nature
The Living Record of Science
《自然》百年科学经典

英汉对照版　套装共十卷

第七卷
1985-1992

总顾问：李政道（Tsung-Dao Lee）

英方主编：Sir John Maddox
Sir Philip Campbell

中方主编：路甬祥

外语教学与研究出版社　·　麦克米伦教育　·　自然科研

FOREIGN LANGUAGE TEACHING AND RESEARCH PRESS　·　MACMILLAN EDUCATION　·　NATURE RESEARCH

北京 BEIJING

图书在版编目（CIP）数据

《自然》百年科学经典：套装共十卷．第七卷：英汉对照 ／（英）约翰·马多克斯（John Maddox），（英）菲利普·坎贝尔（Philip Campbell），路甬祥主编．—— 北京：外语教学与研究出版社，2020.9
　　ISBN 978-7-5213-2021-3

　　Ⅰ．①自…　Ⅱ．①约…　②菲…　③路…　Ⅲ．①自然科学－文集－英、汉　Ⅳ．①N53

中国版本图书馆 CIP 数据核字 (2020) 第 155157 号

地图审图号：GS (2020) 5244 号

出 版 人　徐建忠
项目统筹　章思英
项目负责　刘晓楠　黄小斌
责任编辑　王丽霞
责任校对　黄小斌
封面设计　高　蕾
版式设计　孙莉明
插图设计　麦克米伦提供原图扫描版
出版发行　外语教学与研究出版社
社　　址　北京市西三环北路 19 号（100089）
网　　址　http://www.fltrp.com
印　　刷　北京华联印刷有限公司
开　　本　787×1092　1/16
印　　张　63
版　　次　2021 年 1 月第 1 版　2021 年 1 月第 1 次印刷
书　　号　ISBN 978-7-5213-2021-3
定　　价　8000.00 元

购书咨询：（010）88819926　电子邮箱：club@fltrp.com
外研书店：https://waiyants.tmall.com
凡印刷、装订质量问题，请联系我社印制部
联系电话：（010）61207896　电子邮箱：zhijian@fltrp.com
凡侵权、盗版书籍线索，请联系我社法律事务部
举报电话：（010）88817519　电子邮箱：banquan@fltrp.com
物料号：320210001

《自然》百年科学经典（英汉对照版）

总顾问：李政道（Tsung-Dao Lee）

英方主编：Sir John Maddox 中方主编：路甬祥

Sir Philip Campbell

编审委员会

编译委员会

本卷翻译工作组稿人（以姓氏笔画为序）

王帅帅	王晓蕾	王耀杨	刘　明	刘晓楠	关秀清	李　琦
何　铭	郭红锋	黄小斌	蔡　迪	蔡则怡		

本卷翻译人员（以姓氏笔画为序）

马　颖	王耀杨	牛慧冲	刘皓芳	齐红艳	许向科	李　梅
李　琦	肖　莉	张锦彬	张新彦	陈　林	金世超	周平博
周志华	周晓明	郑建全	侯彦婕	姜　薇	蔡则怡	

本卷校对人员（以姓氏笔画为序）

丁　然	于同旭	马　昊	马　亮	王　敏	王　雷	王帅帅
王丽霞	王晓蕾	王海纳	王德孚	元旭津	公　晗	邓铭瑞
石宇鹏	石爱洁	史未卿	史明澍	朱　玥	任嵫铭	刘俊杰
闫　妍	闫振丽	许晨雨	苏怡汀	李　芳	李　妍	李　昆
李　萌	李　梅	李　静	李永新	李兆升	李盎然	杨　茜
吴兆军	张　敏	张　晴	张欣园	张香香	张梦旋	张琦玮
张瑶楠	陈　雄	罗小青	郑　征	宗伟凯	赵晓非	侯鉴璇
姜　薇	夏　秋	钱　磊	徐　玲	徐　悦	高坛光	郭晓博
黄　瑢	黄　璞	黄小斌	黄雪嫚	梁　瑜	葛聆沨	谢周丽
雷文欣	魏洪淼					

Eric Leher（澳）

Contents
目录

Volume VII

(1985-1992)

Complete Nucleotide Sequence of the AIDS Virus, HTLV-III

L. Ratner *et al.*

Editor's Note

The early 1980s was a period of intense AIDS-related research and discovery. The AIDS-causing virus, then called human T-cell leukaemia virus III (HTLV-III), was identified and isolated, as were its modes of transmission. Here US biologist Robert Gallo and colleagues describe the complete nucleotide sequences of the AIDS virus, a milestone in AIDS research. Overall, the sequence resembles that of other RNA-encoded "retroviruses" containing the three hallmark genes *gag*, *pol* and *env*. But it also contains anomalies, not least the immense heterogeneity between clones. The genome has enabled researchers to define key viral genes and proteins, has shed light on the origins, nature and spread of HIV, and continues to influence diagnostic and drug development.

The complete nucleotide sequence of two human T-cell leukaemia type III (HTLV-III) proviral DNAs each have four long open reading frames, the first two corresponding to the *gag* and *pol* genes. The fourth open reading frame encodes two functional polypeptides, a large precursor of the major envelope glycoprotein and a smaller protein derived from the 3'-terminus long open reading frame analogous to the long open reading frame (*lor*) product of HTLV-I and -II.

HUMAN T-cell leukaemia (lymphotropic) viruses HTLV-I, -II and -III, a family of exogenous retroviruses, are associated with T-cell disorders including adult T-cell leukaemia lymphoma (ATLL) and the acquired immune deficiency syndrome (AIDS)[1-14]. These viruses share a number of biological and structural features: tropism for OKT4+ lymphocytes[10,15-21], the ability to produce giant multinucleated cells in culture[10,17,22-24], immunological cross-reactivity of some virally encoded proteins[12,13], distant nucleic acid sequence similarities[8,9,25-28] and the preference for magnesium of the viral reverse transcriptase[29-31]. Moreover, the genome of HTLV-I and -II as well as the related bovine leukaemia virus (BLV) is somewhat longer than that of other retroviruses[8,9,25,32-34]. A sequence of 1,600–1,800 nucleotides is interposed between the 3' end of the *env* gene and the long terminal repeat (LTR) sequences of these viruses[25,32-37], the 3' portion of which is a long open reading frame (*lor*)[32,35,37]. Another feature that distinguishes HTLV-I, -II, -III and BLV from other retroviruses is the marked increase in the rate of transcription initiated within the viral LTR sequences in infected compared with uninfected cells[38,39]. This phenomenon, *trans*-acting transcriptional regulation, is not observed for other retroviruses[40] and is probably mediated by the *lor* gene product of these retroviruses[38].

艾滋病病毒HTLV-III的完整核苷酸序列

拉特纳等

编者按

20 世纪 80 年代早期是艾滋病相关研究和发现的密集时期。人们鉴定并分离出了引发艾滋病的病毒——后被称为 T 细胞白血病病毒 III（HTLV-III）并弄清了它的传播模式。在本文中，美国生物学家罗伯特·加洛及其同事描述了艾滋病病毒的完整核苷酸序列，这是艾滋病研究领域的一块里程碑。这个序列和其他 RNA 编码的"逆转录病毒"一样，都具有 *gag*、*pol* 和 *env* 这三个标志基因。但它也有一些不同，这些不同不仅仅局限于克隆间巨大的遗传异质性。基因组使得研究人员能够定义关键的病毒基因和蛋白，解释艾滋病的起源、性质和传播，进而影响诊断和药物的发展。

人类两种 T 细胞白血病 III（HTLV-III）的前病毒 DNA 的完整序列各有四个长的开放阅读框，前两个与 *gag* 和 *pol* 基因相关。第四个开放阅读框编码两个功能多肽，主要包膜糖蛋白的大前体和来源于 3′ 末端长开放阅读框的小蛋白，类似于 HTLV-I 和 -II 长开放阅读框（*lor*）的产物。

人类 T 细胞白血病（淋巴性）病毒 HTLV-I, -II 和 -III，属于外源逆转录病毒家族，它们与 T 细胞紊乱有关，包括成人 T 淋巴细胞白血病（ATLL）和获得性免疫综合征（AIDS）[1-14]。这些病毒具有许多共同的生物学和结构特征：对 OKT4+ 淋巴细胞的嗜性 [10,15-21]、在培养基中产生巨型多核细胞的能力 [10,17,22-24]、与一些病毒编码蛋白的免疫学交叉反应 [12,13]、远亲核苷酸序列之间的相似性 [8,9,25-28] 和病毒逆转录酶对镁的偏好 [29-31]。此外，HTLV-I 和 -II 与相关的牛白血病病毒（BLV）一样比其他的逆转录病毒的基因组都略长 [8,9,25,32-34]。在 *env* 基因的 3′ 末端和这些病毒的长末端重复序列（LTR）之间得到一段 1,600~1,800 个核苷酸的序列 [25,32-37]，该序列 3′ 部分是一个长的开放阅读框（*lor*）[32,35,37]。HTLV-I、-II、-III 和 BLV 区别于其他逆转录病毒的另一个特点是，被感染的细胞中 LTR 序列区域起始转录的速率比未被感染的细胞有显著增长 [38,39]。这种反式转录调控的现象在其他逆转录病毒中 [40] 没有观察到，可能是由这些逆转录病毒的 *lor* 基因的产物所介导的 [38]。

Despite the similarity between HTLV-III and the other members of the HTLV-BLV family of viruses, the biology and pathology of HTLV-III differ substantially. Infection with HTLV-III results often in profound immunosuppression (AIDS), consequent on the depletion of the OKT4[+] cell population[10-14,41-43]. This effect is mirrored by a pronounced cytopathic rather than transforming effect of HTLV-III infection upon the OKT4[+] cells in lymphocyte cultures *in vitro*[10,11,20]. In contrast, infection with HTLV-I results in a low incidence of T-cell leukaemia lymphoma (an OKT4[+]-cell malignancy)[1-6]. There is evidence also for some degree of immunodeficiency in HTLV-I patients[6,44]. Infection of primary lymphocytes in culture by HTLV-I and -II results in *in vitro* transformation of predominantly OKT4[+] cells[45,46]. A cytopathic effect of HTLV-I infection on lymphocytes is apparent, but the effect is not as pronounced as that in HTLV-III[16,17,45-48]. HTLV-III differs also from HTLV-I and -II in the extent of infectious virion production *in vivo* and *in vitro*. High titres of cell-free infectious virions can be obtained from AIDS patient semen and saliva and from the supernatant of cultures infected with HTLV-III[10,49-51]. Very few, if any, cell-free infectious virions can be recovered from ATLL patients or from cultures infected with HTLV-I or -II[52].

To investigate the biological activity of these viruses *in vitro* and *in vivo* and to provide information useful for the development of diagnostic and therapeutic reagents for AIDS, we have determined the complete nucleotide sequence of the HTLV-III provirus.

Genomic Structure of HTLV-III

Several closely related clones of HTLV-III DNA were obtained from the H9 cell line infected with HTLV-III present in the blood pooled from several American AIDS patients[10]. The complete primary nucleotide sequence of three unintegrated viral clones of 8.9, 5.3 and 3.6 kilobases (kb) in length[27] was determined with the partial sequence from an integrated proviral clone[53] (Fig. 1).

The HTLV-III provirus is 9,749 base pairs (bp) long. The overall structure of the provirus resembles that of other retroviruses. The sequences that encode viral proteins are flanked by LTR sequences. The LTR itself is flanked by inverted repeated sequences two nucleotides long (Fig. 1). Four long open reading frames are identified in the viral DNA (Fig. 2).

Long Terminal Repeat

A detailed analysis of the HTLV-III LTR is presented elsewhere[54]; it is 634 nucleotides long with U3, R and U5 regions of 453, 98 and 83 nucleotides, respectively. The boundaries of these regions of the LTR were defined by localization of the 5'-cap site by S_1 nuclease mapping and by measurement of the length of the strong stop DNA transcript, as well as by determination of the 3'-terminus of the viral RNA by sequence analysis of cDNA clones. A TATAA sequence typical of eukaryotic promoters, as well as the consensus sequence for polyadenylation, are indicated in Fig. 1. A transfer RNA binding site complementary to the 3' end of tRNA[Lys] is located 3' to the 5' LTR. DNA sequence homologies to the LTR of HTLV-I[32], -II[55] and BLV[56] are indicated in Fig. 3.

尽管 HTLV-III 与 HTLV-BLV 病毒家族其他成员之间有相似性，但是 HTLV-III 与它们的生物学和病理学特征有着根本上的不同。HTLV-III 的感染常常导致完全的免疫抑制（AIDS），随后就是 OKT4+ 细胞数减少 [10-14,41-43]。这一效应是通过 HTLV-III 感染体外淋巴细胞培养物 OKT4+ 造成的细胞病变反映出来的，而非转染效应 [10,11,20]。相反地，细胞感染 HTLV-I 后仅导致一种低发病率的 T 淋巴细胞白血病（一种 OKT4+ 细胞恶性肿瘤）[1-6]，而且也有 HTLV-I 病人存在不同程度的免疫缺陷的例子 [6,44]。HTLV-I 和 -II 体外感染导致培养的原代淋巴细胞大部分变为 OKT4+ 细胞 [45,46]。HTLV-I 感染淋巴细胞引起的细胞病变效应是明显的，但是这一效应不如 HTLV-III 引起的显著 [16,17,45-48]。HTLV-III 与 HTLV-I 和 -II 的不同之处还在于它们在体内和体外产生的具有感染能力的病毒颗粒的数量不同。从艾滋病患者的精液和唾液以及 HTLV-III 感染的细胞培养液上清中能够获得高效价的感染性病毒颗粒 [10,49-51]。从 ATLL 病人或者从 HTLV-I 和 -II 感染的细胞培养基中，很少能够获得游离的病毒粒子 [52]。

为了研究这些病毒在体内和体外的生物学活性并为艾滋病的诊断和治疗药物的开发提供有用的信息，我们完成了 HTLV-III 前病毒完整核苷酸序列的测序。

HTLV-III 的基因组结构

从几个美国艾滋病患者血液中提取 HTLV-III，然后感染 H9 细胞系，从中获得了几个密切相关的 HTLV-III DNA 克隆 [10]。利用一个完整前病毒克隆的部分序列 [53]（图 1），我们测定了长度 [27] 分别为 8,900、5,300 和 3,600 个碱基的三个不完整病毒克隆的全部初级序列。

HTLV-III 前病毒长 9,749 个碱基对。前病毒的总体结构类似于其他的逆转录病毒。编码病毒蛋白的序列两侧为 LTR 序列。LTR 自身的两侧是 2 个核苷酸长度的反向重复序列（图 1）。在病毒 DNA 中发现了四个长的开放阅读框（图 2）。

长末端重复序列

HTLV-III LTR 的详细分析已经被报道过 [54]；该序列长 634 个核苷酸，有 U3、R 和 U5 三个区域，长度分别是 453、98 和 83 个核苷酸。这些区域在 LTR 中的边界是通过 S_1 核酸酶谱和测量强制终止 DNA 转录产物的长度定位 5′ 端帽子位点，以及通过 cDNA 克隆的序列分析来确定病毒 RNA 的 3′ 末端，这些方法来确定的。在图 1 中标明了 TATAA 序列，它是真核启动子的典型序列，保守的多腺嘌呤序列也被标出。与 tRNA[Lys] 的 3′ 末端互补的转运 RNA 结合位点位于 5′LTR 的 3′ 末端。在图 3 中标出了与 HTLV-I[32]、-II[55] 和 BLV[56] 的 LTR 同源的序列。

```
CLONE                                                                                  NUCLEOTIDE   AMINO
                                                                                       POSITION      ACID
                                                                                                   RESIDUE
                                                 |-- U3
                                                 IR
BH10                                             TGGAAGGGCTAATTCACTCCCAACGAAGACAAGA   -420
BH8                                              ----------------------------------
                   (Bam HI)
BH10  TATCCTTGATCTGTGGATCTACCACACACAAGGCTACTTCCCTGATTAGCAGAACTACACACCAGGGCCAGGGAT   -345
BH8   -------------------C---------------------------G------------------------AG-
BH10  CAGATATCCACTGACCTTTGGATGGTGCTACAAGCTAGTACCAGTTGAGCCAGAGAAGTTAGAAGAAGCCAACAA   -270
BH8   -----------------------------------------------------------A------------T--
BH10  AGGAGAGAACACCAGCTTGTTACACCCTGTGAGCCTGCATGGAATGGATGACCCGGAGAGAGAAGTGTTAGAGTG   -195
BH8   ---------------------------------------------T-----------------------------
BH10  GAGGTTTGACAGCCGCCTAGCATTTCATCACATGGCCCGAGAGCTGCATCCGGAGTACTTCAAGAACTGCTGACA   -120
BH8   -------------------------------------------------------------------------T-
BH10  TCGAGCTTGCTACAAGGGACTTTCCGCTGGGGACTTTCCAGGGAGGCGTGGCCTGGGCGGGACTGGGGAGTGGCG    -45
BH8   ---------------------------------------------------------------------------
                   TATA
                   BOX   Pvu II        U3 --|
BH10  AGCCCTCAGATCCTGCATATAAGCAGCTGCTTTTTGCCTGTACT                                  -1
BH8   --------------------------------------------
      |-- R              Bql II        Sst I
BH10  GGGTCTCTCTGGTTAGACCAGATCTGAGCCTGGGAGCTC                                       39

HXB2                                         TCTGGCTAACTAGGGAACCCACTGCTTAAGCCTCAA   75
        Hind III         R ------|------ U5
HXB2  TAAAGCTTGCCTTGAGTGCTTCAAGTAGTGTGTGCCCGTCTGTTGTGTGACTCTGGTAACTAGAGATCCCTCAGA   150
                                   U5 --| -- tRNA-lysine ------|------ Leader sequence
                                     IR
HXB2  CCCTTTTAGTCAGTGTGGAAAATCTCTAGCAGTGGCGCCCGAACAGGGACCTGAAAGCGAAAGGGAAACCA      221
      Sst I
BH10  GAGCTCTCTCGACGCAGGACTCGGCTTGCTGAAGCGCGCACGGCAAGAGGCGAGGGGCGGCGACTGGTGAGTACG   296
BH5   ----------------------------- -- ------------------------------------------
                        Leader sequence ---|--- GAG p17
BH10  CCAAAAATTTTGACTAGCGGAGGCTAGAAGGAGAGAGATGGGTGCGAGAGCGTCAGTATTAAGCGGGGGAGAATT   371
                                             MetGlyAlaArgAlaSerValLeuSerGlyGluLeu           13
BH5   ---------------------------------------------------------------------------

BH10  AGATCGATGGGAAAAAATTCGGTTAAGGCCAGGGGGAAAGAAAAAATATAAATTAAAACATATAGTATGGGCAAG   446
       AspArgTrpGluLysIleArgLeuArgProGlyGlyLysLysLysTyrLysLeuLysHisIleValTrpAlaSer          38
BH5   ---------------------------------------------------------------------------
BH10  CAGGGAGCTAGAACGATTCGCAGTTAATCCTGGCCTGTTAGAAACATCAGAAGGCTGTAGACAAATACTGGGACA   521
       ArgGluLeuGluArgPheAlaValAsnProGlyLeuLeuGluThrSerGluGlyCysArgGlnIleLeuGlyGln          63
BH5   ---------------------------------------------------------------------------
BH10  GCTACAACCATCCCTTCAGACAGGATCAGAAGAACTTAGATCATTATATAATACAGTAGCAACCCTCTATTGTGT   596
       LeuGlnProSerLeuGlnThrGlySerGluGluLeuArgSerLeuTyrAsnThrValAlaThrLeuTyrCysVal          88
BH5   ---------------------------------------------------------------------------
                                            Hind III
BH10  GCATCAAAGGATAGAGATAAAAGACACCAAGGAAGCTTTAGACAAGATAGAGGAAGAGCAAAACAAAAGTAAGAA   671
       HisGlnArgIleGluIleLysAspThrLysGluAlaLeuAspLysIleGluGluGluGlnAsnLysSerLysLys         113
BH5   ---------------------------------------------------------------------------

                  Pvu II                         GAG p17 -----|---- GAG p24
BH10  AAAAGCACAGCAAGCAGCAGCTGACACAGGACACAGCAGTCAGGTCAGCCAAAATTACCCTATAGTGCAGAACAT   746
       LysAlaGlnGlnAlaAlaAlaAspThrGlyHisSerSerGlnValSerGlnAsnTyrProIleValGlnAsnIle         138
BH5   ---------------------------------------------------------------------------
                                               Aha III
BH10  CCAGGGGCAAATGGTACATCaGGCCATATCACCTAGAACTTTAAATGCATGGGTAAAAGTAGTAGAAGAGAAGGC   821
       GlnGlyGlnMetValHisGlnAlaIleSerProArgThrLeuAsnAlaTrpValLysValValGluGluLysAla         163
BH5   ---------------------------------------------------------------------------
                                                                   Aha III
BH10  TTTCAGCCCAGAAGTAATACCCATGTTTTCAGCATTATCAGAAGGAGCCACCCCACAAGATTTAAACACCATGCT   896
       PheSerProGluValIleProMetPheSerAlaLeuSerGluGlyAlaThrProGlnAspLeuAsnThrMetLeu         188
BH5   ---------------G-----------------------------------------------------------
                                                                     Pst I
BH10  AAACACAGTGGGGGGACATCAAGCAGCCATGCAAATGTTAAAAGAGACCATCAATGAGGAAGCTGCAGAATGGGA   971
       AsnThrValGlyGlyHisGlnAlaAlaMetGlnMetLeuLysGluThrIleAsnGluGluAlaAlaGluTrpAsp         213
BH5   ---------------------------------------------------------------------------
BH10  TAGAGTACATCCAGTGCATGCAGGGCCTATTGCACCAGGCCAGATGAGAGAACCAAGGGGAAGTGACATAGCAGG   1046
       ArgValHisProValHisAlaGlyProIleAlaProGlyGlnMetArgGluProArgGlySerAspIleAlaGly         238
BH5   ------G-----------------------C--------------------------------------------
BH10  AACTACTAGTACCCTTCAGGAACAAATAGGATGGATGACAAATAATCCACCTATCCCAGTAGGAGAAATTTATAA   1121
       ThrThrSerThrLeuGlnGluGlnIleGlyTrpMetThrAsnAsnProProIleProValGlyGluIleTyrLys         263
BH5   ---------------------------------------------------------------------------
BH10  AAGATGGATAATCCTGGGATTAAATAAAATAGTAAGAATGTATAGCCCTACCAGCATTCTGGACATAAGACAAGG   1196
       ArgTrpIleIleLeuGlyLeuAsnLysIleValArgMetTyrSerProThrSerIleLeuAspIleArgGlnGly         288
BH5   ------------------------------------G--------T-----------------------------
                                                                     Hind III
BH10  ACCAAAAGAACCTTTTAGAGACTATGTAGACCGGTTCTATAAAACTCTAAGAGCCGAGCAAGCTTCACAGGAGGT   1271
       ProLysGluProPheArgAspTyrValAspArgPheTyrLysThrLeuArgAlaGluGlnAlaSerGlnGluVal         313
BH5   ------G-----C-----------------------------------------------------------A--
                                                                    Aha III
BH10  AAAAAATTGGATGACAGAAACCTTGTTGGTCCAAAATGCGAACCCAGATTGTAAGACTATTTTAAAAGCATTGGG   1346
       LysAsnTrpMetThrGluThrLeuLeuValGlnAsnAlaAsnProAspCysLysThrIleLeuLysAlaLeuGly         338
BH5   ---------------------------------------------------------------------------
BH10  ACCAGCGGCTACACTAGAAGAAATGATGACAGCATGTCAGGGAGTAGGAGGACCCGGCCATAAGGCAAGAGTTTT   1421
       ProAlaAlaThrLeuGluGluMetMetThrAlaCysGlnGlyValGlyGlyProGlyHisLysAlaArgValLeu         363
BH5   ---------------------------------------------------------------------------
BH10  GGCTGAAGCAATGAGCCAAGTAACAAATACAGCTACCATAATGATGCAGAGAGGCAATTTTAGGAACCAAAGAAA   1496
       AlaGluAlaMetSerGlnValThrAsnThrAlaThrIleMetMetGlnArgGlyAsnPheArgAsnGlnArgLys         388
BH5   -----------------------------T--A---------------A--------------------------
                                    SerThr
                            |------- Direct Repeat -------|
BH10  GATGGTTAAGTGTTTCAATTGTGGCAAAGAAGGGCACACAGCCAGAAATTGCAGGGCCCCTAGGAAAAAGGGCTG   1571
       MetValLysCysPheAsnCysGlyLysGluGlyHisThrAlaArgAsnCysArgAlaProArgLysLysGlyCys         413
      A--T----------------------------------T---A----------A----------A----GA----
                                             Ile            Lys            Arg
             |------- Direct Repeat -------|                       |-- POL    Bgl II
BH10  TTGGAAATGTGGAAAGGAAGGACACCAAATGAAAGATTGTACTGAGAGACAGGCTAATTTTTTAGGGAAGATCTG   1646
       TrpLysCysGlyLysGluGlyHisGlnMetLysAspCysThrGluArgGlnAlaAsnPheLeuGlyLysIleTrp         438
                                                                 PhePheArgGluAspLeu           6
BH5   ---------------------------------------------------------------------------
                                      |-------- Direct Repeat ---------|--- Direct
BH10  GCCTTCCTACAAGGGAAGGCCAGGGAATTTTCTTCAGAGCAGACCAGAGCCAACAGCCCCACCATTTCTTCAGAG   1721
       ProSerTyrLysGlyArgProGlyAsnPheLeuGlnSerArgProGluProThrAlaProProPheLeuGlnSer         463
      AlaPheLeuGlnGlyLysAlaArgGluPheSerSerGluGlnThrArgAlaAsnSerProThrIleSerSerGlu          31
BH5   ---------------------------------------------------------------------------

         Repeat ---------------|
BH10  CAGACCAGAGCCAACAGCCCCACCAGAAGAGAGCTTCAGGTCTGGGGTAGAGACAACAACTCCCCCTCAGAAGCA   1796
       ArgProGluProThrAlaProProGluGluSerPheArgSerGlyValGluThrThrThrProProGlnLysGln         488
      GlnThrArgAlaAsnSerProThrArgArgGluLeuGlnValTrpGlyArgAspAsnAsnSerProSerGluAla          56
BH5   ----------------------------------------------------------------T----------
                                                                      Ser
                                                                      Leu
                                                              GAG p15 ------|
BH10  GGAGCCGATAGACAAGGAACTGTATCCTTTAACTTCCCTCAGATCACTCTTTGGCAACGACCCCTCGTCACAATA   1871
       GluProIleAspLysGluLeuTyrProLeuThrSerLeuArgSerLeuPheGlyAsnAspProSerSerGln            512
      GlyAlaAspArgGlnGlyThrValSerPheAsnPheProGlnIleThrLeuTrpGlnArgProLeuValThrIle          81
BH5   ---------------------------------------------------------------------------
BH10  AAGATAGGGGGGCAACTAAAGGAAGCTCTATTAGATACAGGAGCAGATGATACAGTATTAGAAGAAATGAGTTTG   1946
      LysIleGlyGlyGlnLeuLysGluAlaLeuLeuAspThrGlyAlaAspAspThrValLeuGluGluMetSerLeu          106
BH5   ---------------------------------------------------------------------------
BH10  CCAGGAAGATGGAAACCAAAAATGATAGGGGGAATTGGAGGTTTTATCAAAGTAAGACAGTATGATCAGATACTC   2021
      ProGlyArgTrpLysProLysMetIleGlyGlyIleGlyGlyPheIleLysValArgGlnTyrAspGlnIleLeu          131
BH5   ---------------------------------------------------------------------------
BH10  ATAGAAATCTGTGGACATAAAGCTATAGGTACAGTATTAGTAGGACCTACACCTGTCAACATAATTGGAAGAAAT   2096
      IleGluIleCysGlyHisLysAlaIleGlyThrValLeuValGlyProThrProValAsnIleIleGlyArgAsn          156
BH5   ---------------------------------------------------------------------------
                            Aha III
BH10  CTGTTGACTCAGATTGGTTGCACTTTAAATTTTCCCATTAGCCCTATTGAGACTGTACCAGTAAAATTAAAGCCA   2171
      LeuLeuThrGlnIleGlyCysThrLeuAsnPheProIleSerProIleGluThrValProValLysLeuLysPro          181
BH5   -----------------------------------------T--------A------------------------
BH10  GGAATGGATGGCCCAAAAGTTAAACAATGGCCATTGACAGAAGAAAAAATAAAAGCATTAGTAGAAATTTGTACA   2246
      GlyMetAspGlyProLysValLysGlnTrpProLeuThrGluGluLysIleLysAlaLeuValGluIleCysThr          206
BH5   ---------------------------------------------------------------------------
BH10  GAAATGGAAAAGGAAGGGAAAATTTCAAAAATTGGGCCTGAGAATCCATACAATACTCCAGTATTTGCCATAAAG   2321
      GluMetGluLysGluGlyLysIleSerLysIleGlyProGluAsnProTyrAsnThrProValPheAlaIleLys          231
BH5   -----------------------------------------A---------------------------------
BH10  AAAAAAGACAGTACTAAATGGAGAAAATTAGTAGATTTCAGAGAACTTAATAAGAGAACTCAAGACTTCTGGGAA   2396
      LysLysAspSerThrLysTrpArgLysLeuValAspPheArgGluLeuAsnLysArgThrGlnAspPheTrpGlu          256
BH5   ----------------------------------------------------G----------------------
                                                          Arg
BH10  GTTCAATTAGGAATACCACATCCCGCAGGGTTAAAAAAGAAAAAATCAGTAACAGTACTGGATGTGGGTGATGCA   2471
      ValGlnLeuGlyIleProHisProAlaGlyLeuLysLysLysLysSerValThrValLeuAspValGlyAspAla          281
BH5   --------G------------------------------------------------------------------
BH10  TATTTTTCAGTTCCCTTAGATGAAGACTTCAGGAAGTATACTGCATTTACCATACCTAGTATAAACAATGAGACA   2546
      TyrPheSerValProLeuAspGluAspPheArgLysTyrThrAlaPheThrIleProSerIleAsnAsnGluThr          306
BH5   -----------------------------------------------------------------T---------
BH10  CCAGGGATTAGATATCAGTACAATGTGCTTCCACAGGGATGGAAAGGATCACCAGCAATATTCCAAAGTAGCATG   2621
      ProGlyIleArgTyrGlnTyrAsnValLeuProGlnGlyTrpLysGlySerProAlaIlePheGlnSerSerMet          331
BH5   -------G-G-----------------------------------------------------------------
           SerGly
                    Aha III
BH10  ACAAAAATCTTAGAGCCTTTTAAAAAACAAAATCCAGACATAGTTATCTATCAATACATGGATGATTTGTATGTA   2696
      ThrLysIleLeuGluProPheLysLysGlnAsnProAspIleValIleTyrGlnTyrMetAspAspLeuTyrVal          356
BH5   -----------------------G-----------------------T---------------------------
                            Arg

BH10  GGATCTGACTTAGAAATAGGGCAGCATAGAACAAAAATAGAGGAGCTGAGACAACATCTGTTGAGGTGGGGACTT   2771
      GlySerAspLeuGluIleGlyGlnHisArgThrLysIleGluGluLeuArgGlnHisLeuLeuArgTrpGlyLeu          381
BH5   ------------------------------------------------------------------------T--
                                                                              Phe
BH10  ACCACACCAGACAAAAAACATCAGAAAGAACCTCCATTCCTTTGGATGGGTTATGAACTCCATCCTGATAAATGG   2846
      ThrThrProAspLysLysHisGlnLysGluProProPheLeuTrpMetGlyTyrGluLeuHisProAspLysTrp          406
BH5   ---------------------------------------------------------------------------
                                  Pvu II
BH10  ACAGTACAGCCTATAGTGCTGCCAGAAAAAGACAGCTGGACTGTCAATGACATACAGAAGTTAGTGGGAAAATTG   2921
      ThrValGlnProIleValLeuProGluLysAspSerTrpThrValAsnAspIleGlnLysLeuValGlyLysLeu          431
BH5   --GA----------------------------------------------------------------A------
        Ile
BH10  AATTGGGCAAGTCAGATTTACCCAGGGATTAAAGTAAGGCAATTATGTAAACTCCTTAGAGGAACCAAAGCACTA   2996
      AsnTrpAlaSerGlnIleTyrProGlyIleLysValArgGlnLeuCysLysLeuLeuArgGlyThrLysAlaLeu          456
BH5   --------------------T------------------------------------------------------
BH10  ACAGAAGTAATACCACTAACAGAAGAAGCAGAGCTAGAACTGGCAGAAAACAGAGAGATTCTAAAAGAACCAGTA   3071
      ThrGluValIleProLeuThrGluGluAlaGluLeuGluLeuAlaGluAsnArgGluIleLeuLysGluProVal          481
BH5   ---------------------------------------------------------------------------
BH10  CATGGAGTGTATTATGACCCATCAAAAGACTTAATAGCAGAAATACAGAAGCAGGGGCAAGGCCAATGGACATAT   3146
      HisGlyValTyrTyrAspProSerLysAspLeuIleAlaGluIleGlnLysGlnGlyGlnGlyGlnTrpThrTyr          506
BH5   ---------------------------------------------------------------------------
                   Aha III
BH10  CAAATTTATCAAGAGCCATTTAAAAATCTGAAAACAGGAAAATATGCAAGAATGAGGGGTGCCCACACTAATGAT   3221
      GlnIleTyrGlnGluProPheLysAsnLeuLysThrGlyLysTyrAlaArgMetArgGlyAlaHisThrAsnAsp          531
BH5   ---------------------------------------------------------------------------
                                                                        Aha III
BH10  GTAAAACAATTAACAGAGGCAGTGCAAAAAATAACCACAGAAAGCATAGTAATATGGGGAAAGACTCCTAAATTT   3296
      ValLysGlnLeuThrGluAlaValGlnLysIleThrThrGluSerIleValIleTrpGlyLysThrProLysPhe          556
BH5   ---------------------------------------------------------------------------
BH10  AAACTACCCATACAAAAGGAAACATGGGAAACATGGTGGACAGAGTATTGGCAAGCCACCTGGATTCCTGAGTGG   3371
      LysLeuProIleGlnLysGluThrTrpGluThrTrpTrpThrGluTyrTrpGlnAlaThrTrpIleProGluTrp          581
BH5   -----------------A---------------------------------------------------------
                                  Kpn I
BH10  GAGTTTGTTAATACCCCTCCTTTAGTGAAATTATGGTACCAGTTAGAGAAAGAACCCATAGTAGGAGCAGAAACC   3446
      GluPheValAsnThrProProLeuValLysLeuTrpTyrGlnLeuGluLysGluProIleValGlyAlaGluThr          606
BH5   ---------------------------------------------------------------------------
BH10  TTCTATGTAGATGGGGCAGCTAACAGGGAGACTAAATTAGGAAAAGCAGGATATGTTACTAACAAAGGAAGACAA   3521
      PheTyrValAspGlyAlaAlaAsnArgGluThrLysLeuGlyLysAlaGlyTyrValThrAsnLysGlyArgGln          631
BH5   ----------------------G---------------------------------------T-G----------
                           Ser                                        Arg
BH10  AAGGTTGTCCCCCTAACTAACACAACAAATCAGAAAACTGAGTTACAAGCAATTTATCTAGCTTTGCAGGATTCA   3596
      LysValValProLeuThrAsnThrThrAsnGlnLysThrGluLeuGlnAlaIleTyrLeuAlaLeuGlnAspSer          656
BH5   --A------A--------C----------------G-----A------------C-------------------G
               Thr      His                                 Asn
BH10  GGATTAGAAGTAAACATAGTAACAGACTCACAATATGCATTAGGAATCATTCAAGCACAACCAGATAAAAGTGAA   3671
      GlyLeuGluValAsnIleValThrAspSerGlnTyrAlaLeuGlyIleIleGlnAlaGlnProAspLysSerGlu          681
BH5   --------------T------------------------------------------------------------
                                                                   Kpn I
BH10  TCAGAGTTAGTCAATCAAATAATAGAGCAGTTAATAAAAAAGGAAAAGGTCTATCTGGCATGGGTACCAGCACAC   3746
      SerGluLeuValAsnGlnIleIleGluGlnLeuIleLysLysGluLysValTyrLeuAlaTrpValProAlaHis          706
BH5   ---------------------------------------------------------------------------

BH10  AAAGGAATTGGAGGAAATGAACAAGTAGATAAATTAGTCAGTGCTGGAATCAGGAAAATACTATTTTTAGATGGA   3821
      LysGlyIleGlyGlyAsnGluGlnValAspLysLeuValSerAlaGlyIleArgLysIleLeuPheLeuAspGly          731
BH5   ---------------------------------------------------------------------------
BH10  ATAGATAAGGCCCAAGATGAACATGAGAAATATCACAGTAATTGGAGAGCAATGGCTAGTGATTTTAACCTGCCA   3896
      IleAspLysAlaGlnAspGluHisGluLysTyrHisSerAsnTrpArgAlaMetAlaSerAspPheAsnLeuPro          756
BH5   -----------------A---------------------------------------------------------
                             Pvu II
BH10  CCTGTAGTAGCAAAAGAAATAGTAGCCAGCTGTGATAAATGTCAGCTAAAAGGAGAAGCCATGCATGGACAAGTA   3971
      ProValValAlaLysGluIleValAlaSerCysAspLysCysGlnLeuLysGlyGluAlaMetHisGlyGlnVal          781
BH5   ---------------------------------------------------------------------------
BH10  GACTGTAGTCCAGGAATATGGCAACTAGATTGTACACATTTAGAAGGAAAAGTTATCCTGGTAGCAGTTCATGTA   4046
      AspCysSerProGlyIleTrpGlnLeuAspCysThrHisLeuGluGlyLysValIleLeuValAlaValHisVal          806
BH5   ---------------------------------------------------------------------------
                                                                     Aha III
BH10  GCCAGTGGATATATAGAAGCAGAAGTTATTCCAGCAGAAACAGGGCAGGAAACAGCATATTTTCTTTTAAAATTA   4121
      AlaSerGlyTyrIleGluAlaGluValIleProAlaGluThrGlyGlnGluThrAlaTyrPheLeuLeuLysLeu          831
BH5   ---------------------------------------------------------------------------
BH10  GCAGGAAGATGGCCAGTAAAAACAATACATACAGACAATGGCAGCAATTTCACCAGTGCTACGGTTAAGGCCGCC   4196
      AlaGlyArgTrpProValLysThrIleHisThrAspAsnGlySerAsnPheThrSerAlaThrValLysAlaAla          856
BH5   ---------------------------------------------------------------------------
                                 Eco RI
BH10  TGTTGGTGGGCGGGAATCAAGCAGGAATTTGGAATTCCCTACAATCCCCAAAGTCAAGGAGTAGTAGAATCTATG   4271
      CysTrpTrpAlaGlyIleLysGlnGluPheGlyIleProTyrAsnProGlnSerGlnGlyValValGluSerMet          881
BH5   ---------------------------------------------------------------------------
BH10  AATAAAGAATTAAAGAAAATTATAGGACAGGTAAGAGATCAGGCTGAACATCTTAAGACAGCAGTACAAATGGCA   4346
      AsnLysGluLeuLysLysIleIleGlyGlnValArgAspGlnAlaGluHisLeuLysThrAlaValGlnMetAla          906
BH5   ---------------------------------------------------------------------------
                 Aha III
BH10  GTATTCATCCACAATTTTAAAAGAAAAGGGGGGATTGGGGGGTACAGTGCAGGGGAAAGAATAGTAGACATAATA   4421
      ValPheIleHisAsnPheLysArgLysGlyGlyIleGlyGlyTyrSerAlaGlyGluArgIleValAspIleIle          931
BH5   ---------------------------------------------------------------------------
BH10  GCAACAGACATACAAACTAAAGAATTACAAAAACAAATTACAAAAATTCAAAATTTTCGGGTTTATTACAGGGAC   4496
      AlaThrAspIleGlnThrLysGluLeuGlnLysGlnIleThrLysIleGlnAsnPheArgValTyrTyrArgAsp          956
BH5   ---------------------------------------------------------------------------
BH10  AGCAGAAATCCACTTTGGAAAGGACCAGCAAAGCTCCTCTGGAAAGGTGAAGGGGCAGTAGTAATACAAGATAAT   4571
      SerArgAsnProLeuTrpLysGlyProAlaLysLeuLeuTrpLysGlyGluGlyAlaValValIleGlnAspAsn          981
BH5   ---------------------------------------------------------------------------
                      |------- SOR
BH10  AGTGACATAAAAGTAGTGCCAAGAAGAAAAGCAAAGATCATTAGGGATTATGGAAAACAGATGGCAGGTGATGAT   4646
      SerAspIleLysValValProArgArgLysAlaLysIleIleArgAspTyrGlyLysGlnMetAlaGlyAspAsp         1006
                      CysGlnGluGluLysGlnArgSerLeuGlyIleMetGluAsnArgTrpGlnValMetIle          20
BH5   ---------------------------------------------------------------------------
                    POL ----|
BH10  TGTGTGGCAAGTAGACAGGATGAGGATTAGAACATGGAAAAGTTTAGTAAAACACCATATGTATGTTTCAGGGAA   4721
      CysValAlaSerArgGlnAspGluAsp                                                        1015
       ValTrpGlnValAspArgMetArgIleArgThrTrpLysSerLeuValLysHisHisMetTyrValSerGlyLys          45
BH5   --------------------------------------------------------G------------------
                                                              Arg
BH10  AGCTAGGGGATGGTTTTATAGACATCACTATGAAAGCCCTCATCCAAGAATAAGTTCAGAAGTACACATCCCACT   4796
       AlaArgGlyTrpPheTyrArgHisHisTyrGluSerProHisProArgIleSerSerGluValHisIleProLeu          70
BH5   ---------------------------------------------------------------------------

BH10  AGGGGATGCTAGATTGGTAATAACAACATATTGGGGTCTGCATACAGGAGAAAGAGACTGGCATTTGGGTCAGGG   4871
       GlyAspAlaArgLeuValIleThrThrTyrTrpGlyLeuHisThrGlyGluArgAspTrpHisLeuGlyGlnGly          95
BH5   ---------------------------------------------------------------------------
BH10  AGTCTCCATAGAATGGAGGAAAAAGAGATATAGCACACAAGTAGACCCTGAACTAGCAGACCAACTAATTCATCT   4946
       ValSerIleGluTrpArgLysLysArgTyrSerThrGlnValAspProGluLeuAlaAspGlnLeuIleHisLeu         120
BH5   -----------------------G---------------------------------------------------
                            Arg
BH10  GTATTACTTTGACTGTTTTTCAGACTCTGCTATAAGAAAGGCCTTATTAGGACACATAGTTAGCCCTAGGTGTGA   5021
       TyrTyrPheAspCysPheSerAspSerAlaIleArgLysAlaLeuLeuGlyHisIleValSerProArgCysGlu         145
BH5   -C----------T--------------------------------------------------------------
BH10  ATATCAAGCAGGACATAACAAGGTAGGATCTCTACAATACTTGGCACTAGCAGCATTAATAACACCAAAAAAGAT   5096
       TyrGlnAlaGlyHisAsnLysValGlySerLeuGlnTyrLeuAlaLeuAlaAlaLeuIleThrProLysLysIle         170
BH5   -------------------------------------------------------------------------G-
                                                                              Val
BH10  AAAGCCACCTTTGCCTAGTGTTACGAAACTGACAGAGGATAGATGGAACAAGCCCCAGAAGACCAAGGGCCACAG   5171
       LysProProLeuProSerValThrLysLeuThrGluAspArgTrpAsnLysProGlnLysThrLysGlyHisArg         195
BH5   ---------------------------------------------------------------------------
                SOR -------|
BH10  AGGGAGCCACACAATGAATGGACACTAGAGCTTTTAGAGGAGCTTAAGAATGAAGCTGTTAGACATTTTCCTAGG   5246
       GlySerHisThrMetAsnGlyHis                                                            203
BH5   ---A-----------------------------------------------------------------------
BH10  ATTTGGCTCCATGGCTTAGGGCAACATATCTATGAAACTTATGGGGATACTTGGGCAGGAGTGGAAGCCATAATA   5321
BH5   ---------------------------------------------------------------------------
        Eco RI                                Sal I
BH10  AGAATTCTGCAACAACTGCTGTTTATCCATTTTCAGAATTGGGTGTCGACATAGCAGAATAGGCGTTACTCGACA   5396
BH5   -----------------------------------------------------------------------A---
BH10  GAGGAGAGCAAGAAATGGAGCCAGTAGATCCTAGACTAGAGCCCTGGAAGCATCCAGGAAGTCAGCCTAAAACTG   5471
BH5   ---------------------------------------------------------------------------
BH10  CTTGTACCAATTGCTATTGTAAAAAGTGTTGCTTTCATTGCCAAGTTTGTTTCATAACAAAAGCCTTAGGCATCT   5546
BH5   ---------C-----------------------------------------------------------------
                                    (Sst I)
BH10  CCTATGGCAGGAAGAAGCGGAGACAGCGACGAAGACCTCCTCAAGGCAGTCAGACTCATCAAGTTTCTCTATCAA   5621
BH5   ----------------------------------G---
BH8                                   --G---A--G-A-------------------------------
BH10  AGCAGTAAGTAGTACATGTAATGCAACCTATACAAATAGCAATAGTAGCA[ ]TTAGTAGTAGCAATAATAATAGCAA   5696
BH8   --------------------C-----------C-----T--C-A---T-GCC----C--------------------
BH10  TAGTTGTGTGGTCCATAGTAATCATAGAATATAGGAAAATATTAAGACAAAGAAAAATAGACAGGTTAATTGATA   5771
BH8   ---------------------------------------------------------------------------
             |-------- ENV-LOR
BH10  GACTAATAGAAAGAGCAGAAGACAGTGGCAATGAGAGTGAAGGAGAAATATCAGCACTTGTGGAGATGGGGGTGG   5846
               LysGluGlnLysThrValAlaMetArgValLysGluLysTyrGlnHisLeuTrpArgTrpGlyTrp          22
BH8   ---------------------------------------------------------------------------
BH10  AGATGGGGCACCATGCTCCTTGGGATGTTGATGATCTGTAGTGCTACAGAAAAATTGTGGGTCACAGTCTATTAT   5921
      ArgTrpGlyThrMetLeuLeuGlyMetLeuMetIleCysSerAlaThrGluLysLeuTrpValThrValTyrTyr          47
BH8   -------------------------------------------------------------------------T-
                                                                              Phe
        Kpn I
BH10  GGGGTACCTGTGTGGAAGGAAGCAACCACCACTCTATTTTGTGCATCAGATGCTAAAGCATATGATACAGAGGTA   5996
      GlyValProValTrpLysGluAlaThrThrThrLeuPheCysAlaSerAspAlaLysAlaTyrAspThrGluVal          72
BH8   ---------------------------------------------------------------------------
```

CLONE   核苷酸位置   氨基酸残基

Fig. 1. Nucleotide sequence of HTLV-III. The complete nucleotide sequence of clone BH10 is shown together with the predicted amino acid sequence of the four largest open reading frames. The position of sequences encoding *gag* protein p17, the N-terminus of *gag* p24 and the C-terminus of *gag* p15 (which overlaps with the N-terminus of the *pol* protein) are indicated. The open reading frames for *pol*, *sor* and *env-lor* are indicated. The sequence of the remaining 182 bp of the HTLV-III provirus not present in clone BH10 (including a portion of R, U5, the tRNA primer binding site and a portion of the leader sequence) was derived from clone HXB2. The boundaries of R, U5 and U3, the positions of the polypurine tract, inverted repeated sequences (IR) and the transcriptional initiation (TATA) and termination (AATAA) signals are shown. The sequences of BH8 and BH5 are illustrated also; nucleotide and predicted amino acid differences compared with BH10 are listed and dashes are shown for identical sequences. Restriction enzyme sites are listed above the nucleotide sequence and sites present in clone BH8 but not BH10 are in parentheses. Deletions are also noted ([ ]) at nucleotides 251, 254, 5,671 and 6,987–7,001. The nucleotide positions (to the right of each line) start with the transcriptional initiation site and end with the viral RNA transcriptional termination site. The amino acid residues are numbered (to the right of each line) for the four largest open reading frames starting after the preceding termination codon in each case except *gag* which is enumerated from the first methionine codon. A proposed peptide cleavage site (v) and possible asparagine-linked glycosylation sites [77] are shown (*) for the *env-lor* open reading frame. The sequences in the LTR derived from clones BH8 and BH10 listed in the beginning of the figure are derived from the 3′ portion of each clone and are assumed to be identical to those present in the 5′ LTR of the integrated copies of these viral genomes. Clone HXB2 was derived from a recombinant phage library of *Xba*I-digested DNA from HTLV-III-infected H9 cell cloned in λJ1 (ref. 53). Clones BH10, BH8 and BH5 were derived from a library of *Sst*I-digested DNA from the Hirt supernatant fraction of HTLV-III-infected H9 cells cloned in λgtWes·λB (ref. 27). Both libraries were screened with a cDNA probe synthesized from virion RNA using oligo(dT) as a primer[26]. Clones BH8, BH5 and a portion of HXB2 were sequenced as described previously[91]. Clone BH10 was sequenced by the method of Sanger[92] modified by the use of oligonucleotides complementary to the M13 insert sequence as primers and using Klenow fragment of DNA polymerase I or reverse transcriptase as the polymerase.

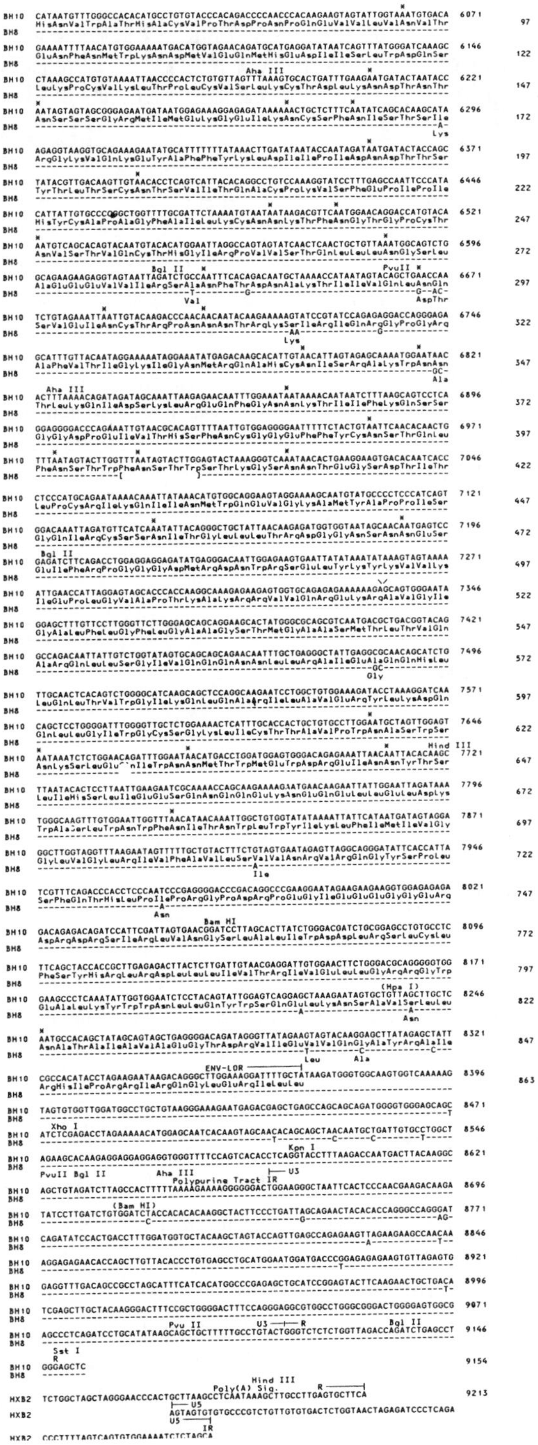

图 1. HTLV-III 的核苷酸序列。对应列出克隆 BH10 的完整核苷酸序列与预测的四个最大的开放阅读框的氨基酸序列。编码 gag 蛋白 p17 的序列位置，p24 的 N 端和 p15 的 C 端（它与 pol 蛋白的 N 端有重叠）序列的位置都已指出。pol，sor 和 env-lor 的开放阅读框都已标出。克隆 BH10 不含有的 182bp HTLV-III 前病毒序列（包括部分 R、U5、tRNA 引物结合位点和部分前导序列）来自克隆 HXB2。图中还标明了 R、U5 和 U3 的边界，多嘌呤序列、反向重复序列（IR）和转录起始（TATA）和终止信号（AATAA）的位置。BH8 和 BH5 的序列也做了说明；图中列出了与 BH10 相比存在差异的核苷酸和预测氨基酸序列，完全相同的序列用破折号来表示。在核苷酸序列上方还标出了限制性酶切位点，圆括号表示的是在 BH8 中出现而 BH10 中未出现的位点。在核苷酸 251、254、5,671 和 6,987～7,001 位中的缺失位点用（[ ]）来表示。核苷酸的位置的标注（每行的右边）由转录起始位点开始到病毒 RNA 转录终止位点结束。在四个大的开放阅读框中，对氨基酸残基进行编号（在每一行的右边），除了 gag 是从第一个甲硫氨酸密码子开始编号，其他开放读框都是从前一个终止密码子开始的。env-lor 开放阅读框中表示了一个已报道的肽剪切位点（v）和可能的天冬酰胺连接型糖基化位点[77]（*）。在图起始处列出的 LTR 中的序列来自克隆 BH8 和 BH10，起源于每个克隆的 3′ 端，被认为和这些病毒基因组整合拷贝的 5′LTR 含有的序列相同。克隆 HXB2 来源于一个重组噬菌体文库，此文库是 HTLV-III 感染的 H9 细胞中的 DNA 经 XbaI 消化后克隆在 λJ1 中获得的（参考文献 53）。克隆 BH10、BH8 和 BH5 所在的 DNA 文库，是 HTLV-III 感染的 H9 细胞中 Hirt 上清部分的 DNA 经 SstI 消化后克隆在 λgtWes·λB 中的（参考文献 27）。以寡聚 dT 为引物利用病毒粒子的 RNA 合成 cDNA 探针[26]，对这两个文库进行筛选。克隆 BH8、BH5 和部分 HXB2 的序列用之前描述的方法进行了测序[91]。克隆 BH10 通过改良的桑格法[92] 进行测序，利用与 M13 插入序列互补的寡聚核苷酸作为引物，并用 DNA 聚合酶 I Klenow 片段或逆转录酶作为聚合酶。

9

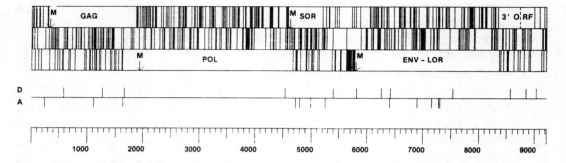

Fig. 2. Distribution of open reading frames in HTLV-III. The positions of termination codons are indicated for each of the three possible reading frames as a vertical line within each box. Thicker lines represent clusters of closely spaced termination codons. The positions of consensus splice donor (D) and acceptor (A) sites[93] are shown below. The nucleotide sequence positions are also indicated below, starting from the transcriptional initiation site. The positions of the four largest open reading frames are identified as *gag*, *pol*, *sor* and *env-lor*, and the position of the first ATG codon (M) in each reading frame is indicated. A fifth open reading frame (*3'-orf*) is found in clone BH8, but not BH10; the broken vertical line indicates the position of a termination codon in BH10.

```
                                                                    PERCENT NUCLEOTIDE
                                                                    IDENTITY TO HTLV-III

HTLV-III BH10 CLONE U3    8824   GAGAAGTTAGAAGAAGCCAACAAAGGAGAGA    8854
HTLV-III BH8  CLONE U3    8824   GAGAAGTAAGAAGAAGCCAATAAAGGAGAGA    8854
HTLV-I            U3       307   AATAAACTAGCAGGAGTCTATAAAAGCGTGG     337              61
                                 * ** *** ** ** * ***** * *
HTLV-II           U3       268   AATAAAAGATGCCGAGTCTATAAAGGCGCAA     298              51
                                 * *** *    ** * ******* * *


HTLV-III          U3      9067   TGGCGAGCCCTCAGATCCTGC ATA   TAA    9093
BLV               U3       152   TGCTGA  CCTCA   CCTGCTGATAAATTAA     178              62
                                 ** **  *****   ***** *** ***


HTLV-III GAG p15          1886   ACTAAAGGAAGCTCTATTAGATACAGGAGCAGATGAT ACAGT ATT AGA AG  1935
HTLV-I BETWEEN GAG & POL  2223   ACTA TCGAAGCTTTACTAGATACAGGAGCAGA CATGACAGTCCTTCCGATAG  2274   76
                                 ****  ****** ** ***************** ** ***** ** ** **


HTLV-III BETWEEN SOR & ENV-LOR  5615  CTATCAAAGCAGTAAGTAGTACATGTAATG    5644
HTLV-I ENV                      5831  CTA CAAAGCACTAATTA TACTTGCATTG     5858              77
                                      *** ******* *** ** *** ** * **
```

Fig. 3. Nucleotide sequence homologies between HTLV-I, -II, -III and BLV. Asterisks indicate identity of nucleotides to that present at the same position in HTLV-III (clone BH10 except where indicated otherwise). The nucleotide position of each sequence is shown.

First Open Reading Frame (*gag*)

The structural proteins of the *gag* gene of retroviruses are derived by proteolytic cleavage of a polypeptide precursor encoded at the 5' end of the genome[57]. Such a precursor, 512 amino acids long, could be encoded by the first long open reading frame of the HTLV-III provirus (nucleotides 310–1,869). The definitive assignment of amino-terminus of the *gag* precursor requires direct amino acid sequencing. A protein of relative molecular mass (M_r) 53,000 (53K) has been detected in immunoprecipitates of HTLV-III-infected cells using sera from an HTLV-III-infected person, as well as sera raised in animals by inoculation of HTLV-III virions[12,13,58]. This 53K protein probably corresponds to the *gag* precursor of HTLV-III.

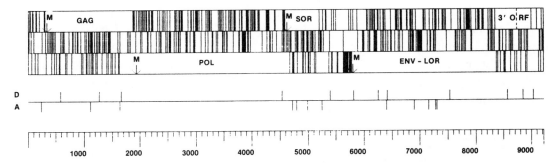

图 2. HTLV-III 中开放阅读框的分布。在每一个方框中，三个可能的阅读框的终止密码子的位置用垂线表示。粗线代表位置比较接近的终止密码子簇。保守的剪接供体 D 和受体 A[93] 的位置也在图中标明。核苷酸序列的位置也在图下方表示，位置编号从转录起始位点开始。四个最大的开放阅读框的位置标注为 gag、pol、sor 和 env-lor，每个开放阅读框的第一个 ATG 密码子（M）也被标出。第五个开放阅读框（3′-orf）在克隆 BH8 中发现，但是在 BH10 中没有；虚垂线表示在 BH10 中终止密码子的位置。

与HTLV-III的相似度（%）

```
HTLV-III BH10 CLONE U3   8824   GAGAAGTTAGAAGAAGCCAACAAAGGAGAGA   8854
HTLV-III BH8  CLONE U3   8824   GAGAAGTAAGAAGAAGCCAATAAAGGAGAGA   8854
HTLV-I            U3      307   AATAAACTAGCAGGAGTCTATAAAAGCGTGG  337        61
                                 x  xx     xx xx x  x  xxxxx  x xx
HTLV-II           U3      268   AATAAAAGATGCCGAGTCTATAAAGGCGCAA  298        51
                                 x  xx     xx xx x  x xxxxxxx xx

HTLV-III          U3     9067   TGGCGAGCCCTCAGATCCTGC  ATA   TAA  9093       62
BLV               U3      152   TGCTGA   CCTCA   CCTGCTGATAAATTAA 178
                                xx       xxx        xx  xx x  xxx

HTLV-III GAG p15         1886   ACTAAAGGAAGCTCTATTAGATACAGGAGCAGATGAT ACAGT ATT AGA AG   1935   76
HTLV-I BETWEEN GAG & POL 2223   ACTA  TCGAAGCTTTACTAGATACAGGACAGA CATGACAGTCCTTCCGATAG    2274
                                xxxx       xxx    xxxxxxxxxxxxxxx        xx   x  x  xx  x

HTLV-III BETWEEN SOR & ENV-LOR  5615   CTATCAAAGCAGTAAGTAGTACATGTAATG   5644   77
HTLV-I ENV                      5831   CTA CAAAGCACTAATTA TACTTGCATTG   5858
                                       xxx xxxxxxx xx  xx  xxx  xx x  xx
```

图 3. HTLV-I，-II，-III 和 BLV 的核苷酸序列的同源性。星号表示在 HTLV-III 相同位置中出现的相同的核苷酸（克隆 BH10 另有注明）。每一条序列的核苷酸位置都已标出。

第一个开放阅读框（gag）

逆转录病毒 gag 基因的结构蛋白是基因组 5′ 末端编码的一段多肽前体经蛋白酶水解的产物 [57]。这个前体有 512 个氨基酸，可能由 HTLV-III 前病毒的第一个长开放阅读框编码（核苷酸 310~1,869）。确认 gag 前体的氨基末端需要进行氨基酸测序。利用感染了 HTLV-III 的人的血清和接种了 HTLV-III 病毒粒子的动物的血清，与得到的感染了 HTLV-III 的细胞进行免疫共沉淀反应，得到了一种相对分子量为 53,000（53K）的蛋白 [12,13,58]。这种 53K 的蛋白可能是 HTLV-III 的 gag 前体。

The identity of the first open reading frame as the *gag* gene is established by the correspondence of the sequence of the amino-terminal 15 amino acids of the p24 major capsid protein (our unpublished observations with S. Oroszolan) with the sequence predicted for the first open reading frame between nucleotides 730 and 774. Moreover, amino acid similarities between the *gag* gene products of HTLV-I and BLV were detected in regions corresponding to the p24 and p15 *gag* products[32,33,59] (Fig. 4).

```
GAG  p24  HTLV-III  133  PIVQNIQGQMVHQAISPRTLNAWVK  157
          HTLV-I    131  PVMHPHGAPPNHRPHQMKDLQAIKQ  155
     BLV            110  PII SEGNRNRHRAWALRELQDIKK  133

     p24  HTLV-III  325  NANPDCKTILKALGPAATLEEMMT ACQGVGGPGHKARVL  363
          HTLV-I    306  NANKECGKLLQARGHTNSPLGDMLRACQTHT PKDKTKVL  364

     p15  HTLV-III  392  CFNCGKEGHTARNCRAPR  409
          HTLV-III  413  CHKCGKEGHGMKDCTERQ  430
          HTLV-I    357  CFRCGKAGHMSRDCTQPR  374
     BLV            347  CYRCLKEGHHARDCQTPTK  364
     BLV            372  CPICKDPSHHKRDCPTLK  389

POL - PEPTIDASE  HTLV-III POL  80   TIKIGGQLKEALLDTGADDTVLEEMSLPGRW  110
                 Mo-MULV POL   14   TLKVGGQPVTFLVDTGAQHSVLTQNPGPLSD  44
                 RSV GAG       601  PVKQRSVYITALLDSGADITIISEEDWPIDM  631
                 HTLV-I BETWEEN GAG & POL  EALLDTGADMTVLPIALFSSNT

                 HTLV-III POL  117  GIGGFIKVR  125
                 Mo-MULV POL   51   GATGGKRYR  59
                 RSV GAG       643  GIGGGIPMR  651

                 HTLV-III POL  152  IIGRNLLTQIG  162
                 Mo-MULV POL   87   LLGRDLLTKLK  97
                 RSV GAG       685  ILGRDCLQGLG  695
                 HTLV-I BETWEEN GAG & POL  IIGRDALQQCQ

REVERSE           HTLV-III  192  PLTEEKIKALVEICTEMEKEGKI  214
TRANSCRIPTASE     HTLV-I    31   PFKPERLQALQHLVRKALEAGHI  53
REGION            BLV       5    PFKLERLQALQDLVHRSLEAGYI  27

                 HTLV-III  224  NTPVFAIKKKDSTKWRKLVDFRELN  248
                 HTLV-I    61   NNPVFPVKKANGT WRFIHDLRATN  84
                 BLV       35   NNPVFPVRKPNGA WRFVHDLRATN  58

POL -  REVERSE        HTLV-III  276  LDVGDAYFSVPLDEDFRKYTAFTIPSINNETPGIRYQYNVLPQGHKGSPAIF  327
       TRANSCRIPTASE  HTLV-I    113  IDLRDAFFQIPLPKQFQPYFAFTVPQQCNYGPGTRYAHKVLPQGFKNSPTLF  164
       REGION         BLV       87   LDLKDAFFHLIPVEDRFRFYLSFTLPSPGGLQPHRREAHRVLPQGFINSPALF  138

                 HTLV-III  349  QYMDDLYVGS  358
                 HTLV-I    186  QYMDDILLAS  195
                 BLV       160  SYMDDILYAS  169

ENDONUCLEASE     HTLV-III  787  IHQLDCTHLEGKVILVAVHVASGYIE A  813
REGION           HTLV-I    660  IHQGDITHHFKYKNTLYRLHVHWDTFSGA  687
                 BLV       622  IHQADITHYKYKQFTYALHVFVDTYSGA  649

                 HTLV-III  840  IHTDNGSNFTSATVKAACWHAGIKQEFGIPYNPQSQGVVESMNKELK  886
                 HTLV-I    718  INTDNGPAYISQDFLNMCTSLAIRHTTHVPYNPTSSGLVERSNGILK  764
                 BLV       680  LNTDGGANYTSKTFVRFCQQFGVSLSHHVPYNPTSSGLDERTNGLLK  726

ENV-LOR - L1  HTLV-III ENV-LOR  519  AV GIGALFLGFLGAAG  534
              HTLV-I ENV        317  AVHLVSALAMGAGVAGG  333
              HTLV-I LOR        1    PCLLSAHFPGFGQSLL  16
              HTLV-II ENV       313  AVHLVPALAAGIGIAGG  329
              BLV ENV           305  A ALTLGLALSVGLTGI  320
              AKV ENV           472  PVSLTLALLLGGLTMGG  488

L2            HTLV-III ENV-LOR  583  LQARILAVERYLKDQ  QL  599
              HTLV-I ENV        376  AQNRRRGLDLLFWEQG  GL  392
              HTLV-II ENV       372  AQNRRGLDLLFWEQG   GL  388
              BLV ENV           365  AQNRRGLDHLYIRLGFQSL  383
              AKV ENV           539  LQNRRGLDLLFLKEG  QL  555

L3            HTLV-III ENV-LOR  690  KLFIMIVGGLVGL  702
              HTLV-I ENV        452  LLLLVILAGPCIL  464
              HTLV-II ENV       448  LLLLVILFGPCIL  460
              BLV ENV           446  ALFLLFLAPPCIL  458
              AKV ENV           621  ILLLILLFGPCIL  633
```

Asterisks indicate amino acids which are identical at the same position as that predicted by the HTLV-III clone BH10 DNA sequence. The positions of the amino acid residues are indicated. Env-lor sequences L1, L2, and L3 are indicated.

Fig. 4. Amino acid homologies between HTLV-III predicted proteins and those of other retroviruses. Asterisks indicate amino acids identical at the same position as that predicted by the HTLV-III clone BH10 DNA sequence. Positions of amino acid residues are indicated. Sequences L1, L2 and L3 in *env-lor* are noted in Fig. 5.

Cleavage of the putative *gag* gene product precursor between amino acids 132 and 133 to yield the observed amino-terminus of p24 would produce an amino-terminal polypeptide 132 amino acids long. This protein would be similar in length to the amino-terminus of the *gag* gene product of HTLV-I (126 amino acids)[32,34]. A 17K virion protein has been identified that probably corresponds to this product[12,20,58].

The immediate juxtaposition of the p24 protein with the amino-terminal p17 protein is like the structure of the *gag* gene products of HTLV-I[32] and BLV[33] which differs from murine, avian, feline and primate type-C and type-D retroviruses in this region, as HTLV-I and BLV seem to lack a short phosphoprotein encoded usually in other retroviruses by sequences between the amino-terminal *gag* protein and the major capsid protein coding sequences[34,57,60,61].

The third HTLV-III *gag* protein (p15) reveals significant amino acid homologies to the p15 proteins of HTLV-I[32,62] and BLV[33] (Fig. 4). There are direct repeats of the DNA sequence in this region of *gag* (Fig. 1), a feature common to both HTLV-I and BLV p15 proteins. The predicted p15 protein of HTLV-III is probably basic and binds nucleic acids, like

通过主要衣壳蛋白 p24（我们和欧罗斯兰未发表的观察结果）的氨基末端 15 个氨基酸序列与第一个开放阅读框 730 和 774 位核苷酸之间的预测序列的相关性，我们确定了 *gag* 基因就是第一个开放阅读框。此外，我们在与 p24 和 p15 *gag* 基因产物对应的区域中，发现了 HTLV -I 和 BLV 的 *gag* 基因产物的氨基酸相似性 [32,33,59]（图 4）。

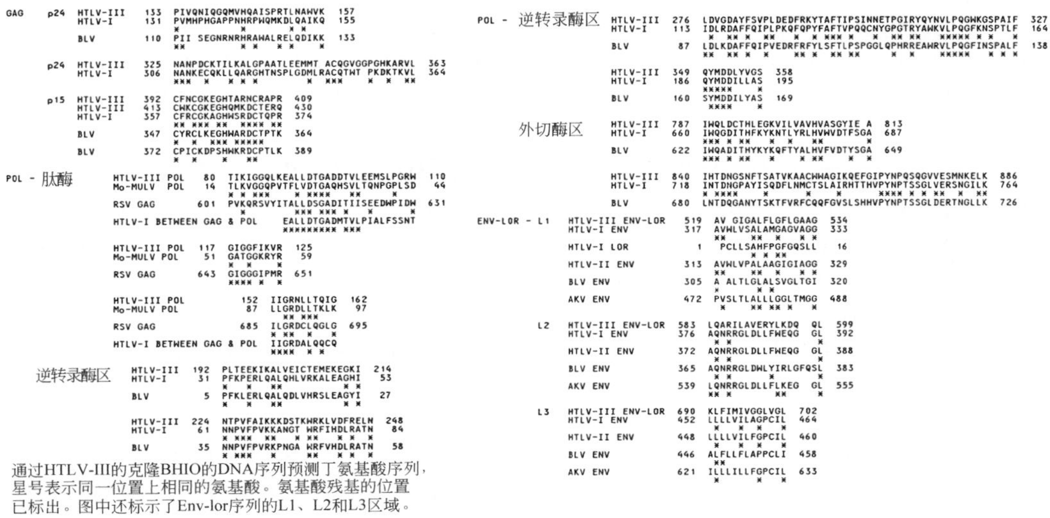

```
GAG   p24  HTLV-III 133 PIVQNIQGQMVHQAISPRTLNAHVK  157     POL - 逆转录酶区  HTLV-III 276 LDVGDAYFSVPLDEDFRKYTAFTIPSINNETPGIRYQYNVLPQGWKGSPAIF  327
           HTLV-I   131 PVMHPHGAPPNKHPWQMKDLQAIKQ  155                      HTLV-I   113 IDLRDAFFQIPLPKQFQPYFAFTVPQQCNYGPGTRYAWKVLPQGFKNSPTLF  164
           BLV      110 PII SEGNRNRHRAWALRELQDIKK  133                      BLV       87 LDLKDAFFQIPRVEDRRFRYLSFTLPSPGGLQPHRREANRVLPQGFINSPALF 138

      p24  HTLV-III 325 NANPDCKTILKALGPAATLEEMMI ACQGVGGPGHKARVL  363                    HTLV-III 349 QYMDDLYVGS  358
           HTLV-I   306 NANKECQKLLQARGHTNSPLGDMLRACQTHT PKDKTKVL  364                    HTLV-I   186 QYMDDILLAS  195
                                                                                          BLV      160 SYMDDILYAS  169
      p15  HTLV-III 392 CFNCGKEGHTARNCRAPR  409
           HTLV-III 413 CWKCGKEGHQMKDCTERQ  430            外切酶区      HTLV-III 787 IWQLDCTHLEGKVILVAVHVASGYIE A   813
           HTLV-I   357 CFRCGKAGHWSRDCTGPT  374                          HTLV-I   660 IHQGDITHFKYKNLYRLHVWVDTFSGA    687
           BLV      347 CYRCLKEGHWARDCTPTK  364                          BLV      622 IWQADITHYKYKQFTYALHVFVDTYSGA   649
           BLV      372 CPICKDPSHWKRDCPTLK  389

POL - 肽酶  HTLV-III POL  80 TIKIGGQLKEALLDTGADTVLEEMSLPGRW  110                 HTLV-III 840 IHTDNGSNFTSATVKAACHWAGIKQEFGIPYNPQSGGVVESMNKELK  886
            Mo-MULV POL   14 TLKVGGQPVTFLVDTGAQHSVLTQNPGPLSD 44                 HTLV-I   718 INDNGPAYISQDFLNMCTSLAIRHTTHVPYNPTSSGLVERSNGILK   764
            RSV GAG      601 PVKQRSVYITALLDSGADITIISEEDWPIDW 631                BLV      680 LNTDQGANYTSKTFVRFCQQFGVSLSHHVPYNPTSSGLDERTNGLLK  726
            HTLV-I BETWEEN GAG & POL     EALLDTGADMTVLPIALFSSNT
                                                           ENV-LOR - L1  HTLV-III ENV-LOR 519 AV GIGALFLGFLGAAG  534
            HTLV-III POL 117 GIGGFIKVR  125                               HTLV-I ENV       317 AVHLVSALAMGAGVAGG 333
            Mo-MULV POL   51 GATGQKRYR  59                                HTLV-I LOR         1 PCLLSAHFPGFGQSLL  16
            RSV GAG      643 GIGGGIPMR  651                               HTLV-I ENV       313 AVHLVPALAAGIGIAGG 329
            HTLV-I BETWEEN GAG & POL                                      BLV ENV          305 A ALTLGLALSVGLTGI 320
                                                                         AKV ENV          472 PVSLTLALLLGGLTMGG 488
            HTLV-III POL 152 IIGRNLLTQIG  162
            Mo-MULV POL   87 LLGRDLLTKLK  97              L2  HTLV-III ENV-LOR 583 LQARILAVERYLKDQ QL  599
            RSV GAG      685 ILGRDCLQGLG  695                 HTLV-I ENV       376 AQNRRGLDLLFWEQG GL  392
            HTLV-I BETWEEN GAG & POL  IIGRDALQQCQ              HTLV-II ENV      372 AQNRRGLDLLFWEQG GL  388
                                                              BLV ENV          365 AQNRRGLDHLYIRLQFQSL 383
逆转录酶区   HTLV-III 192 PLTEEKIKALVEICTEMEKEGKI  214         AKV ENV          539 LQNRRGLDLLFLKEG GL  555
            HTLV-I   31 PFKPERLQALHLVRKALEAGHI   53
            BLV       5 PFKLERLQALQDLVHRSLEAGYI  27        L3  HTLV-III ENV-LOR 690 KLFIMIVGGLVG  702
                                                              HTLV-I ENV       452 LLLLVILAGPCIL 464
            HTLV-III 224 NTPVFAIKKKDSTKHRKLVDFRELN  248        HTLV-II ENV      448 LLLLVILFGPCIL 460
            HTLV-I   61 NNPVFPVKKANGT WRFIHDLRATN   84        BLV ENV          446 ALFLLFLAPPCLI 458
            BLV      35 NNPVFPVRKPNGA WRFVHDLRATN   58        AKV ENV          621 ILLLILLFGPCIL 633
```

通过HTLV-III的克隆BHIO的DNA序列预测了氨基酸序列，星号表示同一位置上相同的氨基酸。氨基酸残基的位置已标出。图中还标示了Env-lor序列的L1、L2和L3区域。

图 4. HTLV-III 预测的蛋白与其他逆转录病毒蛋白的氨基酸同源性。星号表示某个位置的氨基酸与 HTLV-III 克隆 BH10 DNA 序列中预测的相同。氨基酸残基位置被标明。*env-lor* 的 L1、L2 和 L3 的序列见图 5。

蛋白酶在推测的 *gag* 基因前体产物的第 132 和 133 位氨基酸之间切割，能够产生一个 132 个氨基酸的多肽，即已观察到的 p24 的氨基末端。这个蛋白在长度上与 HTLV-I 的 *gag* 基因的氨基末端产物（126 个氨基酸）相似 [32,34]。已发现的一个 17k 的病毒颗粒蛋白可能就是这个产物 [12,20,58]。

p24 蛋白和 p17 蛋白的氨基末端是紧密相邻的，就像 HTLV-I[32] 和 BLV[33] 的 *gag* 基因产物的结构一样，它们不同于啮齿类、鸟类、猫科和灵长类的 C- 型和 D- 型逆转录病毒在该区域的产物，HTLV-I 和 BLV 似乎缺少一段短的磷蛋白，在其他逆转录病毒中通常由 *gag* 蛋白氨基末端和主要衣壳蛋白的编码序列之间的序列所编码 [34,57,60,61]。

第三个 HTLV-III *gag* 蛋白（p15）与 HTLV-I[32,62] 和 BLV[33] 的 p15 蛋白有显著的氨基酸同源性（图 4）。在 *gag* 的这个区域有正向的 DNA 重复序列（图 1），这是 HTLV-I 和 BLV p15 蛋白共有的一个特点。该预测的 HTLV-III 的 p15 蛋白可能是碱

the basic proteins of other retroviruses[34,63,64]. (There is also a proline-rich sequence at the carboxyl end of the *gag* precursor that may encode a small polypeptide similar to the progagtin described by S. Oroszolan and co-authors (personal communication).)

We conclude that the first long open reading frame of the HTLV-III genome encodes the *gag* protein precursor, based on the location of the open reading frame near the 5′ end of the viral genome and the correspondence between sequences predicted for the *gag* gene precursor and those observed for the major capsid p24 protein. The structure of the *gag* precursor resembles more closely that of HTLV-I and BLV than it does other retroviruses, as the amino-terminal *gag* protein is immediately juxtaposed to the major capsid protein.

Second Open Reading Frame (*pol*)

The predicted amino acid sequence of the second long open reading frame (nucleotides 1,629–4,673) that overlaps the first open reading frame by 80 amino acids, reveals numerous regions of amino acid similarity to the *pol* gene products of other retroviruses[34,65,66] (Fig. 4). These regions of conserved sequences are co-linear with those of other retroviruses, therefore we conclude that the second long open reading frame encodes the viral reverse transcriptase protein.

Similarities in amino acid sequences in the virally encoded protease products of other retroviruses are present at the amino-terminus of the HTLV-III *pol* protein precursor[57,60,61,67-70] (Fig. 4). Therefore, we suggest that the second open reading frame, in addition to encoding the reverse transcriptase, also encodes a protease.

The 3′ portion of the *pol* genes of Rous sarcoma virus (RSV) and Moloney murine leukaemia virus (Mo-MuLV) also encode an endonuclease of $M_r \sim 40K$[67,71]. Regions of homology between the polymerase genes of RSV[61] and Mo-MuLV[60] with HTLV-III suggest that the *pol* gene of HTLV-III also encodes an endonuclease.

We note that the region of greatest nucleic acid sequence similarity of HTLV-III to HTLV-I[32] is near the 5′ end of the second open reading frame (nucleotides 1,886–1,935) (Fig. 3), but this region does not encode a protein product in HTLV-I[32].

We conclude that the second open reading frame encodes the *pol* gene, the reverse transcriptase and a protease at its 5′-terminus, plus an endonuclease at its 3′-terminus. We note that HTLV-III differs from HTLV-I in the amino-terminal region of the second open reading frame as the corresponding region of HTLV-I cannot encode a functional protease[32,34].

Third Open Reading Frame (*sor*)

The region between the second and fourth open reading frames (nucleotides 4,674–5,780) also includes an open reading frame (nucleotides 4,588–5,196), capable of encoding

性的且能与核酸结合，就像其他逆转录病毒的碱性蛋白那样[34,63,64]。（在 gag 蛋白前体的羧基末端也有一段富含脯氨酸的序列，它可能编码一个小的多肽，与欧罗斯兰及其合著者（个人交流）描述的 gag 蛋白前体相似）。

我们的结论是 HTLV-III 基因组的第一个长开放阅读框编码 gag 蛋白前体，因为这个开放阅读框的位置靠近病毒基因组的 5′端，而且 gag 基因前体的预测序列和观察到的主要衣壳蛋白 p24 的序列相对应。与其他的逆转录病毒相比较，gag 前体的结构和 HTLV-I 以及 BLV 的更为相似，因为 gag 蛋白的氨基端和主要衣壳蛋白在位置上是紧密相邻的。

第二个开放阅读框（pol）

由第二个长开放阅读框（核苷酸 1,629～4,673）预测的氨基酸序列与第一个开放阅读框有 80 个氨基酸的重叠，揭示了该序列多个区域的氨基酸序列与其他逆转录病毒的 pol 基因产物[34,65,66] 有相似性（图 4）。这些保守区序列与其他逆转录病毒的保守区序列呈共线性，因此我们推测第二个长开放阅读框编码病毒逆转录酶。

HTLV-III pol 蛋白前体的氨基末端与其他逆转录病毒编码的蛋白酶在氨基酸序列上具有相似性[57,60,61,67-70]（图 4）。因此，我们认为第二个开放阅读框除了编码逆转录酶外，还编码蛋白酶。

劳氏肉瘤病毒（RSV）和莫洛尼小鼠白血病病毒（Mo-MuLV）的 pol 基因 3′端也编码一个分子量约 40K[67,71] 的核酸内切酶。RSV[61] 和 Mo-MuLV[60] 与 HTLV-III 聚合酶基因的同源区表明 HTLV-III 的 pol 基因也编码一个核酸内切酶。

我们发现，HTLV-III 和 HTLV-I[32] 之间的核酸序列相似度最大的区域位于第二个开放阅读框的 5′ 末端附近（核苷酸 1,886～1,935）（图 3），但是这个区域在 HTLV-I 中不编码蛋白[32]。

我们推测第二个阅读框编码 pol 基因，其 5′端编码逆转录酶和蛋白酶，同时其 3′端编码核酸内切酶。我们认为 HTLV-III 与 HTLV-I 在第二个开放阅读框的氨基端的不同之处在于 HTLV-I 的相应区域不能编码有功能的蛋白酶[32,34]。

第三个开放阅读框（sor）

第二和第四开放阅读框（核苷酸 4,674～5,780）之间还有一个开放阅读框（核苷酸 4,588 ～ 5,196）能编码一个 203 个氨基酸的蛋白，与 pol 基因的 3′端有 86 个

a protein 203 amino acids long, which overlaps with the 3′ end of the *pol* gene by 86 nucleotides. The 3′ portion of this region contains multiple termination codons in all three reading frames and therefore cannot encode a functional polypeptide (Fig. 2). Both the short open reading frame and non-coding region in this part of the HTLV-III genome have been identified by sequence analysis of two independent clonal isolates, BH5 and BH10. In addition, the restriction map of a biologically active HTLV-III proviral DNA clone is indistinguishable from that of the BH10 provirus throughout this region (our unpublished observations with A. Fisher and E. Collalti). For these reasons, we suggest that this unusual sequence is common to replication-competent HTLV-III viruses. We designate the 5′ portion of this sequence *sor* (short open reading frame).

The predicted product of the *sor* region would be a polypeptide of M_r 21K. This amino acid sequence shows no significant homology to any known viral or mammalian cellular genes, but there is a region of DNA sequence similarity in the non-coding region (nucleotides 5,615–5,644) with the sequences found in the *env* gene of HTLV-I[32] (Fig. 3). Also, the overlap in the open reading frame of the second and third open reading frames is like the structure of the envelope genes of HTLV-I[32] and of BLV[33]. Thus, it is possible that the *sor* region of HTLV-III and the flanking non-coding region represent a vestigial *env* gene.

Fourth Open Reading Frame (*env-lor*)

The fourth open reading frame (nucleotides 5,781–8,369) could encode a protein 863 amino acids long. There is a short tandem duplication (nucleotides 6,972–6,986 and 6,987-7,001) in the DNA sequence in this open reading frame in one of the two HTLV-III clones (BH10) sequenced (Fig. 1).

The predicted product of the fourth reading frame, *env-lor*, shares many features in common with the envelope gene precursors of other retroviruses, the most striking of which is a hydrophobic region near the middle of the protein (amino acids 519-534)[32-34,72-75] (Fig. 4). This region of amino acid conservation is preceded in the HTLV-III and other retroviral proteins by an arginine-rich hydrophilic region[37,76] which includes also the processing site for cleavage of the *env* protein precursors into exterior and transmembrane proteins (see Fig. 5).

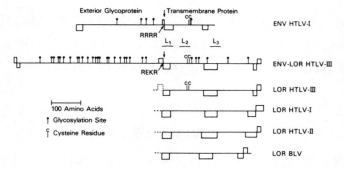

Fig. 5. Structure of *env-lor* product of HTLV-III. The structural features of the predicted *env-lor* product

核苷酸重叠。在三种阅读框中，该区域的 3′ 端均含有多个终止密码子，因此不能编码有功能的多肽（图 2）。通过对两个独立的克隆 BH5 和 BH10 的序列进行分析，我们识别出 HTLV-III 基因组这一区域的短开放阅读框和非编码区。另外，在这部分区域上，有生物学活性的 HTLV-III 前病毒 DNA 克隆的限制性酶切图谱与 BH10 病毒前体的限制性酶切图谱非常相似（我们和费希尔以及科拉尔蒂未发表的观测结果）。由于这些原因，我们认为这个不寻常的序列为有复制能力的 HTLV-III 病毒所共有。我们将这条序列的 5′ 部分命名为 sor（意为短开放阅读框）。

sor 区域的预测编码产物是一个相对分子量为 21K 的多肽。这条氨基酸序列与已知的任何病毒或者哺乳动物细胞基因都没有显著的同源性，但是其非编码区的 DNA 序列（核苷酸 5,615～5,644）与 HTLV-I 的 env 基因中的序列有相似性[32]（图 3）。第二和第三开放阅读框的重叠与 HTLV-I[32] 和 BLV[33] 的包膜基因的结构很相似。因此，HTLV-III 的 sor 区和其相邻的非编码区可能是一个退化的 env 基因。

第四个开放阅读框（env-lor）

第四个开放阅读框（核苷酸 5,781～8,369）编码一个 863 个氨基酸的蛋白。两个已测序的 HTLV-III 克隆中的一个（BH10）在这个开放阅读框的 DNA 序列中有一个短的串联倍增序列（核苷酸 6,972～6,986 和 6,987～7,001）（图 1）。

第四个开放阅读框 env-lor 的预测产物与其他逆转录病毒的包膜基因前体有许多共同特征，最显著的就是靠近蛋白中间部位的疏水区域（氨基酸 519-534 处）[32-34,72-75]（图 4）。这段具有氨基酸保守性的区域在 HTLV-III 中通过富精氨酸疏水区得到延长，在其他逆转录病毒的蛋白中也是如此[37,76]，它还包括将 env 蛋白前体切割为膜外和跨膜蛋白的作用位点（见图 5）。

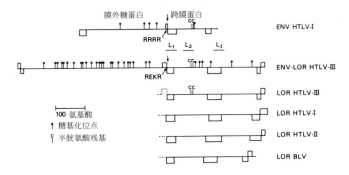

图 5. HTLV-III 的 env-lor 产物结构。将预测的 HTLV-III 的 env-lor 产物的结构特点与 HTLV-I[32]、II[35] 和

of HTLV-III is compared with those of HTLV-I[32], -II[35] and the BLV *lor* products[33,37] and HTLV-I *env* product[32]. Boxes above and below each line represent hydrophilic and hydrophobic regions, respectively[94,95]. Also shown are the positions of potential asparagine-linked glycosylation sites[77] and cysteine residues in the transmembrane proteins. Following asparagine-rich sequences (R, asparagine; E, glutamic acid; K, lysine), the proposed cleavage sites between the exterior glycoprotein and transmembrane protein are shown by an arrow. The scale for amino acid residues is shown at the left. L1, L2 and L3 refer to amino acid sequences which are similar to those of other retroviruses, shown in Fig. 4.

The amino-terminal domain of the translation product of the fourth open reading frame also resembles the *env* protein precursors of other retroviruses[34]. There is a short hydrophobic sequence at the amino-terminus (amino acids 17–37) which may correspond to the signal polypeptide cleaved from the *env* precursor in the maturation process. Moreover, the region of the protein between the putative signal peptide and transmembrane protein is hydrophilic and contains 24 potential asparagine-linked glycosylation sites[77].

The structure of the amino-terminal domain of the predicted transmembrane region resembles closely that of other retroviruses, with respect to both the relative distribution of hydrophobic and hydrophilic residues and the relative location of cysteine residues[34,37,73,78-80] (Fig. 5). The HTLV-III *env-lor* protein, however, differs from envelope proteins of other retroviruses in an additional 180 amino acids at the carboxy-terminus[32,34,37,60,61,73].

In summary, we believe that the fourth open reading frame encodes an *env* precursor, possibly 826 amino acids long, without the signal peptide sequence. In its mature form it is probably cleaved into a large heavily glycosylated exterior membrane protein about 481 amino acids long and a transmembrane protein 345 amino acids long which may be glycosylated (Figs 1,5). The size of these predicted products agrees with the detection of a large glycosylated protein of M_r 120–160K in HTLV-III-infected cells which is probably the glycosylated *env* gene precursor[58] and a smaller, virion-associated gp41 which is probably the transmembrane protein[12,13].

Does a *lor* Gene Exist?

The genomes of HTLV-I, -II and BLV differ from those of the non-acute retroviruses by the presence of a *lor* 3′ to the *env* gene[32,33,35,37,81]. This region of HTLV-I and -II is encoded by a 2-kb mRNA[81,82] which is translated into M_r 42K and 38K proteins, respectively[83,84]. There are several reasons to suspect that the 3′-portion of the fourth open reading frame of HTLV-III also encodes a protein with functions similar to those of the *lor* products of the HTLV-I and -II genomes. Most important is the presence of a 2-kb spliced mRNA species in HTLV-III-infected cells including the 3′, but not the 5′ portion, of the fourth open reading frame (our unpublished observations with S. K. Arya and G. Chan). This mRNA is long enough to include ~1,000 nucleotides of the 3′ portion of the fourth open reading frame.

The overall structure of the *lor* product thought to be synthesized from the carboxy-terminal 1,000 nucleotides of the fourth open reading frame of HTLV-III is similar in

BLV 的 lor[33,37] 产物，HTLV-I 的 env 产物 [32] 相比较。每条线的上面和下面的方框分别代表亲水和疏水区域 [94,95]。同时也标明了潜在的天冬酰胺连接型糖基化位点 [77] 和跨膜蛋白中半胱氨酸残基的位置。富天冬酰胺序列（R，天冬酰胺；E，谷氨酸；K，赖氨酸）膜外糖蛋白和跨膜蛋白之间可能的切割位点用箭头表示。氨基酸残基的比例尺在左边。L1、L2 和 L3 代表与其他逆转录病毒相似的氨基酸序列，如图 4。

第四开放阅读框翻译产物的氨基端区域也类似于其他逆转录病毒 env 蛋白前体 [34]。在氨基末端有一个短的疏水区（氨基酸 17~37），它可能是 env 前体在成熟过程中切下的信号肽。另外，在预测的信号肽和跨膜蛋白之间的区域是亲水的，还包括 24 个潜在的天冬酰胺连接型糖基化位点 [77]。

预测的跨膜区域的氨基末端结构域在结构上由于相关的疏水、亲水残基的分布以及半胱氨酸残基相对位置 [34,37,73,78-80]，而与其他逆转录病毒的蛋白非常相似（图 5）。但是 HTLV-III 的 env-lor 蛋白比其他逆转录病毒包膜蛋白在羧基端多出 180 个氨基酸 [32,34,37,60,61,73]。

总之，我们相信第四开放阅读框编码一个 env 前体蛋白，可能有 826 个氨基酸，没有信号肽序列。它可能被切割为一个约 481 个氨基酸的高度糖基化的膜外蛋白和一个 345 个氨基酸的可能被糖基化的跨膜蛋白，从而进入其成熟形式（图 1、图 5）。预测的蛋白大小与在感染的 HTLV-III 的细胞中检测到大的糖基化蛋白的分子量在 120~160K 之间的结果一致，它可能是糖基化的 env 前体 [58] 和一个小的病毒颗粒相关蛋白 gp41，gp41 可能是跨膜蛋白 [12,13]。

是否存在 lor 基因？

由于 env 基因的 3' 端存在 lor 基因 [32,33,35,37,81]，因此 HTLV-I、-II 和 BLV 的基因组与那些非急性逆转录病毒不同。HTLV-I、-II 的这部分区域由 2,000 个碱基的 mRNA 编码 [81,82]，分别翻译成分子量为 42K 和 38K 的蛋白 [83,84]。有许多理由怀疑，HTLV-III 第四开放阅读框的 3' 端也编码与 HTLV-I 和 -II 基因组上 lor 编码产物有相似功能的蛋白。最重要的是，在感染 HTLV-III 的细胞中出现了 2,000 个碱基的 mRNA 剪接产物，它包含第四阅读框的 3' 端而缺少 5' 端（我们和阿里亚以及尚未发表的结果），这段 mRNA 的长度足够包含第四开放阅读框 3' 端 1,000 个左右的核苷酸。

我们认为 lor 基因产物是由第四开放阅读框羧基端的 1000 个核苷酸所合成的，其整体结构与通过 HTLV-I、-II 和 BLV 的 lor 区域的核苷酸序列预测的结构相似 [32,35,37]。

structure to that predicted by the nucleic acid sequence of the *lor* regions of HTLV-I, -II and BLV[32,35,37]. This similarity includes the size of the *lor* polypeptide, the presence of three hydrophobic regions spaced approximately the same distance apart and the presence of a carboxy-terminal hydrophilic region (Fig. 5). Such a protein may mediate the observed *trans*-activation of transcription of the viral LTR in HTLV-III-infected cells[39], as suggested already for the *lor* product of HTLV-I, -II and BLV[38,85].

There is a sequence of 292 nucleotides between the end of the fourth open reading frame and the beginning of the LTR. The purine-rich sequence preceding the LTR is similar to that of the site of second-strand DNA initiation[86] (Fig. 1).

We propose that the fourth open reading frame encodes two functional polypeptides, one that serves as the precursor for the major envelope glycoprotein and a second derived from the 3' end of the open reading frame, corresponding to the *lor* gene of other HTLV-BLV viruses.

Heterogeneity in HTLV-III Viruses

Sequences from different clones of HTLV-III allow an analysis of the level of sequence diversity of the virus. A comparison of clones BH8 and BH5 with BH10 (Fig. 1) demonstrates a 0.9% base pair polymorphism in the coding regions of the genome and a 1.8% base pair polymorphism in the non-coding regions. In addition, three 1–3-bp deletions are noted in the non-coding regions, as well as a 15-bp sequence present in one copy in clone BH8, but repeated tandemly in the *env-lor* region of clone BH10. In the coding regions, most nucleotide differences are in the third codon positions; of those that predict amino acid differences between clones, most are non-conservative substitutions. The resultant differences in viral protein function remain to be determined. Of note is the presence of a fifth open reading frame (nucleotides 8,344–8,991), designated 3' *orf*, present in clone BH8 but truncated in BH10 (Fig. 2).

The heterogeneity among HTLV-III clones shown here could represent sequence divergence developing in culture in a given individual over a period of time, or polymorphic differences in viruses from different individuals. Diversity among different HTLV-III isolates seems to be greater than that between different HTLV-I isolates[6,53]. Different isolates of HTLV-III comprise a spectrum of closely to distantly related viruses. Heterogeneity of proviruses within a given individual, however, has not been noted. Furthermore, a cloned HTLV-III provirus from another individual differs in 18 of 31 restriction enzyme sites mapped compared with clone BH10; the restriction enzyme map of this isolate did not change over a period of several months in culture (our unpublished observations with B. Hahn and G. Shaw). Thus, it is likely that most of the divergence among the HTLV-III clones analysed here represents differences in strains in different individuals. The full extent of this diversity in the HTLV-III family of viruses, however, remains to be determined, and is probably necessary in estimating possible differences in antigenicity of viral proteins. These differences could be important factors in the design of agents useful for viral detection or for therapeutic agents.

相似性包括 *lor* 多肽的长度，三个间隔距离相似的疏水区和一个羧基端亲水区（图 5）。这个蛋白可以介导实验中观察到的 HTLV-III 感染细胞中病毒 LTR 转录的反式激活现象 [39]，就像 HTLV-I、-II 和 BLV 的 *lor* 产物 [38,85] 一样。

在第四开放阅读框的末尾和 LTR 开始之间有一条 292 个核苷酸长度的序列。LTR 前端的富嘌呤序列与 DNA 第二链起始位点相似 [86]（图 1）。

我们认为第四开放阅读框编码两个功能性多肽，一个是主要包膜糖蛋白的前体，另一个来自开放阅读框的 3′ 端，与其他 HTLV-BLV 病毒的 *lor* 基因相对应。

HTLV-III 病毒的异质性

不同克隆的 HTLV-III 序列可以用于分析病毒序列的多样性。比较克隆 BH8 和 BH5 与 BH10 的差异（图 1），发现在基因编码区有 0.9% 的碱基对多态性，在非编码区有 1.8% 的碱基对多态性。另外，在非编码区发现有三处 1~3 个碱基对的缺失现象，同时存在一个 15 碱基对序列，在克隆 BH8 中以单拷贝形式存在，但是在克隆 BH10 的 *env-lor* 区则为串联重复形式。在编码区，大多数核苷酸的差异出现在密码子第三位；不同克隆之间氨基酸序列的差异，大多数是非保守型的替换。由此导致的病毒蛋白功能的差异有待探究。值得注意的是，在 BH8 中出现了定义为 3′*orf* 的第五开放阅读框（核苷酸 8,344~8,991），但是它在 BH10 中被截短了（图 2）。

本文中 HTLV-III 克隆之间表现出来的异质性说明给定的个体培养一段时间后可能产生序列差异，或者来自不同个体的病毒存在多态性差异。不同 HTLV-III 病毒株之间的多样性似乎高于 HTLV-I 之间的多样性 [6,53]。虽然尚未发现在一个给定个体内前病毒的异质性，但不同的 HTLV-III 分离株包含了相似度从小到大的病毒谱。此外，与克隆 BH10 相比，另一个体的 HTLV-III 克隆的前病毒 31 个限制性酶切位点中有 18 个存在差异；在几个月的时间里，培养的分离株的限制性酶切图谱都不会改变（我们和哈恩以及肖未发表的结果）。因此，这里分析的大部分 HTLV-III 克隆间的差异很可能代表了不同个体之间的差异。然而，HTLV-III 病毒家族之间差异性的范围仍旧需要鉴定，而且评价病毒蛋白抗原性可能的差异也是必要的。这些差异对于设计病毒检测方法和治疗试剂可能是重要的因素。

Discussion

HTLV-III demonstrates structural and functional similarities to other members of the HTLV-BLV family of retroviruses. Like HTLV-I[32] and BLV[33], the *gag* precursor of HTLV-III lacks a small phosphoprotein situated between the amino-terminal *gag* protein and the major capsid protein. Significant amino acid homologies exist between the major capsid and the basic *gag* proteins of HTLV-III and the corresponding proteins of HTLV-I and BLV. These homologies could account for the immunological cross-reactivity among these proteins[12,13]. Similarities of nucleic acid sequence in several areas of the genome are consistent also with previous hybridization data[26,27]. The presence of conserved amino acid sequences in the transmembrane region of the major envelope glycoprotein also might account for the cross-reactivity in the envelope gene products of HTLV-III and HTLV-I, -II and BLV[12,13,87,88]. The possibility that the 3' end of the fourth open reading frame may encode a protein similar to the *lor* product of HTLV-I, -II and BLV[33,35,37,81,83,84] might explain the *trans*-acting transcriptional activation common to these viruses[38,39,85]. Alteration of the cellular transcriptional apparatus by an HTLV-III *lor* product may be responsible, at least in part, for the specific cytotoxic effect of HTLV-III on OKT4[+] cells.

Previous studies also have highlighted differences between HTLV-III and other retroviruses. Although detectable, nucleic acid homology between the genomes of HTLV-III and other members of the HTLV-BLV family of viruses is low, reflected in differences in primary nucleotide sequence. The structure of the envelope glycoprotein of HTLV-III is different also from that of HTLV-I, -II and BLV, consistent with recent reports of differences in the size of the major envelope glycoproteins[58] as well as the differences in the type of cell receptors recognized by these viruses (refs 89, 90 and our unpublished observations with M. Popovic). Another unusual feature of the HTLV-III genome is the presence of a short open reading frame, *sor*, between the *pol* and *env* genes. The location of the *sor* region suggests that it may be evolutionarily related to the *env* gene. Although the function of this region is unknown, it too may account for some of the unusual cytotoxic and immunological properties of the HTLV-III virus.

We thank Drs Craig Rosen, Joseph Sodroski and Takashi Okamoto, Augusto Cordova, Mr Miltiades C. Psallidopoulos, Dennis Perkins, Steven Untersee and Ms Debra Briggs for assistance with these experiments; Drs George Shaw, Beatrice Hahn and Suresh Arya in the Laboratory of Tumor Cell Biology for providing the HTLV-III clones; Dr Yogi Ikawa and co-workers for sharing unpublished BLV sequences and Ms Debra Lomb and Dr David Lipmann for assistance with the computer analysis. Part of this work was supported by NIH grant CA36974 and ACS grant RD-186.

(**313**, 277-283; 1985)

Lee Ratner[*], William Haseltine[†], Roberto Patarca[†], Kenneth J. Livak[‡], Bruno Starcich[*], Steven F. Josephs[*], Ellen R. Doran[‡], J. Antoni Rafalski[‡], Erik A. Whitehorn[‡], Kirk Baumeister[‡], Lucinda Ivanoff[‡], Stephen R. Petteway Jr[‡], Mark L. Pearson[‡], James A. Lautenberger[§], Takis S. Papas[§], John Ghrayeb[||], Nancy T. Chang[||], Robert C. Gallo[*] & Flossie Wong-Staal[*]

讨 论

HTLV-III 的结构和功能与 HTLV-BLV 家族的其他逆转录病毒具有相似性。就像 HTLV-I[32] 和 BLV[33] 那样，HTLV-III 的 gag 前体在 gag 蛋白的氨基末端和主要衣壳蛋白之间缺少一个小的磷蛋白。在 HTLV-III 主要衣壳蛋白和碱性 gag 蛋白之间存在的显著的氨基酸同源性，在 HTLV-I 与 BLV 的对应蛋白之间也存在。同源性可以解释这些蛋白之间免疫交叉反应[12,13]。基因组中几个核酸区域的相似性与先前的杂交数据相一致[26,27]。在主要包膜蛋白的跨膜区域出现保守氨基酸序列能够解释 HTLV-III 与 HTLV-I，-II 和 BLV 的包膜基因产物之间的交叉反应[12,13,87,88]。 第四开放阅读框的 3′ 末端可能编码一个与 HTLV-I,-II 和 BLV[33,35,37,81,83,84] 的 lor 基因产物相似的蛋白，这可以解释这些病毒之间普遍存在的反式转录激活[38,39,85]。HTLV-III 的 lor 产物改变细胞的转录机器可能导致了 HTLV-III 对 OKT4+ 的细胞毒性，至少部分如此。

前面的研究也发现 HTLV-III 与其他逆转录病毒有很大不同。虽然能够检测到同源性，但是 HTLV-III 基因组与 HTLV-BLV 病毒家族其他成员核酸序列同源性很低，仅反映在一级核酸序列上的差异。HTLV-III 包膜糖蛋白的结构与 HTLV-I、-II 和 BLV 也不同，这一结果与近来报道的主要包膜糖蛋白大小的[58]以及这些病毒识别的细胞受体类型的不同相一致（参考文献 89、90 和波波维奇未发表的结果）。HTLV-III 基因组另一个不寻常的特点是短开放阅读框 sor 的出现，它位于 pol 和 env 之间。sor 区域的位置暗示它可能在进化上与 env 基因相关。尽管这个区域的功能还未知，但是它足以说明 HTLV-III 病毒不同寻常的细胞毒性和免疫属性。

我们感谢克雷格·罗森博士、约瑟夫·索德劳斯基博士和冈本鹰司、奥古斯托·科多瓦、米尔蒂亚季斯先生、丹尼斯·珀金斯、史蒂文·翁特塞和德布拉·布里格斯女士对这些实验的帮助；感谢肿瘤细胞生物学实验室的乔治·肖博士，比阿特丽斯·哈恩博士和苏雷什·阿里亚博士提供 HTLV-III 克隆；感谢依仪井川博士和他的合作者们分享未发表的 BLV 序列；感谢德布拉·隆布女士和戴维·李普曼博士进行的计算机分析。这项工作的一部分是由 NIH 基金 CA36974 和 ACS 基金 RD-186 支持的。

（郑建全 翻译；孙军 审稿）

* Laboratory of Tumor Cell Biology, Developmental Therapeutics Program, Division of Cancer Treatment, National Cancer Institute, Bethesda, Maryland 20205, USA

† Dana-Farber Cancer Institute and Department of Pathology, Harvard Medical School, Department of Cancer Biology, Harvard School of Public Health, Boston, Massachusetts 02114, USA

‡ Central Research and Development Department, Experimental Station, E.I. duPont de Nemours, Wilmington, Delaware 19898, USA

§ Laboratory of Molecular Oncology, National Cancer Institute, Frederick, Maryland 21701, USA

‖ Centocor, 244 Great Valley Parkway, Malvern, Pennsylvania 19355, USA

Received 29 November; accepted 14 December 1984.

References:

1. Poiesz, B. J. *et al. Proc. Natl. Acad. Sci. U.S.A.* **77**, 7415-7419 (1980).

2. Kalyanaraman, V. S., Sarngadaharan, M. G., Bunn, P. A., Minna, J. D. & Gallo, R. C. *Nature* **294**, 271-273 (1981).

3. Robert-Guroff, M., Ruscetti, F. W., Posner, L. E., Poiesz, B. J. & Gallo, R. C. *J. exp. Med.* **154**, 1957-1964 (1981).

4. Yoshida, M., Miyoshi, I. & Hinuma, Y. *Proc. Natl. Acad. Sci. U.S.A.* **79**, 2031-2035 (1982).

5. Popovic, M. *et al. Nature* **300**, 63-65 (1982).

6. Gallo, R. C. in *Cancer Surveys* (eds Franks, L. M., Wyke, J. & Weiss, R. A.) 113-159 (Oxford University Press, 1984).

7. Kalyanaraman, V. S. *et al. Science* **218**, 571-573 (1982).

8. Chen, I. S. Y., McLaughlin, J., Gasson, J. C., Clark, S. C. & Golde, D. *Nature* **305**, 502-505 (1983).

9. Gelmann, E. P., Franchini, G., Manzari, V., Wong-Staal, F. & Gallo, R. C. *Proc. Natl. Acad. Sci. U.S.A.* **81**, 993-997 (1984).

10. Popovic, M., Sarngadharan, M. G., Read, E. & Gallo, R. C. *Science* **224**, 497-499 (1984).

11. Gallo, R. C. *et al. Science* **224**, 500-502 (1984).

12. Schupbach, J. *et al. Science* **224**, 503-505 (1984).

13. Sarngadharan, M., Popovic, M., Bruch, L., Schupbach, J. & Gallo, R. C. *Science* **224**, 506-508 (1984).

14. Barre-Sinoussi, F. *et al. Science* **220**, 868-871 (1983).

15. Gallo, R. C. *et al. Proc. Natl. Acad. Sci. U.S.A.* **79**, 4680-4683 (1983).

16. Popovic, M. *et al. Science* **219**, 856-859 (1983).

17. Popovic, M., Lange-Watzin, G., Sarin, P. S., Mann, D. & Gallo, R. C. *Proc. Natl. Acad. Sci. U.S.A.* **80**, 5402-5406 (1983).

18. Gallo, R. C. *et al. Cancer Res.* **43**, 3892-3899 (1983).

19. Wong-Staal, F. *et al. Nature* **302**, 626-628 (1983).

20. Klatzmann, D. *et al. Science* **225**, 59-63 (1984).

21. Chen, I. S. Y., Quan, S. G. & Golde, D. *Proc. Natl. Acad. Sci. U.S.A.* **80**, 7006-7009 (1983).

22. Hoshino, H. *et al. Proc. Natl. Acad. Sci. U.S.A.* **80**, 6061-6065 (1983).

23. Nagy, K., Clapham, P., Cheingong-Popov, R. & Weiss, R. A. *Int. J. Cancer* **32**, 321-328 (1983).

24. Clapham, P., Nagy, K. & Weiss, R. A. *Proc. Natl. Acad. Sci. U.S.A.* **81**, 3082-3086 (1984).

25. Shaw, G. M. *et al. Proc. Natl. Acad. Sci. U.S.A.* **81**, 4544-4548 (1984).

26. Arya, S. K. *et al. Science* **225**, 927-930 (1984).

27. Hahn, B. *et al. Nature* **312**, 166-169 (1984).

28. Shimotohno, K., Golde, D. W., Miwa, M., Sugimura, T. & Chen, I. S. Y. *Proc. Natl. Acad. Sci. U.S.A.* **81**, 1079-1083 (1984).

29. Rho, H. M., Poiesz, B., Ruscetti, F. W. & Gallo, R. C. *Virology* **112**, 355-360 (1981).

30. Yoshida, M., Miyoshi, I. & Hinuma, Y. *Proc. Natl. Acad. Sci. U.S.A.* **79**, 2031-2035 (1982).

31. Rey, M. A. *et al. Biochem. Biophys. Res. Commun.* **111**, 116-133 (1984).

32. Seiki, M., Hattori, S., Hirayama, Y. & Yoshida, M. *Proc. Natl. Acad. Sci. U.S.A.* **80**, 3618-3622 (1983).

33. Sagata, N. *et al. Proc. Natl. Acad. Sci. U.S.A.* (in the press).

34. Haseltine, W. A., Sodroski, J. G. & Patarca, R. *Curr. Topics Microbiol. Immun.* **115** (in the press).

35. Haseltine, W. A. *et al. Science* **225**, 419-421 (1984).

36. Shimotohno, K. *et al. Proc. Natl. Acad. Sci. U.S.A.* **81**, 6657-6661 (1984).

37. Rice, N. R. *et al. Virology* **138**, 82-93 (1984).

38. Sodroski, J., Rosen, C. & Haseltine, W. *Science* **225**, 381-385 (1984).

39. Sodroski, J. *et al. Science* (in the press).

40. Celander, D. & Haseltine, W. *Nature* **312**, 159-162 (1984).

41. Safai, B. *et al. Lancet* i, 1438-1440 (1984).

24

42. Laurence, J. *et al. New Engl. J. Med.* **311**, 1269-1273 (1984).

43. Gottlieb, M. S. *et al. New Engl. J. Med.* **305**, 1425-1431 (1981).

44. Essex, M. *et al.* in *Human T-Cell Leukemia-Lymphoma Virus* (eds Gallo, R. C., Essex, M. & Gross, L.) 355-362 (Cold Spring Harbor Laboratory, New York, 1984).

45. Miyoshi, I. *et al. Nature* **294**, 770-771 (1981).

46. Yamamoto, N., Okada, M., Koyangi, Y., Kanagi, M. & Hinuma, Y. *Science* **217**, 737-739 (1982).

47. Kinoshita, K. *et al.* in *Adult T-Cell Leukemia Related Diseases* (eds Hakaoka, M., Takatsuki, K. & Shimoyama, M.) 167-184 (Plenum, Tokyo, 1982).

48. Markham, P. D. *et al. Int. J. Cancer* **31**, 413-420 (1983).

49. Groopman, J. E. *et al. Science* **226**, 447-449 (1984).

50. Zagury, D. *et al. Science* **226**, 449-451 (1984).

51. Ho, D. D. *et al. Science* **226**, 451-453 (1984).

52. Gallo, R. C. & Wong-Staal, F. *Blood* **50**, 545-557 (1982).

53. Shaw, G. M. *et al. Science* **226**, 1165-1171 (1984).

54. Starcich, B. *et al. Science* (in the press).

55. Sodroski, J. *et al. Proc. Natl. Acad. Sci. U.S.A.* **81**, 4617-4621 (1984).

56. Sagata, N., Yasunaga, T., Ogawa, Y., Tsuzuka-Kawamura, J. & Ikawa, Y. *Proc. Natl. Acad. Sci. U.S.A.* **81**, 4751-4754 (1984).

57. Weiss, R., Teich, N., Varmus, H. & Coffin, J. (eds) *RNA Tumor Viruses* (Cold Spring Harbor Laboratory, New York, 1982).

58. Kitchen, L. *et al. Nature* **312**, 367-369 (1984).

59. Oroszlan, S. *et al. Proc. Natl. Acad. Sci. U.S.A.* **79**, 1291-1294 (1984).

60. Shinnick, T. M., Lerner, R. A. & Sutcliffe, J. G. *Nature* **293**, 543-548 (1981).

61. Schwartz, D. E., Tizard, R. & Gilbert, W. *Cell* **32**, 853-869 (1983).

62. Copeland, T. D., Oroszlan, S., Kalyanaraman, V. S., Sarngadaharan, M. G. & Gallo, R. C. *FEBS Lett.* **162**, 390-395 (1983).

63. Bolognesi, D. P., Luftig, R. & Shaper, J. H. *Virology* **56**, 549-564 (1973).

64. Smith, B. J. & Bailey, J. M. *Nucleic Acids. Res.* **7**, 2055-2072 (1979).

65. Chiu, I-M., Tronick, S. R., Schlom, J. & Aaronson, S. A. *Science* **223**, 364-370 (1984).

66. Patarca, R. & Haseltine, W. A. *Nature* **309**, 728 (1984).

67. Levin, J. G., Hu, S. C., Rein, A., Messer, L. I. & Gerwin, B. I. *J. Virol.* **51**, 470-478 (1984).

68. Von der Helm, K. & Duesberg, P. H. *Proc. Natl. Acad. Sci. U.S.A.* **72**, 614-618 (1975).

69. Vogt, P., Wight, W. & Eisenman, R. *Virology* **98**, 154-167 (1979).

70. Dittmar, K. J. & Moelling, J. K. *J. Virol.* **28**, 106-118 (1978).

71. Schiff, R. D. & Grandgenett, D. P. *J. Virol.* **28**, 279-291 (1978).

72. Herr, W. *J. Virol.* **49**, 471-478 (1984).

73. Sodroski, J. *et al. Science* **225**, 378-381 (1984).

74. Cianciolo, G. J., Kipnis, R. J. & Snyderman, R. *Nature* **311**, 515 (1984).

75. Haseltine, W. A. & Patarca, R. *Nature* **309**, 728 (1984).

76. Lenz, J., Crowther, R., Straceski, A. & Haseltine, W. A. *J. Virol.* **42**, 519-529 (1982).

77. Bahl, O. P. & Shah, R. H. in *The Glycoconjugates* Vol. 1 (eds Horowitz, M. I. & Pigman, W.) 385-422 (Academic, New York, 1977).

78. Pinter, A. & Fleissner, E. *Virology* **83**, 417-422 (1983).

79. Segrest, J. P. & Feldman, R. J. *J. Molec. Biol.* **87**, 853-858 (1974).

80. Koch, W., Zimmerman, W., Oliff, A. & Friedrich, R. *J. Virol.* **49**, 828-840 (1984).

81. Wachsman, W., Shimotohno, K., Clark, S. C., Golde, D. W. & Chen, I. S. Y. *Science* **226**, 177-179 (1984).

82. Franchini, V., Wong-Staal, F. & Gallo, R. C. *Proc. Natl. Acad. Sci. U.S.A.* **81**, 6207-6211 (1984).

83. Lee, T. H. *et al. Science* **226**, 58-60 (1984).

84. Slamon, D. J., Shimotohno, K., Cline, M. J., Golde, D. W. & Chen, I. S. Y. *Science* **226**, 61-63 (1984).

85. Rosen, C., Sodroski, J., Kettman, R., Burney, A. & Haseltine, W. A. *Science* (in the press).

86. Czernilofsky, A. P. *et al. Nucleic Acids Res.* **8**, 2967-2984 (1980).

87. Essex, M. *et al. Science* **220**, 859-862 (1983).

88. Essex, M. E. *et al. Science* **221**, 1061-1064 (1983).

89. Dalgleish, A. *et al. Nature* **312**, 763-766 (1984).

90. Weiss, R. A. *et al.* in *Retroviruses in Human Lymphoma/ Leukemia* (ed. Miwa, M.) (Japan Sci. Soc. Press, Tokyo, in the press).

91. Maxam, A. M. & Gilbert, W. *Meth. Enzym.* **65**, 499-560 (1980).

92. Sanger, F., Nickelen, S. & Coulson, A. R. *Proc. Natl. Acad. Sci. U.S.A.* **74**, 5463-5467 (1977).

93. Mount, S. M. *Nucleic Acids Res.* **10**, 459-472 (1982).

94. Kyte, J. & Doolittle, R. F. *J. Molec. Biol.* **157**, 105-120 (1981).

95. Hopp, T. P. & Woods, K. R. *Proc. Natl. Acad. Sci. U.S.A.* **78**, 3824-3825 (1981).

Does the Ocean–Atmosphere System Have More than One Stable Mode of Operation?

W. S. Broecker *et al.*

Editor's Note

Analyses of cores drilled into polar ice sheets offer records of the temperature history of the Earth over several hundred millennia. Cores from Greenland had recently revealed that superimposed on the cycles of ice ages there are shorter-term fluctuations in global climate. Here palaeoclimatologist Wallace Broecker of the Lamont–Doherty Geological Observatory and his colleagues suggest that these fluctuations may be caused by abrupt switches between different modes of ocean circulation, which alter heat transport around the globe. The switches could be driven by climate changes that alter the rate at which cold deep water accumulates in the oceans. This idea of a two-state operation of the ocean–atmosphere system is now a key feature in models of future climate change.

The climate record obtained from two long Greenland ice cores reveals several brief climate oscillations during glacial time. The most recent of these oscillations, also found in continental pollen records, has greatest impact in the area under the meteorological influence of the northern Atlantic, but none in the United States. This suggests that these oscillations are caused by fluctuations in the formation rate of deep water in the northern Atlantic. As the present production of deep water in this area is driven by an excess of evaporation over precipitation and continental runoff, atmospheric water transport may be an important element in climate change. Changes in the production rate of deep water in this sector of the ocean may push the climate system from one quasi-stable mode of operation to another.

MANY feedback loops that may amplify climatic change have been proposed, one of which has recently caught the imagination of palaeoclimatologists. Suggested by the atmospheric CO_2-content record recovered from the polar ice caps[1-3], this scenario involves interactions between climate and ocean circulation[4-7].

To appreciate the significance of the observations on polar ice, one must be aware of their context. Over the past several decades studies on deep-sea cores have provided a detailed history of climate during the past million years[8-10]. The first picture that emerged was that continental glaciers have waxed and waned on a timescale of 100 kyr[9]. These climate cycles are asymmetric, involving long periods of glacial buildup suddenly terminated with rapid warmings. Further work revealed that these long intervals of glacial buildup were

海洋–大气系统是否存在不止一种稳定运行模态？

布勒克等

编者按

分析从极地冰盖钻取的冰芯可以提供数十万年以来地球温度的历史记录。最近格陵兰的冰芯显示，全球气候在冰期循环上叠加有短期的波动。拉蒙特－多尔蒂地质观测所的古气候学家华莱士·布勒克和他的同事提出，这些波动可能是由于不同的海洋环流模态之间的剧烈转换引起的，这也会改变世界范围的热量传输。这种转换可能由气候变化改变海洋中冷的深层水的积累速率所驱动。海洋－大气系统存在这两态运行方式的观点是未来气候变化模式的主要特点。

两支格陵兰岛长冰芯的气候记录显示，冰期时曾发生过几次短期气候振荡现象。其中最近一次的气候振荡现象在陆地的孢粉记录中也有发现，它对受北大西洋气候影响的区域影响最大，而对美国境内却没有影响。上述事实说明，此类气候振荡是由北大西洋深层水生成速率的波动造成的。而由于目前北大西洋深层水汽的输送是由该地区蒸发量相对于降水量和陆地径流过剩所驱动的，所以大气水的运移可能是引起气候变化的一个重要因素。北大西洋深层水生成速率的变化可能会促使气候系统由一种准稳态模式向另一种准稳态模式转变。

学者们已经提出了许多可能会加剧气候变化的反馈循环，其中之一近来就引起了古气候学家们的想象。从极地冰盖中恢复的大气 CO_2 含量记录 [1-3] 的研究指出，这一情景涉及气候和大洋环流之间的相互作用关系 [4-7]。

要想了解对极地冰川进行观测的重要性，首先必须了解其背景。在过去几十年中，通过对深海岩芯的研究，人们已经对过去几百万年的气候变化有了详尽的认识 [8-10]。人们最初认识到的是大陆冰川在 10 万年的时间尺度上发生着消长变化 [9]。而且这些气候循环是非对称的，包括漫长的冰川增长周期随着气候迅速变暖会突然终止。进一步研究表明，冰川增长的长的间隔时间中叠加着为期两万或四万年左右的小循

modulated by cycles of ~20 and ~40 kyr duration[11,12], closely allied in timing and relative amplitude to variations in seasonal contrast produced by cyclic changes in the Earth's orbital elements[11,12]. Orbital forcing is accepted widely as the primary cause of glacial cycles (Fig. 1). Because the exact linkage between changes in seasonality and changes in climate has yet to be established, however, the issue remains open. Although it is plausible that nonlinearities in the response of snow and ice cover to seasonal variations drive glacial growth and retreat[13], it is not clear whether this mechanism alone is sufficient to do so.

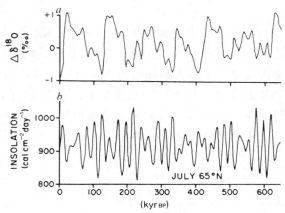

Fig. 1. a, Composite of the $^{18}O/^{16}O$ record for planktonic foraminifera from several deep-sea cores[12]. This record primarily reflects changes in the amount of continental ice in the Northern Hemisphere. The more positive the $\delta^{18}O$ value, the more ice. b, Variation with time of the July insolation at 65° N (ref. 51). The rapid disappearances of the ice that terminate the episodes of very large ice cover correspond to prominent peaks in summer insolation for the latitudes at which the excess ice was located. In addition, there is a strong coherence between the ~20 and ~40 kyr spectral components of ice volume and insolation records. Taken together these ties between insolation and ice volume have convinced most scientists concerned with palaeoclimates that the Earth's glacial cycles are driven by changes in seasonality brought about by cyclic changes in the Earth's orbital elements.

Ice-Core Record

Scientists examining the oxygen isotope record preserved in ice cores from Greenland and Antarctica (see Fig. 2), checked whether the major features of this record matched those found in the deep sea. In one sense they did match. Glacial conditions prevailed from before 50 to ~10 kyr BP at which time a transition to interglacial conditions occurred. Once this transition was complete, climate remained remarkably uniform. No evidence for the 20 and 40 kyr cycles characteristic of orbital forcing appears in the ice-core record, in part because the record extends to only ~100 kyr BP and in part because of the exponential foreshortening with depth of the thickness of ice representing a single year. This flow-induced distortion produces a considerable uncertainty in the ice-core chronology before 10 kyr BP.

环 [11,12]，它们在时间和相对振幅上都与那些由地球轨道参数的周期变化引起的季节性反差变化有着密切联系 [11,12]。轨道驱动被普遍认为是引起冰期旋回的主要因素（图1）。但由于季节性变化与气候变化之间的确切关系尚未得到证实，所以该问题仍需深入探讨。尽管积雪与冰盖对季节性变化的非线性响应有可能驱动冰川的消长 [13]，但仅凭借该机制是否能做到尚不清楚。

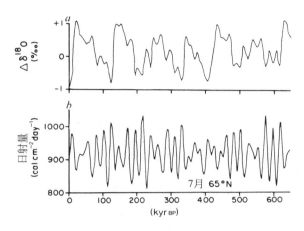

图 1. a，多个深海岩芯中浮游有孔虫 $^{18}O/^{16}O$ 记录的合成曲线 [12]。该记录主要反映了北半球大陆冰的数量变化。$\delta^{18}O$ 值正向越大说明冰越多。b，65°N 地区 7 月份日射量随时间的变化曲线（参考文献 51）。冰川的快速消失标志着大规模冰期的结束，与过量冰所在纬度上的夏季日射量峰值相对应。此外，在距今 2 万年和 4 万年左右时，冰储量的频谱与日射量记录之间的一致性也非常好。综合考虑日射量与冰储量之间的上述关系，使许多古气候学家确信，地球的冰期旋回是由地球轨道参数周期变化引起的季节性变化所导致的。

冰 芯 记 录

科学家对采自格陵兰岛和南极大陆的冰芯中保存的氧同位素记录进行了深入研究（见图 2），对比该记录的主要特征是否与深海岩芯记录一致。从某种意义上来说，它们确实是匹配的。距今约 5 万年至 1 万年前为冰期环境，这个时期发生了向间冰期的过渡。一旦过渡完成，气候又会保持显著一致。在冰芯记录中没有发现关于轨道驱动在距今 2 万年和 4 万年时的旋回特征的证据，一方面是由于记录仅能达到距今 10 万年前左右的时间，另一方面可能是代表一年的冰川厚度随深度呈指数递减所致。水流作用造成的畸变使得利用冰芯测年获得的距今 1 万年以前的结果尚存在不确定性。

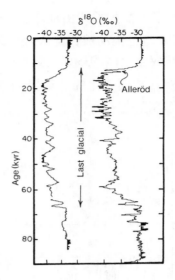

Fig. 2. Oxygen isotope records for ice cores[43] from Camp Century, Greenland (on the right) and Byrd Station, Antarctica (on the left). These records reflect mainly changes in air temperature over the ice cap. The more negative the $\delta^{18}O$ value, the colder the air temperature. The timescales are very approximate as there are as yet no direct radiometric ages for the glacial sections of the ice. Note that the glacial portion of the Greenland record shows a number of events of <1,000 yr duration. These events are muted (or absent) in the Antarctic record.

Although not showing the orbital periodicities, the ice-core record for glacial time does show many brief events during which climatic conditions returned about halfway to their interglacial state. Because such events would be blurred totally by the stirring of worms in all deep-sea sediments with typical accumulation rates (that is, a few centimetres per kyr), this finding is not in conflict with the marine record. However, as these idiosyncrasies of the ice-core record were not seen in other records, the initial temptation was to pass them off as climate "noise" without global significance. A rapid succession of findings has since changed this view of the noise, now the focus of much interest.

First, $^{18}O/^{16}O$ measurements by Dansgaard *et al.* on a second long core from Greenland[14] revealed the same events as the first (see Fig. 3), indicating that the events were both real, and occurred throughout Greenland. Second, the events were recorded not only by $^{18}O/^{16}O$ ratio changes but also by dust[15], ^{10}Be (ref. 16), SO_4, NO_3 and Cl content[17] changes in the ice. The ice formed during the warm events is similar to interglacial ice with respect to these properties. Third, the $^{18}O/^{16}O$ pattern found for the most recent Greenland event was also recorded in $CaCO_3$ from lake sediments in Switzerland[18], which gave credence to a correlation made early on by Dansgaard *et al.*[19] (see Fig. 4). In interpreting their $^{18}O/^{16}O$ results for the Camp Century Greenland ice core, they suggested that the strong oscillation just before the onset of postglacial time was a record of the Alleröd–Younger Dryas oscillation seen in pollen records throughout Europe. During the Alleröd, trees abruptly replaced the grasses and shrubs that had characterized glacial time, only to be replaced by the cold flora characteristic of glacial time (see Fig. 4). This so called "Younger Dryas" cold period lasted ~800 yr (that is, from ~11 to ~10.2 kyr BP) before Holocene forests

30

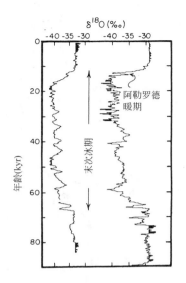

图 2. 分别从格陵兰岛的世纪营地（右）和南极洲伯德站（左）所获冰芯[43]的氧同位素曲线。该曲线反映了冰盖上方空气温度的主要变化。δ18O 值负值越大说明空气温度越低。其中的时间尺度都是近似值，因为目前还没有关于该冰川在冰期时的直接放射性测年结果。格陵兰岛记录的冰期部分显示，期间存在许多周期小于 1,000 年的事件。这些事件在南极冰川记录中则表现得非常弱（或没有）。

　　尽管冰期时的冰芯记录没有体现地球轨道的周期性，但从中可以发现，确实存在一些短周期事件，而这些事件发生时，气候条件可恢复到间冰期环境状态的一半。由于在具有典型堆积速率（也就是说，每千年几厘米）的深海沉积物中，此类事件均很可能会被生物扰动完全破坏，因此这一发现与深海记录并不矛盾。然而，由于冰芯记录的特殊信息在其他记录中并未见到，所以最初的时候，一般将它们作为不具有全球性显著意义的气候"噪声"而过滤掉。但是，一系列发现改变了原来的观点，如今这已成为具有重要意义的焦点所在。

　　首先，丹斯果等发现，对采自格陵兰岛的第二根长冰芯的 $^{18}O/^{16}O$ 测定结果所揭示的事件与第一根相同（见图 3）。这说明，两者所反映的事件确实存在，并且整个格陵兰岛都曾发生过。其次，这些事件不仅反映于 $^{18}O/^{16}O$ 比值的变化中，同样也反映在冰川内尘埃[15]、^{10}Be（参考文献 16）、SO_4、NO_3 以及 Cl 含量[17]的变化上。在这些特征方面，变暖事件期间形成的冰川均与间冰期冰川类似。第三，格陵兰岛上最近一次事件的 $^{18}O/^{16}O$ 特征在瑞士湖泊沉积物的 $CaCO_3$ 中[18]也有记录，这更证实了早期丹斯果等[19]所提出的两者之间的相关性（见图 4）。在解释他们从格陵兰岛世纪营地附近的冰芯中测得的 $^{18}O/^{16}O$ 结果时，丹斯果等提出，冰后期即将开始前发生的强烈振荡是阿勒罗德暖期至新仙女木冷期的记录，在整个欧洲大陆的孢粉记录中都能见到。乔木曾在阿勒罗德期突然取代了作为冰期标志的草本植物和灌木，而此时，它们又被冰期较冷的植物群落所取代（见图 4）。这一时期被称为"新仙女木"

appeared. However, these results did not influence broader thinking about glacial cycles and their causes.

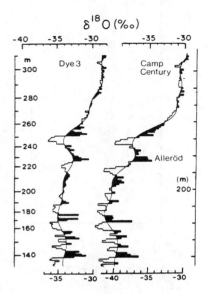

Fig. 3. Comparison between the $^{18}O/^{16}O$ records for the Camp Century and Dye 3 sites in Greenland for the time period ~40 to ~8 kyr BP. For each core a depth scale (metres above bedrock) is given. After some adjustment of the Dye 3 depth scale a good match is achieved between the records in the two cores. (Results obtained by Dansgaard et al.[14].)

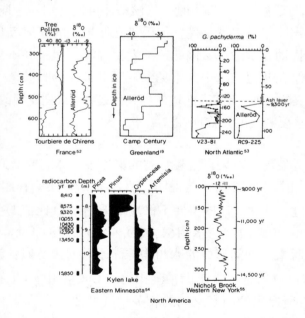

Fig. 4. Examples of records for the time period 13–9 kyr BP from Europe (pollen and $^{18}O/^{16}O$ in CaCO₃), Greenland ($^{18}O/^{16}O$ in ice) and the North Atlantic (% G. pachyderma in the planktonic foraminifera). All show the pronounced Alleröd–Younger Dryas oscillation. By contrast no such oscillation is seen in either pollen diagrams or $^{18}O/^{16}O$ records from the United States.

冷期，在全新世森林出现之前持续了约 800 年（即从距今约 1.1 万年至 1.02 万年）。
不过，上述结果并不影响关于冰期旋回及其成因的更为广泛的思考。

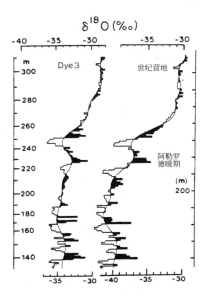

图 3. 来自格陵兰岛世纪营地和 Dye 3 上的距今约 4 万年至 8,000 年的 $^{18}O/^{16}O$ 记录对比。图中分别给两
根冰芯标出了各自的深度标尺（基岩之上的米数）。通过对 Dye 3 站的深度标尺加以调整之后，两冰芯
记录可以很好地匹配。（丹斯果等 [14] 的测定结果）

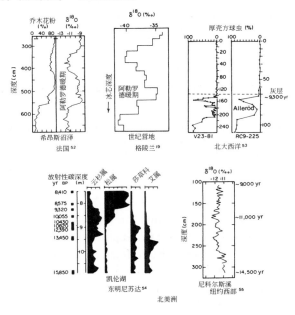

图 4. 分别从欧洲（孢粉和 $CaCO_3$ 的 $^{18}O/^{16}O$ 记录）、格陵兰（冰芯的 $^{18}O/^{16}O$ 记录）和北大西洋（浮游有
孔虫中厚壳方球虫的百分含量）地区得到的距今约 1.3 万年至约 9,000 年期间的记录示例。阿勒罗德
暖期至新仙女木冷期显著的气候振荡在所有记录中均有显示。而相反，来自美国地区的孢粉柱状图或
$^{18}O/^{16}O$ 记录均未发现这样的振荡。

A few years earlier Berner *et al.* found that the CO_2 content of the air trapped in ice from the glacial sections of the Greenland and Antarctic cores was about two-thirds that for air trapped in ice from the interglacial sections[1]. Intrigued by the $^{18}O/^{16}O$ events found in the ice and the apparent correlation of the last of these with an oscillation in plant cover seen throughout Europe, Oeschger and co-workers found that there were CO_2 changes associated with these events[20,21]. In the Dye 3 core, oscillations (as recorded by the $^{18}O/^{16}O$ ratio) were accompanied by CO_2 oscillations of ~60 p.p.m. (see Fig. 5). The CO_2 change was about two-thirds of the change that accompanied the major glacial–interglacial transition[1-3]. Although Fig. 5 shows only the CO_2 records for the oscillations within glacial time, a similar CO_2 change is found during the Alleröd–Younger Dryas interval at the end of glacial time[20].

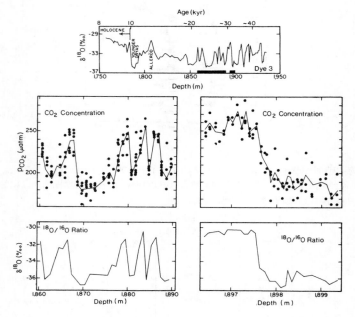

Fig. 5. Detailed P_{CO_2}–$\delta^{18}O$ comparison for two sections of the Dye 3 Greenland core[20,21]. The location of these sections are shown in the upper panel by the dark bands. The longer band represents a time interval of ~8 kyr and the shorter a time interval of ~2 kyr. The sudden air temperature warmings indicated by the rise in ^{18}O are accompanied by sharp rises in CO_2 content of air trapped in the ice. (CO_2 results obtained by Oeschger *et al.*)

Oeschger and co-workers are now searching for the CO_2 events in ice cores from the Antarctic. Whereas the other changes found in Greenland (that is, ^{18}O, ^{10}Be, dust, etc.) may have been restricted to the region under the influence of the northern Atlantic, the CO_2 change must, of course, be global. Until confirmed in Antarctic ice, the possibility remains that the sharp changes in CO_2 content found in Greenland are artefacts of summer melting, which may have occurred during the warm events as it did at this low elevation site during much of the Holocene. We emphasize that although it was the discovery of CO_2 events that prompted serious consideration of possible ocean circulation–climate linkages, our speculations below about possible multiple climatic modes do not depend on the validity of the CO_2 changes.

几年前，伯纳等发现，格陵兰及南极冰芯属于冰期的部分中，所包含空气的 CO_2 含量仅为间冰期的 2/3[1]。受冰川中发现的 $^{18}O/^{16}O$ 事件及其最后一次事件与整个欧洲地区植被覆盖波动之间的显著联系的启发，厄施格尔及其同事发现，伴随着这些事件的发生，CO_2 含量也有变化[20,21]。在 Dye 3 站点冰芯中，伴随振荡（由 $^{18}O/^{16}O$ 比值所记录）发生的 CO_2 含量的波动范围约为 60 ppm（见图 5）。该 CO_2 的变化量约是从主冰期至间冰期过渡时发生的 CO_2 变化量的 2/3[1-3]。虽然图 5 仅给出了冰期内振荡事件的 CO_2 记录，但在冰期末，阿勒罗德暖期至新仙女木冷期时，也发现了类似的 CO_2 含量变化[20]。

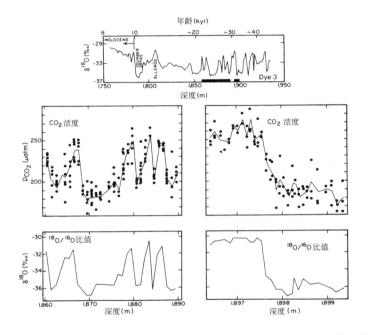

图 5. 格陵兰 Dye 3 站冰芯两个剖面的 P_{CO_2}–$\delta^{18}O$ 的详细对比图[20,21]。最上方图中的黑色条带表示两个剖面的位置。较长的条带代表约 8,000 年的时间段，较短的代表 2,000 年左右。^{18}O 的上升标志着空气温度突然升高，同时也伴随着冰川所包裹的空气中 CO_2 含量的急剧上升。（CO_2 含量由厄施格尔等测定）

厄施格尔和他的同事们目前正在研究南极冰芯中的 CO_2 事件。在格陵兰岛发现的其他变化（即 ^{18}O、^{10}Be、尘埃等）可能仅限于受北大西洋影响的地区，但 CO_2 含量的变化则一定是全球性的。除非由南极冰川所证实，否则在格陵兰岛发现的 CO_2 含量的剧烈变化仍有可能是发生于变暖事件期间由于夏季冰雪消融而产生的假象，正如全新世的多数时间里在这一低海拔的地区所发生的那样。在这里需要强调的是，虽然是 CO_2 事件的发现推动了我们对大洋环流–气候变化之间可能的相互关系进行认真的考量，但我们下面将要讨论的关于多气候模态的推断却并不取决于 CO_2 含量是否变化。

Causes of Atmospheric CO₂ Change

The finding from ice-core studies that the CO_2 content of air extracted from glacial ice was lower than that extracted from postglacial ice[1-3] stimulated investigations as to the origin of natural CO_2 changes, which must be rooted in ocean chemistry[22,23]. The first scenario for the 90-μatm rise in CO_2 content at the close of glacial time called for the deposition of organic residues on the coastal shelves during the transgression of the sea that accompanied deglaciation. The subsequent finding of brief CO_2 events within glacial time, however, led to a re-examination of the question. If these CO_2 changes are typical of the atmosphere, then explanations involving the transfer of nutrient substances between the ocean and its shelf sediments must be abandoned. Such transfers could certainly not occur fast enough to produce 60-p.p.m. CO_2 changes in ~100 yr. To be viable, hypotheses will have to invoke redistributions of C, P and fixed N in the sea. Such redistributions are feasible if the ocean mixing and/or biological cycling change substantially[4-7,24]. This explains why CO_2 measurements on ice cores suggested links between climate and the joint operation of the atmosphere and ocean system.

Three quite different scenarios have been proposed. Broecker[24] pointed out that the evidence from deep-sea cores cited in support of his shelf-deposition hypothesis could also be explained by a change in the C to N and/or C to P ratio in the organic residues falling to the interior of the sea. A 30% decrease in this ratio was needed to explain the CO_2 drop at the end of glacial time.

Broecker and Takahashi[4] pointed out that a change in the transfer rate of water between the cold- and warm-water spheres of the ocean would produce a redistribution of ΣCO_2 between these reservoirs and a consequent change in atmospheric CO_2 content. The reason is that the biological "pumping" of carbon by organisms from the surface ocean to the deep ocean is compensated partly by a flow of CO_2 through the atmosphere from the cold- to the warm-water sphere. Hence, a change in the rate of transfer of water between these spheres alters the balance between these two competing effects. To explain the lower CO_2 content during glacial time, Broecker and Takahashi invoked a several-fold higher rate of transfer of water between these spheres.

Three groups[5-7] have arrived independently at a different ocean scenario. Having pointed out that a reduction in the NO_3 and PO_4 contents of polar surface waters (that is, more effective biological use) would produce the desired glacial CO_2 reduction, all three groups demonstrated that a decrease in the rate of exchange between polar surface waters and the rest of the ocean may result in reduced nutrient content of polar surface waters and, in turn, of the CO_2 content of the atmosphere.

As the Broecker–Takahashi (B–T) ocean mixing scenario requires enhanced mixing during glacial time whereas the Princeton–Bern–Harvard (P–B–H) scenario requires reduced mixing, the balance of evidence must be carried by marine sediments, which would allow one of these hypotheses to be eliminated. Indeed, the P–B–H hypotheses predict higher than Holocene $\delta^{13}C$ values for planktonic forams grown in the Antarctic during

影响大气中 CO_2 含量变化的因素

通过对冰芯的研究发现，从冰期冰川中提取的空气中 CO_2 的含量低于冰后期的冰川 [1-3]，该发现促进了对自然界 CO_2 含量变化起因的研究，这方面的研究必须建立在海洋化学的基础上 [22,23]。首先，在冰期末，CO_2 含量上升了 90×10^{-6} 标准大气压，这一情景的实现需要伴随冰川消退发生的海侵期间所形成的有机残留物沉积于沿海陆架上。然而，随后发现的短暂的冰期 CO_2 事件却促使人们不得不重新审视这一问题。如果这样的 CO_2 含量变化在大气中非常典型，那么，就必须放弃关于海洋与陆架沉积物之间营养物质的迁移这样的解释。因为物质的迁移肯定不能快到 100 年中就可使 CO_2 含量变化 60 ppm。为了可行起见，这种假定必须引入海洋中 C、P 以及固定 N 的再分配。而在海洋混合作用与 / 或生物循环充分变化的条件下，这种再分配是切实可行的 [4-7,24]。这就解释了为什么冰芯中 CO_2 的测定结果可以揭示气候与大气和海洋系统联合运作之间的关系。

学者们已经提出了三种截然不同的情景。布勒克 [24] 曾指出，从深海岩芯中获得的证据（曾被引用支持陆架沉积假说）也可以用沉入海洋内部的有机残留物中 C/N 和 (或)C/P 比值的变化来解释。但是要解释冰末期 CO_2 含量的降低需要使该比值降低 30%。

布勒克和高桥 [4] 指出，在海洋冷暖水域之间水迁移速率的变化可以使 CO_2 总量在这些储库之间进行再分配，从而导致大气中 CO_2 含量发生变化。原因就在于，从海洋表层到深海，因生物"泵"作用移除的碳可以由 CO_2 通过大气从冷水域到暖水域的流动而得到部分补偿。因此，这些水域之间水迁移速率的变化会改变这两种互相竞争的作用之间的平衡。为了解释冰期时 CO_2 含量较低的现象，布勒克和高桥提出把这些水域之间的水迁移速率提高几倍。

有三组科学家 [5-7] 先后独立地获得了不同的海洋响应情景。他们均指出，极地表层水中 NO_3 和 PO_4 含量的降低（即生物利用更加有效）可以使 CO_2 含量降到理想的冰期水平，进而证明，当极地表层水与海洋其他部分之间水体的交换速率降低时，极地表层水中营养盐含量也随之降低，进而造成大气中 CO_2 含量也降低。

布勒克和高桥（B-T）的海洋混合作用情景要求冰期时的混合作用是加强的，而普林斯顿 – 伯尔尼 – 哈佛（P-B-H）的情景则要求混合作用是减弱的，来自海洋沉积物的证据应该可以排除其中之一。实际上，P-B-H 假说预测冰期时生长在南极地区的浮游有孔虫壳体中 $\delta^{13}C$ 的值要高于全新世的值，而 B-T 假说则低于全新世的

glacial time whereas the B–T hypothesis predicts lower values. Unpublished ^{13}C results by N. Shackleton and R. Fairbanks on planktonic foraminifera from Antarctic deep-sea sediments strongly suggest that the reduction in surface water nutrient content required by the P–B–H hypotheses for glacial time did not occur. Radiocarbon age differences (determined by accelerator mass spectrometry) between planktonic and benthic forams from glacial horizons in deep-sea sediments eventually may provide another basis for making a distinction[25,26]. It is possible that neither of these scenarios is correct.

Although little is known about either ocean circulation or biological cycling in the past, one important clue has been found. Evidence from faunal, chemical[27] and isotope studies[23,28-31] of deep-sea sediments suggests that the production of deep water in the northern Atlantic, of great importance to the present-day circulation scheme, was reduced greatly during the peak glacial time. Most convincing is the finding by Boyle that the Cd content of benthic foraminifera from the Atlantic Ocean was higher during glacial time than today[27]. In the present-day ocean, the Cd and PO_4 contents of various water types in the sea are correlated almost perfectly. Thus, the Cd distribution in the glacial ocean is a good substitute for the P distribution. Boyle has demonstrated that the Cd/Ca ratio in benthic foraminifera is proportional to the corresponding ratio in the water in which they grow. In the present-day ocean, the low PO_4 and Cd content of Atlantic relative to Pacific deep water is attributable directly to the formation of deep water in the northern Atlantic. The reduction in this difference (suggested by the glacial foram results) is thus indicative of a reduction in the magnitude of the deep-water production in the northern Atlantic at that time.

Taken together, these arguments for the reduction of deepwater production in the northern Atlantic during glacial time are convincing. Is it possible then that the brief warm events recorded in the ice cores represent periods during which the glacially weakened northern Atlantic deep-water source was rejuvenated?

Distribution of Oscillations

Adequate records are available currently to provide a picture of the geographical distribution for only the most recent fluctuation. This last oscillation appears in the records from both the Camp Century and Dye 3 cores from the Greenland ice cap and is found in pollen and $^{18}O/^{16}O$ ratio records from bog and lake sediments in western Europe. Evidence is also found in sediments in the northern Atlantic with an unusually high accumulation rate. Ruddiman and McIntyre showed that ~13 kyr BP the boundary between polar waters and temperate waters moved from its glacial position to near its present position (see Fig. 6), and remained there ~1 kyr before returning to its glacial position for several hundred years[32]. Finally, it returned to its present position where it remained throughout the Holocene.

值。沙克尔顿和费尔班克斯关于南极深海沉积物中浮游有孔虫 [13]C 的未发表成果有力地说明,P–B–H 假说中所要求的冰期时表层水营养成分的降低并未发生。从深海沉积物获得的冰期地层中浮游有孔虫和底栖有孔虫之间的放射性碳同位素测年差异(采用加速器质谱仪测定)可能为鉴别两种假说的正确性提供另一个基础 [25,26]。也有可能两种假说都是不正确的。

虽然我们对过去的大洋环流和生物循环都不太了解,但已经发现了一条重要线索。深海沉积物的动物群落、化学 [27] 以及同位素 [23,28-31] 证据表明,冰盛期时,在当今大洋环流体系中占据重要地位的北大西洋深层水的生成显著下降。其中最有说服力的证据就是博伊尔的发现,即冰期时大西洋底栖有孔虫中 Cd 的含量比现今要高 [27]。现今的海洋中,不同水体的 Cd 和 PO_4 含量之间均有极好的相关性。因此,冰期的海洋中 Cd 的分布是 P 分布的一个良好替代指标。博伊尔已经证明,底栖有孔虫的 Cd/Ca 比值与其生活的水体中 Cd/Ca 的比值成比例。在现今的海洋中,大西洋深层水中 PO_4 和 Cd 的含量相对于太平洋的要低,这应该直接归因于北大西洋深层水的形成。因此这种差异的减小(如冰川有孔虫研究结果所示)标志着当时北大西洋深层水生成规模的减小。

综上所述,冰期时北大西洋深层水生成量下降的论点是很有说服力的。那么,冰芯中记录的短期变暖事件是否代表着被冰川作用削弱的北大西洋深层水源复原的时期呢?

气候振荡的分布

如今已有充足的记录可以提供最近一次气候波动的地理分布概况。格陵兰岛冰盖的世纪营地和 Dye 3 冰芯都发现了最后一次振荡的记录,而且在西欧地区湖沼沉积物的孢粉和 ^{18}O/[16]O 比值记录中也有发现。在北大西洋沉积物中也发现了证据证明存在一个异常高的堆积速率。拉迪曼和麦金太尔研究发现,距今约 1.3 万年前极地水体与温带水体的界线从冰期时的位置移到了现今的位置附近(见图 6),并且一直保持了约 1,000 年,之后又回到冰期位置,并维持了几百年的时间 [32]。最后,才回到了现今的位置,并且整个全新世一直留在那里。

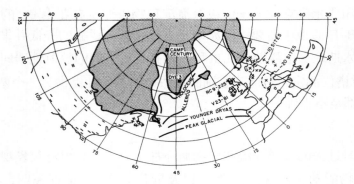

Fig. 6. Map showing the locations of sites at which sediments spanning the 13–9 kyr BP time interval have been studied[33-36]. At sites designated by a+ an oscillation in climate corresponding to the Alleröd–Younger Dryas is found. At sites designated by a– this oscillation has not been reported. The stippling corresponds to the area covered by ice just before the onset of the Alleröd[56]. Positions of the polar front in the northern Atlantic during peak glacial, Alleröd, Younger Dryas and Holocene time, as reconstructed by Ruddiman and McIntyre[32], and the locations of the two long ice borings in Greenland and of the two ocean cores referred to in Fig. 4 are shown.

There are >50 European sites whose pollen records contain an oscillation in the 13–10 kyr period[33]. In contrast to the European pollen record is the lack of evidence for this event in the United States[34]. Recent research on cores from lakes and bogs in New Brunswick, Nova Scotia and Newfoundland[35,36], however, indicate that the oscillation was felt in the eastern regions of maritime Canada. This evidence is summarized in Fig. 6. Thus, as proposed by Mercer[37], we may be dealing with a regional change in climate involving primarily the area under the climatic influence of the northern Atlantic Ocean. Because evidence for such an oscillation has been found elsewhere, that is, in the cordillera of South America[38-41] and in New Zealand[42], the situation may well be more complicated. This event is muted or absent in the $^{18}O/^{16}O$ ratio for the Byrd Station Antarctica record (see Fig. 2)[43].

Climate Impact of Deep-Water Production

The turning on and off of deep-water production in the northern Atlantic would be expected to produce a regional climate change. The rate of production of deep water is now ~20 Sverdrups (that is, 20,000,000 m³ s⁻¹)[44]. The water feeding the source region for the deep water has a temperature of ~10 °C, whereas the new deep water leaving the region has a temperature of ~2 °C. Thus, as a byproduct of deep-water formation ~5×10²¹ cal of heat are released to the atmosphere each year, an amount corresponding to ~30% of the solar heat reaching the surface of the Atlantic Ocean in the region north of 35° N.

To test the geographical distribution of the impact of turning on and off this source of heat, an experiment was performed using the general circulation model for the atmosphere developed by the Goddard Institute for Space Studies. A comparison was made between the air temperature for a model run with present-day ocean conditions and for a model

40

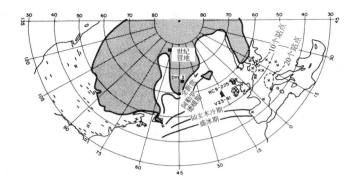

图 6. 已利用距今约 1.3 万年至 9,000 年间生成的沉积物做了研究 [33-36] 的站点位置分布图。在以 "+" 表示的站点上发现了与阿勒罗德暖期至新仙女木冷期相对应的气候振荡现象。以 "−" 表示的站点上未发现这次振荡的记录。点画区域表示就在阿勒罗德暖期刚开始之前，冰川所覆盖的地区 [56]。拉迪曼和麦金太尔分别恢复重建了冰盛期、阿勒罗德暖期、新仙女木冷期以及全新世时，北大西洋极锋的位置 [32]，同时展示了格陵兰岛上两根长冰芯和图 4 中涉及的两根大洋岩芯的钻孔位置。

在欧洲有 50 个以上站点的孢粉记录都揭示了距今约 1.3 万年至 1 万年期间的气候振荡 [33]。与欧洲孢粉记录相反，美国地区则没有关于该事件的记录 [34]。然而，对新不伦瑞克、新斯科舍以及纽芬兰地区 [35,36] 的湖沼岩芯的新近研究表明，该气候振荡影响了加拿大东部海域。证据概括于图 6。因此，正如默瑟 [37] 所提出的，我们面对的可能是气候的区域性变化，而该变化主要包含了受北大西洋气候影响的地区。由于在其他地区，即南美科迪勒拉山系 [38-41] 和新西兰地区 [42]，也发现了这一气候振荡的证据，情况变得越发复杂了。该事件在伯德南极考察站的 $^{18}O/^{16}O$ 比值记录中表现很微弱甚至缺失（见图 2）[43]。

大洋深层水生成对气候的影响

大洋深层水生成的开启和切断可能会引起区域性的气候变化。现今深层水的生成率约为 20 Sv（斯维尔德鲁普，流量单位，相当于 20,000,000 $m^3 \cdot s^{-1}$）[44]。向深层水源区补偿的水温度约为 10℃，而从该区流出的深层水的温度则为 2℃ 左右。因此，作为深层水生成作用的副产物，每年约有 5×10^{21} 卡热量释放到大气中，约相当于 35°N 以北地区大西洋表层每年获得的太阳能的 30%。

为了检验开启和切断该热源所引起的影响的地理分布，我们利用戈达德太空飞行中心建立的大气环流模式进行了一次实验。对比了在当今海洋环境条件下模拟出的大气温度与极锋以北地区（见图 6）海表温度降到 CLIMAP（气候：长期的调查、

run with the surface ocean temperatures in the region north of the glacial polar front (see Fig. 6) cooled to the levels estimated by the CLIMAP (1981) reconstruction for glacial time[45]. The results of this experiment will be published elsewhere. The air-temperature anomaly generated by this change in sea surface temperature spreads across Europe. A cooling is seen in extreme north-eastern North America whereas no corresponding anomaly is seen in the United States or over Antarctica. The results are, therefore, consistent with the pollen and ice-core evidence. Although this experiment does not prove that the Alleröd–Younger Dryas event was caused by changes in the rate of deep-water production in the northern Atlantic, it does suggest that were such changes to have occurred they would have produced climate changes with the observed regional pattern.

Deep-Water Production Changes

The most difficult question is why the production of deep water in the northern Atlantic may have resumed for brief intervals during glacial time. For an answer, we must consider the processes important to the present-day production of deep water in the northern Atlantic and for the absence of equivalent production in the northern Pacific. Oceanographers agree that the contrast between the two northern oceans is rooted in the large salinity difference. The waters of the northern Atlantic are saltier than the mean for the upper ocean, whereas the waters of the Pacific are fresher. The Atlantic's extra salt allows waters of density as great as any found in the deep sea to be generated during the winter months. By contrast, even if cooled to their freezing point, northern Pacific waters achieve a density no greater than that of intermediate depth water.

An approximate fresh water budget for the northern Atlantic and its satellite sea, the Mediterranean, is given in Table 1. Despite the fact that this region receives a sizeable portion of the world's river runoff, it loses an even greater amount of water through an excess in evaporation over precipitation. The resulting net loss of fresh water leads to the salt enrichment observed in the northern Atlantic. The salt budget for the North Atlantic must be balanced by the export of salty deep water to the Pacific and Indian Oceans. On a global scale, the water (and salt) budgets of the surface ocean must balance; thus, the fresh water lost from the Atlantic must re-enter the ocean elsewhere. Polewards of 30° N, atmospheric transport produces a net divergence of water vapour over the North Atlantic and convergence over the North Pacific east of the dateline[46]. Thus, if we are to understand what maintains deep water production in the present-day ocean, we must understand why fresh water is being pumped through the atmosphere from the North Atlantic to the North Pacific.

制图和预报计划）（1981）对冰期所估算的水平时所模拟出的大气温度 [45]。该实验结果将另文发表。海洋表层温度变化引起的大气温度异常遍布整个欧洲。在北美洲的东北部有降温过程出现，而在美国境内以及南极地区则未见到相应的气温异常现象。因此，该实验结果与孢粉和冰芯证据一致。虽然该项实验并未能证明阿勒罗德－新仙女木事件是由北大西洋深层水生成率的变化造成的，但它已经证明，倘若曾发生过类似变化，那么一定会引起所观测到的气候的区域性变化。

大洋深层水生成的变化

目前最大的难题在于，北大西洋深层水的生成为什么会引起冰期时短暂的气候事件。为了找到答案，我们必须考虑这样一个过程：对当今北大西洋深层水生成有重要影响，而对北太平洋地区没有产生相同的生成量的作用的过程。海洋学家们一致认为，两大洋北部的差异源于两者之间存在的较大的盐度差异。北大西洋水体的盐度要高于大洋上层水体盐度的平均值，而太平洋水体的盐度则相对较低。大西洋中过剩的盐分使其水体密度与冬季生成的海洋深层水的密度相当。相反，即使冷却到冰点时，北太平洋水体的密度也达不到中层水的密度。

北大西洋及其附属海地中海的淡水收支情况见表1。尽管本地区汇聚了世界河流径流相当大的一部分，但因蒸发量大于降水量而损失的水量更大。淡水的净损失造就了北大西洋的高盐特性。北大西洋盐分过高必然要通过向太平洋和印度洋输送高盐深层水来达到平衡。而在全球尺度上，大洋表层水（及盐分）的收支必定是平衡的，因此，从大西洋损失的淡水必定会从其他地方重新进入大洋。从 30° N 向北极，大气的输送导致水汽在北大西洋上空形成净辐散，而在国际日期变更线以东的北太平洋地区则发生辐合 [46]。所以，如果我们要想了解当今大洋的深层水生成的维持机制是什么，首先必须弄清楚为什么淡水会通过大气从北大西洋运移到北太平洋地区。

Table 1. Freshwater budget for the North Atlantic Basin, including the Arctic, Mediterranean and Caribbean

Source	Input rate freshwater (m yr^{-1})	Freshwater flux (sverdrup)
River runoff[50]	+0.21	+0.33
Precipitation[50]	+0.87	+1.36
Evaporation[50]	−1.21	−1.89
Mediterranean exchange*	−0.07	−0.10
Net†	−0.20	−0.30

The combined area of the North Atlantic basin (0°–80° N) excluding the Mediterranean Sea is 4.9×10^{13} m^2. For freshwater flux, 1 sverdrup represents a flow of a million cubic metres per second.

* The exchange between the more salty waters of the Mediterranean Sea and the less salty waters of the open Atlantic leads to a loss of fresh water from the Atlantic. This process is driven by the high evaporation rate (relative to precipitation and runoff) for the Mediterranean Sea.

† Using a deep water production rate in the northern Atlantic of 20×10^6 m^3 s^{-1} and a salinity excess for this water of 0.50‰, a fresh water flux of 0.3 sverdrups would be obtained, indicating that no large discrepancy exists between oceanographic and meteorological budgets.

Warren, addressing this question[47], has shown that this pumping can be explained nicely by the temperature difference between the two oceans. The waters north of 30° latitude in the Atlantic are warmer than their Pacific counterparts. Thus, water is being distilled off the "warm" Atlantic and condensed on the "cold" Pacific. If so, then it is the temperature difference on which we must focus. What maintains it?

To some extent the warmer temperatures for the surface of the northern Atlantic must be related to the deep-water formation process. Upper waters in the Atlantic are advected northward into the regions of deep-water production. This advection carries heat to high latitudes. By contrast, in the northern Pacific, deep water upwells to the surface and is carried southward in the upper ocean. In this sense the situation is self-sustaining. Stommel[48] and Rooth[49] have discussed the possibility that thermohaline circulation has more than one stable mode. The deepwater circulation pattern maintains surface temperature of the northern Atlantic at a higher value than that for the Pacific. This temperature difference causes the Atlantic to be enriched in salt, whose excess leads to deep-water formation. At steady state, deep-water production must carry away just the amount of excess salt left behind by the atmospheric transport of water from the Atlantic to the Pacific. The standing excess of salt in the northern Atlantic is presumably just high enough to allow the generation of water sufficiently dense to enter the deep Atlantic.

This brings us to the fundamental question of this review—does the ocean–atmosphere system have more than one mode of operation? The idea that the Earth could, under the same solar heating regime, have quite different temperatures depending on its ice albedo or atmospheric greenhouse gas content is not new. Climate modellers have long been aware of the white Earth catastrophe scenario. If somehow the Earth were to be covered

表 1. 北大西洋海盆（包括北冰洋、地中海和加勒比海）的淡水收支概况

淡水来源	淡水输入速率（m·yr⁻¹）	淡水通量（Sv）
河流径流 [50]	+0.21	+0.33
降水 [50]	+0.87	+1.36
蒸发 [50]	−1.21	−1.89
地中海交换 *	−0.07	−0.10
净值 †	−0.20	−0.30

除去地中海，北大西洋海盆的总面积为（0°～80°N）为 $4.9 \times 10^{13} \, m^2$。对于淡水通量，1 Sv 代表每秒一百万立方米的流量。

* 地中海的高盐水体与开阔大西洋的低盐水体互换导致大西洋中淡水流失。该过程是由地中海的高蒸发速率（相对于降水量和径流量）所驱动的。

† 当北大西洋深水的生成率为 $20 \times 10^6 \, m^3 \cdot s^{-1}$、盐度过剩值为 0.50‰时，得到淡水通量为 0.3 Sv，说明海洋学和气象学收支之间存在的差异不大。

关于这个问题，沃伦 [47] 已经证明，可以通过两大洋之间的温度差异来很好的解释这种泵效应。北纬 30°以北的大西洋水温要高于太平洋相应位置的水温。因此，水分会从"温暖"的大西洋蒸发，然后在"寒冷"的太平洋凝结。倘若如此，那么两者的温差才是我们应该关注的。其维持机制是什么呢？

从某种程度上来说，北大西洋表层较高的温度可能与深层水的形成过程有关。北大西洋的上层水体均向北平流输送至深水生成区。平流将热量携带至高纬度地区。相反，在北太平洋地区，深层水上升至表层后就随大洋表层水向南流去。在这种情况下，这是一种自维持机制。施托梅尔 [48] 和鲁思 [49] 探讨了温盐环流具有一种以上稳定模态的可能性。深水环流模式使得北大西洋表层相对于太平洋有较高的温度。该温度差异造成大西洋盐分富集，而盐分的过剩又导致了北大西洋深层水的形成。在稳定状态下，深水生成作用带走的盐分必定恰好等于通过大气将水从大西洋带到太平洋而留下的多余盐分。北大西洋长期的过剩盐分应该可以生成密度足够大的水以进入大西洋深处。

这就引出了本文要讨论的最基本的问题——海洋－大气系统是否存在不止一种运行模态？在相同的太阳能辐射条件下，根据冰川反照率或大气中温室气体含量的不同，地球的温度变化可能很大，这一观点并非新创。气候模拟学家很早以前就已注意到了白垩突变情景。如果地球被冰川覆盖，那么地表反射率的剧增将会使气温

with ice, the greatly increased reflectivity of its surface would cause the temperature to fall below the freezing point and thereby stabilize the change. They have also considered the greenhouse catastrophe. If somehow the carbon locked up in sediments were to be released to the atmosphere, the enhanced infrared absorption would raise the planetary surface temperature to the point where carbonate minerals and organic residues could no longer form and thereby stabilize the change. Based on the CO_2 results from ice cores, Oeschger suggested that the Earth had two modes of ocean–atmosphere–biosphere–cryosphere operation. Each oscillation observed in the ice cores involves a jump from one mode of operation to the other.

It is tempting to speculate that one of Oeschger's two modes corresponds to the situation when deep-water production in the northern Atlantic is "strong" and the other to the situation when deep-water production is "weak". If this is the case, then the palaeoclimatic record tells us that, for the summer insolation and ice-cover situation that prevailed during the full interglacial time, the system was in the "strong" mode and for the corresponding situation that prevailed during full glacial times it was in the "weak" mode. Because in the present-day ocean the deep-water production corresponds to salt enrichment in the Atlantic, it is tempting to postulate that during full glacial time the opposite was true. Then, salt was being enriched in the Pacific and deep-water flow was the reverse of what it is now (see Fig. 7). Based on oxygen isotope studies on North Pacific cores, deep water may have been produced in the Pacific Ocean during glacial time (N. Shackleton, personal communication). On the other hand, it is possible that the rate of salt enrichment in the Atlantic was considerably less during glacial time, causing a reduction in deep-water production rather than a reversal in flow. Boyle's Cd data favours this latter point of view.

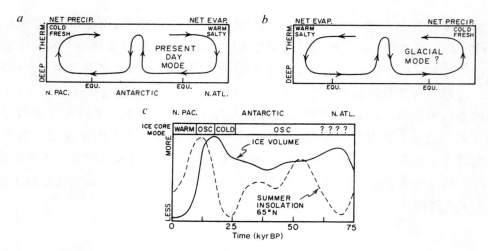

Fig. 7. *a, b,* Two possible extreme modes of ocean circulation are proposed here, corresponding to the warm and cold intervals seen in the ice-core record. *c,* The times when the ice-core record shows the system to have been locked in its warm mode, to have been locked in its cold mode or to have been oscillating between these modes are shown with the ice-volume record and the Northern Hemisphere high-latitude summer insolation record. The intervals of warm Greenland climate correspond to intervals of low ice volume and high summer insolation and the intervals of cold Greenland climate correspond to times of high ice volume and low summer insolation. The intervals when Greenland climate oscillated between warm and cold corresponded to times when the ice volume–summer insolation product had intermediate values. This suggests that the atmospheric transport of water vapour between the Atlantic and Pacific changes with ice cover and summer insolation.

46

降至冰点以下，进而达到稳定状态。他们也考虑了温室突变情景。倘若沉积物中的碳释放到大气中，加强的红外线吸收作用将会使行星地表温度上升到不再形成碳酸岩矿物和有机残留物的程度，从而达到稳定。根据冰芯中 CO_2 的测定结果，厄施格尔提出，地球的海洋－大气圈－生物圈－冰雪圈系统存在两种运行模态。从冰芯中观测到的每次振荡即是由一种模态向另一种模态的一次转变。

对于厄施格尔的两种模态，其中之一对应于北大西洋深层水生成作用"加强"的情形，而另一个则对应于生成作用"减弱"的情形，这一推测是很吸引人的。倘若如此，那么前述古气候记录告诉我们的是，全间冰期夏季日照和冰盖占主导地位的情形中，该体系处于增强模态下；而对应于全冰期的情形时，该体系则处于减弱模态下。由于当今海洋中深层水生成作用对应着大西洋盐分的富集，因此我们推断，全冰期情况应该是相反的。那么，当时盐分应该富集于太平洋中，深层水环流与现在相反（见图7）。根据太平洋岩芯的氧同位素研究结果，冰期时大洋深层水可能形成于太平洋中（沙克尔顿，个人交流）。另一方面，也许冰期时大西洋中盐分的富集速率低得多，使得深层水生成量降低，而不是产生反向环流。博伊尔的 Cd 数据就支持后一种论点。

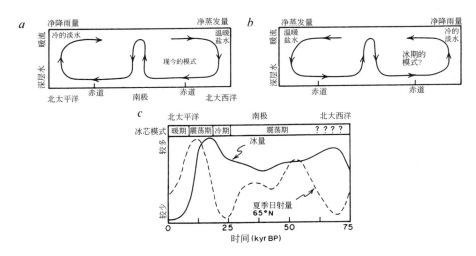

图 7. a 和 b，此处提出了两种可能的极端大洋环流模态，与冰芯记录中的冷暖期相对应。c，冰芯记录显示该体系处于温暖模态、寒冷模态，以及在两种模态间摆动的时间，同时还给出了冰量记录以及北半球高纬度地区夏季的日照情况。格陵兰气候暖期对应于冰量少、夏季日照强，而格陵兰气候冷期则对应于冰量大、日照弱。格陵兰气候在冷暖期之间摆动时，相应的冰量与日照条件处于中间值状态。这表明，大西洋与太平洋之间，大气对水汽的输送随冰川覆盖面积和夏季日照的变化而变化。

The Oeschger climate oscillations occur in intervals with climates lying between those characterizing full glacial and full interglacial time. If, as the summer insolation at high northern latitudes increased and once again the atmospheric vapour transport balance favoured salt buildup in the Atlantic, then the production of deep water would resume (or intensify), releasing excess heat to the atmosphere over the northern Atlantic. This excess heat would lead eventually to increased discharge of ice from the caps surrounding the Atlantic. If 3% of the excess ice present during full glacial time were added to the Atlantic Ocean by melting during a 100 yr interval, the mean freshwater flux would be 0.6 sverdrups (that is, twice the present imbalance between fresh water and loss for the Atlantic). Thus, the melt water generated in this way would significantly reduce deep-water production, returning northern Atlantic climates to their glacial state. This, in turn, would halt ice retreat and allow the northern Atlantic salt buildup to resume. Thus, it is possible that during periods of ice retreat the system oscillates between the North Atlantic "strong" and "weak" modes of deep-water production. Although the physics of such an oscillation has yet to be elucidated, two elements are evident. The first involves water storage in and release from the large Northern Hemisphere glacial ice caps adjacent to the Atlantic. The other involves the transport of salt through the deep sea. As water now resides for many hundreds of years in the deep sea, transients in the deep-ocean salinity distribution created by ventilation changes may be an important element in the oscillator.

Climate Modelling

Until now, our thinking about past and future climate changes has been dominated by the assumption that the response to any gradual forcing will be smooth. But if, as proposed by Oeschger, the system has more than one quasi-stable mode of operation, then the situation is more complex. Present general circulation models will at best allow us to study only the changes that will take place if the system remains in its current operational mode. Thus, if the changes that characterized glacial time and those that will characterize the coming CO_2 superinterglacial time involve mode switches, investigations of the transient climate response have to allow for this possibility.

Despite the tenuous nature of the information presently available and of the difficulties inherent in thinking in terms of mode changes, we must begin to explore this alternate track. The programme elements required are clear. At least we must have a joint ocean–atmosphere general circulation model that will allow the exploration of several possible connections between planetary radiation, atmospheric water transport, ocean circulation, atmospheric trace gas content and the marine and terrestrial biosphere. If we are to have confidence that these models provide reliable analogues to the real world, we must gather more information about how each of the important subsystems operates in the present. Finally, we must extract all possible information from the palaeoclimatic record. Even given the full use of present resources, it will be several decades before we possess sufficient understanding to predict future climates. Unless we intensify research in these areas, the major impacts of CO_2 will occur before we are prepared fully to deal with them.

(**315**, 21-26; 1985)

厄施格尔气候振荡发生于全冰期和全间冰期之间的气候条件下。倘若高北纬度地区的夏季日照增加，大气水汽输送平衡再次有利于大西洋中盐分的富集，那么深层水生成作用将再度启动（或加强），并向北大西洋上空的大气释放过剩的热量。释放的这些热量将最终导致大西洋周围冰盖的消融速率增大。假使冰盛期时约有 3% 过量的冰在 100 年的时间内融化进入了大西洋，那么平均的淡水通量将达 0.6 Sv（相当于现今大西洋中淡水注入与流失差量的两倍）。所以，通过这种方式产生的冰雪融水将显著降低深层水的生成量，进而促使北大西洋气候回到冰期时的状态。而这又会再次终止冰川的消退并使北大西洋盐度重新开始上升。因此，冰川消退期间北大西洋深层水生成作用系统可能在强弱模态之间振荡。虽然此类振荡的物理机制还有待于进一步说明，但其中有两点是很显然的。第一点涉及北半球与大西洋毗连的大冰盖中水的储存和释放。第二点则关于盐分通过深海的转移。由于现在水体已经在深海逗留了几百年的时间，由大气流通变化引起的深海盐度的瞬时分布在振荡作用中可能有重要作用。

气 候 模 拟

到目前为止，我们对过去和未来气候变化的设想主要建立在对所有渐变强迫的响应都是平滑的前提下。但是，倘若如厄施格尔所说，该体系具有不止一种准稳定运行模态，那情况就复杂得多了。当前的大气环流模式最多只能允许我们研究该体系仍处于当前运行模态时将会发生的变化。因此，如果代表冰期以及将要发生的 CO_2 超级间冰期的那些变化涉及系统运行模态的转换，那么关于瞬时气候响应的研究则必须考虑这种可能性的存在。

虽然现在相关资料还很贫乏，关于模态转换的思维方面也存在困难，但我们必须开始着手探索这种交替现象。所需要的各个计划要素已经非常清楚了。至少，我们必须建立一个联合的大气-海洋环流模式，以便于探索地球辐射、大气水的输送、海洋环流、大气中痕量气体的含量以及海洋和陆地生物圈之间可能存在的多种相互关系。要想使这些模型提供可靠的关于真实世界的模拟结果，我们必须搜集到更多关于当前状态下每个子系统的运行资料。最后，我们必须从古气候记录中提取所有可能的信息。即便充分利用现今资源，我们要做到理解并能预测未来气候也还需要几十年的时间。除非我们加强对这些领域的研究，否则在我们做好应付准备之前 CO_2 产生的主要影响可能就已经发生了。

（齐红艳 翻译；刘新 审稿）

Wallace S. Broecker[*], **Dorothy M. Peteet**[†] & **David Rind**[†]
[*] Lamont-Doherty Geological Observatory of Columbia University, Palisades, New York 10964, USA
[†] NASA/Goddard Space Flight Center, Institute for Space Studies, 2880 Broadway, New York, NY 10025, USA

References:

1. Berner, W., Stauffer, B. & Oeschger, H. *Nature* **275**, 53-55 (1979).
2. Delmas, R., Ascencio, J. -M. & Legrang, M. *Nature* **284**, 155-157 (1980).
3. Neftel, A., Oeschger, H., Schwander, J., Stauffer, B. & Zumbrunn, R. *Nature* **295**, 220-233 (1982).
4. Broecker, W. & Takahashi, T. *Climate Processes and Climate Sensitivity* (ed. Hansen, J. & Takahashi, T.) 314-326 (*Geophys. Monogr.* **29**, *Am. Geophys. U.* 1984).
5. Sarmiento, J. & Toggweiler, R. *Nature* **308**, 621-624 (1984).
6. Siegenthaler, U. & Wenk, Th. *Nature* **308**, 624-626 (1984).
7. Knox, F. & McElroy, M. *J. Geophys. Res.* **89**, 4629-4637 (1984).
8. Emiliani, C. *J. Geol.* **63**, 538-578 (1955).
9. Broecker, W. & Van Donk, J. *Rev. Geophys. space Sci.* **8**, 169-198 (1970).
10. Shackleton, N. & Opdyke, N. *Quat. Res.* **3**, 39-55 (1973).
11. Hays, J., Imbrie, J. & Shackleton, N. *Science* **194**, 1121-1132 (1981).
12. Imbrie, J. *et al. Milankovitch & Climate I* (eds Berger, A. *et al.*) 269-305 (Reidel, Dordrecht, 1984).
13. Imbrie, J. & Imbrie, J. Z. *Science* **207**, 943-953 (1980).
14. Dansgaard, W. *et al. Science* **218**, 1273-1277 (1982).
15. Dansgaard, W. *et al. Am. Geophys. Un. Monogr. Ser.* **29** (*M. Ewing Symp.* **3**), 288-298 (1984).
16. Beer, J. *et al. Ann. Glaciol.* **5**, 16-17 (1984).
17. Finkel, R. & Langway, C. *Earth Planet. Sci. Lett.* (in the press).
18. Siegenthaler, U., Eicher, U., Oeschger, H. & Dansgaard, W. *Ann. Glaciol.* **5**, 149-152 (1984).
19. Dansgaard, W., Johnsen, S., Moller, J. & Langway, C. *Science* **166**, 377-381 (1969).
20. Oeschger, H. *et al. Am. Geophys. Un. Monogr. Ser.* **29** (*M. Ewing Symp.* **3**), 299-306 (1984).
21. Stauffer, B., Hofer, H., Oeschger, H., Schwander, J. & Siegenthaler, U. *Ann. Glaciol.* **5**, 160-164 (1984).
22. Broecker, W. in *Climate Variations and Variability: Facts and Theory* (ed. Berger, A.) 109-120 (Reidel, Dordrecht, 1981).
23. Broecker, W. *Prog. Oceanogr.* **11**, 151-197 (1982).
24. Broecker, W. *Geochim. Acta* **46**, 1689-1705 (1982).
25. Broecker, W., Mix, A., Andree, M. & Oeschger, H. *Nucl. Instrum. Meth. Phys. Res.* B5, 331-339 (1984).
26. Andree, M. *et al. Nucl. Instrum. Meth. Phys. Res.* B5, 340-345 (1984).
27. Boyle, E. & Keigwin, L. *Science* **218**, 784-787 (1982).
28. Duplessy, J., Chenouard, L. & Vila, F. *Science* **188**, 1208-1209 (1975).
29. Kellogg, T., Duplessy, J. & Shackleton, N. *Boreas* **7**, 61-73 (1978).
30. Shackleton, N. *The Fate of Fossil Fuel CO$_2$* (eds Andersen, N. & Malahoff, A.) 401-427 (Plenum, New York, 1977).
31. Shackleton, N., Imbrie, J. & Hall, M. A. *Earth Planet. Sci. Lett.* **65**, 233-244 (1983).
32. Ruddiman, W. F. & McIntyre, A. *Palaeogeogr. Palaeoclimatol. Palaeoecol.* **35**, 145-214 (1981).
33. Watts, W. *Studies in the Late-Glacial of North-west Europe* (eds Lowe, J., Gray, J. & Robinson, J.) 1-21 (Pergamon, Oxford, 1980).
34. Wright, H. (ed.) *Late-Quaternary Environments of the United States* Vols 1 and 2 (University of Minnesota Press, 1983).
35. Anderson, T. & Macpherson, J. *6th IPC Conf.* (Calgary, 1984).
36. Mott, J., Grant, D., Stea, R. & Ochietti, S. *6th IPC Conf.* (Calgary, 1984).
37. Mercer, J. *Arctic Alp. Res.* **6**, 227-236 (1969).
38. Van der Hammen, T., Barelds, J., de Jong, H. & De Veer, A. A. *Palaeogeogr. Palaeoclimatol. Palaeoecol.* **32**, 247-340 (1981).
39. Mercer, J. H. & Palacios, O. *Geology* **5**, 600-604 (1977).
40. Wright, H. E. *Quat. Res.* **21**, 275-285 (1984).
41. Heusser, C. J. *Quat. Res.* **22**, 77-90 (1984).
42. Burrows, C. J. *Palaeogeogr. Palaeoclimatol. Palaeoecol.* **27**, 287-347 (1979).
43. Johnsen, S., Dansgaard, W., Clausen, H. & Langway, C. *Nature* **235**, 429-434 (1972).
44. Broecker, W. *J. Geophys. Res.* **4**, 3218-3226 (1979).
45. Climap Project Members *Geol. Soc. Am. Map Chart Ser.* MC-36 (1981).
46. Peixoto, J. & Oort, A. in *Variations in the Global Water Budget* (eds Street-Perott, A. *et al.*) 5-65 (Reidel, Dordrecht, 1983).
47. Warren, B. *J. Mar. Res.* **41**, 327-347 (1983).

48. Stommel, H. *Tellus* **13**, 224-230 (1961).

49. Rooth, Claes. *Prog. Oceanogr.* **11**, 131-149 (1982).

50. Baumgartner, A. & Reichel, E. *Die Weltwasserbilanz Munich* (1975).

51. Berger, A. *Astr. Astrophys.* **51**, 127-135 (1977).

52. Eicher, U., Siegenthaler, U. & Wegmuller, S. *Quat. Res.* **15**, 160-170 (1981).

53. Ruddiman, W., Sancetta, C. & McIntyre, A. *Phil. Trans. R. Soc.* **B280**, 119-142 (1977).

54. Birks, H. & Mathewes, R. *New Phytol.* **80**, 455-484 (1978).

55. Eicher, U. & Siegenthaler, U. *Physische Geographie* **1**, 103-110 (1982).

56. Denton, G. & Hughes, T. *The Last Great Ice Sheets* (Wiley, New York, 1981).

Large Losses of Total Ozone in Antarctica Reveal Seasonal ClO$_x$/NO$_x$ Interaction

J. C. Farman *et al.*

Editor's Note

Fears that human activity on the surface of the Earth will have permanent consequences for the environment have strengthened during the past quarter of a century. One of the first definitive proofs that such threats exist was provided by Joe Farman and his colleagues at the British Antarctic Survey. They reported in this paper that the concentration of stratospheric ozone—a naturally occurring molecule in the upper atmosphere that absorbs potentially harmful ultraviolet solar radiation—had been declining steadily since the 1950s. This seemed to confirm warnings in the 1970s that chlorofluorocarbons—volatile human-made compounds used mainly in refrigerators—could break down in the atmosphere into ozone-destroying substances. In 1987 the industrial use of such compounds began to be phased out according to the internationally ratified agreement called the Montreal Protocol.

Recent attempts[1,2] to consolidate assessments of the effect of human activities on stratospheric ozone (O$_3$) using one-dimensional models for 30° N have suggested that perturbations of total O$_3$ will remain small for at least the next decade. Results from such models are often accepted by default as global estimates[3]. The inadequacy of this approach is here made evident by observations that the spring values of total O$_3$ in Antarctica have now fallen considerably. The circulation in the lower stratosphere is apparently unchanged, and possible chemical causes must be considered. We suggest that the very low temperatures which prevail from midwinter until several weeks after the spring equinox make the Antarctic stratosphere uniquely sensitive to growth of inorganic chlorine, ClX, primarily by the effect of this growth on the NO$_2$/NO ratio. This, with the height distribution of UV irradiation peculiar to the polar stratosphere, could account for the O$_3$ losses observed.

TOTAL O$_3$ has been measured at the British Antarctic Survey stations, Argentine Islands 65° S 64° W and Halley Bay 76° S 27° W, since 1957. Figure 1a shows data from Halley Bay. The mean and extreme daily values from October 1957 to March 1973 and the supporting calibrations have been discussed elsewhere[4,5]. The mean daily value for the four latest complete observing seasons (October 1980–March 1984) and the individual daily values for the current observing season are detailed Fig. 1. The more recent data are provisional values. Very generous bounds for possible corrections would be ±30 matm cm. There was a changeover of spectrophotometers at the station in January 1982; the replacement instrument had been calibrated against the UK Meteorological

南极臭氧总量大量损失揭示季节性 CIO$_x$/NO$_x$ 的相互作用

法曼等

编者按

在过去 25 年中，人们关于人类在地球表面的活动会对环境产生永久后果的忧虑加深了。关于上述影响过程，最早的明确证据之一是由英国南极勘探署的乔·法曼和他的同事提供的。他们在本文中指出，自从 20 世纪 50 年代以来，平流层中臭氧的浓度一直稳步下降，臭氧是高层大气中自然反应形成的分子，这些分子能吸收具有潜在危害的紫外太阳辐射。这似乎证实了 20 世纪 70 年代的警告——氟氯烃（一种主要用于电冰箱的挥发性人造化合物）能够在大气中分解为破坏臭氧层的物质。根据国际签署的协议《蒙特利尔议定书》，从 1987 年开始，工业应用中人们逐步淘汰了这种化合物。

最近，有人尝试[1,2]在 30°N 使用一维模型评估人类活动对于平流层臭氧的影响，结果指出，臭氧总量受到的干扰至少在未来十年中仍然很小。这类模型所得的结果通常默认为是对全球情况的估计[3]。这里，对于上述方法的不足之处给出了观测证据，即南极春季臭氧总量现在已经大幅度下降。平流层下层的循环显然不变，那么必须要考虑到其中可能的化学原因。我们认为，冬季中期至春分后几周盛行的极低温度使南极平流层对无机氯（即 ClX）含量的增长特别敏感，主要是由于该增长对 NO$_2$/NO 比例的影响。基于上述理由，加上极地平流层所特有的高紫外（UV）辐射分布，就可以解释观测到的臭氧损失。

从 1957 年开始，人们一直在英国南极勘探署观测站（位于 65°S，64°W 阿根廷群岛和 76°S，27°W 哈雷湾）监测臭氧总量。图 1a 显示了来自哈雷湾的数据。1957 年 10 月到 1973 年 3 月的日平均值和极值，以及相应的仪器校准已在其他地方进行了讨论[4,5]。图 1 中详细给出了最近四个完整的观测季中（1980 年 10 月~1984 年 3 月）的日平均值，以及当前观测季中每个站点的每日数值。较近期的数据是暂定值。可能的校正具有很宽的界限，达到 ±30 matm·cm。1982 年 1 月对站点的分光光度计进行了更换；更新仪器于 1981 年 6 月以英国气象局的标准进行了校准。由此，有两

Office standard in June 1981. Thus, two spectrophotometers have shown October values of total O$_3$ to be much lower than March values, a feature entirely lacking in the 1957–73 data set. To interpret this difference as a seasonal instrumental effect would be inconsistent with the results of routine checks using standard lamps. Instrument temperatures (recorded for each observation) show that the March and October operating conditions were practically identical. Whatever the absolute error of the recent values may be, within the bounds quoted, the annual variation of total O$_3$ at Halley Bay has undergone a dramatic change.

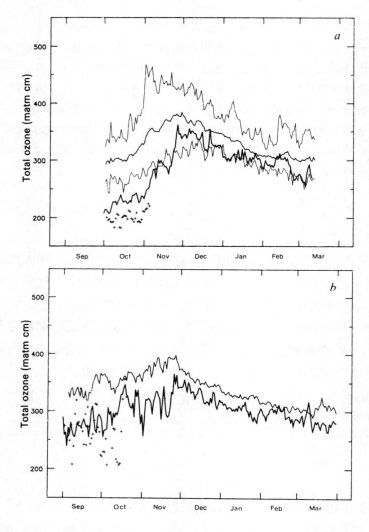

Fig. 1. Daily values of total O$_3$. *a*, Halley Bay: thin lines, mean and extreme values for 16 seasons, 1957–73; thick line, mean values for four seasons, 1980-84; +, values for October 1984. Observing season: 1 October to 13 March. *b*, Argentine Islands: as for Halley Bay, but extreme values for 1957-73 omitted. Observing season: 1 September to 31 March.

Figure 1*b* shows data from Argentine Islands in a similar form, except that for clarity the extreme values for 1957–73 have been omitted. The values for 1980 to the present are

台分光光度计显示的 10 月份臭氧总量比 3 月份数值低很多，这种情况在 1957~1973 年的数据中从未曾出现过。要将这一差异解释为季节性的仪器影响，就会与使用标准光源进行例行检查得到的结果相矛盾。仪器温度（每次观测都做了记录）表明，3 月份和 10 月份的工作条件几乎是相同的。就所引用的范围来看，无论近期数据的绝对误差有多大，哈雷湾年度臭氧总量的变化的确经历了巨大的改变。

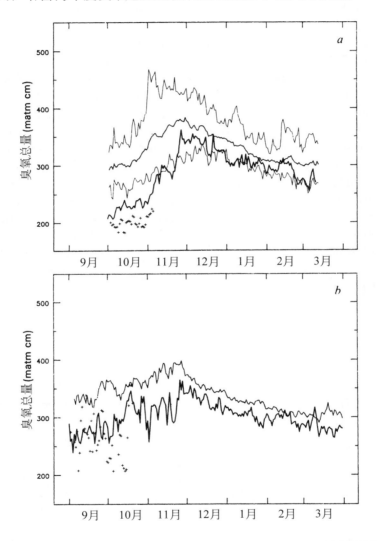

图 1. 臭氧总量的每日数值。*a*，哈雷湾：细线表示 1957~1973 年间，16 个观测季的平均值和极值；粗线表示 1980~1984 年间 4 个观测季的平均值；+ 表示 1984 年 10 月的数值。观测季：10 月 1 日到 3 月 13 日。*b*，阿根廷群岛：与哈雷湾数据类似，但省略了 1957~1973 年的极值。观测季：9 月 1 日到 3 月 31 日。

　　图 1*b* 以类似的形式显示了来自阿根廷群岛的数据，只是为了清晰起见省略了 1957~1973 年数据的极值。1980 年至今的数据是临时的，其最大误差界限还是

provisional, the extreme error bounds again being ±30 matm cm. The changes are similar to those seen at Halley Bay, but are much smaller in magnitude.

Upper-air temperatures and winds are available for these stations from 1956. There are no indications of recent departures from established mean values sufficient to attribute the changes in total O_3 to changes in the circulation. The present-day atmosphere differs most prominently from that of previous decades in the higher concentrations of halocarbons. Figure 2*a* shows the monthly mean total O_3 in October at Halley Bay, for 1957–84, and Fig. 2*b* that in February, 1958–84. Tropospheric concentrations of the halocarbons F-11 ($CFCl_3$) and F-12 (CF_2Cl_2) in the Southern Hemisphere[3] are also shown, plotted to give greatest emphasis to a possible relationship. Their growth, from which increase of stratospheric ClX is inferred, in not evidently dependent on season. The contrast between spring and autumn O_3 losses and the striking enhancement of spring loss at Halley Bay need to be explained. In Antarctica, the lower stratosphere is ~40 K colder in October that in February. The stratosphere over Halley Bay experiences a polar night and a polar day (many weeks of darkness, and of continuous photolysis, respectively); that over Argentine Islands does not. Figure 3 shows calculated amounts of NO_x in the polar night and the partitioning between the species[6] of these, only NO_3 and NO_2 are dissociated rapidly by visible light. The major reservoir, N_2O_5, which only absorbs strongly below 280 nm, should be relatively long-lived. Daytime levels of NO and NO_2 should be much less in early spring, following the polar night, than in autumn, following the polar day. Recent measurements[7] support these inferences. The effect of these seasonal variations on the strongly interdependent ClO_x and NO_x cycles is examined below.

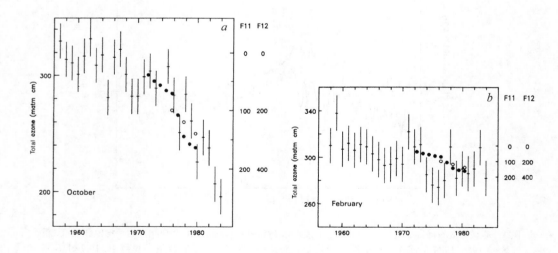

Fig. 2. Monthly means of total O_3 at Halley Bay, and Southern Hemisphere measurements of F-11(●, p.p.t.v. (parts per trillion by volume) $CFCl_3$) and F-12 (○, p.p.t.v. CF_2Cl_2). *a*, October, 1957–84. *b*, February, 1958–84. Note that F-11 and F-12 amounts increase down the figure.

±30 matm·cm。其变化情况类似于在哈雷湾所观测到的，不过强度要小得多。

从 1956 年起，地面站可以测得高空温度和风速。从近期的平均偏差来看，没有任何迹象表明大气环流的改变是引起臭氧总量变化的原因。当今大气与过去数十年相比，最显著的差别就是卤代烃的浓度升高了。图 2a 显示了 1957~1984 年间，哈雷湾 10 月时臭氧总量的月平均值；图 2b 则是 1958~1984 年间 2 月的数据。还显示了南半球对流层中卤代烃 F–11（CFCl$_3$）和 F–12（CF$_2$Cl$_2$）的浓度[3]，图中主要强调可能存在的关系。根据平流层中ClX的增加推测，它们的浓度增加没有明显的季节变化。关于春季与秋季臭氧损失的对比，以及哈雷湾地区春季臭氧损失量的惊人增长，需要加以解释。在南极洲，平流层下层的温度在 10 月份比在 2 月份要低约 40 K。哈雷湾上空的平流层经历了极夜和极昼（分别为持续数周的黑暗和光照）；而在阿根廷群岛上空则没有这种现象。图 3 中显示了极夜时期 NO$_x$ 的计算值以及各种物质间[6]的分布情况，仅 NO$_3$ 和 NO$_2$ 能被可见光快速解离。作为主要吸收库，只对低于 280 nm 电磁波有强烈吸收的 N$_2$O$_5$ 应该有相对较长的寿命。极夜之后，早春时期 NO 和 NO$_2$ 的日间水平应该会比极昼之后的秋季时低很多。最近的观测结果支持上述推测[7]。上述季节性变更对于强烈依赖 ClO$_x$ 与 NO$_x$ 循环的影响在下文进行讨论。

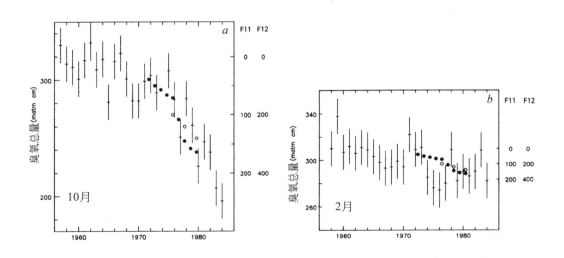

图 2. 哈雷湾臭氧总量的月平均值，以及南半球 F–11（●，CFCl$_3$ 的 pptv（体积混合比，10^{-12}））和 F–12（○，CF$_2$Cl$_2$ 的 pptv）的观测结果。a, 1957~1984 年, 10 月。b, 1958~1984 年, 2 月。注意，图中 F–11 和 F–12 的量向下逐渐增多。

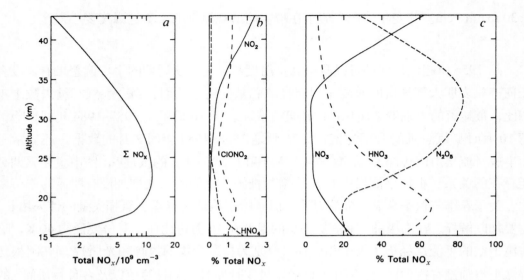

Fig. 3. NO_x during the polar night. a, Total NO_x cm^{-3}, from 15 to 43 km. b, NO_2, $ClONO_2$ and HNO_4 as percentages of total NO_x. c, NO_3, HNO_3 and N_2O_5 as percentages of total NO_x.

The O_3 loss rate resulting from NO_x and ClO_x may be written[8]

$$L = N + C = 2k_2[O][NO_2] + 2k_6[O][ClO] \tag{1}$$

L accounts for over 85% of O_3 destruction in the altitude range 20–40 km. At 40 km, N and C are roughly equal. Lower down, C decreases rapidly to 10% of L at 30 km, 3% at 20 km (refs 6, 8). Equation (1) is based on two steady-state approximations, (see Table 1a for the reactions involved)

$$\psi = \frac{[NO_2]}{[NO]} \sim \frac{k_1[O_3] + k_4[ClO]}{k_2[O] + j_3} \tag{2}$$

and

$$\chi = \frac{[Cl]}{[ClO]} \sim \frac{k_6[O] + k_4[NO]}{k_5[O_3]} \tag{3}$$

valid in daytime, with [O] in steady state with [O_3]. Reaction (4) has a negative temperature coefficient, whereas reaction (1) has large positive activation energy[9], with the result that ψ is strongly dependent on [ClO] at low temperature, as shown in Fig. 4. [ClO] is not simply proportional to total ClX, because $ClONO_2$ formation (reaction (10)) intervenes. Throughout the stratosphere, $\chi \ll 1$, so that [ClO]~[Cl+ClO]. From a steady-state analysis of the reactions given in Table 1b,

$$[Cl + ClO] \sim \frac{k_7[HCl][OH] + j_8[ClONO_2] + j_9[HOCl]}{k_{10}[NO_2] + k_{11}[HO_2] + \chi(k_{12}[CH_4] + k_{13}[HO_2])} \tag{4}$$

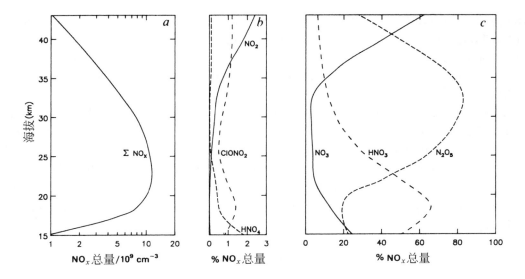

图 3. 极夜时期的 NO$_x$。a，NO$_x$ 总量 cm^{-3}，从 15 km 到 43 km。b，NO$_2$，ClONO$_2$ 和 HNO$_4$ 在全部 NO$_x$ 中所占的百分比。c，NO$_3$，HNO$_3$ 和 N$_2$O$_5$ 在全部 NO$_x$ 中所占的百分比。

由 NO$_x$ 和 ClO$_x$ 导致的臭氧损失率可以用下列式子表示[8]：

$$L = N + C = 2k_2[O][NO_2] + 2k_6[O][ClO] \tag{1}$$

L 描述了 20~40 km 高度范围内超过 85% 的臭氧破坏情况。在 40 km 高度，N 和 C 大致相等。在较低高度时 C 迅速减小，30 km 处的 C 为 L 的 10%，20 km 处为 3%（参考文献 6、8）。等式（1）是基于两个稳态近似而得到（参见表 1a 中涉及的有关反应），

$$\psi = \frac{[NO_2]}{[NO]} \sim \frac{k_1[O_3] + k_4[ClO]}{k_2[O] + j_3} \tag{2}$$

和

$$\chi = \frac{[Cl]}{[ClO]} \sim \frac{k_6[O] + k_4[NO]}{k_5[O_3]} \tag{3}$$

适用于白天，其中 [O] 和 [O$_3$] 为稳态。反应（4）具有负的温度系数，而反应（1）有很大的正活化能[9]，因此 ψ 在低温时高度地依赖于 [ClO]，如图 4 所示。由于 ClONO$_2$ 的形成（反应（10）），[ClO] 的值不是简单地正比于 ClX 总量。在整个平流层中，$\chi \ll 1$，因此 [ClO] ~ [Cl + ClO]。通过对表 1b 中反应进行稳态分析，可以得到：

$$[Cl + ClO] \sim \frac{k_7[HCl][OH] + j_8[ClONO_2] + j_9[HOCl]}{k_{10}[NO_2] + k_{11}[HO_2] + \chi(k_{12}[CH_4] + k_{13}[HO_2])} \tag{4}$$

Values of ψ, χ and [Cl+ClO] obtained from equations (2), (3) and (4) are in good accord with full one-dimensional model results for late summer in Antarctica[6]. Neglecting seasonal effects other than those resulting from temperature and from variation of [NO+NO$_2$], it is possible to solve simultaneously for [NO$_2$] and [ClO], and to derive L. Results are shown in Table 2 as relaxation times[8], [O$_3$]/L, for various conditions. The spring values (lines 2, 3 and 4) are highly dependent on ClX amount (compare columns a and b), the autumn values (line 1) much less so. At Argentine Islands, the sensitivity to ClX growth should resemble that seen in line 2, attributable solely to low temperature. Lines 3 and 4 show the enhanced sensitivity possible at stations within the Antarctic Circle, such as Halley Bay, arising from slow release of [NO+NO$_2$] following the polar night. It remains to be shown how stable O$_3$ budgets were achieved with the relaxation times for the lower chlorine level (Table 2, a).

Table 1. Reaction list

a Governing ψ and χ (see text)		b Governing [Cl+ClO]	
$NO + O_3 \rightarrow NO_2 + O_2$	(1)	$HCl + OH \rightarrow Cl + H_2O$	(7)
$NO_2 + O \rightarrow NO + O_2$	(2)	$ClONO_2 + hv \rightarrow ClO + NO_2$	(8)
$NO_2 + hv \rightarrow NO + O$	(3)	$HOCl + hv \rightarrow Cl + OH$	(9)
$NO + ClO \rightarrow NO_2 + Cl$	(4)	$ClO + NO_2 + M \rightarrow ClONO_2 + M$	(10)
$Cl + O_3 \rightarrow ClO + O_2$	(5)	$ClO + HO_2 \rightarrow HOCl + O_2$	(11)
$ClO + O \rightarrow Cl + O_2$	(6)	$Cl + CH_4 \rightarrow HCl + CH_3$	(12)
		$Cl + HO_2 \rightarrow HCl + O_2$	(13)
c	$HCl + ClONO_2 \rightarrow Cl_2 + HNO_3$		(14)

Table 2. Relaxation times in days, [O$_3$]/L, for maximum chlorine levels 1.5 p.p.b.v. (a)
and 2.7 p.p.b.v. (b) (1980)

Date	Altitude (km)	22		25.5		29		32.5		36		39.5		43	
	Relative NO+NO$_2$	a	b	a	b	a	b	a	b	a	b	a	b	a	b
25 March	1	105	103	38	37	16	15	6.9	5.7	2.6	2.0	1.2	0.9	0.83	0.57
17 September	1	224	210	86	77	32	27	12.2	9.2	4.9	3.4	2.6	1.7	1.90	1.22
17 September	0.75	288	265	107	93	39	31	14.2	10.4	5.7	3.9	3.0	1.9	2.13	1.33
17 September	0.5	398	353	141	118	47	36	17.0	12.0	6.9	4.5	3.5	2.2	2.41	1.46

Noon values at 75.5° S, solar elevation 12.5°. Lower stratosphere at 230 K on 25 March; 190 K on 17 September. The altitudes shown apply to the summer temperature profile used in the model[6].

利用等式（2）、（3）和（4）所得到的 ψ、χ 和 [Cl + ClO] 的值与南极洲夏末时完整的一维模型所得结果吻合得很好[6]。除温度和 [NO + NO₂] 变化导致的结果以外，忽略季节性影响，就有可能同时解出 [NO₂] 和 [ClO]，并进而得到 L。表 2 中显示了不同条件下得到的弛豫时间[8]，[O₃]/L。春季数值（第 2、3 和 4 行）高度地依赖于 ClX 的量（比较 a 和 b 两列），而秋季数值（第 1 行）的依赖性则要弱很多。在阿根廷群岛，对于 ClX 含量增加的敏感性应该与第 2 行中的情况类似，其原因是低温。第 3 和 4 行显示，可能在诸如哈雷湾等位于南极圈内的站点，敏感性会增强，其原因是极夜之后 [NO + NO₂] 的缓慢释放。有待证明的是，在较低氯水平的弛豫时间下，臭氧如何实现稳定的累积（参见表 2，a）。

表 1. 反应列表

a 主要 ψ 和 χ（参见正文）		b 主要 [Cl+ClO]	
$NO + O_3 \rightarrow NO_2 + O_2$	(1)	$HCl + OH \rightarrow Cl + H_2O$	(7)
$NO_2 + O \rightarrow NO + O_2$	(2)	$ClONO_2 + hv \rightarrow ClO + NO_2$	(8)
$NO_2 + hv \rightarrow NO + O$	(3)	$HOCl + hv \rightarrow Cl + OH$	(9)
$NO + ClO \rightarrow NO_2 + Cl$	(4)	$ClO + NO_2 + M \rightarrow ClONO_2 + M$	(10)
$Cl + O_3 \rightarrow ClO + O_2$	(5)	$ClO + HO_2 \rightarrow HOCl + O_2$	(11)
$ClO + O \rightarrow Cl + O_2$	(6)	$Cl + CH_4 \rightarrow HCl + CH_3$	(12)
		$Cl + HO_2 \rightarrow HCl + O_2$	(13)
c		$HCl + ClONO_2 \rightarrow Cl_2 + HNO_3$	(14)

表 2. 弛豫时间（以天为单位），[O₃]/L，最大氯水平为 1.5 ppbv（a）和 2.7 ppbv（b）（1980）

日期	NO+NO₂ 相对含量	海拔（km） 22		25.5		29		32.5		36		39.5		43	
		a	b	a	b	a	b	a	b	a	b	a	b	a	b
3月25日	1	105	103	38	37	16	15	6.9	5.7	2.6	2.0	1.2	0.9	0.83	0.57
9月17日	1	224	210	86	77	32	27	12.2	9.2	4.9	3.4	2.6	1.7	1.90	1.22
9月17日	0.75	288	265	107	93	39	31	14.2	10.4	5.7	3.9	3.0	1.9	2.13	1.33
9月17日	0.5	398	353	141	118	47	36	17.0	12.0	6.9	4.5	3.5	2.2	2.41	1.46

位于 75.5°S 的正午数值，太阳高度角 12.5°。3 月 25 日时平流层下层温度 230 K；9 月 17 日时 190 K。所示海拔适用于模型中所用的夏季温度[6]。

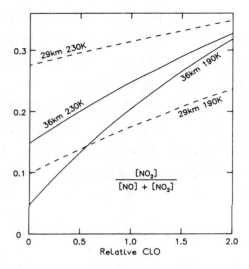

Fig. 4. [NO$_2$]/[NO+NO$_2$] has the status of an efficiency factor for O$_3$ destruction by the NO$_x$ cycle. In terms of the ratio ψ in the text, it is $\psi/(1+\psi)$. The figure shows how this factor varies with [ClO] at 190 K and at 230 K, at altitudes of 29 and 36 km. Values of [O$_3$], [O], [ClO] and j_3 were taken from one-dimensional model results[6] (maximum chlorine 2.7 p.p.b.v) for noon, 25 March at 75.5° S, solar elevation 12.5°. The abscissa is [ClO] relative to the model value. The rate-limiting reaction, (2) in Table 1, for the NO$_x$ cycle has zero activation energy. Note how, nevertheless, O$_3$ was protected against destruction by NO$_x$ at low temperatures in a stratosphere with small amounts of ClX, but is losing this protection as ClX grows.

Much O$_3$ destruction is driven by visible light, but production requires radiation below 242 nm. On the dates shown (Table 2), destruction persists for some 11 h, while, because of the long UV paths, production is weak (except around noon) at 29 km, and is virtually absent below that altitude. Line 1 of Table 2 then demands O$_3$ transport in autumn from the upper to the lower stratosphere, which is consistent with inferred thermally-driven lagrangian-mean circulations[10]. A mean vertical velocity of 45 m per day is in good accord with calculations of net diabatic cooling[11] and gives a realistic total O$_3$ decay rate in an otherwise conventional one-dimensional model[6]. The short relaxation times in the lower stratosphere in autumn are tolerable, with adequate transport compensating for lack of O$_3$ production.

In early spring, on the other hand, wave activity scarcely penetrates the cold dense core of the Antarctic polar vortex and with very low temperatures the net diabatic cooling is very weak[11]. Lagrangian transport in the vortex should then be almost negligible. (The virtual exclusion of Agung dust from the vortex supports this view[5].) The final warming signals the end of this period of inactivity and is accompanied by large dynamically induced changes in O$_3$ distribution. However, before the warming, with low chlorine, total O$_3$ was in a state of near-neutral equilibrium, sustained primarily by the long relaxation times. With higher chlorine, relaxation times of the order seen in line 4, Table 2, entail more rapid O$_3$ losses. With negligible production below 29 km and only weak transport, large total O$_3$ perturbation is possible. The extreme effects could be highly localized, restricted

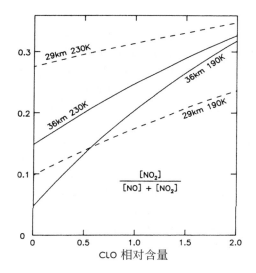

图 4. $[NO_2]/[NO+NO_2]$ 可以作为衡量 NO_x 循环对于臭氧破坏作用的有效因子。用正文中的 ψ 的比例来表示的话，就是 $\psi/(1+\psi)$。图中显示，在 29 km 和 36 km 高度，190 K 和 230 K 温度下，这一因子随 $[ClO]$ 变化的情况。$[O_3]$、$[O]$、$[ClO]$ 和 j_3 的数值是根据一维模型的结果[6]（最大氯浓度为 2.7 ppbv）得到的，条件为 3 月 25 日正午，75.5° S，太阳高度角 12.5°。横坐标为 $[ClO]$ 对于模型数值的相对值。限速反应见表 1 中的反应（2），对于 NO_x 循环而言活化能为 0。不过还要注意到，低温条件下，在含少量 ClX 的平流层中，臭氧免受 NO_x 破坏，而当 ClX 含量增加时臭氧受 NO_x 破坏。

　　可见光促进了大量臭氧被破坏，但是其合成还需要低于 242 nm 的辐射。从已显示的数据（表 2）来看，破坏过程持续大约 11 小时，但是由于紫外光具有长光程，合成在 29 km 处是微弱的（正午时间附近除外），而在此高度以下则根本不会出现。表 2 的第 1 行还明确了秋季时臭氧从平流层上层到下层的输送过程，这与所推测的热驱动下的拉格朗日平均环流量相吻合[10]。每天 45 m 的平均垂直速度可以与净非绝热冷却计算结果吻合得很好[11]，并在另外一种传统一维模型中给出了接近于事实的臭氧总衰减率[6]。秋季时在平流层下层中短暂的弛豫时间是可以容许的，因为有适量的输送过程补偿臭氧合成的缺失。

　　另一方面，早春时期，波运动基本上无法穿过南极极涡稠密寒冷的核心，由于气温非常低，净非绝热冷却是非常微弱的[11]。因此旋涡中的拉格朗日输送几乎可以忽略。（对涡流中阿贡火山尘埃的有效排除可以支持这一观点[5]。）最终的变暖标志着这一静止周期的结束，并伴随着臭氧分布导致的巨大动态变化。不过，在变暖之前，氯含量低时，臭氧总量处于一种近中性平衡状态中，主要由长的弛豫时间来决定。在氯水平较高时，从表 2 的第 4 行数据可以看出，弛豫时间的变化导致更快的臭氧损失。在 29 km 以下，生成过程是可忽略的，并且只存在微弱的输送，臭氧总量的大规模波动就有可能出现了。极端效应可能是集中在有限的区域，仅限于日光

to the period with diurnal photolysis between polar night and the earlier of either the onset of polar day or the final spring warming. At the pole [NO+NO$_2$] rises continuously after the polar night, with the Sun. The final warming always begins over east Antarctica and spreads westwards across the pole. At Halley Bay the warming is typically some 14 days later than at the pole. Maximum O$_3$ depletion could be confined to the Atlantic half of the zone bordered roughly by latitudes 70 and 80° S.

Comparable effects should not be expected in the Northern Hemisphere, where the winter polar stratospheric vortex is less cold and less stable than its southern counterpart. The vortex is broken down, usually well before the end of the polar night, by major warmings. These are accompanied by large-scale subsidence and strong mixing, in the course of which peak O$_3$ values for the year are attained. Hence, sensitivity to ClX growth should be minimal if, as suggested above, this primarily results from O$_3$ destruction at low temperatures in regions where O$_3$ transport is weak.

We have shown how additional chlorine might enhance O$_3$ destruction in the cold spring Antarctic stratosphere. At this time of the year, the long slant paths for sunlight make reservoir species absorbing strongly only below 280 nm, such as N$_2$O$_5$, ClONO$_2$ and HO$_2$NO$_2$, relatively long-lived. The role of these reservoir species should be more readily demonstrated in Antarctica, particularly the way in which they hold the balance between the NO$_x$ and ClO$_x$ cycles. An intriguing feature could be the homogeneous reaction (Table 1c) between HCl and ClONO$_2$. If this process has a rate constant as large as 10^{-16} cm^3 s^{-1} (ref. 2) and a negligible temperature coefficient, the reaction would go almost to completion in the polar night, leaving inorganic chlorine partitioned between HCl and Cl$_2$, almost equally at 22 km for example. Photolysis of Cl$_2$ at near-visible wavelengths would provide a rapid source of [Cl+ClO] at sunrise, not treated in equation (4). The polar-night boundary is, therefore, the natural testing ground for the theory of nonlinear response to chlorine[1,2]. It might be asked whether a nonlinear response is already evident (Fig. 2a). An intensive programme of trace-species measurements on the polar-night boundary could add greatly to our understanding of stratospheric chemistry, and thereby improve considerably the prediction of effects on the ozone layer of future halocarbon releases.

We thank B. A. Thrush and R. J. Murgatroyd for helpful suggestions.

(**315**, 207–210; 1985)

J. C. Farman, B. G. Gardiner & J. D. Shanklin
British Antarctic Survey, Natural Environment Research Council, High Cross, Madingley Road, Cambridge CB3 0ET, UK

Received 24 December 1984; accepted 28 March 1985.

分解时期，这个时期介于极昼开始或最终春季变暖两者中较早的一个时间点与极夜之间。极夜之后，$[NO + NO_2]$ 随着太阳出现而持续增加。最终的变暖总是始于南极东部上空，并穿越极点向西蔓延。在哈雷湾，变暖过程一般比极点要晚大约 14 天。臭氧最大耗损大致位于 70°S 到 80°S 纬度范围内、靠近大西洋那半边的区域。

类似的效应预期不会出现在北半球，与南半球相比，北半球冬季平流层极涡既不那么寒冷，也不那么稳定。通常在极夜结束之前，显著的变暖就会将极涡完全分解。与此同时，还伴随着大范围的沉降和强烈的混合过程，在此期间，臭氧含量将会达到全年中的峰值。因此，如果低温时臭氧输送弱的区域中臭氧破坏的主要原因是上述理由的话，对于 ClX 含量增加的敏感性此时应该是最小的。

我们已经指出，在寒冷的春季，增加的氯含量是如何促进南极平流层中臭氧破坏的。在每年的这一时期，日光具有长的倾斜路径，使得吸收库中的各种物质充分吸收 280 nm 以下的电磁波，这些物质包括 N_2O_5，$ClONO_2$ 和 HO_2NO_2，都有较长的寿命。吸收库中的各种物质在南极地区的作用应该更容易阐释清楚，尤其是它们维持 NO_x 和 ClO_x 循环平衡的方式。一个引人注目之处就是 HCl 与 $ClONO_2$ 之间的均相反应（表 1c）。如果该过程的速率常数达到 10^{-16} cm³ · s⁻¹（参考文献 2），并且温度系数可以忽略，那么在极夜时期就能基本反应完全，使无机氯在 HCl 和 Cl_2 之间进行分配，例如在 22 km 处是各占一半。日出时，Cl_2 在近可见波段的光解过程将快速提供 [Cl + ClO]，这是等式（4）中没有讨论的。因此，极夜的边界为这一关于氯的非线性反应理论提供了天然试验场所 [1,2]。可能有人会问，非线性响应是否已经足够明显（图 2a）。一个关于极夜边界时痕量物质检测的完整计划，可以大大提高我们对于平流层化学的理解，并且大大增强我们关于未来卤代烃排放对臭氧层影响效应的预测。

我们要感谢思拉什和穆加特罗伊德提供的有益建议。

（王耀杨 翻译；安俊岭 审稿）

References:

1. Cicerone, R. J., Walters, S. & Liu, S. C. *J. Geophys. Res.* **88**, 3647-3661 (1983).
2. Prather, M. J., McElroy, M. B. & Wofsy, S. C. *Nature* **312**, 227-231 (1984).
3. *The Stratosphere 1981, Theory and Measurements* (WMO Global Ozone Research and Monitoring Project Rep. No. 11, 1981).
4. Farman, J. C. & Hamilton, R. A. *Br. Antarct. Surv. Sci. Rep.* No. 90 (1975).
5. Farman, J. C. *Phil. Trans. R. Soc.* **B279**, 261-271(1977).
6. Farman, J. C., Murgatroyd, R. J., Silnickas, A. M. & Thrush, B. A. *Q. Jl R. Met. Soc.* (submitted).
7. McKenzie, R. L. & Johnston, P. V. *Geophys. Res. Lett.* **11**, 73-75 (1984).
8. Johnston, H. S. & Podolske, J. *Rev. Geophys. Space Phys.* **16**, 491-519 (1978).
9. *Chemical Kinetics and Photochemical Data for Use in Stratospheric Modelling, Evaluation No. 6* (JPL Publ. 83-62, 1983).
10. Dunkerton, T. *J. Atmos. Sci.* **35**, 2325-2333 (1978).
11. Dopplick, T. G. *J. Atmos. Sci.* **29**, 1278-1294 (1972).

A 150,000-year Climatic Record from Antarctic Ice

C. Lorius *et al.*

Editor's Note

The ratios of stable isotopes of oxygen ($^{18}O/^{16}O$) and hydrogen ($^{2}H/^{1}H$) in ice sheets of the polar regions reflect global temperatures at the time that the ice was formed from falling snow. Since the late 1960s, cores drilled into ice in Greenland and Antarctica have thus provided records of global climate over the past 740,000 years or so. Here French climatologist Claude Lorius and co-workers report the first continuous, accurate and well-dated record for that entire period, obtained at the Soviet Vostok station in Antarctica. It extends over the last ice age and the preceding warmer interglacial, and was a key record for attempts to understand the mechanisms of natural climate change.

During much of the Quaternary, the Earth's climate has undergone drastic changes most notably successive glacial and interglacial episodes. The past 150 kyr includes such a climatic cycle: the last interglacial, the last glacial and the present holocene interglacial. A new climatic–time series for this period has been obtained using $\delta^{18}O$ data from an Antarctic ice core.

ALTHOUGH continuous records of climatic and environmental conditions extending beyond 150 kyr are preserved in polar ice sheets, a reliable time series covering the whole of this climatic cycle has not yet been derived from ice cores. This results from logistic reasons, the favourable sites being located in the central regions of Antarctica and Greenland, and the technical difficulty of deep drilling.

The Quaternary has undergone successive glacial and interglacial episodes[1-3]. Since the first Camp Century drilling in north-west Greenland[4], five deep-ice cores reaching back to the last glacial have been recovered in Antarctica at Byrd[5], Vostok[6] and Dome C[7] and in Greenland at Dye 3[8]. They have been extensively studied for their oxygen-18 content (denoted $\delta^{18}O$ expressed with respect to SMOW) and their chemical impurities, which provide valuable information about the Earth's palaeoclimate and palaeoenvironment (see refs 9, 10).

Of these cores, Camp Century seems to extend back to the last interglacial. As it was drilled down to the bedrock, however, this last interglacial ice is confined to the last few metres of the core, because of the thinning of the ice layers during their sinking in the ice sheets. The complexity of the flow lines makes it difficult to date ice cores reaching the bedrock by flow modelling only. Indirect dating techniques, based on the comparison of

南极冰芯记录的过去15万年以来的气候变化

洛赫由斯等

编者按

极地地区冰盖中氧（$^{18}O/^{16}O$）和氢（$^{2}H/^{1}H$）的稳定同位素比率反映了当时降雪时全球气温的状况并最终保存在冰川冰中。从 20 世纪 60 年代末开始，在格陵兰和南极地区进行的冰芯钻探工作提供了过去约 74 万年以来的全球气候记录。在本文中，法国气候学家克劳德·洛赫由斯及其合作者报道了苏联南极沃斯托克站获得的这整个时期的第一个连续、精确和定年准确的冰芯记录。这一时段包含了整个末次冰期以及末次间冰期，是理解自然气候变化机制的关键记录。

在第四纪的大部分时期，地球上的气候经历了剧烈变化，最显著的是连续的冰期和间冰期旋回。在过去的 15 万年中，包括了一个包含末次间冰期、末次冰期和现在的全新世间冰期的气候周期性变化。而南极冰芯中的 $\delta^{18}O$ 记录提供了这一时期一个新的气候变化时间序列。

尽管在极地冰盖中保存着超过 15 万年的气候环境连续记录，然而，尚未从冰芯中得到整个包括冰期－间冰期旋回的可靠时间序列。这一方面是因为理想的冰芯钻探点位于南极和格陵兰的中部，而后勤保障存在问题；另一方面，深孔钻取也存在技术上的难题。

第四纪期间经历了连续的冰期和间冰期气候波动 [1-3]。在格陵兰西北部的世纪营地进行初次钻探以来 [4]，又陆续在南极洲的伯德站 [5]、沃斯托克站 [6]、冰穹 C [7] 以及格陵兰的 Dye 3 [8] 钻取了直达末次冰期的五根深冰芯。人们对这些冰芯中的氧–18含量（相对于标准平均大洋水（SMOW），表示为 $\delta^{18}O$）和化学杂质进行了广泛研究，为地球的古气候和古环境研究提供了宝贵信息（见参考文献 9 和 10）。

在这些冰芯中，世纪营地冰芯可延伸至末次间冰期。因为冰层沉降入冰盖时会减薄，所以当冰芯到达基岩时，末次间冰期的冰只限于冰芯的最后几米。由于冰川流动线的复杂性，仅仅利用冰川流动模型很难对到达基岩的冰芯进行定年。近来，基于冰芯和深海岩芯 $\delta^{18}O$ 剖面对比的间接定年技术 [7-9] 可用于解决这一问题。由此

$\delta^{18}O$ profiles in ice cores and in deep-sea cores have recently been used[7-9] for this purpose. A new Camp Century timescale was proposed which confirms the presence of last interglacial ice and, accordingly, indicates that the deepest part of the Dye 3 ice core was probably deposited during this period[9]. This is possibly also the case for the Devon Island core drilled through a shallow ice cap in the Canadian Arctic[11].

We have determined a new climatic–time series obtained from $\delta^{18}O$ analysis of a 2,083-m ice core drilled at Vostok Station by the Soviet Antarctic Expeditions. The site is located on the high Antarctic Plateau, where the ice thickness is ~3,700 m. The isotope profile covers the last 150 kyr, back to the ice age which preceded the last interglacial, and has essentially been undisturbed by flow conditions.

Vostok Ice Core

The Soviet Antarctic station of Vostok is located in East Antarctica (78°28′ S and 106°48′ E) at an altitude of 3,488 m (mean annual pressure 624 mbar; mean annual temperature −55.5 °C). The present snow accumulation is between 2.2 and 2.5 g cm^{-2} yr^{-1} (ref. 12) as determined independently from a profile of artificial β activity[13] and detailed stake measurements[14].

The first series of drilling was performed down to 950 m in successive steps between 1970 and 1974. This 950-m core covers all the Holocene and part of the last glacial periods as shown by the $\delta^{18}O$ profiles obtained by Barkov and co-workers[6,15,16]. In 1980, the drilling of a second deep hole was started which has reached a depth of 2,083 m. The $\delta^{18}O$ measurements were completed down to 1,412 m (refs 17, 18), a depth which would correspond, from a preliminary dating, to 115 kyr BP (ref. 19).

The collaboration between Soviet and French scientists which centred around the study of this new 2,083-m Vostok ice core was initiated in 1982. Within this framework, sampling was done in the field during the 1982–83 Austral summer and pieces of ice core were sent to Grenoble. The core analysis now in progress in various Soviet and French laboratories concerns, in particular, the chemical analysis of impurities and gas bubbles including CO_2.

$\delta^{18}O$ Profile

Sampling of ice for isotope analysis was done in the field (1982–83 Austral summer) by cutting a continuous slice from the length of the ice after careful cleaning. Sampling was performed on 1.5–2 m ice increments. Samples were sent in solid form to Grenoble and then melted before isotope analysis in Saclay. Two independent series of samples were obtained: (1) a discontinuous series, duplicated to check reproducibility, with one sample taken each 25 m from the surface down to the bottom of the core; (2) a continuous series between 1,406 and 2,083 m.

Oxygen-18 and deuterium determinations were simultaneously performed on all the samples. Here we will discuss the $\delta^{18}O$ results. The deuterium and deuterium-excess[20]

确立了新的世纪营地时间序列，证实了末次间冰期的存在，并由此表明 Dye 3 冰芯的最深部分有可能是在该时期内沉积而成 [9]。在加拿大北极地区的一个薄冰帽所钻取的德文岛冰芯也可能是相同的情况 [11]。

通过对苏联南极探险队在沃斯托克站所钻取的一根长 2,083 米的冰芯进行 $\delta^{18}O$ 分析，我们得到了一个新的气候 – 时间序列。该站位于高大的南极高原，其冰层厚度约为 3,700 米。该同位素剖面涵盖了过去 15 万年，其时间尺度可以达到倒数第二次冰期，并且基本没有受到冰川流动的干扰。

沃斯托克冰芯

苏联沃斯托克南极站位于南极洲东部（78°28′ S, 106°48′ E），海拔 3,488 米（年平均气压为 624 毫巴；年平均气温为 –55.5℃）。由人工 β 活化度剖面 [13] 和详细的花杆测量 [14] 分别独立确定目前的积雪积累率在 2.2 克 /（厘米² ·年）和 2.5 克 /（厘米² ·年）之间（参考文献 12）。

1970~1974 年间，第一次连续钻到了 950 米。巴尔科夫和他的同事们 [6,15,16] 取得的 $\delta^{18}O$ 剖面显示，这条 950 米的冰芯覆盖了整个全新世以及末次冰期的一部分。1980 年开始钻取第二个深冰芯，其长度达 2,083 米。对 1,412 米以上的部分进行了 $\delta^{18}O$ 测定（参考文献 17 和 18），根据初步定年，其对应的时间应为距今 11.5 万年（参考文献 19）。

1982 年，苏联和法国的科学家开始合作研究这条新的 2,083 米的沃斯托克冰芯。在这项合作下，1982~1983 年间科学家在南半球的夏季进行了野外取样，并把冰芯切片送到格勒诺布尔。现在苏联和法国各有关实验室正在进行冰芯分析，着重对杂质和包含 CO_2 的空气进行化学成分分析。

$\delta^{18}O$ 剖面

科学家在野外（1982~1983 年南半球夏季）采集了用于同位素分析的样品，在小心清理之后，将冰芯按长度切割成连续的切片。每根冰芯以 1.5~2 米的长度取样。样本以固态的形式送往格勒诺布尔，融化后在法国萨克雷环境与气候模拟实验室进行同位素分析。该冰芯被处理成两个独立的系列样本：（1）不连续系列，将整条冰芯从头到尾每间隔 25 米取样，作重复性分析检验；（2）1,406~2,083 米之间的连续系列。

同一时间对所有样本进行了氧 –18 和氘的测定。这里将讨论 $\delta^{18}O$ 的结果。氘和过量氘 [20] 结果将另作讨论。图 1 所示为 $\delta^{18}O$ 随深度的变化，精确度为 ±0.15‰（相

results will be discussed elsewhere. The results, obtained with an accuracy of ±0.15‰ (w.r.t. SMOW), are shown in Fig. 1 as a function of the sample depth. The two sets of samples from the discontinuous series are in good agreement all along the core and their average value at each level is given. For the sake of discussion a continuous line was drawn between each point. There is excellent agreement between the continuous and discontinuous series over all the common parts indicating that the 25-m sampling interval is fine enough to extract reliable palaeoclimatic information. On the other hand, the present data are not detailed enough to document for the Southern Hemisphere such features as the abrupt environmental changes revealed in the Dye 3 ice core between 30 and 40 kyr BP (refs 9, 21).

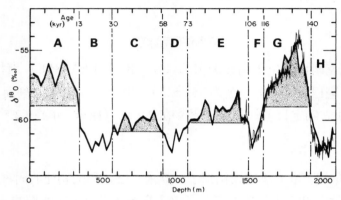

Fig. 1. Oxygen-18 versus depth in the Vostok ice with the definition of the successive stages and indication of the ages corresponding to the limits between these stages. The thick line is drawn from discontinuous data (one for each 25 m), the thin line corresponds to a continuous sampling between 1,400 and 2,083 m. For explanation of A–H, see text.

Down to 1,400 m, the basic features of the $\delta^{18}O$ curve (Fig. 1) are similar to previously published Vostok $\delta^{18}O$ profiles[17,18], with the last glacial maximum around 400 m, and a $\delta^{18}O$ shift between glacial and post-glacial conditions of ~5‰. However, there is a systematic shift towards lower values for the present set of data of ~3‰. Such a shift has already been noticed by Dansgaard et al.[22].

The $\delta^{18}O$ profile presented here gives a complete picture of the last climatic cycle from the end of the previous glaciation. In particular, the last interglacial with the highest $\delta^{18}O$ values around 1,825 m can now be examined in detail. For a further description of this curve and comparison with other palaeoclimatic profiles, we will designate the successive warm and cold stages consecutively from the top of the record downwards. A striking feature of the profile is the existence of four very well-marked cold periods (that is, low $\delta^{18}O$) around 425, 975, 1,525 and 2,050 m with practically the same $\delta^{18}O$ values of around −62‰. This makes the definition of the successive stages shown on Fig. 1 relatively straightforward. Starting from the top, the warm periods (hatched areas), are designated by A, C, E and G and the cold periods by B, D, F and H. Stages A and G have the isotopically richest values lying around −57 and −55‰, respectively. From the solid curve (Fig. 1), one can note a sharp isotope transition (~2‰) inside the G stage at a depth of 1,790 m.

对于标准平均大洋水）。不连续系列的两组样本在整个冰芯中很吻合，并给出了每一层的平均值。为了便于讨论，在各点之间做了连线。连续和不连续系列重叠的部分高度一致，这说明以 25 米间隔取样的部分可以提供可靠的古气候信息。但是，这一间隔取样的数据不足于揭示南半球气候的高频波动，如在格陵兰 Dye 3 冰芯所记录到的距今 3 万年至 4 万年间的气候突变事件（参考文献 9 和 21）。

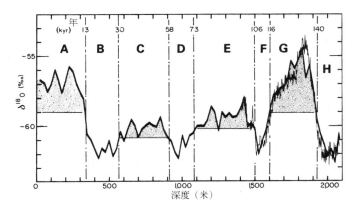

图 1. 沃斯托克冰芯中氧 –18 随深度的变化。图中还划出了冰阶与冰阶之间的对应绝对年代值。粗线是间隔取样数据（每 25 米一点）的连线，而细线是 1,400~2,083 米间的连续样本测量结果。A~H 的说明见正文。

　　直到 1,400 米处，$\delta^{18}O$ 曲线（图 1）的基本特征与之前发表的沃斯托克 $\delta^{18}O$ 的剖面 [17,18] 相似，末次冰盛期出现在约 400 米处，$\delta^{18}O$ 值在冰期和冰后期变化了约 5‰。然而，现在的这一数据相对以前，$\delta^{18}O$ 系统性地偏低了大约 3‰，丹斯果等 [22] 也注意到这一现象。

　　这里的 $\delta^{18}O$ 剖面给出了从倒数第二次冰期末开始的一个气候周期的完整图式。特别地，现在能够对约 1,825 米处、具有 $\delta^{18}O$ 最高值的末次间冰期进行详细研究。为进一步描述这一曲线，并与其他古气候剖面作比较，我们从上到下选出连续的暖期和冷期。剖面的显著特征是存在四个非常明显的冷期（即 $\delta^{18}O$ 的低值），分别位于 425 米、975 米、1,525 米和 2,050 米处，其 $\delta^{18}O$ 值均为 –62‰ 左右。这使得对图 1 中各连续时期的界定相对直观起来。从上部开始，暖期（阴影区）用 A、C、E 和 G 标注，而冷期用 B、D、F 和 H 标注。阶段 A 和 G 的同位素值最高，分别约为 –57‰ 和 –55‰。从图 1 中的实曲线可以看出，在 G 阶段 1,790 米处，有一同位素的跃变（约

Stages E and C are relatively warm interstadials intermediate between full glacial and interglacial conditions.

Dates for the limits between the successive phases are indicated on the top of Fig. 1 (the dating method used is described below). Stage A corresponds to the present Holocene period. Stages B–F cover the last glacial. Stage G includes the peak of the last interglacial and stage H is the last part of the previous glacial.

Ice-Core Chronology

Many techniques, including isotope and chemical stratigraphies and flow modelling, have been used over the past 10 yr to establish dating of the Vostok ice[16,19,23,24]. Further detailed isotope study showed that seasonal $\delta^{18}O$ variations are rapidly smoothed by diffusion[22] indicating that reliable dating cannot be obtained from isotope stratigraphy. Unlike the Camp Century core, where the existence of interglacial ice relies on a comparison with deep-sea core isotope profiles, we propose to establish the timescale using an ice-flow model which is independent of other palaeoindicators.

There are two problems with this type of dating. First, for each depth the rate of accumulation at the time and in that area of origin of snow, $A(z)$, must be determined. Second, the thinning function, that is, the ratio of the thickness of a layer to its initial thickness, has to be calculated. We now describe our approach to these problems.

To estimate the past accumulation rate we adopt a procedure based on the observation that the present precipitation rate on the Antarctic plateau is strongly correlated with surface temperature. Robin[25] has suggested that this correlation exists because precipitation is governed by the amount of water vapour in the atmosphere circulating above the surface inversion layer. As discussed by Lorius *et al.*[7] and Jouzel and Merlivat[26], there is a link between the temperature of formation of precipitation and its oxygen isotope ratio. Assuming that the same relationship has held in the past, it is thus possible to estimate past accumulation rates from the $\delta^{18}O$ profile of the ice. Raisbeck *et al.*[27] and Yiou *et al.*[28] in this issue have noted that the ^{10}Be concentrations of ice at Dome C and Vostok are consistent with accumulation rates deduced by such procedures. We thus estimate the accumulation function in the following way. First, the temperature of formation of precipitation, T_F, is estimated along the profile as described by Lorius *et al.*[10]. Then, the accumulation rate, $A(z)$, is calculated from the product of its present value, $A(0)$, times the ratio of the derivatives of the saturation vapour pressure—with respect to $T_F(z)$ for the time of precipitation and with respect to $T_F(0)$ for the present conditions. This formulation is derived from a simplified unidimensional model neglecting the possible changes in circulation intensity above the area of precipitation.

The use of a two-dimensional glaciological model is well suited to the Vostok area as the ice flowlines are roughly parallel in this region of East Antarctica[29]. The change of the ice thickness upstream of the drilling site is important because of the bedrock topography[30] (Fig. 2) and this has been taken into account when using the analytical model of Lliboutry[31].

2‰）。E 和 C 阶段是相对温暖的间冰阶，是介于全冰期和间冰期之间的一种气候状况。

图 1 的顶部标出了各连续阶段的年代（所使用的定年方法会在下面说明）。阶段 A 与现在的全新世相对应，阶段 B~F 则覆盖了整个末次冰期，阶段 G 包含了末次间冰期的最大值，而 H 阶段则为倒数第二次冰期的最后部分。

冰芯年代学

在过去的十年中，研究者应用了包括同位素、化学地层学以及流动模型技术在内的很多技术来确定沃斯托克冰芯的年代 [16,19,23,24]。更为详细的同位素研究表明，$\delta^{18}O$ 的季节变化很快因扩散而变得不明显 [22]，这表明同位素年层不能得到可靠的年代信息。格陵兰世纪营地冰芯的定年必须依靠与深海氧同位素剖面的对比。而这里我们提出用独立于其他古气候指标的冰川流动模型来定年。

用这种方法定年存在两个问题。第一，需要知道不同深度冰层当初在源地的冰川积累率 $A(z)$ 是多少。第二，必须计算减薄函数，即年层的厚度对原始年层厚度的比率。下面我们来说明如何处理这些问题。

通过观察发现，南极高原当前的降水率和地表温度高度相关，基于此点我们采用一个方法来估算过去的积累率。罗宾 [25] 指出之所以存在这样的关系，是因为降水受控于地面逆温层表面气流内的水汽含量。如洛赫由斯等 [7] 以及茹塞勒和梅利瓦特 [26] 所讨论的那样，降水形成时的温度与其氧同位素比率之间存在关联。假定这种相关性在过去一直存在的话，就可能从冰的 $\delta^{18}O$ 剖面估算出过去的积累率。雷兹贝克等 [27] 和伊奥等 [28] 在本期发表的论文中指出，在冰穹 C 和沃斯托克冰芯的 ^{10}Be（铍）浓度与同这种方法推断的积累率的变化是一致的。为此我们用下列方法估计积累函数。首先，根据洛赫由斯等人 [10] 所描述的，沿剖面估算降水形成时的温度 T_F。然后，用现在的冰川积累率 $A(0)$ 乘以过去饱和水汽压与现代大气饱和水汽压（即降水时的 $T_F(z)$ 和现在的 $T_F(0)$）的导数之比率，计算得到冰川积累率 $A(z)$。该公式基于简化的一维模型得出，忽略了降水地区大气环流强度可能的变化。

二维冰川模型非常适用于沃斯托克地区，因为南极东部这一地区的冰川流线大致是平行的 [29]。由于冰盖下伏地形 [30] 的缘故，冰芯钻取点上游的冰川厚度变化非常重要（图 2），这在使用利布特里分析模型 [31] 时已经考虑在内。最后，用迭代方法确

Finally, ice-core dating is established using an iterative process. Starting from a plausible dating obtained from a simple one-dimensional model the ice origin is determined. Then, the thinning function is calculated and the ice redated all along the core. The process is repeated using the new dates as the initial conditions until the initial and final datings converge.

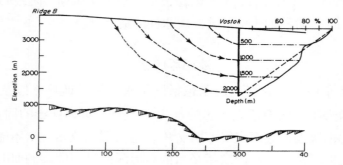

Fig. 2. Surface and bedrock topography along the Ridge B–Vostok axis (lower curve) and the thinning function (top right) expressed as a percentage of the initial thickness, with (solid line) or without (dotted line) taking into account this topography.

To illustrate the influence of the bedrock topography, the thinning functions with (Fig. 2, solid line) and without (Fig. 2, dotted line) taking into account this topography can be compared. This demonstrates the strong effect of bedrock topography between 500 and 1,000 m. For these calculations, ice velocities were approximated by their average values using mass continuity over the entire climatic cycle.

The results are presented in Fig. 3 for three values of the present accumulation. The annual accumulation (expressed with respect to its present value) is obviously correlated to the $\delta^{18}O$ profile with lower values during glacial periods as previously stated from Dome C ice-core studies[7,27] and independently proposed at Vostok from ^{10}Be measurements[28].

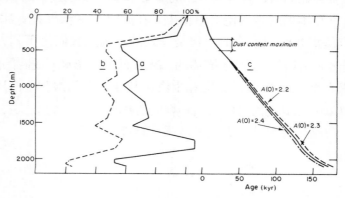

Fig. 3. *a*, Initial thickness of annual layers (accumulation rate $A(z)$); *b*, thickness of these annual layers in the core. Both *a* and *b* are expressed with respect to the present (accumulation rate $A(0)$); *c*, depth–age relationship for different values of $A(0)$ in g cm^{-2} yr^{-1}.

定冰芯年代。从简单的一维模型得到可能的年代，由此确定最初的冰川积累量。然后，计算减薄函数，且沿冰芯重新确定不同深度冰的年代，应用新的年代作为初始条件不断重复计算，直到初始与最终的年代相符合。

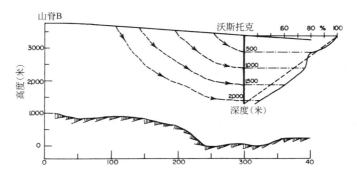

图2. 沿山脊 B－沃斯托克轴的冰盖表面形态与冰盖下伏地形（下面的曲线）；右上侧为冰层减薄函数，表示为不同深度年层的减薄率，有两种情况，一种考虑了地形的影响（实线），一种没有考虑地形的影响（虚线）。

通过对比考虑（图2的实线）和忽略（图2的虚线）地形条件下的减薄函数，可以说明冰盖下伏地形的影响。对比显示，在500~1,000米之间冰盖下伏地形具有重要影响。在计算中，冰的流动速度用整个气候旋回的冰体流动速度的平均值来近似代替。

图3给出了目前三种积累量的结果。历史时间年积累率（表示为与现在年积累量的比率）的大小显然与冰芯 $\delta^{18}O$ 剖面相关，冰期时年积累率最低，这与之前对冰穹 C 冰芯的研究 [7,27] 以及沃斯托克 ^{10}Be 测量所独立获得的结论 [28] 一致。

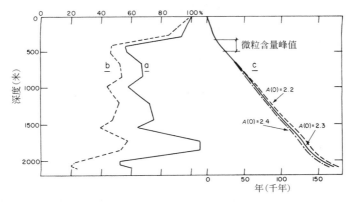

图3. a，为每年各层的初始厚度（积累率 $A(z)$）；b，为冰芯内每年各层的厚度。a 与 b 均表示为与现在的积累率的比率（积累率 $A(0)$）；c，为不同的 $A(0)$ 值所对应的深度－年代关系，单位为克 /（厘米 ^{2} · 年）。

77

From available data[12], an average value of 2.3 g cm^{-2} yr^{-1} was adopted for the present accumulation rate, giving ages of 98 kyr BP at 1,412 m (that is, significantly younger than the previously estimated[19] 115 kyr BP) and of ~160 kyr BP for the bottom of the core.

This accumulation value, although uncertain given the very short period (<10 yr) over which this parameter was determined, seems to be a reasonable average over the Holocene period. Our dating puts the end of the last climatic transition at around 10 kyr BP which compares well with the same event recorded in the Dome C East Antarctic core at ~10.5 kyr BP (ref. 7). The uncertainty on this value is thus ~5%, a value which would give a lower limit for the relative dating uncertainty all along the core. Dating of the first part of the core is also indirectly supported by the existence of a dust content maximum between ~13 and 26 kyr BP (ref. 32), a period of aridity over Australia[33]. However, other sources of errors come from estimations of accumulation changes and, to a lesser degree, of the thinning function. Thus, the age of the bottom of the core is probably not known with a precision better than 10–15 kyr.

Palaeoclimatic Information

The isotope content of polar snow is primarily governed by T_F, but it also depends[9,10,34,35] on several other parameters such as the origin and dynamical history of the air masses and the microphysical processes leading to snow formation. A way of reconstructing the full, space-time variations of isotope contents of vapour and precipitation is to incorporate the isotope cycles in a general circulation model of the atmosphere (GCM)[36].

Until this new approach is fully developed, the climatic interpretation must be based on $\delta^{18}O$–temperature relationships observed in modern precipitation and/or isotope models which give only a simple schematic overview of the dynamic history of the air masses. Although aware of the limitations, we are relatively confident that when the two methods are combined major temperature changes, such as those accompanying glacial-interglacial transitions, can be estimated. This is especially true for central East Antarctica for several reasons. First, the observed $\delta^{18}O$–temperature relationship[37] is quite linear (correlation coefficient, $r = 0.989$ for the -20 to $-55\,°C$ interval) and its slope can be correctly explained on a theoretical basis applying a recently developed kinetic isotopic model[26]. Second, the ice thickness has probably undergone only minor fluctuations and the ice origin can be reliably reconstructed. In addition, our confidence in a temperature reconstruction is reinforced in the Vostok core by the good agreement between accumulation changes derived by transforming the $\delta^{18}O$ profile into a temperature profile and those derived from ^{10}Be (ref. 28).

After correcting for the change in $\delta^{18}O$ of the oceanic water (maximum 1.6‰)[3], this temperature reconstruction is carried out as in ref. 10. With this interpretation, the glacial-interglacial surface temperature shifts are ~10 °C for the H–G transition ($\delta^{18}O$ shift of 6.5‰) and 8 °C for the B–A transition ($\delta^{18}O$ shift of 5‰). C and E interstadials are around 2 and 4 °C, respectively, warmer than full glacial conditions and the four cold stadials H, F, D and B are within ~1 °C. The peak of the last interglacial maximum is

根据已有的资料[12]，采用 2.3 克 /（厘米²·年）的平均值来表示现在的积累率，则计算出 1,412 米处的冰芯年龄约为距今 9.8 万年（比之前估计的[19]距今 11.5 万年显著提前），而冰芯底部的年龄距今约 16 万年。

虽然积累量是在很短的时期（<10 年）内测定的，存在一定的不确定性，但仍可以作为整个全新世的一个合理平均值。我们给出末次冰期结束的年代约为距今 1 万年，与南极东部冰穹 C 冰芯所记录的相同事件的年代 1.05 万年（参考文献 7）一致。因此该值的不确定度为 5% 左右，这也可以为整个冰芯定年的不确定度给出更低的底线。距今约 1.3 万年至 2.6 万年之间（参考文献 32）的微粒含量峰值也为冰芯第一部分的定年提供了间接的支持，这一时期澳大利亚处于干旱期[33]。其他的定年误差可能来源于对积累量变化的估算，减薄函数也会有些影响。因此，冰芯底部的定年误差可能会大于 1 万年至 1.5 万年。

古气候信息

极地雪的同位素含量主要受控于 T_F，同时也依赖[9,10,34,35]于其他几个参数，如气团的源地及运动历史，以及降雪形成的微物理过程。要重建一个完整的大气水汽及降水中同位素含量的时空变化，需要将同位素循环纳入大气环流模式（GCM）[36]。

在新方法全面开发出来之前，我们现在只能通过现代降水和（或）同位素模型中观测到的 $\delta^{18}O$–温度的关系来重建冰芯中的气候记录。这一模型只能简单描述气团的动态历史。尽管意识到其局限性，我们比较确信如果结合两种方法，那么主要的温度变化，例如冰期 – 间冰期的转变，是能够估计出来的。对于南极东部中心区来说尤其如此，这主要基于以下几点原因。首先，观测到的 $\delta^{18}O$–温度的线性关系[37]非常好（–20℃到 –55℃区间，相关系数 $r = 0.989$），并且其斜率可以用近期开发的同位素动力分馏模型[26]作为理论基础准确解释。其次，冰的厚度可能只受到较小的波动，而且能较为可靠地重建冰的来源地。另外，在沃斯托克冰芯中，由 $\delta^{18}O$ 剖面转变到温度剖面所得出的积累量和由 ^{10}Be（参考文献 28）得到的积累量是相当吻合的，由此增强了我们重建古温度的信心。

校正了海水 $\delta^{18}O$ 的变化（最大值 1.6‰）[3]之后，文献 10 中进行了温度的重建。在这一重建工作中，对于 H~G 转变阶段（$\delta^{18}O$ 变化 6.5‰），冰期 – 间冰期地表气温变化约为 10℃，而 B~A 的转变阶段（$\delta^{18}O$ 变化 5‰）约为 8℃。C 与 E 间冰阶则分别约为 2℃ 和 4℃，这比全冰期和 H、F、D 和 B 四个冷冰阶要暖约 1℃ 以内。末次间冰期最大峰值明显地比全新世时期暖，估计相差约 3℃，其中 1℃ 是由于间冰期时

significantly warmer than the Holocene period. The difference is estimated to ~3 °C, 1 °C of this being due to the formation of the interglacial ice 100 km further inland (Fig. 2). All these values do not take into account the possible variations in the ice-cap altitude. These corrections will be done, if necessary, from the total gas content which is under investigation. Preliminary data (D. Raynaud, personal communication) suggest that the isotope signal is essentially of climatic origin which is independently corroborated by some studies tending to demonstrate the relative stability of the East Antarctic ice sheet at the considered timescale[38,39].

Comparison with Other Ice Cores

Concerning the transition between the last glacial maximum (around 18 kyr BP) and the Holocene periods (B–A in our terminology), the present results confirm the excellent agreement between the two East Antarctic sites, with a $\delta^{18}O$ shift, before corrections, of 5.4‰ at Dome C[7] and of ~5‰ at Vostok, and to a lesser degree with the Byrd West Antarctic site (shift of 7‰)[5]. The inferred surface temperature change for Antarctica is ~8–10 °C. These shifts agree well with those deduced for high southern latitudes from GCM ice-age modelling[40,41], although recent simulations predict lower temperature shifts[42,43]. The isotope shift is also 7‰ in southern Greenland (Dye 3)[8,9]. The higher values (>10‰) registered in northern Greenland and adjacent regions (Camp Century, Devon Island) can be partly attributed either to a change in the elevation of the ice formation[44] or to a more drastic climatic change in this area than in southern Greenland or in Antarctica[9].

For the last glacial, a detailed comparison with other ice cores is difficult because only 7% of the Vostok core was analysed down to 1,400 m. In any case, it would be necessary to discuss thoroughly the successive timescales derived for the Byrd, Camp Century and Dye 3 cores. Such a comparison will be undertaken in the near future when a continuous profile becomes available for the Vostok core.

The apparent time elapsed between the interglacial peak and the following $\delta^{18}O$ minimum is more than twice as long at Vostok than at Camp Century. This is not strictly an ice core feature and cannot be discussed further here (see below) as the Camp Century timescale is deduced from a comparison with the deep-sea record[9]. This shows the difficulty of applying such an indirect dating method.

Comparison with $\delta^{18}O$ in Deep-Sea Cores

It is now widely accepted that $\delta^{18}O$ in benthic foraminifera primarily reflects ice-volume changes[3,45,46]. Although the relationship can be distorted by many factors, the CLIMAP project members concluded that there is no compelling evidence to reject the first-order assumptions of isotope synchroneity or fidelity to the ice volume[45]. Although varying in detail, all the cores give similar general trends[3,47], allowing a common definition of isotope stratigraphy. The period of interest here covers Emiliani's stages 1–6 (ref. 48), stage 5 being subdivided in 5a to 5e (ref. 49), as we have illustrated on Fig. 4e.

期冰川向内陆后退了100千米所致（图2）。全部数据均未考虑冰帽可能出现的高度变化。如果需要，现在正在进行的冰芯包裹气体总含量的研究可以帮助校正海拔高度的变化。初步的数据（雷诺，个人交流）表明，同位素信号来源于气候变化。这一结论被其他的独立研究所证实，这些研究指出南极东部冰盖在研究的时间尺度内保持相对稳定状态[38,39]。

与其他冰芯的对比

关于末次冰盛期（距今约1.8万年）到全新世（这里表示为B~A）的转变，南极洲东部两站点现有的结果表现出高度的一致。在校正前，冰穹C的$\delta^{18}O$变化为5.4‰[7]，沃斯托克约为5‰，而与南极洲西部的伯德站（7‰的变化）[5]的吻合程度次之。据此推断，南极的地表气温变化幅度约为8~10℃。这与GCM冰期模型[40,41]所推测的南半球高纬度地区的结果很吻合，尽管最近模拟预测的温度变化幅度较小[42,43]。在格陵兰的南部（Dye 3），同位素的变化也是7‰[8,9]。在格陵兰北部及其邻近地区（世纪营地、德文岛）记录的较高值（>10‰），或者是由于冰形成时高度发生了变化[44]，或者是由于该地区发生了比格陵兰南部或南极地区更剧烈的气候变化[9]。

沃斯托克冰芯还无法与其他冰芯就末次冰期这一时段的详细气候变化进行对比。这是因为下至1,400米，仅分析了整个沃斯托克冰芯7%的样本。无论如何，透彻讨论伯德站、世纪营地与Dye 3冰芯所取得的连续时间尺度都很有必要。在不久的将来，当沃斯托克冰芯的连续时间序列剖面完成后，就可以开展这样的比较研究。

在沃斯托克间冰期峰值和随后的$\delta^{18}O$最小值之间的时间跨度比格陵兰世纪营地冰芯记录长两倍。严格来说，这并不是冰芯的主要特征，因为世纪营地冰芯的时间尺度是从与深海沉积记录的对比中推出的[9]，所以这里就不再作进一步讨论（参见下文）。这说明了应用这样一种间接定年方法导致的困难。

与深海岩芯中$\delta^{18}O$的对比

底栖有孔虫$\delta^{18}O$的值主要反映的是冰量变化[3,45,46]这一观点已经被广泛认可。尽管这种关系可能会受到许多因素的影响，CLIMAP（一项关于气候的长期的调查、制图和预报计划）的成员认为，现在还没有令人信服的证据来否定这个一级假设——即氧同位素变化与冰量变化的一致性与可靠性[45]。虽然有些细节的差异，但所有冰芯记录的总变化趋势是相同的[3,47]。这使得我们可以定义一个共同的冰芯同位素年层序列。我们这里主要讨论的阶段包括伊米利亚尼的深海氧同位素1~6阶段（参考文献48），阶段5可以分成5a至5e几个亚阶段（参考文献49），如图4e所示。

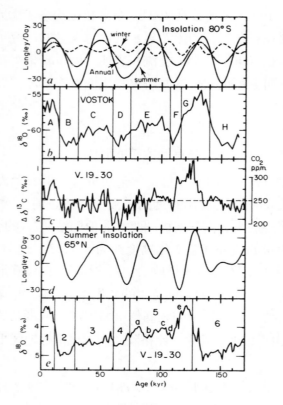

Fig. 4. Variation with time of: *a*, winter, summer and annual insolations at 80° S (ref. 59); *b*, $\delta^{18}O$ in the Vostok ice (this work); *c*, $\Delta\delta^{13}C$ in the V 19–30 deep-sea core[68] and indication of the CO₂ scale on the right; *d*, summer insolation at 65° N (ref. 59); *e*, $\delta^{18}O$ in the V 19–30 deep-sea core[68] for *Uvigerina senticosa* with an indication of the successive climatic stages.

With the adopted Vostok dating, there is a good correspondence between stages 1–4 and Vostok stages A–D. Stage E covers 5a–5c and F corresponds to 5d. However, there is no clear correspondence between 5e and G representing the last interglacial in deep-sea and ice records, respectively (Fig. 4). There is a major difference in the duration of these two stages; 11 kyr for 5e and 24 kyr for G. Also, the last interglacial peak in the Vostok core is around 130 kyr BP whereas the corresponding ice-volume minimum in the deep-sea record is dated earlier at 122-kyr BP (ref. 45).

A doubling of the accumulation rate over this period would lead to a good correspondence between the 5e and G stages. While this possibility cannot be completely ruled out, there is no indication of such a drastic change in the precipitation regime. Part of the time-lag between the two peaks could be real (~3 kyr) as already observed between Southern Hemisphere ocean temperature and ice volume records but dating uncertainties (probably of ~10 kyr at this level) prevent a detailed discussion of this possible lag. On the other hand, the fact that ice stage G probably lasted longer than stage 5e is a key element for understanding the last interglacial climate and the initiation of the last ice age. A detailed interpretation is beyond the scope of the present study and would require knowledge of

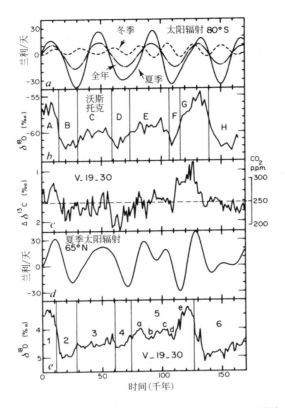

图 4. 时间变化：a，80°S 处冬季、夏季和全年的太阳辐射（参考文献 59）；b，沃斯托克冰芯的 $\delta^{18}O$ 值（本文）；c，V 19~30 深海岩芯的 $\Delta\delta^{13}C$[68] 值，以及右侧的 CO_2 值；d，65°N 处夏季太阳辐射（参考文献 59）；e，刺葡萄虫 V 19~30 深海岩的芯的 $\delta^{18}O$ 值[68]，上面标注了连续的气候变化阶段。

　　采用沃斯托克定年，深海氧同位素阶段 1~4 和沃斯托克 A~D 阶段之间是很一致的。阶段 E 包含了 5a~5c，阶段 F 则对应于 5d。然而，在深海岩芯和冰芯记录中分别代表末次间冰期的 5e 和 G 阶段并不完全对应（图 4）。这两个阶段的持续时间差别较大，5e 为 1.1 万年而 G 为 2.4 万年。在沃斯托克冰芯中末次间冰期的峰值距今约 13 万年，而相对应的深海岩芯记录的冰量最小值距现在要近一些，约为 12.2 万年（参考文献 45）。

　　如果使该阶段的积累率加倍，则 5e 与 G 阶段可以保持很好的一致性。尽管不能完全排除这种可能性，但是也没有任何证据表明降水会发生如此剧烈的变化。在两个峰值之间，部分的时间滞后可能是真实存在的（约三千年），这正如在南半球观测到的海洋温度与冰量之间的变化。但是由于定年本身的不确定性（在该层中可能约一万年），我们无法对这一时间滞后作进一步的讨论。另一方面，冰芯中阶段 G 可能比阶段 5e 持续时间更长这一事实是揭示末次间冰期气候和末次冰期开始的关键因素。要做详细解释就超出了本研究的范围，而且需要有关温度和冰量信息之间的

the exact timing between the temperature and ice volume signals. Recent measurements of $\delta^{18}O$ of air entrapped in ice cores could provide a way of correlating deep-sea and ice-cores $\delta^{18}O$ profiles and then establishing this timing[50].

According to CLIMAP members[45], the last interglacial was similar to the current climate. However, they noted some indications of a slightly warmer climate. The Vostok record brings quantifiable evidence of atmospheric warming over Antarctica during this period. This is useful information because there is some controversy about the behaviour of the East Antarctic ice sheet during the last interglacial[45]. In addition, the Vostok record does not support an interglacial character for marine stage 5c (first part of E), an argument used to suggest an East Antarctic ice surge around 95 kyr BP (ref. 51).

Whereas glacial buildups in the deep-sea record (Fig. 4e) are gradual giving the ice-volume cycles their asymmetrical saw-toothed character[52], the ice record (Fig. 4b) shows that the minimum temperatures were of the same order during cold periods (H, F, D and B stages). This may be linked to the rapid response of the atmospheric system to forcings and feedbacks and also suggests that there is a very stable mode of the climatic system for these cold periods. Such differences in shape were previously noted between ice-volume and temperature signals recorded in some oceanic cores[53].

Forcing and Feedback Factors

Beyond this reconstruction of the East Antarctic climate, we now discuss some current important aspects of the mechanisms which have probably controlled this climate and how the East Antarctic climate is related to the global climate. We will examine the possible role of changes in insolation, atmospheric CO_2 content and global ice volume.

Insolation changes. Over recent years, the Milankovitch hypothesis that orbital variations are the principal causes of the Pleistocene ice ages has received considerable support[45,52-54], and has stimulated many modelling efforts[55-58]. The spectral analysis of proxy records has revealed periodicities statistically correlated to the precessional (19 and 23 kyr), obliquity (41 kyr) and eccentricity (100 kyr) cycles. There is a general consensus that summer insolation at about 65° N might be a plausible forcing as Northern Hemisphere ice sheets have undergone the major changes, and that the dominant 100-kyr cycle would result from a nonlinear response of ice sheets to orbital forcing.

Before discussing the possible link between the Northern Hemisphere insolation changes and the Vostok climate, we will investigate whether there is a relationship between this climate and the local changes of insolation.

The comparison of the $\delta^{18}O$ ice profile (Fig. 4b) with the annual insolation curve for 80° S (ref. 59) (Fig. 4a) reveals a very striking relationship between the cold and warm isotope stages and the minima and maxima of the insolation curve. While discontinuous sampling prevents us from performing reliable spectral analysis, especially for short periodicities, this remarkable correlation strongly supports the role of orbital forcing in climatic change.

精确定年知识。近来，测量冰芯包裹气体中的 $\delta^{18}O$ 有可能把深海岩芯和冰芯的 $\delta^{18}O$ 剖面关联起来，从而建立起共同的时间序列[50]。

按 CLIMAP 成员[45] 的观点，末次间冰期与现在的气候相似。然而，他们注意到末次间冰期比现代气候更温暖一些。沃斯托克记录提供了该段时期南极大气变暖的定量证据。这个结论很有用，因为对末次间冰期南极东部冰盖的运动仍然存在一些争议[45]。另外，沃斯托克记录并不支持深海岩芯同位素阶段 5c（E 的第一部分）的间冰期气候特征。支持这一观点的人认为在南极东部距今约 9.5 万年时冰川发生过跃动（参考文献 51）。

深海氧同位素记录地球冰量的增加是逐渐的（图 4e），从而使得陆地冰量的周期性变化出现不对称的锯齿状特征[52]，冰芯同位素记录（图 4b）显示冷期（H、F、D 和 B 阶段）的最低温度处于同一水平。这可能与大气系统对冰量的强迫和反馈的快速反应有关，同时也说明了冰期的气候系统是非常稳定的。之前的一些海洋岩芯记录也提到了冰量变化与温度变化曲线之间存在的这种不一致性[53]。

强迫与反馈因子

除了重建南极洲东部的气候历史之外，我们现在讨论一些目前非常重要的问题：控制气候变化的机制以及南极洲东部气候变化与全球气候变化之间的关系。我们将检验不同因子的作用，包括太阳辐射、大气 CO_2 浓度和全球冰量变化。

太阳辐射变化。 近年来，米兰科维奇关于轨道变化是更新世冰期的主要起因的假说得到了大量支持[45,52-54]，并由此激发了许多模拟工作[55-58]。气候变化指标的频谱分析揭示出这种周期性与岁差（1.9 万年和 2.3 万年）、地轴倾角（4.1 万年）和地球轨道偏心率（10 万年）的周期在统计上具有相关性。现在大家都意识到，65°N 的夏季太阳辐射变化可能是北半球冰盖发生较大变化的强迫因子，而 10 万年的主周期就是由于冰盖对地球轨道强迫的非线性响应的结果。

在讨论北半球太阳辐射变化与沃斯托克气候之间的联系之前，我们将研究气候与太阳辐射局地变化之间的关系。

对比冰芯 $\delta^{18}O$ 剖面（图 4b）与 80°S 年太阳辐射曲线（参考文献 59）（图 4a），可以发现冷与暖同位素阶段与太阳辐射曲线的最小和最大值之间具有显著联系。尽管由于不连续取样我们无法进行可靠的频谱分析，尤其是对短周期性，但是这种显著的相关性强有力地支持了轨道强迫在气候变化中的作用。

The particular importance of the obliquity cycle, previously suggested from some high-latitude oceanic cores[54], would indicate that orbital forcing acts at a local scale. At 80° S, the maximum change of annual insolation is ~7% (ref. 59) which, from the radiative equilibrium equation, corresponds to a direct temperature effect of 4 °C. This direct effect is certainly important when compared with the 10 °C temperature range inferred from the $\delta^{18}O$ profile.

The apparent climatic synchroneity between the Northern and Southern Hemispheres poses a problem because the seasonality history of the polar insolation at 65° is different for the two hemispheres[60,61]. One explanation[61] could be that, for polar regions, the climate responds to annual insolation changes that are in phase for the two hemispheres. The correlation between the 80° S annual insolation and the $\delta^{18}O$ record gives some support to this hypothesis.

Finally, accepting the role of orbital forcing on the Southern Hemisphere climate, the existence of a roughly 40-kyr cycle in the $\delta^{18}O$ ice core record indirectly supports the Vostok core dating.

Atmospheric CO_2 concentration. CO_2 measurements from the analysis of air bubbles entrapped in ice from Greenland and Antarctic cores have shown that CO_2 changes are associated with climatic changes. Such direct measurements are available for the past 40 kyr (refs 62–65) and show a CO_2 increase of ~40% between the last glacial maximum and the pre-industrial Holocene period. These measurements suggest that CO_2 and its greenhouse warming might be involved in the control of the ice ages[21] and also in their interhemispheric synchroneity[42,60].

Shackleton et al.[66] have used the idea that the difference in carbon isotope ratios in surface and deep oceanic waters varies with CO_2 levels[67] to develop an indirect approach which extends the atmospheric CO_2 record further back in time. They estimate this parameter from the $\delta^{13}C$ difference between planktonic and benthic foraminifera ($\Delta\delta^{13}C$). The validity of this approach is supported by the fact that the estimated CO_2 values are consistent with the polar record over their common part[66] (the past 40 kyr). However, because many assumptions underly this method, it has to be corroborated either from other oceanic cores or, more directly, from ice cores. A study is in progress to obtain a detailed CO_2 profile along the Vostok core to examine directly the CO_2–climate connection over the past 150 kyr. In the following discussion, we will treat the $\Delta\delta^{13}C$ curve as a CO_2 curve.

The first 150 kyr of this $\Delta\delta^{13}C$ record[68] is shown on Fig. 4c. One can easily see the similarities between this curve and the $\delta^{18}O$ Vostok record. A relationship between CO_2 content and atmospheric temperatures is expected. Indeed, climate models predict that the greenhouse CO_2 effect should be amplified in high latitudes especially near ice margins[69,70]. Thus, these observed similarities suggest a CO_2–atmospheric temperature connection all over the last climatic cycle. According to Stauffer et al.[21] a 40-% CO_2 change corresponds to a temperature rise of 2–4.5 °C in high latitudes. Thus, the hypothesis that CO_2 changes

从一些高纬海洋岩芯记录[54]中发现，地轴倾角周期的特殊重要性说明轨道的强迫作用具有地带性。从辐射平衡方程可得到，在80°S，年太阳辐射最大变化约为7%（参考文献59），相当于对温度的直接影响为4℃。和 $\delta^{18}O$ 记录得出的10℃的温度变化相比较，这种直接影响当然是非常重要的。

南半球与北半球明显的气候同时变化也是一个问题，因为对于南半球与北半球来说，65°受到的太阳辐射的季节变化是不同的[60,61]。有一种解释[61]认为，对于极地区域，两个半球气候变化对于年太阳辐射变化的响应是同步的。80°S 年太阳辐射与冰芯 $\delta^{18}O$ 记录之间的相关性，在一定程度上支持该假说。

最后，我们接受南半球气候受地球轨道的强迫作用，南极冰芯 $\delta^{18}O$ 存在的约4万年的周期变化也间接支持了沃斯托克冰芯的定年结果。

大气的 CO_2 浓度。格陵兰和南极冰芯包裹的气泡测量表明，CO_2 浓度的变化与气候变化相关。对过去4万年以来冰芯 CO_2 浓度的直接测定已完成（参考文献62~65）。结果是从末次冰盛期到工业革命前的全新世，CO_2 浓度增加了约40%。这些测量结果表明，CO_2 及其温室效应也参与了控制冰期的周期性变化[21]，以及南北半球气候的同步性变化[42,60]。

沙克尔顿等人[66]发展了一种间接方法进一步延伸了大气 CO_2 记录的尺度，该方法基于这样一个认识，即海洋表层水与深层水的碳同位素比率随 CO_2 水平的变化而变化[67]。他们从浮游有孔虫和底栖有孔虫之间的 $\delta^{13}C$ 差异（$\Delta\delta^{13}C$）估计该参数。因估算的 CO_2 值与在相同年代（过去的4万年）的极地记录是一致的[66]，这一事实说明了上述方法的有效性。然而，由于该方法基于许多假定，所以必须由其他大洋岩芯或更直接地由冰芯记录来验证。目前正在通过沃斯托克冰芯获取15万年以来大气 CO_2 浓度变化序列，以此研究过去大气 CO_2 浓度变化与气候的联系。在下面的讨论中，我们将用 $\Delta\delta^{13}C$ 曲线代表 CO_2 曲线。

图4c 给出了过去15万年的 $\Delta\delta^{13}C$ 记录[68]。我们可以很容易看出该曲线与沃斯托克冰芯 $\delta^{18}O$ 记录之间的相似性，并且可以预料到 CO_2 浓度与大气温度之间存在关系。实际上，气候模型预测，在高纬地区，特别是在冰缘附近[69,70]，CO_2 温室效应会增强。因此，这些观测到的相似性说明，在最后一个完整的冰期－间冰期旋回中，CO_2 与大气温度存在联系。根据施陶费尔等[21]的说法，在高纬度地区 CO_2 上升

are an important factor in controlling high latitude climate is well within the realm of possibility.

There are several other features of the CO_2–climate relationship. CO_2 measurements at Dome C indicate that the increase in CO_2 concentration associated with the end of the last ice age began before, or simultaneously with, the climatic change at high southern latitudes[65]. On the other hand, from the 340-kyr reconstructed CO_2 curve, Pisias and Shackleton[71] inferred that CO_2 lags the orbitals forcing (summer insolation at 65° N) but leads the ice volume, by an average of 2.5 kyr. From this, they made two important points[68,71]: (1) CO_2 changes are not a consequence of climatic changes but may represent part of the mechanisms by which orbital variations induce changes in climate; (2) the presence of a strong obliquity component suggests a high-latitude control for the mechanisms by which CO_2 responds to orbital forcing.

This also puts constraints on the way in which CO_2 levels in the ocean surface, which eventually control the atmospheric CO_2 levels, can vary[68]. Recently, four groups[72-75] have independently explored CO_2 scenarios implying a high latitude control through: the changes in ocean circulation; the influence of the amount of light reaching the polar regions on the utilization of nutrients; and a combination of these two factors.

The Knox and McElroy nutrient scenario[74] includes a mechanism whereby small changes in insolation at high latitudes could result in large changes in CO_2 and thus looks attractive in view of the possible CO_2 climatic role at the timescale considered here although this type of scenario[78] is not supported by recent results on planktonic foraminifera from Antarctic deep-sea sediments.

Ice-volume feedbacks. Although many assumptions are involved, the above discussion suggests that local insolation and possibly the atmospheric CO_2 have played a part in determining the Antarctic climate over the past 150 kyr. The two factors alone, however, would not explain all the climatic variability seen in the $\delta^{18}O$ Vostok record. In particular, we observe that the very cold stage F corresponds to an intermediate inferred CO_2 value.

Note that this stage F corresponds to the time of lowest insolation at 65° N (Fig. 4*d*)[59]. (Indeed, there are similarities between this insolation curve and the $\delta^{18}O$ Vostok record (Fig. 4*b*) over all the past 150 kyr.) Modelling of the growth and retreat of the ice sheets has shown that ice volume changes can be driven by summer radiation in Northern Hemisphere high latitudes[56,57,76,77]. Although all of the models do not specifically refer to 65° N, the generated ice-volume curves resemble, with a few kiloyears lag, the summer insolation at this latitudinal band. As shown in Fig. 4*d*, high volumes correspond to low insolations and vice versa. Such generated ice volume curves differ from ice volumes deduced from benthic foraminifera (Fig. 4*e*). In particular, note the difference during stage F. According to Budd[61] the two approaches of deriving ice volumes can be reconciled if the contribution of ^{18}O-poor Antarctic ice is taken into account. This raises the question of how Northern Hemisphere ice extent can influence Antarctic climate.

40%，则气温相应地上升 2~4.5℃。因此，CO_2 的变化完全有可能是控制高纬度气候的一个重要因子。

CO_2 与气候的关系还有几个特征。测得的冰穹 C 冰芯中 CO_2 浓度变化表明，末次冰期结束时，CO_2 浓度的升高比南半球高纬度地区的气候变化 [65] 超前或两者同时发生。另一方面，皮西亚斯与沙克尔顿 [71] 通过重建过去 34 万年以来的 CO_2 曲线，推测 CO_2 浓度的变化滞后于轨道强迫（在 65°N 夏季的太阳辐射），但却超前于冰川体积变化平均约 2,500 年。由此，他们提出两个重要观点 [68,71]：（1）CO_2 变化不是气候变化的结果，相反，它可能是轨道变化引起气候变化这一机制的一部分；（2）地轴倾角周期的存在说明了高纬度的控制机制，从而导致了 CO_2 对轨道强迫的响应。

这个结果也限制了海洋表面 CO_2 浓度的变化范围，而海洋表面 CO_2 浓度最终控制大气 CO_2 浓度 [68]。最近有 4 个研究小组 [72-75] 各自独立地探索研究高纬地区通过 3 种途径控制大气 CO_2 浓度的情景：通过洋流变化、通过到达极地地区的光的总量对养分利用的影响以及结合以上两种途径。

诺克斯和麦克尔罗伊的营养方案 [74] 包含了一种机制，在这个机制中高纬地区太阳辐射的微小变化就可以导致 CO_2 的较大变化。鉴于在该时间尺度上 CO_2 可能产生的气候控制作用，该机制还是很有吸引力的。但南极深海沉积物中的浮游有孔虫的最新研究结果并不支持这一方案 [78]。

冰川体积的反馈作用。 尽管包含了许多假设，上述讨论表明局地太阳辐射及大气 CO_2 可能对于过去 15 万年的南极气候变化起着部分决定作用。然而，仅有两个因子，并不能解释在沃斯托克冰芯 $\delta^{18}O$ 记录中的全部气候变化。特别地，我们发现，极冷的 F 阶段却对应于 CO_2 的中间值。

我们注意到，F 阶段与 65°N（图 4d）太阳辐射最低值的时间 [59] 相符。（实际上，在过去整个 15 万年里，太阳辐射曲线和沃斯托克冰芯 $\delta^{18}O$ 记录（图 4b）变化相似）。冰盖消长的模拟结果显示，冰体积总量变化受北半球高纬度地区 [56,57,76,77] 夏季辐射变化的影响。尽管没有任何模式特别适用于 65°N 地区，模拟出的冰量曲线却与同纬度带的夏季太阳辐射相似，但存在数千年的滞后。如图 4d 所示，较大冰体积总量对应于较低的太阳辐射，反之亦然。这里所得到的冰体积总量曲线与由底栖有孔虫（图 4e）所推测的冰体积总量不同，特别是 F 阶段的差异。巴德 [61] 认为，如果考虑 ^{18}O 贫化的南极冰的影响，两种方法得到的冰体积总量的变化应该是一致的。这引出了一个问题：北半球的冰川分布范围如何影响南极气候。

Although we cannot answer this question here, we note that recent GCM results[42] show that such a relationship cannot be explained by the interhemispheric exchange of heat in the atmosphere. Other mechanisms would have to be involved, such as a change in the cross-equatorial heat transport by the ocean circulation[42,60,78] or a response of the East Antarctic ice sheets to sea-level changes[61]. This second hypothesis is valid only if its apparent contradiction with the time lead of Antarctic sea-ice compared with the Northern Hemisphere ice volume can be solved as suggested by Budd[61].

Conclusions

We have obtained the first complete and unambiguous isotope description from a deep-ice core of the last climatic cycle. The 2,083-m Vostok record covers the past 150 kyr extending into the end of the previous glacial period. The timescale has been established by combining a glaciological model appropriate here as the core represents only about the first half of the ice sheet, with an original approach for estimating past accumulation rates from the isotope record. While this method has its own limitations, it has the advantage of being independent of other palaeoindicators or climatic forcing series.

This $\delta^{18}O$ record has been interpreted as essentially representing temperature changes over East Antarctica. This interpretation is based on the $\delta^{18}O$–temperature gradient observed for modern precipitation and on a dynamically-simple isotope model. Although aware of the necessity of a more detailed modelling of the atmospheric $\delta^{18}O$ cycle using GCMs, we have confidence in the temperature interpretation as far as major $\delta^{18}O$ changes are concerned.

In this interpretation, the Vostok record provides extremely rich climatic information. The present Holocene period was preceeded by a long glacial period marked by two relatively warm interstadials. The well-marked last interglacial was significantly warmer than the Holocene and the end of the previous glacial was quite similar to the last glacial maximum.

A comparison with $\delta^{18}O$ in deep-sea cores shows that the Antarctic climate and the global ice volume have not evolved in the same way. The last interglacial appears to be about twice as long in the Antarctic temperature record as in the ice-volume record. In addition, there are marked differences in the shapes of the records during the last glacial. Thus, we now have access to another different, but complementary, climatic record fully covering the last climatic cycle.

The presence of a roughly 40-kyr cycle in the Vostok record strongly supports the role of orbital forcing in determining climatic changes. This record is approximately in phase with the annual insolation at 80° S suggesting that this forcing operates at a local scale. There are also some common features between the climatic curve and the summer insolation at 65° N which may be the result of the influence of the Northern Hemisphere ice sheets on the Antarctic climate.

虽然我们无法在本文中回答这个问题，然而我们注意到近期 GCM 模拟结果 [42] 显示，南北半球间大气热量交换并不能解释其中的关系。因此还须包括其他机制，比如大洋环流驱动的跨赤道热量输送的变化 [42,60,78]，或者南极洲东部冰盖对海平面变化的响应 [61] 等。正如巴德 [61] 提出的那样，只有解决了南极海冰的变化先于北半球冰量的变化这一突出矛盾，第二个假说才能得到证实。

结　　论

我们首次从深孔冰芯中获得了包含整个末次冰期 – 间冰期旋回的完整且清晰的同位素记录。长度为 2,083 米的沃斯托克冰芯记录涵盖了过去 15 万年的气候记录，时间尺度延伸至倒数第二次冰期的结束期。通过结合两种方法对该冰芯进行定年，建立时间序列。一种方法是利用适宜的冰川学模型（该冰芯只代表了冰盖的上半部分）。第二种方法是通过冰芯稳定同位素的记录估算过去冰川积累率的变化。虽然这种结合法仍存在局限性，但其优点是它完全独立于其他古气候指标或气候强迫因子的时间序列。

沃斯托克冰芯的 $\delta^{18}O$ 记录可以解释为从根本上反映了南极洲东部的温度变化。这一解释的理论基础是观测到的现代降水中 $\delta^{18}O$–温度梯度以及简单的动力学同位素模型。虽然我们也意识到利用 GCM 模型更为详细地模拟大气 $\delta^{18}O$ 循环是十分必要的，但我们对于该冰芯 $\delta^{18}O$ 解释温度变化的可靠程度仍很有信心，至少对于大的 $\delta^{18}O$ 变化是如此。

在这个解释中，沃斯托克冰芯记录提供了极其丰富的气候变化信息。现在的全新世时期之前有一个较长的冰期，而且该冰期包含了两个相对较暖的间冰阶。我们也发现末次间冰期比全新世要温暖得多，而且倒数第二次冰期的结束与末次冰盛期十分相似。

与深海岩芯 $\delta^{18}O$ 的对比表明，南极的气候和全球的冰量变化并不一致。南极温度记录的末次间冰期持续时间是冰量记录的末次间冰期持续时间的两倍。此外，两个记录在末次冰期时的曲线形状也显著不同。因而，我们现在获得了另一种不同但互补的、覆盖整个末次冰期旋回的气候记录。

沃斯托克冰芯记录存在一个约 4 万年的周期，这强有力地支持了轨道强迫在气候变化中的作用。该记录与 80°S 的年太阳辐射变化几乎同步，说明这种强迫作用限于局地尺度。南极冰芯的气候曲线与 65°N 的夏季太阳辐射之间也有一些共性，这可能反映了北半球冰盖对南极气候的影响。

There are striking similarities between the $\Delta\delta^{13}C$ curve of Shackleton and co-workers[66,68] and the $\delta^{18}O$ record. Following these authors in treating the $\Delta\delta^{13}C$ curve as a CO_2 curve, there appears to be, over a complete climatic cycle, a relationship between atmospheric CO_2 levels and atmospheric temperatures as previously suggested for the past 40 kyr.

There are several other ways to obtain more climatic information from the Vostok ice than the $\delta^{18}O$ method described here. Interesting results concerning ^{10}Be have been obtained[27], and other studies are either in progress or planned for the near future. They include additional deuterium and oxygen-18 determinations and measurements of total gas volume, crystal size, CO_2 in the air bubbles, $^{18}O/^{16}O$ ratio of oxygen in air and aerosol content.

The Vostok ice core offers the possibility of measuring many other parameters and their variation with time. As shown from other ice cores, the number of these parameters of interest is growing. Recent studies include more and more chemical elements[79-83] and trace gases[84] as well as $^{12}C/^{13}C$ ratio in CO_2 (ref. 85). Although their first objective is to reconstruct the Earth's palaeo-environment, some of these parameters also contain, at least indirectly, palaeoclimatic information. Finally, it is hoped to reach greater depths in the Vostok drilling and thus to extend the time scale considerably.

We are very grateful to all Soviet and French participants in drilling, field work and ice sampling which was prepared, in particular, by K. V. Blinov. We thank G. Mondet for isotopic determinations. We also thank W. F. Budd, R. Sadourny, N. J. Shackleton for helpful discussions. The presentation of the work has largely benefited from very constructive criticisms of J. C. Duplessy, G. Raisbeck, D. Raynaud, J. White, and F. Yiou. This work was supported in France by the EPF (Expéditions Polaires Francaises), PNEDC (Programme National d'Etudes de la Dynamique du Climat) and TAAF (Terres Australes et Antarctiques Françaises) and in USSR and Vostok by Soviet Antarctic Expeditions.

(**316**, 591-596; 1985)

C. Lorius[*], J. Jouzel[†], C. Ritz[*], L. Merlivat[†], N. I. Barkov[‡], Y. S. Korotkevich[†] & V. M. Kotlyakov[§]

[*] Laboratoire de Glaciologie et de Géophysique de l'Environnement, CNRS, BP96, 38402 Saint Martin d'Héres Cedex, France

[†] Laboratoire de Géochimie Isotopique DPC, CEN Saclay, 91191 Gif-sur-Yvette Cedex, France

[‡] The Arctic and Antarctic Research Institute, Fontanka 34, Leningrad 191104, USSR

[§] Institute of Geography, Academy of Sciences of USSR, Staronometry, St 29, Moscow 109017, USSR

Received 29 March; accepted 17 May 1985.

References:

1. Shackleton, N. J. *Nature* **215**, 15-17 (1967).

2. Shackleton, N. J. & Opdyke, N. D. *Quat. Res.* **3**, 39-55 (1973).

3. Duplessy, J. C. *Climatic Change* (ed. Gribbin, J.) 46-67 (Cambridge University Press, 1978).

4. Dansgaard, W., Johnsen, S. J. Moeller, J. & Langway, C. C. *Science* **166**, 377-381 (1969).

5. Epstein, S., Sharp, R. P. & Gow, A. J. *Science* **168**, 1570-1572 (1970).

6. Barkov, N. I., Korotkevitch, E. S., Gordienko, F. G. & Kotlyakov, V. M. *IAHS Publ.* **118**, 312-321 (1977).

沙克尔顿和他的同事 [66,68] 得出的 $\Delta\delta^{13}C$ 曲线与冰芯 $\delta^{18}O$ 记录之间有显著的相似性。按照他们的做法，把 $\Delta\delta^{13}C$ 曲线指代成 CO_2 曲线，那么在整个气候旋回内，过去 4 万年的大气 CO_2 水平和大气温度之间似乎存在相关性，正如之前所提出的那样。

除了本文所介绍的 $\delta^{18}O$ 方法，还有其他方式可以从沃斯托克冰芯中得到更多的气候信息。目前已从 ^{10}Be 记录中得到了令人感兴趣的结果 [27]，而其他的研究正在进行中或正计划近期开展。它们包括氘和氧 –18 的进一步测定以及气体总量、冰晶大小、气体包裹体中的 CO_2、气体中的 $^{18}O/^{16}O$ 比率以及气溶胶含量等的测量。

沃斯托克冰芯也使测量许多其他参数及其随时间的变化成为可能。像其他冰芯一样，这些有价值的参数的数量正在不断增加。最近的研究涵盖了越来越多的化学元素 [79-83] 和痕量气体 [84]，以及 CO_2 中 $^{12}C/^{13}C$ 的比率（参考文献 85）。尽管这些参数的首要目标是重建地球的古环境，但有些参数也包含了（至少间接地）古气候信息。最后，我们希望在沃斯托克钻井能钻探至更深的位置，从而大大延伸研究的时间尺度。

我们非常感谢在准备钻探、野外工作和采集冰样工作中的全体苏联和法国的参与者，特别是布利诺夫。我们感谢进行同位素测定的蒙代。我们也感谢与巴德，萨杜尔尼，沙克尔顿进行的有益讨论。迪普莱西、雷兹贝克、雷诺、怀特和伊奥曾提出过很多有建设性的评论意见，使本工作受益匪浅。本研究得到了法国方面 EPF（法国极地探险队）、PNEDC（国家气候动力学研究项目）和 TAAF（法属南方和南极洲领地）的支持以及苏联和沃斯托克的苏联南极探险队的支持。

（蔡则怡 翻译；田立德 审稿）

7. Lorius, C., Merlivat, L., Jouzel, J. & Pourchet, M. *Nature* **280**, 644-648 (1979).

8. Dansgaard, W. *et al. Science* **218**, 1273-1277 (1982).

9. Dansgaard, W. *et al. Geophys. Monogr.* (M. Ewing *Symp.*, 5) **29**, 288-298 (1984).

10. Lorius, C., Raynaud, D., Petit, J. R., Jouzel, J. & Merlivat, L. *Annls Glaciol.* **5**, 88-94 (1984).

11. Paterson, N. S. B. *Nature* **266**, 508-511 (1977).

12. Young, N. W., Pourchet, M., Kotlyakov, V. M., Korolev, P. A., & Dyugerov, M. B. *Annls Glaciol.* **3**, 333-338 (1982).

13. Lorius, C. *et al. IAHS Publ.* **86**, 3-15 (1970).

14. Barkov, N. I. *Antarct. J. U. S.* **10**, 55-56 (1975).

15. Barkov, N. I., Gordienko, F. G., Korotkevich, E. S. & Kotlyakov, V. N. *Dokl. Acad. Sci. USSR* **214**, 1383-1386 (1974).

16. Barkov, N. I., Gordienko, F. G., Korotkevich, E. S. & Kotlyakov, V. M. *Inform. Bull. Soviet Antarct. Expedn* **90**, 39-48 (1975).

17. Gordienko, F. G., Kotlyakov, V. M., Barkov, N. I., Korotkevich, T. E. & Nikolaev, S. D. *Data Glacio Stud. Acad. Sci. USSR* **46**, 168-171 (1983).

18. Grosvald, M. G. *Data Glaciol. Stud. Acad. Sci. USSR* **46**, 171-174 (1983).

19. Shumskii, P. A., Korotkevich, E. S. & Larina, T. B. *Inform. Bull. Soviet Antarct. Expedn.* **100**, 41-48 (1980).

20. Jouzel, J., Merlivat, L. & Lorius, C. *Nature* **289**, 688-691 (1982).

21. Stauffer, B., Hofer, H., Oeschger, H., Schwander, J. & Siegenthaler, U. *Annls Glaciol.* **5**, 160-164 (1984).

22. Dansgaard, W., Barkov, N. I. & Splettstoesser, J. *IAHS Publ.* **118**, 204-209 (1977).

23. Wilson, A. T. & Hendy, C. H. *J. Glaciol.* **27**, 95, 3-9 (1981).

24. Budd, W. F. & Young, N. W. *The Climatic Record in Polar Ice Sheets* (ed. de Q. Robin, G.) 150-176 (Cambridge University Press, 1983).

25. Robin, G. de Q. *Philos. Trans. R. Soc.* B**280**, 143-148 (1977).

26. Jouzel, J. & Merlivat, L. *J. Geophys. Res.* **89**, 11749-11758 (1984).

27. Raisbeck, G. M. *et al. Nature* **292**, 825-826 (1981).

28. Yiou, F., Raisbeck, G. M., Bourles, D., Lorius, C. & Barkov, N. I. *Nature* (**this issue**).

29. Drewry, D. J. *Pol. Rec.* **17**, 359-374 (1975).

30. Drewry, D. J. *Scott Polar Research Institute Rep.* (ed. Drewry, D. J.) (Scott Polar Research Institute, Cambridge, 1983).

31. Lliboutry, L. *Z. Gletscherk. Glaziolgeol.* **15**, 135-148 (1979).

32. de Angelis, M. *et al. J. Atmos. Chem.* **1**, 215-239 (1984).

33. Bowler, J. M., *Earth. Sci. Rev.* **12**, 279-310 (1976).

34. Robin, G. de Q. The Climatic Record in Polar Ice Sheets, (ed. de Q. Robin G.) 180-189 (Cambridge University Press, 1983).

35. Jouzel, J., Merlivat, L., Petit, J. R. & Lorius, C. *J. Geophys. Res.* **88**, 2693-2703 (1983).

36. Joussaume, S., Jouzel, J. & Sadourny, R. *Nature* **311**, 24-29 (1984).

37. Lorius, C. & Merlivat, L. *IAHS Publ.* **118**, 127-137 (1977).

38. Alley, R. B. & Whillans, I. M. *J. Geophys. Res.* **89**, 6487-6493.

39. Drewry, D. J. *Nature* **287**, 214-216 (1980).

40. Gates, W. L. *Science* **191**, 1138-1144 (1976).

41. Manabe, S. & Hahn, D. G. *J. Geophys. Res.* **82**, 3889-3911 (1977).

42. Manabe, S. & Broccoli, A. J. *Annls Glaciol.* **5**, 100-105 (1984).

43. Hansen, J. *et al. Geophys. Monogr.* **29**, 130-163 (1984).

44. Raynaud, D. & Lorius, C. *IAHS Publ.* **118**, 326-335 (1977).

45. CLIMAP Project Members *Quat. Res.* **21**, 123-224 (1984).

46. Mix, A. C. & Ruddiman, W. F. *Quat. Res.* **21**, 1-20 (1984).

47. Imbrie, J. *et al. Milankovitch and Climate* Vol.1, (eds Berger A. L. *et al.*) 269-305 (Reidel, Dordrecht, 1984).

48. Emiliani, C. *J. Geol.* **63**, 538-578 (1965).

49. Shackleton, N. J. *Proc. R. Soc.* B**174**, 135-154 (1969).

50. Bender, M., Labeyrie, L., Raynaud, D. & Lorius, C. *EOS*, **64**, 973 (1984).

51. Hollin, J. T. *Nature* **283**, 629-633.

52. Broecker, W. S. & Van Donk, J. *Rev. Geophys. Space Phys.* **8**, 169-198 (1970).

53. Hays, J. D., Imbrie, J. & Shackleton, N. J. *Science* **194**, 1121-1132 (1976).

54. Ruddiman, W. F. & McIntyre, A. *Science* **212**, 617-627 (1981).

55. Imbrie, J. & Imbrie, Z. *Science* **207**, 943-953 (1980).

56. Budd, W. F. & Smith, I. N. *IAHS Publ.* **131**, 369-409 (1981).

57. Pollard, D, *Nature* **296**, 334-338 (1981).

58. Le Treut, H. & Ghil, M. *J. Geophys. Res.* **88**, 5167-5190 (1983).

59. Berger, A. *Contr.* 37 (Université Catholique de Louvain, Belgique, 1978).

60. Broecker, W. S. *Milankovitch and Climate* Vol. 2 (eds Berger, A. L. *et al.*) 687-698 (Reidel, Dordrecht, 1984).

61. Budd, W. F. *IAHS Publ.* **131**, 441-471 (1981).

62. Delmas, R. J., Ascensio, J. M. & Legrand, M. *Nature* **284**, 155-157 (1980).

63. Neftel, A., Oeschger, H., Schwander, R. J., Stauffer, B., & Zumbrunn, R. *Nature* **295**, 220-223 (1982).

64. Stauffer, B., Hofer, H., Oeschger, H., Schwander, J. & Siegenthaler, U. *Annls Glaciol.* **5**, 160-164 (1984).

65. Raynaud, D. & Barnola, J. M. *Annls Glaciol.* **5**, 224 (1984).

66. Shackleton, N. J., Hall, M. A., Line, J. & Cang Shuxi *Nature* **306**, 319-323 (1983).

67. Broecker, W. S. *Progr. Oceanogr.* **11**, 151-197 (1982).

68. Shackleton, N. J. & Pisias, N. G. *Chapman Conf. on CO₂* (American Geophysical Union, in the press).

69. Manabe, S. & Wetherald, R. T. *J. Atmos. Sci.* **37**, 99-118 (1980).

70. Washington, W. M. & Meehl, A. G. *J. Geophys. Res.* **89**, 9475-9503 (1984).

71. Pisias, N. G. & Shackleton, N. J. *Nature* **30**, 757-759 (1984).

72. Sarmiento, J. L. & Toggweiler, J. R. *Nature* **308**, 621-624 (1984).

73. Siegenthaler, U. & Wenk, T. *Nature* **308**, 624-626 (1984).

74. Knox, F. & McElroy, M. B. *J. Geophys. Res.* **89**, 4629-4637 (1984).

75. Broecker, W. S. & Takahashi, T. *Geophys. Monogr.* (M. Ewing *Symp.*, 5) **29**, 314-326 (1984).

76. Birchfield, G. E., Weertman, J. & Lunde, A. T. *Quat. Res.* **15**, 126-142 (1981).

77. Oerlemans, J. *Nature* **297**, 550-553 (1982).

78. Broecker, W. S., Peteet, D. & Rind, D. *Nature* **315**, 21-26 (1985).

79. Zeller, J. E. & Parker, B. C. *Geophys. Res. Lett.* **8**, 895-898 (1981).

80. Legrand, M. & Delmas, R. J. *Atmos Envir.* **18**, 1867-1874 (1984).

81. Palais, J. & Legrand, M. *J. Geophys. Res.* **90**, 1143-1154 (1985).

82. Neftel, A., Jacob, P. & Klockow, D. *Nature* **311**, 43-45 (1984).

83. Wolff, E. W. & Peel, D. A. *Nature* **313**, 535-540 (1985).

84. Rasmunssen, R. A. & Khalil, M. A. *J. Geophys. Res.* **89**, 11599-11605 (1984).

85. Friedl, I. H., Moor, E., Oeschger, H., Siegenthaler, U. & Stauffer, B. *Geophys. Res. Lett.* **11**, 1145-1148 (1984).

C$_{60}$: Buckminsterfullerene

H. W. Kroto *et al.*

Editor's Note

By the 1980s, students of chemistry throughout the world learned that carbon exists as diamond or graphite. The chemistry of carbon (organic chemistry) was based on the familiar hexagonal structure of molecules of benzene in which atoms form a six-sided ring with carbon atoms at each corner. It was therefore a great surprise that in 1985 British chemist Harry Kroto, working with a team at Rice University, Texas, was able to announce the discovery of a molecule consisting only of carbon atoms—60 of them—in the form of a truncated icosahedron, a figure made up of 12 pentagons and 20 hexagons. This was a design used by the American architect Richard Buckminster Fuller to construct what are known as geodesic domes, whence the name buckminsterfullerene for the molecule. Kroto and his colleagues, Robert Curl and Richard Smalley, were awarded a Nobel Prize in 1996.

During experiments aimed at understanding the mechanisms by which long-chain carbon molecules are formed in interstellar space and circumstellar shells[1], graphite has been vaporized by laser irradiation, producing a remarkably stable cluster consisting of 60 carbon atoms. Concerning the question of what kind of 60-carbon atom structure might give rise to a superstable species, we suggest a truncated icosahedron, a polygon with 60 vertices and 32 faces, 12 of which are pentagonal and 20 hexagonal. This object is commonly encountered as the football shown in Fig. 1. The C$_{60}$ molecule which results when a carbon atom is placed at each vertex of this structure has all valences satisfied by two single bonds and one double bond, has many resonance structures, and appears to be aromatic.

Fig. 1. A football (in the United States, a soccerball) on Texas grass. The C$_{60}$ molecule featured in this letter is suggested to have the truncated icosahedral structure formed by replacing each vertex on the seams of such a ball by a carbon atom.

C₆₀：巴克敏斯特富勒烯

克罗托等

编者按

在 20 世纪 80 年代之前，全世界学化学的人都知道，碳以金刚石和石墨两种形式存在。碳化学（有机化学）是基于我们所熟悉的苯分子的六边形结构，该分子中的原子组成一个六元环，每个顶角上有一个碳原子。1985 年，英国化学家哈里·克罗托与来自得克萨斯州莱斯大学的研究小组合作并宣称发现了一种全部由碳原子（60 个碳原子）组成的分子，该分子形如一个截角二十面体，是一种由 12 个五边形和 20 个六边形围成的图形，这着实令人惊奇。美国建筑师理查德·巴克敏斯特·富勒在建造通常所称的多面穹顶时曾经使用过这种设计结构，因此将该物质命名为巴克敏斯特富勒烯。克罗托与他的同事们（罗伯特·柯尔和理查德·斯莫利）因而获得了 1996 年诺贝尔奖。

在探索长碳链分子于星际空间和星周壳中的形成机制而进行的实验中[1]，石墨在激光照射下气化，产生出一种由 60 个碳原子组成的非常稳定的簇状分子。关于 60 个碳原子以何种类型的结构才能产生出超稳定物质这一问题，我们提出一种截角二十面体结构，这种多面体具有 60 个顶点和 32 个面，其中 12 个面为正五边形，20 个为正六边形。这个多面体和我们经常看到的足球一样，如图 1 所示。将上述结构中的每个顶点放置一个碳原子，就可以形成一个 C₆₀ 分子，为符合碳原子的价态，其中所有原子均为两个单键和一个双键，该分子具有多重共轭结构，属于芳香族化合物。

图 1. 得克萨斯草坪上的一个足球（在美国称为英式足球）。本文中描述的 C₆₀ 分子让人想起截角二十面体结构，就是将图示足球中接线上的每个顶点用一个碳原子代替形成的结构。

THE technique used to produce and detect this unusual molecule involves the vaporization of carbon species from the surface of a solid disk of graphite into a high-density helium flow, using a focused pulsed laser. The vaporization laser was the second harmonic of Q-switched Nd:YAG producing pulse energies of ~30 mJ. The resulting carbon clusters were expanded in a supersonic molecular beam, photoionized using an excimer laser, and detected by time-of-flight mass spectrometry. The vaporization chamber is shown in Fig. 2. In the experiment the pulsed valve was opened first and then the vaporization laser was fired after a precisely controlled delay. Carbon species were vaporized into the helium stream, cooled and partially equilibrated in the expansion, and travelled in the resulting molecular beam to the ionization region. The clusters were ionized by direct one-photon excitation with a carefully synchronized excimer laser pulse. The apparatus has been fully described previously[2-5].

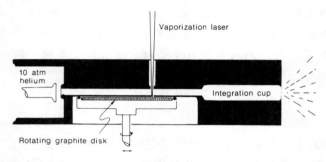

Fig. 2. Schematic diagram of the pulsed supersonic nozzle used to generate carbon cluster beams. The integrating cup can be removed at the indicated line. The vaporization laser beam (30–40 mJ at 532 nm in a 5-ns pulse) is focused through the nozzle, striking a graphite disk which is rotated slowly to produce a smooth vaporization surface. The pulsed nozzle passes high-density helium over this vaporization zone. This helium carrier gas provides the thermalizing collisions necessary to cool, react and cluster the species in the vaporized graphite plasma, and the wind necessary to carry the cluster products through the remainder of the nozzle. Free expansion of this cluster-laden gas at the end of the nozzle forms a supersonic beam which is probed 1.3 m downstream with a time-of-flight mass spectrometer.

The vaporization of carbon has been studied previously in a very similar apparatus[6]. In that work clusters of up to 190 carbon atoms were observed and it was noted that for clusters of more than 40 atoms, only those containing an even number of atoms were observed. In the mass spectra displayed in ref. 6, the C_{60} peak is the largest for cluster sizes of >40 atoms, but it is not completely dominant. We have recently re-examined this system and found that under certain clustering conditions the C_{60} peak can be made about 40 times larger than neighbouring clusters.

Figure 3 shows a series of cluster distributions resulting from variations in the vaporization conditions evolving from a cluster distribution similar to that observed in ref. 3, to one in which C_{60} is totally dominant. In Fig. 3c, where the firing of the vaporization laser was delayed until most of the He pulse had passed, a roughly gaussian distribution of large, even-numbered clusters with 38–120 atoms resulted. The C_{60} peak was largest but not dominant. In Fig. 3b, the vaporization laser was fired at the time of maximum helium

　　用来产生并检测这种不同寻常的分子的技术包括：利用聚焦的脉冲激光使含碳物质从固体石墨盘表面气化，进入高密度的氦气流。气化激光是 Q 开关 Nd：YAG（钕钇铝石榴石）激光器产生的二次谐波，脉冲能量约为 30 mJ。生成的碳簇在超声分子束中膨胀，经准分子激光器光电离后，利用飞行时间质谱进行检测。图 2 中所示为气化室。实验中，脉冲阀首先打开，在精确控制的一段延迟时间之后气化激光点亮。含碳物质气化并进入氦气流中，在膨胀过程中冷却并建立了局部平衡，最终以分子束的形式进入电离区域。碳簇在精确同步准分子激光脉冲下直接单光子激发而被电离。这个装置此前有过完整的描述[2-5]。

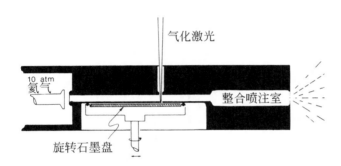

图 2. 用来产生碳簇分子束的脉冲超声喷嘴示意图。整合喷注室可以沿图示线移开。气化激光束（30~40 mJ，532 nm，5 ns 脉冲）在喷口处聚焦，击打在缓慢旋转的石墨盘上，以产生均匀的气化表面。高密度氦气沿着这个气化区域通过脉冲喷口。这种氦气载气提供了令气化的石墨等离子中的物质冷却、反应以及簇聚所必需的热碰撞，还提供了携载簇状产物通过喷管剩余部分所必需的气流。这种满载簇状产物的气体在喷管末端自由膨胀，形成了超声束，在下游 1.3 m 处被飞行时间质谱仪检测到。

　　以前曾用非常类似的装置对碳的气化进行过研究[6]。在该研究中曾观测到多达 190 个碳原子的簇状物，同时注意到，在超过 40 个碳原子的簇状物中，只有偶数个碳原子的簇状物才能被观测到。在参考文献 6 提供的质谱图中，C₆₀ 的峰值在大于 40 个原子的簇状物中是最大的，但也不完全是占绝对优势的。最近，我们重新检验了该体系，并发现在特定的簇聚条件下，可以使 C₆₀ 的峰值达到邻近簇峰值的约 40 倍以上。

　　图 3 显示了通过气化条件的变动而得到的一系列簇状物分布结果，最初得到与参考文献 3 中非常类似的分布，逐渐改进，得到了 C₆₀ 具有绝对优势的结果。图 3c，是等到大部分氦脉冲通过之后点亮气化激光所得，结果得到了含 38~120 个碳原子的大型偶数原子簇的近似高斯分布。C₆₀ 峰是最大的但不是占绝对优势的。图 3b 是在氦密度达到最大时点亮气化激光得到的；C₆₀ 峰值增强，大约比相邻峰强

density; the C$_{60}$ peak grew into a feature perhaps five times stronger than its neighbours, with the exception of C$_{70}$. In Fig. 3a, the conditions were similar to those in Fig. 3b but in addition the integrating cup depicted in Fig. 2 was added to increase the time between vaporization and expansion. The resulting cluster distribution is completely dominated by C$_{60}$, in fact more than 50% of the total large cluster abundance is accounted for by C$_{60}$; the C$_{70}$ peak has diminished in relative intensity compared with C$_{60}$, but remains rather prominent, accounting for ~5% of the large cluster population.

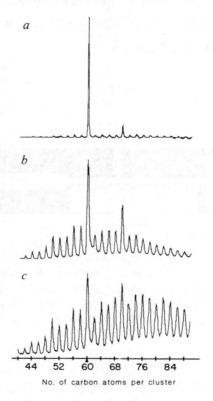

Fig. 3. Time-of-flight mass spectra of carbon clusters prepared by laser vaporization of graphite and cooled in a supersonic beam. Ionization was effected by direct one-photon excitation with an ArF excimer laser (6.4 eV, 1 mJ cm^{-2}). The three spectra shown differ in the extent of helium collisions occurring in the supersonic nozzle. In c, the effective helium density over the graphite target was less than 10 torr—the observed cluster distribution here is believed to be due simply to pieces of the graphite sheet ejected in the primary vaporization process. The spectrum in b was obtained when roughly 760 torr helium was present over the graphite target at the time of laser vaporization. The enhancement of C$_{60}$ and C$_{70}$ is believed to be due to gas-phase reactions at these higher clustering conditions. The spectrum in a was obtained by maximizing these cluster thermalization and cluster-cluster reactions in the "integration cup" shown in Fig. 2. The concentration of cluster species in the especially stable C$_{60}$ form is the prime experimental observation of this study.

Our rationalization of these results is that in the laser vaporization, fragments are torn from the surface as pieces of the planar graphite fused six-membered ring structure. We believe that the distribution in Fig. 3c is fairly representative of the nascent distribution of larger ring fragments. When these hot ring clusters are left in contact with high-density

五倍，除了相对 C$_{70}$ 以外。图 3a 的获得条件与图 3b 类似，不过加入了图 2 中描述的整合喷注室，以增加气化与膨胀过程之间的时间。C$_{60}$ 在所得到的簇状物分布中完全占绝对优势，事实上，它占据了大型原子簇总数的 50% 以上；与 C$_{60}$ 相比，C$_{70}$ 峰值的相对强度减小了，但仍然相当显著，在大型原子簇总数中约占 5%。

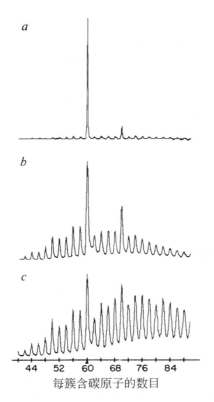

图 3. 将石墨进行激光气化并在超声束中冷却得到的碳簇的飞行时间质谱图。电离是利用 ArF 准分子激光器（6.4 eV，1 mJ·cm^{-2}）进行直接单光子激发。展示的三张谱图只是在发生于超声喷嘴中的氦撞击的程度上存在差异。在图 c 中，经过石墨靶上方的有效氦密度不到 10 torr——这里所观测到的簇状物的分布，应单纯地归结为在初级气化过程中喷射出的石墨片层碎片。谱图 b 是在气化激光激发时，以大约 760 torr 的氦气流经石墨靶上方所得。相信 C$_{60}$ 和 C$_{70}$ 峰值的增强应归结为在这种较强簇聚条件下发生的气相反应。谱图 a 是利用图 2 所示的"整合喷注室"最大化簇的热能化及簇间反应所得。以特别稳定的 C$_{60}$ 形式出现的簇状物质的浓度是这项研究中的主要实验观测焦点。

我们对于上述结果的解释是，在激光气化的过程中，碎片以稠合六元环结构的石墨层片断形式从其表面剥离。我们相信，图 3c 中的分布情况基本代表了最初生成的大型稠环碎片的分布。当这些热的稠环簇状物与高密度氦保持接触时，簇通过两

helium, the clusters equilibrate by two- and three-body collisions towards the most stable species, which appears to be a unique cluster containing 60 atoms.

When one thinks in terms of the many fused-ring isomers with unsatisfied valences at the edges that would naturally arise from a graphite fragmentation, this result seems impossible: there is not much to choose between such isomers in terms of stability. If one tries to shift to a tetrahedral diamond structure, the entire surface of the cluster will be covered with unsatisfied valences. Thus a search was made for some other plausible structure which would satisfy all sp^2 valences. Only a spheroidal structure appears likely to satisfy this criterion, and thus Buckminster Fuller's studies were consulted (see, for example, ref. 7). An unusually beautiful (and probably unique) choice is the truncated icosahedron depicted in Fig. 1. As mentioned above, all valences are satisfied with this structure, and the molecule appears to be aromatic. The structure has the symmetry of the icosahedral group. The inner and outer surfaces are covered with a sea of π electrons. The diameter of this C$_{60}$ molecule is ~7 Å, providing an inner cavity which appears to be capable of holding a variety of atoms[8].

Assuming that our somewhat speculative structure is correct, there are a number of important ramifications arising from the existence of such a species. Because of its stability when formed under the most violent conditions, it may be widely distributed in the Universe. For example, it may be a major constituent of circumstellar shells with high carbon content. It is a feasible constituent of interstellar dust and a possible major site for surface-catalysed chemical processes which lead to the formation of interstellar molecules. Even more speculatively, C$_{60}$ or a derivative might be the carrier of the diffuse interstellar lines[9].

If a large-scale synthetic route to this C$_{60}$ species can be found, the chemical and practical value of the substance may prove extremely high. One can readily conceive of C$_{60}$ derivatives of many kinds—such as C$_{60}$ transition metal compounds, for example, C$_{60}$Fe or halogenated species like C$_{60}$F$_{60}$ which might be a super-lubricant. We also have evidence that an atom (such as lanthanum[8] and oxygen[1]) can be placed in the interior, producing molecules which may exhibit unusual properties. For example, the chemical shift in the NMR of the central atom should be remarkable because of the ring currents. If stable in macroscopic, condensed phases, this C$_{60}$ species would provide a topologically novel aromatic nucleus for new branches of organic and inorganic chemistry. Finally, this especially stable and symmetrical carbon structure provides a possible catalyst and/or intermediate to be considered in modelling prebiotic chemistry.

We are disturbed at the number of letters and syllables in the rather fanciful but highly appropriate name we have chosen in the title to refer to this C$_{60}$ species. For such a unique and centrally important molecular structure, a more concise name would be useful. A number of alternatives come to mind (for example, ballene, spherene, soccerene, carbosoccer), but we prefer to let this issue of nomenclature be settled by consensus.

体或三体碰撞向形成最稳定物质的方向平衡转化，结果显示最稳定的物质就是含有 60 个原子的独特簇状分子。

石墨破碎自然会形成边界，当考虑到边界处带有不饱和键的很多种含稠环异构体时，这种结果似乎是不可能的：因为从稳定性角度来看不足以在这些异构体之中作出选择。如果试图用正四面体的金刚石结构来解释，那么簇状分子的整个表面都会被不饱和键所覆盖。因此要研究出另外一些合理结构以满足所有 sp^2 价键。看来只有类球形结构能够符合这一标准，由此我们想到了巴克敏斯特·富勒的研究（例如，见参考文献 7）。一个非常漂亮（也许还是独一无二）的选择，就是图 1 中描绘的截角二十面体。如同上面所提到的，所有的价态用这个结构都得到满足，而且分子呈芳香性。该结构具有二十面体群的对称性。分子内表面和外表面均为 π 电子海所覆盖。这种 C_{60} 分子的直径约为 7 Å，提供了一个有可能容纳各种原子的内部空腔[8]。

假设我们推测的结构是正确的，那么这类化合物的存在就会衍生出许多重要分支。它是在最剧烈的条件下形成的，由于它的稳定性，该分子有可能广泛存在于宇宙之中。例如，它可能是含有大量碳的星周壳中的主要成分。它有可能是星际尘埃的组成成分，并可能是导致星际分子形成的表面催化化学过程中的主要位点。甚至可以进一步猜测，C_{60} 或者其某一衍生物，可能是弥散星际线的携带者[9]。

如果能找到一种大规模合成 C_{60} 这类化合物的方法，也许就能证明它具有极高的化学研究和实际应用价值。人们可以很容易地设想出多种 C_{60} 的衍生物，诸如 $C_{60}Fe$ 等 C_{60} 与过渡金属形成的化合物，以及像 $C_{60}F_{60}$ 这样可以作为超级润滑剂的卤化物。我们还有证据表明，可以将一个原子（例如镧[8]和氧[1]）置于其内腔中，制备出具有特殊性质的分子。例如，由于有环电流的存在，在中心原子的 NMR 谱中应该具有显著的化学位移。如果这种分子稳定存在于宏观量的凝聚相中，C_{60} 类化合物就能为有机和无机化学的新分支提供一种具有全新拓扑性质的芳基核。最后，C_{60} 这种具有独特稳定性和对称性的碳结构，为模拟起源化学提供了一个可能的催化剂和（或）中间体。

在标题中用到这类 C_{60} 化合物的颇为怪异又极为恰当的名称时，我们为其字母和音节的数目而感到困扰。对于这样一种独特且极为重要的分子结构来说，更为简洁的名字将会是有所助益的。我们还想到了很多选择（比如球烯、球面烯、英式足球烯、碳球），但还是决定把这个命名问题交给大家来解决。

We thank Frank Tittel, Y. Liu and Q. Zhang for helpful discussions, encouragement and technical support. This research was supported by the Army Research Office and the Robert A. Welch Foundation, and used a laser and molecular beam apparatus supported by the NSF and the US Department of Energy. H.W.K. acknowledges travel support provided by SERC, UK. J.R.H. and S.C.O'B. are Robert A. Welch Predoctoral Fellows.

(**318**, 162-163; 1985)

H. W. Kroto[*], J. R. Heath, S. C. O'Brien, R. F. Curl & R. E. Smalley

Rice Quantum Institute and Departments of Chemistry and Electrical Engineering, Rice University, Houston, Texas 77251, USA

[*] Permanent address: School of Chemistry and Molecular Sciences, University of Sussex, Brighton BN1 9QJ, UK

Received 13 September; accepted 18 October 1985.

References:

1. Heath, J. R. *et al. Astrophys. J.* (submitted).

2. Dietz, T. G., Duncan, M. A., Powers, D. E. & Smalley, R. E. *J. Chem. Phys.* 74, 6511-6512(1981).

3. Powers, D. E. *et al. J. Phys. Chem.* **86**, 2556-2560 (1982).

4. Hopkins, J. B., Langridge-Smith, P. R. R., Morse, M. D. & Smalley, R. E. *J. Chem. Phys.* 78, 1627-1637(1983).

5. O'Brien, S. C. *et al. J. Chem. Phys.* (submitted).

6. Rohlfing, E. A., Cox, D. M. & Kaldor, A. *J. Chem. Phys.* 81, 3322-3330 (1984).

7. Marks, R. W. *The Dymaxion World of Buckminster Fuller* (Reinhold, New York, 1960).

8. Heath, J. R. *et al. J. Am. Chem. Soc.* (in the press).

9. Herbig, E. *Astrophys. J.* **196**, 129-160 (1975).

我们要感谢弗兰克·蒂特尔、刘元（音译）和张清玲（音译）所提供的有益的讨论、鼓励和技术性支持。本研究得到了美国陆军研究办公室和罗伯特·韦尔奇基金会的支持，并使用了由美国国家科学基金会和美国能源部资助的激光和分子束装置。克罗托要感谢英国科学与工程研究委员会提供的旅行赞助。希思和奥布赖恩是罗伯特·韦尔奇基金会的博士前奖学金获得者。

（王耀杨 翻译；周江 审稿）

2.5-Myr *Australopithecus boisei* from West of Lake Turkana, Kenya

A. Walker *et al.*

Editor's note

From the late 1970s, palaeoanthropologists began to realise that the story of human evolution was far from simple. The tale was shaped less like a ladder than a bush, with many evolutionary "experiments", some of which terminated without issue. This was certainly the case for the "robust" australopithecines, a group of primitive, small-brained, large-jawed hominids specialised for eating tough vegetable matter. Here Alan Walker and colleagues add a very robust-looking and extremely ancient "Black Skull" from Kenya to the well-known *Australopithecus robustus* form from South Africa and *A. boisei* from East Africa. Eventually named *Australopithecus aethiopicus*, this Black Skull illustrated the complexity of human evolution and how little we still knew about it.

Specimens of *Australopithecus boisei* have been found in 2.5-Myr-old sediments west of Lake Turkana, Kenya. The primitive morphology of these early *A. boisei* suggests that robust and hyper-robust *Australopithecus* developed many of their common features in parallel and further that *A. africanus* is unlikely to have been ancestral to *A. boisei*.

THE "hyper-robust" hominid *Australopithecus boisei* is well-known from several East African Plio-Pleistocene deposits dated between 2.2 and 1.2 Myr (refs 1, 2). It has been thought of variously, as: the northern vicar of the equally well-known *A. robustus*[3]; the extremely specialized end-member of the robust clade[4]; an already developed species which immigrated from another, unknown area[5]; and as representing individuals at the large end of a single *Australopithecus* species that also encompasses *A. robustus* and *A. africanus*[6].

There is a growing consensus that the east and south African samples are different enough to allow them to be placed in separate species[1-4]. The type specimen of *A. boisei* is Olduvai Hominid 5[7,8].

These two robust species are placed in the genus *Paranthropus* by some authors[9]. Although recognizing that the two known samples overlap in time, some have advocated an ancestor–descendant relationship with *A. robustus* giving rise to *A. boisei*. Perhaps the most compelling recent evidence for this last view is Rak's exemplary study of the structure and function of the australopithecine face[4]. He has followed an evolutionary scheme in which the origins of the robust clade are in *A. africanus*, which is thereby removed from consideration as a

肯尼亚图尔卡纳湖以西250万年前的
南方古猿鲍氏种

沃克等

编者按

自 20 世纪 70 年代晚期起，古人类学家们开始意识到人类的演化历史远非人们想象的那么简单。与其说人类演化是按阶梯进行，不如说这段历史是由许多演化"实验"构成的繁芜庞杂的灌木丛，这些"实验"中许多还没有结果便终结了。南方古猿"粗壮种"显然是其中之一。这是一群原始、颅容量小、具有适应摄食粗糙植物的大颌骨的人科动物。本文中艾伦·沃克与其同事们将产自肯尼亚的外观十分粗壮且极为古老的"黑色颅骨"归入产自南非的著名南方古猿粗壮种和产自东非的南方古猿鲍氏种。最终，这件黑色颅骨被命名为南方古猿埃塞俄比亚种，它揭示了人类演化的复杂性以及我们对这段历史的浅见寡识。

在肯尼亚图尔卡纳湖西侧距今 250 万年的沉积物中发现了南方古猿鲍氏种标本。这些早期南方古猿鲍氏种原始的形态表明，粗壮的和超级粗壮的南方古猿发育了许多与南方古猿非洲种平行演化出的共同特征，并且进一步表明了南方古猿非洲种不可能是南方古猿鲍氏种的祖先。

众所周知，"超级粗壮的"人科动物——南方古猿鲍氏种产自距今 220 万年至 120 万年的几处东非上新世–更新世沉积物（参考文献 1、2）。对于鲍氏种有多种解释：同等著名的南方古猿粗壮种的北方替代物种 [3]；粗壮种分支极端特化的终端成员 [4]；从另一未知地区迁徙而来的已经独立的物种 [5]；包括南方古猿粗壮种和南方古猿非洲种在内的单一的南方古猿种的末期代表性个体 [6]。

越来越多的人认同，东非和南非标本与其他地区标本的不同之处足以将他们划分到不同的物种中 [1-4]。南方古猿鲍氏种的模式标本是奥杜威人科 5 号 [7,8]。

有些学者将这两个粗壮种物种归入傍人属中 [9]。尽管有些人认识到这两种已知的标本在时间上有重叠，但他们还是主张是南方古猿粗壮种衍生出了南方古猿鲍氏种，二者具有祖裔关系。可能最近对于后一个观点的最有说服力的证据就是拉克对南方古猿面部结构和功能的典型研究 [4]。他所遵循的演化图解中，粗壮种分支起源于南方古猿非洲种，因此不能把粗壮种看作是人类祖先 [10]。这种方案还没有得到普遍

human ancestor[10]. This scheme has not found universal acceptance[11,12].

Localities

Prospecting was carried out in 1985 in Pliocene sediments to the west of Lake Turkana, Kenya. It led to the recovery of two *A. boisei* specimens. A cranium and a partial mandible were discovered at two separate localities: sediments in the Lomekwi and Kangatukuseo drainages (see Fig. 1) at approximately 3°45' N, 35°45' E.

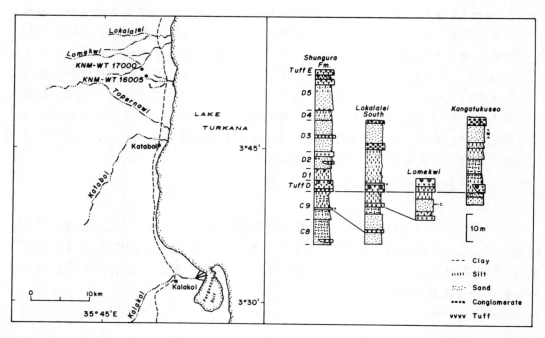

Fig. 1. Map and sections showing geographical and stratigraphic positions of KNM-WT 17000 and KNM-WT 16005. C, cranium; M, mandible.

The general dip of strata is to the east in the Lomekwi drainage, but the strata at Lomekwi I from which the cranium was derived are deformed into a syncline by drag along a fault that truncates the section about 50 m east of the site. Several small faults cut the section west of the site, but it has been possible to link the short sections together by analysis of volcanic ash layers in the sequence. The total thickness of section immediately surrounding the site is less than 15 m, and the volcanic ash layer which caps the section is compositionally indistinguishable from Tuff D of the Shungura Formation. Earlier[13], this tuff was referred to the informally designated Upper Burgi Tuff of the Koobi Fora Formation. With more numerous analyses it is now clear that the Upper Burgi Tuff also correlates with Tuff D, and an additional correlation datum is provided between the Shungura Formation and the Koobi Fora Formation. Tuff D has been dated at 2.52 ± 0.05 Myr[14]. This age is an average computed from samples from the Shungura Formation in Ethiopia, and from the correlative unit at Kangatukuseo. The cranium derives from a level 3.8 m below Tuff D. Around 10 m below Tuff D there is a second ash layer. In the Lokalalei drainage, about 4 km northwest of the site, there are three ash layers exposed in

108

认同 [11,12]。

地 点

1985 年，研究人员在肯尼亚图尔卡纳湖西侧的上新世沉积物中进行了勘查工作。这次工作出土了两件南方古猿鲍氏种标本。在两处地点——大约位于北纬 3°45′，东经 35°45′ 处的罗埋奎流域和坎噶图库涩流域的沉积物中（见图 1）分别发现了一件颅骨和一件不完整的下颌骨。

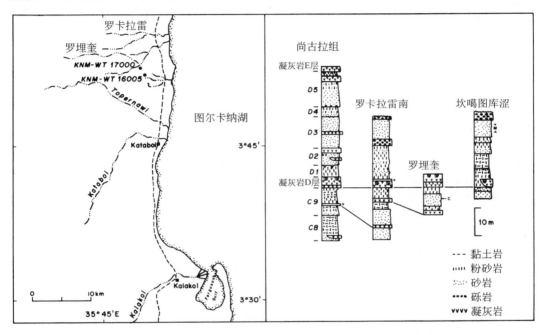

图 1. KNM-WT 17000 和 KNM-WT 16005 的地理位置和地层位置及柱状剖面。C，颅骨；M，下颌骨。

地层总体倾斜至罗埋奎流域的东部，但是发现颅骨的罗埋奎Ⅰ号地点的地层由于沿断层的拖曳作用而形变成为向斜，该断层截去了这一遗址东面约 50 米的剖面。几处小断层则切去了该遗址西侧的剖面，但还是有可能通过分析地层层序中的火山灰层来将这些短的剖面联系起来。直接围绕该遗址的剖面总厚度不到 15 米，覆盖在该剖面之上的火山灰层在组分上与尚古拉组的凝灰岩 D 层几乎区分不出来。早先 [13]，该凝灰岩层被认为是库比福勒组中非正式命名的上布基凝灰岩层。随着更多的分析，现在已经明确了上布基凝灰岩层也与凝灰岩 D 层层位相当，并且又提出了一个尚古拉组和库比福勒组之间的对比基准。经测定，凝灰岩 D 层的年龄为 252 万年 ±5 万年 [14]。这一年龄是根据在埃塞俄比亚的尚古拉组采集的样本和在坎噶图库涩研究地的相当层位采集的样本计算出来的平均值。颅骨是从凝灰岩 D 层之下 3.8 米的地层中得到的。凝灰岩 D 层之下约 10 米处还有一个灰层。在该遗址西北部约 4 千米处的罗

sequence. The lowest correlates with a tuff in submember C9 of the Shungura Formation, and the upper two correlate with the two ash layers exposed at the site of the cranium. On this basis, the cranium is shown to lie within strata correlative with submember C9 of the Shungura Formation. Based on the K/Ar chronology of the Shungura Formation and scaling on the basis of constant sedimentation rates there, the cranium is estimated to be 2.55 Myr old. Using palaeomagnetic polarity boundaries as the basis of chronological placement, the age of the cranium would be ~2.45 Myr, as there is a slight discordance between the two chronologies[15]. Therefore, we believe that the age of the cranium can be confidently stated as 2.50 ± 0.07 Myr, including all errors. The sediments from which the cranium derives are overbank deposits of a large perennial river, probably the ancestral Omo.

The mandible from Kangatukuseo III derives from a level about 19 m above Tuff D. Tuff E is not exposed in Kangatukuseo, but it is exposed in the northern part of the Lomekwi drainage, and in the southern Lokalalei drainage. There, sediments correlative with Member D of the Shungura Formation are at least 26 m thick. On this basis, the mandible is assigned to the central part of Member D of the Shungura Formation, the best age estimate for which is 2.45 ± 0.05 Myr. The section is faulted east of the mandible site, and older sediments are exposed along the drainage east of that point. In fact, the entire section exposed in Kangatukuseo lies within an interval from ~25 m above Tuff D to 5 m below that tuff. The mandible was collected from a sandstone layer ~6 m thick, deposited by a large river system. Thin basalt pebble conglomerates intercalated in this part of the section show that the site lay near the boundary between sediments deposited by this large river, and alluvial fan deposits derived from the west.

The interval of section from which the australopithecine specimens were collected has also yielded over 200 fossils representing more than 40 other mammalian species (Table 1), including the skeleton of a ground-dwelling colobine and a relatively complete camel mandible. Bovids are the most common elements of the fauna at this level and most represent species that are otherwise known from the lower portion of the Omo Shungura succession. But whereas alcelaphines and impalas predominate at lower horizons west of Lake Turkana, reduncine bovids are the commonest fossils at the australopithecine sites reported here and are taxonomically different from those recovered slightly higher in the sequence. *Elephas recki shungurensis* is the common elephant at the localities considered here while *Notochoerus scotti* and *Kolpochoerus limnetes* are the common suids. Although all three taxa have lengthy Pliocene distributions, the West Turkana specimens closely match samples of these species from Omo Shungura Members C and D—thus supporting the estimate of age derived from the tuff analyses. The age estimate is corroborated by the apparent absence of the elephantids *Loxodonta adaurora*, *Loxodonta exoptata* and *Elephas recki brumpti*, and of the suids *Nyanzachoerus kanamensis*, *Notochoerus euilus*, *Kolpochoerus afarensis* and *Potamochoerus* sp., all of which occur in older horizons in the upper reaches of the Laga Lomekwi. Also missing from the australopithecine-bearing assemblage are the reduncine bovid *Menelikia lyrocera* and equids of the genus *Equus*, both of which occur higher in the sequence.

卡拉雷流域，有三个灰层依次出露。最底层灰层与尚古拉组亚段 C9 中的一个凝灰岩层相当，上面两层与在发现颅骨的遗址处出露的两个灰层相当。基于这个对比，证明该颅骨的层位与尚古拉组亚段 C9 相当。根据尚古拉组的钾／氩年表以及对此处恒定沉积速率的测算，估计该颅骨的年龄为 255 万年。使用古地磁极性界限作为测年依据，得出该颅骨的年龄约为 245 万年，这种差异是由于两种测年方法之间存在微小的差异 [15]。因此，考虑到所有的误差，我们可以确信该颅骨的年龄为 250 万年 ±7 万年。出土该颅骨的沉积物是一条大型常流河的河漫滩沉积物，这一常流河可能是古时的奥莫河。

在坎噶图库涩 III 发现的下颌骨是从位于凝灰岩 D 层之上约 19 米处的层位得到的。凝灰岩 E 层在坎噶图库涩没有出露，但是在罗埋奎流域的北部以及罗卡拉雷流域南部都有出露。在那里，与尚古拉组 D 段层位相当的沉积物至少有 26 米厚。根据这一点，该下颌骨被划分到了尚古拉组 D 段的中部，对其最佳的年代估计值是距今 245 万年 ±5 万年。该剖面在发现下颌骨的地点的东侧发生断层，沿该点东侧的流域有更为古老的沉积物出露。事实上，在坎噶图库涩出露的整个剖面都位于从凝灰岩 D 层之上约 25 米到凝灰岩 D 层之下 5 米之间。该下颌骨是从由一个大型水系沉积下来的厚约 6 米的砂岩层中发掘出来的。薄层玄武岩质砾岩嵌入到该剖面的这一部分中，这表明该处遗址位于这条大河沉积形成的沉积物与来自西部的冲积扇沉积物的分界线附近。

采集到南方古猿标本的剖面的间隔带中也发现了 200 多件分属 40 余种其他哺乳动物的化石（表 1），包括一副地表疣猴的骨架和一件相对完整的骆驼下颌骨。牛科动物是在该层位中最常见的动物群成员，也是已知的在奥莫尚古拉组下部发现的其他物种中最具代表性的种类。但是狷羚和黑斑羚在图尔卡纳湖西侧较低的层位占优势，在本文报道的南方古猿遗址处，小苇羚牛类是最常见的化石，与稍高层位上发掘的标本在分类学上存在差异。尚古拉巨象是研究地常见的一种象，而斯氏南方猪和沼泽裂尾猪是常见的猪科动物。尽管这三个类群在上新世时期都具有漫长的分布史，但是图尔卡纳西侧的标本与这些来自奥莫尚古拉组 C 段和 D 段的标本非常匹配——由此支持了根据凝灰岩分析得到的年代估计值。该年代估计值通过象科动物非洲祖象、扇羽非洲象和一种古菱齿象及猪科动物肿颊猪、南方猪、阿法裂尾猪和河猪属未定种等的明显缺失得到证实，所有这些物种在拉伽罗埋奎上游较古老的层位上都出现了。包含南方古猿的化石组合中还缺失了小苇羚牛类 *Menelikia lyrocera* 和（马科的）马属动物化石，这两者都是在较高的地层中出现。

Table 1. Fossil mammals from the new australopithecine localities west of Lake Turkana

Theropithecus brumpti	*Giraffa* sp.
T. cf. brumpti	*Aepyceros* sp.
Cercopithecidae large	*Connochaetes* sp.
Cercopithecidae medium	*Parmularius cf. braini*
Cercopithecidae small	Alcelaphini medium
Papionini medium/large	Alcelaphini small
Parapapio ado	*Menelikia* sp.
Paracolobus mutiwa	*Kobus sigmoidalis*
Australopithecus boisei	*Kobus* sp. A
Hyaena sp.	*Kobus* sp. B
Homotherium sp.	*Kobus* sp. C
Felidae	*Kobus* sp. D
Viverridae	*Kobus* sp. E
Carnivora indet.	*Kobus* sp. F
Deinotherium bozasi	Reduncini indet.
Elephas recki shungurensis	Reduncini large
Hipparion hasumensis	Reduncini medium
Ceratotherium sp.	Reduncini small
Diceros bicornis	*Tragelaphus nakuae*
Notochoerus scotti	*Tragelaphus* sp.
Kolpochoerus limnetes	Bovini
Hexaprotodon protamphibius	*Gazella aff. granti*
Hippopotamus imagunculus	*Antidorcas recki*
Camelus sp.	Antilopini
Sivatherium maurusium	

Specimens

KNM-WT 17000 is an adult cranium with the following parts missing: all of the tooth crowns except a half molar and the right P^3; some facial bone fragments which have spalled off the infilled maxillary sinus; most of the frontal processes and temporal plates of the zygomatics; the zygomatic arches themselves; a large part of the frontal and parietals superiorly (but a piece of the sagittal crest on the anterior part of the parietal is preserved); parts of both pterygoid regions inferiorly and the posterior part of the maxilla and palate on the right side; and the inferior part of the nuchal region of the occipital. There is no bilateral asymmetry and all bony contacts are sharp. There is no evidence of any plastic deformation and the brain case has retained its spheroidal shape (Fig. 2).

表1. 图尔卡纳湖西侧南方古猿新遗址出土的哺乳动物化石

布兰普特兽猴	长颈鹿未定种
布兰普特兽猴相似种	高角羚未定种
大型长尾猴	角马未定种
中型长尾猴	*Parmularius cf. braini*
小型长尾猴	中型狷羚亚科
中 / 大型狒狒	小型狷羚亚科
阿拉伯狒狒	*Menelikia* 未定种
傍疣猴	S 型弯角水羚
南方古猿鲍氏种	水羚属未定种 A
缟鬣狗未定种	水羚属未定种 B
似剑虎未定种	水羚属未定种 C
猫科	水羚属未定种 D
灵猫科	水羚属未定种 E
食肉目科属种未定	水羚属未定种 F
恐象	小苇羚属种未定
尚古拉巨象	大型小苇羚
哈苏门三趾马	中型小苇羚
白犀未定种	小型小苇羚
双角犀	*Tragelaphus nakuae*
斯氏南方猪	林羚未定种
沼泽裂尾猪	牛科
原两栖六齿河马（中新古河马）	葛氏瞪羚近亲种
Hippopotamus imagunculus	*Antidorcas recki*
骆驼未定种	羚羊科
西瓦兽	

标　本

KNM-WT 17000 是一件成人颅骨，它的如下部分丢失了：除了半颗臼齿和右 P³ 外的所有齿冠；一些从已被填充的上颌窦剥落的面骨碎片；大部分额突和颧骨的颞板；颧弓自身；额骨的大部分和顶骨上部（但是在顶骨前部的一块矢状嵴保存了下来）；两侧翼状区下部与上颌骨后部的部分骨骼及右侧腭骨；枕骨颈区的下部。此颅骨双侧对称，所有骨质接触部位都很清晰。没有证据表明存在任何的塑性变形，因此该脑颅保留下了其球形形状（图2）。

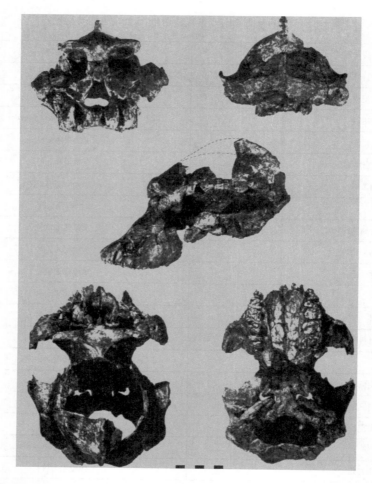

Fig. 2. Anterior, posterior, left lateral, superior and inferior views of cranium KNM-WT 17000. Scale in cm.

It is a massively-built cranium with a very large facial skeleton, palate and large cranial base, but with a small brain case. The palate and cranial base are roughly the same size as in Olduvai Hominid (O.H.) 5. The cranial base is about the same size as, but the palate is slightly larger than in, KNM-ER 406 (ref. 16). The cranial capacity is 410 ml (mean of five determinations by water displacement with a standard error of 4.32). This measurement is probably accurate since the orbital plates of the frontals, the cribiform plate region of the ethmoid, one anterior clinoid and both posterior clinoid processes are preserved together with the rest of the cranial base. The missing cranial vault fragments can be reconstructed with fair certainty by following the internal contours all around them. This is the smallest published cranial capacity for any adult fossil hominid, although A.L. 162-28 from Hadar[17] must have been smaller. Given the massive face and palate combined with a small brain case, it is not surprising that the sagittal crest is the largest ever in a hominid. Further, the sagittal crest joins completely to compound temporal-nuchal crests with no intervening bare area[18]. The foramen magnum position is far forward as in other robust *Australopithecus* specimens[19].

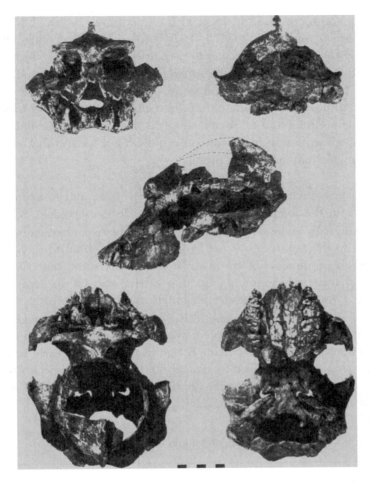

图 2. 颅骨 KNM-WT 17000 的前、后、左侧、上、下视图。标尺单位为厘米。

　　这是一件厚重的颅骨，具有很大的面部骨骼、腭骨和大的颅底，但是脑颅很小。腭骨和颅底与奥杜威人科（OH）5 号的尺寸大致相同。该颅底与 KNM-ER 406（参考文献 16）的大小几乎相同，但是颚骨稍大。其颅容量为 410 毫升（通过水置换法测得的五次测量值的平均值，标准误差为 4.32）。该测量值应该是准确的，因为额骨的眶板、筛骨的筛板区、一个前床突和两个后床突都与颅底的其余部分一起被保留了下来。丢失的颅骨碎片可以根据其周围所有的内部轮廓非常准确地予以重建。这是目前已公布的所有成年人科化石中颅容量最小的标本，尽管在哈达尔[17] 发现的A.L.162-28 肯定更小。鉴于该标本具有较大的面部和颚骨以及小型的脑颅，其矢状嵴在已发现的人科动物中最大就不足为奇了。此外，矢状嵴与颞 – 颈复合嵴完全接合在一起，中间没有裸区[18]。枕骨大孔的位置与其他粗壮的南方古猿属标本一样，位置都很靠前[19]。

The one complete tooth crown, right P[3], is 11.5 mesiodistally by 16.2 buccolingually. This is bigger mesiodistally (md) than O.H. 5 (10.9) and smaller buccolingually (bl) (17.0)[7,8]. These dimensions are completely outside the recorded range for *A. robustus* (9.2–10.7 md, 11.6–15.2 bl) and at the high end of the range for *A. boisei* (9.5–11.8 md, 13.8–17.0 bl)[20]. Only the largest *A. boisei* mandibles found so far (for example, KNM-ER 729 and 3230[21]) would fit this cranium. It is unfortunate that the region of the occipital which would show the grooves for the occipital and marginal sinuses is missing, but the small sigmoid sinuses appear to have no contribution from transverse ones. Thus we feel that enlarged occipital and a marginal sinuses may have been present.

Most of the previously recorded differences between *A. boisei* and *A. robustus* have involved greater robustness in the former. In fact for those parts preserved in KNM-WT 17000, the definitions originally given by Tobias[8] include only two characters that cannot be simply attributed to this robustness. One is that the supraorbital torus is "twisted" along its length. Subsequent discoveries of *A. boisei* specimens show that O.H. 5 is extreme in its supraorbital torus development and that others are not so "twisted". The other character is that *A. boisei* palates are deeper anteriorly than those of *A. robustus*, in which they tend to be shallow all along the length. Recently, Rak[4] has undertaken a study of the australopithecine face and has documented structural differences between the faces of all four species. Skelton *et al.*[22] have just made a cladistic analysis of early hominids; Table 2 lists some of the characteristics given as typical of *Australopithecus* species by these authors (see ref. 22 and refs therein) as well as the condition found in KNM-WT 17000. For most features the new specimen resembles *A. boisei*.

Table 2. Compilation of features of *Australopithecus* species

Feature	A. afarensis	A. africanus	A. robustus	A. boisei	KNM-WT 17000
Position of I[2] roots relative to nasal aperture margins	Lateral	Medial	Medial	Medial	Medial
Divergence of temporal lines relative to lambda	Below	Above	Above	Above	Below
Lateral concavity of nuchal plane	Present	Absent	Absent	Absent	Probably present
Depth of mandibular fossa	Shallow	Deep	Deep	Deep	Shallow
Temporal squama pneumatization	Extensive	Weak	Weak	Weak	Extensive
Flat, shallow palate	Present	Absent	Absent	Absent	Present
Subnasal prognathism	Pronounced	Intermediate	Reduced	Reduced	Pronounced
Orientation of tympanic plate	Less vertical	Intermediate	Vertical	Vertical	Intermediate
Flexion of cranial base	Weak	Moderate	Strong	Strong	Weak
Relative sizes of posterior to anterior temporalis	Large	Intermediate	Small	Small	Large
Position of postglenoid process relative to tympanic	Completely anterior	Variable	Merge superiorly	Merge superiorly	Completely anterior
Tubular tympanic	Present	Intermediate	No	No	Intermediate

那颗完整的齿冠右 P³，近远中径（md）是 11.5 mm，颊舌径（bl）是 16.2 mm。其近远中径比 OH 5（10.9 mm）的要大，而颊舌径比 OH 5（17.0 mm）[7,8] 要小些。这些尺寸完全不在已记录的南方古猿粗壮种的范围（md 9.2~10.7 mm, bl 11.6 ~15.2 mm）之内，而处于南方古猿鲍氏种范围（md 9.5~11.8 mm, bl 13.8~17.0 mm）[20] 的上限。只有迄今发现的最大的南方古猿鲍氏种的下颌骨（例如，KNM-ER 729 和 3230[21]）与该颅骨尺寸对应。不幸的是，这件标本上能够显示出枕骨窦和边缘窦沟的枕骨区不见了，而从横窦处，小型的乙状窦似乎没有什么贡献。因此我们认为扩大的枕骨和边缘窦可能已经存在了。

之前所记录的南方古猿鲍氏种和南方古猿粗壮种之间的差异，大部分都提到前者更加粗壮。实际上，对于那些 KNM-WT 17000 中保存下来的部分，最初托拜厄斯 [8] 给出的描述仅包括两种特征，这两种特征不能简单地被归为粗壮性。一个特征是眶上圆枕沿其长轴是"扭曲的"。后来发现的南方古猿鲍氏种标本表明 OH 5 的眶上圆枕的发育是一种极端情况，并且其他标本的眶上圆枕并没有如此"扭曲"。另一个特征是南方古猿鲍氏种的腭在前部比南方古猿粗壮种的要深，后者似乎在其整个长轴上都较浅。最近，拉克 [4] 正在进行一项对南方古猿面部的研究，并且已经证明了所有四个物种的面部之间存在结构性差异。斯凯尔顿等 [22] 刚刚对早期人科进行了支序分析；表 2 列出了由这些作者给出的南方古猿物种的一些典型特征（见参考文献 22 及其中的参考文献）以及在 KNM-WT 17000 中发现的一些特征。新标本的大部分特征与南方古猿鲍氏种相似。

表 2. 南方古猿属物种特征汇总

特征	南方古猿阿法种	南方古猿非洲种	南方古猿粗壮种	南方古猿鲍氏种	KNM-WT 17000
I² 根部相对于鼻孔边缘的位置	外侧	内侧	内侧	内侧	内侧
λ 形的颞线分歧	下方	上方	上方	上方	下方
项平面侧凹	存在	缺失	缺失	缺失	可能存在
下颌窝深度	浅	深	深	深	浅
鳞颞部气腔形成	广泛	弱	弱	弱	广泛
平、浅的腭	存在	缺失	缺失	缺失	存在
鼻下颌前突	显著	中等	减弱	减弱	显著
鼓板方向	略垂直	中度垂直	垂直	垂直	中度垂直
颅底屈曲	弱	中度	强	强	弱
颞骨从前至后的相对尺寸	大	中等	小	小	大
下颌窝后突相对于鼓骨的位置	完全在前部	位置多样	在上部融合	在上部融合	完全在前部

Continued

Feature	A. afarensis	A. africanus	A. robustus	A. boisei	KNM-WT 17000
Articular eminence	Weak	Intermediate	Strong	Strong	Weak
Foramen magnum relative to tympanic tips	Anterior	Intermediate	Anterior	Anterior	Anterior
Coronally placed petrous temporals	No	Variable	Yes	Yes	Yes
Distance between M^1 and temporomandibular joint	Long	Variable	Short	Short	Long
P^3 outline	Asymmetric	Intermediate	Oval	Oval	Oval
Relative size of C	Very large	Medium	Small	Small	Small
Anterior projection of zygomatic	Absent	Intermediate	Strong	Very Strong	Very Strong
Height of masseter origin	Lowest	Intermediate	High	High	High
Canine jugum separate from margin of pyriform aperture	Yes	Variable	No	No	No
Distinct subnasal and intranasal parts of clivus	Yes	Intermediate	No	No	No
Relative size of post-canine teeth	Moderate	Large	Very large	Very large	Very large
Robustness of zygomatic arches	Moderate	Strong	Very Strong	Very Strong	Very Strong
Common origin of zygomatic arch	M^1/P^4	P^4	P^4	P^3	P^3
C jugum	Prominent	Pronounced	Reduced	Lost	Lost
Inclination of nuchal plane	Steep	Less steep	—	Variable	Less steep
Compound temporonuchal crest	Present	Absent	Males only	Males only	Present
Asterionic notch	Present	Absent	Absent	Absent	Probably Present
Medial inflection of mastoids	Strong	Reduced	Reduced	Reduced	Reduced
Anterior facial pillars	Absent	Present	Present	Absent	Absent
Length of nuchal plane relative to occipital	Long	Intermediate	Long	Long	Long
Braincase relative to face	—	High	Low	Low	Low
Nasals wide above frontonasal suture	—	No	Yes	Yes	Yes
Nasoalveolar gutter present	No	No	Yes	Yes	Yes
Infraorbital foramen high	Yes	Yes	No	No	No
Maxillary fossula present	No	Yes	Yes	No	No
Inferior orbital margins soft laterally	—	No	Yes	No	Yes
Greatest orbital height	—	Middle	Middle	Medial	Middle
Foramen magnum heart-shaped	—	No	No	Yes	Yes

There are some features of **KNM-WT 17000** that differ from all other "hyper-robust" specimens as well as from robust ones. The most obvious and important is the prognathic mid- and lower facial region. In superior view all other robust crania are so orthognathic

特征	南方古猿阿法种	南方古猿非洲种	南方古猿粗壮种	南方古猿鲍氏种	KNM-WT 17000
管状鼓板	存在	中等	无	无	中等
关节隆起	弱	中等	强	强	弱
枕大孔相对于鼓部尖端的位置	前部	中部	前部	前部	前部
颞岩骨冠状位排列	否	多样	是	是	是
M^1与颞颌关节的距离	长	距离不等	短	短	长
P^3轮廓	非对称	中度对称	卵形	卵形	卵形
C的相对尺寸	非常大	中等	小	小	小
颧骨前突度	缺失	中度	强	非常强	非常强
咬肌起点高度	最低	中等	高	高	高
犬齿轭从梨状孔边缘脱离	是	形式多样	否	否	否
斜坡的鼻下与鼻腔部分独特	是	中等	否	否	否
颊齿的相对尺寸	中等	大	非常大	非常大	非常大
颧弓的粗壮性	中等	强	非常强	非常强	非常强
颧弓的共同起点	M^1/P^4	P^4	P^4	P^3	P^3
犬齿隆突	突出	显著	减弱	丢失	丢失
项平面的倾斜程度	陡	略陡	—	多样	略陡
颞/项复合脊	存在	缺失	仅雄性个体存在	仅雄性个体存在	存在
星穴	存在	缺失	缺失	缺失	可能存在
乳突内弯曲	强	减弱	减弱	减弱	减弱
前部面柱	缺失	存在	存在	缺失	缺失
项平面相对于枕骨的长度	长	中等	长	长	长
脑颅相对于面部的位置	—	高	低	低	低
额鼻缝上方的鼻部宽	—	否	是	是	是
存在鼻槽沟	否	否	是	是	是
眶下孔较高	是	是	否	否	否
存在上颌窝	否	是	是	否	否
下眶缘侧向柔软	—	否	是	否	否
最大眶高位置	—	位于中间	位于中间	位于内侧	位于中间
枕骨大孔心形	—	否	否	是	是

KNM-WT 17000 的有些特征与所有其他的"超级粗壮"标本以及粗壮标本的都不同。最显著且最重要的是突颌的面中部和下部区域。从俯视图看，所有其他的粗

that only a small part of the incisor region projects past the supraorbital tori. In KNM-WT 17000 the midface projects strongly past the tori and the anterior maxilla projects well forwards as a square muzzle. In summary, we regard this specimen as part of the *A. boisei* clade and view its differences from the younger sample as being either primitive, or part of normal intraspecific variation that has not been documented before, or both.

Mandible KNM-WT 16005 has the body preserved to the M_3 alveoli on the left and the M_2 alveoli on the right. The base is missing. The incisors and canines are, as judged from their roots, relatively very small and the post-canine teeth relatively very large. In its size, shape and proportions, KNM-WT 16005 is very similar to the Peninj mandible[23], except that the P_4 and M_1 of the latter are a little larger and the M_2 a little smaller than this specimen. KNM-WT 16005 is smaller than the mandible which KNM-WT 17000 possessed. Tooth measurements are given in Table 3, and the specimen is shown in Fig. 3.

Table 3. Tooth measurements of KNM-WT 16005 (mm)

	Mesiodistal	Buccolingual
Left P_3	10.7	13.8
P_4	(12.0)	(15.0)
M_1	15.7	14.3
M_2	(17.0)	16.7

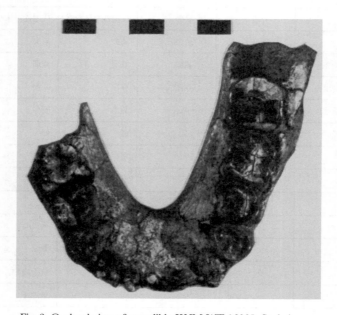

Fig. 3. Occlusal view of mandible KNM-WT 16005. Scale in cm.

Although future finds may show that KNM-WT 17000 is well within the range of

壮颅骨都为直颌型，以至于只有一小部分门齿区突出越过眶上圆枕。在 KNM-WT 17000 中，面中部非常突出，越过圆枕，前面的上颌向前突出成一个正方形的吻突。总之，我们认为该标本属于南方古猿鲍氏种分支的一例，并且将其与年代较晚的标本比较后，认为其与其他标本的不同点较为原始，或者，该标本是尚无资料记载的正常种内差异的一部分，或许二者兼有。

下颌骨 KNM-WT 16005 的下颌体在左侧保存至 M_3 齿槽，在右侧保存至 M_2 齿槽。下颌骨的基底丢失了。正如依据齿根判断的那样，门齿和犬齿相对较小，而颊齿相对较大。KNM-WT 16005 与佩宁伊下颌骨[23] 在大小、形状和比例上很相似，除了后者的 P_4 和 M_1 比该标本大些，以及 M_2 比该标本小些。KNM-WT 16005 比与 KNM-WT 17000 对应的下颌骨小。表3 给出了牙齿尺寸，图3 展示了该标本。

表 3. KNM-WT 16005 的牙齿测量数据（毫米）

	近远中径	颊舌径
左 P_3	10.7	13.8
左 P_4	(12.0)	(15.0)
左 M_1	15.7	14.3
左 M_2	(17.0)	16.7

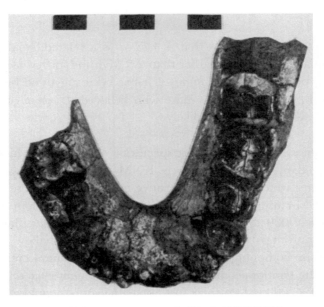

图 3. 下颌骨 KNM-WT 16005 嚼面视。标尺单位为厘米。

variation of *A. boisei*, it is also possible that the differences will prove sufficient to warrant specific distinction. If the latter proves to be the case we suggest that some specimens from the same time period and from the same sedimentary basin (for example, Omo 1967-18 from the Shungura Formation) will be included in the same species. Omo 1967-18 is the type specimen of *Paraustralopithecus aethiopicus* Arambourg and Coppens[24]. In our view, the appropriate name then would be *Australopithecus aethiopicus*.

Conclusions

The new specimens show that the *A. boisei* lineage was established at least 2.5 Myr ago and further that, in robustness and tooth size, at least some members of the early population were as large as any later ones. Although one authority suggested that the robust australopithecines became smaller in skull and tooth size with time[25], most have pointed out that the available sample showed the opposite, that within *A. boisei* there has been an increase in size and robustness of the skull and jaws. This was apparently an artefact of sampling and is no longer correct.

Although recognizing that at least some populations of *A. robustus* and *A. boisei* overlapped in their time ranges, Rak[4] hypothesized that the former was ancestral to *A. boisei*. This is no longer tenable. *A. robustus* shares with younger examples of *A. boisei* several features which are clearly derived from the condition seen in KNM-WT 17000. These include the cresting pattern—with the emphasis on the anterior and middle parts of the temporalis muscle—the orthognathism and the deep temporomandibular joint with strong eminence. At the same time KNM-WT 17000 is clearly a member of the *A. boisei* lineage, as demonstrated by the massive size, extremely large palate and teeth, the build of the infraorbital and nasal areas and the anterior position and low take-off of the zygomatic root.

Therefore, this new specimen shows that *A. robustus* is a related, smaller species that was either derived from ancestral forms earlier than 2.5 Myr and/or has evolved independently in southern Africa, perhaps from *A. africanus*. It has been suggested before that *A. robustus* was derived from *A. africanus*[4], but by those who believed *A. robustus* then gave rise to *A. boisei*—an interpretation that is now unlikely.

The idea that *A. africanus* was the earliest species of a lineage in which *A. robustus* led to *A. boisei* is challenged by the new evidence. KNM-WT 17000 shows that all known *A. africanus* share features which are derived relative to it. Many of these same features were cited by White *et al.*[20] in arguing that *A. afarensis* is more primitive than *A. africanus*. Features showing KNM-WT 17000 to be more primitive than *A. africanus* that were also used to distinguish the primitiveness of *A. afarensis* are: a very flat, shallow palate; pronounced subnasal prognathism; compound temporal/nuchal crests; sagittal crest with emphasis on posterior fibres of the temporalis muscle; an extensively pneumatized squamous temporal, which in KNM-WT 17000 is 11.5 thick just above the supraglenoid gutter; small occipital relative to nuchal plane; pneumatization of lateral cranial base to produce strongly flared

尽管将来的发现可能会显示 KNM-WT 17000 正好处于南方古猿鲍氏种的变异范围之内，但是也有可能这些差异足以成为物种差异的根据。如果事实证明是后者的话，那么我们主张，有些来自同一时间段、同一沉积盆地的标本（例如，来自尚古拉组的奥莫1967-18）可被归入同一物种中。奥莫1967-18 是由阿朗堡和科庞 [24] 命名的埃塞俄比亚副猿的模式标本。那么在我们看来，其适当的名字应该是南方古猿埃塞俄比亚种。

结　论

这些新标本表明南方古猿鲍氏种谱系是在至少250万年前建立起来的，并且在粗壮性和牙齿大小方面，至少早期种群的一些成员与后来的成员是一样大的。尽管有位权威人士认为，粗壮种南方古猿的颅骨和牙齿会随着时间变小 [25]，但是大部分学者指出，已得到的标本表明了相反的情况，即南方古猿鲍氏种的颅骨和颌骨的大小及其粗壮性都有所增加。这显然是由于取样造成的假象，不再是正确的。

尽管意识到至少有些南方古猿粗壮种和南方古猿鲍氏种群在其时间分布范围上有重叠，但拉克 [4] 还是假设前者是南方古猿鲍氏种的祖先。现在这一观点已经站不住脚。南方古猿粗壮种与年代较近的南方古猿鲍氏种有些特征是相同的，这些特征明显是从 KNM-WT 17000 中见到的特征衍生而来的。这些特征包括颅骨的嵴型——着重颞肌的前部和中部——直颌型和具有显著隆起的较深的颞颌关节。同时，KNM-WT 17000 明显是南方古猿鲍氏种谱系中的一员，通过较大的标本尺寸、极大的腭和牙齿、眶下和鼻区的构造以及颧骨根的前位和低的出发点可以证明。

因此，这一新发现的标本表明，南方古猿粗壮种是一个有亲缘关系的、较小的物种，该物种或者起源于早于250万年前的祖先，而且（或者）是在南非（可能是由南方古猿非洲种）独立进化而来的。以前就有人提出，南方古猿粗壮种起源于南方古猿非洲种 [4]，但是现在对于那些相信南方古猿粗壮种后来演化成了南方古猿鲍氏种的人来说，这种解释是不太可能的。

南方古猿非洲种是谱系中最早的物种、在该谱系中南方古猿粗壮种产生了南方古猿鲍氏种，这一观点受到了新证据的挑战。KNM-WT 17000 表明所有已知的南方古猿非洲种都具有衍生而来的与其相关的特征。在关于南方古猿阿法种比南方古猿非洲种更加原始的证明中，怀特等 [20] 引用过很多这些相同的特征。表明 KNM-WT 17000 比南方古猿非洲种更加原始的特征也被用来区分南方古猿阿法种的原始性，这些特征包括：一个非常平坦的、浅的腭板；显著的鼻下突颌；颞/项复合嵴；以附着颞肌后纤维为主的矢状嵴；一个广泛布有气腔的鳞状的颞部，在 KNM-WT 17000 中有 11.5 mm 厚，其位置刚好在盂上沟之上；与项平面关联的小枕骨；侧向颅骨基底

parietal mastoid angles; shallow and mediolaterally broad mandibular fossae; tympanics completely posterior to the postglenoid process. In KNM-WT 17000, the asterionic region is poorly preserved, but an asterionic notch was probably present, which is an additional feature also cited to demonstrate the primitiveness of *A. afarensis.*

Other primitive features found in KNM-WT 17000, but not known or much discussed for *A. afarensis*, are: very small cranial capacity; low posterior profile of the calvaria; nasals extended far above the frontomaxillary suture and well onto an uninflated glabella; low calvaria with receding frontal squama; and extremely convex inferolateral margins of the orbits such as found in some gorillas. Thus there are many features in which KNM-WT 17000 is more primitive than *A. africanus* and similar to *A. afarensis* yet KNM-WT 17000 is clearly a member of the *A. boisei* clade. Further, although the dating of the South African sites is admittedly still imprecise and populations of ancestral species may survive a speciation event, the time sequence of the fossils is becoming increasingly less supportive of the idea of an *africanus–robustus–boisei* lineage.

Finally, it is striking that many of the features of this cranium shared by *A. afarensis* are primitive and not found in *A. robustus* or later specimens of *A. boisei*. These primitive features shared by KNM-WT 17000 and *A. afarensis* are almost exclusively confined to the calvaria, despite the largely complete face of KNM-WT 17000 and the existence of several partial facial specimens at Hadar. However, not one individual adult specimen of *A. afarensis* preserves a facial skeleton attached to a calvaria. This observation raises two alternatives: first, that these features are primitive to the Hominidae and therefore not of great taxonomic value in determining relationships among hominids; second, that, as Olson[26] has suggested, the specimens identified as *A. afarensis* include two species, one of which gives rise directly to *A. boisei*. Whatever the final answer, these new specimens suggest that early hominid phylogeny has not yet been finally established and that it will prove to be more complex than has been stated.

We thank the Government of Kenya and the Governors of the National Museums of Kenya. This research is funded by the National Geographic Society, Washington, D.C., the Garland Foundation and the National Museums of Kenya. F.H.B. was funded for analyses by NSF grant BNS 8406737. We thank Bw. Kamoya Kimeu and his team for invaluable help. Many colleagues, but especially M. G. Leakey and P. Shipman, helped in various ways.

(**322**, 517-522; 1986)

A. Walker[*], R. E. Leakey[†], J. M. Harris[‡] & F. H. Brown[§]

[*] Department of Cell Biology and Anatomy, Johns Hopkins University School of Medicine, 725 North Wolfe Street, Baltimore, Maryland 21205, USA

[†] National Museums of Kenya, PO Box 40658, Nairobi, Kenya

[‡] Los Angeles County Museum of Natural History, 900 Exposition Boulevard, Los Angeles, California 90007, USA

[§] Department of Geology and Geophysics, University of Utah, Salt Lake City, Utah 84112, USA

的气腔形成以产生强烈伸展的顶骨乳突角；浅的沿内外侧方向宽阔的下颌窝；完全在下颌后突之后的鼓室。在 KNM-WT 17000 中，星穴区保存状况差，但是星穴凹可能还存在，这是用以证实南方古猿阿法种原始性的另外一个特征。

已在 KNM-WT 17000 中发现、但在南方古猿阿法种中还未知或者探讨不多的其他原始特征包括：非常小的颅容量；低的颅盖后轮廓；鼻骨延伸远至额颌缝之上并恰好位于隆起的眉间之上；具有退化的额鳞的低的颅盖；极端凸出的眼眶下侧边缘，正如在某些大猩猩中所见到的。因此 KNM-WT 17000 有许多特征比南方古猿非洲种的更加原始，与南方古猿阿法种相似，然而 KNM-WT 17000 很显然是南方古猿鲍氏种分支的一员。而且，尽管不可否认南非遗址年代的测定仍不精确，祖先种的某些种群可能在一个物种形成事件后保留下来，然而这些化石的时序变得越来越无法为南非古猿非洲种 – 粗壮种 – 鲍氏种这一谱系提供支持。

最后，值得注意的是，该颅骨与南方古猿阿法种共有的许多特征都是原始的，这些原始特征在南方古猿粗壮种或者后来的南方古猿鲍氏种标本中都没有发现过。尽管我们有 KNM-WT 17000 基本完整的面部骨骼以及若干在哈达尔发现的部分面部骨骼标本，这些 KNM-WT 17000 和南方古猿阿法种共有的原始特征几乎只限于颅盖。然而，没有一个南方古猿阿法种的成年个体标本保存有与颅盖衔接的面部骨骼。这一观察结果产生了两种可能：首先，这些特征对人科来讲比较原始，因此在确定人科动物间的关系时没有太大的分类学价值；第二，正如奥尔森[26] 提出的那样，这些被鉴定为南方古猿阿法种的标本包括两个物种，其中一个直接演化成南方古猿鲍氏种。无论最终的答案是什么，这些标本暗示着早期人科的系统发育尚未最终建立，并且系统发育将被证明其比已确定的关系更加复杂。

我们向肯尼亚政府和肯尼亚国家博物馆的管理者表示表示感谢。该研究得到了华盛顿哥伦比亚特区的国家地理学会、加兰基金会和肯尼亚国家博物馆的资助。布朗的研究受到了美国国家科学基金会 BNS 8406737 项拨款的资助。我们感谢卡莫亚·基梅乌及其团队提供的宝贵协助。许多同事，尤其是利基和希普曼都以不同方式提供了帮助。

（刘皓芳 翻译；董为 审稿）

Received 7 April; accepted 2 July 1986.

References:

1. Howell, F. C. in *Evolution of African Mammals* (eds Maglio, V. J. & Cooke, H. B. S.) 154-248 (Harvard, Cambridge, 1978).

2. Coppens, Y. in *Morphologie Evolutive—Morphogenese du Crane at Origine de l'Homme* (ed. Sakka, M.) 155-168 (CRNS, Paris, 1981); *Bull Mem. Soc. Anthrop. Paris* **3**, 273-284 (1983).

3. Tobias, P. V. *A. Rev. Anthrop.* **2**, 311-334 (1973).

4. Rak, Y. *The Australopithecine Face*, 1-169 (Academic, New York, 1983); *Am. J. Phys. Anthrop.* **66**, 281-288 (1985).

5. Boaz, N. T. in *New Interpretations of Ape and Human Ancestry* (eds Ciochon, R. L. & Corruccini, R. S.) 705-720 (Plenum, New York, 1983).

6. Wolpoff, M. H. *Palaeoanthropology* 131-157 (Knopf, New York, 1980).

7. Leakey, L. S. B. *Nature* **184**, 491-493 (1959).

8. Tobias, P. V. *Olduvai Gorge* Vol. 2 (Cambridge University Press, 1967).

9. Robinson, J. T. in *Evolution and Hominisation* (ed. Kurth, G.) 120 (Fischer, Stuttgart, 1962); in *Evolutionary Biology* (eds Dobzhansky, T., Hechi, M. K. & Steere, W.) (Appleton-Century Crofts, New York, 1967).

10. Johanson, D. C. & White, T. D. *Science* **203**, 321-330 (1979).

11. Tobias, P. V. *Palaeont. afr.* **23**, 1-17 (1980).

12. Olson, T. R. in *Aspects of Human Evolution* (ed. Stringer, C. B.) 99-128 (Taylor & Francis, London, 1981).

13. Harris, J. M. & Brown, F. H. *National Geographic Res.* **1**, 289-297 (1985).

14. Brown, F. H., McDougall, L., Davies, T. & Maier, R. in *Ancestors: the Hard Evidence* (ed. Delson, E.) 82-90 (Liss, New York, 1985).

15. Hillhouse, J. J., Cerling, T. E. & Brown F. H. *J. Geophys. Res.* (in the press).

16. Leakey, R. E. F., Mungai, J. M. & Walker, A. C. *Am. J. Phys. Anthrop.* **35**, 175-186 (1971).

17. Kimbel, W. H., Johanson, D. C. & Coppens, Y. *Am. J. Phys. Anthrop.* **57**, 453-499 (1982).

18. Dart, R. A. *Am. J. Phys. Anthrop.* **6**, 259-284 (1948).

19. Dean, M. C. & Wood, B. A. *Am. J. Phys. Anthrop.* **59**, 157-174 (1982).

20. White, T. D., Johanson, D. C. & Kimbel, W. H. *S. Afr. J. Sci.* **77**, 445-470 (1981).

21. Leakey, M. G. & Leakey, R. E. *Koobi Fora Research Project*, 100, 169 (Clarendon, Oxford, 1978).

22. Skelton, R. R., McHenry, H. & Drawhorn, G. M. *Curr. Anthrop.* **27**, 21-43 (1986).

23. Leakey, L. S. B. & Leakey, M. D. *Nature* **202**, 5-7 (1964).

24. Arambourg, C. & Coppens, Y. *C. r. hebd. Séanc. Acad. Sci., Paris* **265**, 589-590 (1967).

25. Robinson, J. T. *Early Hominid Posture and Locomotion* (University of Chicago Press, 1972).

26. Olson, T. R. in *Ancestors: the Hard Evidence* (ed. Delson, E.) 102-119 (Liss, New York, 1985).

Forty Years of Genetic Recombination in Bacteria: A Fortieth Anniversary Reminiscence

Joshua Lederberg

Editor's Note

In 1944, Canadian-born researcher Oswald Avery and colleagues demonstrated that DNA was the molecule responsible for inheritance. Inspired by this discovery, US molecular biologist Joshua Lederberg began investigating his own hypothesis that, instead of reproducing asexually and passing down exact copies of genetic information, bacteria can sometimes enter a sexual phase in which genetic information is combined and merged. Here he reminisces on the experiments that were to later earn him and colleague Edward Tatum the 1958 Nobel Prize, which demonstrated that bacteria can mate and exchange genes. The results, which challenged dogma, prompted lively discussion when they were presented at the 1946 Cold Spring Harbor Symposium, but bacterial genetic recombination was soon incorporated into the textbooks and mainstream molecular biological research.

Between April and June 1946, Joshua Lederberg and Edward L. Tatum carried out a series of experiments that proved that bacteria can exchange their genes by sexual crossings. The experiments were reported in *Nature* just 40 years ago[1]. In the following pair of articles*, Joshua Lederberg first provides a personal reminiscence of the circumstances of the discovery and then, together with Harriet Zuckerman, considers it as a possible case of "postmature" scientific discovery.

Lederberg in 1945

A Fortieth Anniversary Reminiscence

IN September 1941, when I started as an undergraduate at Columbia University, the genetics of bacteria was still a no-man's-land between the disciplines of genetics

---

* Only the first of these two articles is reproduced here.

128

细菌遗传重组四十年——四十周年纪念

乔舒亚·莱德伯格

编者按

1944 年加拿大裔研究者奥斯瓦尔德·埃弗里和他的同事证明 DNA 分子对遗传起作用。美国分子生物学家乔舒亚·莱德伯格受这一结论的启发，开始研究他自己提出的假说，即细菌有时可以进行有性生殖，在此过程中基因信息重组和融合，而不是通过无性生殖来传递精确拷贝的过程。在本文中，他回顾了证明细菌可交配并交换基因的实验，这项工作为莱德伯格和同事爱德华·塔特姆赢得了 1958 年的诺贝尔奖。当这些挑战传统法则的结果在 1946 年冷泉港学术研讨会上被提出时，引起了热烈讨论，而不久之后，细菌遗传重组理论就被纳入教科书和主流的分子生物学研究中。

从 1946 年 4 月到 6 月，乔舒亚·莱德伯格和爱德华·塔特姆开展的一系列实验证实了细菌可以通过有性杂交交换其基因。这些实验结果发表在 40 年前的《自然》杂志上 [1]。在随后文章中*，乔舒亚·莱德伯格首次对这一发现的详细情况进行了个人回顾，在这之后他又与哈丽雅特·朱克曼共同对此进行了评价，将之称为一个"晚熟"的科学发现。

1945 年的莱德伯格

四十周年纪念

1941 年 9 月，当我开始在哥伦比亚大学读本科的时候，细菌遗传学仍然是介于遗传学和（医学的）细菌学之间的一个未知领域。关于"细菌是否像所有其他生物

---

* 本书只收录了两篇论文中的第一篇。

and (medical) bacteriology. The question whether "bacteria have genes, like all other organisms" was still unanswered, indeed rarely asked. My own thoughts at that moment lay elsewhere. I looked forward to a career in medical research applying chemical analysis to problems like cancer and the malfunctions of the brain. Cytotoxicology then appeared to be the most promising approach to cell biochemistry. It was Francis J. Ryan (d. 1963) who turned my attention to the sharper tools of genetics.

Ryan had spent 1941–42 as a postdoctoral fellow at Stanford University, where he had met G. W. Beadle and E. L. Tatum (d. 1975), and had become fascinated with their recent invention of nutritional mutations in *Neurospora* as a tool for biochemical genetic analysis[2]. Although working on a fungus like *Neurospora* did not go down smoothly in a Department of Zoology as at Columbia, where Ryan had accepted an instructorship, he established a laboratory to continue these studies. In January 1943 I was fortunate to get a job in his laboratory assisting in the preparation of media and handling of *Neurospora* cultures. Ryan's personal qualities as a teacher and the setting of serious research, discussion with him, other faculty members and graduate students in the department nourished my education as a scientist. On 1 July 1943, I was called to active duty in the United States Naval Reserve, and my further months at Columbia College alternated with spells of duty at the United States Naval Hospital, St Albans, Long Island. There, in the clinical parasitology laboratory, I had abundant opportunity to observe the life cycle of *Plasmodium vivax*. This experience dramatized the sexual stages of the malaria parasite, which undoubtedly sensitized me to the possibility of cryptic sexual stages in other microbes (perhaps even bacteria). In October 1944, I was reassigned to begin my studies at Columbia Medical School; but I continued working with Ryan at the Morningside Heights campus.

Discovery

The important biological discovery of that year, by Avery, MacLeod and McCarty, was the identification of DNA as the substance responsible for the *Pneumococcus* transformation[3]. This phenomenon could be viewed as the transmission of a gene from one bacterial cell to another; but such an interpretation was inevitably clouded by the obscure understanding of bacterial genetics at the time. Avery's work, at the Rockefeller Institute in New York, was promptly communicated to Columbia biologists by Theodosius Dobzhansky (who visited Rockefeller) and by Alfred Mirsky (of the Rockefeller faculty) who was a close collaborator of Arthur Pollister in the Zoology Department. The work was the focus of widespread and critical discussion among the faculty and students. Mirsky was a vocal critic of the purported chemical identification of the transforming agent, while applauding the central importance of the work. For my own part, the transcendent leap was simply the feasibility of knowing the chemistry of the gene. Whether this was DNA or protein would certainly be clarified quickly, provided the *Pneumococcus* transformation could be securely retained within the conceptual domain of gene transmission. I read the Avery, MacLeod and McCarty paper on 20 January 1945, prompted by Harriett Taylor (later Ephrussi-Taylor) a graduate student in Zoology who planned to pursue her postdoctoral studies with Avery. My excited response is recorded as..."unlimited in its implications... Direct demonstration of the multiplication of transforming factor... Viruses are gene-type

一样含有基因"的问题一直没有答案，甚至都无人问津。当时，我对这方面也不感兴趣。我渴望从事将化学分析应用于癌症和大脑功能障碍等问题的医学研究方面的工作。于是，细胞毒理学似乎成为进入细胞生物化学研究的最有希望的途径。后来，我遇到了弗朗西斯·瑞安（于 1963 年去世），正是他使我的研究兴趣转移到这个更有效的研究工具——遗传学上。

1941 年到 1942 年间瑞安在斯坦福大学开展博士后研究，他在那里遇到了比德尔和塔特姆（于 1975 年去世），并开始对将脉孢菌的营养缺陷型突变体作为工具进行生物化学遗传分析产生浓厚的兴趣 [2]。尽管在动物系对诸如脉孢菌的真菌的研究工作并不如在哥伦比亚（他在那里获得了讲师职位）那般顺利，但是他建立了实验室并继续从事这些研究。1943 年 1 月，我有幸在他的实验室得到了一份工作，帮助准备培养基和处理脉孢菌培养物。受到瑞安作为教师的个人品质、严谨的研究态度的影响以及与他、动物系的其他教员及研究生的讨论使我受益匪浅。1943 年 7 月 1 日，我被征召进入美国海军预备队服役，本该在哥伦比亚学院度过的几个月，转而用于长岛圣奥尔本斯的美国海军医院工作。在那里的临床寄生虫学实验室，我有充足的机会观察间日疟原虫的生命周期。这一经历使我注意到了疟原虫的有性阶段，并促使我开始探索其他微生物（甚至是细菌）中是否也可能有隐蔽的有性阶段。1944 年10 月，我再次被分到了哥伦比亚医学院学习，但依然继续在晨边高地校区与瑞安共事。

发 现

那一年重要的生物学发现之一是埃弗里、麦克劳德和麦卡蒂发现 DNA 是肺炎球菌转化的物质基础 [3]。这一现象可以被看作是一个细菌细胞的基因转移到另一个细菌细胞中；不过这种解释不可避免地因当时对细菌遗传学的模糊认识而变得疑云重重。艾弗里在纽约洛克菲勒研究所的工作被特奥多修斯·多布然斯基（曾访问过洛克菲勒）和阿尔弗雷德·米尔斯基（洛克菲勒的教员）迅速传达给了哥伦比亚的生物学家。阿尔弗雷德·米尔斯基与动物学系的阿瑟·波利斯特有密切的合作。当时这一研究成为倍受教员和学生关注的重要讨论焦点。米尔斯基毫无保留地批判所谓的转化物质的化学鉴定，但对艾弗里的核心工作非常推崇。在我看来，这一飞跃只不过是了解了基因的化学本质后的必然结果。如果说肺炎球菌的转化确实是基因传递，那么这一物质是 DNA 还是蛋白质肯定很快就被证明了。在动物系一个即将跟随埃弗里开展博士后研究的研究生——哈丽雅特·泰勒（后来改名为埃弗吕西·泰勒）的推荐下，我阅读了艾弗里、麦克劳德和麦卡蒂在 1945 年 1 月 20 日发表的论文。以下文字记录了我兴奋的反映："……意义深远……直接证明了转化因子的增殖……病毒是基因类型的复合物"。

compounds."

At once, I thought of attempting similar transformations by DNA in *Neurospora*. This organism had a well understood lifecycle and genetic structure. The biochemical mutants opened up by Beadle and Tatum also allowed the efficient detection of nutritionally self-sufficient (prototrophic) forms, even if these were vanishingly rare. This would facilitate the assay of transformational events.

Between January and May, 1945, I shared this idea with Francis Ryan; in June, he invited me to work on the subject with him. To our dismay, we soon discovered that the leucine-minus *Neurospora* mutant would spontaneously revert to prototrophy[4], leaving us with no reliable assay for the effect of DNA in mediating genetic change in *Neurospora*. Questions about the biology of transformation would remain inaccessible to conventional genetic analysis if bacteria lacked a sexual stage. But was it true that bacteria were asexual? Rene Dubos' monograph, *The Bacterial Cell*[5], footnoted how inconclusive the claims were for or against any morphological exhibition of sexual union between bacterial cells.

My notes dated 8 July 1945 detail hypothetical experiments both to search for mating among *Monilia* (medically important yeast-like fungi) and to seek genetic recombination in bacteria (by the protocol that later proved to be successful). These notes coincide with the beginning of my course in medical bacteriology. They were provoked by the contrast of the traditional teaching that bacteria were *Schizomycetes*, asexual primitive plants, with an appreciation of sexuality in yeast[6], which was represented at Columbia by the graduate research work of Sol Spiegelman and Harriett Taylor.

Dubos[5] cited many unclear, and two clear-cut negative results[7,8] for sexuality in bacteria using genetic exchange methodology. But these two studies had no selective method for the detection of recombination and so would have overlooked the process had it occurred less often than perhaps once per thousand cells. With the use of a pair of nutritional mutants, say A^+B^- and A^-B^+, one could plate out innumerable cells in a selective medium and find a single A^+B^+ recombinant. In early July, I began experiments along these lines. In the first instance I used a set of biochemical mutants in *Escherichia coli*, which I began to accumulate in Ryan's laboratory. To avoid the difficulty that had arisen in our *Neurospora* experiments, a spontaneous reversion from A^-B^+ to A^+B^+, the strategy would be to use a pair of double mutants: $A^-B^-C^+D^+$ and $A^+B^+C^-D^-$. Sexual crossing should still generate $A^+B^+C^+D^+$ prototroph recombinants. These would be unlikely to arise by spontaneous reversions which, in theory, requires the coincidence of two rare events; $A^- \rightarrow A^+$ and $B^- \rightarrow B^+$. Much effort was devoted to control experiments to show that double reversions would follow this model, and so occur at a negligible frequency in the cultures handled separately. Thus the occurrence of prototrophs in the mixed cultures would be presumptive evidence of genetic recombination.

132

我立刻开始考虑在脉孢菌中使用 DNA 进行类似的转化实验，人们对于这种生物的生活史以及遗传结构有着比较清楚的认识。比德尔和塔特姆构建的生化突变体使营养自足型（原养型）的高效检测成为可能，即使其数量稀少。这也为转化事件的检测提供了便利。

1945 年 1 月到 5 月期间，我和弗朗西斯·瑞安讨论了这个想法；6 月份，他邀请我和他一起研究这个课题。让我们沮丧的是，不久我们发现脉孢菌的亮氨酸缺陷型突变体会自发回复成原养型 [4]，这使得我们无法建立一个可靠的检测方法来验证 DNA 在介导脉孢菌的遗传改变方面的作用。如果细菌不存在有性生殖的话，那么有关转化的生物学过程的问题也就无法用传统的遗传分析方法来解释。但是，细菌真的是无性生殖么？勒内·杜博斯的专论——《细菌细胞》[5] 中明确指出，任何支持或否定细菌细胞间存在性连接的形态学表现都无明确的结论。

我在 1945 年 7 月 8 日详细记录了用于寻找念珠菌（一种医学上十分重要的类似酵母的真菌）中的交配以及细菌中的遗传重组（所采取的实验方案后来证明是成功的）的假设性实验。这些记录与我在医学细菌学课程一开始的内容一致。它们挑战了传统教科书认为细菌是裂殖类、属于无性生殖的原始植物的观点，并且赞同索尔·施皮格尔曼和哈丽雅特·泰勒主张酵母存在性别差异 [6] 的观点，这是两人在哥伦比亚研究生时期的研究工作。

杜博斯 [5] 引用了很多利用遗传交换方法研究细菌有性生殖的阴性结果 [7,8]，其中很多结果尚不清楚，但有两个阴性结果很明确。不过这两个研究结果并没有建立用于检测重组的筛选方法，因此如果发生重组的概率低于千分之一，可能会忽略这个过程。通过使用一对营养突变体，分别命名为 A^+B^- 和 A^-B^+，就可以将无数的细胞涂布在选择性培养基上，而只有 A^+B^+ 型的重组细胞可以长出单克隆。在 7 月初，我开始按照这些方法开展实验。在第一个实验中，我使用了一系列大肠杆菌的生物化学突变体（来自瑞安的实验室）。为了避免在脉孢菌实验中出现的困境，即由 A^-B^+ 自发回复突变 A^+B^+，我们使用了下面一对双突变体：$A^-B^-C^+D^+$ 和 $A^+B^+C^-D^-$。有性杂交应该仍然会产生 $A^+B^+C^+D^+$ 型的原养型重组子。这些不太可能由自发性回复突变产生，因为在理论上，这需要从 A^- 到 A^+ 和 B^- 到 B^+ 同时发生两个小概率的突变。我们在对照实验上投入了很多精力，实验结果显示，双回复突变也按照这一模式进行，所以其发生的概率非常低以致可以忽略。因此，在混合培养物中出现的原养型突变体将证明有遗传重组发生。

Long Shot

Meanwhile at Stanford, Ed Tatum, whose doctoral training at Wisconsin had been in the biochemistry of bacteria, was returning to bacteria as experimental subjects, having published two papers on the production of biochemical mutants in *E. coli*[9], including double mutants like those described here. During the summer of 1945 Francis Ryan learned that Tatum was leaving Stanford to set up a new programme in microbiology at Yale. He suggested that, rather than merely ask Tatum to share these new strains, I apply to work with him and get the further benefit of his detailed experience and general wisdom. Tatum agreed and suggested that I arrive in New Haven in late March, to give him time to set up his laboratory. He hinted that he had some similar ideas of his own, but never elaborated them. The arrangement suited him by leaving him free to complete his work on the biochemistry of *Neurospora*, perform the heavy administrative duties of his new programme, and still participate in the long-shot gamble of looking for bacterial sex.

It took about six weeks, from the first serious efforts at crossing in mid-April 1946, to establish well-controlled, positive results. These experiments could be done overnight, so the month of June allowed over a dozen repetitions, and the recruitment of almost a dozen genetic markers in different crosses. Besides the appearance of $A^+B^+C^+D^+$ prototrophs, it was important to show that additional unselected markers in the parent stocks would segregate and recombine freely in the prototrophic progeny. This result left little doubt as to the interpretation of the experiments.

An immediate opportunity for public announcement presented itself at the international Cold Spring Harbor Symposium in July. This was dedicated to the genetics of microorganisms, signalling the postwar resumption of major research in a field that had been invigorated by the new discoveries with *Neurospora*, phage, and the role of DNA in the *Pneumococcus* transformation. Tatum was already scheduled to talk about his work on *Neurospora*. We were granted a last-minute improvisation in the schedule to permit a brief discussion of our new results.

The discussion was lively. The most principled criticism came from Andre Lwoff who worried about cross-feeding of nutrients between the two strains without their having in fact exchanged genetic information. Having taken great pains to control this possibility, I felt that the indirect genetic evidence was quite conclusive. Fortunately, Max Zelle mediated the debate, and generously offered to advise and assist me in the direct isolation of single cells under the microscope. These subsequent observations did quiet remaining concerns of the group that Lwoff had assembled at the Pasteur Institute, including Jacques Monod, Francois Jacob and Elie Wollman, who were to make the most extraordinary contributions to the further development of the field. The single cell methods were also useful in later investigations in several fields. A direct result of the Cold Spring Harbor meeting was the prompt ventilation of all the controversial issues. With a few understandable, but minor, points of resistance, genetic recombination in bacteria

展　望

与此同时，毕业于威斯康星大学从事细菌生化研究的爱德华·塔特姆博士在斯坦福大学也重新开始使用细菌作为实验对象进行研究，并发表了两篇论文报道了他构建的大肠杆菌生物化学突变体[9]，其中也包括上文中提到的双突变体。在1945年的夏天，弗朗西斯·瑞安了解到塔特姆即将离开斯坦福大学并将在耶鲁大学启动一个新的微生物学研究项目。他建议我与其仅仅向塔特姆索取这些新的菌株来开展实验，还不如干脆申请和他一起工作从而获得更多这方面的经验和指导。塔特姆同意了我的申请，并建议我在三月下旬到纽黑文来，这期间他可以建立他的实验室。他向我提到，他自己也有一些类似的想法，不过并没有深入考虑。如此安排使得他可以在继续完成对脉孢菌的生物化学研究的同时，既能够有时间完成他新项目繁重的管理工作，又可以在细菌的性别方面开展一些探索性的远景研究。

从1946年4月中旬第一次尝试杂交实验开始，我花了大约6个星期的时间来得到一个拥有良好对照的阳性结果。这些实验可以过夜进行，因此我在6月份得以进行了超过12次重复实验，并且在不同的杂交实验中发现近12个遗传标记。很重要的是除了实验中出现的 $A^+B^+C^+D^+$ 原养型外，那些亲本中未用于筛选的其他遗传标记也会在原养型子代中自由地发生分离和重组。这些结果符合对实验的解释。

随后在7月举行的冷泉港国际论坛上，这一结果得以公布于众。这一成果被归到微生物遗传学，这也标志着在脉胞菌、噬菌体以及DNA在肺炎球菌转化中的作用等新发现的带动和鼓舞下，一个主流研究领域在战后的复苏。按照既定日程，塔特姆介绍了他在脉胞菌中开展的研究工作。我们则被允许在会议日程的最后进行一个即席演讲，来简短地讨论一下我们的新发现。

讨论开展得非常热烈，其中最主要的争议来自于安德烈·利沃夫，他提出两个菌株也可能会在营养上交互共生而事实上它们之间并没有发生遗传信息的交换。基于之前已经花了大量的精力来排除这种可能，我认为间接的遗传证据已经非常具有说服力了。幸运的是，马克斯·泽尔调停了这场争论，他慷慨地给出建议并帮助我在显微镜下直接分离出单个细胞。这些后续的观察确实解决了在巴斯德研究所的利沃夫研究组所提出的质疑，这个小组中还有雅克·莫诺、弗朗西斯·雅各布和伊利·沃尔曼，他们对该领域的进一步发展做出了非凡的贡献。单细胞研究方法在后来的多个领域的研究中都有应用。冷泉港会议的直接结果是各种争议可以迅速得到沟通。虽然存在一些无可厚非的小阻力，细菌的遗传重组仍旧很快被纳入分子生物学的前沿研究的主流，并在大概十年后被写入细菌学的权威教科书里。人们仍然需要花上

was soon incorporated into the mainstream of the burgeoning research in molecular biology, and after another decade or so into the standard texts of bacteriology. It still took some years to work out the intimate details of crossing in *E. coli*; some, including the crucial question of the physical mechanism of DNA transfer between mating cells, are still obscure.

The public image of the scientific fraternity today has seldom been so problematic and the system cannot avoid putting a high premium on competition and self-assertion. We can recall with gratification how the personalities of Ryan[10] and Tatum[11] exemplified norms of nurture, dignity, respect for others, and above all a regard for the advance of knowledge.

Experimental Luck

1. We have learned[12] that *E. coli* strain K-12 itself was a remarkably lucky choice of experimental material: only about one in twenty randomly chosen strains of *E. coli* would have given positive results in experiments designed according to our protocols. In particular, strain B, which has become the standard material for work on bacteriophage, would have been stubbornly unfruitful. Tatum had acquired K-12 from the routine stock culture collection in Stanford's microbiology department when he sought an *E. coli* strain to use as a source of tryptophanase in work on tryptophan synthesis in *Neurospora*[13]. The same strain was then in hand when he set out to make single, and then double mutants in *E. coli*[9]. In 1946, I was very much aware of strain specificities and was speculating about mating types (as in *Neurospora*). I have no way to say how many other strains would have been tried, or in how many combinations, had the June 1946 experiments not been successful.

2. An equally important piece of luck was that the selected markers Thr (threonine) and Leu (leucine) are found almost at the origin of the *E. coli* chromosome map[14]. The cognoscenti will recognize that in a cross $B^-M^-T^+L^+F^+ \times B^+M^+T^-L^-F^-$, the configuration used in June 1946, these chromosome localizations offer almost a maximum yield of selectible recombinants. We were therefore led stepwise into the complexities of mapping.

(**324**, 627-628; 1986)

Joshua Lederberg is at the Rockefeller University, New York, NY 10021. The research summarized in this article was supported in 1946 by a fellowship of the Jane Coffin Childs Fund for Medical Research.

References:

1. Lederberg, J. & Tatum, E. L. *Nature* **158**, 558 (1946).

2. Beadle, G. W. & Tatum, E. L. *Proc. Natl. Acad. Sci. U.S.A.* **27**, 499-506 (1941).

3. Avery, O. T., MacLeod, C. M. & McCarty, M. *J. exp. Med.* **79**, 137-158 (1944).

4. Ryan, F. J. & Lederberg, J. *Proc. Natl. Acad. Sci. U.S.A.* **32**, 163-173 (1946).

5. Dubos, R. *The Bacterial Cell* (Harvard, Cambridge, 1945).

136

好几年的时间来阐明大肠杆菌有性杂交的内在细节，有些关键问题，如 DNA 在交配细胞间如何转移的物理机制等依然不清楚。

今天公众对科学界的质疑很少，并且这个体系不可避免采用高额奖金来鼓励竞争和独立思考。我们非常高兴地回忆起瑞安 [10] 和塔特姆 [11] 如此杰出的人格，他们为其他人在育人、尊严与尊重方面做出了示范，以及最重要的以知识为先的精神。

实验的运气

我们已经知道 [12] 选取大肠杆菌 K-12 菌株做实验材料本身就是一件非常幸运的事：根据我们的实验方案在随机挑选的 20 个大肠杆菌菌株中，只有大约 1 株可以在实验中得到阳性结果。尤其是 B 菌株，它成为了噬菌体研究的标准实验材料，并且该菌株是高度不育的。塔特姆从斯坦福大学微生物系的常规培养物库存中得到了 K-12，那时他打算寻找一个大肠杆菌菌株作为脉胞菌色氨酸合成研究 [13] 中色氨酸酶的来源。当他开始构建大肠杆菌的单突变体以及之后的双突变体 [9] 时，很快就得到了相同的菌株。1946 年，我对菌株的特异性非常了解，并开始推断交配的方式（就像在脉胞菌中一样）。如果 1946 年 6 月的实验不成功的话，我不知道还要尝试多少其他的菌株，也不知道需要尝试多少种组合。

另一个同样重要的运气在于，实验所使用的筛选标记——苏氨酸和亮氨酸几乎位于大肠杆菌染色体图谱的起始部位 [14]。内行人士都会知道，在 1946 年 6 月使用的 B⁻M⁻T⁺L⁺F⁺ × B⁺M⁺T⁻L⁻F⁺ 杂交组合中，这些染色体定位有利于产生几乎最高产量的重组子，因此我们被逐步引导进入定位的复杂性中。

（张锦彬 翻译；肖景发 审稿）

6. Winge & Lausten, O. *C. R. Lab. Carlsberg, Ser. physiol.*, **22**, 99-119 (1937).

7. Sherman, J. M. & Wing, H. U. *J. Bact.* **33**, 315-321 (1937).

8. Gowen, J. W. & Lincoln, R. E. *J. Bact.* **44**, 551-554 (1942).

9. Gray, C. H. & Tatum, E. L. *Proc. Natl. Acad. Sci. U.S.A.* **30**, 404-410 (1944).

10. Lederberg, J. *in University on the Heights.* (ed. First, W.)105-109. (Doubleday, Garden City, New York, 1969).

11. Lederberg, J. *A. Rev. Genet.* **13**, 1-5 (1979).

12. Lederberg, J. *Science* **114**, 68-69 (1951).

13. Tatum, E. L. & Bonner, D. M. *Proc. Natl. Acad. Sci. U.S.A.* **30**, 30-37 (1944).

14. Bachmann, B. J. *Microb. Revs.* **47**, 180-230 (1983).

Mitochondrial DNA and Human Evolution

R. L. Cann *et al.*

Editor's Note

Before this paper, our understanding of human prehistory had come almost entirely from studying ancient bones and stones. But here Allan Wilson, a pioneer of "molecular evolution" techniques, and his colleagues use modern people as windows on the past. By comparing the mitochondrial DNA from 147 people of diverse origins, they show that modern humans shared a common, African ancestry some 200,000 years ago. This conclusion has since been validated by traditional palaeontological methods, but the paper caught the popular imagination by creating a virtual "ancestral celebrity". Because mitochondrial DNA is inherited maternally, Wilson and colleagues postulated the existence of a single woman from whom we all descended: "mitochondrial Eve".

Mitochondrial DNAs from 147 people, drawn from five geographic populations have been analysed by restriction mapping. All these mitochondrial DNAs stem from one woman who is postulated to have lived about 200,000 years ago, probably in Africa. All the populations examined except the African population have multiple origins, implying that each area was colonised repeatedly.

MOLECULAR biology is now a major source of quantitative and objective information about the evolutionary history of the human species. It has provided new insights into our genetic divergence from apes[1-8] and into the way in which humans are related to one another genetically[9-14]. Our picture of genetic evolution within the human species is clouded, however, because it is based mainly on comparisons of genes in the nucleus. Mutations accumulate slowly in nuclear genes. In addition, nuclear genes are inherited from both parents and mix in every generation. This mixing obscures the history of individuals and allows recombination to occur. Recombination makes it hard to trace the history of particular segments of DNA unless tightly linked sites within them are considered.

Our world-wide survey of mitochondrial DNA (mtDNA) adds to knowledge of the history of the human gene pool in three ways. First, mtDNA gives a magnified view of the diversity present in the human gene pool, because mutations accumulate in this DNA several times faster than in the nucleus[15]. Second, because mtDNA is inherited maternally and does not recombine[16], it is a tool for relating individuals to one another. Third, there are about 10^{16} mtDNA molecules within a typical human and they are usually identical to one another[17-19]. Typical mammalian females consequently behave as haploids, owing to a bottleneck in the genetically effective size of the population of mtDNA molecules within each oocyte[20]. This maternal and haploid inheritance means that mtDNA is more sensitive

线粒体DNA与人类进化

卡恩等

编者按

在这篇文章发表之前，我们对史前时代的了解全部来源于对古人骨骼和石器的研究。但是"分子进化"技术的先锋艾伦·威尔逊和他的同事们用现代人类作为了解过去的窗口。通过比较来源不同的 147 个人的线粒体 DNA，他们发现现代人类共同拥有的 20 万年以前的非洲血统。这个结论已经通过传统的古生物学方法证实，但是这篇文章创造了一个虚拟的"祖先名人"从而吸引了大众的兴趣。因为线粒体 DNA 是母系遗传的，所以威尔逊和他的同事们假设了一个女人的存在，我们都是她的后裔，这就是"线粒体夏娃"。

我们分析了来自五个不同地域的群体、共 147 例人线粒体 DNA 的限制性酶切图谱。所有这些线粒体 DNA 都源于同一个我们假设的、生活在约 20 万年以前的非洲女性。除来自非洲的群体外，其他所有的群体都有多个起源，这暗示了每个地域的群体被入侵群体反复占据多次。

如今，分子生物学已是关于人类进化历史的量化和客观信息的主要来源。它为我们揭示人类自猿以来的遗传分化 [1-8] 和人与人之间遗传上相关联的方式 [9-14] 提供了新视角。然而人类遗传进化的研究被蒙上了一层迷雾，因为之前的研究主要基于细胞核基因的比较，而核基因突变的积累是很慢的。此外，核基因遗传自父母双方并在每一代中混合。这种混合模糊了个体的遗传背景，两亲本基因组之间可以发生遗传重组。如果不研究那些紧密连锁的位点，遗传重组会使得特定 DNA 片段的遗传历史难以追踪。

在全世界范围内对线粒体 DNA（mtDNA）的调查研究在以下三个方面加强了我们对人类基因库历史的认识：第一，因为 mtDNA 的突变积累速度比核基因快好几倍 [15]，这使我们更容易观察到人类基因库中的遗传多样性；第二，mtDNA 是母系遗传，不会发生遗传重组 [16]，从而能够将个体之间关联起来；第三，人体中约有 10^{16} 个 mtDNA 分子，它们的 DNA 序列通常是完全相同的 [17-19]。由于每个卵母细胞中 mtDNA 分子遗传上有效群体大小的瓶颈效应 [20]，所以典型的雌性哺乳动物是以单倍体遗传的。mtDNA 的母系遗传和单倍体遗传意味着 mtDNA 对生物群体中个体数量

than nuclear DNA to severe reductions in the number of individuals in a population of organisms[15]. A pair of breeding individuals can transmit only one type of mtDNA but carry four haploid sets of nuclear genes, all of which are transmissible to offspring. The fast evolution and peculiar mode of inheritance of mtDNA provide new perspectives on how, where and when the human gene pool arose and grew.

Restriction Maps

MtDNA was highly purified from 145 placentas and two cell lines, HeLa and GM 3043, derived from a Black American and an aboriginal South African (!Kung), respectively. Most placentas (98) were obtained from US hospitals, the remainder coming from Australia and New Guinea. In the sample, there were representatives of 5 geographic regions: 20 Africans (representing the sub-Saharan region), 34 Asians (originating from China, Vietnam, Laos, the Philippines, Indonesia and Tonga), 46 Caucasians (originating from Europe, North Africa, and the Middle East), 21 aboriginal Australians, and 26 aboriginal New Guineans. Only two of the 20 Africans in our sample, those bearing mtDNA types 1 and 81 (see below) were born in sub-Saharan Africa. The other 18 people in this sample are Black Americans, who bear many non-African nuclear genes probably contributed mainly by Caucasian males. Those males would not be expected to have introduced any mtDNA to the Black American population. Consistent with our view that most of these 18 people are a reliable source of African mtDNA, we found that 12 of them bear restriction site markers known[21] to occur exclusively or predominantly in native sub-Saharan Africans (but not in Europeans, Asians or American Indians nor, indeed, in all such Africans). The mtDNA types in these 12 people are 2–7, 37–41 and 82 (see below). Methods used to purify mtDNA and more detailed ethnographic information on the first four groups are as described[17,22]; the New Guineans are mainly from the Eastern Highlands of Papua New Guinea[23].

Each purified mtDNA was subjected to high resolution mapping[22-24] with 12 restriction enzymes (*Hpa*I, *Ava*II, *Fnu*DII, *Hha*I, *Hpa*II, *Mbo*I, *Taq*I, *Rsa*I, *Hinf*I, *Hae*III, *Alu*I and *Dde*I). Restriction sites were mapped by comparing observed fragment patterns to those expected from the known human mtDNA sequence[25]. In this way, we identified 467 independent sites, of which 195 were polymorphic (that is, absent in at least one individual). An average of 370 restriction sites per individual were surveyed, representing about 9% of the 16,569 base-pair human mtDNA genome.

Map Comparisons

The 147 mtDNAs mapped were divisible into 133 distinct types. Seven of these types were found in more than one individual; no individual contained more than one type. None of the seven shared types occurred in more than one of the five geographic regions. One type, for example, was found in two Australians. Among Caucasians, another type occurred three times and two more types occured twice. In New Guinea, two additional types were found three times and the seventh case involved a type found in six individuals.

的锐减比核基因更敏感[15]。一对可育个体只遗传一种类型的 mtDNA 到后代中，但却有四套单倍体核基因遗传给后代。mtDNA 的快速进化和独特的遗传模式将有助于我们重新理解人类基因库是何时何地以及怎样起源和演化的。

限制性酶切图谱

我们从 145 个胎盘和 HeLa、GM3043 两个细胞系中得到了高度纯化的 mtDNA，这两个细胞系分别来源于一个美国黑人和一个南非土著居民（布须曼昆人）。大部分胎盘（98 个）是从美国医院里获得的，其余则来自于澳大利亚和新几内亚。样本中有 5 个地理区域的代表：20 个非洲人（代表撒哈拉以南地区），34 个亚洲人（来自中国、越南、老挝、菲律宾、印度尼西亚和汤加），46 个高加索人（来自欧洲、北非和中东地区），21 个澳大利亚土著居民和 26 个新几内亚原住民。我们样本中的 20 个非洲人中只有两个出生在撒哈拉沙漠以南的非洲地区，他们的 mtDNA 为 1 型和 81 型（见下文）。其他的 18 个人都是美国黑人，他们拥有许多非非洲人群核基因，这些基因可能主要来自于高加索男性。这些高加索男性不可能将任何 mtDNA 引入美国黑人群体中。与我们的观点相一致，这 18 个美国黑人大多数是非洲人 mtDNA 的可靠来源，我们发现其中 12 个携带有撒哈拉以南非洲土著居民（而不是欧洲人、亚洲人或美洲第安人，当然也不是所有这些非洲人）所特有的或者主要的限制性酶切位点遗传标记[21]。这 12 例的 mtDNA 类型为 2~7、37~41 和 82（见下文）。mtDNA 的纯化方法和最初四组更详细的人群信息如前文献所述[17,22]，新几内亚人样本主要来自巴布亚新几内亚的东部高地[23]。

每一个纯化得到的 mtDNA 都用 12 个限制性酶（*Hpa*I、*Ava*II、*Fnu*DII、*Hha*I、*Hpa*II、*Mbo*I、*Taq*I、*Rsa*I、*Hinf*I、*Hae*III、*Alu*I 和 *Dde*I）进行酶切，然后绘制出高分辨率的图谱[22-24]。将限制性酶切后观察到的片段和已知的人 mtDNA 序列[25] 中期望出现的片段相比较从而得到限制性酶切图谱。通过这种方法，我们鉴定出了467 个独立酶切位点，其中 195 个呈现出多态性（即至少在一例个体中缺少这个位点）。平均每个个体中分析了 370 个限制性酶切位点，代表了人 mtDNA 全基因组16,569 个碱基对中的 9%。

图 谱 比 对

147 个样品的 mtDNA 酶切图谱可分成 133 个不同的类别。其中有 7 类出现在了多个个体中，并且每个个体中只含一种类型的 mtDNA。这 7 类中的每一类也只出现在五个地理区域中的一个，例如在两个澳大利亚人中只发现了一种类型的 mtDNA；在高加索人样本中，有一类出现了三次，有两种类型出现了两次；在新几内亚人样本中，另两类出现了三次，第七种类型被发现存在于六个个体中。

A histogram showing the number of restriction site differences between pairs of individuals is given in Fig. 1; the average number of differences observed between any two humans is 9.5. The distribution is approximately normal, with an excess of pairwise comparisons involving large numbers of differences.

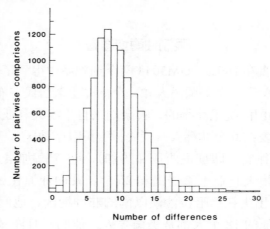

Fig. 1. Histogram showing the number of site differences between restriction maps of mtDNA for all possible pairs of 147 human beings.

From the number of restriction site differences, we estimated the extent of nucleotide sequence divergence[26] for each pair of individuals. These estimates ranged from zero to 1.3 substitutions per 100 base pairs, with an average sequence divergence of 0.32%, which agrees with that of Brown[17], who examined only 21 humans.

Table 1 gives three measures of sequence divergence within and between each of the five populations examined. These measures are related to one another by equation (1):

$$\delta = \delta_{xy} - 0.5(\delta_x + \delta_y) \tag{1}$$

where δ_x is the mean pairwise divergence (in percent) between individuals within a single population (X), δ_y is the corresponding value for another population (Y), δ_{xy} is the mean pairwise divergence between individuals belonging to two different populations (X and Y), and δ is a measure of the interpopulation divergence corrected for intrapopulation divergence. Africans as a group are more variable ($\delta_x = 0.47$) than other groups. Indeed, the variation within the African population is as great as that between Africans and any other group ($\delta_{xy} = 0.40$–0.45). The within-group variation of Asians ($\delta_x = 0.35$) is also comparable to that which exists between groups. For Australians, Caucasians, and New Guineans, who show nearly identical amounts of within-group variation ($\delta_x = 0.23$–0.25), the variation between groups slightly exceeds that within groups.

　　直方图图1显示了成对比较的个体间的限制性酶切位点差异的数量，观察任何两个人的限制性酶切位点的数量平均差异数量为9.5。其分布近似服从正态分布，超出正态分布的两两比较包含了大量差异。

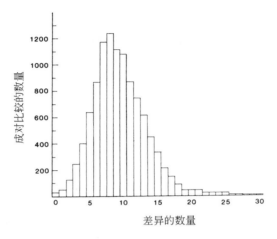

图1. 直方图显示了147个人中所有可能成对的mtDNA限制性酶切图谱之间的位点差异的数量。

　　根据限制性酶切位点差异的数量，我们估算了每对个体间核苷酸序列分化的程度[26]。每100个碱基对中估计有0~1.3个碱基对发生了替换，平均序列分化程度为0.32%，此结果与之前布朗得到的结果[17]一致，但是他们只研究了21例人的样本。

　　表1给出了对我们所研究的五个群体内或群体间序列分化程度的三种度量。所得到的值通过等式（1）计算群体之间的关联：

$$\delta = \delta_{xy} - 0.5\,(\delta_x + \delta_y) \tag{1}$$

其中δ_x为单个群体（X）内个体差异平均值（百分比形式），δ_y为另一个群体（Y）的对应值，δ_{xy}为两个不同群体（X和Y）的个体之间分化的平均值，δ是进行过群体内序列分化校正的群体间分化的度量值。非洲人群内变异（$\delta_x = 0.47$）比其他群体内大。实际上，非洲人群内部的变异程度与非洲人群和其他群体之间的分化程度（$\delta_{xy} = 0.40\sim0.45$）一样大。亚洲人群内分化程度（$\delta_x = 0.35$）也近似于群体之间的分化程度。澳大利亚人群、高加索人群和新几内亚人群的群体内的变异程度近似相等（$\delta_x = 0.23\sim0.25$），群体之间的分化程度稍稍大于群体内的变异程度。

Table 1. MtDNA divergence within and between 5 human populations

Population	% sequence divergence				
	1	2	3	4	5
1. African	0.47	0.04	0.04	0.05	0.06
2. Asian	0.45	0.35	0.01	0.02	0.04
3. Australian	0.40	0.31	0.25	0.03	0.04
4. Caucasian	0.40	0.31	0.27	0.23	0.05
5. New Guinean	0.42	0.34	0.29	0.29	0.25

The divergence is calculated by a published method[26]. Values of the mean pairwise divergence between individuals within populations (δ_x) appear on the diagonal. Values below the diagonal (δ_{xy}) are the mean pairwise divergences between individuals belonging to two different populations, X and Y. Values above the diagonal (δ) are interpopulation divergences, corrected for variation within those populations with equation (1).

When the interpopulational distances (δ_{xy}) are corrected for intrapopulation variation (Table 1), they become very small ($\delta = 0.01$–0.06). The mean value of the corrected distance among populations ($\delta = 0.04$) is less than one-seventh of the mean distance between individuals within a population (0.30). Most of the mtDNA variation in the human species is therefore shared between populations. A more detailed analysis supports this view[27].

Functional Constraints

Figure 2 shows the sequence divergence (δ_x) calculated for each population across seven functionally distinct regions of the mtDNA genome. As has been found before[24,27,28], the most variable region is the displacement loop ($\bar{\delta}_x = 1.3$), the major noncoding portion of the mtDNA molecule, and the least variable region is the 16S ribosomal RNA gene ($\bar{\delta}_x = 0.2$). In general, Africans are the most diverse and Asians the next most, across all functional regions.

表 1. 五个群体内和群体间的 mtDNA 分化程度

人群	序列分化程度（%）				
	1	2	3	4	5
1. 非洲人	0.47	0.04	0.04	0.05	0.06
2. 亚洲人	0.45	0.35	0.01	0.02	0.04
3. 澳大利亚人	0.40	0.31	0.25	0.03	0.04
4. 高加索人	0.40	0.31	0.27	0.23	0.05
5. 新几内亚人	0.42	0.34	0.29	0.29	0.25

通过已发表文献中的方法计算了分化程度[26]。对角线为群体内不同个体之间的平均成对分化值（δ_x）。对角线之下的为两个不同群体 X 和 Y 的个体之间的平均成对分化值（δ_{xy}）。对角线之上为群体之间的平均成对分化值（δ），该值已由等式（1）进行群体内变异的校正。.

群体间的分化程度（δ_{xy}）经群体内分化校正后（表 1）就非常小了（$\delta = 0.01\sim0.06$）。群体间校正后的平均值（$\delta = 0.04$）小于同一群体内不同个体间分化程度的七分之一（0.30）。因此大多数人群的 mtDNA 分化是发生在群体之间的。有一个更为详尽的分析能够支持此观点[27]。

线粒体基因组功能区的不同选择压力

图 2 显示了计算出的每一群体中 mtDNA 基因组全部七个不同功能区域的序列分化程度（δ_x）。正如同以前所发现的[24,27,28]，最容易发生变异的区域就是 mtDNA 控制区（D 环），是 mtDNA 分子中一段非编码区（$\overline{\delta}_x = 1.3$）；变异最小的区域是 16S 核糖体 RNA 基因（$\overline{\delta}_x = 0.2$）。通常来说，非洲人群在所有的功能区域中是最具多样性的，亚洲人群次之。

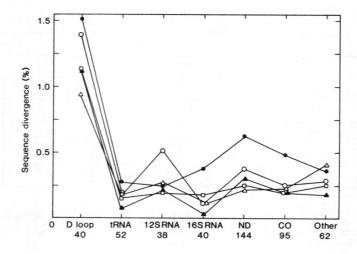

Fig. 2. Sequence divergence within 5 geographic areas for each of 7 functional regions in human mtDNA. Sequence divergence (δ_x) was estimated from comparisons of restriction maps[26]. Symbols for the 5 races are: ●, Africa; ○, Asia; △, Australia; □, Caucasian; ▲, New Guinea. Along the horizontal axis are the numbers of restriction sites in each functional region (D loop, transfer RNA genes, 12S and 16S ribosomal RNA genes, NADH dehydrogenase subunits 1-5, cytochrome oxidase subunits and other protein-coding regions).

Evolutionary Tree

A tree relating the 133 types of human mtDNA and the reference sequence (Fig. 3) was built by the parsimony method. To interpret this tree, we make two assumptions, both of which have extensive empirical support: (1) a strictly maternal mode of mtDNA transmission (so that any variant appearing in a group of lineages must be due to a mutation occurring in the ancestral lineage and not recombination between maternal and paternal genomes) and (2) each individual is homogeneous for its multiple mtDNA genomes. We can therefore view the tree as a genealogy linking maternal lineages in modern human populations to a common ancestral female (bearing mtDNA type a).

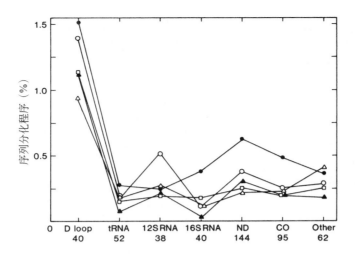

图 2. 五大地理区域人群 mtDNA 中的 7 个功能区域的序列分化程度。该序列分析程度（δ_s）是通过比较限制性酶切图谱来估算的 [26]。五个族群的符号是：●，非洲；○，亚洲；△，澳大利亚；□，高加索；▲，新几内亚。横坐标为每一个功能区域（D 环、tRNA 基因、12S 核糖体 RNA 基因、16S 核糖体 RNA 基因、NADH 脱氢酶亚基 1-5、细胞色素氧化酶亚基和其他蛋白质编码区域）内限制性酶切位点的数目。

进 化 树

通过简约法构建了 133 种类型的人 mtDNA 和参照序列（图 3）的进化树。为了能够诠释此进化树，我们做了两个有大量实证支持的假设：（1）mtDNA 是严格遵守母系遗传模式的（即任何出现在直系亲属中的变异都是由直系亲属祖先的 mtDNA 发生变异造成的，并且母本和父本之间不会发生遗传重组）；（2）每个个体在多个 mtDNA 基因组上是同质的。因此我们可以把此进化树看成是现代人群与一位共同的女性祖先（携带了 a 型 mtDNA）之间的母系谱系关系。

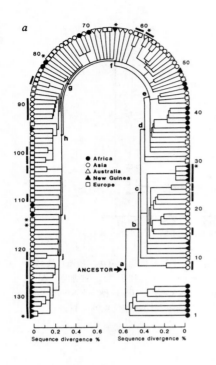

b **D LOOP:** *8j* 2 5 8 9 23 81-83 85 86 118; *64i (16494)* 26 ; *134l* 3; *207h* 128-134; *255l* 39; *259a* 106; *340j* 112 **12S rRNA:** *663e* 43 48 53; *712l* 90; 740j 16-19; *748b* 49; 1240a 7-9 37 110; *1403a (1448)* 11-18 20-29 34 49 50 55-57; 1463e 14; 1484e 2 4 5 8-11 14-17 19 23-25 30 32-35 41-43 45 52-58 61 107 110 120; *1536l* 31 **VAL tRNA:** 1610a 2 3 44 45 104; 1637c 47 102 108; 1667c 47 **16S rRNA:** 1715c 22 23 27 123; 1917a 70; 2208a 87; *2223a (2635)* 37; *2384a (2472)* 106; *2390j* 2 3 8 9 49 79 93; 2734a 18 22 54 73 101; 2758k 1-8; 2849k 112; 3123k 119 **ND 1:** 3315e 11; 3337k 94 118 133; *3391e* 41 105 122; 3537a 44; *3592h* 2-7 9 37-41; 3698f 130-132; *3842e* 44; 3849e 5 46; *3899l* 14 18 22 23 32 71 92 102 110 120; *3930c* 110; 3944 l 127 132; *4092g* 112 **MET tRNA:** 4411a 23 35 36 57; 4464k 129 **ND 2:** *4481b (10933)* 111 112; 4631a 2; *4643k* 87 100; *4732k* 115; 4769a 110; *4793e* 76 85; 5176a 21 25 54-57; 5261e 118; 5269l 71; *5351l* 17-19 **TRP tRNA:** *5538l* 130; 5552c 10 **L. ORIGIN:** 5742l 15 44; *5754i (5755)* 81 **CO I:** 5978a 52; *5984b/5983g* 87; *5985k/5983g* 133 134; 5996a 87; 6022a 74; *6166l (6168)* 63; 6211g 37-41 82; 6260e 95; *6356c* 5 9; 6377c 68; *6409l (7854)* 68; *6501i* 78; *6610g* 12; *6699b (8719,8723)* 78; 6871g 18 19; *6915k* 5 49; 6931g 48; 6957e 44 45; 7025a 75-86 93 94 103-112; 7055a 3 6 7; *7241k* 72; 7335l 6 7 30 92 120; 7347e 124 **SER tRNA:** 7461l 71; 7474a 121 **CO II:** *7617l* 55 73; 7750c 3-9 37 40 41 98; 7859j 120; *7970g* 10 24 71-74 77; 8074a 68; 8112l 1; 8150l 1 126 ; *8165e* 10; *8249 b (8250) /8250e* 1 61 132 **LYS tRNA:** *8299k* 126 **ATP 8:** 8391e 31 120; 8515c 27 **ATP 6:** 8592j 21 23; 8783g 6 7; *8852l (8854, 8856)* 109 110; 8994e60 61; *9009a* 15 16; 9053l 52 91-93 95-102 112; *9070l* 5-7; *9150j* 7 103 104 **CO III:** 9266e 28 49 67; 9294e 25; 9342e 27; 9380l 90; *9429k* 56 57; 9553e 37 117; *9714e* 98; 9746k 62; 9751l 48; *9859g* 86 **GLY tRNA:** 10028a 126 **ND 3:** *10066l* 45; 10094 l 45; 10352a 110; 10364e 96; *10394c* 1-29 39-45 49 50 84-89 94-100 111 120-123 **ARG tRNA:** *10413a (10536)* 16 46 56 85 98 **ND 4L:** *10644k* 19 20; 10689e 96; 10694a 104; *10725e* 22 46 96 **ND 4:** *10806g* 1-7 50 83 124; *10893l* 34; 11146c 61 110; *11161l* 6 7; *11329e (11690)* 2 4; *11350a* 15 37 110; *11806a* 65; 11922j 7; 12026h 124 **ND 5:** *12345k (12350,12528)* 88 127-134; 12406h 91-93; 12560a 19 52 93; *12795j (12798,12806,13374)* 40 90 98 99; *12810k* 5-7; *12925g* 7; *12990a (13642)* 27; *13004j (13018,13182,13194)* 20; 13031g 1-6 9-16 18-23 26-35 37 39 40 42 43 45-64 82 83 92 93; 13051e 23 38-41; *13068a* 128; *13096k* 26; *13100i* 107; 13103g 7; *13208l* 4 5 7 15 75 88; 13268g 65; 13367b 40 88 90 99; 13404l 8 9 79 ; *13635l (13641)* 39 115; 13702e 38-41; 14015a 14; *14050l (14366)* 125 **ND 6:** 14279e 1; *14279j* 23; *14322a* 92; *14385c* 10; 14509a 68 123-126; *14567i* 68; 14608c 5 **CYT b:** *14749e* 87; 14869j 86 126; 14956l 115; *15005g* 56 57; 15172e 10; *15195j (15221)* 44; 15234g 113; 15238c 84 100; 15250c 14-18 20 21 24 25 54 81 90 111; *15606a* 65 127-134; 15723g 43; *15790l (16373)* 82; 15883e 7 45 58 59 112 **THR tRNA:** 15897k 97 129; *15925l* 15 81 90 **PRO tRNA:** 15996c/16000g 48 **D LOOP:** 16049k 15 22 46 74 81; 16065g 121 122; *16089k* 21; 16096k 119; 16125k 3 9 74 78 88-91 93 105 119 122; *16178l* 26-29; 16208k 11 15 51 52 55; *16217l* 95; *16246g* 46; *16254a* 127 132; 16303k 36 58 59 82 89-93 111 112 131 132; 16310k 1-3 5 6 8-14 20 26-31 58 73 78 82 94-97 99-102 120 125 126 133 134; *16389g*/16390b 11 35-41 82 89; *16398e* 5 11 34 37 66 118 119; *16490g* 10; 16517e 2 11-13 15-24 26-29 51-55 58 59 82 97 105-134.

Fig. 3. *a*, Genealogical tree for 134 types of human mtDNA (133 restriction maps plus reference sequence); *b*, comprehensive list of polymorphic restriction sites used. The tree accounts for the site differences observed between restriction maps of these mtDNAs with 398 mutations. No other order of branching tested is more parsimonious than this one. This order of branching was obtained (using the computer program PAUP, designed by Dr. David Swofford) by ignoring every site present in only one type of mtDNA or absent in only one type and confining attention to the remaining 93 polymorphic sites. The computer program produces an unrooted network, which we converted to a tree by placing the root (arrow) at the midpoint of the longest path connecting the two lineages (see ref. 58). The numbers refer to mtDNA types, no. 1 being from the aboriginal South African (!Kung) cell line (GM 3043), no. 45 being from the HeLa cell line and no. 110 being the published human sequence[25]. Black bars, clusters of mtDNA types specific to a given geographic region; asterisks, mtDNA types found in more than 1 individual: type 134 was in six individuals, types 29, 65 and 80 each occurred thrice, and other types flagged with asterisks occurred twice. To place the nodes in the tree relative to the percent divergence scale, we took account of the differences observed at all 195 polymorphic sites. *b*, The numbering of sites is according to the published human sequence[25], with 12 restriction enzymes indicated by the following single letter code: a, *Alu*I; b, *Ava*II; c, *Dde*I; d, *Fnu*DII; e, *Hae*III; f, *Hha*I; g, *Hinf*I; h, *Hpa*I; i, *Hpa*II; j, *Mbo*I; k, *Rsa*I; l, *Taq*I. Italicized sites are present in the indicated mtDNA types and nonitalicized sites are absent in the indicated types; parentheses refer to alternative placements of inferred sites; sites separated by a slash are polymorphic for two different restriction enzymes caused by a single inferred nucleotide substitution; letters in bold face refer to noncoding regions and genes for transfer RNA, ribosomal RNA and proteins (ND, NADH dehydrogenase; CO, cytochrome oxidase; ATP, adenosine triphosphatase; CYT b, cytochrome *b*). For example, *8j* indicates a *Mbo*I site beginning at nucleotide position 8 in the D loop that was not found in mtDNA type 1 but was present in type 2, etc. Note that since this site is not present in the reference sequence (type 110), the sequence beginning at position 8 is actually a semisite, differing from the *Mbo*I recognition sequence at one position (see ref. 23 for a detailed description of the method of mapping such inferred sites). Not all sites were scored in all individuals: *8j*, 1484e and 7750c were not determined for types 1, 31, 59, 63, 68, and all of the New Guinea mtDNAs; mtDNAs 114 and 121 could not be typed with *Rsa*I. The locations of some sites differ from those reported before[23,24], as do the individuals in which some sites occur; these revisions are based on re-examination of previously-studied mtDNAs.

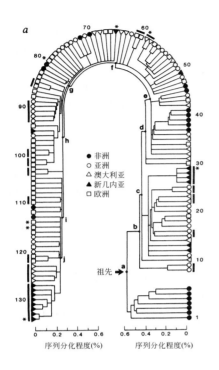

b D LOOP: *8j* 2 5 8 9 23 81-83 85 86 118; *64i (16494)* 26 ; *134l* 3; *207h* 128-134; *255l* 39; *259a* 106; *340j* 112 **12S rRNA:** *663e* 43 48 53; *712l* 90; *740j* 16-19; *748b* 49; *1240a* 7-9 37 110; *1403a (1448)* 11-18 20-29 34 49 50 55-57; *1463e* 14; *1484e* 2 4 15 18 14-17 19 23-25 30 32-35 41-43 45 52-58 60-67 96 107 110 120; *1536f* 31 **VAL tRNA:** 1610a 2 3 44 45 104; 1637c 47 102 108; 1667c 47 **16S rRNA:** 1715c 22 23 27 123; 1917a 70; 2208a 87; *2223a (2635)* 37; *2384a (2472)* 106; *2390j* 2 3 8 9 49 79 93; 2734a 18 22 54 73 101; 2758h 1-8; 2849k 112; 3123k 119 **ND 1:** 3315e 11; 3337k 94 118 133; *3391e* 41 105 122; 3537a 44; *3592h* 2-7 9 37-41; 3698f 130-132; *3842e* 44; 3849e 5 46; *3899l* 14 18 22 23 32 71 92 102 110 120; *3930c* 110; 3944 l 92; *4092g* 112 **MET tRNA:** 4411a 23 35 36 57; 4464k 129 **ND 2:** *4481b (10933)* 111 112; 4631a 2; *4643k* 87 100; *4732k* 115; *4769a* 110; *4793e* 76 85; 5176a 21 35 54-57; 5261e 118; 5269l 71; *5351f* 17-19 **TRP tRNA:** *5538l* 130; 5552c 10 **L. ORIGIN:** 5742i 15 44; *5754i (5755)* 81 **CO I:** 5978a 52; *5984b/5983g* 87; *5985A/5983g* 133 134; 5996a 87; 6022a 74; *6166l (6168)* 63; 6211g 37-41 82; 6260e 95; *6356c* 5 9; 6377c 68; *6409l (7854)* 68; *6501i* 78; *6610g* 12; *6699b (8719,8723)* 78; 6871g 18 19; *6915k* 5 49; 6931g 48; 6957e 44 45; 7025a 75-86 93 94 110-112; 7055a 3 6 7; 7247e 5 6 7 30 92 120; *7347e* 124 **SER tRNA:** 7461l 71; 7474a 121 **CO II:** *7617l* 55 73; 7750c 3-9 37 40 48 99; *7859j* 120; 7943k 2 20 71-74 77; 8074a 68; 8112i 1; 8150l 1 126 ; *8165e* 10; *8249 b (8250)* /8250e 1 61 132 **LYS tRNA:** *8299k* 126 **ATP 8:** 8391e 31 120; 8515c 27 **ATP 6:** *8592j* 21 23; 8783g 6 7; *8852f (8854, 8856)* 109 110; 8994e60 61; *9009a* 15 16; 9053f 52 91-93 95-102 112; *9070l* 5-7; *9150j* 7 103 104 **CO III:** 9266e 28 49 67; 9294e 25; 9342e 27; *9393l* 90; 9429k 56 57; 9553e 37 117; *9714e* 98; 9746k 62; 9751l 48; *9859g* 86 **GLY tRNA:** 10028a 106 **ND 3:** *10066l* 45; 10084l 45; 10081l 6 10; *10394c* 1-29 39-45 49 50 84-89 94-100 111 120-123 **ARG tRNA:** *10413a (10536)* 16 46 56 85 98 **ND 4L:** *10644k* 19 20; 10689e 96; *10694a* 104; *10725e* 22 46 96 79; *13635l (13641)* 39 115; 13702e 38-41; 14015a 14; *14050l (14366)* 125 **ND 6:** 14279e 1; *14279j* 23; *14322a* 92; *14385c* 10; *14509a* 68 123; *14567l* 68; 14608c 5 **CYT b:** *14749e* 87; 14869j 86 126; 14956l 115; *15005g* 56 57; 15172e 10; *15195j (15221)* 44; 15234g 113; 15238c 84 100; 15250c 14-18 22 25 54 84 90 111; *15606a* 65 127-134; 15723g 43; *15790l (16373)* 82; 15883e 7 45 58 59 112 **THR tRNA:** *15897k* 97 116; *15912l* 81; *15925i* 15 81 90 **PRO tRNA:** 15996c/16000g 48 **D LOOP:** 16049k 15 22 46 74 81; 16065g 121 122; *16089k* 21; 16090k 119; *16125k* 3 9 74 88-91 93 105 119 122 124-127; *16178l* 26-29; 16208k 11 15 51 52 55; *16217l* 95; *16246g* 46; *16254a* 127 132; 16303k 36 58 59 82 89-93 111 112 132; 16310k 1-3 5 6 10 20 26-31 58 73 78 82 94-97 99-102 120 125 126 133 134; *16389g/16390b* 11 35-41 82 89; *16398e* 5 11 34 37 66 118 119; *16490g* 10; 16517e 2 11-13 15-24 26-29 51-55 58 59 82 97 105-134.

图 3. *a* 为根据 134 类人 mtDNA（133 个限制性酶切位点图谱和一个参照序列）构建的系统树；*b* 为多态性限制性酶切位点总表。系统树由包括 398 个突变的 mtDNA 的限制性酶切图谱之间的位点差异性构建而成。经测试其他任何的分支排布都不及此树简约。忽略每一个位点只在一种类型的 mtDNA 中出现或缺失的情况，将注意力集中到剩余的 93 个多态性位点，基于此而计算（使用了戴维·斯沃福德博士设计的计算机程序 PAUP）得到了系统树中各分支的排布顺序。计算机程序产生的是一个无根的网络，我们通过把最长一条路径的中点设置为树根（箭头所指）将该网络转化为一个系统树，这条路径将两个支系联系起来（见参考文献 58）。系统树中的数字代表了 mtDNA 的类型，1 型来自南非土著居民（布须曼昆人）的细胞系（GM3043），45 型来自 HeLa 细胞系，110 型是已发表的人的 mtDNA 序列[25]。黑色线条包含一个地域特异的 mtDNA 类型簇；星号表示在多个个体中发现的 mtDNA 类型：134 型出现在六个个体中，29、65 和 80 型 mtDNA 都出现了三次，其他由星号标记的 mtDNA 类型出现了两次。我们考虑到了所有 195 个多态性酶切位点之间的差异，以使系统树的节点与分化百分比相对应。*b* 图中，根据已发表的人类 mtDNA 序列[25]对酶切位点进行编号，分别用 12 个单字母对限制性酶编号：a，*Alu*I；b，*Ava*II；c，*Ded*I；d，*Fnu*DII；e，*Hae*III；f，*Hha*I；g，*Hinf*I；h，*Hpa*I；i，*Hpa*II；j，*Mbo*I；k，*Rsa*I；l，*Taq*I 。斜体字标示的位点为出现在目的 mtDNA 类型中的位点，而非斜体字标示的位点为在目的 mtDNA 类型中没有的位点；括号内是推测位点的其他替代位置；由斜线分开的位点为由一个推断的核苷酸替换导致的两种不同限制性内切酶的多态性位点；黑体加粗的字母为非编码区和 tRNA、核糖体 RNA 及一些蛋白质（ND，NADH 脱氢酶；CO，细胞色素氧化酶；ATP，腺苷三磷酸酶；CYT b，细胞色素 b）的基因。例如，*8j* 就表示酶切位点 *Mbo*I 的起始位置是在 D 环 8 位核苷酸处，它存在于 2 型 mtDNA 中但不存在于 1 型 mtDNA 中。由于参照序列（110 型 mtDNA）中并没有此位点，8 位起始位置其实是一个半位点，不同于 1 位的 *Mbo*I 识别序列（参见参考文献 23 中确定这些位点位置的方法）。并不是所有的酶切位点在所有个体中都能找到，如在 1、31、59、63、68 型 mtDNA 和所有新几内亚人的 mtDNA 中没有找到 *8j*、1484e 和 7750c 的位点；114 和 121 型 mtDNA 中没有 *Rsa*I 位点。一些位点的位置与之前报道的结果[23,24]不同，一些位点出现的个体也与之前报道的结果不同；所做的这些修正是通过对所研究的 mtDNA 的复查得到的。

Many trees of minimal or near-minimal length can be made from the data; all trees that we have examined share the following features with Fig. 3. (1) two primary branches, one composed entirely of Africans, the other including all 5 of the populations studied; and (2) each population stems from multiple lineages connected to the tree at widely dispersed positions. Since submission of this manuscript, Horai et al.[29] built a tree for our samples of African and Caucasian populations and their sample of a Japanese population by another method; their tree shares these two features.

Among the trees investigated was one consisting of five primary branches with each branch leading exclusively to one of the five populations. This tree, which we call the population-specific tree, requires 51 more point mutations than does the tree of minimum length in Fig. 3. The minimum-length tree requires fewer changes at 22 of the 93 phylogenetically-informative restriction sites than does the population-specific tree, while the latter tree required fewer changes at four sites; both trees require the same number of changes at the remaining 67 sites. The minimum-length tree is thus favoured by a score of 22 to 4. The hypothesis that the two trees are equally compatible with the data is statistically rejected, since $22:4$ is significantly different from the expected $13:13$. The minimum-length tree is thus significantly more parsimonious than the population-specific tree.

African Origin

We infer from the tree of minimum length (Fig. 3) that Africa is a likely source of the human mitochondrial gene pool. This inference comes from the observation that one of the two primary branches leads exclusively to African mtDNAs (types 1–7, Fig. 3) while the second primary branch also leads to African mtDNAs (types 37–41, 45, 46, 70, 72, 81, 82, 111 and 113). By postulating that the common ancestral mtDNA (type a in Fig. 3) was African, we minimize the number of intercontinental migrations needed to account for the geographic distribution of mtDNA types. It follows that b is a likely common ancestor of all non-African and many African mtDNAs (types 8–134 in Fig. 3).

Multiple Lineages per Race

The second implication of the tree (Fig. 3)—that each non-African population has multiple origins—can be illustrated most simply with the New Guineans. Take, as an example, mtDNA type 49, a lineage whose nearest relative is not in New Guinea, but in Asia (type 50). Asian lineage 50 is closer genealogically to this New Guinea lineage than to other Asian mtDNA lineages. Six other lineages lead exclusively to New Guinean mtDNAs, each originating at a different place in the tree (types 12, 13, 26–29, 65, 95 and 127–134 in Fig. 3). This small region of New Guinea (mainly the Eastern Highlands Province) thus seems to have been colonised by at least seven maternal lineages (Tables 2 and 3).

152

从数据中可以得到很多最小长度或者接近最小长度的进化树，从图3中可以看出所有这些进化树有以下共同的特点：（1）两个一级分支中，一个全部由非洲人群组成，而另外一个一级分支则包括了五个地域的所有人群；（2）每个群体都源自在广泛分散的位置上与进化树相连接的多个谱系。就在我们提交本文后，宝来等人[29]将他们的日本人群样本结合我们的非洲人和高加索人样本，通过另外一种方法构建了进化树，他们的进化树也同样具有上述的两个特点。

在所研究的进化树中，其中一个进化树有五个一级分支，每个分别只代表了五大地域人群中的一个。此进化树我们称之为群体特异性进化树，与图3中最小长度的进化树相比它还需要51个点突变。在93个系统发育信息性限制性酶切位点中，与群体特异性进化树相比，最小长度的进化树需要在22个酶切位点发生更少数量的变异。然而群体特异性进化树需要在4个限制性酶切位点处发生更少的变异。在剩下的67个限制性酶切位点处两种进化树需要有相同数量的变异。因此最小长度进化树以22：4占优势。22:4与预期的13:13相差太大，因此可以否定关于两种进化树在同等程度上与所得到统计数据相符的猜测。因此最小长度进化树就远比群体特异性进化树简约了。

人群的非洲起源

我们从最小长度的进化树（图3）推测非洲可能是人类线粒体基因库的起源地。这种推测是因为观察到进化树中的两个一级分支中的一个全部指向非洲人群mtDNA（图3中的1~7型），第二个也指向非洲人群mtDNA（37～41、45、46、70、72、81、82、111、113型）。假设非洲人是所有人群mtDNA（图3中的a型）的共同祖先，要满足不同类型mtDNA的地理分布需要在地域之间发生一定数量的迁移，我们将此数量进行了最小化。b可能是所有非非洲人群和许多非洲人群mtDNA的共同祖先（图3中的8~134型）。

每个族群的多个亲缘系

进化树（图3）给我们的第二个暗示就是每一个非非洲人群有多个起源，这可以用最简单的新几内亚人的例子来阐述。以49型mtDNA为例，与它亲缘关系最近的并不是新几内亚人，而是亚洲人群（50型mtDNA）。与其他亚洲人群的亲缘性相比，亚洲的50型谱系与新几内亚49型谱系的亲缘关系更近一些。指向新几内亚人群mtDNA的另外六个系，每一个都起源于进化树中不同的位置（图3中的12、13、26~29、65、95、127~134等型）。因此新几内亚的这个小区域（以东部高地省份为主）似乎已经经过了至少七个母系血统的繁衍（表2和3）。

Table 2. Clusters of mtDNA types that are specific to one geographic region

Geographic region	Number of region-specific clusters	Mean pairwise distance within clusters*	Average age of clusters†
Africa	1‡	0.36	90–180
Asia	27	0.21	53–105
Australia	15	0.17	43–85
Europe	36	0.09	23–45
New Guinea	7	0.11	28–55

* For clusters represented by two or more individuals (and calculated for individuals, not for mtDNA types) in Fig. 3.

† Average age in thousands of years based on the assumption that mtDNA divergence occurs at the rate of 2–4% per million years[15,30].

‡ Assuming that Africa is the source, there is only one African cluster.

Table 3. Ancestors, lineages and extents of divergence in the genealogical tree for 134 types of human mtDNA

Ancestor	No. of descendant lineages or clusters specific to a region							Age*
	Total	Africa	Asia	Australia	Europe	N. Guinea	% divergence	
a	7	1	0	0	0	0	0.57	143–285
b	2	0	1	0	0	0	0.45	112–225
c	20	0	7	3	1	3	0.43	108–215
d	2	0	0	1	1	0	0.39	98–195
e	14	2	2	4	2	0	0.34	85–170
f	19	1	7	4	4	1	0.30	75–150
g	10	2	3	2	2	1	0.28	70–140
h	30	2	4	0	15	1	0.27	68–135
i	8	1	0	0	6	0	0.26	65–130
j	22	1	3	1	5	1	0.25	62–125
All	134	10	27	15	36	7	—	—

* Assuming that the mtDNA divergence rate is 2–4% per million years[15,30].

In the same way, we calculate the minimum numbers of female lineages that colonised Australia, Asia and Europe (Tables 2 and 3). Each estimate is based on the number of region-specific clusters in the tree (Fig. 3, Tables 2 and 3). These numbers, ranging from 15 to 36 (Tables 2 and 3), will probably rise as more types of human mtDNA are discovered.

Tentative Time Scale

A time scale can be affixed to the tree in Fig. 3 by assuming that mtDNA sequence divergence accumulates at a constant rate in humans. One way of estimating this rate is

表 2. 特定地理区域的 mtDNA 类型簇

地理区域	区域特异性簇的数量	簇内平均比对距离 *	簇的平均年代 †
非洲	1‡	0.36	90~180
亚洲	27	0.21	53~105
澳大利亚	15	0.17	43~85
欧洲	36	0.09	23~45
新几内亚	7	0.11	28~55

* 为图 3 中两个及两个以上个体（针对个体，而非 mtDNA 类型）中出现的簇。
† 根据 mtDNA 分化速率为每一百万年 2%~4% 的假设计算的平均年代（千年）[15,30]。
‡ 假设非洲是共同起源地，那么只有一个非洲人群 mtDNA 簇。

表 3. 人类 134 种 mtDNA 的系统树中的祖先、世系和分化程度

祖先	一个地区特定的后代世系或簇的数量							年代 *
	总数	非洲	亚洲	澳大利亚	欧洲	新几内亚	分化程度(%)	
a	7	1	0	0	0	0	0.57	143~285
b	2	0	1	0	0	0	0.45	112~225
c	20	0	7	3	1	3	0.43	108~215
d	2	0	0	1	1	0	0.39	98~195
e	14	2	2	4	2	0	0.34	85~170
f	19	1	7	4	4	1	0.30	75~150
g	10	2	3	2	2	0	0.28	70~140
h	30	2	4	0	15	1	0.27	68~135
i	8	1	0	0	6	0	0.26	65~130
j	22	1	3	1	5	1	0.25	62~125
总数	134	10	27	15	36	7	—	—

* 假设每一百万年 mtDNA 的分化速率是 2%~4%[15,30]。

用同样的方法，我们计算了在澳大利亚、亚洲和欧洲繁衍所需的母系血统的最小数量（表 2 和 3）。每个值都是基于系统树中的区域特异性簇的数量而估算出来的（图 3，表 2 和 3）。随着更多类型的人类 mtDNA 的发现，这些范围在 15 到 36 之间（表 2 和 3）的估算值可能也会增加。

尝试构建年代时间表

假定人类中 mtDNA 序列分化是以恒定的速率积累的，我们就能够在图 3 中的进化树上标示出进化的年代时间表。估计此积累速率的一种方法是考虑发生于新几

to consider the extent of differentiation within clusters specific to New Guinea (Table 2; see also refs 23 and 30), Australia[30] and the New World[31]. People colonised these regions relatively recently: a minimum of 30,000 years ago for New Guinea[32], 40,000 years ago for Australia[33], and 12,000 years ago for the New World[34]. These times enable us to calculate that the mean rate of mtDNA divergence within humans lies between two and four percent per million years; a detailed account of this calculation appears elsewhere[30]. This rate is similar to previous estimates from animals as disparate as apes, monkeys, horses, rhinoceroses, mice, rats, birds and fishes[15]. We therefore consider the above estimate of 2–4% to be reasonable for humans, although additional comparative work is needed to obtain a more exact calibration.

As Fig. 3 shows, the common ancestral mtDNA (type a) links mtDNA types that have diverged by an average of nearly 0.57%. Assuming a rate of 2–4% per million years, this implies that the common ancestor of all surviving mtDNA types existed 140,000–290,000 years ago. Similarly, ancestral types b–j may have existed 62,000–225,000 years ago (Table 3).

When did the migrations from Africa take place? The oldest of the clusters of mtDNA types to contain no African members stems from ancestor c and included types 11–29 (Fig. 3). The apparent age of this cluster (calculated in Table 3) is 90,000–180,000 years. Its founders may have left Africa at about that time. However, it is equally possible that the exodus occurred as recently as 23–105 thousand years ago (Table 2). The mtDNA results cannot tell us exactly when these migrations took place.

Other mtDNA Studies

Two previous studies of human mtDNA have included African individuals[21,28]; both support an African origin for the human mtDNA gene pool. Johnson et al.[21] surveyed ~40 restriction sites in each of 200 mtDNAs from Africa, Asia, Europe and the New World, and found 35 mtDNA types. This much smaller number of mtDNA types probably reflects the inability of their methods to distinguish between mtDNAs that differ by less than 0.3% and may account for the greater clustering of mtDNA types by geographic origin that they observed. (By contrast, our methods distinguish between mtDNAs that differ by 0.03%.) Although Johnson et al. favoured an Asian origin, they too found that Africans possess the greatest amount of mtDNA variability and that a midpoint rooting of their tree leads to an African origin.

Greenberg et al.[28] sequenced the large noncoding region, which includes the displacement loop (D loop), from four Caucasians and three Black Americans. A parsimony tree for these seven D loop sequences, rooted by the midpoint method, appears in Fig. 4. This tree indicates (1) a high evolutionary rate for the D loop (at least five times faster than other mtDNA regions), (2) a greater diversity among Black American D loop sequences, and (3) that the common ancestor was African.

内亚（表 2；参考文献 23 和 30）、澳大利亚[30]和新世界[31]各自簇内特异的分化程度。人类近期才在这些地区进行殖民：新几内亚、澳大利亚和新世界，开始的时间分别至少为 3 万年[32]、4 万年[33]和 1.2 万年[34]以前。通过这些时间我们可以计算出mtDNA 分化的平均速率为每一百万年 2%~4%；关于此计算详细说明可参见其他文献[30]。此 mtDNA 分化速率与之前从猿、猴、马、犀牛、小鼠、大鼠、鸟类和鱼等不同的动物中得出的速率[15]相近。因此我们所估算的 2%~4% 的速率值对人类来说是一个相对合理的值，即使仍需要进一步的比较来做更准确的校正。

如图 3 所示，共同 mtDNA 祖先（a 型）与平均分化程度为 0.57% 的 mtDNA 类型相联系。假如进化速率为每一百万年 2%~4%，那么所有存留下来的 mtDNA 类型的共同祖先出现在 14 万年至 29 万年以前。同样推算，祖先类型 b～j 可能出现在6.2 万年至 22.5 万年前（表 3）。

从非洲向外迁移是什么时候开始的呢？最古老的不含非洲人群 mtDNA 的mtDNA 类型簇起源于祖先 c，包括了 11~29 类型（图 3）。此类型 mtDNA 的表观年龄达 9 万年至 18 万年（计算值见表 3），其祖先可能在这个时间已经离开了非洲。然而，大批迁移同样有可能发生在 2.3 万年至 10.5 万年前（表 2）。分析 mtDNA 的结果并不能准确地告诉我们迁移发生的时间。

其他 mtDNA 的研究

之前的两个关于人类 mtDNA 的研究所用的样本包括非洲的个体[21,28]，它们的结果都支持人类 mtDNA 基因库是从非洲人群起源的。约翰逊等人[21]在非洲、亚洲、欧洲和新世界的 200 例 mtDNA 样品中检测了约 40 个限制性酶切位点，发现了35 种类型的 mtDNA。这么少的 mtDNA 类型的数目反映出他们的方法不能区分差别小于 0.3% 的 mtDNA，可能还解释了他们所观察到的由于地域起源而产生的更大的mtDNA 类型簇（相比之下，我们的方法能够区分差异仅为 0.03% 的 mtDNA）。尽管约翰逊等人偏向于认为亚洲人群是人类 mtDNA 的起源，但他们也发现了非洲人群的 mtDNA 变异度最大，并且他们进化树中一个中点树根指向了非洲起源。

格林伯格等人[28]测定了四个高加索人和三个美国黑人 mtDNA 中包括替代环（D环）在内的大段非编码区序列。图 4 是这 7 个 D 环序列的简约进化树，通过中点法得出树根。从进化树中可以看出：（1）D 环的进化速率很高（至少是其他 mtDNA 区域的五倍）；（2）D 环在美国黑人中的多样性要更大些；（3）共同祖先是非洲人群。

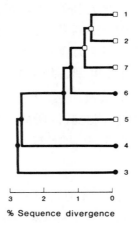

Fig. 4. Genealogical tree relating the nucleotide sequences of D loops from seven human mtDNAs. This tree, which requires fewer mutations than any other branching order, was constructed by the PAUP computer program from the 900-bp sequences determined by Greenberg *et al.*[28] and was rooted by the midpoint method. Symbols: ●, African origin (Black American); □, Caucasian.

Nuclear DNA Studies

Estimates of genetic distance based on comparative studies of nuclear genes and their products differ in kind from mtDNA estimates. The latter are based on the actual number of mutational differences between mtDNA genomes, while the former rely on differences in the frequencies of molecular variants measured between and within populations. Gene frequencies can be influenced by recombination, genetic drift, selection, and migration, so the direct relationship found between time and mutational distance for mtDNA would not be expected for genetic distances based on nuclear DNA. But studies based on polymorphic blood groups, red cell enzymes, and serum proteins show that (1) differences between racial groups are smaller than those within such groups and (2) the largest gene frequency differences are between Africans and other populations, suggesting an African origin for the human nuclear gene pool[11,12,35]. More recent studies of restriction site polymorphisms in nuclear DNA [14,36-42] support these conclusions.

Relation to Fossil Record

Our tentative interpretation of the tree (Fig. 3) and the associated time scale (Table 3) fits with one view of the fossil record: that the transformation of archaic to anatomically modern forms of *Homo sapiens* occurred first in Africa[43-45], about 100,000–140,000 years ago, and that all present-day humans are descendants of that African population. Archaeologists have observed that blades were in common use in Africa 80–90 thousand years ago, long before they replaced flake tools in Asia or Europe[46,47]. But the agreement between our molecular view and the evidence from palaeoanthropology and archaeology should be treated cautiously for two reasons. First, there is much uncertainty about the ages of these remains. Second, our placement of the common ancestor of all human mtDNA diversity in Africa 140,000–280,000 years ago need not imply that the transformation to anatomically modern *Homo sapiens* occurred in Africa at this time. The

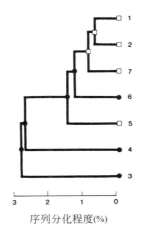

序列分化程度(%)

图 4. 根据来自七个人 mtDNA 分子的 D 环核甘酸序列而构建的系统树。此树是根据格林伯格等 [28] 测出的 900 个碱基对序列通过 PAUP 程序构建的；与其他任何分支顺序相比，此树需要更少数量的突变；中点法确定树根。符号：●，起源于非洲的人群（美国黑人）；□，高加索人。

对核 DNA 的研究

基于比较核基因以及它们的产物而估算出的遗传距离与通过 mtDNA 进化而估算出的遗传距离是不同的。后者基于 mtDNA 基因组之间突变差异的实际数目，而前者依赖于群体间或群体内分子变异的频率差异。而基因重组、遗传漂变、自然选择和迁移都能够影响基因频率，因此 mtDNA 中时间与突变距离之间的直接关系与基于核 DNA 的遗传距离是不能等同的。但是对于血型、红细胞酶和血清蛋白多态性的研究显示：（1）族群之间的差异要小于族群内的差异，（2）基因频率差异最大的是非洲人群和其他人群之间的差异，这也暗示了人类核基因库 [11,12,35] 起源于非洲人群。最近的一些关于核 DNA 限制性酶切位点多态性 [14,36-42] 的研究也支持这些结论。

与化石记录的联系

我们对系统树尝试性的阐述（图 3）和相关的年代时间表（表 3）与一定的化石记录相符合：化石记录显示解剖学上从远古人到现代人群智人的转化最初发生在 10 万年至 14 万年前的非洲 [43-45]，所有现在的人都是那时候非洲人群体的后裔。考古学家发现 8 万年至 9 万年前刀片在非洲非常常用，很久之后在亚洲和欧洲所使用的石片工具才被这种刀片取代 [46,47]。然而我们应该谨慎对待我们在分子水平上的观点与古人类学以及考古学证据的一致性，原因有两点。首先，这些遗物的年代还有很大的不确定性；其次我们提出的观点是所有人类 mtDNA 类型的共同祖先出现在 14 万年至 28 万年前的非洲，此观点不需要揭示解剖学上远古人到现代人的转化就

mtDNA data tell us nothing of the contributions to this transformation by the genetic and cultural traits of males and females whose mtDNA became extinct.

An alternative view of human evolution rests on evidence that *Homo* has been present in Asia as well as in Africa for at least one million years[48] and holds that the transformation of archaic to anatomically modern humans occurred in parallel in different parts of the Old World[33,49]. This hypothesis leads us to expect genetic differences of great antiquity within widely separated parts of the modern pool of mtDNAs. It is hard to reconcile the mtDNA results with this hypothesis. The greatest divergences within clusters specific to non-African parts of the World correspond to times of only 90,000–180,000 years. This might imply that the early Asian *Homo* (such as Java man and Peking man) contributed no surviving mtDNA lineages to the gene pool of our species. Consistent with this implication are features, found recently in the skeletons of the ancient Asian forms, that make it unlikely that Asian *erectus* was ancestral to *Homo sapiens*[50-52]. Perhaps the non-African *erectus* population was replaced by *sapiens* migrants from Africa; incomplete fossils indicating the possible presence of early modern humans in western Asia at Zuttiyeh (75,000–150,000 years ago) and Qafzeh (50,000–70,000 years ago) might reflect these first migrations[45,53].

If there was hybridization between the resident archaic forms in Asia and anatomically modern forms emerging from Africa, we should expect to find extremely divergent types of mtDNA in present-day Asians, more divergent than any mtDNA found in Africa. There is no evidence for these types of mtDNA among the Asians studied[21,54-56]. Although such archaic types of mtDNA could have been lost from the hybridizing population, the probability of mtDNA lineages becoming extinct in an expanding population is low[57]. Thus we propose that *Homo erectus* in Asia was replaced without much mixing with the invading *Homo sapiens* from Africa.

Conclusions and Prospects

Studies of mtDNA suggest a view of how, where and when modern humans arose that fits with one interpretation of evidence from ancient human bones and tools. More extensive molecular comparisons are needed to improve our rooting of the mtDNA tree and the calibration of the rate of mtDNA divergence within the human species. This may provide a more reliable time scale for the spread of human populations and better estimates of the number of maternal lineages involved in founding the non-African populations.

It is also important to obtain more quantitative estimates of the overall extent of nuclear DNA diversity in both human and African ape populations. By comparing the nuclear and mitochondrial DNA diversities, it may be possible to find out whether a transient or prolonged bottleneck in population size accompanied the origin of our species[15]. Then a fuller interaction between palaeoanthropology, archaeology and molecular biology will allow a deeper analysis of how our species arose.

We thank the Foundation for Research into the Origin of Man, the National Science

发生在此时的非洲。从已经灭绝的古人类到现代人在遗传和文化特征方面发生了什么样的转化，我们是无法从 mtDNA 的数据中找到答案的。

有证据表明人在亚洲和非洲都存在了至少一百万年 [48]，因此有另外一种关于人类进化的观点，即认为从远古人到解剖学意义上的现代人的转化并行发生在旧世界的不同区域 [33,49]。这个假设使得我们期望看到广泛分布有现代人类 mtDNA 库的地域在远古时候就有明显的基因差异。但是很难将 mtDNA 结果与该假设对应起来。世界上非非洲人群特异性簇内最大分化所对应的时间仅有 9 万年至 18 万年。这也许暗示了早期亚洲人属（比如爪哇猿人和北京猿人）没有存留下来的 mtDNA 血统贡献于当今人群的基因库。与此暗示相符的是，最近发现的一些古亚洲人骨骼的特征说明亚洲直立人不可能是智人的祖先 [50-52]。也许非洲以外的直立人被来自非洲的智人移民替换了，不完整的化石记录显示在西亚的祖提耶（7.5 万年至 15 万年以前）和卡夫泽（5 万年至 7 万年前）可能出现了最初的现代人群，这也许反映了这些最初的移民 [45,53]。

如果亚洲古代居民与非洲出现的解剖学意义上的现代人发生交配，我们应该能在当今亚洲人的 mtDNA 类型里找到一些极端分化的类型，其分化程度要比在非洲发现的 mtDNA 类型分化程度更高。但对亚洲人的研究中 [21,54-56] 没有任何这种 mtDNA 类型存在的证据。尽管这些古老的 mtDNA 类型可能在种群之间的杂交过程中会丢失，但是 mtDNA 血统在一个膨胀的种群中灭绝的可能性是很低的 [57]。因此我们推测亚洲的直立人被入侵的非洲智人取代了，而且他们之间基本没有遗传混合。

结论和展望

对人类 mtDNA 的研究为我们揭示了现代人是在何时何地以何种方式起源的，这些结果与古人类骨骼和所使用工具的证据相符。仍然需要更多的分子水平上的比较来改善我们构建的 mtDNA 进化树的树根和校正人类 mtDNA 的分化速率。这样能够提供更加可信的人群扩散时间表，也能够更加准确地估算在所发现的非非洲人群体里所包含的母系血统的数量。

获得更多人类和非洲猿的核 DNA 多样性整体程度的定量估计也很重要。通过比较核 DNA 和 mtDNA 的多样性，我们有可能发现伴随在人类起源历史中的 [15] 种群大小瓶颈效应究竟是短暂的还是长期的。古人类学、考古学和分子生物学的充分互动将有利于更深入地分析我们人类是怎样起源的。

在此我们要感谢人类起源研究基金、国家科学基金会和美国国立卫生研究院的

Foundation and the NIH for support. We also thank P. Andrews, K. Bhatia, F. C. Howell, W. W. Howells, R. L. Kirk, E. Mayr, E. M. Prager, V. M. Sarich, C. Stringer and T. White for discussion and help in obtaining placentas.

(**325**, 31-36; 1987)

Rebecca L. Cann[*], Mark Stoneking & Allan C. Wilson
Department of Biochemistry, University of California, Berkeley, California 94720, USA.

Received 17 March; accepted 7 November 1986.

References:

1. Goodman, M. *Hum. Biol.* **35**, 377-424 (1963).

2. Sarich, V. M. & Wilson, A. C. *Science* **158**, 1200-1203 (1967).

3. King, M. C. & Wilson, A. C. *Science* **188**, 107-116 (1975).

4. Ferris, S. D., Wilson, A. C. & Brown, W. M. *Proc. Natl. Acad. Sci. U.S.A.* **78**, 2432-2436 (1981).

5. Brown, W. M., Prager, E. M., Wang, A. & Wilson, A. C. *J. Molec. Evol.* **18**, 225-239 (1982).

6. Sibley, C. G. & Ahlquist, J. E. *J. Molec. Evol.* **20**, 2-15 (1984).

7. Bianchi, N. O., Bianchi, M. S., Cleaver, J. E. & Wolff, S. *J. Molec. Evol.* **22**, 323-333 (1985).

8. O'Brien, S. J. *et al. Nature* **317**, 140-144 (1985).

9. Cavalli-Sforza, L. L. *Proc. R. Soc. Lond.* B**164**, 362-379 (1966).

10. Cavalli-Sforza, L. L. *Sci. Am.* **231**(3), 81-89 (1974).

11. Nei, M. & Roychoudhury, A. K. *Evol. Biol.* **14**, 1-59 (1982).

12. Nei, M. in *Population Genetics and Molecular Evolution* (eds Ohta, T. & Aoki, K.) 41-64 (Japan Sci. Soc. Press, Tokyo, 1985).

13. Constans, J. *et al. Am. J. Phys. Anthrop.* **68**, 107-122 (1985).

14. Wainscoat, J. S. *et al. Nature* **319**, 491-493 (1986).

15. Wilson, A. C. *et al. Biol. J. Linn. Soc.* **26**, 375-400 (1985).

16. Olivo, P. D., Van de Walle, M. J., Laipis, P. J. & Hauswirth, W. W. *Nature* **306**, 400-402 (1983).

17. Brown, W. M. *Proc. Natl. Acad. Sci. U.S.A.* **77**, 3605-3609 (1980).

18. Monnat, R. J. & Loeb, L. A. *Proc. Natl. Acad. Sci. U.S.A.* **82**, 2895-2899 (1985).

19. Monnat, R. J., Maxwell, C. L. & Loeb, L. A. *Cancer Res.* **45**, 1809-1814 (1985).

20. Hauswirth, W. W. & Laipis, P. J. in *Achievements and Perspectives in Mitochondrial Research*, Vol. 2 *Biogenesis* (eds E. Quagliariello, E. C. Slater, F. Palmieri, C. Saccone & A. M. Kroon) 49-60 (Elsevier, New York, 1986).

21. Johnson, M. J. *et al. J. Molec. Evol.* **19**, 255-271 (1983).

22. Cann, R. L. Ph. D. Thesis, Univ. California, Berkeley, California (1982).

23. Stoneking, M., Bhatia, K. & Wilson, A. C. in *Genetic Variation and Its Maintenance in Tropical Populations* (eds Roberts, C. F. & Destefano, G.) 87-100 (Cambridge University Press, Cambridge, 1986).

24. Cann, R. L., Brown, W. M. & Wilson, A. C. *Genetics* **106**, 479-499 (1984).

25. Anderson, S. *et al. Nature* **290**, 457-465 (1981).

26. Nei, M. & Tajima, F. *Genetics* **105**, 207-217 (1983).

27. Whittam, T. S., Clark, A. G., Stoneking, M., Cann, R. L. & Wilson, A. C. *Proc. Natl. Acad. Sci. U.S.A.* (in the press).

28. Greenberg, B. D., Newbold, J. E. & Sugino, A. *Gene* **21**, 33-49 (1983).

29. Horai, S., Gojobori, T. & Matsunaga, E. *Jap. J. Genet.* **61**, 271-275 (1986).

30. Stoneking, M., Bhatia, K. & Wilson, A. C. *Cold Spring Harb. Symp. Quant. Biol.* **51**, 433-439 (1986).

31. Wallace, D. C., Garrison, K. & Knowler, W. C. *Am. J. phys. Anthrop.* **68**, 149-155 (1985).

32. Jones, R. *A. Rev. Anthrop.* **8**, 445-466 (1979).

33. Wolpoff, M. H., Wu, X. Z. & Thorne, A. G. in *Origins of Modern Humans: A World Survey of the Fossil Evidence* (eds Smith, F. H. & Spencer, F.) 411-484 (Liss, New York, 1984).

34. Owen, R. C. in *Origins of Modern Humans: A World Survey of the Fossil Evidence* (eds Smith, F. H. & Spencer, F.) 517-564 (Liss, New York, 1984).

35. Mourant, A. E. *et al. The Distribution of the Human Blood Groups and Other Polymorphism* (Oxford University Press, Oxford, 1978).

36. Murray, J. C. *et al. Proc. Natl. Acad. Sci. U.S.A.* **81**, 3486-3490 (1984).

支持。还要感谢安德鲁斯、巴蒂亚、豪厄尔、豪厄尔斯、柯克、普拉格、迈尔、普拉格、萨里奇、斯特林格和怀特在研究结果讨论和获得胎盘样本方面的帮助。

（周晓明 姜薇 翻译；吕雪梅 审稿）

37. Cooper, D. N. & Schmidtke, J. *Hum. Genet.* **66**, 1-16 (1984).

38. Cooper, D. N. *et al. Hum. Genet.* **69**, 201-205 (1985).

39. Hill, A. V. S., Nicholls, R. D., Thein, S. L. & Higgs, D. R. *Cell* **42**, 809-819 (1985).

40. Chapman, B. S., Vincent, K. A. & Wilson, A. C. *Genetics* **112**, 79-92 (1986).

41. Chakravarti, A. *et al. Proc. Natl. Acad. Sci. U.S.A.* **81**, 6085-6089 (1984).

42. Chakravarti, A. *et al. Am. J. Hum. Genet.* **36**, 1239-1258 (1984).

43. Rightmire, G. P. in *Origins of Modern Humans: A World Survey of the Fossil Evidence* (eds Smith, F. H. & Spencer, F.) 295-326 (Liss, New York, 1984).

44. Bräuer, G. *Courier Forsch. Int. Senckenberg* **69**, 145-165 (1984).

45. Bräuer, G. in *Origins of Modern Humans: A World Survey of the Fossil Evidence* (eds Smith, F. H. & Spencer, F.) 327-410 (Liss, New York, 1984).

46. Isaac, G. *Phil. Trans. R. Soc. Lond.* B**292**, 177-188 (1981).

47. Clark, J. D. *Proc. Br. Acad. Lond.* **67**, 163-192 (1981).

48. Pope, G. G. *Proc. Natl. Acad. Sci. U.S.A.* **80**, 4988-4992 (1983).

49. Coon, C. S. *The Origin of Races* (Knopf, New York, 1962).

50. Stringer, C. B. *Courier Forsch. Inst. Senckenberg* **69**, 131-143 (1984).

51. Andrews, P. *Courier Forsch. Inst. Senckenberg* **69**, 167-175 (1984).

52. Andrew, P. *New Scient.* **102**, 24-26 (1984).

53. Stringer, C. B., Hublin, J. J. & Vandermeersch, B. in *Origins of Modern Humans: A World Survey of the Fossil Evidence* (eds Smith, F. H. & Spencer, F.) 51-136 (Liss, New York, 1984).

54. Horai, S., Goobori, T. & Matsunaga, E. *Hum. Genet.* **68**, 324-332 (1984).

55. Bonne-Tamir, B. *et al. Am. J. Hum. Genet.* **38**, 341-351 (1986).

56. Horai, S. & Matsunaga, E. *Hum. Genet.* **72**, 105-117 (1986).

57. Avise, J. C., Neigel, J. E. & Arnold, J. *J. Molec. Evol.* **20**, 99-105 (1984).

58. Farris, J. S. *Am. Nat.* **106**, 645-668 (1972).

Multi-channel Seismic Imaging of a Crustal Magma Chamber along the East Pacific Rise

R. S. Detrick *et al.*

Editor's Note

New ocean crust is formed by the upwelling of magma at a "divergent" plate junction along a mid-ocean ridge, where two tectonic plates move in opposite directions. The upwelling is fed by a magma chamber at relatively shallow depths within the Earth's crust. This paper by Robert Detrick and colleagues was the first to offer a direct view of such a chamber, answering long-standing questions about their size and shape. The researchers used seismic waves as probes of the deep crustal structure: such waves travel more slowly in softer rock. They find a chamber that is rather narrow—just 4–6 km wide—and probably mushroom-shaped, being supplied with magma by a narrower plume rising from below.

A reflection observed on multi-channel seismic profiles along and across the East Pacific Rise between 8°50′ N and 13°30′ N is interpreted to arise from the top of a crustal magma chamber located 1.2–2.4 km below the sea floor. The magma chamber is quite narrow (<4–6 km wide), but can be traced as a nearly continuous feature for tens of kilometres along the rise axis.

THE presence of a shallow crustal magma chamber at active spreading centres is an important element of current geological models for the formation of ocean crust[1-3]. However, the shape, longevity and along-strike variability of ridge-crest magma chambers remain the subject of considerably controversy[4,5]. The feasibility of using modern multi-channel seismic techniques to image magma chambers at ridge crests was demonstrated a decade ago when three 24-channel seismic reflection profiles were obtained across the East Pacific Rise (EPR) near 9° N[6,7]. In May–June, 1985, we returned to this area and carried out a much more extensive two-ship multi-channel seismic survey of the EPR between 8°50′ N and 13°30′ N. This experiment was designed to provide new information on the shape and dimensions of the axial magma chamber, and to investigate how the magma chamber varies along the rise axis over distances of tens to hundreds of kilometers.

The geological and tectonic setting of the EPR in this area has been well-established from Sea Beam and Sea MARC I surveys[8-10] extensive dredging along the rise axis[11,12], and very high-resolution investigations using bottom photography and manned submersibles[13]. This portion of the EPR is spreading at relatively fast rates of 5–6 cm yr⁻¹ (half-rate)[14] and contains one major transform fault (the Clipperton at 10°15′ N), two large overlapping spreading centres (OSCs) at 9°03′ N and 11°45′ N and several smaller non-transform offsets including OSCs and other small deviations in axial linearity (Devals)[9-11]. Our

沿东太平洋海隆的地壳岩浆房多道地震成像

德特里克等

编者按

沿大洋中脊在"分离的"板块结合带上涌的岩浆形成了新的洋壳，在那里两个构造板块相背运动。岩浆的上涌是由位于地壳内深度相对较浅的岩浆房驱动的。在本文中，罗伯特·德特里克及其同事首次给出了这个岩浆房的直观图像，解答了长期存在的关于岩浆房大小和形状的问题。研究人员利用地震波探测地壳深部构造：地震波在较软的岩石中传播较慢。他们发现了一个很狭窄的岩浆房——只有 4~6 km 宽，而且很可能是蘑菇状，一根更为狭窄的地幔柱从下向该岩浆房供给岩浆。

在沿着和横穿位于 8°50′N 到 13°30′N 之间的东太平洋海隆的多道地震剖面上可以观测到一个反射，我们认为它源于海底以下 1.2~2.4 km 的地壳岩浆房顶部。这个岩浆房相当窄（宽小于 4~6 km），但是沿着隆起轴可以对它近乎连续地追踪数十公里。

活跃型扩张中心浅部地壳岩浆房的存在是目前有关洋壳形成的地质模型中 [1-3] 一个重要的元素。然而，洋脊顶部岩浆房的形态、寿命及其沿走向的变化性仍然是一个极具争议的课题 [4,5]。十年前在 9°N 附近获得了三条 24 道横穿东太平洋海隆（EPR）的反射地震剖面 [6,7]，这表明利用现代多道地震技术对洋脊顶部岩浆房进行成像是可行的。1985 年 5~6 月期间，我们重返该地区，在 EPR 8°50′N 至 13°30′N 的范围内，进行了更为广泛的双船多道地震调查。这项调查试图为轴部岩浆房的形状和大小提供新的信息，并研究沿海隆轴向几十到几百公里距离内岩浆房的变化情况。

在 Sea Beam 型多波束测深仪和 Sea MARC Ⅰ 型侧扫系统的调查中 [8-10]，沿隆起轴 [11,12] 进行了广泛的拖网，并用海底摄像和载人潜水器 [13] 进行了高分辨率的探测，这很好地确定了 EPR 在这一地区的地质和构造环境。EPR 的这部分地区正在以每年 5~6 cm（半扩张速率）[14] 的较高速率扩张，它包含了一个主要的转换断层（位于 10°15′N 的克利珀顿断层）、两个大的重叠扩张中心（OSC）（分别位于 9°03′N 与 11°45′N）以及几个较小的非转换断错（包括 OSC 和其他一些小的相对于轴线的偏

seismic survey was primarily concentrated in two areas—between the 9°03′ N OSC and the Clipperton transform, and in a second area just north of the 12°54′ N OSC (Fig. 1). Seismic refraction data are available in both areas indicating the existence of a crustal low velocity zone (LVZ), interpreted as a magma chamber[15-18], at the rise axis. However, our survey also encompasses part of the ROSE refraction area (~11°30′ N to 12°30′ N) where evidence for a large crustal magma chamber is generally lacking[19,20].

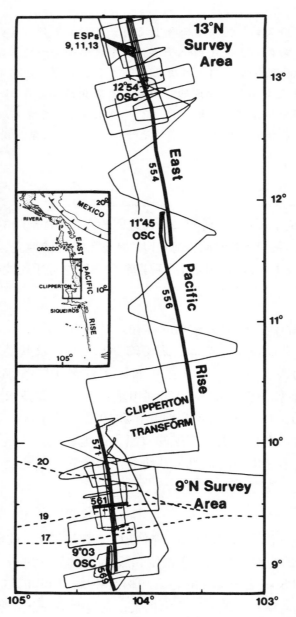

Fig. 1. Map showing the East Pacific Rise (EPR) and the track coverage obtained during our 1985 multi-channel seismic experiment. Labelled profiles (thick solid lines) are shown in Figs 2 and 3 or interpreted in Fig. 5. Dashed lines show the location of the reflection profiles described by Herron *et al*.[6,7].

移体（Deval）[9-11]）。我们的地震探测主要集中在两个区域——位于 9°03′N 处 OSC 和克利珀顿转换断层之间的区域以及 OSC 12°54′N 处的北部区域（图 1）。这两个区域的地震折射数据揭示了在隆起轴线上存在着一个地壳低速带（LVZ），我们将它解释为一个岩浆房 [15-18]。然而，我们也勘测了部分 ROSE 折射区（约 11°30′N 到 12°30′N），该区一般来说缺少巨大的壳内岩浆房存在的证据 [19,20]。

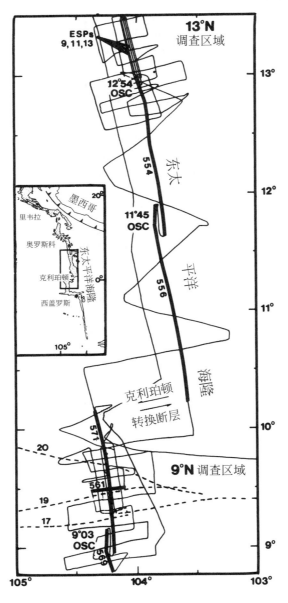

图 1. 1985 年我们进行的多道地震实验获得的东太平洋海隆（EPR）和测线覆盖区图。标注的剖面（粗的实线）将在图 2 和图 3 展示或在图 5 中作出解释。虚线展示了赫伦等 [6,7] 报告的反射剖面的位置。

The experiment involved two ships, the *Robert D. Conrad* of Lamont–Doherty Geological Observatory and the *Thomas Washington* of Scripps Institution of Oceanography. More than 3,500 km of conventional, 48-channel common-depth-point (CDP) reflection data were obtained including 30 new profiles across the EPR and a series of CDP reflection lines along the crest of the EPR between 8°50′ N and 13°30′ N (Fig. 1). The seismic velocity structure of the crust and upper mantle in the axial region was determined using the two-ship expanding spread profiling (ESP) technique[21]. The ESPs were oriented parallel to the rise axis and shot using airguns and, in some cases, explosives. In the 9° N area, ESPs were shot on the rise crest, and at two and five km away from the ridge crest on either side. In the 13° N area, five ESPs were located within ±3.6 km of the rise axis.

Single-ship stacked time sections form the basis of our preliminary observations. About two-thirds of the cross-axis lines have been migrated after stack using the wave equation technique in the F–K domain[22]. Analysis of the ESPs has mainly involved P-wave velocity travel-time inversions on the airgun portions of the ESPs. An initial velocity–depth function was constructed using the tau-sum technique after transformation of the data into tau-p[23]. The velocity–depth function was then iteratively refined by forward travel-time and WKBJ synthetic seismogram modelling.

Results

Two representative CDP reflection profiles across and along the EPR are shown in Figs 2 and 3. A large amplitude reflection is present about 0.6 s below the sea floor on both profiles. On the cross-ridge profile, this high-amplitude event is centred beneath the rise axis and is less than 3 km in width, although a weak continuation of this reflector appears to extend beneath the ridge flanks, especially west of the rise axis. An event is present at about 6 s two-way travel time that may be a Moho reflection based on its position in the section. On the reflection profile shot along the rise axis, a large-amplitude, relatively flat-lying reflector is present at about 4 s two-way travel time that corresponds to the event seen on the cross-ridge profiles. This event can be traced for distances of tens of kilometres along the crest of the EPR, and in a few locations, the amplitude of this reflector is strong enough that it can be observed on single channel monitor records. Some weaker, low frequency events are present below this strong reflection that may also be real, but no obvious Moho reflection is observed.

这个实验使用了两条船，拉蒙特 – 多尔蒂地质观测中心的"罗伯特·康拉德号"和斯克里普斯海洋研究所的"托马斯·华盛顿号"。我们得到了 3,500 多千米长的常规 48 道共深度点（CDP）反射数据，它包括横跨东太平洋海隆的 30 条新剖面和 8°50′N 和 13°30′N 之间（图 1）沿 EPR 顶部的一系列 CDP 反射剖面。用双船扩展排列剖面（ESP）法 [21] 得到轴区地壳和上地幔的地震波速结构。将这些 ESP 平行于隆起轴设置，并用气枪对其放炮，有时也用炸药。在 9°N 的区域，在海隆顶部和距离隆起顶部任一边两到五公里远的位置对这些 ESP 放炮。在 13°N 的区域，在距离隆起轴 ±3.6 km 的范围内设置了 5 条 ESP。

单船叠加时间剖面构成了我们初步观测的基础。大约三分之二的横轴测线都在 F–K 域 [22] 用波动方程技术进行了叠后偏移。对 ESP 的分析主要包括对 ESP 进行气枪放炮的部分进行 P 波波速的走时反演。将数据进行 τ-p 变换之后，利用 τ-sum 技术构建一个初始的速度 – 深度关系式 [23]。然后，将这个速度 – 深度关系式通过走时正演和 WKBJ 合成地震图模拟进行迭代改进。

结　果

图 2 与图 3 分别展示了横穿和沿着 EPR 的两条典型的 CDP 反射剖面。在这两条剖面上，一个大振幅反射波出现在海底以下约 0.6 秒处。在横穿洋脊剖面上，这个高振幅同相轴集中于隆起轴的下方，其宽度小于 3 km，尽管该反射层微弱的连续性看似可延续至海隆的侧翼之下，特别是海隆轴部的西侧。一个同相轴出现在约 6 秒双程走时的深度，基于其在剖面上的位置推测，它可能是来自莫霍面的反射。在沿隆起轴放炮的反射剖面上，一个大振幅、相对平伏的反射层出现在约 4 秒双程旅行时的深度上，它与在海隆横向剖面上观测到的同相轴相对应。这个同相轴可以沿 EPR 顶部被连续追踪数十公里，在几个地方该反射层的振幅甚至强到可以在单道记录上观测到。一些较弱的低频同相轴出现在该强反射层的下方，这些弱的反射层可能也是真实存在的，但没有观测到明显的莫霍面反射。

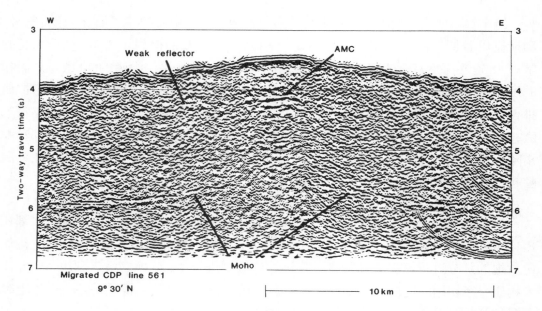

Fig. 2. Migrated time section for CDP Line 561 which crosses the EPR near 9°30′N. These data were shot using a 29.31 (1785 in³) airgun array and recorded on a 48-channel, 2.4-km streamer with an active group length of 50 m. The data were bandpass filtered 5–40 Hz, corrected for spherical divergence, predictively deconvolved (filter length 250 ms; prediction distance 40 ms), stacked and migrated using the F–K wave equation technique[22]. The data are displayed with a time variable gain and a 3-trace additive mix. The relatively flat, high-amplitude event beneath the rise axis is believed to be a reflection from the top of an axial magma chamber (AMC). A weak event at the same depth as the AMC reflector can be traced out beneath the ridge flanks and could represent the top of a frozen chamber. Moho reflections can be traced within 2–3 km of the rise axis.

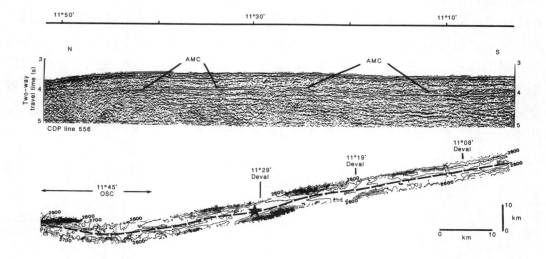

Fig. 3. Time section of a 100-km-long segment of CDP line 556 along the EPR south of the 11°45′N OSC illustrating the alongstrike continuity of the magma chamber reflection. Lower panel shows a 20-m Sea Beam map of this portion of the EPR crest and the location of the MCS profile (dashed line). The reflection data have been bandpass filtered 5–40 Hz, corrected for spherical divergence, predictively deconvolved (filter length 750 ms; prediction distance 40 ms) and filtered again 6–20 Hz. The data are displayed as in Fig. 2. Deval locations after Langmuir *et al.*[11]; stars indicate areas of reported hydrothermal activity[24].

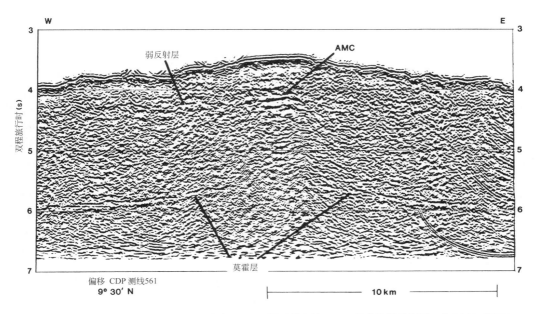

图 2. CDP 测线 561 的时间偏移剖面，它在 9°30′N 附近横穿过 EPR。这些数据是利用一个 29.31（1785 in³）气枪阵列放炮并利用一个 2.4 km 长的、带有 50 m 长活动组的 48 道漂浮电缆记录。对这些数据进行了 5~40 Hz 的带通滤波、球面扩散校正、预测反褶积（滤波器长度为 250 ms；预测距离为 40 ms），并利用 F–K 域波动方程进行叠加和偏移[22]。数据显示是通过一个时变增益和 3 道累积混合技术。隆起轴下方相对平的高振幅同相轴被认为是来自一个轴部岩浆房（AMC）顶部的反射。与轴部岩浆房反射层深度相同的较弱同相轴可以被追踪至洋脊侧翼的下方，它可能代表了一个冷却的岩浆房顶部。莫霍面反射可以在距离隆起轴部 2~3 km 的范围内被追踪到。

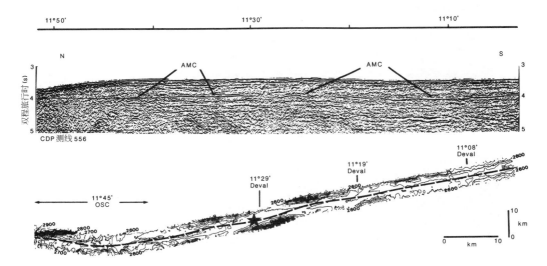

图 3. OSC 11°45′N 以南沿 EPR 的 CDP 测线 556 上一段长 100 km 的时间剖面，它展示了岩浆房反射沿走向的连续性。下图显示了 EPR 顶部这部分 20 m 的 Sea Beam 型多波束测深图以及 MCS 剖面（虚线）的位置。反射数据已经经过 5~40 Hz 的带通滤波，球面扩散校正，预测反褶积（滤波器长度为 750 ms；预测距离为 40 ms）以及 6~20 Hz 滤波的再次处理。数据显示方式与图 2 中的一样。Deval 的位置是根据兰米尔等[11]确定的；五角星代表已报道的热液活动区域[24]。

173

Evidence for a crustal magma chamber. Several lines of evidence indicate that the shallow event seen in these records at the rise axis is a reflection from the top of a crustal LVZ. The reflection is seen on single channel monitor records and in common mid-point gathers and thus is not an artefact of the stacking process. The stacking velocity of this event (2.3–2.4 km s^{-1}) is much higher than the value of 1.5 km s^{-1} expected for a waterpath sidescatter event or a high-order water bottom multiple. This stacking velocity yields an interval velocity of 4.9 km s^{-1} for the crust above this reflector which is a reasonable average value for the upper 1 km of the oceanic crust near the EPR[25]. At several locations along the ridge, the polarity of this event observed on the near-offset trace in CDP gathers is clearly reversed relative to the sea floor return, as would be expected for a reflection from the top of a LVZ. However, the waveform is quite variable, even from CDP to CDP, and in other locations a phase-reversal is not apparent. The strongest evidence that this event is associated with an axial LVZ comes from the ESPs shot along the rise axis. They display a pronounced shadow zone for crustal arrivals beyond 11 km range that is very diagnostic of a LVZ[18] (Fig. 4). Although ESPs were obtained at only two locations along the ridge (9°35′ N and 13°10′ N), sonobuoys collected elsewhere along the rise axis also frequently display this same strong attenuation of refracted energy beyond 10–12 km range.

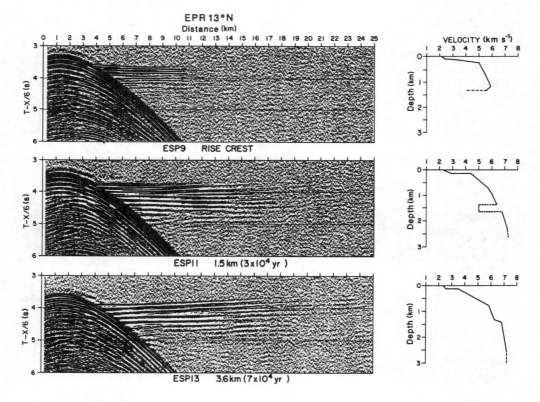

Fig. 4. Record sections for three ESPs shot along and parallel to the EPR near 13° N. ESP 9 (top) was shot along the rise axis, ESP 11 (middle) and ESP 13 (bottom) are 1.5 and 3.6 km from the ridge axis, respectively. The source in each case was a 35.21 (2145 in³) airgun array. The data have been gathered into 50-m bins, summed, bandpass filtered 6–40 Hz, and plotted with a reducing velocity of 6 km s^{-1} and a gain that is scaled linearly with range. Compressional wave velocity solutions for each ESP are shown on the right derived from travel-time modeling.

地壳岩浆房存在的证据。数条测线的证据表明在这些记录上观测到的位于洋脊轴部的浅层同相轴是来自地壳中一个低速带顶部的反射。该反射在单道记录和共中心点道集上均可看到，因此不是叠加过程中产生的假象。该同相轴的叠加速度（2.3~2.4 km/s）要比水道侧向散射或高阶水底多次波的叠加速度值 1.5 km/s 高得多。对于这个反射层以上的地壳而言，该叠加速度产生了一个 4.9 km/s 的层间速度，对于 EPR 附近上部 1 km 厚的洋壳来说，这是一个合理的平均值 [25]。在沿着海隆的几个地点，CDP 道集中近偏移距道上观测到的该同相轴的极性相对于海底反射而言明显发生了倒转，这正如所预期的低速带顶部反射会出现极性倒转一样。然而，波形变化很大（即使在 CDP 与 CDP 之间），而在其他地点，相位反转不是很明显。能证明这个同相轴与轴部低速带有关的最有力证据来自沿着隆起轴线的 ESP 测线炮集资料。对于在地壳中超过 11 km 范围的波至，它们显示出了一个明显的阴影区，这是低速带非常明显的特征 [18]（图 4）。尽管仅在沿轴的两个地方获得 ESP（9°35′N 和 13°10′N），但是在沿着隆起轴的其他地方收集的声呐浮标也经常显示出这种类似的超过 10~12 km 范围的折射能量的强烈衰减。

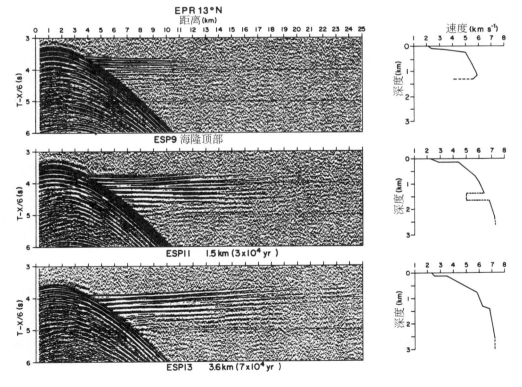

图 4. 三条沿着或平行于 13°N 附近 EPR 的 ESP 的记录剖面。ESP 9（顶部）是沿着隆起轴放炮，ESP 11（中部）和 ESP13（底部）分别是距离海隆轴部 1.5 km 和 3.6 km 处放炮。每一种情况的震源都是 35.21（2145 in³）气枪阵列。数据已经进行了 50 m 间隔的重采样、累加以及 6~40 Hz 的带通滤波，然后利用了一个 6 km/s 的折合速度和一个与距离成比例的增益作图。每一个 ESP 的纵波速度解如右图所示，它们是通过走时模拟得到的。

We interpret this LVZ to be an axial magma chamber (AMC) or zone of melt within the crust beneath the rise axis and use the reflections from the top of this LVZ to infer the width, depth and along-axis variation in the magma chamber.

Width of the magma chamber. The results from this experiment provide very tight constraints on the width of the magma chamber at the EPR. The section shown in Fig. 2 appears to be typical of the rise crest south of the Clipperton transform. The reflection from the top of the magma chamber migrates into a relatively flat, high-amplitude event with a maximum width of 2–3 km. We have not yet been able to image either the walls or floor of the magma chamber, but Moho reflections can be confidently traced to within at least 2–3 km of the rise axis on both the eastern and western flanks of the ridge, placing an upper bound of 4–6 km on the total width of any crustal magma chamber along this portion of the EPR. A weak, discontinuous reflector can be traced out onto the ridge flanks at the same depth as the magma chamber reflection that could represent the top of a frozen magma chamber, perhaps marking the contact between the sheeted dykes and the underlying isotropic gabbros. This is the first time, as far as we are aware, that an event such as this has been seen in marine reflection profiles.

In the 13° N area, a magma chamber reflection is observed on only a few profiles crossing the ridge, and Moho reflections are generally not seen, possibly due to somewhat rougher ridge-flank topography. Where magma chamber reflections are observed, they appear to be no more than 2 km wide. The existence of a very narrow crustal magma chamber near 13° N is strongly supported by an analysis of the three ESPs shown in Fig. 4. Although a seismic LVZ is present 1.2 km below the sea floor at the rise crest (ESP 9), only 3.6 km away (ESP 13) a typical oceanic velocity structure is present with a well-developed lower crustal (layer 3) refractor and no evidence for a crustal LVZ. Even at ESP 11, 1.5 km from the rise crest, arrivals with phase velocities of 7 km s^{-1}, characteristic of the lower crust, are clearly seen beyond 9–10 km range. However, these arrivals are not continuously connected with arrivals at shorter ranges having phase velocities typical of the upper crust (layer 2). The existence of this small shadow zone indicates the presence of a thin (<300 m thick) LVZ sandwiched between the upper and lower crust. However, the total width of the magma chamber in this area is probably less than 4–6 km, and only 1.5 km from the ridge axis the seismic LVZ, if present at all, is extremely thin.

Our estimate of the width of the magma chamber at the EPR is thus well-constrained by the width of the reflections from the roof of the chamber, the gap in the Moho reflection at the rise axis and the crustal velocities from ESPs in the axial region. The narrow magma chamber we have found (4–6 km maximum, generally <3–4 km wide) is incompatible with the large (>10–20 km), funnel-shaped bodies proposed on the basis of some ophiolite models[3,26], but is consistent with the results of recent refraction experiments at the EPR[17-19].

Depth of the magma chamber. The depth of the top of the magma chamber is also well-constrained in our experiment by the ESPs shot along the rise axis and the two-way travel

我们将这个低速带解释为一个轴部岩浆房（AMC）或隆起轴下方地壳中的熔融带，并利用来自这个低速带顶部的反射来推测岩浆房的宽度、深度及其沿轴变化情况。

岩浆房的宽度。这项实验的结果对 EPR 下方的岩浆房宽度提供了十分牢靠的约束。图 2 中展示的剖面看似是克利珀顿转换断层以南海隆顶部的典型。来自岩浆房顶部的反射迁移至一个相对平缓而高振幅的同相轴之中，其最大宽度为 2~3 km。我们还不能对岩浆房的侧翼或底部进行成像，但是在洋脊东西两翼上，莫霍面反射波可以被有效追踪至隆起轴的至少 2~3 km 处，将沿 EPR 这部分下方地壳岩浆房的总宽度的上界限定在 4~6 km。在与岩浆房反射相同的深度上，一个弱的不连续反射层能被追踪至洋脊的侧翼，它可能代表了一个冷却的岩浆房的顶部，有可能标志着席状岩墙与下覆的各向同性辉长岩的接触带。据我们所知，这是第一次在海洋反射剖面上发现这种现象。

在 13°N 的区域，岩浆房反射只能在横穿洋脊的几条剖面上被观测到，一般观测不到莫霍面反射波，这可能是由洋脊侧翼更为粗糙的地形导致的。在可以观测到岩浆房反射波的地方，它们的宽度一般不超过 2 km。通过图 4 中显示的三个 EPS 分析结果，可以发现在 13°N 附近很可能存在着一个非常窄的地壳岩浆房。尽管在海隆顶部（ESP 9）处海床 1.2 km 以下存在一个 LVZ，但是在仅相隔 3.6 km 的地方（ESP 13）却出现了典型的海洋速度结构，它拥有一个发育良好的下地壳（层 3）折射层，并且没有证据表明地壳低速带的存在。甚至在 ESP 11 处（距离海隆顶部 1.5 km），具有 7 km/s 相速度的波至（是下地壳的特征），在超过 9~10 km 的范围内能够被清晰地观测到。然而，这些波至不能与较短距离范围内的波至连续地衔接，后者具有上地壳的典型相速度特征（层 2）。这个小阴影区的存在表明存在一个薄的低速带（厚度小于 300 米），它镶嵌在上下地壳之间。但是，这个地区岩浆房的总宽度很可能小于 4~6 km，并且在距离洋脊轴部仅 1.5 km 的地方如果存在地震低速带的话，也极其薄。

因此，来自岩浆房顶部反射的宽度、隆起轴部莫霍面反射的间隔以及轴部地区 ESP 提供的地壳速度共同为我们对 EPR 岩浆房宽度的估计提供了较好的约束。我们发现的窄岩浆房（宽度最大为 4~6 km，一般小于 3~4 km）与基于蛇绿岩模型得到的大型（大于 10~20 km）漏斗状岩浆房不一致 [3,26]，但是与最近在 EPR 获得的折射实验结果相一致 [17-19]。

岩浆房的深度。在我们的实验中，沿着隆起轴部对 ESP 放炮的实验以及海底与 AMC 反射波之间的双程走时都为岩浆房顶部深度的确定提供了良好的约束。沿着

time between the sea floor and the AMC reflection. Along the portion of the EPR we have surveyed, the roof of the magma chamber varies in depth between 1.2 and 2.4 km below the sea floor, a result which is consistent with previous estimates based on seismic refraction studies at the EPR[15-18]. The most interesting new observation made in this study is the correlation between the depth of the magma chamber (that is, the thickness of the crustal lid above the chamber) and the depth of the rise axis. Although the depth of the EPR varies <300 m along the 500 km of ridge we surveyed, the depth of the magma chamber changes by more than a kilometer. In general, the shallowest parts of the rise axis (south of Clipperton, between 11° N and 11°40′ N, north and south of the 12°54′ N OSC) are associated with the thinnest crustal lids, While the magma chamber reflection is deeper, more discontinuous and, in some cases, absent altogether where the rise axis is deep (north of Clipperton, near the OSC at 9°03′ N and 11°45′ N). These results are a striking confirmation of the inferences of MacDonald *et al.*[9] of magmatic budget based on axial geomorphology.

Along-strike variation in the magma chamber. As part of this experiment, we obtained a unique series of reflection profiles along the crest of the EPR between 8°50′ N and 13°30′ N, using Sea Beam to keep the vessel positioned atop the axial high. An AMC reflection is observed along slightly more than half (61%) of the 500 km of ridge crest we surveyed (Fig. 5). The most continuous magma chamber reflection is found south of the Clipperton transform, where a high amplitude event can be traced more than 90 km from just north of the large 9°03′ N OSC to a point about 10 km south of the Clipperton transform (line 571). There are three locations, dashed on the interpretive section, where the AMC event becomes weak and somewhat discontinuous. However, in each instance we believe this was caused by the vessel sliding off the axial high rather than a physical discontinuity in the magma chamber. Several other small gaps in the AMC reflection (for example, 11° N, 11°29′ N, 11°40′ N, 11°50′ N) may have a similar origin. Magma chamber reflections that are laterally continuous for 40–50 km are also observed south of the 12°54′ N OSC on line 554 and between 11° N and 11°40′ N on line 556. These results are the first geophysical evidence for the continuity of an axial magma chamber over distances of several tens of kilometres at the EPR.

我们所调查的 EPR 部分，岩浆房顶部的深度在海床以下 1.2~2.4 km 之间变化，这一结果与先前在 EPR 基于地震折射的研究结果一致 [15-18]。在此项研究中最有意思的新发现是岩浆房深度（也就是岩浆房之上地壳盖层的厚度）与隆起轴的深度之间存在相关性。尽管 EPR 的深度沿着我们所调查的长 500 km 的洋脊变化幅度小于 300 m，但是岩浆房深度的变化却超过 1 km。一般而言，隆起轴最浅的部分（在克利帕顿以南位于 11°N 与 11°40′N 之间，12°54′N 处 OSC 以南和以北）与最薄的地壳盖层有关；而在隆起轴深的地方（克利珀顿以北，位于 9°03′N 和 11°45′N OSC 附近），岩浆房反射波更深、更不连续，有时甚至完全消失。这些结果是对麦克唐纳等 [9] 基于轴部地貌学而推断的岩浆收支的一种有力证实。

岩浆房沿走向的变化。作为这项实验的一部分，我们沿着 8°50′N 与 13°30′N 之间的 EPR 顶部采集了一系列独特的反射剖面，利用波束定位来保持船体位于轴部高地的顶部。AMC 反射波在沿着我们所调查的长 500 km 的洋脊顶部的多半（61%）区域均有发现（图 5）。最连续的岩浆房反射波出现在克利珀顿转换断层以南，在那里能够从 9°03′N 处巨大的 OSC 以北到克利珀顿转换断层以南约 10 km 处的一点（测线 571）连续追踪一个高振幅的同相轴超过 90 km。在三个位置上（在剖面上解释线以虚线表示），轴部岩浆房同相轴变弱，且变得有些不连续。然而，我们认为这些微弱的非连续同相轴是由船体偏离轴部高地所致，而非由于岩浆房存在物理不连续性。在 AMC 反射波上出现的其他几个间隙（例如位于 11°N、11°29′N、11°40′N 以及 11°50′N 等处）可能也是由相似原因造成的。横向延续 40~50 km 的岩浆房反射在 12°54′N OSC 以南的测线 554 和 11°N 与 11°40′N 之间的测线 556 上也有发现。这些结果提供了在 EPR 的轴部岩浆房延绵数十公里的首个地球物理证据。

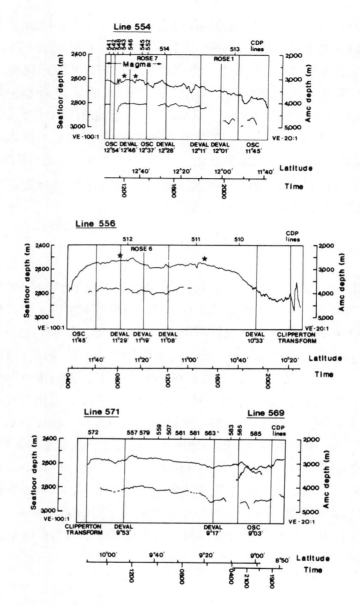

Fig. 5. (Left) Interpretive line drawing of a longitudinal section along the EPR extending from the 9°03′ N OSC to the Clipperton Transform (lower panel), from the Clipperton Transform to the 11°45′ N OSC (middle panel) and from the 11°45′ N OSC to the 12°54′ N OSC (upper panel). In each drawing the top curve, plotted using the scale on the left, is the sea floor depth derived from the centre beam of the Sea Beam swath. The lower curve, plotted using the scale on the right, is the depth of the AMC reflection below the sea surface derived from the observed two-way travel time assuming an interval velocity of 4.9 km s[-1] for the crust between the sea floor and this reflector. Each panel is annotated with the location of the ridge crossing profiles (labelled ticks) and various ridge axis discontinuities including transforms, OSC and Devals (vertical bars). The stars mark the locations of known hydrothermal activity[13,24,27].

The largest gap in the AMC reflection (~77 km) occurs north of the Clipperton transform. This ridge segment is deep (>2,700 m) and relatively narrow (<4 km wide), plunging over

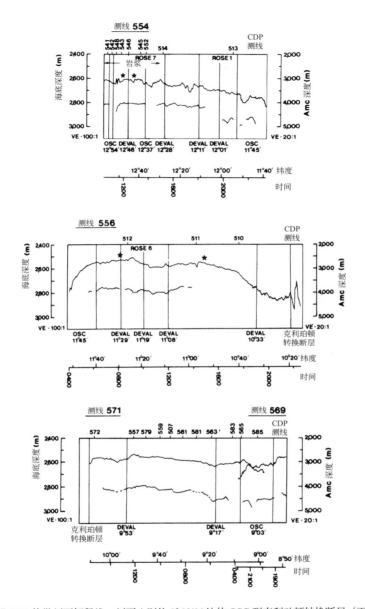

图 5.（左）沿 EPR 的纵剖面解释线，剖面分别从 9°03′N 处的 OSC 到克利珀顿转换断层（下图）、从克利珀顿转换断层到 11°45′N 处的 OSC（中图）以及从 11°45′N 处的 OSC 到 12°54′N 处的 OSC（上图）。在每一个图中，上部曲线代表由多波束带测深仪获得的海底深度，其标尺显示在左边；下部曲线是根据双程走时获得的轴部岩浆房反射在海面以下的深度，假设海底与该反射层之间地壳的层间速度为 4.9 km/s，其标尺显示在右边。每个图都标注有洋脊横剖面的位置（标注于每个图的下方）和各种洋脊轴部不连续体，包括转换断层、OSC 以及 Deval（垂直棒）。五角星标注的是已知的热液活动地点 [13,24,27]。

　　AMC 反射波的最大间隙（约 77 km）出现在克利珀顿转换断层以北。这部分洋脊很深（大于 2,700 m），并且相对较窄（宽度小于 4 km），向克利珀顿洋脊与

200 m toward the Clipperton ridge–transform intersection (Fig. 5). The absence of an AMC reflection along this part of the EPR indicates that a magma chamber, if present at all, is much smaller than to the south. Seismic refraction studies had previously suggested the possible absence of a crustal magma chamber in the vicinity of ROSE line 6 near 11°19′ N[20]. We observe a clear, phase-reversed AMC event on line 556 in this area (Fig. 3). However, no corresponding event is seen on the cross-axis profiles, again suggesting that the magma chamber is quite small or partially solidified. The presence of a small, seismically unresolvable AMC along a substantial length of the ridge segment north of the Clipperton transform is the strongest geophysical evidence so far that crustal magma chambers are not steady-state features at these spreading rates.

The AMC reflection deepens toward the large OSCs at 9°03′ N and 11°45′ N. It can be traced into the region where the spreading centres overlap, but in each case the magma chamber reflections disappear before reaching the tip of the overlapping ridges (Fig. 5). Reflection profiles across and through the overlap basins at both OSCs do not reveal an AMC reflection, suggesting that the axial magma chamber is physically disrupted. These observations, and the small dimensions of the magma chamber documented above, clearly favour the OSC model of MacDonald et al.[9,28]. However, both their model and Lonsdale's[29,30] model predict a continuous magma chamber beneath small-offset OSCs. We observe a gap in the AMC reflection across the small OSCs at 12°54′ N and 12°37′ N (Fig. 5), suggesting that the magma chamber is disrupted as predicted by Langmuir et al.[11] on petrological grounds. However, the AMC reflector is generally continuous across many of the smaller ridge axis discontinuities located between OSCs, including seven of the ten Devals identified along this portion of the EPR (Fig. 5). It may be significant that several Devals (9°17′ N, 9°53′ N, 11°08′ N, 12°28′ N) are located near or close to prominent dips in the AMC reflection, although in these areas it is difficult to keep a ship located precisely on top of the axial high.

Discussion

We have not yet been able to image either the walls or floor of the magma chamber, but some aspects of its shape can be constrained by our data. Figure 6 shows a model that is consistent with our observations. The magma chamber is modelled as a flat-topped body with a roof 2–3 km wide. We include a thin region of liquid melt in the top of the chamber to explain the high amplitude of the AMC reflector and its reversed polarity. However, both of these observations require only a strong, negative velocity contrast and do not necessitate the presence of a liquid. A chamber consisting, for example, of a partially solidified crystal mush[31] would also be consistent with our results. The observation of Moho reflections very close to the rise axis, and our ESP data, indicate that the chamber does not widen with depth but remains quite narrow.

One of the major remaining uncertainties concerns the thickness of the chamber. In Fig. 6 we envision a mushroom-shaped magma chamber with a bulbous shallow top and a narrower central stalk that extends to depths equivalent to Moho in the adjacent crust. We base this model on the assumption that, were the chamber much thinner (for example,

转换断层交叉区域插入超过 200 m（图 5）。沿 EPR 的这部分 AMC 反射波缺失，表明岩浆房，如果存在的话，要比南部的小得多。先前的地震折射研究表明在 11°19′N 附近的 ROSE 测线 6 周边可能并不存在地壳岩浆房[20]。在这区域的测线 556 上我们观测到一个清晰的相位倒转的 AMC 同相轴（图 3）。然而，在横轴剖面上没有发现相应的同相轴，这再一次表明这个岩浆房的规模可能很小或已经部分固化。在克利珀顿转换断层以北沿相当长的一段洋脊发现一个十分小、地震波无法分辨的 AMC，这是迄今为止能够证明在这些扩张速率下地壳岩浆房并非是稳态特征的最有力的地球物理证据。

AMC 反射朝位于 9°03′N 和 11°45′N 处的巨大 OSC 方向加深。它能被追踪到扩张中心重叠的区域，但是在每一种情形中岩浆房反射波在到达重叠洋脊顶端之前都消失了（图 5）。在两个 OSC 的重叠洋盆横向和纵向反射剖面上都没有发现 AMC 反射，表明轴部岩浆房发生物理中断。这些观测结果，加上上述记录的小规模岩浆房，明显支持麦克唐纳等提出的 OSC 模型[9,28]。然而，他们的模型和朗斯代尔的模型[29,30]都预测在小型断错 OSC 的下方存在一个连续的岩浆房。在位于 12°54′N 和 12°37′N 的小型 OSC 地震波横剖面上，我们发现轴部岩浆房反射存在一个间隙，表明岩浆房发生中断，正如兰米尔等[11]以岩石学为依据预测的一样。然而，在横穿过许多位于 OSC 之间的较小洋脊轴间断面，包括沿 EPR 这一区域识别出的十个 Deval 中的七个（图 5），AMC 反射面一般是连续的。几个 Deval（9°17′N、9°53′N、11°08′N、12°28′N）位于 AMC 反射显著倾斜的部位附近，这可能有重要意义，尽管在这些地方很难将船精确地定位于轴部高地的顶部。

讨 论

我们尚不能对岩浆房的侧壁或顶部进行成像，但是我们的数据能为岩浆房形态的某些方面提供约束。图 6 展示了一个与我们观察结果相一致的模型。岩浆房被模拟成一个带有 2~3 km 宽顶盖的顶部平坦物体。我们在岩浆房的顶部引入了一个薄的熔融流体区域，以解释 AMC 反射层的高振幅及其极性倒转。然而，这两种观测都只需要大的负速度差存在，并不一定表明有流体存在。例如，一个由部分固化的晶粥状岩浆组成的岩浆房也能与我们的结果保持一致[31]。十分靠近洋脊轴部的莫霍面反射以及我们的 ESP 数据都表明岩浆房没有随深度而变宽，而是仍保持很窄的形状。

一个重要的遗留问题是关于岩浆房的厚度。如图 6 所示，我们设想了一个蘑菇状的岩浆房，它具有一个球形的浅顶部和一个向下延伸至相当于邻近地壳莫霍面深度的更窄的中央茎部。这个模型基于如下假设：如果岩浆房要薄得多（例如，是一

a partially molten sill), unreasonable values of the elastic attenuation factor, Q would be required to explain the complete extinction of arrivals beyond 11 km range on the ridge axis ESPs. However, we have no direct knowledge of the physical properties of the material within the chamber or its thickness and, consequently, the root structure of the magma chamber shown in Fig. 6 is still largely speculative.

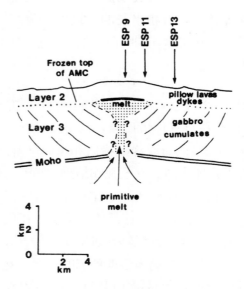

Fig. 6. Schematic drawing of the shape and dimensions of the AMC at the EPR based on the multi-channel seismic results presented in this paper. Location of ESPs shown in Fig. 4 is indicated for comparison. See text for discussion.

There is a good correlation between some of the geochemical and petrological variations in basalts dredged from this portion of the EPR[11] and our seismic results. The basalts with the most homogeneous compositions and highest eruption temperatures were dredged from the ridge segment south of the Clipperton transform where we record some of the strongest, most continuous magma chamber reflections. Low eruption temperatures and more heterogeneous compositions are found in basalts along the ridge segment north of Clipperton where we do not observe a magma chamber event. The gaps we observe in the magma chamber reflection across both large- and small-offset OSCs also appear to substantiate petrological evidence for a lack of magmatic continuity and mixing across OSCs[11]. However, the smaller offsets between OSCs, such as Devals, are generally not associated with breaks in the magma chamber reflection, and we can trace the AMC reflector continuously across Devals that appear to separate regions of distinctly different petrology (for example, 9°53′ N, 11°08′ N, 12°28′ N).

Based on the geochemical variability of basalts erupted along the ridge, Langmuir *et al.*[11] have recently argued for a much smaller scale magmatic segmentation of the EPR than previously proposed[32-34]. Instead of a single, centrally supplied magma chamber underlying each tectonically defined spreading centre cell, they propose that the AMC can

个部分熔融的岩床），就需要弹性衰减因子 Q 的不合理值，来解释在超过洋脊轴部 ESP 11 km 的范围波至完全消失的现象。然而，我们对岩浆房内物质的物理性质及其厚度还不甚了解，因此图 6 所示的岩浆房根部结构大部分仍是推测的。

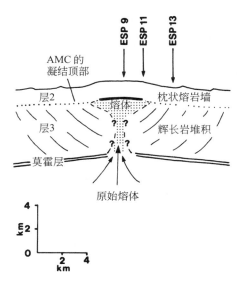

图 6. 以本文多道地震结果为基础绘制的 EPR 的 AMC 的形状和大小示意图。图 4 所示的 ESP 位置用于对比。讨论部分见正文。

在 EPR 的这部分区域 [11]，利用拖网获得的玄武岩的一些地球化学和岩石学变化情况与我们的地震结果之间存在着较好的相关性。拖网获得的具有最均匀组成和最高喷发温度的玄武岩来自克利珀顿转换断层以南的洋脊分段，在那里我们记录到了一些最强、最连续的岩浆房反射波。沿克利珀顿转换断层以北的洋脊分段发现的玄武岩则具有较低的喷发温度和较不均匀的组成，在此我们没有观测到岩浆房同相轴。我们在横穿大型和小型偏移距 OSC 的岩浆房反射剖面上观察到的间隙似乎也证实了 OSC 缺失岩浆连续性与混合性的岩石学证据 [11]。然而，OSC 之间较小的断错，例如 Deval，一般与岩浆房反射波的中断无关，并且我们穿过 Deval 能连续地追踪到 AMC 反射层，这些 Deval 似乎可以分隔岩性显著不同的区域（例如在 9°53′N、11°08′N、12°28′N 等处）。

在沿洋脊喷发的玄武岩的地球化学性变化的基础上，兰米尔等 [11] 最近指出在 EPR 中存在一个比先前提出 [32-34] 的规模小得多的岩浆分离。他们提出 AMC 在单个扩张中心单元之内是物理不连续的，它沿着洋脊分布有多重喷发中心，而不是在每

be physically discontinuous within a single cell with multiple injection centres distributed along the ridge. We have seismic data on the along-strike continuity of the AMC reflection from three tectonically defined spreading centre cells: 9°03′ N to Clipperton, Clipperton to 11°45′ N, 11°45′ N to Orozco. In each of these cells we can trace the AMC reflection laterally for distances of at least 40–50 km along strike. We believe a physically continuous magma chamber must exist at this scale along at least portions of the EPR. South of Clipperton transform, where morphological[9], petrological[11] and seismic evidence all indicate a large, robust magma chamber is present, the entire spreading cell (>90 km) appears to be associated with a single, laterally continuous magma chamber. However, in the other two cells, significant gaps in the AMC reflection may indicate that the magma chamber is much more discontinuous along strike, although the absence of an AMC reflection does not necessarily preclude the presence of a magma chamber.

The picture that emerges from both the seismic and petrological data is of a magma chamber that is quite narrow (<4–6 km wide), but continuous for several tens of kilometres along the ridge axis. Where the magmatic budget is high (for example, south of Clipperton), a single magma chamber can extend along an entire, tectonically-defined spreading centre cell. The chamber will be relatively large and well-mixed, and erupting basalts will be geochemically homogeneous. Where the magmatic budget is low (for example, north of Clipperton), the magma chamber is smaller, or absent altogether, incompletely mixed and disrupted by both large and small OSCs. Lavas will be geochemically and petrologically diverse. Although smaller offsets between OSCs are not generally associated with physical disruptions in the AMC, geochemical anomalies associated with these features may reflect multiple regions of supply from below the crust or a magma chamber that is incompletely mixed and heterogeneous in its composition. The correlation of this morphological, geochemical and seismic variability along the rise axis appears to offer great promise for an improved understanding of the magmatic and tectonic processes occurring at the EPR.

We thank the officers and crew of the RVs *Conrad* and *Washington* and the members of the scientific parties on both ships for their help at sea. Jeff Fox and Ken MacDonald provided us with large-scale versions of their Sea Beam maps prior to our cruise which were essential in planning and carrying out this experiment. We also thank Joe Cann, Jeff Fox, Alistair Harding, Charlie Langmuir, Ken Macdonald and Janet Morton for their comments or reviews. This work was supported by NSF grants OCE-8314653 (URI), OCE-8315466 (L-DGO), OCE-8316549 (Scripps) and OCE-8409509 (WHOI).

(**326**, 35-41; 1987)

R. S. Detrick[*], P. Buhl[†], E. Vera[†], J. Mutter[†], J. Orcutt[‡], J. Madsen[*] & T. Brocher[§]

[*] Graduate School of Oceanography, University of Rhode Island, Kingston, Rhode Island 02881, USA

[†] Lamont-Doherty Geological Observatory, Columbia University, Palisades, New York 10964, USA

[‡] Scripps Institution of Oceanography, University of California, San Diego, La Jolla, California 92093, USA

[§] US Geological Survey, MS 977 345 Middlefield Road, Menlo Park, California 94025, USA

个构造定义的扩张中心单元之下由单个的、中心式的喷发来供给。我们从三个构造定义的扩张中心单元：9°03′N 到克利珀顿、克利珀顿到 11°45′N、11°45′N 到奥罗斯科，获取了有关轴部岩浆房反射沿走向连续性的地震数据。在每一个扩张中心构造单元上，我们能沿着走向横向追踪轴部岩浆房反射至少 40~50 km。我们认为至少沿着 EPR 的某些部分肯定存在一个这样尺度的物理连续的岩浆房。在克利珀顿转换断层以南，形态学[9]、岩石学[11]以及地震学证据都表明有一个巨大坚固的岩浆房存在，整个扩张单元（大于 90 km）似乎与单个横向连续的岩浆房相关联。然而，在另外两个单元中，轴部岩浆房反射中的显著间隙可能表明岩浆房沿走向很不连续，尽管轴部岩浆房反射的缺失并不一定排除岩浆房存在的可能性。

根据地震学和岩石学数据可以描绘一幅岩浆房的图像：它十分窄（宽小于 4~6 km），但是沿洋脊轴线能延续数十公里。在岩浆房收支高的地方（例如，克利珀顿以南），单个岩浆房能沿整个构造界定的扩张中心单元延伸。这种岩浆房相对较大且混合均匀，而且其喷发玄武岩的地球化学组成是均质的。在岩浆房收支低的地方（例如克利珀顿以北），岩浆房更小或者完全缺失，混合不充分，并且被大型和小型 OSC 所中断。岩浆的地球化学和岩石学特征均较多样。尽管 OSC 之间的较小断错一般与 AMC 的物理中断无关，但是与这些特征相关的地球化学异常可能反映了岩浆源区的多样性，这些岩浆来源于地壳以下或混合不充分的岩浆房，并且组成也不均匀。沿隆起轴的这种形态学、地球化学和地震学变化之间的相关性为增进人们对 EPR 地区岩浆和构造过程的了解提供了广阔前景。

我们感谢康拉德号和华盛顿号的全体船员和官员以及两艘船上的科考人员在出海期间给予的帮助。杰夫·福克斯和肯·麦克唐纳在我们航次开始前提供了他们的大尺度 SeaBean 型多波束测深图，这对于我们在计划和执行这项实验的过程中起了十分重要的作用。我们也感谢乔·卡恩、杰夫·福克斯、阿利斯泰尔·哈丁、查利·兰米尔、肯·麦克唐纳和珍妮特·莫顿的意见或评论。这项工作由美国国家科学基金会项目 OCE-8314653（罗得岛大学）、OCE-8315466（拉蒙特 – 多尔蒂地质观测中心）、OCE-8316549（斯克里普斯海洋研究所）和 OCE-8409509（美国伍兹霍尔海洋研究所）资助。

（陈林 张新彦 翻译；张忠杰 审稿）

Received 17 September 1986; accepted 9 January 1987.

References:

1. Cann, J. R. *Geophys. J. R. Astr. Soc.* **39**, 169-187 (1974).

2. Bryan, W. B. & Moore, J. *Bull. Geol. Soc. Am.* **88**, 556-570 (1977).

3. Pallister, J. & Hopson, C. *J. Geophys. Res.* **86**, 2593-2644 (1981).

4. Macdonald, K. C. *A. Rev. Earth Planet. Sci.* **10**, 155-190 (1982).

5. Lewis, B. T. R. *Science* **220**, 151-157 (1983).

6. Herron, T. J., Ludwig, W., Stoffa, P., Kan, T. & Buhl, P. *J. Geophys. Res.* **83**, 798 (1978).

7. Herron, T. J., Stoffa, P. & Buhl, P. *Geophys. Res. Lett.* **7**, 989-992 (1980).

8. Gallo, D., Fox, P. J. & MacDonald, K. C. *J. Geophys. Res.* **91**, 3455-3468 (1986).

9. Macdonald, K. C., Sempere, J. C. & Fox, P. J. *J. Geophys. Res.* **89**, 6049-6069 (1984).

10. Kastens, K., Ryan, W. B. F. & Fox, P. J. *J. Geophys. Res.* **91**, 3439-3454 (1986).

11. Langmuir, C., Bender, J. & Batiza, R. *Nature* **322**, 422-429 (1986).

12. Thompson, G., Bryan, B., Ballard, R., Hanuro, K. & Melson, W. *Nature* **310**, 429-433 (1985).

13. Hekinian, R. *et al. Mar. Geophys. Res.* **7**, 359-377 (1985).

14. Klitgord, K. D. & Mammerickx, J. *J. Geophys. Res.* **87**, 6725-6750 (1982).

15. Orcutt, J. A., Kennett, B., Dorman, L. & Prothero, W. *Nature* **256**, 475-476 (1975).

16. Rosendahl, B. R. *et al. J. Geophys. Res.* **81**, 5244-5304 (1976).

17. McClain, J. S., Orcutt, J. & Burnett, M. *J. Geophys. Res.* **90**, 8627-8640 (1985).

18. Orcutt, J. A., McClain, J. S. & Burnett, M. in *Ophiolites and Oceanic Lithosphere* 7-16 (Spec. Publs geol. Soc., London, 1985).

19. Lewis, B. T. R. & Garmany, J. D. *J. Geophys. Res.* **87**, 8417-8425 (1982).

20. Bratt, S. R. & Solomon, S. C. *J. Geophys. Res.* **89**, 6095-6110 (1984).

21. Stoffa, P. L. & Buhl, P. *J. Geophys. Res.* **84**, 7645-7660 (1979).

22. Stoffa, P. L., Kan, T. K., Buhl, P. & Kutschale, H. *Geohysics* **42**, 7-14 (1977).

23. NAT Study Group *J. Geophys. Res.* **90**, 10321-10341 (1985).

24. Hekinian, R. *et al. Science* **219**, 1321-1324 (1983).

25. Bratt, S. R. & Purdy, G. M. *J. Geophys. Res.* **89**, 6111-6125 (1984).

26. Casey, J. F. & Karson, J. A. *Nature* **292**, 295-301 (1981).

27. Ballard, R., Hekinian, R. & Francheteau, J. *Earth Planet. Sci. Lett.* **69**, 176-186 (1984).

28. Macdonald, K. C., Sempere, J. C. & Fox, P. J. *J. Geophys. Res.* **91**, 10501-10511 (1986).

29. Lonsdale, P. *J. Geophys. Res.* **88**, 9393-9406 (1983).

30. Lonsdale, P. *J. Geophys. Res.* **91**, 10493-10500 (1986).

31. Morton, J. & Sleep, N. *J. Geophys. Res.* **90**, 11345-11353 (1985).

32. Francheteau, J. & Ballard, R. *Earth Planet. Sci. Lett.* **64**, 93-116 (1983).

33. Whitehead, J., Dick, H. J. B. & Schouten, H. *Nature* **312**, 146-148 (1984).

34. Crane, K. *Earth Planet. Sci. Lett.* **72**, 405-414 (1985).

188

Transmission Dynamics of HIV Infection

R. M. May and R. M. Anderson

Editor's Note

By 1987, it was clear that the disease called AIDS had become an international epidemic. There were many schemes for developing vaccines against the causative virus (known as HIV) and formal treatments of the epidemiology of the infective process, of which this is one of the most significant. Robert May (now Lord May of Oxford) was at the time at Princeton University in the United States; an Australian, he was trained as a physicist at the University of Sydney, before converting to biology and, after migrating to Oxford, England, became Chief Scientific Adviser to the British government and president of the Royal Society. Notice that, in 1987, the authors were unsure whether heterosexual transmission was significant.

Simple mathematical models of the transmission dynamics of human immunodeficiency virus help to clarify some of the essential relations between epidemiological factors, such as distributed incubation periods and heterogeneity in sexual activity, and the overall pattern of the AIDS epidemic. They also help to identify what kinds of epidemiological data are needed to make predictions of future trends.

DESPITE remarkable advances in understanding the basic biology of human immunodeficiency virus (HIV—the aetiological agent of AIDS, acquired immune deficiency syndrome)[1-5] public health planning continues to be hampered by uncertainties about epidemiological parameters[4-6]. Accurate information about the typical duration and intensity of infectiousness, or about the fraction of those infected who will go on to develop AIDS (and after how long), will emerge only from carefully designed studies on these same timescales, which is to say many years. In the absence of such information, mathematical models of the transmission dynamics of HIV cannot be used at present to make accurate predictions of future trends in the incidence of AIDS, but they can facilitate the indirect assessment of certain epidemiological parameters, clarify what data is required to predict future trends, make predictions under various specified assumptions about the course of infection in individuals and patterns of sexual activity within defined populations (or changes therein) and, more generally, provide a template to guide the interpretation of observed trends[7,8].

Whether an infection can establish itself and spread within a population is determined by the key parameter R_0, the basic reproductive rate of the infection[7]. R_0 is the average number of secondary infections produced by one infected individual in the early stages of an epidemic (when essentially all contacts are susceptible); clearly the infection can

190

HIV的传播动力学

到 1987 年，很显然艾滋病已成为国际性传染病。已有许多开发疫苗的研究，都是致力于抵抗这种致病病毒（我们所知的 HIV）和其感染过程中流行病学方面的正规治疗，下面发表的文章就是其中之一。当时，澳大利亚人罗伯特·梅（即现在牛津的梅勋爵）在美国普林斯顿大学，在转到生物专业之前，他在悉尼大学学习物理学。移居到英国牛津以后，他担任英国政府首席科学顾问和英国皇家学会主席。值得注意的是，在 1987 年作者尚不确定异性传染是否为主要的传染方式。

人类免疫缺陷病毒传播动力学的简单数学模型帮助我们阐明了一些流行病学因素之间的重要关系，比如分布式潜伏期和异性之间的性活动以及艾滋病传染的所有形式。这些简单的数学模型也帮助我们确定了预测艾滋病的发展趋势都需要哪些类型的流行病学数据。

尽管在人类免疫缺陷病毒（HIV——艾滋病，即获得性免疫缺陷综合征的发病原因）[1-5] 的基本生物学特性上的认识已有显著进展，但是公共卫生计划仍然受到流行病学不确定因素的阻碍 [4-6]。要想获得关于感染性的典型持续时间和感染强度，或者被感染者发展为艾滋病的比例（以及多久之后发展为艾滋病）这些方面的准确信息，只有在这些事件发生的同时进行仔细设计的研究才可以，也就是说这需要很多年。缺少这些数据，目前 HIV 传播动力学的数学模型就不能用来准确预测艾滋病将来的发展趋势，但是它们有助于间接评价某些流行病学参数，弄清楚预测未来发展趋势需要哪些数据，在多种特定推测的基础上，对个人的传染过程和限定人群中性活动的模式（或者改变）做出预测，通俗地讲，也就是提供一个模板来指导对于已观察到的趋势进行解释 [7,8]。

感染是否可以自身发生并在人群中传播是由关键的参数 R_0，即感染的基本再生率决定的 [7]。R_0 是指在感染的早期阶段（这时基本上所有接触都是易感的）一个受感染的个体引起的继发性感染的平均数；很明显只要 R_0 超过 1 [9,10]，病毒传染就可以

maintain itself within the population only if R_0 exceeds unity[9,10]. For a sexually transmitted disease (STD), R_0 depends on c, which is essentially the average rate at which new sexual partners are acquired, on β, the average probability that infection is transmitted from an infected individual to a susceptible partner (per partner contact) and on D, the average duration of infectiousness[7,11]. In what follows, we mainly restrict attention to the spread of HIV among homosexual males, now responsible for the bulk of AIDS cases (about 70–80% in the United States, and a similar proportion in European countries[6,12,13]).

Initial Stages of the Epidemic

The characteristics of most STDs cause their epidemiology to differ from that of common childhood viral infections[11,14,15]. Unlike infections caused by airborne transmission, the rate at which new infections are produced is not dependent on the density of the host. Second, the carrier phenomenon in which certain individuals harbour asymptomatic infection is often important (as in the spread of herpesvirus). Third, many STDs induce little or no acquired immunity on recovery (for example, gonorrhoea) and fourth, net transmission depends on the degree of heterogeneity in sexual activity prevailing in the population.

As Hethcote and Yorke[11] have shown in their studies of gonorrhoea, mathematical models for the dynamics of STDs need to take account of the substantial variations of sexual activity within the population at risk. A particular risk group (such as male homosexuals in San Francisco[12]) of total size N may be roughly partitioned into subgroups of size N_i, each of whom on the average acquire i new sexual partners per unit time (when $N = \Sigma_i N_i$). The probability that susceptible individuals in this ith group will become infected, per unit time, is thus $i\lambda$, where λ is the probability that infection is acquired from any one new partner. In turn, λ is equal to the product of the transmission probability β defined above and the probability that any one randomly-chosen partner is infected (with such partners being more likely to come from the sub-groups of individuals with high degrees of sexual activity).

Exponential Growth

When these assumptions are incorporated into a model for the transmission dynamics of HIV infection, the infected fraction of the population at risk (who are seropositive in tests for HIV) rises exponentially, as $\exp(\Lambda t)$, in the early stages of the epidemic. The exponential growth rate, Λ, is related to the basic epidemiological quantities defined above by:

$$\Lambda = \beta c - 1/D \qquad (1)$$

The effective average over the distribution by degrees of sexual activity, c, is given explicitly as

$$c = \Sigma i^2 N_i / \Sigma_i N_i = m + \sigma^2/m \qquad (2)$$

where m is the mean and σ^2 the variance of the distribution of the number of new sexual partners per unit of time[8]. Thus, c is not simply the mean but the mean plus the ratio

在人群中维系。对于性传播疾病（STD），R_0 受 c（获得新的性伙伴的平均速率）、β（从一个感染者传播到易感伙伴——每次与伙伴接触的平均概率）和 D（具有感染性的平均持续时间）的影响 [7,11]。在下文中，我们的注意力主要集中在 HIV 在男性同性恋之间的传播，现在这在艾滋病病例中占有大部分的比例（在美国大概有70%~80%，在欧洲国家比例也差不多 [6,12,13]）。

流行病的最初阶段

大多数 STDs 的特点导致其与常见的儿童病毒感染的流行病学不同 [11,14,15]。第一，不像空气传播引起的感染，新感染的概率不取决于宿主的密度。第二，某些个体感染后没有任何症状，这种携带者现象通常很重要（如疱疹病毒的传播）。第三，许多 STDs 在恢复期导致很少或没有获得性免疫力（如淋病）。第四，网状传播主要依赖于人群中性活动的异质性的程度。

就像赫思克特和约克 [11] 在淋病研究中发现的那样，STDs 动力学数学模型需要考虑危险人群中性活动的实质性变量。一个总数为 N 的特定的危险群体（比如旧金山的男性同性恋群体 [12]）可以大致分成几个亚群 N_i，单位时间内平均每个人找到 i 个新的性伙伴（$N=\Sigma_i N_i$）。$i\lambda$ 是单位时间内，第 i 组易感个体被感染的可能性，λ 是来自任何一个新的性伙伴的感染概率。反过来，λ 等于上述定义的传染率 β 与任何一个随机选择的性伙伴被感染的概率的乘积（这些性伙伴更有可能来自具有高频率性活动的亚群）。

指 数 增 长

当把这些假设与 HIV 感染的传播动力学模型结合起来时，在流行病的早期阶段，危险人群（HIV 检测呈阳性）被感染的比例呈指数上升，记作指数随机变量 (Λt)。指数增长速率（Λ）与上面定义的基本流行病学数量相关。

$$\Lambda = \beta c - 1/D \tag{1}$$

性活动程度分布的有效平均数 c，如下面公式所描述

$$c = \Sigma i^2 N_i/\Sigma_i N_i = m + \sigma^2/m \tag{2}$$

其中 m 是平均数，σ^2 是单位时间内新的性伴侣的数量分布的方差 [8]。因此，c 就不仅仅是平均值，而是平均值加上方差比例，通过高度活跃的个体（在性活动分布概

of variance to mean, which reflects the disproportionate role played by highly active individuals (in the tail of the probability distribution of sexual activity), who are both more likely to acquire infection and more likely to transmit it. The basic reproductive rate for HIV infection, R_0, is related to the parameters β, c and D, and hence to Λ by the formula

$$R_0 = \beta c\, D \tag{3}$$

In contrast with standard epidemiological models in homogeneous populations (where the exponential phase of rising incidence lasts until something like half the pool of susceptibles have been infected), the early exponential phase is of relatively short duration in our HIV models, giving way to a more nearly linear rise in the fraction infected (see Fig. 2).

This is because most susceptibles in the sexually highly active categories are infected in the early stages of the epidemic, producing saturation effects in these categories which decrease the exponential rise in incidence within them; although the incidence of infection continues to rise among individuals in less sexually active categories, the overall rate of increase is now slower than exponential.

Much less information is available about the rise in the number of individuals infected with HIV, as a function of time, than about the rise in the subsequent incidence of AIDS[46,12,13], largely because information about infection requires serological examination for antibodies to the HIV virus. Although the initial infection may produce symptoms[3,16,17] and, in some cases acute encephalopathy[18] and meningitis[16], it is not clear that such symptoms are always evoked: in any event, the symptoms are usually sufficiently mild to preclude systematic reporting. By contrast, the opportunistic infections cancers[4,5,12,19], and subsequent mortality characteristic of the destruction of the immune system in AIDS, leads to fairly reliable reporting[20]. There is, however, one study of hepatitis B virus (HBV) in a cohort of 6,875 homosexual and bisexual males in San Francisco, which resulted in serum samples being taken and preserved as early as 1978[12,21,22]; stored sera of a representative sample of 785 of these individuals gives the rise in the fraction seropositive for HIV, from 1978 to 1985, shown in Fig. 1.

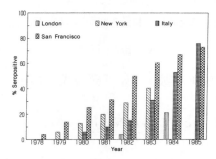

Fig. 1. The rise in seropositivity to HIV antigens in cohorts of patients over the period 1978–1985. The studies in San Francisco[12], London[23] and New York[35] were of homosexual/bisexual males. The study in Italy[24] is of drug addicts.

率的尾部）不成比例的作用，反映了这部分人群既更加有可能被传染也更有可能传播 HIV。HIV 传染的基本再生率 R_0 与 β，c 和 D 几个参数有关，并且根据 Λ 得到下面公式

$$R_0 = \beta c\, D \qquad\qquad (3)$$

与同类人群中标准流行病学模型（发病率指数上升阶段持续到半数的易感人群已被感染）相比，在我们的 HIV 模型中，早期的指数阶段的持续时间相对较短，被感染的比例几乎呈直线上升（见图 2）。

这是因为性高度活跃人群中的大多数易感染者在疫情的早期阶段被感染，在这些人群中产生饱和效应，抑制了他们疾病发生率的指数增长。尽管在性活动较少的人群中感染的发生率持续增长，但是总的增长率仍低于指数增长速率。

随着时间的变化，与艾滋病并发率的增长相比，很少有关于感染 HIV 个体的数目增长的信息可以利用 [46,12,13]。主要是因为感染信息需要 HIV 病毒抗体的血清学检测。尽管感染初期可能会产生症状 [3,16,17]，如某些病例中的急性脑病 [18] 和脑膜炎 [16]，但是这些症状是否总是被诱发尚不清楚：通常情况下，这些症状十分温和不会引起预警系统报告。相比之下，机会性感染的癌症 [4,5,12,19] 和随后的艾滋病引起的免疫系统破坏的死亡特性产生清楚可靠的报告 [20]。然而，有一项对旧金山的 6,875 个男性同性恋和双性恋群体进行的乙肝病毒（HBV）的研究，使得早在 1978 年就开始采集和保存血清标本 [12,21,22]，储存的这些有代表性的血清标本中，从 1978 年到 1985 年，这些个体中有 785 个人的 HIV 血清阳性反应比例呈上升趋势，见图 1。

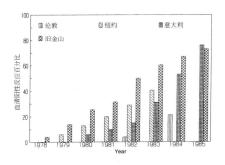

图 1. 1978~1985 年期间，被统计的病人中 HIV 抗原血清阳性反应呈增长趋势。在旧金山 [12]、伦敦 [23] 和纽约 [35] 研究的是男性同性恋和双性恋。在意大利 [24] 研究的是吸毒者。

The pattern of roughly linear rise shown in Fig. 1 is uncharacteristic of standard epidemics (in homogeneously mixed populations), but is suggested by our HIV models. In Britain and other countries in Europe, the virus seems first to have appeared several years later than in the United States (Fig. 2a, b and c), and the spread of infection is still in its early stages. As a result there are serological studies focused on HIV roughly from its initial appearance in Europe[23,24] (Fig. 1). The initially exponential rise in HIV infection may be characterized by a doubling time, t_d, related to the growth rate, Λ, of (1) by $t_d = (\ln 2)/\Lambda$.

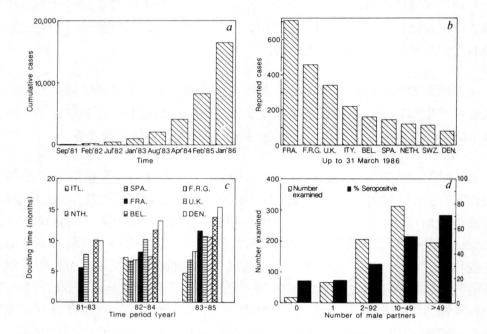

Fig. 2. a, The rise in the cumulative number of reported cases of AIDS in the USA over the interval September 1981–January 1986[13]. b, Reported cases of AIDS in 9 countries of the European Community up to 31 March 1986[40]. c, Doubling times in the cumulative incidence of AIDS (t_d) recorded in months for various European countries[40] over various time intervals (1981–83, 1982–84, 1983–85; DEN, Denmark; BEL, Belgium; NTH, Netherlands; FRA, France; E.C., European Community in total; F.R.G., Federal Republic of Germany; SPA, Spain; ITL, Italy; UK, United Kingdom). d, The relationship between sexual activity amongst a sample of homosexual/bisexual males (from San Francisco, USA) as measured by the number of male partners over a two-year period, and the percentage of each group (based on sex partners) who were seropositive for HIV antibodies (data from ref. 26).

Table 1 summarizes information about doubling times deduced from serological and case notification studies, which lead to a surprisingly consistent estimate of $t_d \sim 8$–10 months in the early stages of the epidemic (Fig. 2d) giving an estimate of Λ of about 1.0 yr^{-1}. The characteristic duration of infection (and infectiousness), D, is probably not significantly less than the characteristic time from HIV infection to manifestation of AIDS.

我们的 HIV 模型表明，如图 1 中所示的大致呈直线增长的模式，并不是标准流行病（在同类的混合群体中）的特点。在英国和其他的欧洲国家，这种病毒首次出现的时间要比美国晚几年（图 2a，b 和 c），传染病的蔓延仍旧处于早期阶段。结果大概从它最初在欧洲出现以后 [23,24]（图 1），才有集中于 HIV 的血清学研究。HIV 感染的最初指数增长可以用倍增时间来描述，t_d，与生长速率 Λ 有关。公式（1）变为 $t_d = (\ln 2)/\Lambda$。

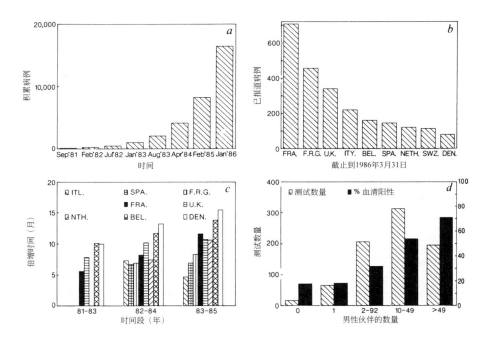

图 2. a，在美国，1981 年 9 月到 1986 年 1 月这段时间里 [13]，所报道的艾滋病病例总数的增长。b，欧共体 9 个国家，截止到 1986 年 3 月 31 日报道的艾滋病病例的数量 [40]。c，多个欧洲国家 [40] 在不同时间段内艾滋病累积发生的倍增时间 (t_d)（1981~83、1982~84、1983~85；DEN，丹麦；BEL，比利时；NTH，荷兰；FRA，法国；E.C.，欧共体总计；F.R.G.，德国；SPA，西班牙；ITL，意大利；UK，英国）。d，取样男性同性恋/双性恋（美国旧金山），记录两年内男性伙伴的数量，比较性活动与每组（性伴侣为基础）HIV 抗体反应阳性百分比（数据来自参考文献 26）之间的关系。

表 1，通过推断血清学和呈报病例的研究，总结了关于倍增时间的信息，给出了一个令人吃惊的一致性估计，在传染期的早期 t_d 约为 8~10 个月（图 2d），得出 Λ 的估计值为大约每年 1.0。传染（和传染性）的典型持续时间——D，可能不是显著少于从感染 HIV 到表现出 AIDS 的特征时间。

Table 1. Doubling time of the HIV epidemic (in the early stages)

Serological data		
Area	Period	Doubling time t_d (in months)
(a) Male homosexuals		
San Francisco, USA	1978–80	10–11
New York City, USA	1979–80	10–11
London, UK	1982–84	9–10
(b) Intravenous drug users		
Italy	1980–83	15–16
London, UK	1983–85	11–12
Switzerland	1983–84	8–9
Case notifications		
(a) All risk groups		
Australia	1982–85	4–5
Austria	1983–85	15–16
Belgium	1982–84	11–12
Canada	1981–85	9–10
Denmark	1982–84	13–14
Europe(EC)	1982–84	8–9
France	1982–84	8–9
Italy	1982–84	7–8
Netherlands	1982–84	7–8
Spain	1982–84	6–7
Sweden	1983–85	8–9
Switzerland	1983–85	9–10
United Kingdom	1982–84	10–11
United States	1982–83	5–6
West Germany	1982–84	6–7
(b) Heterosexuals		
United States	1982–84	9–10
Average		9–10

But D may be significantly longer if a substantial proportion of infected individuals remain asymptomatic carriers (with the epidemiology similar to hepatitis B virus[25]). On the other hand, recent studies observing that measurable HIV antigen (HIV-Ag, the

表 1. HIV 流行的倍增时间（在早期阶段）

血清学数据		
地区	时期	倍增时间t_d（月）
（a）男同性恋		
美国旧金山	1978~80	10~11
美国纽约	1979~80	10~11
英国伦敦	1982~84	9~10
（b）静脉注射吸毒者		
意大利	1980~83	15~16
英国伦敦	1983~85	11~12
瑞士	1983~84	8~9
呈报病例		
（a）所有危险群体		
澳大利亚	1982~85	4~5
奥地利	1983~85	15~16
比利时	1982~84	11~12
加拿大	1981~85	9~10
丹麦	1982~84	13~14
欧洲	1982~84	8~9
法国	1982~84	8~9
意大利	1982~84	7~8
荷兰	1982~84	7~8
西班牙	1982~84	6~7
瑞典	1983~85	8~9
瑞士	1983~85	9~10
英国	1982~84	10~11
美国	1982~83	5~6
西德	1982~84	6~7
（b）异性恋		
美国	1982~84	9~10
平均数		9~10

如果被感染个体表现为无症状携带者（流行病学与乙肝病毒相似[25]）的话，D可能明显更长。另外，最近的研究表明可测量的 HIV 抗原（HIV-Ag，它的出现表明

presence of which indicates the presence of the virus) appears early and transiently in primary HIV infection, that antibody production follows (1–3 months after infection) and that HIV-Ag may then disappear could imply lower estimates of D, as would the apparent correlation of this persistence or reappearance of antigen with clinical, immunological and neurological deterioration[3].

In the absence of conclusive data on infectiousness during the incubation period, we shall assume that D is equal to the incubation period. Studies of cases of AIDS associated with transfusion suggest that the average incubation period is 4–5 years[31], but as such studies are extended, this estimate will rise (Fig. 3). The true average may be 8–10 years or more. Our estimate of Λ in conjunction with equation 1 then leads to the rough estimate.

$$\beta c \simeq 1 \ \text{yr}^{-1} \tag{4}$$

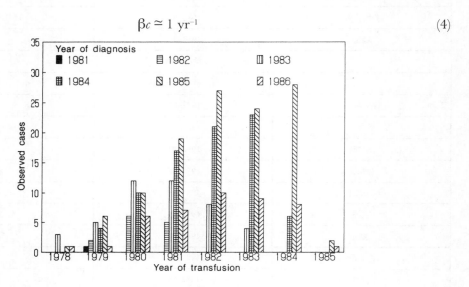

Fig. 3. Data on the distribution of the incubation period of AIDS derived from longitudinal studies of transfusion recipients (data from ref. 31). Observed cases of AIDS are recorded as a function of the year of transfusion (the assumed point of acquisition of infection) and the year of diagnosis. A Weibull distribution provides a good empirical description of this data with a mean incubation period of ~4–5 years.

Note that $\Lambda \simeq \beta c$ provided D is large (4–5 years plus). Thus data on changes in seropositivity over time have allowed us to infer the approximate magnitude of the combination of epidemiological parameters β and c, neither of which can easily be estimated directly.

Is this estimate consistent with what is known about β and c separately? Unfortunately, nearly all the information about degrees of sexual activity among male homosexuals has focused on average numbers of sexual partners, as distinct from average number of new partners per unit time[26,27] (Fig. 4). For less active individuals (say, 1–3 partners per 6-month interval), the rate of acquisition of new partners will be seriously overestimated by the average number of partners. On the other hand, the quantity c is disproportionately influenced by highly active individuals, most of whose partners are likely to be new, so that

病毒的出现）在 HIV 传染初期出现较早而且短暂,随后抗体产生（感染后 1~3 个月），然后 HIV-Ag 会消失，这意味着对 D 的估计值较低，这种抗原的持久性或再现与临床上、免疫学上和神经学上的恶化之间有明显的关系 [3]。

在潜伏期，由于缺少关于传染性的确凿数据，我们假定 D 等于潜伏期。和输血相关的艾滋病病例研究表明平均潜伏期是 4~5 年 [31]，但是随着研究的扩展，这个估计值将会上升（图 3）。真实的平均值可能是 8~10 年或者更高。Λ 的估值与方程 1 相关联，得到这个粗略估计。

$$\beta c \simeq 1 \ yr^{-1} \tag{4}$$

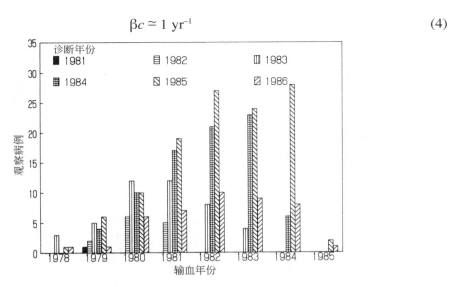

图 3. 来源于对输血接受者纵向研究的艾滋病潜伏期的分布数据（数据来自参考文献 31）。 将观察到的艾滋病病例作为输液年份（假定的感染点）和诊断年份的函数。韦伯分布给出了数据的一个很好的实证描述，潜伏期的平均值大约为 4~5 年。

倘如 D 很大（4~5 年），那么 $\Lambda \approx \beta c$。超过一定时间，血清反应阳性随时间改变的数据使得我们可以推断出流行病学参数 β 和 c 组合的大概量值，二者的值都不容易进行直接估计。

这个估计是否分别与已知的 β 和 c 相符合？不幸的是几乎所有的关于男性同性恋之间性活动程度的信息都集中在性伴侣的平均数量上，它与单位时间里获得新性伴侣的平均数是不同的 [26,27]（图 4）。对于性活动少的个体来说（比如，每 6 个月 1~3 个伴侣），性伴侣的平均数大大超出他们获得新的性伴侣的几率。另外，c 的量受高度性活跃个体不成比例地影响，他们的性伴侣可能是新的，因此仅仅依据性伴

studies based simply on numbers of partners may give a rough guide to the magnitude of c (Fig. 4). Quantitative information on average values of β, whether for homosexuals or heterosexuals, is very limited at present. Estimates vary widely (from 0.05 to 0.5) although it appears that the average probability of transmission per partner contact is higher among male homosexuals than among heterosexuals, perhaps as a result of more frequent sexual activity that results in epithelial damage (for example anal intercourse)[26,29]. Our estimates of $\beta c \sim 1$ yr^{-1} together with the high estimates of c for homosexuals suggest that β may be small (~ 0.05). But estimates of c based on the reported number of partners per unit of time may significantly overestimate the number of new partners per unit of time, which, or that equating D to the incubation period, may overestimate the average duration of infectiousness. It may also be that the high values of c arise from sampling biased towards the high activity groups of homosexual communities.

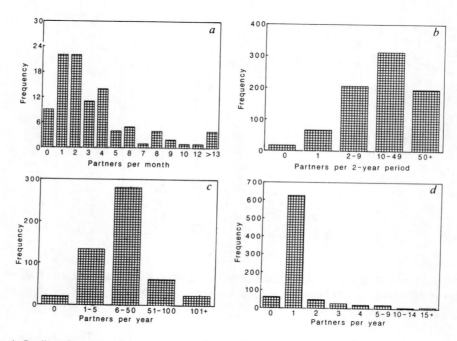

Fig. 4. Studies of sexual activity amongst *a–c*, male homosexual and *d* heterosexual communities. The graphs record frequency distributions of the number of sex partners per defined time period in samples of homosexual/bisexual males and heterosexuals. *a*, Homosexual/bisexual males resident in London surveyed in 1986 (unpublished data from C. A. Carne and I. V. Weller) ($m = 4.7$ per month, $\sigma^2 = 56.7$). Data denote male partners per month. *b*, Homosexual/bisexual males resident in San Francisco surveyed in 1984–85 (data from ref 26). Data denote male partners per 2-year period. *c*, Homosexual/bisexual males resident in London surveyed in 1984 (unpublished data from T. McManus). Data denote male partners per year. *d*, Heterosexuals between the ages of 18–44 years in England surveyed in November 1986 (unpublished data, Harris Research Organisation; R.M.A. and G. F. Medley). Data denote partners of the opposite sex per 1 year period (sample size = 823, $m = 1.41$, $\sigma^2 = 4.36$). A further survey of homosexual men (ref. 27) in San Francisco reveals a decline in the mean partners per month over the period November 1982 to November 1984 from 5.9 to 2.5.

侣数量进行的研究，可能对 c 值的大小给出一个粗略的指导（图 4）。不论是同性恋还是异性恋，β 的平均值的量化信息目前还很受限。尽管可能由于较频繁的性活动会导致上皮损伤（比如肛交）[26,29]，男性同性恋之间每次接触感染的平均可能性似乎大于异性恋之间的，但是估值范围很大（从 0.05 到 0.5）。结合同性恋的高 c 估值，我们对 βc 每年约等于 1 的估值表明 β 可能很小（约为 0.05）。以单位时间里得到的性伴侣的数目为基础的 c 的估值明显超过单位时间里新的性伴侣数量，如果将 D 等同于潜伏期，则会高估传染性的平均持续时间。高 c 值可能是由于取样偏向于同性恋群体中的高度活跃人群。

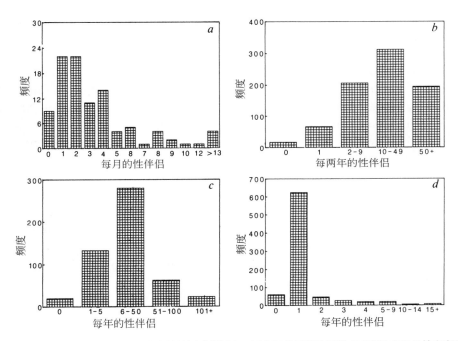

图 4. a~c 男同性恋和 d 异性恋群体内的性活动的研究。图表记录了男性同性恋或双性恋和异性恋者在一定时间里性伴侣数量的分布频率。a，1986 年调查的伦敦同性恋和双性恋男性居民（来自卡恩和韦勒的未发表数据）（m 的值为每月 4.7，σ^2=56.7）。数据表示每个月男性伴侣数量。b，1984~85 年，在旧金山调查到的男性同性恋和双性恋（数据来自参考文献 26）。数据表示每两年男性伴侣的数量。c，在 1984 年，伦敦调查到的同性恋和双性恋男性居民（来自麦克马纳斯未发表的数据）。数据表示每年的男性伴侣的数量。d，1986 年 11 月，在英格兰调查到的 18~44 岁之间的异性恋居民（哈里斯研究组织；安德森和梅德利未发表数据）。数据表示每年异性性伴侣的数量（样本大小 =823，m=1.41，σ^2=4.36）。进一步的调查发现（参考文献 27），从 1982 年 11 月到 1984 年 11 月，旧金山的男同性恋每月的伴侣平均数下降，从 5.9 降为 2.5。

As public awareness about AIDS has increased, there have been changes in patterns of sexual activity among male homosexuals in the United States (reflected, for example, in marked decreases in the incidence of rectal gonorrhoea[29,30]) which have presumably resulted in changes both in β and in c[27]. Our discussion, therefore, pertains mainly to the relatively early stages — 1978 to the early 1980s — of the epidemic.

Incubation Period

Although much more information is available about the incidence of AIDS than of HIV infection (Table 1), it is harder to tease estimates of epidemiological parameters out of these. Incidence of AIDS depends not only on the transmission factors β and c, but also on the incubation period and on the fraction, f, of those infected who will eventually develop AIDS.

Significantly, estimates of both the incubation period and f have tended systematically to increase since the epidemic was first recognized[4,5,28,31,32]. Estimates of f range from 10% to 75% or more[19,28,33,37], with an incubation period of 4–5 years or more[31]. The progressive sequence of steps which eventually impair the ability of the immune system to respond to opportunistic infection seem not to be reversible. But whether all those infected with HIV are moving toward AIDS at different rates, or whether some will develop AIDS while others never will, remains unclear. Variability in the incubation period, and whether or not an infected person develops AIDS, could be accounted for by genetic heterogeneity within the host population (HLA-linked[38,39]), or could be associated with specific strains of the antigenically variable HIV virus[1,6].

Studies of the incubation period for those who develop AIDS suggest that the "hazard function", the probability of the disease manifesting itself as a function of the time since infection, increases with time (Fig. 3). Lui and co-workers[31] have assumed a Weibull distribution (a flexible two parameter probability distribution) for the incubation period with probability density function

$$h(t) = \gamma v^{-\gamma} t \exp[-(t/\gamma)^v] \qquad (5)$$

If indeed the probability per unit time, to develop AIDS (for that fraction f who do indeed develop it) increases linearly with time from infection as αt, the result is a Weibull distribution with $\gamma = 2$ and $v = \alpha$ for the hazard function[8]. This assumption differs from conventional epidemiological models, where infected individuals move through the incubation interval either at a fixed rate, or in a fixed time. But none of this resolves the question of what proportion of those infected will develop AIDS on what timescale: That issue will be resolved only by very long term (many decades) studies.

Fraction Eventually Infected

In a closed and homogeneously mixed population, the total fraction eventually infected depends only on the basic reproductive rate of the infection, R_0, defined above as shown[7]

由于公众对艾滋病的认识有所提高，美国男性同性恋之间的性活动模式已发生改变（比如，表现为直肠淋病的发病率明显下降 [29,30]），可能导致 β 和 c 的改变 [27]。因此，我们的讨论主要适合于流行病相对早期的阶段——1978 年到 20 世纪 80 年代初。

潜 伏 期

尽管艾滋病发病率比 HIV 感染有更多可利用的信息（表 1），但是从这些数据中更难找到流行病学参数的估值。艾滋病的发病率不仅与传播因素 β 和 c 有关，也与潜伏期和那些最终发展为艾滋病的感染者的比例（f）有关。

值得注意的是，自从第一次认识到这种流行病 [4,5,28,31,32]，潜伏期和 f 的估计值都趋向于系统性的增加。f 的估计值介于 10%~75% 或者 75% 以上之间 [19,28,33,37]，潜伏期 4~5 年或者更长 [31]。这种渐进性的过程最终损害了免疫系统，导致其不能对机会感染作出应答，而且这个过程似乎是不可逆的。但是否所有感染了 HIV 的人正在以不同速率发展成艾滋病，或者是否有些人会发展为艾滋病而其他的永远不会，这些尚不清楚。潜伏期的变化以及感染者是否会发展成艾滋病，可以通过宿主（连接有 HLA[38,39]）基因异质性或者结合抗原变异的 HIV 病毒的特殊关系来确定 [1,6]。

对发展为艾滋病的那些人的潜伏期的研究显示，风险函数即感染后显示出疾病的可能性，随时间而增加（图 3）。卢伊和他的同事 [31] 结合概率密度函数推测出一个潜伏期的韦伯分布公式（一个灵活的双参数的概率分布）

$$h(t) = \gamma v^{-\gamma} t \exp[-(t/\gamma)^v] \tag{5}$$

如果从感染后定义为 αt，单位时间里发展为艾滋病的几率随时间的变化呈线性增长，那么韦伯公式得出的风险率是 $\gamma = 2$ 和 $v = \alpha$[8]。这一假说与传统的流行病模型不同，在传统模型中受感染的个体以固定的几率或固定的时间度过潜伏期。但是这个解说也没有解决感染 HIV 的群体有多大比例及多长时间里会发展为艾滋病的问题：这个问题只有通过长期（数十年）的研究才能解决。

最终感染率

在一个封闭单一混合人群中，最终总体感染率仅仅与传染的基本再生率 R_0 有关，如图 5 中最上面的曲线图所示 [7]。对性传染疾病比如 HIV，这个结果可以引申

by the uppermost curve in Fig. 5. For sexually-transmitted infections such as HIV, the result can be extended to include the complications associated with a wide diversity in degrees of sexual activity.

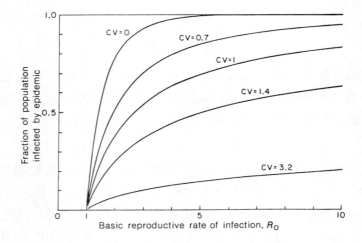

Fig. 5. The relationship between the eventual fraction infected (seropositive) in an epidemic of HIV and the basic reproductive rate R_0 (see text). The predictions are based on a model which assumes that sexual activity (defined as the number of new partners per unit of time) obeys a gamma distribution with varying coefficients of variation (CV) (mean m and variance σ^2; see text).

In a closed population, the eventual fraction seropositive will depend both on R_0 and on the actual distribution of rates of acquisition of sexual partners. Assuming a gamma distribution[8], we may characterize it by c and by its coefficient of variation (CV = σ/m). The resulting overall fraction infected is shown as a function of R_0, for a range of values of CV, in Fig. 5; for fixed R_0, the eventual seropositive fraction can be much lower than for CV = 0, if the variability in degrees of sexual activity (measured by CV) is high. This makes intuitive sense: the highly active individuals acquire infection, and eventually are removed, relatively early in the epidemic; transmission among the remaining, less active, individuals may be relatively weak.

Figure 5 may be used, in combination with two factual observations, to make a rough assessment of R_0 for HIV among male homosexuals. First, the studies indicate great variability in degrees of sexual activity among male homosexuals (with CV significantly in excess of unity[8,26,27]), thus confining attention to the lower curves. The second observation is that levels of seropositivity to HIV among male homosexuals in San Francisco in 1985 are variously reported as 70% or more[12] (in the HBV study which is probably biased towards more active individuals) and as around 50% (in a study carefully constructed to avoid bias[26]), providing a lower bound of 50–70% on the proportion ever seropositive. For CV noticeably in excess of unity, this can be achieved only if R_0 is in excess of 5.

Thus our early estimate of $\beta c \sim 1$ yr^{-1}, in conjunction with the assessment that R_0 exceeds

为与性活动程度多样化有关的综合征。

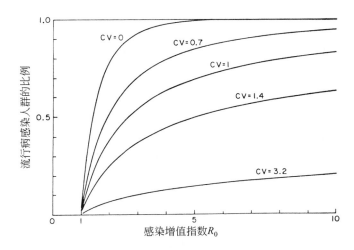

图 5. 在 HIV 流行病中，最终的感染比例（血清反应阳性）与基本再生数 R_0（见正文）之间的关系。推测是以模型为基础，该模型假定性活动（定义为单位时间内性伴侣的数量）遵从伽马分布，该分布的变异系数（CV）（平均值 m 及方差 σ；见正文）是变化的。

在一个封闭的人群里，最终血清反应阳性的比例与 R_0 以及获得性伴侣的比率的实际分布有关。假定一个伽马分布 [8]，我们以 c 和它的变异系数（CV=σ/m）来表示。最终的总感染比例用 R_0 的函数来表示，范围为 CV 的值，如图 5；对于固定的 R_0 来说，如果性活动程度的变化（通过 CV 来测量）很大，那么最终血清反应阳性的比例可能更低，因为 CV=0。这会造成这样一种直觉：在流行病的早期，高度活跃的个体被感染，最后被排除；剩余的不太活跃的个体之间的传播可能相对较弱。

利用图 5，并结合两个实际观察结果，得出一个男性同性恋之间 HIV 的 R_0 粗略估值。首先，研究表明，男性同性恋之间的性活动程度有很大的可变性（CV 明显超过整体 [8,26,27]），因此我们将注意力集中在较低的曲线上。第二个调查结果是，1985 年旧金山男同性恋的 HIV 血清反应阳性水平的报道分别为 70% 或高于 70%[12]（在 HBV 的研究中，很可能会偏向于更活跃的个体）和 50% 左右（一个为消除偏差而仔细构建的研究 [26]），这给出了血清反应阳性比例的下界为 50%~70%。对于 CV 显著超过整体的，只有在 R_0 超过了 5 才能够实现。

因此结合 R_0 超过 5 的估值，我们早期 βc 每年约等于 1 的估值间接导致 D 的估

5, leads to an indirect estimate that D exceeds 5 years. Although R_0, like β and c changes with changing social and sexual habits, the data leading to our earlier estimate for βc come from the early stages of the rise in HIV infection, before such changes were significant. The estimate of R_0 depends importantly on observed levels of seropositivity, but these were also high before social changes became pronounced. Consequently, our estimate of D which depends only on the basic biology of HIV, is reasonably consistent. This independent estimate of $D \sim 5$ years accords with current estimates that the incubation period is 4–5 years or more.

An estimate of the value of R_0 in the early stages of the epidemic is also valuable in indicating the magnitude of the social changes needed to bring R_0 below unity. If R_0 is around 5–10 or more, then reductions by a factor of 5–10 or more in βc are needed. Because c depends disproportionately on those in the highly sexually active category, programmes aimed at getting them to change their habits—both to fewer partners and to "safe sex"—are most efficient. But if such individuals are less likely to respond to public health education, it will be harder to bring R_0 below unity.

Mortality

The frequent assumption that the severity of the epidemic, in terms of cumulative mortality, will be greatest if all those infected eventually develop AIDS and subsequently die is not necessarily true. Mortality depends critically on the duration of infectiousness of both those infected who develop AIDS and those infected who do not. If the latter have a similar life expectancy to those not infected, but remain infectious for life, they may contribute more to the net transmission of the virus, R_0, than those who die of AIDS. Much may be understood by recognizing that the overall net reproductive rate of the virus, R_0, is made up of two components, the reproductive rate of those who develop AIDS (R_{01}) and the equivalent rate of those who do not (R_{02}). If a fraction f develop AIDS

$$R_0 = fR_{01} + (1-f)R_{02} \tag{6}$$

where the two reproductive rates are defined by equation (3) with different parameters for the separate groups. Even if the asymptomatic carriers are less infectious than those who develop AIDS, if they remain infectious over, say, a 30-year span of sexual activity, R_{02} may be much larger than R_{01}, and, depending on f, the contribution of the asymptomatic carriers to R_0 may be dominant.

At present, it is not possible to tell whether the severity of the epidemic will be increased or decreased if a larger fraction of those infected develop AIDS, for the relative infectiousness of the two categories is unknown. For public health planning it is clearly important to attempt to acquire such data.

Dynamics of the Epidemic

The dynamics of an HIV epidemic within a homosexual community are represented by the results of our calculations given in Fig. 6, which shows the proportion seropositive

值超过了 5 年。尽管像 β 和 *c* 一样，R_0 随着社会习性和性习惯的改变而改变，但是在这些改变变得很显著之前，我们用 HIV 感染早期阶段的增长水平来估计之前 β*c* 的值。R_0 的估值主要受血清反应阳性水平的影响，但是在社会习性改变很明显之前，这些值也是很高的。因此，仅仅依据 HIV 的基本生物学所得 *D* 的估值是合理的。*D* 的独立估计值大约是 5 年，与潜伏期的现行估计值（4~5 年或更长）一致。

对在染病早期阶段 R_0 的估值是有用的，它可以表明使 R_0 低于整体值的社会习性变化幅度。如果 R_0 的值在 5~10 左右或者更高，那么 β*c* 需要减小 5~10 倍或更多。因为 *c* 不成比例地取决于那些使高度性活跃群体中的人改变自己习惯——较少的性伴侣和安全的性行为——的项目是最有效的。但是如果这些人不太可能响应公共健康教育，那么使 R_0 低于整体值是很困难的。

死 亡 率

如果感染者最终都发展为艾滋病并随后死亡，那么流行病的严重程度，也就是累计死亡率就会达到最大，这种推测是不准确的。死亡率主要取决于已经发展为 AIDS 的感染者和没有发展为 AIDS 的感染者二者的传染性的持续时间。如果后者与未被感染的人有相似的预期寿命，但是他们生活中仍保持传染性，那么他们对病毒的净繁殖率 R_0 比那些死于艾滋病的人起的作用更大。认识了病毒总的净繁殖率 R_0 是由那些发展为艾滋病的繁殖率（R_{01}）和那些没有发展成艾滋病的等同的繁殖率（R_{02}）两部分组成后，我们可以理解更多。如果发展为艾滋病的比例为 *f*，那么

$$R_0 = fR_{01} + (1-f)R_{02} \tag{6}$$

公式（3）定义了两种繁殖率，两个单独的群体用不同的参数表示。即使无症状的携带者比发展为艾滋病的人有更小的传播性，如果他们在 30 年的性活动中保持传染性，那么 R_{02} 可能比 R_{01} 大很多，并且与 *f* 有关，无症状的携带者对 R_0 的影响可能比较明显。

目前，由于两类群体的相对传染力是未知的，如果较大比例感染者发展为艾滋病，那么就不可能预测到传染病的严重程度是增加还是降低。对于公共健康计划，显然努力获得这些数据是很重要的。

流行病的动力学

根据我们的计算结果建立的同性恋群体中 HIV 流行病的动力学如图 6 所示，它

and the incidence of cases of AIDS as a function of time since the start of the epidemic. It is assumed that 30% of those infected eventually manifest AIDS, with the incubation intervals obeying a Weibull distribution such that the average incubation period is 5 years[31]. Individuals who are incubating AIDS are assumed infectious throughout the incubation interval, and the 70% who remain asymptomatic are assumed to remain infectious for similar periods.

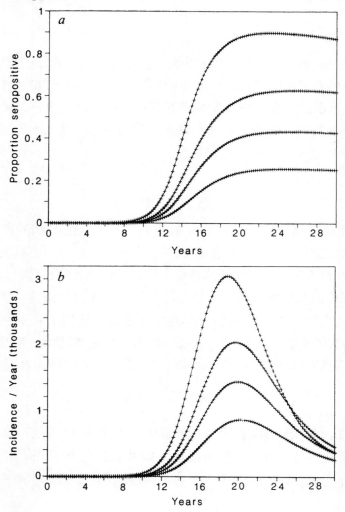

Fig. 6. The predictions of a model (see ref. 8) incorporating variable incubation periods, heterogeneity in sexual activity and recruitment of susceptibles. The two graphs record changes in seropositivity through time from the point of introduction of HIV into a community of 100,000 homosexual/bisexual males (graph *a*) and the incidence of AIDS yr[-1] (graph *b*). Heterogeneity in sexual activity is described by a gamma distribution with a mean fixed at 5 partners yr[-1] and variances 5, 25, 50 and 100 representing the predictions recorded by the four lines depicted in each graph. In *a* and *b* the smallest epidemic arises when the variance is largest and vice versa. Parameter values, $R_0 = 5$, $D = 5$ yr, $f = 0.3$ with the life expectancy of AIDS patient set at 1 yr from diagnosis and for the susceptible sexually active community at 32 yr from the point of joining the sexually active class. The 70% of infecteds who do not develop AIDS are assumed to be infectious for a period equal to D. The immigration of new susceptibles into the sexually active community was set at 100,000 per 32 yr.

以时间函数的形式描述了从流行病开始以来，血清反应阳性的比例和艾滋病的发病率。如果潜伏期遵从韦伯分布，即平均潜伏期为 5 年 [31]，据推测约 30% 的感染者最终会发展为艾滋病患者。我们推测处于艾滋病潜伏期的个体在整个潜伏期都有传染性，70% 的无症状者在同一时期也保持传染性。

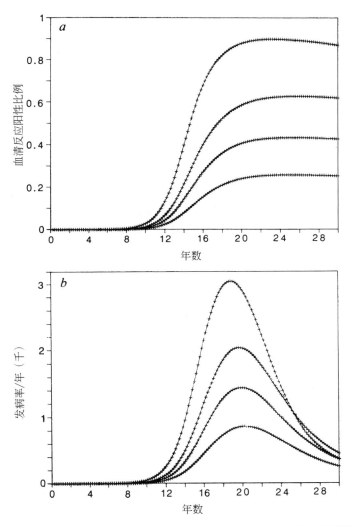

图 6. 一个结合可变的潜伏期、性活动不均一性和易感人群募集的模型（见文献 8）的预测。这两幅图记录了从 HIV 传入到 100,000 个男性同性恋和双性恋的群体的时间内，血清反应阳性的变化（表 a）和每年 AIDS 的发生率（表 b）。性活动的异质性以伽马分布描述，固定平均值为每年 5 个性伴侣，变量 5、25、50 和 100 代表了在表中描述的四条线的预测值。在表 a 和 b 中当变量最大时，传染增长最小，反之亦然。参数值：R_0=5，D=5 年，f=0.3，艾滋病人的预期寿命设定为诊断后的一年，性活跃的易感人群的预期寿命设定为加入性活跃类别后的 32 年。假设 70% 没有发展成艾滋病的感染者在长度为 D 的时期内有传染性。性活跃群体中新的易感人数设定为每 32 年 100,000 人。

Many of the features presented in Fig. 6 show qualitative agreement with observation. The rise in incidence of infection (seropositivity) is initially exponential, but soon shows a more linear rise. And, the rise in incidence of AIDS lags that in the proportion infected, as seen.

It is easy to build epidemiological models of arbitrary complexity, which may appear beguilingly realistic, but we think there is little point in constructing them until more is known about the relevant epidemiological parameters. We distrust predictions made by using statistical procedures to fit polynomial or exponential curves to existing data on the incidence of AIDS, and then extrapolating[40,44]. The HIV epidemic is a dynamic process; to predict future trends, models must be based on the underlying epidemiological phenomena.

Heterosexual Transmission

In developed countries, the extent to which HIV infection can be transmitted by heterosexual contacts is uncertain[43,48]. HIV infections in females come from contact with bisexual males (the dominant sexually-transmitted route at present), transfusion recipients, haemophiliacs and intravenous drug users[45]. If such females are not themselves a significant source of infection back into the homosexual/bisexual community (through contacts with uninfected bisexuals), we would expect the incidence of HIV infections among the female partners of bisexuals initially to rise roughly in proportion to the incidence among homosexual males.

Specifically, we would expect the ratio of HIV infection among female partners of bisexuals to that among bisexual males to be $\sim \beta'c'/\beta c$, where β and c are as previously defined, β' is the transmission probability for male-to-female contact, and c' is the mean number of new female partners acquired by a bisexual male, per unit time. We expect this ratio to be significantly less than unity, because β' is less than β, and c' significantly less than c. The data (Table 1) suggest the doubling time for heterosexually-transmitted HIV infection is roughly equal to that among homosexual males, which is in accord with our simple expectation.

As the epidemic progresses, a high proportion of homosexual males become infected (Fig. 2e). On the other hand, the pool of female partners for bisexual males may be large, and we would expect incidence of HIV infection still to be rising roughly linearly among women at and beyond the point at which saturation effects limit the epidemic among homosexual/bisexual males. How long this rise continues, and how many females are eventually likely to be infected, depends on the average duration of infectiousness in the transmitting group of males (which could be long if a substantial fraction remain asymptomatic carriers).

The transmission of HIV infection to females by bisexual males is a process whose initial dynamics is essentially determined by R_0 for transmission among homosexual males, thereafter the question of its transmission and maintenance by purely heterosexual contact arises. The basic reproductive rate for such heterosexual transmission of HIV, R_0', is given by

图 6 中呈现出的许多特征与观察到的特征在性质上相一致。感染（血清反应阳性）最初呈指数增长，但是很快就表现为直线上升。如我们所见，艾滋病发生率增长滞后于感染比例增长。

建立任意复杂的流行病学模型是很容易的，但是它可能出现现实欺骗性，除非我们对相关流行病学参数有更多的了解，否则我们认为建立这个模型是没有意义的。利用统计学程序对已有的艾滋病发生率数据套用多项式和指数曲线然后进行推测[40,44]，对这样的预测结果我们深表怀疑。HIV 流行病是一个动力学过程；要预测未来的发展趋势，模型必须以根本的流行病学现象为基础。

异性性传播

在发达国家，通过异性性接触传播的 HIV 传染程度是不确定的[43,48]。女性感染 HIV 是由于与双性恋男性（目前最主要的性传播途径）、受血者、血友病患者和静脉吸毒者接触[45]。如果这样的女性自身不是一个再传染同性恋和双性恋群体的重要感染源（通过接触未被感的双性恋），那么我们预测女性双性恋性伴侣之间的 HIV 传染率最初大致上与男性同性恋之间的几率成比例上升。

特别是，我们预期双性恋的女性伴侣的 HIV 感染率与双性恋男性感染率的比值大约为 $\beta'c'/\beta c$，β 和 c 在前面已经定义过，β' 是男性与女性接触传染的可能性，c' 是单位时间内双性恋男性获得新女性性伴侣的平均数。我们预期这个比率显著小于整体，因为 β' 小于 β，c' 显著小于 c。表 1 的数据显示，异性传染 HIV 的倍增时间约等于男性同性恋之间的倍增时间，与我们的预期值相同。

随着流行病的进一步发展，男性同性恋感染的比率很高（图 2e）。另一方面，双性恋男性的女性性伴侣范围可能比较广，我们预计女性之间的 HIV 感染率仍旧大致以线性方式增长，大于或等于同性恋或异性恋男性流行病的饱和效应限定点。这种增长持续多久，以及多少女性最终会被感染与男性传染群体具有传染性的平均持续时间有关（如果很大一部分能保持无症状携带者的状态，那么这段时间可能会很长）。

双性恋男性传染 HIV 给女性只是一个过程，它最初的动力学主要是由同性恋男性之间的传播 R_0 决定的，其后出现了纯粹异性恋接触的传播和持续时间的问题。这种异性恋之间 HIV 传播的感染增值指数 R_0' 的计算公式是

$$R_0' = (\beta_1\beta_2 c_1 c_2)^{1/2}D \tag{7}$$

Here β_1 and β_2 are the transmission parameters for contacts between infected females and susceptible males and between infected males and susceptible females, respectively; c_1 and c_2 are as before given by (2), for the distribution in rates of acquiring new partners of the other sex by females and males, respectively.

Data are very limited on the transmission and sexual activity parameters, but the data in Fig. 4 suggest that c_1 and c_2 are significantly smaller than c among homosexual males. Further, it seems likely that $\beta_1 < \beta_2$ and that both are less than the MM for homosexual males. Thus overall, the factor $(\beta_1\beta_2 c_1 c_2)^{1/2}$ seems likely to be much smaller than c for homosexual males, which suggests that in developed countries, R_0 for purely heterosexual transmission is probably significantly smaller than R_0 for purely male homosexual transmission. Whether R_0 is greater than unity, such that HIV infection can maintain itself and spread by purely heterosexual transmission, is at present unclear. There is an urgent need for studies to measure c_1 and c_2 in different communities (stratified by age and social status) and to assess how these parameters change as a consequence of educational programmes and publicity campaigns on AIDS. The use of professional opinion poll organizations to gather quantitative data on rates of partner change over a series of specified time intervals by interview and questionnaire (Fig. 4d) could help to fill this gap in our knowledge, but estimates of β_1 and β_2 will come only from long term studies of the heterosexual partners of infected patients.

If R_0' does exceed unity, the incidence of HIV infection in the heterosexual community will initially grow exponentially, at a rate given by the analogue of equation (1):

$$\Lambda = (\beta_1\beta_2 c_1 c_2)^{1/2} - 1/D = (R_0' - 1)D \tag{8}$$

The estimates above indicate that initial doubling times will be significantly longer than the 9 months or so for HIV among homosexual males; the slow initial growth will be difficult to discern against a background of homosexual transmission among males and bisexual transmission to females.

These observations are not necessarily inconsistent with the epidemiological situation for HIV in sub-Sahara Africa[6,49,56,57]. In contrast to the United States and the United Kingdom, where male/female ratios of AIDS cases have been of the order of 14:1 to 20:1, in certain parts of central Africa including areas in Zaire, Rwanda and Uganda, sex ratios approaching unity have been reported[45,50-53,56,57]. Very high prevalences of HIV antibodies have been found in males and females from surveys in urban and rural areas[52,56,57]. These points suggest that heterosexual transmission has been frequent in both directions and horizontal studies have shown that infection is associated with the age-related degree of sexual activity amongst heterosexuals[27,47,48,56,57]. We note, however, that in the early and approximately exponential phase of the epidemic, the ratio of the number of seropositive males to seropositive females is not unity, but is roughly $(\beta_1 c_1/\beta_2 c_2)^{1/2}$.

214

$$R_0' = (\beta_1\beta_2 c_1 c_2)^{1/2} D \tag{7}$$

β_1 和 β_2 分别是被感染的女性和易受感染的男性之间接触以及被感染的男性和易受感染的女性之间接触的传播参数；c_1 和 c_2 在前面（2）中已经给出，分别是女性和男性获得新的异性性伴侣的比率分布。

虽然数据受传播和性活动的参数的限制，但是图 4 的数据显示 c_1 和 c_2 明显地比男性同性恋之间的 c 小。此外，似乎 $\beta_1 < \beta_2$，它们两个都小于男性同性恋之间的 MM。因此，总的来说，$(\beta_1\beta_2 c_1 c_2)^{1/2}$ 因素似乎可能比男性同性恋的 c 小得多，表明在发达国家，纯粹异性传染的 R_0 可能明显的小于纯粹男性同性恋传染的 R_0。R_0 是否大于整体的值，譬如 HIV 感染可以通过单纯的异性传播来维持自身和传播，目前还不清楚。在不同群体（按照年龄和社会地位分类）中测量 c_1 和 c_2 的值以及评估这些参数如何随着关于艾滋病的教育项目和宣传活动而改变的研究急待开展。利用专业的民意测验系统，通过访谈和调查问卷收集一系列特定时间间隔内性伴侣改变速率的定量数据（图 4d），能够填补我们在这方面认识的空缺。但是只能通过对被感染病人的异性性伴侣进行长期研究才能获得 β_1 和 β_2 的估值。

如果 R_0' 确实超过了整体，那么在异性恋群体中，HIV 的传染发生率最初会以指数形式增长，通过模拟公式（1），给出了这个增长速率：

$$\Lambda = (\beta_1\beta_2 c_1 c_2)^{1/2} - 1/D = (R_0' - 1)D \tag{8}$$

上面的估值显示，在男性同性恋之间，HIV 最初的倍增时间显著长于 9 个月左右；最初的慢速增长在男性同性恋之间的传播和双性恋传染给女性的背景下很难识别。

这些观察结果不一定与非洲撒哈拉以南地区的 HIV 流行状况不一致 [6,49,56,57]。与美国和英国不同，那里的男性和女性感染艾滋病的比例分别是 14：1 到 20：1，在中非的某些区域包括扎伊尔（刚果民主共和国的旧称）、卢旺达和乌干达，报道称他们的性别比例接近整体的性别比例 [45,50-53,56,57]。在城市和农村地区的调查中发现男性和女性中普遍具有 HIV 的抗体 [52,56,57]。这些观点表明异性传染很频繁，纵向和横向的研究表明传染与异性恋年龄相关的性活动程度有关 [27,47,48,56,57]。然而，我们发现在流行病学的早期和近似指数期，血清反应阳性的男性数量与女性数量的比例不是统一的，但是近似等于 $(\beta_1 c_1/\beta_2 c_2)^{1/2}$。

It is generally thought that β_1 is less than β_2 for HIV, although the facts are uncertain (for gonorrhea, for instance, male-to-female transmission, β_2 is roughly twice β_1). Obviously the average number of heterosexual partners of females and males, m_1 and m_2, are equal, but c_1 could significantly exceed c_2 if the variance of the distribution of rate of acquiring new sexual partners by females (associated with the concentrated activities of female prostitutes) is greater than that for males. This effect could partly offset β_1 being smaller than β_2. Although there is no *a priori* reason to expect the ratio $\beta_1 c_1 / \beta_2 c_2$ to be exactly unity, its square root could easily be close to unity, which would explain the roughly equal proportions of seropositive males and females. Alternatively, the roughly equal proportions could be explained if homosexual transmission among males had coincidentally raised the seropositive proportion among males to around the level among females, or by transmission by contaminated needles in public and private medical services[6]. In any event, the rough equality of the seropositive proportions among males and females is a puzzle to be explained, and is not by itself evidence for purely heterosexual transmission.

Discussion

The ideas presented above are based on relatively simple mathematical models, with the aim of making clear some of the essential relations between epidemiological parameters and the overall course of HIV infection within various populations. Such models help to clarify what kinds of epidemiological data are needed to make predictions. As such data become available, the models can be made more detailed and realistic.

For public health planning, the dominant unknown is f, the fraction infected who will eventually develop AIDS. Estimates of this parameter have been increasing in recent years, but on present evidence the possibility cannot be ruled out that it is as low as 20% or as high as virtually 100%. Thus any current predictions about the number of homosexuals likely to acquire AIDS are uncertain by at least a factor 5 or so. Better understanding of the mechanisms of interactions between virus and host may help to determine f, but it is possible that only epidemiological data gathered on a decade-long timescale, as cases accumulate, will resolve this question.

The duration of infectiousness, and the way this duration is distributed among different infectives, is also relevant to estimates of R_0 and thence of the eventual number infected; more studies directed towards eliciting this information, including looking for virus in the blood, excretions and secretions of infected individuals over time, together with longitudinal studies of the partners of infected patients, are needed[3].

More generally, there is need for more studies that combine information about the epidemiological history of individuals with information about their sexual habits, such as the important study by Winkelstein *et al.*[26] of an unbiased sample of homosexuals in San Francisco, which demonstrated the association between the number of sexual partners and probability of acquiring infection. We emphasize that what is epidemiologically important is the average rate of acquiring new sexual partners, not necessarily the same as the

尽管还不确定，但是一般认为对 HIV 来说 β_1 小于 β_2（以淋病为例，男性传染给女性，β_2 大概是 β_1 的两倍）。很明显，男性和女性的异性性伴侣的平均值 m_1 和 m_2 相等，但是如果女性获得性的性伴侣的几率分布的方差高于男性（与妓女的集中活动有关），那么 c_1 就会明显的超过 c_2。这个效应会部分抵消 β_1 比 β_2 小的部分。没有先验的理由认为比率 $\beta_1 c_1 / \beta_2 c_2$ 必须精确地等于 1，但是它的平方根很容易接近 1，这可以解释男性和女性血清反应阳性的比例大致相等。或者说，如果男性同性恋之间传播或者通过公共和私人医疗服务污染的针头传播碰巧将男性血清反应阳性比例增长到与女性相同的水平，那么也可以解释大略相等的比例 [6]。不管怎样，男性和女性血清反应阳性比例的大致相等都很难解释，而且它本身不是一个纯粹异性传播的证据。

讨　论

为了弄清楚流行病学参数和 HIV 在多种人群中传染的全过程之间的重要联系，上述观点是以较简单的数学模型为依据的。这些模型帮助我们阐明做出预测都需要什么类型的流行病学数据。当可以获得这样的数据时，模型可以做得更加详细和实际。

对于公共健康计划，关键的未知数是 f，也就是最终会发展为艾滋病感染者的比例。最近几年这个参数的估值已经增加了，但是在当前的证据下，低至 20% 或几乎高达 100% 的可能性都不能够排除。因此，当前与可能得艾滋病的同性恋数目有关的预测都是不确切的，至少在 5 倍左右范围内。更好地理解病毒和宿主之间的相互作用机制可以帮助我们确定 f，但是只有以长达十年的时间为标度来，随着病例的积累收集流行病学数据，才有可能解决这个问题。

感染的持续时间和不同感染阶段持续的方式，都与 R_0 的估值和从那以后终被传染的人数有关；更多的研究直接指向引出这些信息，包括这段时间里的血液病毒检查、被感染个体的排泄物和分泌物检查以及对被感染病人性伴侣进行纵向研究也是必需的 [3]。

更为普遍的是，我们需要将个体的流行病史和他们的性习惯方面的信息结合起来进行更多的研究，如温克尔斯坦等 [26] 在旧金山所做的一个同性恋无偏样本的研究，揭示了性伴侣的数量和被感染的概率之间的联系。我们强调，流行病学上最重要的是获得新的性伴侣的平均几率不一定要和单位时间里性伴侣的平均数相同。一些作者认识到，高度性活跃的个体在传播动力学中起到了不成比例的重要作用；公式（2）

average number of partners per unit time. Some authors have recognized that sexually highly active individuals play a disproportionate role in the transmission dynamics; equation (2) quantifies this observation, making it clear that the epidemiologically relevant quantity is not the mean number of new partners but, rather, the mean-square divided by the mean.

In developed countries, at present and into the near future, it is probable that sexually-transmitted HIV infections among females are likely to come mainly from bisexual males. Whether subsequent spread of infection from such females to heterosexual male partners is likely to reach significant levels, and more importantly whether purely heterosexual transmission of HIV infection may be selfsustaining ($R_0' > 1$), depends on estimates of the transmission parameters β_1, β_2, c_1 and c_2.

We have shown how c for transmission among homosexual males can be estimated indirectly from data on initial doubling times, but corresponding estimates of $\beta_1 c_1$ and $\beta_2 c_2$ are much harder, partly because the corresponding doubling rates are likely to be longer and partly because these infections are likely to be masked by homosexual/bisexual transmission among males, and by bisexual-to-female transmission among females (both of which processes depend simply on c). Attempts to estimate these quantities directly, and thence to estimate R_0, are urgently needed.

From present knowledge, it is not possible to assess whether R_0' is greater or less than unity in developed countries, and it is thus not possible to say whether HIV infections could spread epidemically by purely heterosexual transmission. The evidence from Africa, however, clearly argues that the sexually active population as a whole should be regarded as at risk[6,47,56,57].

We have greatly benefited from discussions with Anne Johnson, Mike Adler, John Pickering, Graham Medley, Stephen Blythe and Jenny Crombie. Financial support from the MRC and the NSF is gratefully acknowledged. We thank C. A. Carne, I. V. Weller and T. McManus for permission to quote unpublished data (Fig. 4).

(**326**, 137-142; 1987)

Robert M. May is in the Biology Department, Princeton University, Princeton, New Jersey 08544, USA. Roy M. Anderson is in the Parasite Epidemiology Research Group, Department of Pure and Applied Biology, Imperial College, University of London, London SW72BB, UK.

References:

1. Hahn B. H. *et al. Science* **232**, 1548-1552 (1986).

2. Goedert, J. J. *et al. Lancet* ii 711-715 (1984).

3. Goudsmit, J. *et al. Lancet* ii 177-180 (1986).

4. Peterman, T. A., Drotman, D. P. & Curran, J. W. *Epidem. Rev.* **7**, 1-21 (1985).

5. Curran, J. W. *Ann. Intern. Med.* **103**, 657-662 (1985).

量化了这个观察结果，明确了流行病相关的数量不是新伴侣的平均值，而是均方除以平均值之后的结果。

在现在和不久的将来，在发达国家女性中通过性传播 HIV 可能主要来自男性双性恋。从这样的女性到异性恋的男性伴侣随后的传播是否有可能达到显著的水平和最重要的是纯粹的异性恋之间的 HIV 传播是否可以自我维持（$R_0' > 1$），都取决于传播参数 β_1，β_2，c_1 和 c_2 的估计值。

我们已经阐明如何间接地从原始的倍增时间估算出男性同性恋之间的传染 c 值，但是 $\beta_1 c_1$ 和 $\beta_2 c_2$ 相应的估算较困难，一部分是因为相应的倍增几率可能比较长，一部分是这些传染可能会被男性同性恋、双性恋和双性恋男性传染给女性（这两个过程只与 c 有关）所遮盖。尽量直接估计这些数据然后再估计 R_0 是急切需要的。

就现在的知识，我们很难估计出发达国家的 R_0 是否大于或小于 1，因此我们不可能确定 HIV 传染能否纯粹依靠异性传播。尽管来自非洲的证据明确指出性活跃群体作为一个整体应该被认为是高危人群 [6,47,56,57]。

我们从和安妮·约翰逊、迈克·阿德勒、约翰·皮克林、格雷厄姆·梅德利、斯蒂芬·布莱思和珍妮·克龙比的讨论中获益匪浅，资金支持来自医学研究理事会和国家科学基金会。我们感谢卡恩、韦勒和麦克马纳斯准许我们使用他们尚未发表的数据（图 4）。

（郑建全 翻译；孙军 审稿）

6. Acheson, E. D. *Lancet* i 662-676 (1986).

7. Anderson, R. M. & May, R. M. *Nature* **318**, 323-329 (1985).

8. Anderson, R. M., May, R. M., Medley, G. F. & Johnson, A. *IMAJ. Math. Med. Biol.* (in the press).

9. Dietz, K. *Lect. Notes. Biomaths.* **11**, 1-15 (1976).

10. Anderson, R. M. in *Theoretical Ecology* (ed. May, R. M.) 318-355 (Blackwell, Oxford, 1981).

11. Hethcote, H. W. & Yorke, J. A. *Lect. Notes. Biomaths.* **56**, 1-105 (1984).

12. Centers for Disease Control MMWR **34**, 573-589 (1985).

13. Centers for Disease Control MMWR **35**, 17-20 (1986).

14. Anderson, R. M. & May, R. M. *Nature* **280**, 361-367 (1979).

15. May, R. M. & Anderson, R. M. *Nature* **280**, 455-461 (1979).

16. Ho, D. D. *et al. New Engl. J. Med.* **313**, 1606 (1985).

17. Ho, D. D. *et al. Ann. Intern. Med.* **103**, 880-883 (1985).

18. Carne, C. A. *et al. Lancet* ii 1206-1208 (1985).

19. Wong-Staal, F. & Gallo, R. C. *Nature* **317**, 395-403 (1985).

20. Centers for Disease Control MMWR **34**, 373-375 (1985).

21. Schreeder, M. T. *et al. J. Infect. Dis.* **146**, 7-15 (1982).

22. Jaffe, H. W. *et al. Ann. Intern. Med.* **103**, 210-214 (1985).

23. Carne, C. A. *et al. Lancet* i, 1261-1262 (1985).

24. Angarano, G. *et al. Lancet* ii 1302 (1985).

25. Francis, D. P. *Rev. Infect. Dis.* **5**, 322-329 (1983).

26. Winkelstein, W. *et al. J. Am. Med. Assoc.* **257**, 321-325 (1987).

27. McKusick, L. *et al. Pub. Hlth. Repts.* **100**, 622-628 (1985).

28. Curran, J. W., Morgan, W. M. & Hardy, A. M. *Science* **229**, 1352-1357 (1985).

29. Weller, I. V. D., Hindley, D. J. & Adler, M. W. *Brit. med. J.* **289**, 1041 (1984).

30. Centers for Disease Control MMWR **34**, 613-615 (1985).

31. Lui, K. J. *et al. Proc. Natl. Acad. Sci. U.S.A.* **83**, 3051-3055 (1986).

32. Peterman, T. A. *et al. J. Am. med. Ass.* **254**, 2913-2917 (1985).

33. Moss, A. R. *et al. J. infect. Dis.* **152**, 152-161 (1985).

34. Weber, J. N. *et al. Lancet* i 1179-1182 (1986).

35. Stevens, C. E. *et al. J. Am. med. Assoc.* **255**, 2167-2171 (1985).

36. Goedert, J. J. *et al. Science* **231**, 992-995 (1986).

37. Brodt, H. R. *et al. Dtsch. med. Wschr.* **111**, 1175-1180 (1986).

38. Weiss, R. A. in *Virus Resistance* (eds Mahy, B. W. J., Mison, A. C. & Dorby, G. K.) 267-288 (Cambridge Univ., London, 1982).

39. Scorza Smeraldi, R. *et al. Lancet* ii 1187-1189 (1986).

40. McEvoy, M. & Tillett, H. *Lancet* ii, 541-542 (1985).

41. Artalego, F. R. *et al. Lancet* i 378 (1986).

42. Downs, A. M., Ancelle, R. & Brunet, J. B. (in the press).

43. Barnes, D. M. *Science* **232**, 1589-1590 (1986).

44. Gonzalez, J. J. & Keoch, M. G. *W. H. O. Report on Euro meeting on AIDS containment* (WHO, Geneva, 1986).

45. Vogt, M. W. *et al. Lancet* i, 525-527 (1986).

46. Wofsy, C. *et al. Lancet* i, 527-529 (1986).

47. Centers for Disease Control MMWR, **34**, 561-563 (1985).

48. de Perre, P. V. *et al. Lancet* ii 524.

49. Harris, C. *et al. New Engl. J. Med.* **308**, 1181-1184 (1985).

50. Centers for Disease Control MMWR **31**, 697-698 (1984).

51. Newmark, P. *Nature* **322**, 6 (1986).

52. Biggar, R. J. *Lancet* i 79-82 (1986).

53. Kreiss, J. K. *et al. New Engl. J. Med.* **314**, 414-417 (1985).

54. Papervangelou, G., Roumeliotou-Karayannis, A., Kallinikos, G. & Papoutsakis, G. *Lancet* ii 1018 (1985).

55. Tirelli, U. *et al. Lancet* ii 1424 (1985).

56. Quinn, T. C., Mann, J. M., Curran, J. W. & Piot, P. *Science* **234**, 955-963 (1986).

57. Melbye, M. *et al. Lancet* ii 1113-1117 (1986).

Interstellar Diamonds in Meteorites

R. S. Lewis *et al.*

Editor's Note

Meteorites are pieces of debris left over from the formation of the solar system that have landed on Earth. Some types of meteorites contain a very fine-grained type of carbon, which Roy Lewis in Chicago and colleagues here show to be microscopic diamonds containing less than 100 atoms. Normally, diamonds are formed when carbon is put under pressure, but those in the meteorites seem to have formed directly in the diamond phase from carbon ejected in the winds of old stars or supernovae into the interstellar medium. When the solar system was forming out of interstellar gas, the diamonds were incorporated into the growing bodies, and eventually arrived on Earth as meteorites.

Primitive meteorites contain up to 400 p.p.m. of a very fine-grained type of carbon, noncommittally called $C\delta$[1]. It apparently comes from outside the Solar System, as it carries isotopically anomalous krypton and xenon ("Xe-HL" or "CCFXe", enriched twofold in the lightest and heaviest isotopes[2]) and nitrogen ($\delta^{15}N = -330‰$[3]; that is, depleted in ^{15}N by $-330‰$ relative to atmospheric nitrogen), although the carbon itself is within the terrestrial range ($\delta^{13}C = -38‰$[1]). Expanding on a preliminary report[4], we now present evidence that part or all of $C\delta$ is diamond—not shock-produced but primary, formed by stellar condensation as a metastable phase. It appears that interstellar dust contains diamond.

THINKING that $C\delta$ might be the C_{60} cluster "buckminsterfullerene"[5], we isolated a new sample from the Allende C3V chondrite, aiming for maximum purity rather than maximum yield. After dissolving the major minerals in HF-HCl, we generated a colloid from the remaining 0.5% residue, leaving behind coarse-grained spinel and chromite[2,6]. The major gas-poor part ($C\gamma$) of the colloidal carbon was removed by oxidation with 16 M and 21 M HNO_3 (16 h, 70 °C) and concentrated $HClO_4$ (2 h, 140 °C). Surprisingly, the residue (Allende CH, 109 p.p.m.) was not black but light tan. As it contained some silicate contaminants, we reprocessed it with HCl and HF, obtaining Allende CJ (89 p.p.m.) of unchanged colour.

On the scanning electron microscope (SEM) Allende CJ showed no elements above oxygen (Mg, Al and Si <2.5 wt% if evenly dispersed or <<1% if in grains of >0.5 μm). X-ray diffraction showed only three very broad, diffuse lines, which to our surprise matched the

陨石中的星际金刚石

刘易斯等

编者按

陨石是太阳系形成时坠落在地球上的残余的碎块。某些种类的陨石中含有一种非常细小的晶粒状的碳，在本文中，芝加哥大学的罗伊·刘易斯和他的合作者们指出这种晶粒是含有少于 100 个碳原子的金刚石微晶。通常，当碳处于一定压力下时会形成金刚石，但是陨石中的金刚石似乎是由老的恒星或者超新星的风喷射入星际介质的碳直接形成的金刚石相。在太阳系由星际间的气体形成的过程中，这些金刚石嵌入了成长中的星体，并最终以陨石的形式到达地球。

原始的陨石中包含多达 400 ppm 的非常细小的晶粒状的碳，它们被模糊地称为 Cδ[1]。它显然来自太阳系之外，因为它携带了同位素含量异常的氖、氙（被称为"Xe-HL"或者"CCFXe"，其中最轻和最重的同位素富集了两倍[2]）和氮（$\delta^{15}N = -330‰$[3]；这表明相对大气中的氮 ^{15}N 贫化为 $-330‰$），而碳元素本身在地球分布的范围之内（$\delta^{13}C = -38‰$[1]）。通过对一个初步研究结果[4]进行扩展，我们在此给出证据表明部分或者全部的 Cδ 是金刚石——它们并非由冲击产生，而是在星体凝聚过程中原生的亚稳相。这表明星际尘埃中包含有金刚石。

考虑到 Cδ 可能是 C$_{60}$（"巴克敏斯特富勒烯"[5]）的团簇，我们从球粒状陨石阿连德 C3V 中分离得到了一个新的样品，以期获得最高的纯度而不是最高的产率。在将矿石主体溶于氢氟酸 – 盐酸混合液之后，弃去大颗粒的尖晶石和铬铁矿，我们从剩余的 0.5% 物质中得到了一种胶体物质[2,6]。胶状碳中主要的贫气部分（Cγ）用 16 M 和 21 M 的硝酸（16 小时，70℃）和浓高氯酸（2 小时，140℃）氧化除去。令人惊奇的是，残余物（阿连德 CH，109 ppm）并非黑色而为浅黄褐色。由于其中含有一些硅酸盐污染物，我们将它用盐酸和氢氟酸又处理了一遍，得到了同样颜色的样品阿连德 CJ（89 ppm）。

在扫描电子显微镜（SEM）中，阿连德 CJ 显示其中没有重于氧的元素（均匀分散的话，镁、铝和硅的含量小于 2.5wt%；如果只考虑大于 0.5 μm 的颗粒的话，它们的含量远小于 1%）。X 射线衍射只显示出三条非常宽的弥散的衍射线，令我们感到惊奇的是它们与金刚石的三条主要衍射线相吻合。在透射电子显微镜（TEM）中，

three principal lines of diamond. On the transmission electron microscope (TEM), the grains turned out to be typically 50 Å in size (Fig. 1). Electron diffraction (Fig. 2) confirmed that most grains were diamond, as shown by the agreement of the observed spacings with accepted values (shown in parentheses): 2.06 (2.06), 1.26 (1.26), 1.07 (1.075), 0.893 (0.8916), 0.817 (0.8182), 0.73 (0.728), 0.68 (0.686) Å. Elemental analysis by analytical electron microscopy showed a small amount of Cl (contamination or surface-bound Cl from HCl?) as well as Cr and Fe (submicrometre-sized ferrichromite[7]). Examination by high-resolution mass spectrometry at 70–550 °C showed only small amounts of volatile material, probably contamination. Peaks appeared up to at least $m/e = 733$, but none of the more abundant ones corresponded to C_{60} or other C_n ions.

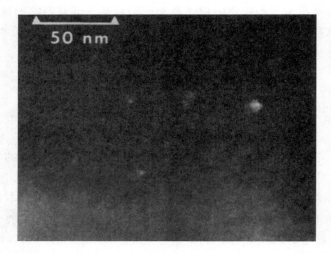

Fig. 1. Dark-field transmission electron micrograph of Allende CJ, in which bright areas are diamond grains diffracting electrons into one part of the innermost ring of the diffraction pattern shown in Fig. 2. As most grains do not have the proper orientation, the true abundance of diamond is perhaps five times higher than indicated by the bright areas in the picture.

Fig. 2. Selected-area electron diffraction pattern from Allende CJ. This is a typical ring powder pattern, with d-values matching those of diamond.

可以看出颗粒的典型尺寸为 50 Å（图 1）。电子衍射（图 2）确认了大部分的颗粒均为金刚石，获得的晶面间距与公认值（显示在括号中）一致：2.06（2.06）Å、1.26（1.26）Å、1.07（1.075）Å、0.893（0.8916）Å、0.817（0.8182）Å、0.73（0.728）Å、0.68（0.686）Å。分析型电子显微镜的元素分析显示样品中有很少量的氯（污染物或者来自盐酸的键合在表面的氯?）、铬和铁（微米尺寸以下的铬铁矿 [7]）。在 70~550℃进行的高分辨质谱检测表明仅有少量的挥发性物质，很可能是污染物。出现的峰的质荷比至少可以达到 733，但是没有哪个含量较多的组分的峰对应于 C_{60} 或者其他的 C_n 离子。

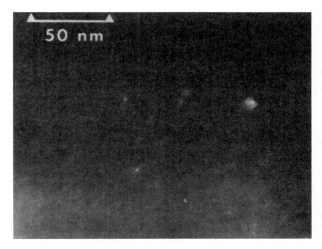

图 1. 样品阿连德 CJ 的暗场透射电子显微镜图片，其中亮的区域是金刚石颗粒，其衍射电子形成如图 2 中的衍射图样中最内环的一部分。由于大部分的颗粒没有适当的取向，实际的金刚石的数量可能是图片中亮的区域标示出来的数量的 5 倍以上。

图 2. 样品阿连德 CJ 的选区电子衍射图样。这是一个粉末样品的典型环状图样，其 d 值与金刚石吻合。

To check whether such diamonds are present in other meteorites containing Xe-HL, we isolated similar residues from Murchison (C2), Murray (C2) and Indarch (EH4), using $HClO_4$ at higher temperature (190–206 °C) to remove the more reactive forms of carbon. Residues Murchison GL1 (white, 225 p.p.m.) and Indarch CF (dark grey, 36 p.p.m.) both showed diamond by electron diffraction. Murray A2C (white, 250 p.p.m.) was not checked by electron diffraction but showed only minor Al and Si on the SEM.

From the TEM work it appears that some amorphous, low-atomic-number material is present in addition to diamond, perhaps radiation-damaged diamond or unrelated extraneous material. (As we note later, Xe-HL seems to have been trapped by ion implantation, and presumably was accompanied by large amounts of other ions.) This is supported by density-gradient centrifugation, showing that Murchison GL1 has an effective bulk density of 2.22–2.33 g cm^{-3}, well below the density of pure diamond (3.51 g cm^{-3}). This material is not graphite or amorphous carbon, else the sample would not be pure white. But its amount must be less than implied by the low effective density, as the particles sink not singly but as aggregates, containing much interstitial liquid immobilized in angstrom-sized voids.

Curiously the infrared spectrum strongly resembles that of soot, with peaks at 2.93, 3.17, 5.59, 6.13 and 7.14 µm. For soot, these features are attributed to the reaction of surface atoms with H and O, and presumably such surface alteration also occurs for fine-grained diamond. Approximately 9% of the atoms in 50-Å diamond are at the surface.

On heating, Cδ showed a surface graphitization behaviour consistent with that of diamond. A sample wrapped in platinum foil did not change when heated in air (19 days at 165 °C, 3 days at 280 °C, 1 day at 380 °C), but blackened visibly at ~10^{-2} torr (1 day at 380 °C). A sample heated in a Pyrex tube in high vacuum darkened only slightly (1 h at 100–550 °C, 3 min at 550 °C). Diamond behaves similarly, darkening at low O_2 pressures but not in high vacuum or at high O_2 pressures (where any graphite formed is rapidly oxidized).

Given that Cδ is mainly diamond, is the diamond the actual carrier of the isotope anomalies? We cannot get absolute proof, as our samples are not pure diamond; the best we can do is establish correlations between the anomalies and the diamond content of the samples.

The Xe-HL content is indicated by ^{136}Xe-HL (Table 1). It is generally highest in the white samples, although black Allende B1B is close and white Murray A2C (which contained some extraneous phases) is lower. Apparently Xe-HL stays with the diamond when other phases are destroyed. The highest values for Allende and Murchison are similar (17–19×10^{-8} cm^3 g^{-1}), as expected if both meteorites contained the same kind of Cδ.

为了确定这种金刚石是否存在于其他含有 Xe-HL 的陨石中，我们用高氯酸从默奇森（C2），默里（C2）和因达奇（EH4）中分离出了类似的剩余物，这是采用在更高的温度（190~206℃）除去具有更高活性形式的碳得到的。剩余物默奇森 GL1（白色，含量 250 ppm）和因达奇 CF（深灰色，含量 36 ppm）在电子衍射中均显示出了金刚石的存在。样品默里 A2C（白色，含量 250 ppm）没有用电子衍射进行确认，但 SEM 表明其中仅有少量的铝和硅。

在 TEM 研究中显示，除了金刚石外还有一些无定形的低原子序数物质存在，它们可能是被辐射损伤的金刚石或者是无关的其他物质。（正如我们之后所注意到的那样，Xe-HL 似乎是通过离子注入被捕获的，同时很可能也含有大量的其他离子。）这一结果得到了密度梯度离心实验的支持，实验表明默奇森 GL1 的有效体相密度为 2.22~2.33 g·cm^{-3}，明显低于纯金刚石的密度（3.51 g·cm^{-3}）。这种材料不是石墨或无定形碳，否则样品不会是纯白色。但是它的含量一定少于用于解释低的有效密度的量，这是由于这些颗粒并非单独沉降而是聚集之后沉降，其中含有很多颗粒间隙中的液体，它们被固定在埃尺度的缝隙中。

很奇怪的是，红外光谱与炭黑非常相似，在 2.93 μm、3.17 μm、5.59 μm、6.13 μm 和 7.14 μm 处有峰。就炭黑而言，这些特征被归因于表面原子与氢和氧的反应，那么很有可能这种表面替换在细小的金刚石晶粒中也会发生。尺寸为 50 Å 的金刚石中有大约 9% 的原子位于表面。

在加热过程中，Cδ 表现出了表面石墨化的行为，这与金刚石的行为一致。包裹在铂箔中的样品在空气中加热（165℃ 加热 19 天，280℃ 加热 3 天，380℃ 加热 1 天）没有发生变化，但是在约 10^{-2} 托的气压下加热（380℃ 加热 1 天）会变黑。派莱克斯玻璃（译者注：一种耐热玻璃）管中高真空加热的样品仅会稍稍变黑（100~550℃ 加热 1 小时，550℃ 加热 3 分钟）。金刚石的行为类似，在较低的氧压条件下会变黑，而在高真空或者高的氧压下不会变黑（这种条件下任何生成的石墨都会被快速地氧化掉）。

既然 Cδ 主要是金刚石，那么金刚石是否为异常同位素的载体？由于我们的样品不是纯的金刚石，我们无法获得确凿的证据；我们能做到的就是确立同位素异常与样品中金刚石含量的相关性。

Xe-HL 的含量由 ^{136}Xe-HL 表示（表 1）。它在白色样品中含量通常最高，尽管黑色的样品阿连德 B1B 中含量与之接近而白色样品默里 A2C（包含一些额外的相）的含量较低。当其他相被除去后，表观上 Xe-HL 与金刚石在一起。阿连德和默奇森的最高含量接近（17×10^{-8} ~ 19×10^{-8} cm^3·g^{-1}），这与两种陨石含有相同种类的 Cδ 的假设相一致。

Table 1. Anomalous Xe in diamond-rich meteorite separates

Sample		Class	Mass fraction* p.p.m.	Gas content $10^{-8}\,cm^2\,g^{-1}$		$\dfrac{^{136}Xe}{^{132}Xe}$	References
				^{132}Xe	^{136}Xe-HL†		
Allende	CJ‡	C3V	89	30±6	19±4	0.642±3	This paper
Allende	CH‡	C3V	109	24±2	15±1	0.649±3	This paper
Allende	B1B	C3V	390	25±3	16±2	0.644±5	3
Allende	CC	CeV	180	21±2	14±1	0.653±23	3
Allende	B1E	C3V	180	16±2	10±1	0.636±8	This paper
Allende	CG	C3V	250	12±1	8±1	0.652±3	6
Murchison	GL1‡	C2	225	37±7§	17±3	0.550±2§	This paper
Murchison	2C10f	C2	780	18±2§	8±1	0.537±2§	23
Murray	A2C‡	C2	250	28±2§	12±1	0.535±2§	This paper
Indarch	CF	EH4	36	9±2	5±1	0.593±4	This paper

* Mass fraction of separate relative to bulk meteorite. Values for different samples are not directly comparable. In the earlier samples they are high due to extraneous phases and in the later, highly purified, samples they are low due to mechanical losses.

† ^{136}Xe-HL is the calculated excess ^{136}Xe in the sample, relative to planetary Xe with $^{136}Xe/^{132}Xe = 0.32$.

‡ White; all other samples are black (except Indarch CF, which is dark grey) owing to the presence of graphitic carbon.

§ Excluding an isotopically normal Xe component released at 800 °C, before the release of Xe-HL ($>1,000$ °C). It occurs only in C2 chondrites[23]. Its carrier, Cζ is carbonaceous but totally uncharacterized.

The correlation with other anomalies is more tenuous, as no data are available yet on the new samples. Earlier measurements by stepped combustion show that light N, light C, and Xe-HL are all released in the same temperature range of 500–600 °C[1,3,8], and hence may be located in the same phase. However, this correlation must be checked on diamond-enriched samples. (The combustion temperature of terrestrial diamond under identical conditions is ~250 °C higher[9], but that is a trivial consequence of the coarser grain size. At an activation energy of 60 kcal mol^{-1}, the combustion rate per unit area is 4.8×10^3 times higher at 800 °C than at 550 °C, but this difference would be exactly offset by a 70-fold difference in grain size, that is, 3,500 Å rather than 50 Å).

Diamonds have been previously found in some meteorites (most ureilites and two iron meteorites), but they apparently formed by shock, in terrestrial or asteroidal impacts[10,11]. It seems unlikely that the Cδ diamonds originated in this way. First, although all four meteorites in which these diamonds have been found are somewhat brecciated (Allende least so), none shows the strong shock effects, high post-shock temperatures, or both, that characterize other diamond-bearing meteorites. Second, all the Cδ-bearing meteorites also contain 10^3–10^4 p.p.m. of graphitic or amorphous carbon that has no Xe-HL or light N and is isotopically heavier ($\delta^{13}C = -15‰$, compared with $-38‰$ for Cδ[1,12]). If the diamonds were made from graphite grains in the meteorite parent bodies by shock, why

表 1. 异常氙在富含金刚石的陨石分离产物中的分布

样品		类别	质量含量[*] (ppm)	气体含量 $10^{-8}\,cm^2\cdot g^{-1}$		$^{136}Xe/^{132}Xe$	参考文献
				^{132}Xe	^{136}Xe-HL[†]		
阿连德	CJ[‡]	C3V	89	30 ± 6	19 ± 4	0.642 ± 3	本文
阿连德	CH[‡]	C3V	109	24 ± 2	15 ± 1	0.649 ± 3	本文
阿连德	B1B	C3V	390	25 ± 3	16 ± 2	0.644 ± 5	3
阿连德	CC	CeV	180	21 ± 2	14 ± 1	0.653 ± 23	3
阿连德	B1E	C3V	180	16 ± 2	10 ± 1	0.636 ± 8	本文
阿连德	CG	C3V	250	12 ± 1	8 ± 1	0.652 ± 3	6
默奇森	GL1[‡]	C2	225	37 ± 7§	17 ± 3	0.550 ± 2§	本文
默奇森	2C10f	C2	780	18 ± 2§	8 ± 1	0.537 ± 2§	23
默里	A2C[‡]	C2	250	28 ± 2§	12 ± 1	0.535 ± 2§	本文
因达奇	CF	EH4	36	9 ± 2	5 ± 1	0.593 ± 4	本文

[*] 分离产物相对于陨石块体质量分数。不同样品的数值并非直接可比。在较早的样品中由于其他相的存在其数值较大，而后来的样品经过了高度的纯化，由于存在机械损失所以数值较低。

[†] ^{136}Xe-HL 是计算得到的样品中多余的 ^{136}Xe，这是相对于比例为 $^{136}Xe/^{132}Xe = 0.32$ 的行星中的氙而言的。

[‡] 白色；由于石墨碳的存在，所有其他的样品均为黑色（除了样品因达奇 CF，其为深灰色）。

§ 排除了在 Xe-HL 释放（不小于 1,000℃）之前于 800℃ 释放的同位素含量正常的氙。它仅在 C2 球粒型陨石中出现 [23]。它的载体 Cζ 含有碳，但完全无法表征。

与其他同位素异常的相关性就更弱了，这是由于目前还没有获得关于新样品的数据。之前的分步燃烧测量显示，少量氮、少量碳和 Xe-HL 都在同样的温度区间（500~600℃）被释放 [1,3,8]，这表明它们可能处在同一相中。然而，这种相关性必须在金刚石含量高的样品中进行确认。（在相同条件下陆生金刚石的燃烧温度较之高约 250℃ [9]，但这是较为粗大的颗粒尺寸的一个寻常结果。当活化能为 60 kcal·mol^{-1} 时，800℃ 下单位面积的燃烧速率是 550℃ 的 4.8×10^3 倍，但是这个差异会被晶粒尺寸 70 倍的差异完全抵消，也就是说尺寸为 3,500 Å 而非 50 Å）。

以前金刚石在一些陨石中也被发现过（大部分的橄辉无球粒陨石和两种铁陨石），但是它们显然是由于在地球上或太空中的撞击形成的 [10,11]。看上去 Cδ 并非由这种途径产生。首先，尽管有这种金刚石存在的四种陨石被发现时都在某种程度上被撞成了碎片（阿连德陨石程度最轻），但是没有证据表明存在像其他含金刚石的陨石那样强烈的冲击效应，以及冲击后产生的高温，或两者兼而有之。其次，所有含有 Cδ 的陨石也含有 10^3~10^4 ppm 的石墨或者无定形碳，而其中并无 Xe-HL 或只含少量氮，并且碳的同位素更重（$\delta^{13}C = -15‰$，对 Cδ 而言，其值为 $-38‰$ [1,12]）。如果金刚石是由陨石母体中的石墨颗粒经撞击形成的，为什么撞击（在三个或四个不同的陨石

did the shock (in three or four different parent bodies) singlemindedly transform only the Xe-HL-bearing grains, while ignoring the more abundant, gas-poor carbon grains? Third, all four meteorites have essentially similar $C\delta$, with comparable gas contents and isotopic compositions (Table 1). If the diamonds were shock-produced, we would expect greater variations, depending on the proportions of the two types of carbon converted to diamond and on post-shock diffusion losses. Ureilites, for example, show a ~100-fold variation in gas concentration[13].

By default, it seems necessary to invoke an extra-solar origin for the diamond. But diamond has not been seriously considered a possible constituent of the cosmos outside the Solar System, as no astronomical object except planets has the right pressure–temperature conditions for its formation as a stable phase (40–400 kbar, 1,200–4,000 K), and any diamonds formed in planets could not get out because of the high escape velocity. (Landau[14] has pointed out that diamond of a steep size distribution would give a good match to the interstellar extinction curve, but he did not consider the origin of the diamonds.) Although shocks are common in the cosmos, they too, do not give the combination of high pressure and moderate temperature required for formation of diamond. The only feasible mechanism would seem to be metastable formation of diamond from a hot gas at low pressures, as recently demonstrated in the laboratory[15]. Let us see how this mechanism can be incorporated in a scheme that accounts for Xe-HL.

Xe-HL apparently formed in a supernova[16] and (along with other noble gases, H and N) was trapped in carbon grains by ion implantation[17]. The high relative velocities (~10^3 km s^{-1}) required for the latter process imply that the grains predate the supernova, and presumably formed in the gas shell ejected by the pre-supernova during its red giant or planetary nebula stage some 10^2–10^4 yr earlier[18]. Carbon is the first solid expected to condense from a carbon-rich gas at equilibrium[19], and although graphite is the stable phase, diamond, being metastable by only ~2 kJ mol^{-1}, could form instead. Indeed, such preferential formation of diamond has been observed in the laboratory[15]. The processes studied so far involve decomposition of CH_4 or organic compounds in the presence of large amounts of hydrogen, either by ordinary pyrolysis or by plasma reactions. The mechanism is not yet known, but seems to involve CH_3 radicals and H atoms. Although CH_3 is not an abundant radical in red giants, other radicals or molecules, such as CH, C_2H and C_2H_2, may be able to serve in its place. Whatever the mechanism, it now seems necessary to add diamond to the list of interstellar grain constituents. We review here some of the prospects opened up by this work.

First, diamond should be looked for in space wherever graphite is thought to be present: circumstellar, interstellar and interplanetary dust (including dust from comets). Perhaps the abundance of interstellar graphite has been overestimated; Nuth[20] has pointed out that most of the carbon in primitive meteorites is a complex organic polymer, not graphite, and now that $C\delta$ has turned out to be diamond, the balance is even more lopsided: graphite constitutes $\leqslant$2,000 p.p.m., compared to 100–400 p.p.m. diamond and (2–3)$\times10^4$ p.p.m. organic carbon. But meteorites may not be representative of interstellar matter. Several

母体中）只单单对含有 Xe-HL 的颗粒进行了转化，而忽略了更为大量的贫气的碳颗粒呢？第三，所有的四种陨石都含有非常相似的 Cδ 以及可比拟的气体含量和同位素含量（表 1）。如果金刚石是由于撞击生成的，我们预期这些数值变化的范围应该更大，这有赖于两种类型的碳颗粒转化成金刚石的比例和撞击之后的扩散损失。比如，橄辉无球粒陨石的气体含量的变动范围约有 100 倍 [13]。

自然而然地，似乎必须为这种金刚石寻找一个太阳系外的起源。但是金刚石并未被认定为是太阳系外的宇宙的可能组成部分，由于除了行星之外还没有其他宇宙天体具有适合金刚石作为一种稳定相生成的压力和温度条件（40~400 kbar，1,200~4,000 K），而且因为逃逸速度很高，任何在行星上形成的金刚石不会脱离该行星。（兰多 [14] 曾经指出金刚石窄的尺寸分布与星际间的消光曲线吻合得很好，但他并未考虑金刚石的起源。）尽管宇宙中撞击很普遍，它们也并不能够同时满足金刚石形成需要的高压和中等温度的要求。仅有的可行的机制似乎是亚稳相的金刚石在低压下的热气体中生成，正如最近在实验室中所证实的一样 [15]。让我们看看这个机制怎样与解释 Xe-HL（的形成）的理论体系结合起来。

Xe-HL 显然形成于超新星爆发 [16]，并与其他一些稀有气体（如氢和氮）一起通过离子注入 [17] 而被碳颗粒捕获。后续步骤所要求的高的相对速度（约 10^3 km·s^{-1}）意味着碳颗粒的形成早于超新星爆发，而很可能定在超新星爆发 10^2~10^4 年前，生成于其红巨星或行星状星云阶段所喷射出的气体壳中 [18]。碳是富碳气体在平衡状态下凝聚时最先形成的固体 [19]，并且尽管石墨是稳定相，而金刚石与之相差仅约 2 kJ·mol^{-1}，属亚稳相，但在这种情况下金刚石却优先形成。实际上，这种金刚石的优先生成已经在实验室中被观察到了 [15]。到目前为止研究过的过程包括了甲烷或有机化合物在大量氢存在情况下的分解，不是通过普通的热裂解，就是通过等离子体反应。反应机制目前并不清楚，但是可能涉及 CH$_3$ 自由基和氢原子。尽管 CH$_3$ 并不是在红巨星中大量存在的自由基，但其他的自由基或者分子，比如 CH，C$_2$H 和 C$_2$H$_2$ 也可能能够替代它。无论何种机制，现在看来似乎将金刚石加入星际颗粒组分的名单是必需的。我们在这里综述一下这个工作所展现出来的部分前景。

首先，太空中凡是目前认为存在石墨的地方都应该去探寻金刚石：环恒星，恒星间以及行星间尘埃（包括彗星尘埃）。或许恒星间石墨的丰度被高估了；努 [20] 已经指出原始陨石中大部分碳以复杂的有机高分子形式存在，而非石墨，既然现在 Cδ 已被证明是金刚石，这一（碳存在形式的）"天平"更为倾斜了：与 100~400 ppm 的金刚石和 (2~3)×10^4 ppm 的有机碳相比，石墨组分将少于或等于 2,000 ppm。但是

authors have argued that a single, massive supernova exploded near the forming Solar System, injecting short-lived radionuclides as well as excess amounts of the stable isotopes ^{12}C, ^{16}O and ^{20}Ne (refs 21, 22). If the Solar System is indeed enriched in supernova products, then $C\delta$ and Xe-HL (whether from the same or another supernova) may be atypically high.

Second, if diamond is detected in circumstellar dust, its formation conditions (as inferred from the atmosphere of the central star) should be determined and duplicated, insofar as possible, in the laboratory. Possibly nature makes diamond more efficiently than even the best laboratory synthesis discovered so far.

Finally, meteoritic diamond should be isotopically analysed for all detectable elements. If the xenon was trapped by ion implantation from a supernova, then it ought to be accompanied by the remainder of the periodic table. Diamond, owing to its extreme durability, may be an informative record of stellar nucleosynthesis and chemistry and of the prehistory of the Solar System.

This work was supported in part by NASA.

(**326**, 160-162; 1987)

Roy S. Lewis[*], Tang Ming[*], John F. Wacker[*‡], Edward Anders[*] & Eric Steel[†]

[*] Enrico Fermi Institute and Department of Chemistry, University of Chicago, Chicago, Illinois 60637, USA
[†] Center for Analytical Chemistry, National Bureau of Standards, Gaithersburg, Maryland 20899, USA
[‡] Present address: Geological Research Division, Scripps Institution of Oceanography, La Jolla, California 92093, USA

Received 24 February; accepted 2 March, 1987.

References:

1. Swart, P. K., Grady, M. M., Pillinger, C. T., Lewis, R. S. & Anders, E. *Science* **220**, 406-410 (1983).
2. Lewis, R. S., Srinivasan, B. & Anders, E. *Science* **190**, 1251-1262 (1975).
3. Lewis, R. S., Anders, E., Wright, I. P., Norris, S. J. & Pillinger, C. T. *Nature* **305**, 767-771 (1983).
4. Lewis, R. S., Tang, M., Wacker, J. F. & Steel, E. *Lunar planet. Sci.* **18**, 550-551 (1987).
5. Heymann, D. *J. Geophys. Res.* **91**, E135-E138 (1986).
6. Lewis, R. S., Anders, E., Shimamura, T. & Lugmair, G. W. *Science* **222**, 1013-1015 (1983).
7. Fraundorf, P., Flynn, G. J., Shirck, J. R. & Walker, R. M. *Earth Planet. Sci. Lett.* **37**, 285-295 (1977).
8. Frick, U. & Pepin, R. O. *Earth Planet. Sci. Lett.* **56**, 64-81 (1981).
9. Swart, P. K., Grady, M. M., Wright, I. P. & Pillinger, C. T. *J. Geophys. Res.* **87**, 283-288 (1982).
10. Lipschutz, M. E. & Anders, E. *Geochim. Cosmochim. Acta* **24**, 83-105 (1961).
11. Clarke, R. S. Jr, Appleman, D. E. & Ross, D. R. *Nature* **291**, 396-398 (1981).
12. Ott, U., Kronenbitter, J., Flores, J. & Chang, S. *Geochim. Cosmochim. Acta* **48**, 267-280 (1984).
13. Göbel, R., Ott, U. & Begemann, F. *J. Geophys. Res.* **83**, 855-867 (1978).
14. Landau, R. *Nature* **226**, 924 (1970).
15. Roy, R. *Nature* **325**, 17-18 (1987).
16. Heymann, D. & Dziczkaniec, M. *Proc. Lunar planet. Sci. Conf.* **10**, 1943-1959 (1979).
17. Lewis, R. S. & Anders, E. *Astrophys. J.* **247**, 1122-1124 (1981).
18. Clayton, D. D. *Proc. Lunar planet. Sci. Conf.* **128**, 1781-1802 (1981).
19. Larimer, J. W. & Bartholomay, M. *Geochim. Cosmochim. Acta* **43**, 1455-1466 (1979).

陨石并不能代表星际物质。有几个作者主张靠近形成中的太阳系区域的一个单独的质量巨大的超新星爆发，不但喷射短寿命的放射性核素，而且还有大量 ^{12}C、^{16}O 和 ^{20}Ne 的稳定同位素（参考文献 21 和 22）。如果太阳系确实富集了超新星的产物，那么 $C\delta$ 和 Xe-HL（无论是来自同一个或者不同的超新星）含量会明显地高。

其次，如果金刚石在星际尘埃中被检测到，它的生成条件（从中心恒星的大气层进行推断）将会被确定，并尽可能在实验室中复制这一过程。可能大自然制造金刚石比目前最好的实验室发现的合成技术的效率更高。

最后，对于陨石中的金刚石，应该对其中所有可检测的元素进行同位素分析。如果氙可以通过来自超新星的离子注入被捕获，那么它应该伴随有元素周期表中的其他元素。由于具有非比寻常的耐受性，金刚石可能记录了含有恒星的核合成和化学信息以及太阳系形成前的信息。

本研究部分由美国国家航空航天局支持。

（李琦 翻译；顾镇南 审稿）

20. Nuth, J. A. *Nature* **318**, 166-168 (1985).
21. Cameron, A. G. W. & Truran, J. W. *Icarus* **30**, 447-461 (1977).
22. Schramm, D. N. & Olive, K. A. *Ann. N. Y. Acad. Sci.* **395**, 236-241 (1982).
23. Alaerts, L., Lewis, R. S., Matsuda, J. & Anders, E. *Geochim. Cosmochim. Acta* **44**, 189-209 (1980).

Oceanic Phytoplankton, Atmospheric Sulphur, Cloud Albedo and Climate

R. J. Charlson *et al.*

Editor's Note

In the 1970s James Lovelock developed the Gaia hypothesis, which postulates that the Earth's climate is held in homeostatic equilibrium by feedback mechanisms like those of living organisms, in which the biosphere is central. Here Lovelock teams up with atmospheric scientists to propose how one such feedback might work. Planktonic algae emit a sulphur-containing gas called DMS, which becomes converted in the atmosphere into small aerosol particles of sulphate salts. These may act as seeds for the nucleation of cloud droplets, altering the radiation balance of the planet via reflection of sunlight from bright cloud tops. The paper stimulated intense interest in the climate role of aerosols, although the role of this component of the sulphur cycle remains in debate.

The major source of cloud-condensation nuclei (CCN) over the oceans appears to be dimethylsulphide, which is produced by planktonic algae in sea water and oxidizes in the atmosphere to form a sulphate aerosol. Because the reflectance (albedo) of clouds (and thus the Earth's radiation budget) is sensitive to CCN density, biological regulation of the climate is possible through the effects of temperature and sunlight on phytoplankton population and dimethylsulphide production. To counteract the warming due to doubling of atmospheric CO_2, an approximate doubling of CCN would be needed.

CLIMATIC influences of the biota are usually thought of in connection with biological release and uptake of CO_2 and CH_4 and the effect of these gases on the infrared radiative properties of the atmosphere[1]. However, the atmospheric aerosol also participates in the radiation balance, and Shaw[2] has proposed that the aerosol produced by the atmospheric oxidation of sulphur gases from the biota may also affect climate. So far the physical and biological aspects of this intriguing hypothesis have not been quantified, but three recent discoveries may make this possible for the remote marine atmosphere. (1) Most species of phytoplankton, ubiquitous in the oceans, excrete dimethylsulphide (DMS) which escapes to the air where it reacts to form a sulphate and methane sulphonate (MSA) aerosol. (2) This non-sea-salt sulphate (NSS—SO_4^{2-}) aerosol is found everywhere in the marine atmospheric boundary layer. (3) Aerosol particles which act as cloud-condensation nuclei (CCN) in the marine atmosphere are principally, perhaps almost exclusively, these same NSS—SO_4^{2-} particles.

In this paper we show that emission of DMS from phytoplankton is sufficient to justify

海洋浮游植物、大气硫、云反照率与气候

查尔森等

编者按

20 世纪 70 年代，詹姆斯·洛夫洛克发展了盖亚假说，假设地球气候是由处于中心位置的生物圈的反馈机制维持稳态平衡的，就像生物体那样。在本文中，洛夫洛克与大气学家们共同提出了这样一种反馈机制可能的运作模式。浮游藻类排放出名为二甲硫醚的含硫气体，其在大气中转化成硫酸盐气溶胶颗粒。它们可以作为云滴核化的种子，通过反射明亮云层顶部的太阳光来改变地球的辐射平衡。虽然硫循环中这一组分的作用仍然存在争议，但本文却激起了人们对气溶胶在气候变化中的角色的浓厚兴趣。

二甲硫醚是大洋上空云凝结核（CCN）的主要来源，它是由海水中的浮游藻类产生的，之后在大气中发生氧化形成硫酸盐气溶胶。由于云的反照率（以及随之变化的地球辐射平衡）对云凝结核的密度非常敏感，气候的生物调控可能是通过温度效应、浮游植物接受的光照以及二甲硫醚的生成来实现。要抵消大气 CO_2 倍增引起的气候变暖效应，就需要将云凝结核的含量也大约提高一倍。

通常认为生物群的气候效应与生物对 CO_2 和 CH_4 等气体的吸收和释放以及这些气体对大气红外辐射特性的影响有关 [1]。不过，大气气溶胶也参与辐射的收支平衡，并且肖 [2] 曾提出，生物群产生的含硫气体在大气中氧化后形成的气溶胶可能也会影响气候状况。到目前为止，这一颇具吸引力的假说在物理和生物方面还未得到量化，不过对于偏远的海洋大气圈来说，近来的三个发现可能会促使这种量化成为可能。（1）普遍生长于海洋中的绝大多数浮游植物都可以分泌二甲硫醚（DMS），这些二甲硫醚逸入大气后发生化学反应，生成硫酸盐和甲烷磺酸盐（MSA）气溶胶。（2）这种非海盐硫酸盐（NSS—SO_4^{2-}）气溶胶在海气边界层中到处都是。（3）气溶胶颗粒是海洋大气圈中的云凝结核（CCN），它们可能几乎全部都是这样的非海盐硫酸盐。

本文我们将证明，在未受污染的偏远海洋大气圈中，由浮游植物分泌出二甲硫

its consideration as the gaseous precursor of CCN in the remote and unpolluted marine atmosphere. We re-examine the physical role of the sulphate aerosol in atmospheric radiative transfer, particularly in clouds, which are responsible for most of the Earth's albedo, and estimate the sensitivity of the Earth's temperature to changes in the abundance of CCN. Finally we examine the geophysiology[3] of the system comprising phytoplankton, DMS, CCN and clouds, as a putative planetary thermostat.

Production of Sulphur-Containing Gases

Assuming that sulphuric acid and sulphate aerosols are indeed the only significant contributors to CCN over the oceans (as will be concluded below), we have to consider what processes are responsible for the production of the volatile sulphur compounds that are the precursors of sulphuric acid in the atmosphere. In this discussion, we shall ignore the perturbations of the atmospheric sulphur cycle by manmade fluxes of SO_2 (mostly from burning of coal and oil) and shall consider only the natural fluxes, which currently represent about 50% of the total flux of gaseous sulphur to the atmosphere, and which still dominate the atmospheric sulphur cycle in the Southern Hemisphere[4-6].

The only significant non-biological natural flux is the emission of SO_2 and H_2S by volcanoes and fumaroles. This process releases of the order of 0.4 Tmol yr^{-1}, about 10–20% of the total natural flux of gaseous sulphur to the atmosphere[4,5]. The emission of sulphur by volcanoes is highly variable in space and time. Consequently, the production of sulphate aerosol by the oxidation of volcanic sulphur during the quiescent stage of a volcano is of regional importance only. Large eruptions, on the other hand, which emit enough gaseous sulphur compounds to influence wider areas, are relatively rare events. For this discussion, we shall assume that the contribution of CCN from volcanic sulphur to the global atmosphere is proportional to its contribution to the total sulphur flux, that is, 10–20% of the natural component at present.

Volatile sulphur compounds are emitted both by terrestrial and marine biota. The marine emissions are almost exclusively in the form of DMS, whereas the emissions from land are in a variety of chemical species, including H_2S, DMS, methanethiol, CS_2, COS and others. This difference is related to the biological processes which are responsible for the production of the sulphur volatiles. Most sulphur at the Earth's surface is present as sulphate, which is the thermodynamically stable form of sulphur in the presence of oxygen. Sulphate is reduced by organisms through two mechanisms, "assimilatory" and "dissimilatory" sulphate reduction. The dissimilatory pathway is restricted to sulphate-reducing bacteria in anaerobic environments; due to physical and microbial restrictions only a small fraction of the H_2S produced by this process can escape to the atmosphere[7]. The products of the assimilatory pathway are a variety of organosulphur compounds, the largest fraction being the amino acids cysteine and methionine, which are incorporated into proteins.

On the continents, the breakdown of organosulphur compounds during fermentative decomposition of organic matter is probably the most important mechanism for the

醚的量足以使其成为云凝结核的气相前驱体。我们重新检测了大气辐射传输过程中，特别是地球反照率主要影响因素的云层之中，硫酸盐气溶胶的物理作用，同时对地球温度对云凝结核丰度的敏感性作了估算。最后，我们还从地球生理学[3]角度研究了由浮游植物、二甲硫醚、云凝结核以及云层组成的系统，该系统是推定的地球恒温器。

含硫气体的生成

倘若硫酸和硫酸盐气溶胶确实是海洋上空云凝结核最主要的来源（后面我们将证明确实如此），我们就必须考虑是何种过程影响着挥发性含硫化合物的生成，而挥发性含硫化合物是大气中硫酸的前驱体。在这里我们将人为因素形成的 SO_2 通量（多数来自煤和石油的燃烧）对大气中硫循环的影响忽略不计，而仅考虑 SO_2 的自然通量的大小。目前，天然的硫约占大气中气态硫总量的 50%，并且在南半球，其在大气硫循环中仍占主导地位[4-6]。

从火山口和火山喷气孔排出的 SO_2 和 H_2S 是最重要的非生物天然硫通量。由此释放进入大气的气态硫量级为 $0.4\ \text{Tmol} \cdot \text{yr}^{-1}$，约占大气中天然气态硫总量的 10% 到 20%[4,5]。火山喷发排出的硫随时间和空间变化较大。因此，火山处于休眠期时所排放的硫经氧化作用形成的硫酸盐气溶胶仅具有区域性意义。然而，大型的火山喷发虽能够喷发出足够多的气态含硫化合物影响广泛区域，但却是稀有事件。在本研究中，我们假定来自火山硫的云凝结核对全球大气的贡献量与其对总的硫通量的贡献量成正比，即目前约占自然组分的 10% 到 20%。

陆地和海洋生物群都能排放挥发性含硫化合物。海洋生物产生的挥发性含硫化合物几乎全部为二甲硫醚，而陆地上的排放物则呈现为各种形态，包括 H_2S、DMS、甲硫醇、CS_2、COS 等。这种差异源于产生挥发性含硫化合物的生物过程不同。地表的多数硫都是以硫酸盐的形式存在的，它是有氧条件下硫的一种热力学稳定形态。生物体还原硫酸盐有两种机制："同化"和"异化"硫酸盐还原作用。其中，异化途径仅限于厌氧条件下的硫酸盐还原细菌；由于物理以及微生物条件的限制，由此产生的 H_2S 仅有一小部分可以进入大气[7]。同化作用的产物为各种有机含硫化合物，其中最多的一部分是半胱氨酸和蛋氨酸，它们是蛋白质的组成部分。

在陆地上，有机质的发酵分解过程中，有机含硫化合物的分解可能是挥发性硫释放的最重要机制。由于从陆地生物群中获取代表性数据比较困难，因此至今我们

release of sulphur volatiles. Due to the difficulty in obtaining representative data from land biomes, the magnitude of this flux is still poorly known. Estimates range from about 0.15 to 1.5 Tmol yr^{-1}; the best estimate appears to be around 0.25 Tmol yr^{-1} for the total land surface, or about 2 mmol m^{-2} yr^{-1}, which turns out to be a slightly smaller flux per unit area than is emitted from the oceans (about 3±1.5 mmol m^{-2} yr^{-1}). Preliminary data from the tropical regions suggest that there may be a net transport of biogenic sulphur from the marine to the continental atmosphere, consistent with a smaller emission flux per unit area on the continents[8]. Coastal wetlands play a surprisingly small role in the global sulphur cycle; at present we estimate their contribution to be about 2% of the total gaseous emissions[5]. This is because although the emission per unit area may be relatively high, the total area of coastal wetlands is quite small.

In the marine environment, most volatile sulphur is emitted in the form of DMS which is excreted by living planktonic algae. In contrast to microbial decomposition which produces a complex mixture of volatile sulphur species, algal metabolism yields DMS as the only volatile sulphur species. The biological function of the production of DMS is still unclear. The substance from which DMS originates, dimethylsulphonium propionate (DMSP), is important in osmoregulation in a number of phytoplankton types[9] and also participates in the biochemical cycle of methionine. DMSP is also excreted by algae, and its breakdown in sea water may release additional amounts of DMS.

Even though DMS is excreted by phytoplankton, its concentration in surface sea water, and consequently its emission rate to the atmosphere, is only weakly correlated with the usual measures or phytoplankton activity, for example, chlorophyll concentration or ^{14}C-uptake rate. In fact, the calculated flux of DMS from the tropical oceans, which have a low primary productivity, is essentially the same per unit area (2.2 mmol m^{-2} yr^{-1}) as from the much more productive temperate oceans (2.4 mmol m^{-2} yr^{-1})[5]. Recent evaluations of seasonal effects[10,11] suggest that the annually averaged flux from temperate regions may even be considerably lower than the value given here. Even the highly productive coastal and upwelling regions do not support much higher DMS fluxes (5.7 and 2.8 mmol m^{-2} yr^{-1}, respectively, based on a large body of data from several research groups[5]). It appears that, independent of the rate of primary production, the warmest, most saline, and most intensely illuminated regions of the oceans have the highest rate of DMS emission to the atmosphere. This is a key fact to keep in mind when discussing possible climatic feedback mechanisms.

Two reasons can be given for this unexpected behaviour. First, the concentration of DMS in surface sea water depends not only on the rate of DMS production, but also on its rate of removal. The two dominant removal processes are ventilation to the atmosphere and the photochemical and microbial breakdown of DMS in the water column[12,13]. The rate of microbial removal of DMS will increase both with the density of bacteria which are able to metabolize DMS and, in a nonlinear fashion, with the concentration of DMS in sea water. The density of bacterioplankton is a function of the densities of phytoplankton and of grazing organisms. Due to these diverse and nonlinear

对其通量大小仍知之甚少。估算的范围大致在 0.15~1.5 Tmol · yr^{-1} 之间，最佳估计值似乎为：总陆地表面为 0.25 Tmol · yr^{-1} 左右，或约 2 mmol · m^{-2} · yr^{-1}。该单位面积通量略小于海洋逸出量（约 3 ± 1.5 mmol · m^{-2} · yr^{-1}）。热带地区的初步数据表明，从海洋到陆地大气圈可能存在生源硫的净运移，这与陆地上单位面积的排放通量较小是一致的 [8]。沿海湿地在全球硫循环中起的作用惊人的小，据我们估计，目前其贡献仅占气体硫排放物总量的 2% 左右 [5]。这是因为，虽然其单位面积上的排放量可能较高，但沿海湿地的总面积却很小。

在海洋环境下，多数挥发性含硫化合物以二甲硫醚的形式排出，它是由活体浮游藻类分泌的。与微生物的分解作用产生气态硫化物的复杂混合物相反，藻类代谢释放出的挥发性含硫化合物只有二甲硫醚这一种形态。生成二甲硫醚的生物功能尚不清楚。二甲硫醚的前驱体是二甲基磺基丙酯（DMSP），它是许多浮游植物中起渗透压调节作用的重要物质 [9]，同时它还参与蛋氨酸的生化循环。二甲基磺基丙酯也是由藻类分泌的，而它在海水中分解后还可释放额外的二甲硫醚。

尽管二甲硫醚是由浮游植物分泌的，但它在表层海水中的浓度及其向大气的释放速率与普通测定结果或浮游植物活动的相关性却很弱，如叶绿素浓度或 ^{14}C 的吸收速率。事实上，就初级生产力较低的热带海洋而言，其二甲硫醚的单位面积通量（2.2 mmol · m^{-2} · yr^{-1}）与生产力高得多的温带海洋中单位面积的通量（2.4 mmol · m^{-2} · yr^{-1}）差别不大 [5]。对季节性效应的最新研究 [10,11] 表明，温带地区的年平均通量甚至可能比这里所给出的值还要低得多。即使在沿海地区以及上升流区这些高生产力区，其二甲硫醚通量也不是很高（基于多个研究小组的大量数据 [5]，分别为 5.7 mmol · m^{-2} · yr^{-1} 和 2.8 mmol · m^{-2} · yr^{-1}）。海洋中最温暖、盐度最高且日照最强烈的区域向大气释放二甲硫醚的速率似乎也最高，并与初级生产率无关。这是我们在讨论可能的气候反馈机制时必须注意的关键问题。

关于这种意外现象可能有两个原因。首先，表层海水中二甲硫醚的浓度不仅仅取决于二甲硫醚的生成速率，还取决于其移除速率。两种主要的移除作用分别为向大气的通风量以及水体中二甲硫醚的光化学分解和微生物分解作用 [12,13]。微生物对二甲硫醚的移除作用会随海水中可代谢生成二甲硫醚细菌的密度而增加，也会随海水中二甲硫醚本身的浓度呈非线性增加。而浮游细菌的密度又是浮游植物密度和海洋草食动物密度的函数。由于调节二甲硫醚生成与移除的各变量之间是复杂多样的非

relationships between the variables which regulate DMS production and removal, we cannot expect to find a simple, linear relationship between phytoplankton density and DMS concentration. Furthermore, the production rate of DMS shows variations over three orders of magnitude among different phytoplankton species (ref. 14 and M.O.A., unpublished data). It appears that some algal groups, such as the coccolithophorids, which are most abundant in tropical, oligotrophic waters, have the highest rate of DMS excretion per unit biomass. We conclude, therefore, that the global input of DMS into the atmosphere is much less sensitive to changes in total primary production than to variations in phytoplankton speciation. In other words, we can accommodate rather large swings in marine productivity without changing the climatic effects produced by the sulphur cycle, and on the other hand, we could essentially eliminate the marine input of sulphur to the atmosphere without significantly changing the total primary productivity, for example by replacing all coccolithophorids with diatoms. The concentration of SO_4^{2-} in sea water is so large ($\sim$29 mmol kg^{-1}) that it does not limit the emission of DMS.

We can now evaluate the role of sulphur gases in general (and DMS in particular) as sources of NSS—SO_4^{2-} and of CCN in the unpolluted marine troposphere. Because submicrometre NSS—SO_4^{2-} particles are not directly emitted by land or ocean surfaces, they are created in the atmosphere only by chemical reactions. As far as is known, the only significant gaseous sulphur precursors of NSS—SO_4^{2-} of biological origin are DMS from the oceans and H_2S, DMS and perhaps other sulphur species from land biota. These gases are oxidized in air, largely by OH[15,16,75], to form SO_4^{2-}. At the low NO_x concentrations typical of the unpolluted marine troposphere, the oxidation of DMS by NO_3 can be considered negligible[17,18]. In addition to SO_2 the oxidation of DMS by OH also produces MSA. At low NO_x levels, however, the fraction of MSA produced is less than 20%, as suggested both by laboratory experiments (ref. 19 and unpublished manuscript by I. Barnes, V. Bastian and K. H. Becker, 1986) and by the ratio of MSA to NSS—SO_4^{2-} observed on marine aerosols from remote regions[20,21]. MSA is mostly present as aerosol particles (M.O.A., unpublished data) and due to its high solubility is also likely to be effective as CCN.

The oxidation of DMS to DMSO by the IO radical, which has recently been proposed (unpublished manuscript by I. Barnes et al.), is probably not important as a sink for DMS because the concentrations of DMSO in the atmosphere and in marine rain have been found to be very low compared to those of DMS, MSA and NSS—SO_4^{2-} (ref. 22 and M.O.A., unpublished data). The present evidence thus suggests that SO_2 is the major oxidation product of DMS in the unpolluted marine atmosphere. In the presence of cumulus clouds, which are abundant in the marine boundary layer, conversion of SO_2 to NSS—SO_4^{2-} is rapid and significantly exceeds the rate of dry deposition of SO_2 (refs 18, 21).

The rates of DMS oxidation obtained from laboratory experiments, and the corresponding lifetimes, are consistent with observed concentrations, the observed flux out of the atmosphere in rain and the calculated flux into the atmosphere from the ocean

线性关系，我们无法找出浮游植物密度和二甲硫醚浓度之间一个简单的线性关系。此外，二甲硫醚的生成速率在不同的浮游植物种类间也有差异，该差异超过三个数量级（参考文献 14 及安德烈埃，未发表数据）。有些藻类，如热带贫营养海域最为丰富的颗石藻，其单位生物量的二甲硫醚释放量最高。因此我们认为，相比于初级生产力总量的变化，全球二甲硫醚向大气的输入量对浮游植物种类的变化要敏感得多。也就是说，我们可以调节海洋初级生产力大幅度的变化而保持硫循环产生的气候效应不变；另一方面，我们也可以基本消除海洋向大气的硫输入而不显著改变总的初级生产力，比如，用硅藻来代替所有的颗石藻。海水中 SO_4^{2-} 的浓度非常大（约 29 mmol·kg^{-1}），因此二甲硫醚的释放不会受限。

现在我们可以大概评估一下，在未受污染的海洋对流层中，气态硫（特别是二甲硫醚）作为非海盐硫酸盐和云凝结核的来源所发挥的作用。由于陆地或海表并不直接排出亚微米级的非海盐硫酸盐颗粒，因此它们只能在大气中通过化学反应生成。据目前所知，对于生源非海盐硫酸盐来说，其最重要的前驱体就是海洋中的二甲硫醚和来自陆地生物群的 H_2S、二甲硫醚，或许还有其他一些硫化物。这些气体在空气中被氧化（主要被 OH 氧化[15,16,75]）形成 SO_4^{2-}。在未受污染的海洋对流层中氮氧化物（NO_x）的含量很低，NO_3 对二甲硫醚的氧化作用可忽略不计[17,18]。二甲硫醚经 OH 氧化后，除生成 SO_2 外，还可生成甲烷磺酸盐。然而，根据室内实验结果（参考文献 19 以及巴恩斯、巴斯蒂安和贝克尔未发表的稿件，1986 年）以及偏远区域海洋气溶胶中观测到的甲烷磺酸盐和非海盐硫酸盐的比值[20,21]，当 NO_x 含量较低时，生成的甲烷磺酸盐比重不足 20%。甲烷磺酸盐多以气溶胶颗粒的形式存在（安德烈埃，未发表数据），而由于其溶解度较高，也有可能成为有效的云凝结核。

新近提出的 IO 自由基将二甲硫醚氧化为二甲基亚砜的过程（巴恩斯等，未发表的数据）可能并不是二甲硫醚一个重要的汇，因为研究发现，相对于二甲硫醚、甲烷磺酸盐以及非海盐硫酸盐来说，大气及海洋降雨中二甲基亚砜的浓度非常低（参考文献 22 和安德烈埃，未发表数据）。因此目前的证据显示，SO_2 是未受污染的海区大气中二甲硫醚主要的氧化产物。当存在积云时（这在海洋边界层中大量存在），从 SO_2 到非海盐硫酸盐的转化速度非常快，远远超过 SO_2 的干沉降速率（参考文献 18、21）。

根据室内实验得到的二甲硫醚的氧化速率及其对应的生命周期与观测到的二甲硫醚的浓度、大气降水输出通量以及计算得到的海洋表面向大气的输入通量结果相

surface[5,17,18]. Thus, the lack of alternative sources of sulphur-bearing gases and the internal consistency of mass-balance calculations support the hypothesis that these biologically derived gases are the probable main sources of NSS—SO_4^{2-} in the remote marine boundary layer. It is therefore reasonable to assume that any change in atmospheric DMS concentration would cause a corresponding change in NSS—SO_4^{2-} concentration and hence in the number of particles which act as CCN. This could be due to changes in the number-concentration of particles, changes of the mass of water-soluble material in existing particles, or both.

Effect on Radiative Properties of Clouds

Clouds of liquid water droplets form only in the presence of CCN. In the unpolluted marine atmosphere, the concentration of particles capable of being CCN varies from about 30 to 200 cm^{-3}, depending on aerosol content, supersaturation and meteorological conditions[23]. In this same environment, the total number of submicrometre particles is often about 200 cm^{-3}, such that a significant fraction of them must be CCN. Bigg[24] made observations of CCN at Cape Grim, Tasmania, when the total number-concentration of particles was less than 300 cm^{-3}. Results for relative humidities between 100.3 and 101% (values believed to be typical of marine clouds) showed that 40 to 80% of the particles in that marine setting were active CCN. Thus, changes in NSS—SO_4^{2-} in marine air are expected to result in changes in the number-density of cloud droplets, contrary to the widely held belief supported by Fletcher[25] that the atmosphere always has an overabundance of particles that could act as CCN. Present-day continental air, by contrast, probably is consistent with Fletcher's generalization.

Koehler[26] argued that most CCN are composed of water-soluble materials, such that the marine NSS—SO_4^{2-} should qualify. It is observed that sea-salt particle concentrations at cloud height are typically not more than 1 cm^{-3}, so that sea-salt itself cannot be the main CCN[23,27,28]. Water-soluble materials other than sea-salt and NSS—SO_4^{2-} do exist in marine air but the data are not extensive. Nitrates probably are found on coarser particles, and hence do not contribute substantially to the number population[29]. Organic compounds exist in the submicrometer particles, but their mass-concentration is probably only a tenth that of NSS—SO_4^{2-} (W. H. Zoller, personal communication). Their number-concentration and sources are unknown.

The idea that natural CCN in marine air consist of sulphates has been believed for decades and that they have a widespread gaseous precursor was suggested by Hobbs[27]. DMS was identified as the likely source of most particles in marine air by Bigg et al.[30]. The size distribution of submicrometre NSS—SO_4^{2-} as deduced from size-resolved samples[31,32] is about right for activation at supersaturation between 0.1% and 1% which is appropriate for marine clouds and is comparable to the values used by Bigg[24]. The mass-concentration of NSS—SO_4^{2-} in the remote marine troposphere is about 0.3 µg m^{-3} (refs 31, 33) which, if the number-mean radius is 0.07 µm (which is reasonable[76]) yields a total number-population of about 100 cm^{-3}, in agreement with measured CCN populations.

符 [5,17,18]。因此，含硫气体其他来源的缺乏与质量守恒计算的内部一致性有力地支持了"生源气体很可能是偏远的海洋边界层中非海盐硫酸盐的主要来源"这一假说。那么，"大气中二甲硫醚浓度的任何变化都将引起非海盐硫酸盐浓度发生相应变化，进而导致作为云凝结核的颗粒数量的变化"这一假定就是合理的。这可能是由于颗粒数浓度的变化或颗粒中水溶性物质质量的变化引起，或者二者兼有。

对云层辐射特性的影响

只有在凝结核存在时，液态水滴才会形成云。在未受污染的海洋大气层中，可作为云凝结核的颗粒的浓度约在 30~200 cm⁻³ 之间，具体取决于气溶胶含量、过饱和度和气象条件等 [23]。在相同的环境下，亚微米级颗粒的总数一般约为 200 cm⁻³，由此其中大部分必定是云凝结核。比格 [24] 在塔斯马尼亚的格里姆角，对颗粒的数浓度低于 300 cm⁻³ 条件下的云凝结核作了观测。结果表明，在那样的海洋条件下，当相对湿度为 100.3%~101%（海洋云层的典型值）时，有 40%~80% 的颗粒都是活跃的云凝结核。因此我们预期海洋空气中非海盐硫酸盐的变化会导致云滴数密度的变化，这与弗莱彻 [25] 已得到广泛认可的观点恰恰相反，他认为大气中总是有过量的颗粒可以作为云凝结核。相比之下，现今陆地空气的特性很可能与弗莱彻的结论一致。

克勒 [26] 认为，多数云凝结核是由水溶性物质组成的，这样海洋非海盐硫酸盐就可以作为云凝结核。据观测，在云层的高度上，海盐的粒子浓度一般不高于 1 cm⁻³，所以，海盐本身不会成为云凝结核的主体 [23,27,28]。除海盐与非海盐硫酸盐之外，海洋空气中确实还存在其他水溶性物质，但数量不大。硝酸盐可能在较粗的颗粒中找到，故硝酸盐对总体数量的贡献不大 [29]。亚微米级颗粒中存在有机化合物，但其质量浓度大概仅为非海盐硫酸盐的十分之一（佐勒，个人交流）。它们的数浓度及来源尚不清楚。

几十年来，人们一直认为海洋空气中天然云凝结核是由硫酸盐组成的，并且霍布斯 [27] 曾提出这些天然云凝结核具有广泛分布的气相前驱体。比格等 [30] 认为，二甲硫醚是海洋空气中多数颗粒物可能的来源。根据粒级样品 [31,32] 得到了亚微米级非海盐硫酸盐的粒度分布，这种分布正适合过饱合度在 0.1%~1% 之间（适合于海洋云层，而且与比格 [24] 所用的值一致）时发生活化作用。偏远地区海洋对流层中非海盐硫酸盐的质量浓度约为 0.3 μg·m⁻³（参考文献 31、33），当其数平均半径为 0.07 μm（这是一个合理值 [76]）时，得到的总数量浓度约为 100 cm⁻³，这与所测定的云凝结核总数是一致的。偏远地区海洋降水中，非海盐硫酸盐的浓度为 $2 \times 10^{-6} \sim 5 \times 10^{-6}$ M 左

The concentration of NSS—SO_4^{2-} in remote marine rain water is around 2–5×10^{-6} M (ref. 34), which agrees with a simple nucleation scavenging calculation with 0.2–0.5 µg m^{-3} of NSS—SO_4^{2-} aerosol and 1 g m^{-3} liquid water in the cloud[35].

Other data also support the idea that NSS—SO_4^{2-} particles are the main contributor to the CCN. Much of the light-scattering aerosol in marine air is volatile at elevated temperatures, evaporating in a fashion identical to sulphates with a range of compositions from H_2SO_4 to $(NH_4)_2SO_4$, as deduced from temperature-and-humidity-controlled nephelometry[76,77]. The droplet-nucleating property of particles in marine air is also heat-labile, with CCN disappearing at $T > 300°C$ (ref. 36). Finally, the turnover time of CCN from purely physical data in the atmosphere has been deduced to be of the order of one day[37], which is the same as results from an estimate for turnover time of NSS—SO_4^{2-} based on mass-concentration, rainfall concentration and rainfall amount, as follows. If we take an NSS—SO_4^{2-} flux, F, of 0.3 g m^{-2} yr^{-1} as representative of remote marine sites[34], 0.3 µg m^{-3} as the typical concentration, C, of NSS—SO_4^{2-} aerosol, and 3,000 m as its scale height, H, the turnover time, $\tau = HC/F \sim 1$ day.

We now consider the potential effects of NSS—SO_4^{2-} variations on cloud properties. Changing the size distribution or concentration of the CCN causes the size distribution of cloud droplets to change[38], which could affect the coalescence and rain production process and possibly the time-averaged cloud cover. However, the effect which is well established (and which we think to be the most significant effect) is that changes in the size distribution of droplets would change the reflectance (albedo) of clouds. This step of the proposed climatic feedback loop is at present more readily quantified than the other steps, so it is presented in some detail. How the average liquid water content of clouds would change is unknown, so we hold it constant in our analysis.

The liquid water content L (g m^{-3}), the number-density of droplets N (m^{-3}), and the droplet radius r (for a monodispersion) are related by

$$L = (4/3)\,\pi r^3 \rho N$$

where ρ is the density of water in the appropriate units. Various studies have examined the effect of holding one of these three variables constant while the other two change. Paltridge[39], Charlock[40], and Somerville and Remer[41] considered cloud albedo changes due to a climatic warming which might increase the liquid water content of clouds. They held r fixed so that the increase in cloud albedo was due to increase of N. Bohren[42] showed that the increase of albedo would be somewhat less if N was instead held fixed (that is, assuming that CCN concentration did not change), so that the droplets increased in size rather than number.

For our hypothesis, we must instead consider the effect of holding L constant while increasing N. This leads to a decrease in mean radius, which causes an increase in total surface area of droplets in the cloud and thus an increase of cloud albedo. The study of

右（参考文献 34），与云层中非海盐硫酸盐气溶胶的浓度为 0.2~0.5 μg·m⁻³、液态水含量为 1 g·m⁻³ 时简单的核化清除计算结果一致 [35]。

非海盐硫酸盐颗粒是云凝结核的主要组成部分，这点也得到了其他资料的支持。根据温湿度控制比浊法的测定结果 [76,77]，高温条件下，海洋空气中多数光散射气溶胶都具有挥发性，其挥发方式与由 H_2SO_4、$(NH_4)_2SO_4$ 等合成的硫酸盐的挥发方式相同。海洋空气中颗粒的水滴成核特性也具有热不稳定性，当 $T > 300℃$ 时，云凝结核会消失（参考文献 36）。最后，根据纯物理数据推算，大气中云凝结核的周转时间约为 1 天左右 [37]，这与根据质量浓度、降水集中度和降水量推算出的非海盐硫酸盐的周转时间相同，具体推算如下。如果我们取偏远地区海洋站位 [34] 上非海盐硫酸盐通量 F 为 0.3 g·m⁻²·yr⁻¹，非海盐硫酸盐气溶胶的典型浓度 C 为 0.3 μg·m⁻³，均质大气高度 H 为 3,000 m，则周转时间 $\tau = HC/F$，约为 1 天。

现在我们来看一下非海盐硫酸盐的变化对云层性质的可能影响。改变云凝结核的粒度分布或浓度，会引起云滴粒度分布的变化 [38]，进而影响到云滴的并合及降雨形成过程，还可能影响平均时间上云层的覆盖量。不过，目前已得到充分证明的效应（而且也是我们认为最重要的效应）是云滴粒度分布的变化会改变云的反照率。目前来说，所提出的气候反馈回路中这一阶段比其他阶段量化得都好，因此我们将提供一些详细说明。云层中液态水的平均含量发生怎样的变化尚不清楚，因此我们在分析过程中将其看作常量。

设液态水含量为 L（g·m⁻³），云滴的数密度为 N（m⁻³），云滴半径为 r（看作单分散性粒子），则：

$$L = (4/3)\,\pi r^3 \rho N$$

其中，ρ 为近似环境单元水的密度。人们进行了很多这样的研究，即令三个变量中的一个保持不变，而改变另外两个，从而检测不同的效果。帕尔特里奇 [39]、查洛克 [40] 及萨默维尔和雷默 [41] 认为云反照率的变化是由气候变暖造成的，因为气候变暖可能会使云中液态水的含量增大。他们令 r 保持不变，则云的反照率的增加是由 N 的增大引起的。博伦 [42] 则证明，倘若 N 保持不变（即假定云凝结核浓度不变），那么云的反射率的增加量会小一些，因此，增加的是云滴的大小而不是其数量。

为了证明我们的假说，我们必须转而考虑令 L 不变而使 N 增大时产生的效应。这样一来云滴平均半径将变小，导致云中云滴总表面积增加，进而使云的反照率增

this effect was pioneered by Twomey[43]. His Figs 12.5 and 12.6 show the albedo, a, at cloud top at visible wavelengths as a function of cloud thickness for a reference plane-parallel cloud with uniform droplet radius $r = 8$ μm ("fairly clean maritime conditions"), as well as the albedo which resulted if N was multiplied or divided by 8, causing r to decrease or increase respectively by a factor of 2. (Much of Twomey's subsequent work on this topic examined the competing effects on cloud albedo due to absorption of sunlight by dark aerosol particles and the increased number of droplets. Only the latter effect is considered here, because H_2SO_4 and its ammonium salts are transparent in the solar spectrum.) However, his calculations apparently assumed an overhead sun (zenith angle $\theta_0 = 0°$) and a black underlying surface. To study the effects on the global radiation budget we have repeated Twomey's calculations using the global average zenith angle $\theta_0 = 60°$ (which causes the cloud albedo to increase relative to $\theta_0 = 0°$) and assuming an ocean surface as the lower boundary, for many different values of N. Figure 1 shows the change in albedo Δa from that of Twomey's reference cloud, caused by variation of N/N_0 in the range 8 to 1/8, where N_0 is the number-density of droplets in the reference cloud. Different thicknesses of the reference cloud are represented on the vertical axis by their albedos. The information in Twomey's Fig. 12.6 is therefore contained in the right and left edges of Fig. 1 here, which also shows the effect of any smaller changes in N. Our results agree with those of Twomey where they overlap, showing that the change in albedo due to changing N is not sensitive to solar zenith angle if the results are expressed as a function of the reference albedo rather than of the cloud thickness. Figure 1 shows that the cloud albedo is most sensitive to N at $a = 0.5$ but that Δa is essentially independent of a for $0.3 < a < 0.8$, for small changes in N/N_0. Figure 1 was calculated for effective droplet radius of the reference cloud $r_{eff}^0 = 8$ μm, but it is approximately valid also for any value of r_{eff}^0 in the range 4–500 μm (see Fig. 1 legend).

加。图米 [43] 是研究该效应的先驱。如他的图 12.5 和图 12.6 所示，对于所参照的具有统一云滴半径 $r = 8$ μm 的平面平行云层来说（"非常清洁的海上环境"），在云层顶部的可见光波长下，云的反照率 a 是云层厚度的函数；图米的图还展示了当将 N 乘以或除以 8，半径 r 分别减小为原来的 1/2 或增大至原来的 2 倍时云的反照率。（图米关于该问题的后续工作多致力于研究黑色气溶胶颗粒对日光的吸收作用和云滴数量增加对云的反照率的竞争效应。在这里我们仅考虑后一种效应，因为在太阳光谱中 H_2SO_4 及其铵盐都是透明的。）不过，显然他计算的前提是：太阳直射（天顶角 $\theta_0 = 0°$）且下垫面为黑色。为了研究全球辐射平衡效应，我们采用全球平均天顶角 $\theta_0 = 60°$（使得云反照率相对于 $\theta_0 = 0°$ 时有所增加），以洋面为下边界，对多个不同 N 值按图米的方法进行重新计算。图 1 所示为图米提出的参考云层的反照率变化 Δa，它是由 N/N_0 在 8~1/8 之间变化所引起的，其中 N_0 是参考云层中云滴的数密度。参考云层的不同厚度在竖轴上以其反照率表示。因此，图米的图 12.6 给出的信息就包含于本文图 1 的左右两边，同时图 1 还展示了 N 发生任何微小变化将引起的效应。重叠部分是我们的研究结果与图米的结果相一致的部分，这说明，如果将结果表示为参考云的反照率的函数而不是云层厚度的函数，则因 N 变化而引起的反照率的变化对太阳天顶角并不敏感。由图 1 可知，当 $a = 0.5$ 时，云的反照率对 N 最敏感，但当 $0.3 < a < 0.8$ 且 N/N_0 变化较小时，Δa 基本独立于 a。取参考云层的有效云滴半径 $r^0_{\text{eff}} = 8$ μm，对图 1 作了计算，但对于 r^0_{eff} 在 4~500 μm 之间的任一值也几乎同样有效（见图 1 中图例所示）。

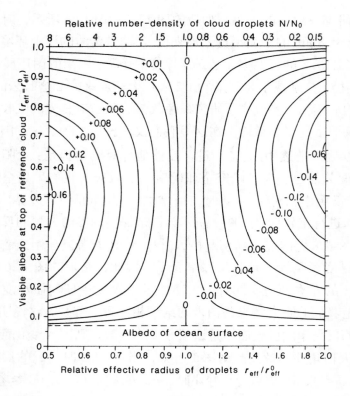

Fig. 1. Change (Δa) of visible albedo (0.6-μm wavelength) at cloud top caused by changing droplet number-density N while holding vertically integrated liquid water content (liquid water path, LWP) constant. Δa is plotted as a function of the albedo of the reference cloud and the effective radius (r_{eff}, the surface-areaweighted mean radius[65]) of the dropsize distribution relative to that of the reference cloud (r_{eff}^0). The corresponding change in top-of-atmosphere albedo (needed for estimating the effect on Earth radiation budget) can be obtained approximately by multiplying these values by 0.8, as described in footnote of Table 1. The different albedos for the reference cloud (vertical axis) correspond to different values of LWP. When LWP and the shape of the dropsize distribution are held fixed, the number-density of cloud droplets N is related to r_{eff} by $N/N_0 = (r_{eff}/r_{eff}^0)^{-3}$, shown on the scale at the top of the figure. These calculations used $r_{eff}^0 = 8$ μm, but the figure also is approximately valid for other reference clouds: the plotted values of Δa are in error by less than 20% if albedo < 0.9 and $4 \leqslant r_{eff}^0 \leqslant 500$ μm (that is, anywhere in the range of r_{eff} found in real clouds by Hegg[66]). The size distributions used for the calculations are almost monodisperse, broadened just enough to average over the oscillations in the Mie-scattering quantities. However, the calculations are also valid for any realistic size distributions with the same r_{eff}, as Hansen and Travis[65] showed that the scattering properties of a cloud are controlled essentially by r_{eff}, with very little influence from other moments of size distribution. These calculations assume a direct solar beam at the global average zenith angle $\theta_0 = 60°$, incident on a cloud of spherical droplets of pure water, above an ocean surface. The albedo of an ocean surface under a cloud is essentially independent of wavelength and averages 0.06–0.08 (refs 67–69); these calculations assumed 0.07 (dashed horizontal line). The computation of phase function, single-scattering albedo and extinction efficiency for individual cloud droplets used the Mie program of Wiscombe[70] assuming the refractive index for water is $1.332 - 1.09 + 10^{-8}i$ at 0.6 μm wavelength[71]. The computation of radiative transfer in the cloud used the delta-Eddington approximation[72]. This leads to absolute errors in albedo (for water-clouds at visible wavelengths and $\theta_0 = 60°$) of 0.00 to 0.03 depending on cloud optical thickness (Fig. 8 of ref. 73), but the error in albedo differences plotted here is much smaller, generally by a factor of 10.

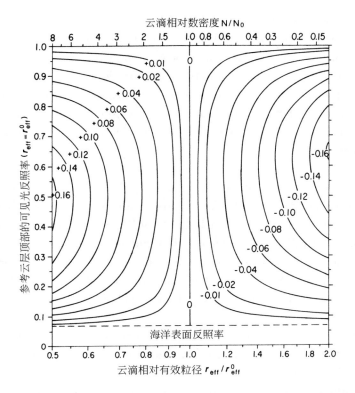

图 1. 在保持垂直积分的液态水含量（液态云水路径，LWP）不变的前提下，改变云滴的数密度 N 时，云层顶部可见光反照率（波长 0.6 μm）的变化量（Δa）。其中 Δa 是参考云层的反照率以及云滴粒度分布的有效半径（r_{eff}，表面积加权平均半径 [65]）相对于参考云层的有效半径（r_{eff}^0）的函数。将这些值乘以 0.8 可大致得出大气层顶部反照率的相应变化（用于计算对地球辐射平衡的影响），如表 1 的脚注所示。参考云层的不同反照率（纵轴）对应着不同的 LWP 值。当 LWP 和云滴粒度分布的形状保持不变时，云滴的数密度 N 与 r_{eff} 的关系为：$N/N_0 = (r_{eff}/r_{eff}^0)^{-3}$，见图中顶部的标尺。上述计算均采用 $r_{eff}^0 = 8$ μm，但对于其他云层来说，该图也基本上是有效的：当云的反照率 <0.9 且 4 μm ≤ r_{eff}^0 ≤ 500 μm 时（即赫格 [66] 在实际云层中发现的 r_{eff} 的全部范围），图中所示 Δa 的误差小于 20%。这些计算所采用的半径分布几乎都是单分散性的，将其宽度扩展至刚好可以计算在米氏散射量波动范围内的平均值，然而这些计算对于具有相同 r_{eff} 的任意实际半径分布也是有效的，汉森和特拉维斯 [65] 已证明，云层的散射性质实际上主要是受 r_{eff} 控制的，而其他的半径分布力矩对其影响很小。这些计算的前提是：对于全球平均天顶角 $\theta_0 = 60°$，太阳是直射的，入射于海面上空由球形纯水水滴组成的云层之上。云层之下的海洋表面反射率与波长无关，平均为 0.06~0.08（据参考文献 67~69），此处的计算所采用的值为 0.07（水平虚线）。单个云滴的相函数、单次散射反照率以及消光率的计算采用维斯科姆 [70] 的米氏散射程序，即假定波长为 0.6 μm 时，海水的折射指数为 $1.332 – 1.09 + 10^{-8}i$ [71]。云层中辐射传输量的计算采用爱丁顿近似法 [72]。得出云的反照率的绝对误差（在可见光波长和 $\theta_0 = 60°$ 情况下的水云）为 0.00~0.03，具体取决于云层的光学厚度（参考文献 73 中的图 8），不过本图中反照率差异的误差则小得多，一般是该值的 1/10。

Real clouds are not homogeneous, and the albedo of a cloud with a horizontally inhomogeneous distribution of droplets is always less than that of a hypothetical homogeneous cloud[44,45], because the albedo-versus-optical-depth function is nonlinear, concave downwards. We therefore compare observed clouds to modelled clouds not by comparing their optical depths but rather by comparing their albedos. (The changes Δa will also be somewhat smaller for an inhomogeneous cloud than for a plane-parallel cloud, but not by much if the albedos of the different cloud elements are all in the range 0.3–0.8, as can be seen from Fig. 1.)

The top-of-atmosphere (TOA) albedo (or "planetary" albedo) measured by satellites in the 0.5–0.7 µm wavelength channel over marine stratus and stratocumulus (St/Sc) varies in the range 0.25–0.65 (ref. 46). Channel albedo at TOA is usually smaller than channel albedo at top-of-cloud (TOC) by a factor of about 0.9 (ref. 47 and S.G.W. and W. J. Wiscombe, personal communication), because ozone above the cloud absorbs radiation at 0.6 µm, so most marine St/Sc probably have visible TOC albedos, a, in the middle region of Fig. 1 where Δa is insensitive to a for small relative changes of N.

Table 1 illustrates the use of Fig. 1. Stratiform water clouds that probably have visible TOC albedos in the range 0.3–0.8 cover about 45% of the ocean (Table 1a). As an example (Table 1b), we increase N by 30% over the ocean only (because DMS cannot compete with anthropogenic sulphur over land), which causes r_{eff} to decrease by 10%. From Fig. 1, this causes visible-channel albedo at TOC to increase by 0.02, which causes an increase of 0.016 in planetary albedo averaged over the solar spectrum above these marine clouds, or 0.005 averaged over the entire Earth. (This increase in whole-Earth albedo is smaller than the value 0.006 shown in Fig. 6b of Twomey *et al.*[48] for this example, because we assume the changes in planetary albedo to apply only to the ocean areas.)

实际的云层是不均匀的，且在水平方向上云滴呈不均匀分布的云的反照率总是低于所假定的均匀云层[44,45]，因为反照率与光学厚度之间的函数是非线性且向下凹的曲线。因此，在比较所观测到的云层与模拟云层时，我们比较的是其反射率而非光学厚度。（对于不均匀的云层，其反照率变化量 Δa 也要小于平面平行云层，不过，如果不同云层要素的反照率均在 0.3~0.8 之间，这一差别就不会太大，如图 1 所示。）

在海洋层云和层积云（St/Sc）上空，利用人造卫星在 0.5~0.7 μm 波长通道下测定的大气层顶部（TOA）反照率（又称"行星"反照率）在 0.25~0.65 之间变化（参考文献 46）。大气层顶部通道反射率通常小于云层顶部（TOC）的通道反射率，大约是 TOC 通道反射率的 0.9 倍（参考文献 47 及沃伦和维斯科姆，个人交流），因为云层上方的臭氧层吸收 0.6 μm 的辐射，因此，大部分海洋 St/Sc 很可能会具有 TOC 可见光反照率 a，位于图 1 的中间部分，其中当 N 的相对变化较小时，Δa 对 a 的响应不敏感。

表 1 阐明了图 1 的用途。层状水云的 TOC 可见光反射率在 0.3~0.8 之间，覆盖了 45% 的海洋（表 1a）。举例来说（表 1b），我们只将海洋上空的 N 增加 30% 时（因为在陆地上，二甲硫醚无法与人为成因的硫相比），导致 r_{eff} 减小了 10%。从图 1 可以看出，由此将导致 TOC 可见光通道的反射率增加 0.02，从而使该海洋云层上方整个太阳光谱的平均行星反射率提高 0.016，即将整个地球上的平均值提高 0.005。（这里全球反照率的增加值要小于图米等[48]的图 6b 中给出的值 0.006，这是因为在这里我们假定行星照率的变化仅适用于海洋区域。）

Table 1. Climatic effect caused by increasing CCN concentration over the ocean

a Global annual average cloud cover (ocean areas only)			*b* Example: effect on surface climate due to increasing CCN concentration N by 30% while holding liquid water path fixed		
Cloud type*	Ocean area covered (%)	Earth covered by oceanic clouds (%)		For area covered by oceanic stratiform water clouds	Averaged over Earth's surface area
Non-overlapped St/Sc†	25.2	17.6	Imposed change in N	+30%	
Non-overlapped As/Ac‡	10.8	7.5	Change in r_{eff}	−10%	
As/Ac overlapped with St/Sc§	8.8	6.1	Change in 0.5–0.7-μm albedo at TOC #	+0.02	
Nimbostratus, cumulus, cumulonimbus	not applicable (optically thick; high albedo)		Change in 0.5–0.7-μm albedo at TOA**	+0.018	
Cirrus‖	not applicable (ice)		Change in solar albedo at TOA**	+0.016	+0.005
Total cover of oceanic stratiform water clouds (As/Ac+St/Sc) not overlapped with cumuliform clouds	44.8¶	31.2	Equivalent change in solar constant††		−0.7%
			Change in global-average surface temperature‡‡		−1.3 K

* Only the areas covered by low stratus and stratocumulus (St/Sc) clouds and middle altostratus and altocumulus (As/Ac) are considered, because the change in albedo is smaller for convective clouds and for nimbostratus because they are thicker and may have albedos greater than 0.8.

† The zonal average amount (fractional areal coverage) of St/Sc over the oceans varies from 18% at low latitude to 50% at high latitude[61] and averages 34% for the world ocean, average of all four seasons (ref. 61 and additional data from S.G.W. *et al.*, in preparation). The daytime (sunlit) amount is close to the diurnal average amount. When St/Sc is observed over the ocean, As/Ac is also present above it about 52% of the time[62]. The amount-when-present of oceanic As/Ac is 50% (S.G.W. *et al.*, in preparation), so 50%×52% = 26% of the St/Sc amount is overlapped by As/Ac. Non-overlapped St/Sc thus covers 34%×(1.0−0.26) = 25.2% of the ocean area or 17.6% of the Earth's surface.

‡ As/Ac covers 22.4% of the ocean during the daytime (ref. 61 and S.G.W. *et al.*, in preparation) but only 10.8% of the ocean is covered by As/Ac which does not overlap St/Sc, cumulus, or cumulonimbus (using a procedure parallel to that used in the St/Sc analysis above).

§ We assume that this two-layer cloud is still optically thin enough for its albedo to be less than 0.8, that is, in the region of Fig. 1 where Δa is insensitive to a.

‖ A change in albedo of low or middle water-clouds may be muted at TOA when those clouds are partially hidden by higher ice clouds (cirrus). Here we assume that cirrus is thin enough that the change in planetary albedo due to the water-clouds is the same as if cirrus were absent.

¶ If cumulus is also included, the total areal coverage of clouds whose albedo is sensitive to CCN concentration changes from 44.8% to 56.6%.

From Fig. 1.

** Because of absorption in the 0.6-μm band of ozone above the cloud, the visible-channel albedo at TOA is smaller than at TOC, by a factor of about 0.9 (ref. 47). A further factor of about 0.9 is needed to convert visible-channel TOA albedo to solar TOA albedo[47,63], because cloud albedo is lower in the near-infrared than in the visible. The same factors apply to Δa.

†† The global average planetary albedo is now 0.30 (ref. 64), so a change in planetary albedo Δa causes the same change in the amount of solar energy absorbed by the Earth–atmosphere system as would a fractional change in solar constant of $(1.0-0.3)\Delta a$.

‡‡ From Table 1 of ref. 49.

表 1. 海洋上空云凝结核浓度增加带来的气候效应

a 全球年平均云层覆盖率（仅海洋地区）			b 实例：云凝结核浓度 N 增加 30% 而云液水柱含量保持不变时，对地表气候的影响		
云型 *	海洋面积覆盖率 (%)	海洋云层覆盖的地球百分率 (%)		海洋层状水云覆盖的区域	地球表面的平均值
非重叠 St/Sc†	25.2	17.6	令 N 发生的变化量	+30%	
非重叠 As/Ac‡	10.8	7.5	r_{eff} 的变化量	−10%	
与 St/Sc 重叠的 As/Ac §	8.8	6.1	TOC 在 0.5~0.7 μm 波段上反照率的变化 #	+0.02	
雨层云、积云、积雨云	不适用（光学厚度大，反射率高）		TOC 在 0.5~0.7 μm 波段上反照率的变化 **	+0.018	
卷云 ‖	不适用（冰晶云）		TOA 太阳反照率的变化 **	+0.016	+0.005
不与积状云重叠的海洋层状水云层（As/Ac+St/Sc）总覆盖区域	44.8¶	31.2	太阳常数的等效变化 ††		−0.7%
			全球平均地表温度的变化 ‡‡		−1.3 K

* 仅考虑了低层云和层积云（St/Sc）以及中层高层云和高积云（As/Ac）覆盖的区域，因为对流云和雨层云中反照率的变化较小，原因是这些云比较厚且其反照率高于 0.8。

† 海洋上空 St/Sc 的纬向平均值（部分覆盖区）在低纬度地区的 18% 到高纬度地区的 50% 之间变化[61]，全球海洋的平均值为 34%，季节平均值（参考文献 61 及沃伦等的其他资料，完稿中）。白天（受日光照射）接近于日平均值。当海洋上空观测到 St/Sc 时，约有 52% 的时间也会在其上方看到 As/Ac[62]。当海洋 As/Ac 的量占到 50% 时（沃伦等，完稿中），则有 50%×52%=26% 的 St/Sc 与 As/Ac 重叠。那么，非重叠 St/Sc 所覆盖的大洋面积比就为 34%×(1.0−0.26)=25.2%，即地表的 17.6%。

‡ 白天 As/Ac 对海洋的覆盖率为 22.4%（参考文献 61 及沃伦等，完稿中），但与 St/Sc、积云或积雨云不重叠的 As/Ac 对海洋的覆盖对率仅为 10.8%（分析方法同上面 St/Sc 分析的方法）。

§ 我们假定该双层云的光学厚度仍足够薄，使其反照率低于 0.8，即位于图 1 中 Δa 对 a 响应不敏感的区域。

‖ 当低层或中层水云部分被较高的冰晶云（卷云）遮住时，其 TOA 反射率的变化可忽略不计。在这里我们假定卷云足够薄，使因水云引起的地球反射率变化和没有卷云时一样。

¶ 倘若将积云也包含在内，则云层的总覆盖率将在 44.8%~56.6% 之间，其反照率对云凝结核的浓度非常敏感。

\# 来自图 1。

** 由于云层上方的 0.6 μm 臭氧带的吸收作用，TOA 的可见光反照率小于 TOC，差异系数约为 0.9（参考文献 47），将 TOC 可见光反射率转化为太阳光反照率时，还需要再加一个 0.9 的系数[47,63]，因为在红外区附近云层的反射率要低于可见光区。Δa 适用相同的系数。

†† 目前全球的平均行星反照率为 0.30（参考文献 64），因此，行星反照率变化 Δa 与太阳常数变化（1.0~0.3）Δa 对地球 – 大气圈系统吸收的太阳能变化量具有相同的影响。

‡‡ 据参考文献 49 的表 1。

If none of the climatic feedbacks causes cloud albedo to change, the increase in planetary albedo of 0.005 is equivalent to a decrease of the solar constant by 0.7% in a climate model, which causes a decrease of 1.3 K in global mean surface temperature T_s when water-vapour and snow-albedo feedbacks (both positive) are accounted for (Table 1 of ref. 49). This reduction in T_s caused by reducing the effective radius of cloud droplets by 10% everywhere over the world ocean is about one-third as large as the increase in T_s predicted for a doubling of atmospheric CO_2 (ref. 1).

Of course we do not know the relationship between a change in aerosol concentration over the ocean and the resulting change in cloud-droplet concentration N. Theory and experiments (equations 9–1 and 13–41 of ref. 23) indicate that N is proportional to $[CCN]^p$, with $p \approx 0.8$. Setting $p = 1$ for simplicity, we can show that the cloud-mediated effect on planetary albedo discussed above is much larger than the direct radiative effect of non-nucleated aerosol. Using a mass extinction coefficient of 10 m^2 g^{-1} for NSS—SO_4^{2-} (ref. 50), a column-mass of 10^{-3} g m^{-2}, and a ratio of backscattering to total scattering of 0.2, the average total backscattering optical depth, δ_{bsp}, of aerosol particles is 3×10^{-3}, smaller than the Rayleigh backscattering optical depth due to air itself which is ~0.1. This empirically derived quantity is similar to the estimates of Shaw[2]. A 30% increase in the number of particles (over the oceans only) with no change in their mean size would increase δ_{bsp} by 9×10^{-4}, increasing the planetary albedo over dark surfaces by the same amount, but having no effect in areas where clouds are present. The average cloud cover over the oceans is 64% (S.G.W. *et al.*, in preparation) so the increase in planetary albedo from aerosol alone is $9\times10^{-4}\times(1-0.64) = 3.2\times10^{-4}$ for the ocean or 2.3×10^{-4} for the whole Earth; that is, only about 5% as large as the cloud-mediated increase.

The example we chose for illustration (a 30% change in N) is actually relatively small compared to observed variations. CCN concentrations over the remote ocean can vary with season and time of day, and from one cloud to another, by an order of magnitude or more[23]; thus even the extreme left and right sides of Fig. 1 may be applicable for some models of climatic change.

This analysis of the climatic effect of changing the CCN population has assumed that the radiative properties of clouds will change only in the solar spectrum, not in the thermal infrared (beyond 4 μm wavelength). Changing the size of droplets will not significantly affect the thermal-infrared emissivity of most water clouds, because they are in effect optically semi-infinite and are nearly black bodies at those wavelengths[51]. Cirrus is the only type of cloud which is normally thin enough for its emissivity to be sensitive to optical thickness, but the ice-particle sizes are unlikely to be affected by variations in the concentration of CCN because ice nuclei are normally much rarer and from different origins than CCN.

Global Climate and DMS Emission

Although we do believe that increased DMS emission should influence both the mass concentration and number population of CCN composed of NSS—SO_4^{2-} (and hence

　　假设任何气候反馈都不会引起云反照率的变化，那么地球反照率增加 0.005 就等效于气候模式中太阳常数减小 0.7%，这将使全球平均地表温度 T_s 降低 1.3 K，这种增加是由水蒸气和积雪反射率的反馈机制（两者均为正反馈）造成的（参考文献 49 中表 1）。倘若全球海洋上空云滴的有效半径均减小 10%，那么由此带来的 T_s 的减少量约为大气 CO_2 浓度增加一倍时 T_s 增加量（参考文献 1）的 1/3。

　　当然，我们对海洋上气溶胶浓度的变化与由此导致的云滴浓度 N 的变化之间的关系并不清楚。理论与实验（参考文献 23 中的方程 9~1 和 13~41）表明 N 值与 $[CCN]^p$ 成比例，其中 $p \approx 0.8$。为了简便起见，令 $p=1$，我们可以证明，上述讨论的云对行星反照率的媒介效应要比作用于非成核气溶胶的直接辐射效应大得多。设非海盐硫酸盐的质量消光系数为 10 $m^2 \cdot g^{-1}$（参考文献 50），柱体质量浓度为 $10^{-3} g \cdot m^{-2}$，背散射与总散射的比值为 0.2，则气溶胶颗粒的总背散射光学厚度的平均值 δ_{bsp} 为 3×10^{-3}，小于由空气本身造成的瑞利背散射光厚度值（约 0.1）。根据经验得到的这个量与肖 [2] 的估算值接近。颗粒数增加 30%（仅海洋上空），而保持其平均半径不变，则 δ_{bsp} 将增加 9×10^{-4}，进而使黑面上（不反射的面）的行星反照率也增加同样的量，但对有云地区则没有影响。海洋上空的平均云层覆盖率为 64%（沃伦等，完稿中），那么仅由气溶胶引起的行星反照率的增加值对于海洋为 $9 \times 10^{-4} \times (1-0.64)=3.2 \times 10^{-4}$，对于全球为 2.3×10^{-4}；也就是说，这仅为云媒介效应引起的增加量的 5% 左右。

　　我们所举的例子（N 增大 30%）与观测到的变化相比，实际上是比较小的。偏远海洋上空的云凝结核浓度会随季节以及一天中时间的不同而变化，且云与云之间也不一样，其差异可达 1 个数量级甚至更多 [23]；因此，即使是图 1 的左右两极端也可适用某些气候变化模式。

　　此处对云凝结核数量变化引起的气候效应的分析，其前提是，云层的辐射特性仅在太阳光谱中变化，而不包含热红外部分（波长 >4 μm）。对多数水云来说，改变云滴大小对其热红外辐射率的影响并不显著，这是因为其光学厚度实际上是半无限的，在这些波长下近似于黑体 [51]。卷云是唯一一类足够薄的云层，其辐射率对光学厚度的变化十分敏感，但其冰粒的大小并不受云凝结核浓度变化的影响，因为一般情况下冰核比云凝结核要少得多，而且两者的来源也不相同。

全球气候与二甲硫醚的排放

　　虽然我们确信提高二甲硫醚的排放量对由非海盐硫酸盐组成的云凝结核的质量浓度和总量都有影响（进而影响云的反照率），但我们对二甲硫醚的源强度与云凝结

cloud albedo), we do not understand quantitatively the relationship of source strength of DMS to CCN number concentration. It seems likely that increased DMS fluxes would increase the CCN population, based for example on the observation in polluted air that gas-to-particle conversion produces new particles[52].

When looking for feedbacks which link the sea-to-air mass flux F of DMS to global climate (Fig. 2), we can consider the variables which make up the flux equation:

$$F = A \cdot k \cdot \Delta c$$

We can change either the total ocean surface area (A) available for gas exchange, the transfer velocity (k), or the concentration gradient across the air/sea interface (Δc). Because the ocean is highly oversaturated (by at least three orders of magnitude) relative to the atmosphere, the concentration gradient term is essentially identical to the DMS concentration in surface sea water.

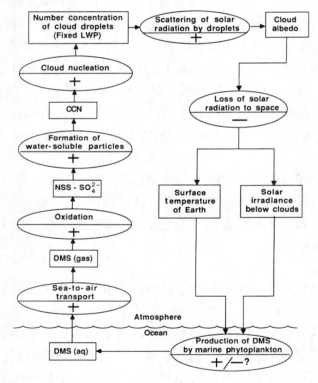

Fig. 2. Conceptual diagram of a possible climatic feedback loop. The rectangles are measurable quantities, and the ovals are processes linking the rectangles. The sign (+ or −) in the oval indicates the effect of a positive change of the quantity in the preceding rectangle on that in the succeeding rectangle, following Kellogg's[74] notation. The most uncertain link in the loop is the effect of cloud albedo on DMS emission; its sign would have to be positive in order to regulate the climate.

A 10% decrease in ice-free ocean-surface area accompanied the last glacial maximum[53]. During an ice age, the areas covered by ice on the continents and oceans increase, and

核的数浓度之间的定量关系尚不清楚。二甲硫醚通量的增大可能会导致云凝结核总量增加，比如，对受污染空气的观测发现，由气态到颗粒态的转化可以形成新的颗粒[52]。

在寻找二甲硫醚由海洋向大气输入的质量通量 F 与全球气候之间的反馈机制（图2）时，我们可以从组成通量方程的变量入手：

$$F = A \cdot k \cdot \Delta c$$

我们可以改变发生气体交换的大洋总表面积（A）、传输速度（k）或气－海界面上的浓度梯度（Δc）中的任何一个。相对于大气来说，海洋是高度超饱和的（至少超出3个数量级），所以浓度梯度这一变量实际上相当于表层海水中二甲硫醚的浓度。

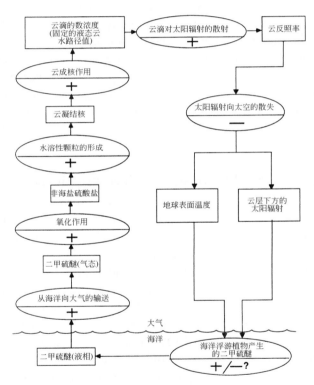

图2. 一种可能的气候反馈循环概念图解。矩形内为可测定量，椭圆内为连接矩形内各个量的作用。椭圆内的＋、－号表示前一个矩形内的量的正向改变对后一个矩形内的量的影响，采用凯洛格[74]的符号表示法。该循环中最不确定的关系是云的反照率对二甲硫醚排放量的影响；要起到调节气候的作用，其符号应为正号。

末次盛冰期时，无冰洋面面积减少了10%[53]。冰期期间，被冰川覆盖的陆地和

there is some exposure of continental shelf now under water. The decrease in ocean area during an ice age could lead to a drop in the global flux of DMS to the atmosphere. Climatic changes would also affect the wind field over the ocean (perhaps only slightly[54]) and thereby the transfer velocity k. The magnitude of this effect on CCN would depend on the relative rates of loss of DMS to the atmosphere and in the water column.

Empirically, we find that the largest flux of DMS comes from the tropical and equatorial oceans[5]. This suggests that the most important climatic role of DMS is to contribute to elevated cloud albedo over the warmest ocean regions, and thus to reduce the input of heat into the low-latitude oceans. A cooling of the oceans or a reduction in area of the tropical seas could thus lead to a smaller DMS flux, providing a stabilizing negative feedback.

On the other hand, the sea-to-air flux of DMS and consequently the albedo of marine clouds could significantly change as a result of ecological changes which would favour phytoplankton species with large DMS output rates over those with low output rates, or vice versa. At this time we have only examined a few species for their DMS emission rates. Although we know that there are large interspecific differences, we cannot yet relate them to phytoplankton taxonomy. In particular, we are not yet able to use the data on phytoplankton speciation during the geological past, which has been obtained by the CLIMAP program[53], to predict the DMS flux during periods of glaciation. As a result, we are left with an incomplete story: we are convinced that the emission of DMS into the marine atmosphere plays a crucial climatic role, but we cannot yet define precisely the processes which regulate the rate of DMS emission.

Geophysiology and Homoeostasis

Gaia theory[3] suggests that in order to maintain thermostasis on Earth, CO_2 is continuously and increasingly pumped from the atmosphere. There is a constant input from tectonic processes, and the long-term sink is the burial of carbonate rock in the sediments. The sink for CO_2 is almost wholly biologically determined; without life, CO_2 would rise to an abundance of well over 1% by volume. Lovelock and Whitfield[55] observed that if climate regulation does take place by pumping of CO_2 then the mechanism is now close to the limit of its capacity to operate. Atmospheric CO_2 has been reduced from about 30% of the atmosphere at the start of life to the present 300 p.p.m.v., a factor of 1,000. It was suggested that the decrease of CO_2 through its declining greenhouse effect had compensated for the monotonic increase of solar luminosity and so the climate had remained constant and suited for life. It cannot be much more reduced without seriously impairing the growth of mainstream plants whose limit is near 150 p.p.m.v.; not much less than the minimum, 180 p.p.m.v., of the last glaciation[78].

DMS emission, through its effect on the planetary albedo, shares with CO_2-pumping a cooling tendency. So if the DMS production increases with temperature and/or solar irradiance, the sign of its climatic effect would be in the right direction to offset what seems, for the biota, to be an excessive solar flux.

海洋面积增加，同时，现今位于水下的部分大陆架也暴露出来。冰期中海洋面积的减少将导致全球进入大气的二甲硫醚通量下降。气候变化还会影响海洋上的风场（可能较微弱[54]），进而影响传输速度 k。该作用对云凝结核的影响的大小取决于二甲硫醚在大气和水体中的相对损失速率。

根据经验我们发现，二甲硫醚的最大通量来自热带和赤道洋区[5]。这说明，二甲硫醚所起的最重要的气候作用是增大了热带海区的云的反照率，从而减少热量向低纬度海洋的输入。所以，海洋温度的降低或热带海面积的减少将导致二甲硫醚通量减小，形成稳定的负向反馈机制。

另一方面，生态变化将会引起海洋输入大气的二甲硫醚通量发生明显变化，进而造成云反射率的显著变化，因为生态变化有利于二甲硫醚输出速率较大的浮游植物的生长，反之亦然。这一次我们只研究了少数几种浮游植物的二甲硫醚释放速率。虽然我们知道各浮游植物种间的差异非常大，但还无法将其与浮游植物的分类联系起来。尤其是，我们还无法利用地质历史时期浮游植物物种形成的有关资料（来自 CLIMAP 计划[53]——"气候长期调查、制图与预报"计划）来预测冰期时二甲硫醚的通量。因此，我们只能得到一个不完整的结果：我们确信二甲硫醚向海洋大气层的释放对气候具有重要意义，但还无法精确地定义调节二甲硫醚释放速率的各个过程。

地球生理学及稳态

盖亚假说[3]提到，为了维持地球温度的恒定，要不断地将越来越多的 CO_2 从大气中抽出。构造作用的输入是恒定的，而沉积物中碳酸盐岩的埋藏就是 CO_2 的一个长期的汇。CO_2 的汇几乎全部是由生物作用决定的；如果没有生命，CO_2 的体积将增加 1% 以上。洛夫洛克和惠特菲尔德[55]观察发现，如果通过 CO_2 的抽取可以进行气候调节，那么如今该机制已接近其运行极限了。大气中 CO_2 含量已从生命出现之初的 30% 降到了现在的 300 ppmv，相差 1,000 倍。有人认为，温室效应的降低造成 CO_2 含量的减少补偿了太阳亮度的单调增加，因此气候仍保持恒定，适于生命生存。如果主要植物的生长未受到严重影响，CO_2 含量不会显著降低，其临界值为 150 ppmv 左右；略低于末次冰期时的最低浓度 180 ppmv[78]。

通过影响行星反照率，二甲硫醚排放与 CO_2 的泵作用共同造成了温度的下降。因此，倘若二甲硫醚的生成速率随温度和（或）太阳辐射而增加，其对气候的影响将表现为朝着抵消太阳辐射通量的方向发展，而对于生物区系来说，现在的太阳辐射过量。

How could the local activity of species living in the ocean evolve to serve in the altruism of planetary regulation? The biogeochemical cycles of carbon and of sulphur are intimately linked and appear to be connected with the regulation of redox potential in both oxic and anoxic ecosystems[56,57]. The first indication of a geophysiological role for sulphur came from the observations of Challenger[58] that marine algae emitted DMS. He found that some species of shoreline algae of the order *Polysiphonia* contained as much as 15% of their dry weight as the sulphur betaine, DMSP. Until recently it has been difficult to envisage any geophysiological link between DMS production in the oceans or on the shoreline and the need of land-based ecosystems for sulphur. Why should an algal community of the ocean make the extravagant altruistic gesture of producing DMS for the benefit of, among other things, elephants and giraffes? One possible answer is that the biosynthesis of DMS began as a local activity that grew to become an unconscious benefit for the system.

With algae it seems likely that the local problem that led to the biosynthesis of DMSP was salt stress. As a result of tidal movement algae are left exposed and drying on the beach at least twice daily. Neutral solutes, such as glycerol or dimethyl sulphoxide are well known to protect against the adverse effects of freezing or drying. The mechanism of the protective effect is simply the solvent effect for salt of these involatile compounds[59]. Among solutes able to protect cells against desiccation are the betaines. These compounds although ionic are charge-neutral; the negative and positive moieties are on the same molecule. DMSP, $(CH_3)_2S^+ \cdot CH_2CH_2COO^-$ (a thionium betaine), is widely distributed among marine algae and serves to protect them against drying or increased salinity. Thus the requirement of an osmoregulatory substance by intertidal organisms may have been the original reason for DMSP synthesis.

We begin to see a possible geophysiological link between the local self interest of salt-stress prevention and the global sulphur cycle. The accidental by-product of DMSP production is its decomposition product DMS. This compound or its aerosol oxidation products will move inland from the shore and deposit sulphur over the land surface downwind of the ocean. The land tends to be depleted of sulphur and the supply of this nutrient element from the ocean would increase productivity and the rate of weathering and so lead to a return flow of nutrients to the ocean ecosystems. What seems a naive altruism is in fact an unconscious self-interest. Sulphur from DMS can travel farther than the sea-salt aerosol because several steps are involved in the conversion of gaseous DMS to aerosol sulphate; also the resulting aerosol particles are smaller and so have much longer lifetimes.

A large proportion of the current biosynthesis of DMSP is in the open oceans distant from the land surfaces. Is this DMSP also made for the relief of salt stress, or is it a redundant mechanism kept in action because of glacial epochs when the sea or part of it was saltier? Interglacials have occupied only one tenth of the time during the current series of glaciations; this may be too short a period for the devolution of DMSP biosynthesis. Alternatively, it may be that production of DMSP in the open ocean has a different geophysiological basis from that in the continental shelf regions and one that is unconnected with salinity as such.

海洋中物种的局部活动是如何发展以在地球调节的利他行为中发挥作用呢？碳和硫的生物地球化学循环是密切相关的，而且不管在喜氧还是厌氧生态系统中似乎都与氧化还原电位的调节有关[56,57]。查林杰[58]首次发现硫的地球生理作用的意义，即海洋藻类会释放二甲硫醚。他发现，沿海地区多管藻目的有些藻种中硫代甜菜碱（二甲基磺基丙酯）的含量占其干重的比例可达15%。直到最近，仍很难弄清海洋或沿海地区二甲硫醚的生产力与陆地生态系统对硫的需求之间的地球生理学联系。为什么海洋中的藻群要额外地生成对其他生物（包括大象和长颈鹿）有益的二甲硫醚呢？一种可能的解释就是，二甲硫醚的生物合成最开始只是局部活动，后来才逐渐演变成了对系统有利的无意识活动。

对于藻类来说，引起二甲基磺基丙酯的生物合成的局部因素可能是盐胁迫。在潮汐运动的作用下，藻类每天至少两次暴露在海滩上并逐渐变干，而中性溶质，如甘油或二甲基亚砜，可以抵御冰冻或干燥作用的负效应。该保护作用的机制很简单，就是这些不挥发化合物对盐具有溶剂效应[59]。甜菜碱就是一种可以保护细胞不被干燥的溶质。虽然这些化合物是离子态的，但总体是电中性的，其正负两部分的分子相等。二甲基磺基丙酯、$(CH_3)_2S^+ \cdot CH_2CH_2COO^-$（一种硫基甜菜碱）广泛分布于海洋藻类中，可以保护其免受干燥作用和高盐度的破坏。因此潮间带生物对渗透压调节物质的需求可能是合成二甲基磺基丙酯的起因。

我们终于开始看到出于盐胁迫保护的局部利己行为与全球硫循环之间的地球生理学关系了。二甲基磺基丙酯生成作用中的副产物就是其分解产物二甲硫醚。该化合物或其气溶胶氧化产物会从沿海地区向内陆输送，并在海洋下风向位置的陆地表面形成硫沉降。陆地上的硫是趋于减少的，而来自海洋的这种营养元素可以提高生产力以及风化速率，进而导致营养盐回流至海洋生态系统。表面上朴素的利他行为实际上是一种无意识的利己行为。来自二甲硫醚的硫比海盐气溶胶的传输距离要远，因为气态二甲硫醚转变成气溶胶硫酸盐要经过多个步骤；而且所形成的气溶胶颗粒较小，因此其生命周期也长得多。

目前，二甲基磺基丙酯的合成作用大部分发生于远离陆表的开阔海洋中。二甲基磺基丙酯的生成也是为了缓解盐胁迫，还是从冰期海水盐度过高时留下来的一种尚在运行的冗余机制呢？间冰期只占当前一系列冰川作用时期的1/10，对于生物合成二甲基磺基丙酯的退行进化来说这段时间可能太短了。还有一种可能，即在开阔海洋中二甲基磺基丙酯生成作用的地球生理学机制不同于陆架区，这种机制可能与盐度没有那样的相关性。

We have seen how the local self-interest of shoreline algae could lead to the mutual sharing of sulphur and nutrients with land-based organisms. The evolution of a link between ocean climate and DMS production could have happened in a similar way. Ocean organisms are often deficient in nitrogen and to some extent vulnerable to solar ultra-violet. Cloud formation with rainfall would return nitrogen to the ocean and also serve as a sunshade. If either or both of these effects were significant for the health of phytoplankton then species that emitted DMS might be at an advantage.

Is the sulphur cycle also involved in global climate control? Evapotranspiration is known to modify the climate of forests in the humid tropics. The additional cloud cover that comes from the vast water vapour flux of the trees increases the planetary albedo and further cools the surface. The emission of DMS from the oceans seems to act similarly. Through its aerosol oxidation products it alters the properties of clouds, increasing the albedo of the oceanic regions and hence of the greater part of the planet. The link between the biota and climate in both of these processes of cloud formation could be a mechanism for climate control, the clouds serving as do white daisies in the "Daisyworld" model of Gaian climate regulation[60].

Lastly, DMS is the principal component of the present biogeochemical flux of sulphur to the atmosphere. But it is not the only one; some sulphur is emitted as H_2S, COS and CS_2. COS, both from direct emission and as an oxidation product of CS_2, is stable in the troposphere long enough to be an important source of sulphur to the stratosphere. COS in the stratosphere would be oxidized and produce a sulphate aerosol there. Such stratospheric aerosols scatter sunlight back to space and lead to a cooler climate. The biological variation of COS output is therefore another possible geophysiological means of regulating climate.

Future Research Needs

We propose that sulphate aerosols derived from the sulphur gases produced by the marine biota are important determinants of cloud albedo and, as a consequence, the climate. It also seems likely that the rate of DMS emission from the oceans is affected by the climate, thus closing a feedback loop.

There are significant gaps in our knowledge of this proposed feedback system. Most importantly, we need to understand the climatic factors affecting DMS emission. Because some species produce much more DMS than others, we must include the necessary understanding of controls on phytoplankton species abundance. We also need to understand the relationship between DMS concentration in the air and the CCN population, through the intervening aerosol physical processes. Knowing how the area of cloud cover is influenced by CCN is also important.

Nonetheless, the role of the CCN population in controlling albedo, the production of CCN in marine air by the oxidation of DMS from the biota and the sensitivity of the

我们已经知道沿海藻类的局部利己行为如何最终使它们与陆地生物之间实现硫和多种营养素的相互共享。海洋气候与二甲硫醚生产力之间相互关系的演化方式可能与此类似。海洋生物通常缺乏氮，而且，从某种程度上来说较易受到太阳紫外线的破坏。云层形成带来的降雨可使氮回到海洋中，同时云层还可以起到遮阳的作用。倘若两种效应中的一种或两者都对于浮游植物的健康有重要意义，那么可以释放二甲硫醚的种类将占据一定的优势。

硫循环是否对全球气候也有影响呢？我们都知道，在湿润的热带地区，蒸散作用可以改变森林的气候。树木产生的巨大的水蒸气通量形成了额外的云层，使行星反照率增加，进而导致地表温度降低。海洋中二甲硫醚的释放也起着类似的作用。它可以通过其气溶胶氧化产物改变云层的性质，增加海洋区域的反照率，进而使地球反照率增加。上述云层形成过程中生物区系与气候之间的相互关系就是一种气候调节机制，云层的作用就好比盖亚气候调节理论的"雏菊世界"模型中白色雏菊的作用 [60]。

最后，二甲硫醚是当前输入大气中硫的生物地球化学通量的主要组分，但并不是唯一组分，有些硫是以 H_2S、COS 和 CS_2 的形式释放的。COS 既可以直接释放，也可以由 CS_2 氧化形成，它在对流层中可长期保持稳定，构成平流层中硫的重要来源。平流层中的 COS 可被氧化并在那里形成硫酸盐气溶胶。这种平流层气溶胶可将阳光散射回太空，从而导致气候变冷。因此，由生物引起的 COS 输出量的变化可能是气候调节的另一种地球生理学方式。

未来的研究方向

我们认为，由海洋生物产生的含硫气体所形成的硫酸盐气溶胶是影响云的反照率的决定性因素，因此也是影响气候的决定性因素。同时，海洋中二甲硫醚的释放速率可能也受气候的影响，由此组成一个封闭的反馈循环。

我们对该反馈系统的认识还存在许多不足。最重要的是，我们需要弄清楚影响二甲硫醚释放的气候因素。因为有些物种比其他物种生成的二甲硫醚多得多，所以我们还必须对浮游植物物种丰度的影响因素有一定认识。此外，我们还需要通过干预气溶胶物理过程，找出空气中二甲硫醚浓度与云凝结核总量之间的关系。了解云凝结核对云层覆盖面积的影响机制也很重要。

不管怎样，我们已基本确立了云凝结核总量在控制反照率中所起的作用、海洋空气中生物群释放出的二甲硫醚被氧化后形成云凝结核的机制以及地球温度对云凝

Earth's temperature to the CCN population seem to be established. Although we do not understand the details of the climatic feedback, it seems that CCN from biogenic DMS currently act to cool the Earth. It is possible that the Earth's climate has been mediated in the past (for instance, that this feedback has helped to counteract the increasing luminosity of the Sun and/or that it has already counteracted the influence of the recent increase in CO_2 and other "greenhouse" gases). However, the data required to demonstrate the latter effect have not been and are not now being acquired.

The portion of this work done in the USA was supported in part by NSF grants ATM-82-15337, ATM-83-18028, OCE-83-15733 and ATM-84-07137. The computations were done at the National Center for Atmospheric Research. We thank Marcia Baker, Keith Bigg, Robert Chatfield, Ian Galbally, Dean Hegg, Ann Henderson-Sellers, Kendal McGuffie, Henning Rodhe and Starley Thompson for commenting on an early draft, and Antony Clarke for discussions.

(**326**, 655-661; 1987)

Robert J. Charlson[*], James E. Lovelock[†], Meinrat O. Andreae[‡] & Stephen G. Warren[*]

[*] Department of Atmospheric Sciences AK-40, University of Washington, Seattle, Washington 98195, USA
[†] Coombe Mill Experimental Station, Launceston, Cornwall PL15 9RY, UK
[‡] Department of Oceanography, Florida State University, Tallahassee, Florida 32306, USA

References:

1. Dickinson, R. E. & Cicerone, R. J. *Nature* **319**, 109-115 (1986).

2. Shaw, G. *Climatic Change* **5**, 297-303 (1983).

3. Lovelock, J. E. *Bull. Am. Met. Soc.* **67**, 392-397 (1986).

4. Andreae, M. O. in *The Biogeochemical Cycling of Sulfur and Nitrogen in the Remote Atmosphere* (eds Galloway, J. N., Charlson, R. J., Andreae, M. O. & Rodhe, H.) 5-25 (Reidel, Dordrecht, 1985).

5. Andreae, M. O. in *The Role of Air-Sea Exchange in Geochemical Cycling* (ed. Buat-Menard, P.) 331-362 (Reidel, Dordrecht, 1986).

6. Cullis, C. F. & Hirschler, M. M. *Atmos. Environ.* **14**, 1263-1278 (1980).

7. Andreae, M. O. in *Microbial Mats: Stromatolites* (eds Cohen, Y., Castenholz, R. W. & Halverson, H. O.) 455-466 (Liss, New York, 1984).

8. Andreae, M. O. & Andreae, T. W. *J. Geophys. Res.* (submitted).

9. Vairavamurthy, A., Andreae, M. O. & Iverson, R. L. *Limnol. Oceanogr.* **30**, 59-70 (1985).

10. Turner, S. M. & Liss, P. S. *J. Atmos. Chem.* **2**, 223-232 (1985).

11. Bates, T. S., Cline, J. D., Gammon, R. H. & Kelly-Hansen, S. R. *J. Geophys. Res.* (in the press).

12. Andreae, M. O. *Limnol. Oceanogr.* **30**, 1208-1218 (1985).

13. Brimblecombe, P. & Shooter, D. *Mar. Chem.* **19**, 343-353 (1986).

14. Andreae, M. O., Barnard, W. R. & Ammons, J. M. *Ecol. Bull.* (Stockholm) **35**, 167-177 (1983).

15. Niki, H., Maker, P. D., Savage, C. M. & Breitenbach, L. P. *Int. J. Chem. Kinet.* **15**, 647-654 (1983).

16. Yin, F., Grosjean, D. & Seinfeld, J. H. *J. Geophys. Res.* (in the press).

17. Ferek, R. J., Chatfield, R. B. & Andreae, M. O. *Nature* **320**, 514-516 (1986).

18. Andreae, M. O. *et al. J. Geophys. Res.* **90**, 12891-12900 (1985).

19. Tyndall, G. S., Burrows, J. P., Schneider, W. & Moortgat, G. K. *Chem. Phys. Lett.* **130**, 463-466 (1986).

20. Saltzman, E. S., Savole, D. L., Prospero, J. M. & Zika, R. G. *J. Atmos. Chem.* **4**, 227-240 (1986).

21. Andreae, M. O., Berresheim, H., Andreae, T. W., Kritz, M. A., Bates, T. S. & Merrill, J. T. *J. Atmos. Chem.* (in the press).

22. Harvey, G. R. & Lang, R. F. *Geophys. Res. Lett.* **13**, 49-51 (1986).

23. Pruppacher, H. R. & Klett, J. D. *Microphysics of Clouds and Precipitation* (Reidel, Dordrecht, 1978).

24. Bigg, E. K. *Atmos. Res.* **20**, 82-86 (1986).

25. Fletcher, N. H. *The Physics of Rainclouds* 98 (Cambridge University Press, 1962).

结核总量的敏感度。虽然我们对气候反馈的细节还不太清楚，但目前，生源二甲硫醚形成的云凝结核可能正使地球变冷。过去地球气候可能就发生过这样的调节作用（例如，该反馈机制帮助抵消了太阳亮度的增加，而且（或者）它已抵消了近来 CO_2 和其他"温室气体"增加所产生的影响）。然而，不管是从前还是现在，我们还没有获得能证明后一种效应的数据。

本研究在美国进行的部分得到了美国国家科学基金会 ATM-82-15337、ATM-83-18028、OCE-83-15733 以及 ATM-84-07137 项目的部分资助。计算工作在美国国家大气研究中心进行。感谢马西娅·贝克、基思·比格、罗伯特·查特菲尔德、伊恩·加尔巴利、迪安·赫格、安·亨德森－塞勒斯、肯德尔·麦古菲、亨宁·罗德以及斯塔利·汤普森对本文初稿提出的意见，安东尼·克拉克参与了研讨，在此一并感谢。

（齐红艳 翻译；刘新 审稿）

Oceanic Phytoplankton, Atmospheric Sulphur, Cloud Albedo and Climate

26. Koehler, H. *Trans. Faraday Soc.* **32**, 1152 (1936).

27. Hobbs, P. V. *Q. Jl R. Met. Soc.* **97**, 263-271 (1971).

28. Radke, L. F. *thesis,* Univ. Washington, Seattle (1968).

29. Charlson, R. J., Chameides, W. & Kley, D. in *The Biogeochemical Cycling of Sulfur and Nitrogen in the Remote Atmosphere* (eds Galloway, J. N., Charlson, R. J., Andreae, M. O. & Rodhe, H.) 67-80 (Reidel, Dordrecht, 1985).

30. Bigg, E. K., Gras, J. L. & Evans, C. *J. Atmos. Chem.* **1**, 203-214 (1984).

31. Andreae, M. O. *J. Geophys. Res.* **87**, 8875-8885 (1982).

32. Savoie, D. L. & Prospero, J. M. *Geophys. Res. Lett.* **9**, 1207-1210 (1982).

33. Prospero, J. M., Savoie, D. L., Nees, R. T., Duce, R. A. & Merrill, J. *J. Geophys. Res.* **90**, 10586-10596 (1985).

34. Galloway, J. N. in *The Biogeochemical Cycling of Sulfur and Nitrogen in the Remote Atmosphere* (eds Galloway, J. N., Charlson, R. J., Andreae, M. O. & Rodhe, H.) 143-175 (Reidel, Dordrecht, 1985).

35. Charlson, R. J. & Rodhe, H. *Nature* **295**, 683-685 (1982).

36. Twomey, S. A. *J. Atmos. Sci.* **28**, 377 (1971).

37. Wallace, J. M. & Hobbs, P. V. *Atmospheric Science, an Introductory Survey* 212 (Academic, New York, 1977).

38. Hobbs, P. V., Harrison, H. & Robinson, E. *Science* **183**, 909-915 (1974).

39. Paltridge, G. W. *Q. Jl R. Met. Soc.* **106**, 895-899 (1980).

40. Charlock, T. P. *Tellus* **34**, 245-254 (1982).

41. Somerville, R. C. J. & Remer, L. A. *J. Geophys. Res.* **89**, 9668-9672 (1984).

42. Bohren, C. F. *J. Geophys. Res.* **90**, 5867 (1985).

43. Twomey, S. *Atmospheric Aerosols* (Elsevier, Amsterdam, 1977).

44. Welch, R. M. in *Fifth Conference on Atmospheric Radiation* 505-507 (American Meteorological Society, Boston, 1983).

45. Gabriel, P., Lovejoy, S., Austin, G. & Schertzer, D. in *Sixth Conference on Atmospheric Radiation* 230-235 (American Meteorological Society, Boston, 1986).

46. Coakley, J. A. Jr & Davies, R. *J. Atmos. Sci.* **43**, 1025-1035 (1986).

47. Wiscombe, W. J., Welch, R. M. & Hall, W. D. *J. Atmos. Sci.* **41**, 1336-1355 (1984).

48. Twomey, S. A. Piepgrass, M. & Wolfe, T. L. *Tellus* **36B**, 356-366 (1984).

49. Wetherald, R. T. & Manabe, S. *J. Atmos. Sci.* **32**, 2044-2059 (1975).

50. Waggoner, A. P. *et al. Nature* **261**, 120-122 (1976).

51. Paltridge, G. W. & Platt, C. M. R. *Radiative Processes in Meteorology and Climatology* 191 (Elsevier, Amsterdam, 1976).

52. McMurry, P. H. & Wilson, J. C. *J. Geophys. Res.* **88**, 5101-5108 (1983).

53. McIntyre, A. *et al. Science* **191**, 1131-1144 (1976).

54. Bryan, K. & Spelman, M. J. *J. Geophys. Res.* **90**, 11679-11688 (1985).

55. Lovelock, J. E. & Whitfield, M. *Nature* **296**, 561-563 (1982).

56. Garrels, R. M. & Lerman, A. *Proc. Natl. Acad. Sci. U.S.A.* **78**, 4652-4656 (1981).

57. Holland, H. D. *The Chemical Evolution of the Atmosphere and Oceans* (Princeton University Press, 1984).

58. Challenger, F. *Adv. Enzymol.* **12**, 429-491 (1951).

59. Lovelock, J. E. *Biochim. Biophys. Acta* **11**, 28-34 (1953).

60. Watson, A. J. & Lovelock, J. E. *Tellus* **35B**, 284-289 (1983).

61. Warren, S. G., Hahn, C. & London, J. in *Fifth Conference on Atmospheric Radiation* 313-314 (American Meterological Society, Boston, 1983).

62. Warren, S. G., Hahn, C. & London, J. *J. Clim. Appl. Meteor.* **24**, 658-667 (1985).

63. Shine, K. P., Henderson-Sellers, A. & Slingo, A. *Q. Jl R. Met. Soc.* **110**, 1170-1179 (1984).

64. Stephens, G. L., Campbell, G. G. & Vonder-Haar, T. H. *J. Geophys. Res.* **86**, 9739-9760 (1981).

65. Hansen, J. E. & Travis, L. D. *Space Sci. Rev.* **16**, 527-610 (1974).

66. Hegg, D. A. *J. Atmos. Sci.* **43**, 399-400 (1986).

67. Briegleb, B. & Ramanathan, V. *J. Appl. Met.* **21**, 1160-1171 (1982).

68. Kondratyev, K. *Radiation in the Atmosphere* (Academic, New York, 1969).

69. Payne, R. E. *J. Atmos. Sci.* **29**, 959-970 (1972).

70. Wiscombe, W. *J. Appl. Opt.* **19**, 1505-1509 (1980).

71. Hale, G. M. & Querry, M. R. *Appl. Opt.* **12**, 555-563 (1973).

72. Joseph, J. H., Wiscombe, W. J. & Weinman, J. A. *J. Atmos. Sci.* **33**, 2452-2459 (1976).

73. King, M. D. & Harshvardhan *J. Atmos. Sci.* **43**, 784-801 (1986).

74. Kellogg, W. W. in *Climate of the Arctic* (eds Weller, G. & Bowling, S. A.) 111-116 (Geophysical Institute, Fairbanks, Alaska, 1975).

75. Graedel, T. E. *Geophys. Res. Lett.* **6**, 329-331 (1979).

76. Clarke, A. D., Ahlquist, N. C. & Covert, D. S. *J. Geophys. Res.* **92** (in the press).

77. Covert, D. S. *J. Geophys. Res.* (submitted).

78. Neftel, A. *et al. Nature* **295**, 220-223 (1982).

Structure of the Repressor–Operator Complex of Bacteriophage 434

J. E. Anderson *et al.*

Editor's Note

In 1967, molecular biologist Mark Ptashne demonstrated negative gene regulation in the form of a repressor protein binding directly to specific DNA sequences. Two decades later, with the help of colleagues John E. Anderson and Stephen C. Harrison, Ptashne describes the crystal structure of a specific complex between the DNA-binding domain of a bacteriophage repressor protein and a synthetic operator DNA. The structure reveals how the repressor recognizes both a particular conformation of DNA and an array of base-pair contacts, a phenomenon driving repressor specificity. Structures such as this have enabled the controlled switching of gene expression to become a reality and provided a framework for understanding the mechanisms governing gene regulation.

The crystal structure of a specific complex between the DNA-binding domain of phage 434 repressor and a synthetic 434 operator DNA shows interactions that determine sequence-dependent affinity. The repressor recognizes its operators by its complementarity to a particular DNA conformation as well as by direct interaction with base pairs in the major groove.

WE describe here the structure of a specific complex between the DNA-binding domain of a bacteriophage repressor protein and a synthetic operator DNA. The description is based on an X-ray crystallographic analysis of crystals that diffract to 3.2 Å resolution in some directions and to about 4.5 Å in others. The repressor is encoded by coliphage 434, a close relative of phage λ. It binds to a set of six similar but non-identical 14-base-pair (bp) operators in the phage genome. Its differential affinity for these sites, coupled with the distinct differential affinity of the homologous cro protein, creates a regulatory switch determining the choice between lysogeny and lytic growth[1]. The structure of the repressor-operator complex, taken together with experiments reported in an accompanying paper and elsewhere[2,3], reveals the basis of specific binding and its modulation by the exact DNA sequence of the operator.

In an account of this structure at 7 Å resolution[4], we described the general features of the complex. The repressor DNA-binding domain (R1-69), contains the first 69 residues of the complete polypeptide. Its conformation is predominantly α-helical, similar to the first four helices of the λ repressor[5]. The second and third alpha helices (α2 and α3) form a

噬菌体434阻遏蛋白–操纵基因复合物的结构

安德森等

编者按

1967年，分子生物学家马克·普塔什尼证明了基因负调控以阻遏蛋白直接结合于特异DNA片段的形式实现。二十年后，在其同事约翰·安德森和斯蒂芬·哈里森的协助下，普塔什尼描述了一种噬菌体阻遏蛋白的DNA结合域与人工合成的操纵基因DNA所形成的特异复合物的晶体结构。这一结构揭示了阻遏蛋白如何同时识别DNA的特殊构象并与一排碱基对相接触的，该现象使阻遏蛋白具有了特异性。这样的结构使基因表达的可控开关成为可能，并为了解基因调控机制提供了框架。

噬菌体434阻遏蛋白的DNA结合域与人工合成的434操纵基因DNA所形成的特异复合物的晶体结构显示了决定序列依赖性亲和力的相互作用方式。阻遏蛋白通过和特异DNA构象的互补作用及与DNA大沟中的碱基对直接作用的方式识别其操纵基因。

本文所描述的是噬菌体阻遏蛋白的DNA结合域与人工合成的操纵基因DNA所形成的特异复合物的结构。所有描述都是基于对晶体的X射线晶体学衍射图谱的分析，该晶体的衍射分辨率在某些方向上达到3.2 Å，在其余方向约为4.5 Å。阻遏蛋白是由与λ噬菌体非常相似的大肠杆菌噬菌体434基因编码的。它结合于噬菌体基因组中六个长度为14个碱基对、序列相似但不完全相同的操纵基因上。它对六个位点的不同亲和力，加上和同源的cro蛋白有着明显的亲和性差异，形成了一个调控开关来决定噬菌体的生长处于溶源还是裂解周期[1]。这个阻遏蛋白–操纵基因复合物的结构，加上本期杂志中另一篇相关文章及其他文献报道的实验结果[2,3]，揭示了特异结合的原理以及操纵基因中特定DNA序列对它的调节。

在过去该结构的分辨率为7 Å时[4]，我们描述了这一复合物的大致特征。阻遏蛋白的DNA结合域（R1-69）包含该蛋白全长多肽起始的69个氨基酸残基。它的构象主要是α-螺旋，类似于λ噬菌体阻遏蛋白起始的四个螺旋[5]。第二和第三个α螺旋（α2和α3）形成一个螺旋–转角–螺旋基序，这在其他某些DNA结合蛋白的

271

helix–turn–helix motif, found in crystal structures of certain other DNA binding proteins[6-8] and believed on the basis of amino-acid sequence similarity to occur in many more[9]. The conformation of the 14-bp synthetic operator (14-mer) is B-DNA-like, and individual 14-mers are stacked end-to-end to form pseudocontinuous double helices running through the crystals. Two R1-69 subunits are bound to each 14-mer, and α3 of each monomer rests in the major groove of a half-site.

The higher resolution structure presented here shows the interaction in molecular detail. Hydrogen bonds between amide nitrogens of the peptide backbone and phosphate groups on DNA strongly constrain the fit of DNA to protein, and three glutamine side chains on α3 are in position to form a pattern of van der Waals and hydrogen-bond contacts with the five outer base pairs. Thus, the repressor recognizes in DNA both a particular conformation and an array of base-pair contacts.

Structure Determination

Crystals of R1-69 and the 14mer were prepared as described previously[10]. Data-collection procedures and statistics are presented in Table 1. Initial single isomorphous replacement (SIR) phases were obtained using crystals with DNA containing 5-bromodeoxyuracil instead of thymine at position 7. Phases between 15 Å and 7 Å were refined using real space noncrystallographic symmetry averaging[11-13] about a local 3_1 axis parallel to [1$\bar{1}$1] and intersecting [110] 33.5 Å from the origin[4]. The small magnitude of the heavy-atom differences and weak intensities beyond 7 Å made conventional refinement of heavy-atom positions impractical. We therefore used a two-step strategy to extend phases, first from 7 Å to 5 Å and then from 5 Å to 3.2 Å. In the first step, heavy-atom positions were refined at 7 Å resolution by averaging a 15–7 Å heavy-atom difference map about a series of local 3_1 axes, parallel to [1$\bar{1}$1] and intersecting [110] in the neighbourhood of 33.5 Å from the origin. The position of the 3_1 axis that gave the strongest average heavy-atom peaks was selected, and new heavy-atom positions were determined by inspection of the corresponding map. SIR phases between 7 and 5 Å resolution were computed using these positions, combined with the previously refined 15 to 7 Å phases, and used to generate a 5 Å map. Eight cycles of noncrystallographic symmetry averaging[13] about the new local 3_1 (34.0 Å from the origin along [110]) gave an averaging R-factor, $R_{av} = 0.28$. In the second step, refined phases to 5 Å resolution were used in an analogous way to adjust the origin of the threefold screw axis and to improve the heavy-atom coordinates. The noncrystallographic symmetry phase refinement was unstable if all phases from 15 to 3.2 Å were allowed to change, but fixing phases from 15 to 5 Å at their best values from the 5 Å refinement allowed the computation to converge with $R_{av} = 0.30$ for all data from 15 to 3.2 Å (Table 2, upper part). This way of refining heavy-atom coordinates is similar to the procedure introduced by Hogle for work on poliovirus[14].

晶体结构中也有发现[6-8]，并且基于氨基酸序列的相似性可以相信在更多的 DNA 结合蛋白中均有该基序的存在[9]。14 个碱基对的人工合成操纵基因 (14 碱基对) 具有类 B 型 DNA 构象，单独的 14 碱基对以末端相接的方式堆积成伪连续的双螺旋贯穿晶体。每个 14 碱基对结合两个 R1-69 亚基，每个亚基中的 α3 螺旋位于一个半位点的大沟中。

本文所描述的更高分辨率的结构显示了分子细节上的相互作用。蛋白质多肽骨架中氨基氮和 DNA 的磷酸基团之间的氢键极大地限制了 DNA 对蛋白质的匹配，而 α3 螺旋中三个谷氨酰胺侧链则与五个外缘碱基对形成范德华力和氢键模式的接触。这样，阻遏蛋白对 DNA 的识别既依赖 DNA 的特殊构象，又需要与一串碱基对的接触。

结 构 测 定

R1-69 和 14 碱基对 DNA 复合物的晶体制备参见前述[10]。数据收集步骤和统计学结果如表 1 所示。初始的单对同晶置换（SIR）相位来自在 DNA 第七位上用 5– 溴代尿苷取代了胸腺嘧啶的晶体。15 Å 到 7 Å 之间的相位修正采用的是实空间非晶体学对称平均[11-13] 的方法，围绕一个平行于 [1Ī1] 并在距离原点 33.5 Å 处与 [110] 交叉的局部 3_1 轴[4] 进行。重原子差异很小，分辨率超过 7 Å 的信号强度也很弱，因此不能使用常规的重原子位置修正。为此我们采用两步法来拓展相位，先从 7 Å 到 5 Å，再由 5 Å 到 3.2 Å。第一步，通过将围绕着一系列局部 3_1 轴的 15~7 Å 分辨率的重原子差值图进行平均，使重原子的位置在 7 Å 的分辨率上得到修正，这些局部 3_1 轴距原点 33.5 Å，平行于 [1Ī1] 并交叉于 [110]。选择平均重原子峰值最高的 3_1 轴的位置，通过观察相应图谱确定新的重原子位置。利用这些位置信息，再结合先前修正的 15 Å 到 7 Å 的相位信息，计算出 7 Å 到 5 Å 间单对同晶置换的相位，并用来生成 5 Å 分辨率的密度图。围绕新的局部 3_1 轴（沿着 [110] 的方向距原点 34 Å）进行了八轮非晶体学对称平均[13]，得到 R 因子平均值，$R_{av}=0.28$。第二步，利用 5 Å 分辨率的修正相位通过类似的方式来调整三次螺旋轴的起点，并修正重原子的坐标。如果 15 Å 到 3.2 Å 的相位都设置为可变，则非晶体学对称相位的修正就不稳定。但是将 15 Å 到 5 Å 的相位固定在 5 Å 修正的最佳值，便使得从 15 Å 到 3.2 Å 的所有数据中计算出的 R 因子收敛于 0.30，即 $R_{av}=0.30$（表 2，上部）。这种修正重原子坐标的方法与霍格尔在脊髓灰质炎病毒研究中使用的方法类似[14]。

Table 1. Statistics for data between 45 and 3.2 Å resolution

		Native		
d_{min} (Å)	$<F>$	R_{sym} (N_{mult})	N (% $F > 2\sigma$)	N_{poss} (% $F > 2\sigma$)
9.90	7,568	0.080 (148)	368 (98.4)	622 (58.2)
7.08	6,559	0.096 (585)	929 (98.5)	622 (58.2)
5.81	3,476	0.107 (721)	1,099 (97.0)	1,260 (84.6)
5.04	2,916	0.138 (815)	1,283 (95.9)	1,466 (83.9)
4.51	2,955	0.157 (920)	1,399 (94.1)	1,651 (79.8)
4.12	3,022	0.170 (951)	1,535 (94.2)	1,817 (79.6)
3.82	2,695	0.212 (982)	1,675 (92.0)	1,961 (78.6)
3.58	2,491	0.242 (941)	1,705 (88.7)	2,090 (72.3)
3.37	2,161	0.284 (921)	1,756 (82.8)	2,237 (65.0)
3.20	2,535	0.212 (834)	1,708 (79.7)	2,328 (58.5)
Overall	3,129	0.161 (7,818)	13,457(90.7)	16,444(74.2)
		Derivative		
d_{min} (Å)	$<F>$	R_{sym} (N_{mult})	N (% $F > 2\sigma$)	N_{poss} (% $F > 2\sigma$)
9.90	7,194	0.041 (59)	229 (97.4)	622 (35.9)
7.08	6,225	0.047 (240)	664 (96.8)	1,013 (63.5)
5.81	3,341	0.093 (387)	866 (88.6)	1,260 (60.9)
5.04	2,879	0.135 (442)	970 (84.7)	1,466 (56.1)
4.51	2,902	0.179 (471)	1,079 (85.1)	1,651 (55.6)
4.12	2,905	0.212 (424)	1,132 (83.7)	1,817 (52.2)
3.82	2,790	0.282 (366)	1,244 (79.7)	1,961 (50.6)
3.58	2,630	0.313 (274)	1,200 (75.5)	2,090 (43.3)
3.37	2,430	0.274 (244)	1,141 (70.9)	2,237 (36.2)
3.20	3,405	0.194 (261)	1,089 (75.0)	2,328 (35.1)
Overall	3,224	0.169 (3,168)	9,614 (81.6)	16,444(47.7)

Mean isomorphous difference $= \sum |F_{nat} - F_{der}| / \sum |F_{nat}| = 0.22$, calculated after exclusion of data (between 45 and 3.2 Å) for which $|F_{nat} - F_{der}| > 5\sigma(\Delta F)$.

$R_{sym} = \sum_i \sum_j |I_{ij} - \bar{I}_i| / \sum_i \sum_j I_{ij}$

N_{mult} = number of reflections measured more than once; only these contribute to R_{sym}.

N = number of reflections measured (after rejections) including those measured only once.

N_{poss} = maximum number of reflections possible in corresponding resolution range.

The percentage of observed and possible data with $F > 2\sigma$ (F) is indicated. Data from native crystals were collected to 3.2 Å using CEA-25 X-ray film and oscillation photography with Elliot GX-6 and GX-13 X-ray generators. The films were scanned with an Optronics P1000 film scanner on a 50 µm raster. Integrated intensities were obtained with the film-scanning program SCANFILM, a derivative of SCAN12 (ref. 34). Data to 7 Å were also collected on a prototype Xentronics area detector with the Harvard software package[35]. These measurements provided intensities for native reflections that were too bright to be measured on film. Derivative data to 3.2 Å were collected on the area detector from isomorphous crystals prepared with DNA containing 5-bromodeoxyuracil instead of thymine at position 7 of the 14mer[4]. The native data from detector and film were processed and merged, then scaled to the processed derivative data. All programs for data processing and scaling were from P. Evans (MRC Laboratory of Molecular Biology).

表 1. 分辨率 45 Å 到 3.2 Å 间的数据统计

d_{min}(Å)	$<F>$	$R_{sym}(N_{mult})$	$N(\% F>2\sigma)$	$N_{poss}(\% F>2\sigma)$
母体				
9.90	7,568	0.080 (148)	368 (98.4)	622 (58.2)
7.08	6,599	0.096 (585)	929 (98.5)	622 (58.2)
5.81	3,476	0.107 (721)	1,099 (97.0)	1,260 (84.6)
5.04	2,916	0.138 (815)	1,283 (95.9)	1,446 (83.9)
4.51	2,955	0.157 (920)	1,399 (94.1)	1,651 (79.8)
4.12	3,022	0.170 (951)	1,535 (94.2)	1,817 (79.6)
3.82	2,695	0.212 (982)	1,675 (92.0)	1,961 (78.6)
3.58	2,491	0.242 (941)	1,705 (88.7)	2,090 (72.3)
3.37	2,161	0.284 (921)	1,756 (82.8)	2,237 (65.0)
3.20	2,535	0.212 (834)	1,708 (79.7)	2,328 (58.5)
总体	3,129	0.161 (7,818)	13,457 (90.7)	16,444 (74.2)
衍生物				
d_{min}(Å)	$<F>$	$R_{sym}(N_{mult})$	$N(\% F>2\sigma)$	$N_{poss}(\% F>2\sigma)$
9.90	7,194	0.041 (59)	229 (97.4)	622 (35.9)
7.08	6,225	0.047 (240)	664 (96.8)	1,013 (63.5)
5.81	3,341	0.093 (387)	866 (88.6)	1,260 (60.9)
5.04	2,879	0.135 (442)	970 (84.7)	1,466 (56.1)
4.51	2,902	0.179 (471)	1,079 (85.1)	1,651 (55.6)
4.12	2,905	0.212 (424)	1,132 (83.7)	1,817 (52.2)
3.82	2,790	0.282 (366)	1,244 (79.7)	1,961 (50.6)
3.58	2,630	0.313 (274)	1,200 (75.5)	2,090 (43.3)
3.37	2,430	0.274 (244)	1,141 (70.9)	2,237 (36.2)
3.20	3,405	0.194 (261)	1,089 (75.0)	2,328 (35.1)
总体	3,224	0.169 (3,168)	9,614 (81.6)	16,444 (47.7)

平均同型差异 $= \sum |F_{nat} - F_{der}|/ \sum |F_{nat}| = 0.22$，是将 45 Å 到 3.2 Å 的数据中 $|F_{nat} - F_{der}| > 5\sigma(\Delta F)$ 的数据排除后计算得到的结果。

$R_{sym} = \sum_i \sum_j |I_{ij} - \bar{I}_i|/ \sum_i \sum_j I_{ij}$

N_{mult} = 测到多次的反射数；仅限于对 R_{sym} 有贡献的反射。

N = 测到的反射数（除掉了不符合条件的数据），包括只测到一次的反射。

N_{poss} = 在相应分辨率范围内可能的最大反射数。

观察到的与可能的数据中符合 $F > 2\sigma (F)$ 的百分比在表中列出。母体晶体收集到了分辨率达 3.2 Å 的数据，使用的是 CEA-25 型 X 射线胶片和振荡摄影术以及埃利奥特 GX-6、GX-13 型 X 射线发射机。胶片用 Optronics P1000 型胶片扫描仪以 50 μm 光栅产生的光进行扫描。积分强度则由程序 SCAN12（参考文献 34）衍生出的一个胶片扫描程序 SCANFILM 获得。分辨率达 7 Å 的数据也是在使用哈佛软件包的 Xentronics 面探测器原型机上收集的 [35]。这些测量提供了因光太强而不能在胶片上进行测量的母体反射强度。分辨率达 3.2 Å 的衍生物数据由同晶置换的晶体在面探测器上收集，该同晶置换中将 14 碱基 DNA 中第七位的胸腺嘧啶改变为 5–溴代脱氧核糖 [4]。由面探测器和胶片得到的母体数据经过处理和合并后，缩放到与处理过的衍生物数据一样的大小。数据处理和缩放的所有软件来自埃文斯实验室（医学研究协会，分子生物学实验室）。

Table 2. Phase refinement by noncrystallographic symmetry averaging

		Refinement of SIR phases*				
	Phases refined 15→3.2 Å			Phases refined 5→3.2 Å		
Cycle	R_{av}	r	Mean phase change	R_{av}	r	Mean phase change
1	0.58	0.537	53.3	0.55	0.346	75.3
2	0.45	0.734	40.1	0.41	0.600	34.7
3	0.39	0.785	21.9	0.35	0.678	17.1
4	0.38	0.791	14.5	0.33	0.718	10.2
5	0.38	0.780	11.4	0.31	0.737	7.3
6	0.39	0.780	10.2	0.31	0.750	5.7
7	0.40	0.781	10.5	0.30	0.758	4.8
8	0.43	0.747	11.0	0.30	0.785	4.1
Overall			65.5			82.0
		Refinement of phases determined from initial model†				
Cycle	R_{av}		r		Mean phase change	
1	0.37		0.792		23.2	
2	0.32		0.837		9.2	
3	0.30		0.858		6.3	
4	0.29		0.866		4.7	
5	0.28		0.873		3.8	
6	0.28		0.878		3.3	
7	0.27		0.881		2.7	
Overall					43.4	

* SIR phases were refined by symmetry averaging maps calculated with coefficients $(2F_o–F_c)$ exp $(i\alpha_c)$. The molecular envelopes required for symmetry averaging[13] were generated from model coordinates by enclosing each atom in a sphere of 7 Å radius. The initial model for the R1-69 : 14mer complex (Anderson *et al.* 1985), used to produce the envelope for 5 Å symmetry averaging (see text), contained idealized straight B-DNA. Inspection of the 5 Å map revealed that a 14mer with a slight bend would fit the density better. We therefore adjusted the positions of the two half-sites as rigid bodies using the real space refinement option of FRODO, and carried out the eight cycles of 3.2 Å refinement using an envelope from this model. Mean phase changes $(\sum|\Phi_c–\Phi_o|/N)$, for cycles subsequent to the first, are for all data present in the native data set, whether or not present in the initial SIR data set.

† Phases calculated from coordinates fit to the averaged maps from *a* were refined by averaging F_o exp $(i\alpha_c)$ maps. The envelope was constructed from the coordinates on which the initial phases were based. $R_{av} = \sum|F_o–F_c|/\sum|F_o|$

$$r = \frac{\sum|F_o||F_c|–(\sum|F_o|\sum|F_c|)}{[\sum|F_o|^2–(\sum|F_o|)^2]\cdot[\sum|F_o|^2–(\sum|F_c|)^2]}$$

表 2. 经过非晶体学对称平均的相位修正

单对同晶置换（SIR）相位修正 *					
	相位修正 15 → 3.2Å			相位修正 5 → 3.2Å	
轮数	R_{av}	r	平均相位改变	R_{av}	r	平均相位改变
1	0.58	0.537	53.3	0.55	0.346	75.3
2	0.45	0.734	40.1	0.41	0.600	34.7
3	0.39	0.785	21.9	0.35	0.678	17.1
4	0.38	0.791	14.5	0.33	0.718	10.2
5	0.38	0.780	11.4	0.31	0.737	7.3
6	0.39	0.780	10.2	0.31	0.750	5.7
7	0.40	0.781	10.5	0.30	0.758	4.8
8	0.43	0.747	11	0.30	0.785	4.1
总体			65.5			82.0

初始模型的相位修正†			
轮数	R_{av}	r	平均相位改变
1	0.37	0.792	23.2
2	0.32	0.837	9.2
3	0.30	0.858	6.3
4	0.29	0.866	4.7
5	0.28	0.873	3.8
6	0.28	0.878	3.3
7	0.27	0.881	2.7
总体			43.4

* 通过用系数 $(2F_o - F_c)$ exp $(i\alpha_c)$ 计算的对称平均图来进行 SIR 相位修正。用于对称平均[13]的分子边界来自囊括半径为 7 Å 的球体内每个原子的模型坐标。R1-69 和 14 碱基对 DNA 复合物的初始模型（安德森等，1985）用来产生 5 Å 平均对称的分子边界（见正文），其包含的是理想的、直链 B 型 DNA。对 5 Å 分辨率图谱的观察提示 14 碱基对的 DNA 微弱弯曲将使密度匹配的更好。于是我们使用软件 FRODO 的实空间修正选项将两个半位点作为刚体调整其位置，然后使用这个模型的分子边界进行八轮 3.2 Å 的修正。随后的每一轮相对第一轮的平均相位改变 ($\sum |\Phi_o - \Phi_i|/N$) 是针对所有的母体数据集合，不论其是否存在于初始的 SIR 数据集合中。

† 与 a 的平均密度图相匹配的坐标系计算得到的相位通过平均 $F_o$exp $(i\alpha_c)$ 图来修正。分子边界是基于初始相位的坐标而建立的。 $R_{av} = \sum |F_o - F_c| / \sum |F_o|$

$$r = \frac{\sum |F_o||F_c| - (\sum |F_o| \sum |F_c|)}{[\sum |F_o|^2 - (\sum |F_o|)^2] \cdot [\sum |F_o|^2 - (\sum |F_c|)^2]}$$

The map thus computed showed clear double-helical DNA density, each deoxyribose-phosphate backbone having a staircase like shape, with sugars corresponding to the risers. Base pairs were poorly defined by density, but an unambiguous model could be built using backbone density and hydrogen-bonding restraints as a guide. Four α-helices of the protein appeared as twisted rods. A number of side chains were well-defined; others appeared as truncated bulges. For model-building, we used the program FRODO[15] with separate files for DNA and protein coordinates. The 14mer was broken into single stranded mono-, di- and trinucleotide segments, the phosphates and sugars were fitted to the DNA backbone density, and the torsion angles were adjusted to restore approximately correct base-pair geometry. The Hendrickson-Konnert restrained least squares refinement programs[16], modified by G. Quigley (MIT) to accept nucleic acid coordinates, were used with base-pair hydrogen bonding restraints to restore idealized geometry. Further manual adjustment followed, with periodic regularization. Residues 1–58 of the protein were built into the map and adjusted with the regularization routines in FRODO. Finally, protein and DNA coordinates were regularized with the constrained-restrained least squares refinement program CORELS[17], with base-pair hydrogen bonding restraints imposed on the DNA.

The initial model, constructed as just described, was used to obtain starting phases for a second round of noncrystallographic symmetry phase refinement. The order in the crystals is anisotropic, with intensities measurable to spacings of 3.2 Å in the directions of noncrystallographic symmetry axes formed by stacked protein–DNA complexes, but only to about 4.5 Å in other directions[10]. The map can therefore be regarded as density at 3.2 Å resolution, selectively "smeared" in directions perpendicular to the non-crystallographic symmetry axis. When building a model, however, stereochemical constraints couple positions along the local symmetry axis with those normal to it. Therefore, the effective resolution is intermediate between the two limits. To 5 Å, the intensity fall-off is relatively isotropic and computed structure factors at this resolution were used in a translation search program (A. Aggarwal, personal communication) to carry out a final adjustment of the position of the 3_1 axis. The anisotropy and non-crystallographic symmetry were incorporated into FFT (fast Fourier transform) structure factor calculations[18] by using the Bricogne density reconstitution procedure[13] to generate a full crystallographic asymmetric unit from a half-complex "map" that is computed in a coordinate frame with the noncrystallographic symmetry axis along Z. This choice of frame simplified introduction of a uniaxial, anisotropic "temperature factor". Various ratios of Bx = By to Bz were examined, by comparing calculated and observed amplitudes. The optimum occurred at 1.75, as judged both by R factor minimum and by relative lack of noise in corresponding $2F_o–F_c$ and $F_o–F_c$ maps.

Phases from the initial model were used to initiate eight further cycles of noncrystallographic symmetry refinement of phases between 15 and 3.2 Å. The computation converged stably to $R_{av} = 0.27$, with an overall phase change of 43° (Table 2, lower part). Significant adjustments were indicated by this map, and we extended the model from residue 58 to residue 63 (Fig. 1). Two further rounds of smaller adjustments

278

这样计算得到的密度图可以清晰地看到 DNA 双螺旋的密度，每个脱氧核糖－磷酸骨架的形状就像是楼梯，而糖对应着楼梯的侧板。碱基对在密度图中并不清晰，但是利用骨架的密度和氢键的限制作为指导，可以得到一个很清楚的模型。蛋白质的四个 α 螺旋就像扭缠在一起的棒。一些侧链可以很清晰地看到，另一些则如同被截去一部分的凸起。我们利用 FRODO 程序 [15] 以及 DNA 和蛋白质各自的坐标文件构建了模型。含 14 碱基对的片段被打碎成单链的单核苷酸、双核苷酸和三核苷酸片段的形式，磷酸和糖与 DNA 骨架的密度相匹配，扭转角则经调整恢复至大致正确的碱基对几何学结构。亨德里克森－康纳特的限制最小二乘修正程序 [16]，经由奎格利（麻省理工学院）改进后可以接受核酸的坐标，用于加入碱基对的氢键限制，从而重构理想的几何图形。接下来进行更深入的手动调整，进行周期性正则化。使用 FRODO 程序，蛋白质 1~58 位的氨基酸残基被构建到密度图中，并进行正则化调整。最后，利用约束－限制最小二乘法修正软件 CORELS [17]，将碱基对的氢键限制加到 DNA 上，使蛋白质和 DNA 坐标正则化。

按如上所述构建的初始模型，可用来获得第二轮非晶体学对称相位修正的初始相位。该晶体存在各向异性，堆积的蛋白质–DNA 复合物在非晶体学对称轴的方向上可以在 3.2 Å 的分辨率处测得强度，而在其他方向则只能在 4.5 Å 的分辨率处测得 [10]。因此，可以将密度图看作是 3.2 Å 分辨率处获得的，但在垂直于非晶体学对称轴的方向上有些选择性"模糊"。然而，在搭建模型时，沿着常规对称轴的位置伴随着立体化学的限制。因此有效的分辨率介于两个极限之间。就 5 Å 的分辨率而言，衍射强度的衰减相对来说是各向相同的，在此分辨率下计算得到的结构因子被用于一个转化搜索程序（阿加沃尔，个人交流）来进行 3_1 轴位置的最终调整。通过布里科涅密度重建程序 [13] 将各向异性和非晶体学对称性结合到快速傅里叶变换（FFT）结构因子计算当中 [18]，从以非晶体学对称轴为 Z 轴的坐标系中计算出的半复合物"密度图"得到了完整的晶体学非对称单元。这种坐标系的选择简化了单轴向、各向异性的"温度因子"的引入。通过对振幅计算值和观察值的比较，测定了 Bx=By 与 Bz 的不同比值。结合 R 因子最小值和相应 $2F_o$–F_c 和 F_o–F_c 差值图噪音的相对缺乏判定最佳比值为 1.75。

利用初始模型的相位对 15 Å 到 3.2 Å 之间的非晶体学对称相位进行进一步的八轮修正。计算值稳定地收敛于 R_{av}=0.27，整体的相位角改变为 43°（表 2，下部）。重要的调整在密度图中做了标示，并且我们将模型从第 58 位的残基拓展到 63 位（图 1）。根据 $2F_o$–F_c 和 F_o–F_c 差值密度图又进一步进行了两轮更小的调整。不同阶段的密度

were based on $2F_o-F_c$ and F_o-F_c maps. Maps and coordinates at various stages are shown in Fig. 2. It is evident that the second round of non-crystallographic-symmetry refinement substantially improved phase determination. Base-pair and side-chain densities became far clearer and peptide-backbone density more continuous. Poor placement of some side chains of the initial model did not prevent appearance of density in correct positions in the final map, showing that errors in that model did not unduly bias the outcome of the phase refinement (Fig. 2b and c). The use of an intermediate model to initiate a second round of phase refinement was used in determining the turnip crinkle virus structure, where similar corrections to an actual structure were generated[19]. The power of threefold non-crystallographic redundancy in phase refinement has been amply demonstrated in previous work—for example, in the determination of the influenza virus haemagglutinin structure, with data of comparable accuracy to ours[20]. Reciprocal-space refinement of the model is in progress. The R-factor of the model presented here is 0.44. (H. Holley, J.E.A. and S.C.H. unpublished data).

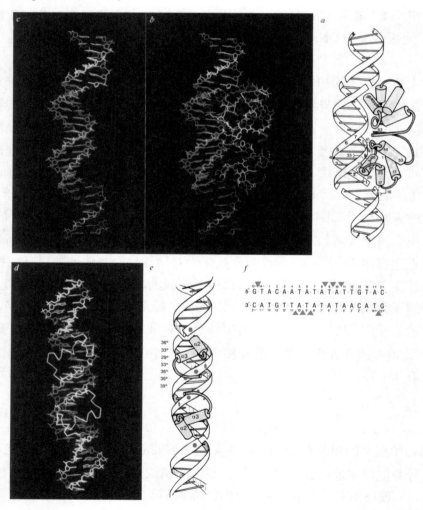

Fig. 1. Diagram summarizing the elements of the 434 repressor–operator complex, in an orientation

图和坐标系如图 2 所示。很明显，非晶体学对称性的第二轮修正从根本上改善了相位的确定。碱基对和侧链的密度变得更加清晰，多肽骨架的密度也更加连续。起始模型中某些侧链较差的定位并没有影响其在最终密度图中的正确位置，这说明模型中的错误没有使相位修正后的结果偏移（图 2b 和 c）。在芜菁皱缩病毒结构的测定过程中曾利用中间模型来起始第二轮的相位修正，也生成了对实际结构的类似修正[19]。三重非晶体学冗余度在相位修正中的作用已在先前的工作中得到充分展示——例如，在测定流感病毒血细胞凝集素的结构时，数据的准确度与我们的相近[20]。模型的倒易空间修正正在进行中。本文中模型的 R 因子为 0.44（霍利、安德森和哈里森，未发表数据）。

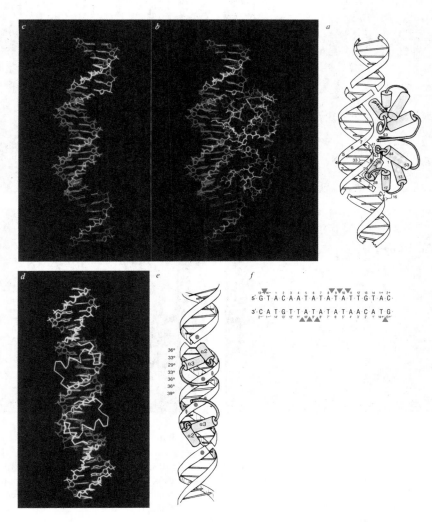

图 1. 434 阻遏蛋白-操纵基因复合物中各要素的总结性图示，其方向与图 b 所示的计算机模拟图对应。

corresponding to the computer-graphics display in *b*. R1-69 α-helices are represented as cylinders and non-helical polypeptide chain as tubes. In the lower R1-69 monomer, key residues are shown and the numbers of the first and last residues in each α-helix are also entered. Numbers along ribbon indicate DNA base pairs (See *f*). *b*, Overall view of the 434 repressor-operator complex. The central 14mer (red) is bound to two R1-69 domains (light blue and dark blue). Adjacent 14mers, stacked as in the crystal, are also shown (violet). The view is perpendicular to the operator dyad, which lies in the centre of the diagram. *c*, DNA alone, viewed as in *b*, to show bend. Note variation of minor groove width. *d*, DNA and part of protein, seen as if viewed from the right in *a* or *b*. Residues 16–44 are represented by Cα backbone. *e*, Diagram summarizing DNA conformation and backbone contacts, drawn to correspond to the view in *d*. The numbers to the left of the diagram indicate twist in degrees between base pairs, calculated using the method of Kabsch[36] after obtaining the best visual superposition of each base pair on the next. *f*, Sequence of 14mer, together with numbering scheme used in the text. Symbols + and − refer to adjacent 14mers as packed in the crystal. Two base pairs of each adjacent 14mer are shown. Arrows refer to phosphates at which ethylation interferes with binding[22].

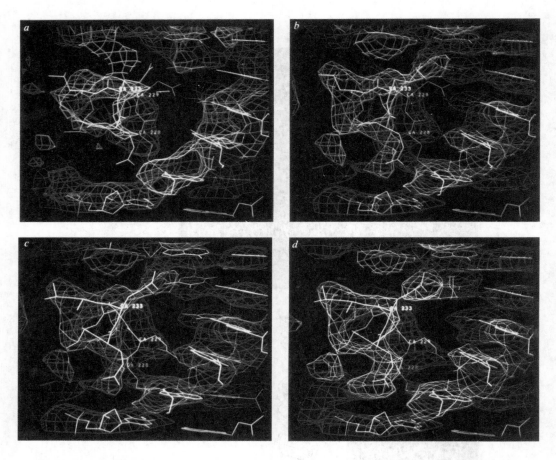

Fig. 2. Part of the electron density maps at different stages of the structure determination, showing the N-terminal half of α3 and portions of base pairs 1–4. Models are superimposed on density. The helix α3 is viewed from the C-terminal end, with residues 28–34 (QQSIEQL) shown and α-carbons of residues 28, 29 and 33 labelled (228, 229 and 233, respectively). *a*, Map after refinement of SIR phases, with initial model superimposed. *b*, Map after refinement of phases determined from initial model, with initial model superimposed. Note clear indications for repositioning of side chains, especially Gln 28 and Gln 29 (background) and Gln 32 (foreground). *c*, Same map as in *b*, but with rebuilt model. *d*, Final $(2F_o–F_c)$ map, with rebuilt model.

R1-69 的 α 螺旋显示为柱状图形，非螺旋的多肽链则显示为管状。在位于下方的 R1-69 单体中显示了关键残基，也标注了每个螺旋起始和结束的残基序号。在 DNA 带上的数字则是 DNA 的碱基对编号（见图 f）。b，434 阻遏蛋白-操纵基因复合物的整体视图。中间的 14 碱基对（红色）DNA 序列与两个 R1-69 结构域（浅蓝色和深蓝色）结合。在晶体中堆叠的相邻 14 碱基对 DNA 在图中也有显示（紫色）。观察方向与反向重复的操纵基因是垂直的，它位于图的中央。c，将 DNA 单独画出以显示其弯曲，观察方向与 b 一样。请注意小沟宽度的变化。d，DNA 和部分蛋白质，观察方向是从 a 或 b 的右侧看过来。残基 16～44 用 Cα 骨架标出。e，DNA 构象和骨架接触的总结性图示，观察方向与 d 对应。图形左侧的数字为碱基对之间的扭转角，在获得了每个碱基对相对于下一个的最佳视觉重合效果之后使用卡卜什法 [36] 计算得到。f，14 碱基对的序列以及正文中使用的编号体系。符号 + 和 − 表示在晶体中相邻的 14 碱基对。图中标示了两头相邻的 14 碱基对中的两个碱基对。箭头指示乙酰化会干扰其结合能力的磷酸基团 [22]。

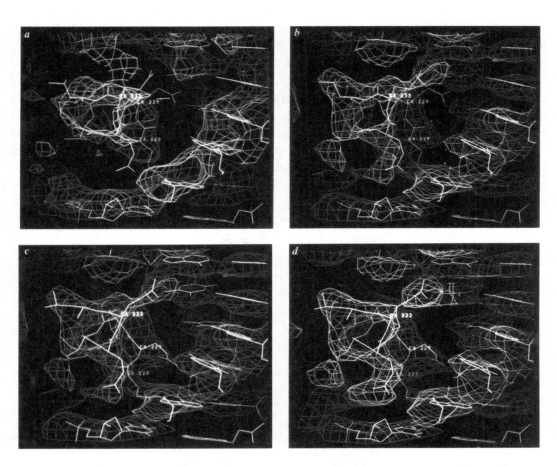

图 2. 结构测定过程中不同阶段的部分电子密度图，显示的是 α3 的 N 末端和碱基对 1~4 的部分。模型叠加在密度图上。观察方向是从螺旋 α3 的 C 端看该螺旋，显示了残基 28~34（QQSIEQL）和标记的残基 28、29 和 33 的 α 碳原子（分别对应 228、229 和 233）。a，单对同晶置换相位修正后的密度图，初始模型叠加其上。b，起始模型相位修正后的密度图，初始模型叠加其上。注意侧链位置变清晰了，特别是第 28 位谷氨酰胺（Gln 28）和 Gln 29（背景）以及 Gln 32（前景）。c，和 b 中相同的密度图，但叠加了重建的模型。d，最后的 $(2F_o - F_c)$ 图，叠加了重建的模型。

As in any structure determination at this resolution, interactions such as hydrogen bonds must be inferred from the position and orientation of the participating groups. We believe our present structure to be sufficiently well determined that the protein–DNA interactions can be described correctly and that likely hydrogen bonds can be assigned. More precise conformational details, accurate hydrogen-bond geometry, contact distances and features such as the positions of water molecules—all of which may be significant for complete understanding of specificity—will only be visible at the higher resolution afforded by a different R1-69–operator crystal currently being studied (A. Aggarwal and S.C.H. unpublished data).

DNA Conformation

The DNA of the 14mer forms a B-type helix throughout its length. The 14mers are stacked accurately on adjacent DNA segments to form a pseudocontinuous helix. The local twist varies from about 39° to 29° per base pair—that is, from 9.2 to 12.3 base pairs per turn (Fig. 1e). A similar range of variation in twist has been found in crystalline B-DNA[21]. With respect to the average of 10.5 base pairs per turn, the 14mer is overwound at its centre and underwound at its ends. The helix axis bends somewhat, causing the DNA to curl slightly around helix 3 of each monomer. The bend is sharpest between base pairs 4 and 5 (and 10 and 11), with relatively more gentle bending between base pairs 1 and 4, between base pairs 5 and 10, and between base pairs 11 and 14. Overwinding and bending in the centre of the DNA fragment narrows the minor groove. Underwinding and bending widens it at the ends. This variation is evident in Figs 1 and 3.

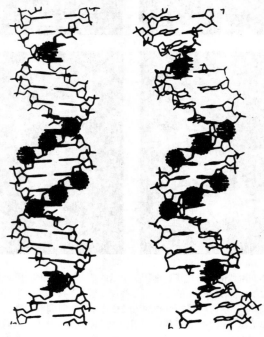

Fig. 3. Conformation of DNA in the crystalline complex (right) compared with idealized, 10.5-bp-per-turn B-DNA (left). Contacted phosphates are highlighted. It is clear from this figure, and from Fig. 1, that model building with idealized B-DNA could not correctly predict the protein–DNA contacts.

　　如同在这个分辨率下的任何结构测定，像氢键这样的相互作用必须从参与基团的位置和取向来推断。我们相信现在的结构已经得到了非常好的确定，可以正确的显示蛋白质–DNA 的相互作用以及可能的氢键。更多精确的构象细节、准确的氢键几何图形、作用距离及其他特征，如水分子的位置等——所有这些都可能对完全理解 DNA 与蛋白质结合的特异性具有重要的意义——将会在一个不同的 R1-69 阻遏蛋白晶体所提供的更高分辨率结构中得以展示，该晶体目前还在研究中（阿加沃尔和哈里森，未发表数据）。

DNA 的构象

　　14 碱基对的 DNA 在其整个长度上形成了一个 B 型螺旋。相邻的 14 碱基对 DNA 精确地堆叠成伪连续螺旋。每个碱基对形成的局部扭转从 39°到 29°不等——这样每一圈就有 9.2 到 12.3 个碱基对（如图 1e）。类似的扭转变化范围在结晶的 B 型 DNA 中已经发现 [21]。就平均每圈 10.5 个碱基对而言，14 碱基对的 DNA 在中心部分卷得太紧，而在末端则太松。DNA 螺旋轴轻微弯曲，使得它围着每个蛋白单体中的螺旋 3 微小卷曲。这种弯曲在碱基对 4 和 5（及 10 和 11）之间最剧烈，而在碱基对 1 到 4、5 到 10 及 11 到 14 之间相对缓和。DNA 片段在中心的过度扭转和弯曲使得小沟变窄，扭转不足和弯曲则使得末端变宽。在图 1 和图 3 中这种变化非常明显。

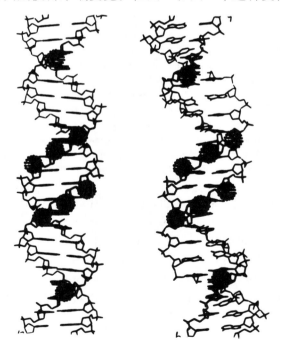

图 3. 结晶复合物中 DNA 的构象（右）与理想状态下每圈 10.5 个碱基对的 B 型 DNA（左）对比。参与接触的磷酸加亮。从这幅图和图 1 中可以很清楚地看到，依据理想的 B 型 DNA 构建的模型不能正确预测蛋白质与 DNA 的接触。

Protein Conformation

R1-69 is a cluster of four α-helices, with a C-terminal extension. Two of the helices, α2 and α3, form a helix–turn–helix motif. The residues found in each of the four helices are shown in Table 3. For comparison, the corresponding residues in the N-terminal domain of λ repressor[5], determined by comparison of the two models, are also listed. As observed in our earlier paper[4], if the 434 and λ α2–α3 structures are superposed, the axes of α1 and α4 in the two repressors coincide to within about 2–3 Å. The α-carbon positions suggest that 434 repressor has "deletion" with respect to λ repressor of two residues between α1 and α2 and of one residue at the beginning of α4. The two models diverge at residue 58 of 434 (corresponding to 75 of λ), precisely the point at which the two amino-acid sequences cease to be similar. Various hydrophobic side-chains form the interior of the four-helix cluster, which is also stabilized by several polar linkages—notably, Gln 17–Glu 32 and Arg 5–Glu 35. The last six residues of R1-69 are poorly defined in our map. They appear to extend toward DNA backbone near P11.

Table 3. Amino-acid residues in α-helices

	434 repressor	λ repressor
α1	1–13	9–23
α2	17–23	33–39
α3	28–36	44–52
α4	44–53	61–69

The Cα backbone of λ repressor N-terminal domain[5] was superimposed on the R1-69 backbone, optimizing coincidence of α2 and α3 (ref. 4). Assignments of helical residues were made by visual inspection of backbone conformation. Residue 15 of λ repressor closely corresponds in three-dimensional position to residue 1 of 434 repressor; 434 repressor lacks the N-terminal arm of λ repressor and the first few residues of α1. The first helix of λ repressor, as built by Pabo and Lewis, ends "earlier" than α1 of 434 repressor (residue 23 of λ corresponds to 9 of 434). The region at the end of α1 was not well-defined in the original λ repressor map, however, and the actual Cα coincidence in α1 may be even greater than suggested by the assignments above. In the present 434 repressor model, residue 27 might also be assigned to helix 3, since its carbonyl appears to hydrogen bond to N31.

Interactions occur between the two R1-69 subunits bound to one 14mer. The two monomers are in contact across the dyad near residues 57–58. The aliphatic chain of Arg 41 and a residue near the C-terminus in one subunit lie against the aromatic ring of Phe 44 in the other subunit. These contacts may be important in determining the relative orientations of the DNA-binding surfaces of the two monomers, thereby defining the required spatial orientation of one operator half-site with respect to the other.

蛋白质的构象

R1-69 是一个由 4 个 α 螺旋构成的簇，并且在 C 端存在延伸。其中螺旋 α2 和 α3 形成一个螺旋－转角－螺旋基序。4 个螺旋中每个螺旋的氨基酸残基如表 3 所示。为了方便比较，在表中还列出了 λ 阻遏蛋白[5] N 端结构域中相应的残基，这些位置是通过比较两个模型而确定的。如我们以前发表的文章所述 [4]，若将噬菌体 434 阻遏蛋白和 λ 阻遏蛋白的螺旋 α2~α3 重叠，可以发现这两个阻遏蛋白的 α1 和 α4 的轴几乎重合，仅有 2~3Å 的微小差别。α 碳的位置显示，相比于 λ 阻遏蛋白，434 阻遏蛋白缺失了螺旋 α1 和 α2 间的两个残基以及 α4 起始处的一个残基。两个模型在 434 的 58 位残基（对应于 λ 的 75 位残基）出现分歧，也正是从这个位置开始两个蛋白的氨基酸序列不再相似。各种疏水侧链组成四螺旋簇的内部结构，该结构还因几个极性键而得以稳定——尤其是 Gln 17–Glu 32 间和 Arg 5–Glu 35 间的联接。R1-69 的最后六个残基在我们的电子密度图上不是很明确。它们似乎朝着 P11 附近的 DNA 骨架延伸。

表 3. α 螺旋中的氨基酸残基

	434 阻遏蛋白	λ 阻遏蛋白
α1	1~13	9~23
α2	17~23	33~39
α3	28~36	44~52
α4	44~53	61~69

λ 阻遏蛋白 N 端结构域的 Cα 骨架[5] 叠加在 R1-69 骨架上，使 α2 和 α3 的相合性最佳（参考文献 4）。α 螺旋残基的分配是根据骨架构象的视图而定的。三维位置中 λ 阻遏蛋白的 15 位残基与 434 阻遏蛋白的第 1 位残基相对应；434 阻遏蛋白缺少 λ 阻遏蛋白的 N 末端臂和 α1 起始位置的一些残基。λ 阻遏蛋白的第一个螺旋是由帕博和刘易斯构建的，比 434 阻遏蛋白的 α1 结束的"更早"（λ 的残基 23 与 434 的残基 9 相对应）。然而，在原先的 λ 阻遏蛋白密度图中 α1 的末端区域并不清晰，实际的 α1 的 Cα 相合性可能要比上述残基分配所得到的更好些。在现有的 434 阻遏蛋白的模型中，27 位残基也可能属于螺旋 3，因为它的羰基似乎与 N31 形成氢键。

与一个 14 碱基对的 DNA 结合的两个 R1-69 亚基间会发生相互作用。两个单体在残基 57~58 处相接触。一个亚基中的 Arg 41 的脂肪族侧链和邻近 C 端的一个残基依靠在另一个亚基的 Phe 44 的芳香族环上。这些接触可能在确定两个单体的 DNA 结合表面的相对取向上很重要，从而决定了操纵基因的半位点相对于另一个半位点所需的空间取向。

Protein–DNA Contacts

The polypeptide chain is so folded that in the complex the N-termini of α-helices 2, 3 and 4 all point toward the DNA backbone, α3 lies in the major groove, and the loop joining α3 and α4 runs along the DNA backbone (Fig. 1*d*). Contacts to DNA backbone from one R1-69 subunit occur on both sides of the major groove that is occupied by α3 and possibly across the minor groove that contains the operator dyad. Major-groove interactions with base pairs 1–5 and 10–14 are made by three glutamine side chains projecting from α3. These relationships are summarized in Figs 1*d* and *e*, and described in detail below.

Backbone contacts. Four phosphate groups per half-site, corresponding precisely to the phosphates implicated by ethylation interference experiments[22], appear to interact with protein. Considering half of the complex, the contact phosphate groups lie 5′ to bases 14-, 9′, 10′ and 11′ (see Fig. 1*f* for numbering scheme). The P14- contact occurs between different complexes in the crystal. Because the stacking of 14mers mimics continuous DNA, we believe that the interaction we observe at P14- closely reflects the one actually made in continuous DNA.

The three tightest contacts (as judged both from the structure and by the strength of ethylation interference) all appear to involve peptide backbone NH groups. At P14-, the NH of Gln 17 approaches the phosphate oxygens closely enough to form a hydrogen bond. Residue 17 is at the N-terminus of α2, and its peptide NH group is expected to make a particularly strong hydrogen bond to a negatively charged ion, as a result of oriented peptide dipoles in the α-helix[23]. Analogous interactions occur in the *Salmonella typhimurium* sulphate binding protein, where peptide NH groups at the N-termini of α helices are ligands of bound SO_4^{2-} ions[24]. The side chain of Asn 16 also appears to be involved in the contact to P14-. At P9′, there is close approach of the main chain NH groups of Lys 40 and Arg 41; the side-chain conformation of Arg 41 permits a salt link with the same phosphate (Fig. 4). At P10′, there is close approach of the peptide NH groups of both Arg 43 and Phe 44 (Fig. 4). Phe 44 is the amino-terminal residue of α4. The use of peptide NH groups to contact phosphates may be a common feature in proteins that bind DNA and nucleotides. Dreusicke and Schulz[25] have described a "giant anion hole" at the site in adenylate kinase where a nucleotide phosphoryl group is believed to be located. The polypeptide chain loops in such a way that five peptide NH groups coordinate a bound sulphate in their crystal structure.

蛋白质-DNA 的相互作用

复合物中的多肽链高度折叠，以至于 α 螺旋 2、3 和 4 的 N 端都指向 DNA 骨架，α3 位于 DNA 大沟内，且连接 α3 和 α4 的环也沿着 DNA 的骨架行走（如图 1d）。一个 R1-69 亚基与 DNA 骨架的接触发生在被 α3 占据的大沟的两侧，并有可能穿过包含有反向重复操纵基因的小沟。与碱基对 1~5 以及 10~14 发生的大沟相互作用是通过从螺旋 α3 中伸出的三个谷氨酰胺侧链实现的。这些作用关系在图 1d 和 e 中进行了总结，详情如下所述。

骨架的接触。每个半位点有四个磷酸基团可能与蛋白质相互作用，这些磷酸基团精确对应于乙酰化干扰实验所指向的磷酸基团 [22]。就复合物的一半而言，参与接触的磷酸基团位于碱基 14-、9′、10′ 和 11′ 的 5′ 端（见图 1f 的编号体系）。P14- 的接触发生在晶体中不同的复合物之间。因为 14 碱基对的堆叠模拟了连续的 DNA，所以我们认为我们观察到的 P14- 的接触作用近似地体现了连续 DNA 实际发生作用时的情况。

三个最紧密的接触（根据结构和乙酰化干扰强度来判断）看来都涉及多肽骨架的 NH 基团。在 P14- 位，氨基酸 Gln 17 的 NH 基团足够接近磷酸基团中的氧，形成氢键。残基 17 位于螺旋 α2 的 N 末端，由于 α 螺旋中定向的肽偶极 [23]，使得肽的 NH 基可以与负离子产生非常强烈的氢键作用。相似的相互作用见于鼠伤寒沙门氏杆菌硫酸结合蛋白中，α 螺旋 N 末端的肽 NH 基团是其上结合的硫酸根离子的配体 [24]。Asn 16 的侧链也可能与 P14- 相接触。在 P9′ 位点上，主链上 NH 基团与 Lys 40 和 Arg 41 很接近；Arg 41 侧链的构象可以使其与同一个磷酸基团形成盐键（图 4）。在 P10′ 位点上，肽链 NH 基团与 Arg 43 和 Phe 44 都非常接近（图 4）。Phe 44 是螺旋 α4 的氨基末端的残基。利用肽 NH 基团与磷酸基团作用可能是结合 DNA 和核苷酸的蛋白质的普遍特征。德勒西克和舒尔茨 [25] 已经描述了在腺苷酸激酶中有一个"巨大的阴离子洞"，该位置被认为结合了一个核苷酸磷基团。它们的晶体结构中多肽链以一定的方式环化，使五个肽 NH 基团与一个硫酸根相协调。

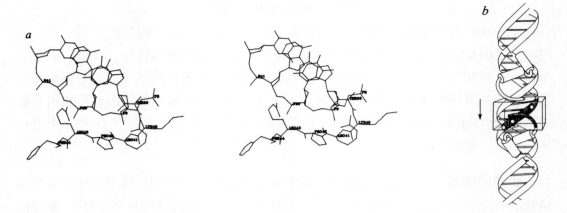

Fig. 4. Stereo view of contacts between protein and DNA phosphates P9' and P10'. *b*, Schematic diagram as a key to *a*. The view is of the region indicated in the (shaded structures), looking approximately along the DNA axis (arrow). Compare key with Fig. 1*e*. Residues 39–44 of the protein are shown, together with nucleotides 8'–11'. (Primes are omitted in the labels.)

The side chain of Arg 43 projects into the minor groove near base pair 7. The groove is somewhat narrower than average at this position, and the guanidinium group could probably have significant coulombic interaction with phosphates 9 and 10' on either side of the groove (Fig. 4). The possibility of direct interaction with base pair 7 is discussed in the next section and in the accompanying paper.

The ethylation of P11 interferes more weakly with binding than ethylation of P14-, P9' or P10' (ref. 22). Thr 26 appears to contact P11', and the C-terminal residues of the other monomer may also lie in this vicinity. Because the C-terminal residues are not well defined in our map, we cannot at present determine whether any actually engage in backbone contacts. If they do, the interaction may help establish the favoured relative orientation of the two operator half-sites, because an R1-69 domain bound in one half-site would make contact by its C terminus with DNA backbone in the other half-site.

Base-pair contacts. Three glutamines (residues 28, 29 and 33) project from α3 into the major groove (Fig. 5). Gln 28 approaches A1 (base pair 1) in such a way that hydrogen bonds can readily form between N7 of the base and Nε of the glutamine and between N6 and Oε. "Bidentate" H-bonding of this type was suggested as a mode of adenine-specific interaction by Seeman *et al.*[26]. Gln 29 lies along α3. Its Cβ and Cγ are in van der Waals contact with the 5-methyl group of T12' (base pair 3), and its Nε can hydrogen bond to O6 (and perhaps also N7) of G13' (base pair 2). The Oε of Gln 29 may hydrogen bond to its main chain NH, an interaction occasionally seen with glutamine at amino termini of α-helices[27]. This hydrogen bond would fix the orientation of the glutamine and point the Nε donor group directly at G13'. Gln 33 projects toward T11' and A10' (base pairs 4 and 5). There could be a hydrogen bond between Nε of Gln 33 and O4 of T11' (base pair 4), and perhaps between Oε and N6 of A10' (base pair 5); a refined model will be required for confident assignment.

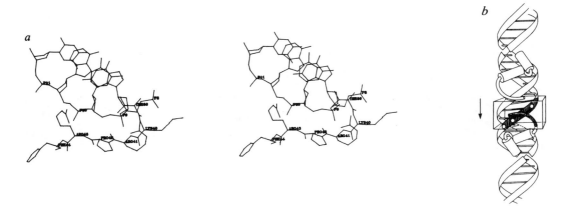

图 4. 蛋白质和 DNA 磷酸基团 P9′ 和 P10′ 接触的立体视图。b，作为 a 图索引的概要图。图中标出了 a 图所描述的具体位置（阴影结构），观察方向是沿着 DNA 的轴向（箭头所指）。参考图 1e 的标示。显示的是蛋白质 39~44 的残基和核酸的 8′~11′ 的碱基对。（标注省略了）

Arg 43 的侧链伸入小沟中第 7 个碱基对附近。此位置的小沟要比平均宽度更窄些，胍基很可能与位于小沟任一侧的磷酸 9 和 10′ 有显著的库仑相互作用（图 4）。与碱基对 7 直接作用的可能性将在下一节和本期另一篇相关文章里讨论。

P11 的乙酰化对结合的干扰作用比 P14-、P9′ 或 P10′ 弱（参见参考文献 22）。Thr 26 看来与 P11′ 相接触，而另一个单体的 C 端残基可能也位于这一区域附近。由于在我们的密度图上 C 端残基不清晰，因而现在不能确定其是否参与了骨架的接触。如果它们参与了接触，这个相互作用可能会帮助两个操纵基因半位点建立最惠的相对取向，因为结合在一个半位点上的 R1-69 结构域会使其 C 末端与另一个半位点的 DNA 骨架相接触。

碱基对的接触。螺旋 α3 中的三个谷氨酰胺（残基 28、29 和 33）从大沟中伸出（如图 5）。Gln 28 接近 A1（碱基对 1），从而使碱基的 N7 与 Gln 的 Nε、碱基的 N6 与 Gln 的 Oε 之间形成氢键。这种"双配位"氢键类型被西曼等人描述为腺嘌呤特异性的相互作用模式[26]。Gln 29 位于螺旋 α3。它的 Cβ 和 Cγ 与 T12′（碱基对 3）的 5-甲基基团通过范德华作用相接触，其 Nε 可以与 G13′（碱基对 2）的 O6（也可能是 N7）形成氢键。Gln 29 的 Oε 可能与其主链上的 NH 基团形成氢键，这种相互作用偶尔存在于 α 螺旋氨基末端的 Gln[27]。这个氢键可以固定 Gln 的取向，将 Nε 供体基团直接指向 G13′。Gln 33 指向 T11′ 和 A10′（碱基对 4 和 5）。在 Gln 33 的 Nε 和 T11′（碱基对 4）的 O4 之间可能有氢键，在 Oε 和 A10′（碱基对 5）的 N6 之间也可能有；这需要一个修正的模型来准确地推断。

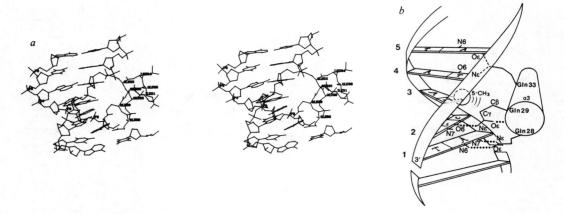

Fig. 5. *a*, Stereo view of helix α3 and base pairs 1–5, viewed from the N-terminus of α3. One base pair of the adjacent 14-mer is also present. Included are residues 28–35 of R1-69. *b*, Schematic diagram as a key to *a*. Note the similarity to view of α3 and surrounding structure in the lower monomer of Fig. 1*c*. Gln 28, Gln 29 and Gln 33 are shown, with hydrogen bonds suggested by the current model drawn in dotted lines. Functional groups on bases and on Gln 33 that might participate in additional hydrogen bonds are also shown. The proposed non-polar contact between the 5-CH₃ group of T12′ (base pair 3) and Cβ and Cγ of Gln is indicated.

The present model shows no direct interactions with base-pairs 6 and 7. Although residues 64–69 are not well defined in the map they are clearly excluded from the major groove on the near side of the operator by α3 and from the minor groove by residues 40–44. Moreover, model building indicates that there is no reasonable possibility of base-pair contact from these residues in the major groove on the far side of the DNA.

Contributions to Specificity

Three different features of the DNA structure appear to be significant for specificity: (1) the groups accessible in the major groove on base pairs 1–5, (2) the conformational details of the half-sites, and (3) the overwinding of the central base pair steps with a narrowing of the minor groove. These features are relevant to different classes of interactions made by the protein. (1) Side chains from α3 contact base pairs in the major groove. (2) Peptide amino groups, as well as side chains from various residues, contact backbone phosphates in ways that constrain the conformation of the operator half-sites. (3) Dimer interactions between repressor monomers favour a particular spatial relationship between half-sites.

Base-pair contacts. The interactions of Gln 28 with base pair 1 and of Gln 29 with base-pairs 2 and 3 are consistent with the conservation of base pairs 1–3 in all 12 operator half-sites, because changes in any of these base pairs would destroy one or more of the hydrogen bonds or disturb van der Waals contacts with the thymine methyl group. (For a list of all naturally-occurring operator sequences, see accompanying paper, ref. 2.) Wharton[3] used a random mutagenesis scheme to generate all possible changes in amino acids 28 and 29. No viable mutants were detected, and indeed no likely substitutions in the model can be imagined. Wharton and Ptashne[28] have also shown that a mutant operator

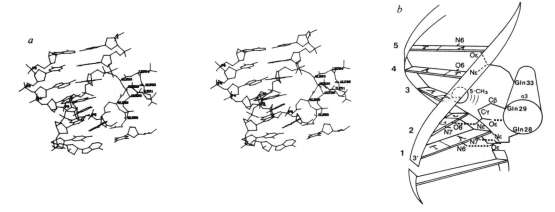

图 5. a，螺旋 α3 和碱基对 1~5 的立体视图，从 α3 的 N 末端观察。并显示了与 14 碱基对相邻的一个碱基对。包括的残基从 R1-69 的 28 至 35 位。b，作为 a 图索引的概要图。注意本图与图 1c 下方单体中 α3 及周围的结构相似。图中显示了 Gln 28、Gln 29 和 Gln 33，当前模型中的氢键用虚线表示。碱基 Gln 33 中可能参与附加氢键作用的功能基团也有所显示。我们提出的 T12′（碱基对 3）的 5-甲基基团与 Gln 的 Cβ 和 Cγ 之间的非极性接触也标示了。

目前的模型显示碱基对 6 和 7 之间没有直接作用。虽然残基 64~69 在密度图上不能很清晰地看到，然而它们清楚地被螺旋 α3 排除在操纵基因近侧大沟外并被残基 40~44 排除在小沟外。而且，模型构建显示位于 DNA 大沟较远一侧的残基没有合理的可能性去参与碱基对接触。

对特异性的贡献

DNA 结构的三个不同特征似乎对于特异性有重要意义：（1）大沟中碱基对 1~5 的基团是容易接近的，(2) 半位点的构象细节,(3) 中间碱基对的过旋使得小沟变窄。这些特征是和蛋白质不同类型的相互作用相关的。（1）α3 的侧链与大沟中的碱基对接触。(2) 肽链上的氨基基团以及来自不同残基的侧链与磷酸骨架接触，从而限制操纵基因半位点的构象。(3) 阻遏蛋白单体之间形成二聚体的相互作用促成半位点之间形成的特殊空间关系。

碱基对的接触。Gln 28 与碱基对 1 以及 Gln 29 与碱基对 2 和 3 的相互作用与所有 12 个操纵基因半位点中碱基对 1~3 的保守性是一致的，因为这些碱基对中任意一个的改变都会破坏一个或者多个氢键，或者打乱与胸腺嘧啶甲基基团的范德华接触。（所有天然操纵基因序列的清单请参见本期另一篇相关文章，参考文献 2）沃顿[3] 使用了一种随机突变策略在氨基酸 28 和 29 位置上产生所有可能的变化。我们没有检测到可行的突变，事实上，在模型中不可能存在合适的取代。沃顿和普塔什尼[28] 已

with T instead of A at position 1 is recognized specifically by a mutant repressor with alanine at position 28. These coordinated changes can be built into the model, generating a van der Waals contact between the —CH_3 group of T1 and the —CH_3 side chain of Ala 28.

The side chain of Gln 33 is in position to contact base pairs 4 and 5. The model shows that this residue could hydrogen bond to either base 11' or 10', or to both (Fig. 5). Wharton[3] has studied the effects of substituting Ala for Gln 33 on the binding of repressor to various operators. His results, taken with others (R. Wharton and M.P. unpublished data), are consistent with the idea that residue 33 indeed contacts positions 4 and 5.

Backbone contacts. Within a half-site, contacts to the DNA backbone position a subunit of the protein against the operator. The relationship is likely to be quite exact, because main-chain peptide amino groups participate in the contacts and the main chain of a folded protein is generally less flexible than the side chains. The backbone contacts, especially the one at P14-, require a gently bent outer operator[22]. This curvature is essential for at least one of the major groove contacts: without it, the interaction between Gln 28 and A1 would not have the correct geometry. It is not yet clear whether the bend is present in unbound operator DNA, or whether protein binding induces it.

Central base pairs. The configuration of the operator at its central base pairs is consistent with sequence preferences at positions 6–9. A more detailed discussion appears in the accompanying paper, but we summarize the arguments here. The twist is about 36° between base pairs 6 and 7 and base pairs 8 and 9 and 39° between base pairs 7 and 8 (Fig. 1e). The minor groove is consequently 2.5 Å narrower than in idealized B-DNA. It is believed that GC or CG base pairs are not well accommodated in a narrow minor groove[29], and repressor indeed discriminates against GC or CG at positions 6–9 (ref. 2). The sequence preferences at central base pairs persist when alanine is substituted for Arg 43, which projects into the minor groove. The position of the guanidinium group in the present model does not indicate hydrogen bonding to bases, and the binding affinities of the Ala 43 mutant show that any minor-groove contacts that are made do not contribute significantly to sequence discrimination at positions 6–9. We therefore believe that it is the DNA conformation, rather than contacts to the bases themselves, that influences binding.

How does the structure in the centre of the operator influence affinity? One explanation is that a particular conformation is required for correct relative orientation of the two half-sites. Though monomeric at most concentrations in solution, the two R1-69 domains in the complex with DNA have significant interactions, including complementary packing of parts of each subunit that are important for DNA backbone contacts (especially residues 41–44: see Fig. 4). Thus, the relative orientation of monomer DNA-binding surfaces is influenced by interactions between individual R1-69 subunits. The tightly structured repressor domain binds to a half-site in a precise way. Any variation in twist or bend at the central base pairs changes the spatial relationship of the two half-sites and requires compensatory variation in the protein dimer contacts, with a corresponding loss

经证实第一位的 A 突变为 T 的操纵基因可以被 28 位突变为丙氨酸的阻遏蛋白特异性识别。这些相互协调的改变可以构建进模型中，在 T1 的甲基基团和 Ala 28 的甲基侧链之间产生范德华接触。

Gln 33 的侧链所处的位置使其能与碱基对 4 和 5 相接触。模型显示这个残基可以与碱基 11′ 或 10′ 或二者形成氢键（图 5）。沃顿[3] 已经研究了将阻遏蛋白的 Gln 33 突变为丙氨酸后与不同操纵基因的结合能力。他的结果与其他人的结果（沃顿和普塔什尼的未发表数据）一致，即残基 33 的确与碱基对 4 和 5 位点相接触。

骨架的接触。 在一个半位点内，与 DNA 骨架的接触促使阻遏蛋白的一个亚基处于与操纵基因相对的位置。这种关系可能是非常精确的，因为主链的多肽氨基基团参与到了接触中，且已经折叠好的蛋白质的主链通常不如侧链柔软。骨架的接触，特别是在 P14- 处的接触，需要一个微微向外弯曲的操纵基因[22]。这种弯曲对至少一个数量的大沟接触是必要的：如果没有它，Gln 28 与 A1 间的相互作用将不会有正确的几何结构。目前还不清楚这种弯曲是否存在于未被结合的操纵基因 DNA 中，或者是否由蛋白的结合所诱导。

中央的碱基对。 操纵基因中央碱基对的构型与其在 6~9 的位置上的序列偏好性一致。在本期另一篇文章中有更加详尽的讨论，这里我们只进行观点的总结。在碱基对 6 和 7 之间、8 和 9 之间的扭转角都为 36°，在碱基对 7 和 8 之间的扭转角为 39°（图 1e）。结果，小沟比理想状态的 B 型 DNA 窄了 2.5 Å。据信碱基对 GC 或 CG 碱基对不能很好地安置在狭窄的小沟中[29]，事实上阻遏蛋白不识别位于 6~9 的 GC 和 CG（参考文献 2）。当 Arg 43 突变为丙氨酸后，伸入小沟中，中间碱基对序列的偏好性依旧存在。在本模型中胍基并没有与碱基形成氢键，Ala 43 突变体的结合亲和力实验显示任何与小沟的接触没有明显影响其对 6~9 序列的辨别力。因此，我们认为是 DNA 的构象而不是与碱基对自身的接触影响了结合。

位于操纵基因中央的结构是怎样影响亲和性的呢？一种解释是两个半位点之间正确的相对取向需要特定的构象。尽管在多种浓度的溶液中该蛋白均以单体形式存在，然而在与 DNA 形成的复合物中两个 R1-69 的结构域有显著的相互作用，包括每个亚基中对 DNA 骨架的接触非常重要的那些部分互补堆积（特别是残基 41~44：见图 4）。因此与 DNA 结合的单体表面的相对取向受到单个 R1-69 亚基间相互作用的影响。结构紧密的阻遏蛋白结构域精确地结合到半位点上。中央碱基扭转或弯曲的任何变化都会改变两个半位点的空间关系，要求在蛋白二聚体的接触上做出补偿性的改变，导致复合物的整体能量得到相应的损失。我们估计完整的阻遏蛋白二聚

in the overall energy of the complex. We expect dimer contacts to be more extensive and less deformable in the intact repressor, and indeed alterations in central base-pair sequence have greater effects on the binding of the intact molecule than on R1-69 (ref. 2). Analogous mechanisms have been suggested on the basis of indirect evidence as a contribution to the specificity of SV40 T antigen[30].

The conformation of operator bound to a dimer of R1-69 is likely to differ from the equilibrium structure of the DNA in solution, but the base sequence will in any case affect flexibility and hence its propensity to reconfigure on binding. An even greater perturbation has been seen in the complex of *Eco*RI endonuclease with its DNA binding site, where an effective unwinding of about 25° occurs at the centre of the symmetrical sequence[31]. The unwinding induced by the endonuclease is important for appropriate alignment of protein–DNA interactions on either side.

The general notion that sequence-dependent aspects of DNA conformation can influence affinity of specific binding proteins has been discussed by Dickerson[32]. The characteristics that we see here to be necessary for a good fit, both within a half-site and between half-sites, appear to be examples of such conformational effects, but the specific "rules" developed by Dickerson[32] may not be straightforwardly applicable[2].

Operator Recognition

The tight fit between 434 repressor and DNA could not be achieved with a random 14-bp sequence. We suppose that in a non-specific complex, the repressor would be displaced by 2–3 Å outward from the DNA axis, to accommodate non-optimal major-groove interactions, and that the peptide backbone–DNA backbone hydrogen bonds would be lost. Residues such as Arg 41 (which must curl back toward a phosphate in the specific complex) and Arg 43 (which lies in the minor groove) could extend to provide compensating electrostatic stabilization. Such non-specific complexes may be intermediates in operator binding, because proteins like 434 repressor are believed to locate their sites by initial nonspecific interaction with distant sequences, followed by diffusion along the backbone. Record *et al.*[33] have postulated a similar distinction between complexes of *lac* repressor with operator and non-operator sequences.

We do not yet have a complete description of how the 434 repressor distinguishes among its six naturally-occurring operator sites. To summarize our current picture of specific repressor–operator interactions, it is useful to distinguish three zones in a 7-bp half-site. (1) The first three base pairs (ACA...), invariant in all operators (see ref. 2), interact directly with Gln 28 and Gln 29 on α3. Changes at any one of these positions decrease repressor affinity over 150-fold (R. Wharton, personal communication), and indeed no other DNA sequence can be properly complementary to the contact surface presented by the glutamine side chains. (2) The fourth and fifth base pairs both interact with Gln 33. We therefore expect effects of altered base sequence at these positions to be correlated. One of the naturally-occurring operators (O_R3) differs from the others at position 4 in

体的接触范围更广且更不易改变，事实上中央碱基对序列的改变对完整分子的结合能力的影响比对 R1-69 单体更大（参考文献 2）。已有间接证据提示类似的机制对 SV40 T 抗原的特异性有贡献 [30]。

结合了 R1-69 二聚体的操纵基因的构象很可能与在溶液中 DNA 的平衡结构不同，但不论在何种状态，碱基序列都会影响蛋白质的柔性，进而影响其在结合时发生重新装配的倾向。在 EcoRI 限制性内切酶和 DNA 结合位点形成的复合物中发现了一个更大的扰动，在该复合物中回文序列中心产生了大约 25° 的有效解旋 [31]。这种由限制性内切酶诱导产生的解旋对在回文序列任一侧的蛋白质–DNA 相互作用的适当对齐是重要的。

关于 DNA 构象的序列依赖性可以对特异性结合蛋白质的亲和力产生影响的一般观点，迪克森已经讨论过 [32]。我们这里看到的对于无论是在单个半位点内还是半位点间形成好的匹配所必需的构象特征，看来可以作为这种构象效应的一个范例，而迪克森 [32] 推导的特殊"规则"可能并不能直接应用 [2]。

操纵基因的识别

434 阻遏蛋白和 DNA 的紧密匹配并不能用随机的 14 个碱基对序列实现。我们假设在非特异性的复合物中，阻遏蛋白将从 DNA 轴外移 2~3Å，以适应非最佳的大沟相互作用，则多肽骨架和 DNA 骨架之间的氢键作用也将消失。像 Arg 41（在特异性复合物中它必定向磷酸基团后回旋）和 Arg 43（它位于小沟中）这样的残基将可能伸展以补偿静电稳定。这种非特异性的复合物可能是与操纵基因结合的中间体，因为像 434 阻遏物这样的蛋白被认为首先通过非特异性的相互作用与距离较远的序列结合，然后再沿着骨架扩散来定位。雷科德等人 [33] 对 lac 阻遏蛋白与操纵基因和与非操纵基因形成的复合物的区别提出过类似的假说。

我们现在还不能完整地解释 434 阻遏蛋白是如何区分其天然存在的六个操纵基因的位点的。为了总结我们现有的对特异的阻遏蛋白－操纵基因相互作用的理论框架，在 7 个碱基对的半位点中区分三个区域是很有帮助的。（1）前三位的碱基对（ACA…），在所有的操纵基因中是不变的（参见参考文献 2），直接与螺旋 α3 上的 Gln 28 和 Gln 29 作用。改变这些位置中的任何一个碱基都会使阻遏蛋白的亲和力下降超过 150 倍（沃顿，个人交流），事实上，其他 DNA 序列都不能与谷氨酰胺侧链的接触表面正确地互补。（2）第四和第五位碱基对，都与 Gln 33 作用。因此我们预计在这些位置替换碱基序列所造成的影响将是相关的。有一个天然操纵基因（O$_R$3） one half-site, and there is considerable variation among sites at position 5. (3) The sixth and seventh base pairs form no direct contact with protein, and modulation of affinity by sequence variation at these positions occurs through effects on DNA conformation. The corresponding free energy changes are modest (1–2 kcal mol⁻¹), but natural operator sites differ in binding free energy by just such small amounts. The sequences of the six sites vary widely in this zone.

The distinction between these zones is only heuristic and it is clear that a perturbation at one position will affect the fit elsewhere. For example, the entire operator half-site must be configured correctly against the repressor monomer for any of the interactions with base pairs to be meaningful. Given such a configuration, the present description appears to explain many of the observed effects of operator mutations.

We thank Marie Drottar for laboratory assistance and preparation of crystals; R. Crouse for maintaining X-ray apparatus; J. Katz for artwork; A. Aggarwal, A. Mondragon, J. Moulai and G. Quigley for programs and advice; J. Koudelka and R. Wharton for discussion of unpublished results; C. Wolberger and D. C. Wiley for comments and suggestions. J. E. Anderson was a Burroughs Wellcome Fund Fellow of the Life Sciences Research Foundation. The work was supported by a grant from the NIH to S.C.H. and M. P.

(**326**, 846-852, 1987)

J. E. Anderson*, M. Ptashne & S. C. Harrison
Department of Biochemistry and Molecular Biology, Harvard University, Cambridge, Massachusetts 02138, USA
* Present address: Cold Spring Harbor Laboratory, Cold Spring Harbor, Long Island, New York 11724, USA

Received 8 January; accepted 1 April 1987.

References:

1. Ptashne, M. *A Genetic Switch* (Cell Press, Cambridge, Massachusetts, 1986).

2. Koudelka, J., Harrison, S. C. & Ptashne, M. *Nature* **326**, 886-888 (1987).

3. Wharton, R. thesis, Harvard Univ. (1985).

4. Anderson, J., Ptashne, M. & Harrison, S. C. *Nature* **316**, 596-601 (1985).

5. Pabo, C. O. & Lewis, M. *Nature* **298**, 443-447 (1982).

6. Anderson, W. F., Ohlendorf, D. H., Takeda, Y. & Matthews, B. W. *Nature* **290**, 754-758 (1981).

7. McKay, D. B. & Steitz, T. A. *Nature* **290**, 744-749 (1981).

8. Schevitz, R. W., Otwinowski, Z., Joachimiak, A., Lawson, C. L. & Sigler, P. B. *Nature* **317**, 782-786 (1985).

9. Pabo, C. O. & Sauer, R. *Ann. Rev. Biochem.* **53**, 293-321 (1984).

10. Anderson, J., Ptashne, M. & Harrison, S. C. *Proc. Natl. Acad. Sci. U.S.A.* **181**, 1307-1311 (1984).

11. Rossmann, M. G. & Blow, D. M. *Acta crystallogr.* **16**, 39-45 (1973).

12. Bricogne, G. *Acta crystallogr.* A**130**, 395-405 (1974).

13. Bricogne, G. *Acta crystallogr.* A**132**, 832-847 (1976).

14. Hogle, J., Chow, M. & Filman, D. *Science* **229**, 1359 (1985).

15. Jones, T. A. *J. appl. Crystallogr.* **11**, 268-272 (1978).

16. Hendrickson, W. A. & Konnert, J. H. *Biomolecular Structure, Conformation, Function and Evolution* Vol. I (ed. Srinivasan, R.) 43-57 (Pergamon, Oxford, 1981).

17. Sussmann, J., Holbrook, S. R., Church, G. M. & Kim, S.-H. *Acta crystallogr.* **33**, 800-804 (1977).

18. Ten Eyck, L. *Acta. crystallogr.* A**33**, 486-492 (1977).

19. Hogle, J., Maeda, A. & Harrison, S. C. *J. Molec. Biol.* **191**, 625-638 (1986).

在一个半位点中的位置 4 与其他操纵基因不同，而且在位置 5 的位点中有相当大的改变。（3）第六和第七个碱基，与蛋白质没有直接相互作用，这些位置的序列变化可以通过影响 DNA 的构象来调节与蛋白质的亲和力。相应的自由能变化是不大的（1~2 kcal · mol⁻¹），然而天然操纵基因位点在结合自由能上的区别就是通过这样微小的量来体现的。这个区域内六个位点的序列变化是很广泛的。

这些区域间的区别仅仅是启发式的，很显然一个位置的扰动将影响其他位置的匹配。例如，完整的操纵基因半位点必须有对于阻遏蛋白正确的构型从而使得其与碱基对的任何相互作用有意义。有了这样的构型，目前的描述看来能够解释观察到的许多操纵基因突变所产生的影响。

感谢玛丽·德罗塔尔协助实验室工作并制备晶体；感谢克劳斯维护 X 射线装置；感谢卡茨为本文作插图；感谢阿加沃尔、蒙德拉贡、穆莱和奎格利提供程序和建议；感谢考德尔卡和沃顿对未发表结果的讨论；感谢沃尔贝格和威利的评论和建议。安德森是生命科学研究基金会伯勒斯·韦尔科姆基金研究员。这项研究受到国立卫生研究院给予斯蒂芬·哈里森和马克·普塔什尼的基金支持。

（侯彦婕 翻译；吴琳 审稿）

20. Wilson, I. A., Wiley, D. C. & Skehel, J. J. *Nature* **289**, 373-378 (1981).

21. Drew, H. R. *et al. Proc. Natl. Acad. Sci. U.S.A.* **78**, 2179-2183 (1981).

22. Bushman, R., Anderson, J. E., Harrison, S. C. & Ptashne, M. *Nature* **316**, 651-653 (1985).

23. Hol, W. G. J., van Duijnen, P. T. & Berendsen, H. J. C. *Nature* **273**, 443-446 (1978).

24. Pflugrath, J. W. & Quiocho, F. A. *Nature* **314**, 257-260 (1985).

25. Dreusicke, D. & Schulz, G. *FEBS Lett.* **208**, 301-304 (1986).

26. Seeman, N. C., Rosenberg, J. N. & Rich, A. *Proc. Natl. Acad. Sci. U.S.A.* **173**, 804-808 (1976).

27. Baker, E. N. & Hubbard, R. E. *Progr. Biophys. molec. Biol.* **144**, 97-179 (1984).

28. Wharton, R. & Ptashne, M. *Nature* **326**, 888-891 (1987).

29. Drew, H. R. & Travers, A. A. *Cell* **37**, 491-502 (1984).

30. Ryder, K., Silver, S., DeLucia, A. L., Fanning, E. & Tegtmeyer, P. *Cell* **44**, 719-725 (1986).

31. McClarin, J. A. *et al. Science* **234**, 1526-1541 (1986).

32. Dickerson, R. E. *J. Molec. Biol.* **166**, 419-441 (1983).

33. Record, M. T., deHaseth, P. L. & Lohman, T. M. *Biochemistry* **16**, 4791-4796 (1977).

34. Crawford, J. thesis, Harvard Univ. (1977).

35. Durbin, R. *et al. Science* **232**, 1127-1132 (1986).

36. Kabsch, W. *Acta crystallogr.* A **33**, 922 (1976).

Iron Deficiency Limits Phytoplankton Growth in the North-East Pacific Subarctic

John H. Martin and Steve E. Fitzwater

Editor's Note

Oceanographer John Martin discovered that in several regions of the world's oceans the main inorganic nutrients of plant plankton are incompletely consumed, because plankton growth is curtailed by shortage of another vital nutrient: dissolved iron, delivered to the sea largely as wind-blown mineral dust. Martin concluded that if iron is added artificially to these iron-depleted waters, more plankton will grow. This would bind atmospheric carbon dioxide into the organisms' tissues, and so could offer a way to "engineer" climate by removing this greenhouse gas: the "iron fertilization" hypothesis. Here Martin and Steve Fitzwater present the first direct evidence that adding iron stimulates plankton growth in seawater. Whether this can (and should) be used on a large scale is still contentious.

An interesting oceanographic problem concerns the excess major plant nutrients (PO_4, NO_3, SiO_3) occurring in offshore surface waters of the Antarctic[1-3] and north-east Pacific subarctic Oceans[4]. In a previous study[5], we presented indirect evidence suggesting that inadequate Fe input was responsible for this limitation of growth; recently we had the opportunity to seek direct evidence for this hypothesis in the north-east Pacific subarctic. We report here that the addition of nmol amounts of dissolved iron resulted in the nearly complete utilization of excess NO_3, whereas in the controls—without added Fe—only 25% of the available NO_3 was used. We also observed that the amounts of chlorophyll in the phytoplankton increased in proportion to the Fe added. We conclude that Fe deficiency is limiting phytoplankton growth in these major-nutrient-rich waters.

WATER, with its resident phytoplankton, was collected from a depth of 20 m at Ocean Station "PAPA" (50.0° N; 145.0° W), using ultra-clean trace-element sampling techniques (30-litre Go-Flo bottles on Kevlar line; samples processed inside a positive pressure portable laboratory)[6,7]. Aliquots of the raw water were placed in 2-1 acid-washed polycarbonate bottles, to which various amounts of unchelated Fe (1,000 p.p.m. Fe in HNO_3, diluted appropriately) were added (Table 1, Fig. 1). In the oxygenated seawater (pH 8), the Fe was presumed to be in the ferric (III) state in the form of hydroxy complexes[8]. Additional methodological details will be published elsewhere.

亚北极区东北太平洋海域铁缺乏对浮游植物生长的限制

约翰·马丁，史蒂夫·菲茨沃特

编者按

海洋学家约翰·马丁发现在大洋中的某些地区，浮游植物主要的无机营养盐未被全部消耗，因为浮游植物的生长受限于另一种关键养分——溶解铁的缺失。溶解铁主要以矿物粉尘的形式被吹入大海的。马丁得出结论，如果人为地将铁加入到这些缺铁的水中，就会有更多的浮游植物生长。这会把大气中的二氧化碳带入有机体组织中，于是就提供了一种去除温室气体从而"改变"气候的方法："铁施肥"假说。在本文中，马丁和史蒂夫·菲茨沃特首次提出了加入铁能促进海水中浮游植物的生长的直接证据。这种方法是否能够（并且应该）大规模使用目前仍存在争议。

南极近海表层水体 [1-3] 和亚北极区东北太平洋海域 [4] 出现了一种关于常量植物营养盐（PO_4、NO_3、SiO_3）过剩的有趣海洋学问题。在之前的研究中 [5]，我们已给出了间接证据证明，Fe 输入的不足是造成这种生长限制的原因；近期我们又有机会得以在亚北极区太平洋东北海域寻找支持该理论的直接证据。本文我们将报道，加入很低浓度的溶解铁可以使过剩 NO_3 几乎完全被利用，而在不加 Fe 的对照组中，仅有 25% 的 NO_3 得到利用。我们还观测到，浮游植物中叶绿素的含量随铁的增加成比例升高。由此我们得出结论，在这些常量营养盐富集的水体中，Fe 的缺乏限制着浮游植物的生长。

采用超净痕量元素取样技术（系于凯芙拉线上的 30 升郭福洛瓶；样品处理在一个正压力便携实验室中进行）[6,7] 采集了 "PAPA" 海洋观测站（50.0°N；145.0°W）水深 20 m 处的水样，连同其中的浮游植物一起采集。将水样等份分装于 2 升的聚碳酸酯瓶（聚碳酸酯瓶用酸洗过）中，然后向其中分别加入不同量的非螯合铁（用 HNO_3 将 Fe 稀释至 1,000 ppm 左右）（表 1，图 1）。我们认为，在含氧的海水（pH 值为 8）中，Fe 以三价铁的氢氧化物形式存在 [8]。关于方法的具体细节将另文发表。

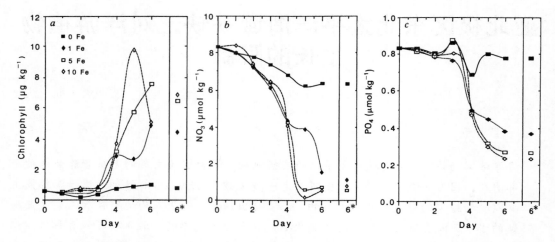

Fig. 1. Chlorophyll concentrations versus experimental day (*a*) in control (no added Fe) and experimental bottles with 1 nmol Fe, 5 nmol Fe and 10 nmol Fe added per kg. The data shown for day 6* represent a second set of replicates that were opened only upon the completion of the experiment. Nitrate (*b*) and phosphate (*c*) concentrations versus day are also shown. Because of the unintentional addition of 3 μmol NO₃ kg⁻¹, the data for the experimental bottles with 10 nmol Fe plus 1.0 nmol Mn and 0.1 nmol Co per kg are not included in this figure (see Table 1). Bottles were placed in three plastic bags and maintained in an all plastic deck-top incubator. Light levels were ~20% of those at the sea surface; temperatures were kept at ~14 °C via running seawater.

Table 1. Nutrient uptake and chlorophyll production by phytoplankton from 20 m depth

Day	Fe added (nmol kg⁻¹)				
	0	1	5	10	10+*
Chlorophyll (μg kg⁻¹)					
0	0.69 (initial value)				
1	0.49	0.46	0.52	0.46	0.49
2	0.35	0.68	0.67	0.77	0.67
3	0.41	0.84	0.67	0.84	0.92
4	0.77	2.98	3.31	3.85	3.65
5	0.92	2.77	5.97	10.16	9.09
6	1.07	5.21	7.91	5.26	6.95
6‡	0.85	4.63	6.81	7.17	14.70
NO₃ (μmol kg⁻¹)					
0	8.37 (initial value)				
1	8.04	7.94	8.03	8.37	11.43†
2	7.72	7.19	7.22	7.34	10.58
3	7.34	6.10	6.40	6.40	9.75
4	6.80	4.32	4.24	4.04	7.57
5	6.25	3.84	0.60	0.15	2.69
6	6.34	1.51	0.75	0.50	0.52
6‡	6.38	1.14	0.58	0.77	0.56

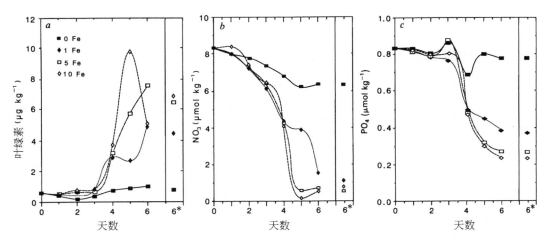

图 1. 对照瓶（未加入 Fe）和每 kg 分别加入了 1 nmol Fe、5 nmol Fe 和 10 nmol Fe 的实验瓶中叶绿素浓度相对于实验天数的变化（a）。6* 天表示的数据为一组仅在实验结束时才打开的平行样品的浓度。图中还给出了硝酸盐（b）和磷酸盐（c）浓度相对于天数的变化情况。由于不小心多加入了 3 μmol·kg^{-1} 的 NO$_3$，每千克水中加入 10 nmol Fe，1.0 nmol Mn 和 0.1 nmol Co 的实验瓶数据并未包含在图中（见表 1）。样品瓶均放置于三个塑料袋中，保存在甲板上一个全塑的培养器中。光照水平约是海洋表面的 20%，利用流动的海水使温度保持在 14℃左右。

表 1. 20 m 水深处浮游植物对营养盐的吸收及其叶绿素生产率

天数	Fe 加入量（nmol·kg^{-1}）				
	0	1	5	10	10+*
叶绿素（μg·kg^{-1}）					
0	0.69（初始值）				
1	0.49	0.46	0.52	0.46	0.49
2	0.35	0.68	0.67	0.77	0.67
3	0.41	0.84	0.67	0.84	0.92
4	0.77	2.98	3.31	3.85	3.65
5	0.92	2.77	5.97	10.16	9.09
6	1.07	5.21	7.91	5.26	6.95
6$^\ddagger_\ddagger$	0.85	4.63	6.81	7.17	14.70
NO$_3$（μmol·kg^{-1}）					
0	8.37（初始值）				
1	8.04	7.94	8.03	8.37	11.43†
2	7.72	7.19	7.22	7.34	10.58
3	7.34	6.10	6.40	6.40	9.75
4	6.80	4.32	4.24	4.04	7.57
5	6.25	3.84	0.60	0.15	2.69
6	6.34	1.51	0.75	0.50	0.52
6$^\ddagger_\ddagger$	6.38	1.14	0.58	0.77	0.56

Continued

PO$_4$ (µmol kg^{-1})					
0	0.83 (initial value)				
1	0.83	0.82	0.83	0.83	0.83
2	0.80	0.78	0.79	0.79	0.79
3	0.86	0.76	0.86	0.80	0.80
4	0.68	0.50	0.48	0.47	0.48
5	0.80	0.44	0.32	0.30	0.33
6	0.78	0.38	0.27	0.23	0.09
6‡	0.74	0.42	0.22	0.23	0.07
SiO$_3$ (µmol kg^{-1})					
0	16.13 (initial value)				
1	16.94	16.96	16.88	17.01	17.04
2	17.24	17.22	17.19	16.86	17.14
3	19.49	18.51	18.53	18.08	17.96
4	18.40	17.65	17.21	17.40	16.65
5	18.80	–	16.90	15.82	15.81
6	–	–	17.31	15.82	14.43
6‡	–	18.60	–	15.34	11.69

The daily chlorophyll and nutrient data are from control and experimental bottles with 0, 1, 5 and 10 nmol added Fe kg^{-1} at Ocean Station PAPA (50.0° N; 145.0° W): water was collected on 6 August 1987 from depth of 20 m. Data from a second set of replicates opened only at end of experiment are also shown.

* 10+ = 10 nmol Fe + 1 nmol Mn + 0.1 nmol Co kg^{-1}.

† About 3 µmol NO$_3$ kg^{-1} inadvertently added with Co.

‡ The second replicate that was not opened until day 6.

Chlorophyll concentrations remained fairly constant for all treatments on days 1–3 (Table 1, Fig. 1). On day 4, however, rapid growth began and substantial chlorophyll increases were observed in all of the bottles with added Fe. Accelerated growth continued into day 5 and appeared to peak in the 10 and 10+ (10 nmol Fe with 1.0 nmol Mn and 0.1 nmol Co kg^{-1} added) experimental bottles. Similar chlorophyll concentrations were found in replicate experimental bottles opened for the first time on day 6. In contrast, both control bottles had very low chlorophyll concentrations (1.07 and 0.85 µg kg^{-1}) on day 6 that were scarcely higher than the initial day 0 values (0.69 µg kg^{-1}).

Nearly identical NO$_3$ uptake was observed in the 1, 5 and 10 nmol added Fe kg^{-1} bottles on days 1–4. On day 5 substantial NO$_3$ depletion continued in the 5 and 10 nmol Fe bottles, although it appeared to slow in the 1 nmol Fe bottle (Fig. 1, Table 1). Once again, the control bottles with no added Fe were completely different. The bottle sampled each day showed very slow NO$_3$ utilization and at the end of the experiment on day 6, 75% of the NO$_3$ originally present remained. The concentration in the other replicate initially opened on day 6 was nearly identical (6.38 versus 6.34 µmol NO$_3$ kg^{-1}). Much the same uptake pattern was also observed for PO$_4$ (Fig. 1). In the case of SiO$_3$, however, hardly any differences

PO₄（µmol·kg⁻¹）					
0	0.83（初始值）				
1	0.83	0.82	0.83	0.83	0.83
2	0.80	0.78	0.79	0.79	0.79
3	0.86	0.76	0.86	0.80	0.80
4	0.68	0.50	0.48	0.47	0.48
5	0.80	0.44	0.32	0.30	0.33
6	0.78	0.38	0.27	0.23	0.09
6‡	0.74	0.42	0.22	0.23	0.07
SiO₃（µmol·kg⁻¹）					
0	16.13（初始值）				
1	16.94	16.96	16.88	17.01	17.04
2	17.24	17.22	17.19	16.86	17.14
3	19.49	18.51	18.53	18.08	17.96
4	18.40	17.65	17.21	17.40	16.65
5	18.80	–	16.90	15.82	15.81
6	–	–	17.31	15.82	14.43
6‡	–	18.60	–	15.34	11.69

每天的叶绿素值和营养盐数据均来自 PAPA 海洋观测站（50.0°N；145.0°W）的对照瓶和实验瓶，瓶中分别加入 0 nmol·kg⁻¹、1 nmol·kg⁻¹、5 nmol·kg⁻¹ 和 10 nmol·kg⁻¹ 的 Fe；水样是 1987 年 8 月 6 日从水深 20 m 处采集得到的。表中还给出了实验结束才打开的第二组平行样品瓶的结果。

* 10+ 表示每千克水中加入 10 nmol Fe、1.0 nmol Mn 和 0.1 nmol Co。

† 不小心多加入了约 3 µmol·kg⁻¹ 的含有 Co 的 NO₃。

‡ 第二组平行样品，直到第 6 天才打开。

　　第 1~3 天，各种处理方法下的叶绿素浓度均基本保持不变（表 1，图 1）。然而，到第 4 天时，所有加了 Fe 的实验瓶中都观察到了浮游植物的快速生长，并且叶绿素浓度也明显增加。加速生长过程一直持续到第 5 天，并在 10 和 10+（每千克水中加入 10 nmol Fe、1.0 nmol Mn 和 0.1 nmol Co）的瓶中出现最大值。在第 6 天首次打开的平行实验瓶中叶绿素的浓度与之相同。相反，两个对照瓶中到第 6 天时叶绿素的浓度仍然很低（分别为 1.07 µg·kg⁻¹ 和 0.85 µg·kg⁻¹），相对于第 0 天的初始值（0.69 µg·kg⁻¹）来说几乎没有变化。

　　第 1~4 天，在分别加入了 1 nmol·kg⁻¹、5 nmol·kg⁻¹ 和 10 nmol·kg⁻¹ Fe 的瓶中 NO₃ 的消耗量几乎相等。第 5 天，在加入 5 nmol·kg⁻¹ 和 10 nmol·kg⁻¹ Fe 的瓶中 NO₃ 继续显著减少，尽管 1 nmol Fe 的瓶中 NO₃ 的消耗速度变慢了（图 1，表 1）。未加 Fe 的对照瓶情况则完全不同。每天从瓶中取样分析显示，NO₃ 的消耗很慢，到第 6 天实验结束时，仍有 75% 的 NO₃ 剩余。第 6 天打开的其他平行试验瓶中 NO₃ 的浓度基本相同（分别为 6.38 µmol·kg⁻¹ 和 6.34 µmol·kg⁻¹）。PO₄ 的情形与此类似（图 1）。

were observed between bottles (Table 1). This was surprising because scanning electron microscope examinations showed substantial diatom (*Nitzschia* spp.) growth in the experimental bottles, in contrast to the controls, which had abundant coccoliths but few diatoms.

Similar experiments were also performed 625 km north-west (55.5° N; 147.5° W) and 625 km south-east (45.0° N; 142.89° W) of Ocean Station "PAPA" (50.0° N; 145.0° W). Essentially the same results were found; chlorophyll data are shown in Fig. 2. These data, together with those in Fig. 1, provide consistent evidence that Fe limits phytoplankton growth in the north-east Pacific subarctic. With appropriate independent confirmation, this area could become a classic marine example of Liebig's law of the minimum[9]. This research also exemplifies the necessity of using ultraclean techniques, without which the control bottles would have had enough contaminate Fe to stimulate growth and make the control results indistinguishable from those with intentionally added Fe.

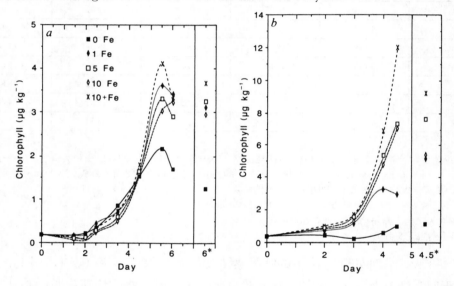

Fig. 2. Chlorophyll concentrations versus experimental day at 45.5° N; 142.89° W (*a*) and at 55.5° N; 147.5° W (*b*) in control (no added Fe) and experimental bottles with 1 nmol Fe, 5 nmol Fe, 10 nmol Fe, and 10 nmol Fe plus 1.0 nmol Mn and 0.1 nmol Co per kg. Day 6* and day 4.5* data represent second sets of replicates that were opened only at the end of the experiment. Initial conditions in *a* (15 m depth, 3 August 1987)=0.18 µg chlorophyll kg^{-1}, 6.43, 0.70 and 10.2 µmol kg^{-1} of NO_3, PO_4 and SiO_3, respectively. Initial conditions in *b* (30 m depth, 11 August 1987) = 0.35 µg chlorophyll kg^{-1}, and 7.53, 0.88 and 23.06 µmol kg^{-1} of NO_3, PO_4 and SiO_3, respectively.

The essential roles of Fe in living systems are well known[10], and it is not surprising that chlorophyll levels increase with increased Fe, as this element is required for the synthesis of this pigment[11]. Iron is also required for the synthesis of several photosynthetic electron transport proteins and for the reduction of CO_2, SO_4 and NO_3 during the photosynthetic production of organic compounds[12].

In addition to the necessity for Fe at the cellular level, it is possible that oceanic Fe availability may be important in determining global atmospheric CO_2 levels and, hence,

但对于 SiO_3，则几乎没有观察到各瓶之间存在任何差异（表 1）。这一点比较出乎意料，因为扫描电子显微镜分析结果显示，在实验瓶中存在大量硅藻（菱形藻），而对照瓶中则主要为颗石藻，硅藻很少。

在"PAPA"海洋观测站（50.0°N；145.0°W）西北 625 km 处（55.5°N；147.5°W）和东南 625 km 处（45.0°N；142.89°W）的两个站位上也进行了相似的实验。得出的结果也基本相同，其中叶绿素的相关数据见图 2。上述数据加上图 1 的数据均证明，在亚北极区东北太平洋海域，Fe 限制着浮游植物的生长。通过适当的独立实验证实，该区可以作为李比希最小因子定律在海洋中的一个典型实例 [9]。本研究还可以作为超净技术利用的实例，倘若不采用该技术，对照瓶中将会受到足量外来 Fe 的污染，从而刺激浮游植物的生长，导致对照结果与特意加入 Fe 的实验结果无法区分开来。

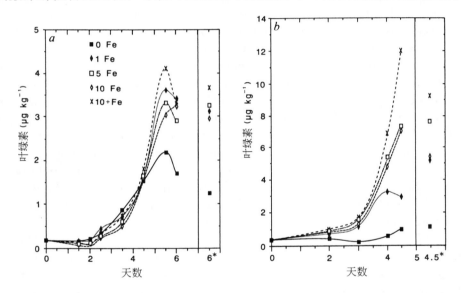

图 2. 在 45.0°N 142.89°W 处（a）和 55.5°N 147.5°W 处（b），对照瓶（未加入 Fe）和每千克中分别加入 1 nmol Fe、5 nmol Fe、10 nmol Fe 和 10 nmol Fe + 1 nmol Mn + 0.1 nmol Co 的实验瓶中叶绿素浓度随实验天数的变化。6* 和 4.5* 天表示的数据为仅在实验组结束时才打开的第二组平行实验瓶中的浓度。图 a（1987 年 8 月 3 日采集于水深 15 m 处）的初始条件为：叶绿素浓度 0.18 μg·kg⁻¹，NO_3、PO_4 和 SiO_3 的浓度分别为 6.43 μmol·kg⁻¹、0.70 μmol·kg⁻¹ 和 10.2 μmol·kg⁻¹。图 b（1987 年 8 月 11 日采集于水深 30 m 处）的初始条件为：叶绿素浓度 0.35 μg·kg⁻¹，NO_3、PO_4 和 SiO_3 的浓度分别为 7.53 μmol·kg⁻¹、0.88 μmol·kg⁻¹ 和 23.06 μmol·kg⁻¹。

众所周知，Fe 在生命系统中具有重要作用 [10]，因而叶绿素水平随 Fe 的增加而增加这一点并不令人惊奇，因为这种色素的合成需要有 Fe 元素参与 [11]。Fe 还是多种光合电子传递蛋白质合成以及在光合生产中还原 CO_2、SO_4 和 NO_3 从而生成有机化合物所必需的元素 [12]。

除了在细胞水平上是必需元素，大洋中 Fe 的可利用率可能对大气中 CO_2 水平

affecting global climate. The major role of the Antarctic Ocean in the removal of CO_2 from the atmosphere has been noted in several studies[13-17]. It is argued that the lower ice age atmospheric CO_2 levels (200 p.p.m.v) measured in ancient air[18-21] trapped in ice resulted from the increased biological productivity and CO_2 removal at high latitudes. When high-latitude surface nutrients are completely used up by the phytoplankton, the biological removal mechanism operates at maximum efficiency and CO_2 is withdrawn from the atmosphere[14,15]. In contrast, when surplus nutrients are left unutilized, the biological pump is inefficient and CO_2 levels increase. The range in these two extremes results in a factor of three difference in the atmospheric CO_2 content[16].

We believe that a situation similar to that in the Gulf of Alaska also exists in offshore Southern Ocean waters, where surface concentrations of major nutrients such as NO_3 (25.2 $\mu mol\ kg^{-1}$), PO_4 (1.68 $\mu mol\ kg^{-1}$) and SiO_3 (54.9 $\mu mol\ kg^{-1}$) are 2–3 times higher (examples from GEOSECS Station 287; 2 m depth, 69°5′ S; 173°30′ W)[22]. We postulate[5] that Fe supplies from local Antarctic continental margin sources are rapidly used up in the highly productive neritic waters of this region and little, if any, Fe mixes out into the open Southern Ocean. Also, atmospheric Fe input is limited, as Southern Ocean dust fluxes between 40° S and the Antarctic continent are among the lowest in the world because of the absence of land masses; that is, only the tip of South America and the southern island of New Zealand are in this region of strong prevailing westerly winds[23]. This low dust input is exemplified by the small amounts of Al found in present-day interglacial Antarctic Vostok ice core samples. De Angelis *et al.*[24] report that mean Al concentrations are 2.5±0.9 ng g^{-1} during the present interglacial (Holocene) and are not significantly different from those of the previous interglacial (3.0±1.5 ng Al g^{-1}, 127 kyr BP). This would be ~0.03–0.04 nmol of Fe g^{-1} based upon Taylor's[25] crustal abundance estimates (8.23% Al and 5.63% Fe; Fe:Al ratio=0.68). Levels of CO_2, in the same Vostok ice core, were highest during these interglacials, on the order of 270–280 p.p.m.v.[21].

In contrast to interglacials, glacial periods had increased amounts of atmospheric dust Al and Fe and low CO_2 concentrations; for example, during the last glacial maximum, when Al levels were 50 times higher (~125 ng Al g^{-1})[24], CO_2 concentrations were <200 p.p.m.v.[21]. The larger glacial period Al amounts are expected as tropical arid zones were five times larger, wind speeds 1.3–1.6 times higher, and atmospheric dust loads 10–20 times greater during the ice ages[26]. We postulate that the enhanced supply of Fe from the atmosphere stimulated photosynthesis, which led to the drawdown in atmospheric CO_2 levels during glacial maxima.

We thank Mike Gordon, Sara Tanner and Ginger Elrod for their help with the field work. The VERTEX nutrient data were supplied by Sandy Moore and Larry Small of Oregon State University. This research was supported by grants from the NSF Marine Chemistry Programme and the US Office of Naval Research Oceanic Chemistry Programme.

(**331**, 341-343; 1988)

也有重要影响，进而影响全球气候。多项研究[13-17]发现，南极海域在促进大气中CO_2含量的减少中起着重要作用。对冰川包裹的古大气的测量[18-21]表明，冰期时大气的CO_2水平较低（200 ppmv），这是由于生物生产力提高，高纬度地区CO_2从大气中移除所致。当高纬度海域表层营养盐被浮游植物完全消耗时，生物移除机制的效率达到最大，大气CO_2浓度降低[14,15]。相反，当过剩的营养盐没有得到充分利用时，生物泵的效率就较低，CO_2水平随之上升。在上述两种极端情况下，大气CO_2含量可相差3倍[16]。

我们相信，南大洋近岸水体中也存在类似于阿拉斯加湾的情形，并且其中常量营养盐如NO_3（25.2 μmol·kg^{-1}）、PO_4（1.68 μmol·kg^{-1}）和SiO_3（54.9 μmol·kg^{-1}）的表层浓度是其的2~3倍（采样地点为 GEOSECS 287 站；水深 2 m，69°5′S 173°30′W）[22]。我们假定[5] Fe 的供给来自当地的南极大陆边缘，在该区的高生产力浅海水体中很快就被耗尽，只有极少量的 Fe（如果有的话）通过混合作用进入开阔的南大洋。同样，由大气输入的 Fe 也非常有限，因为40°S到南极大陆之间南大洋上空的飘尘量是世界上最低的，主要原因是这里的陆源物质很少；也就是说，该区仅有南美洲南端和新西兰南岛位于盛行西风带[23]。现代间冰期南极沃斯托克冰芯样品中 Al 的含量很低，就是该区低浮尘输入量的一个例证。据德安杰利斯等[24]的报告，现代间冰期（全新世）Al 的平均浓度为 2.5±0.9 ng·g^{-1}，并且与之前的间冰期（3.0±1.5 ng·g^{-1}，距今 127,000 年）无明显区别。根据泰勒[25]的地壳丰度估计值（Al 为 8.23%，Fe 为 5.63%；Fe∶Al = 0.68），其 Fe 的浓度约为 0.03~0.04 nmol·g^{-1}。在同一根沃斯托克冰芯中，CO_2水平在间冰期时达最高值，约为 270~280 ppmv[21]。

与间冰期相反，冰期时大气沉降的 Al 和 Fe 尘埃增多，CO_2浓度则相对较低。例如，末次盛冰期时，当 Al 的浓度约为现今的 50 倍（约为 125 ng·g^{-1}）[24] 时，CO_2浓度则小于 200 ppmv[21]。冰期时热带干旱地区的面积约为现今的 5 倍左右，风速为现今的 1.3~1.6 倍，大气中的尘埃负荷是现今的 10~20 倍，故其中 Al 的浓度也较高[26]。我们假定，盛冰期时来自大气 Fe 供给量的增加可促进光合作用，从而导致大气中CO_2水平降低。

感谢迈克·戈登、萨拉·坦纳和金杰·埃尔罗德对野外工作的帮助。感谢俄勒冈州立大学的桑迪·穆尔和拉里·斯莫尔提供的 VERTEX 营养盐资料。本研究受到美国国家科学基金会海洋化学计划和美国海军研究办公室海洋化学计划的资金支持。

（齐红艳 翻译；孙松 审稿）

John H. Martin and Steve E. Fitzwater

Moss Landing Marine Laboratories, Moss Landing, California 95039, USA

Received 9 September; accepted 11 December 1987.

References:

1. Hart, T. J. *Discovery Rep.* **XXI**, 261-356 (1942).

2. Hardy, A. C. *Great Waters* (Harper and Row, New York, 1967).

3. Holm-Hansen, O. in *Antarctic Nutrient Cycles and Food Webs* (eds Siegfriend, W. R., Condy, P. R. & Laws, R. M.) 6-10 (Springer, Heidelberg, 1985).

4. McAllister, C. D., Parsons, T. R. & Strickland, J. D. H. *J. Cons.* **25**, 240-259 (1960).

5. Martin, J. H. & Gordon, R. M. *Deep Sea Res.* (in the press).

6. Martin, J. H., Bruland, K. W. & Broenkow, W. W. in *Marine Pollutant Transfer* (eds Windom, H. & Duce, R.) 159-184 (Heath, Lexington, 1976).

7. Bruland, K. W., Franks, R. P., Knauer, G. A. & Martin, J. H. *Analytica chim. Acta* **105**, 223-245 (1979).

8. Stumm, W. & Morgan, J. J. *Aquatic Chemistry* 2nd edn (Wiley, New York, 1981).

9. Liebig, J. *Chemistry in its Application to Agriculture and Physiology* 4th edn (Taylor and Walton, London, 1847).

10. Bowen, H. J. M. *Environmental Chemistry of the Elements* (Academic, London, 1979).

11. O'Kelley, J. C. in *Botanical Monographs, Vol. 10, Algal Physiology and Biochemistry* (ed. Stewart, W. D. P.) 610-635 (University of California Press, Berkeley, 1974).

12. Bassham, J. A. in *Plant Biochemistry* (eds Bonner, J. & Varner, J. E.) 875-902 (Academic, New York, 1965).

13. Sarmiento, J. L. & Toggweiler, J. R. *Nature* **308**, 621-624 (1984).

14. Broecker, W. S. *Prog. Oceanogr.* **11**, 151-197 (1982).

15. Broecker, W. S. *Geochim. Cosmochim. Acta* **46**, 1689-1705 (1982).

16. Knox, F. & McElroy, M. B. *J. Geophys. Res.* **89**, 4629-4637 (1984).

17. Siegenthaler, U. & Wenk, T. H. *Nature* **308**, 624-626 (1984).

18. Bernier, W., Stauffer, B. & Oeschger, H. *Nature* **276**, 53-55 (1978).

19. Delmas, R. J., Ascencio, J.-M. & Legrand, M. *Nature* **282**, 155-157 (1980).

20. Neftel, A., Oeschger, H., Schwander, J., Stauffer, B. & Zumbrunn, R. *Nature* **295**, 220-223(1982).

21. Barnola, J. M., Raynaud, D., Korotkevich, Y. S. & Lorius, C. *Nature* **329**, 408-414 (1987).

22. Broecker, W. S., Spencer, D. W. & Craig, H. *GEOSECS Pacific Expedition: Hydrographic Data, 3* (US Government Printing Office, Washington, 1982).

23. Hasse, L. in *Air-Sea Exchange of Gases and Particles* (eds Liss, P. S. & Slinn, W. G. N.) 1-51 (Reidel, Dordrecht, 1983).

24. De Angelis, M., Barkov, N. I. & Petrov, V. N. *Nature* **325**, 318-321 (1987).

25. Taylor, S. R. *Geochim. Cosmochim Acta* **28**, 1273-1285 (1964).

26. Petit, J. R., Briat, M. & Royer, A. *Nature* **293**, 391-394 (1981).

Evidence for Global Warming in the Past Decade

P. D. Jones *et al.*

By the late 1980s, the possibility that rising concentrations of atmospheric carbon dioxide, caused by human activities, could alter climate by the greenhouse effect had become a serious concern. The underlying science was clear, but it was conceivable that natural processes might offset such warming. The first step was to establish whether climate really had warmed since the industrial era of the mid-nineteenth century. From 1940 to about 1980, temperatures changed rather little. But here Philip Jones of the University of East Anglia and colleagues use the latest data to reveal significant warming in the past decade: an apparent return to the pre-1940 trend. Establishing a likely anthropogenic cause was to require another decade of painstaking effort.

THE global-mean surface air temperature is the most common measure of the state of the climate system. Variations of this parameter are probably determined largely by the sensitivity of the climate system to external forcing factors such as solar output, explosive volcanic eruptions and the changes in concentration of CO_2 and other radiatively active gases. Understanding the climate's response to changes in forcing is essential if we are ever to forecast future climatic change.

Increases of CO_2 and other radiatively active trace gases (methane, chlorofluorocarbons, nitrous oxide and tropospheric ozone) are expected to raise global equilibrium general circulation models[1] for a doubling of atmospheric CO_2. Up to now, the rise in equivalent CO_2 concentration (incorporating the radiative effects of the other trace gases) has lifted levels about 40% above their preindustrial level of around 280 p.p.m.v. (ref. 2).

In 1986, some of us reported[3] the first compilation of global mean temperature estimates, spanning the period 1861–1984. We have now extended this analysis to include 1985–87 and to improve the ocean and land coverage for the 1980s. The improved coverage for the 1980s slightly alters the original values for 1980–84. Our new estimates use the comprehensive ocean atmosphere data set (COADS) sea-surface temperature (SST) data for 1980–86. For the marine regions for 1987, we used SST data from the UK Meteorological Office. SST data are a good substitute for air temperature over the oceans[4]. These two sources of SST data are in excellent agreement during the 1980s. We have also updated the land temperature series for the two hemispheres[5-7].

The time series for the land and marine areas for 1901–87 is shown in the figure. 1987 is the warmest year recorded, 0.05 °C above the next warmest, 1981 and 1983. The warmth of the 1980s is most evident in the Southern Hemisphere. Here, seven of the eight

过去十年中全球变暖的证据

琼斯等

编者按

自 20 世纪 80 年代末以来，由于人类活动造成大气中 CO_2 浓度升高并可能通过增强温室效应改变全球气候的问题引起了人们的广泛关注。其潜在的科学道理是很清晰的，但自然过程也许有可能抵消这种人为变暖。我们首先要明确的是，自 19 世纪中期工业革命以来气候是否真的变暖了。1940~1980 年间，全球温度变化很小，但是东安格利亚大学的菲利普·琼斯及其同事利用最新的资料研究发现，过去 10 年温度明显升高，这与 1940 年之前的变暖过程十分相似。可见，证实由人为原因引起的气候变暖还需要 10 年更加辛苦的工作。

全球平均地表气温是衡量气候系统状态最常用的指标。该参数的变化主要取决于气候系统对各种外强迫因子的敏感度，如太阳辐射、火山活动以及 CO_2 和其他影响辐射的温室气体浓度。我们要想预测未来的气候变化，就必须了解气候对这些外强迫因子的响应机制。

在大气环流模式[1] 中提高 CO_2 和其他影响辐射的痕量气体（甲烷、氯氟烃、氧化亚氮及对流层臭氧）浓度，比如使 CO_2 浓度加倍，是研究全球变暖的通常做法。到目前为止，等价的 CO_2 浓度（包括其他痕量气体的辐射效应）相对于工业化以前的 280 ppmv 已升高了 40%（参考文献 2）。

1986 年，本文的部分作者[3] 首次发布了 1861~1984 年全球平均气温数据集。现在我们对该数据集做了扩展，使之包含 1985~1987 年的数据，并且提高了 80 年代海洋和陆地资料的覆盖率。80 年代站点覆盖率的提高略微改变了 1980~1984 年的原有值。我们新的估算利用的是综合海洋大气数据集（COADS）中 1980~1986 年的海表温度（SST）数据。对于 1987 年的海洋数据，我们采用的是英国气象局的海表温度资料。海表温度是海洋上空大气温度的一个较好的代用指标[4]。20 世纪 80 年代，这两种不同来源的海表温度数据变化非常一致。我们还更新了南北半球的地面温度资料[5-7]。

1901~1987 年间的海陆温度时间序列如图所示。1987 年是记录中最暖的一年，比次暖的年份 1981 年和 1983 年高出 0.05℃。20 世纪 80 年代变暖现象在南半球表现得最明显。南半球最温暖的 8 个年份中有 7 年发生于 80 年代，并且以 1987 年

warmest years have occurred during the 1980s, with 1987 being the warmest. Warmth over the Northern Hemisphere in the 1980s is not so startling, yet the two warmest years are 1981 (the warmest) and 1987.

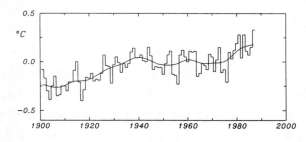

Global surface air temperature, 1901–1987.

The global land air temperature in 1987 is about the same as the previous maximum in 1981 (updating ref. 8), the difference in the analysed temperatures for these years being less than the uncertainty caused by incomplete station coverage. The warmth is not just a surface phenomenon. The global radiosonde data network[9], which began in 1958, also confirms the warmth of the 1980s both at the surface and in the lower troposphere, particularly in 1981, 1983 and 1987. The network also provides data for the stratosphere, a region that models suggest should become increasingly cold as CO_2 levels increase. For global mean lower-stratospheric temperatures, the coldest years are 1985, 1986 and 1987.

It is likely that the record warmth in 1987 partly resulted from the strong 1986–87 El Niño/Southern Oscillation (ENSO) event [10,11], although this event was not as intense as the one in 1982–83. It is also possible that the stratospheric coldness in recent years is partly associated with the recent ozone depletion[12,13]. Nevertheless, the persistent surface and tropospheric warmth of the 1980s which, together with ENSO, gave the exceptional warmth of 1987 could indicate the consequences of increased concentrations of CO_2 and other radiatively active gases in the atmosphere.

(**332**, 790; 1988)

P. D. Jones & T. M. L. Wigley[*], **C. K. Folland & D. E. Parker**[†], **J. K. Angell**[‡], **S. Lebedeff & J. E. Hansen**[§]

[*] Climatic Research Unit, University of East Anglia, Norwich NR4 7TJ, UK.

[†] Meteorological Office, Bracknell RG12 2SZ, UK.

[‡] Air Resources Laboratory, NOAA Environmental Research Labs, Silver Spring, Maryland 20910, USA.

[§] NASA Goddard Space Flight Center, New York, NY 10025, USA.

References:

1. Report of the International Conference on the Assessment of the role of carbon dioxide and of other greenhouses gases in climate variations and associated impacts, World Meteorological Organization No. 661 (Geneva, 1986).

2. Wigley, T. M. L. *Geophys. Res. Lett.* **14**, 1135 (1987).

3. Jones, P. D., Wigley, T. M. L. & Wright, P. B. *Nature* **322**, 430-434 (1986).

4. Folland, C. K., Parker, D. E. & Kates, F. E. *Nature* **310**, 670-673 (1984).

5. Jones, P. D. *et al. J. clim. appl. Meteorol.* **25**, 161 (1986).

的温度最高。北半球的升温在 80 年代则没有这么明显，最温暖的两个年份分别为 1981 年（最暖）和 1987 年。

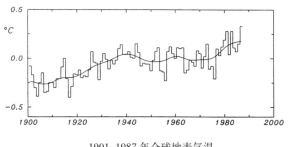

1901~1987 年全球地表气温

1987 年全球的陆地气温与之前 1981 年出现的最高值几乎相等（据参考文献 8 更新内容），两个年份的温度差异要小于因站点覆盖不完全而引起的不确定性。变暖现象的发生并不仅限于地表。始于 1958 年的全球无线电探空数据网 [9] 也证实 20 世纪 80 年代的变暖现象同时发生于地表以及对流层低层，特别是在 1981 年、1983 年和 1987 年。该网络还提供了平流层的相关数据，根据模拟结果，随着 CO_2 含量的增加该区域应该越来越冷。平流层低层的全球平均温度最低的年份分别为 1985 年、1986 年和 1987 年。

1986~1987 年发生的强烈的厄尔尼诺 / 南方涛动（ENSO）事件可能是引起 1987 年气温变暖的部分原因 [10,11]，尽管该事件的强度不如 1982~1983 年。近年来平流层变冷可能也与臭氧层损耗有关 [12,13]。虽然如此，20 世纪 80 年代以来地表和对流层的持续增温，再加上厄尔尼诺 / 南方涛动事件，使得 1987 年异常温暖，从中我们可以看出大气中 CO_2 及其他影响辐射的温室气体增加带来的后果。

（齐红艳 翻译；闻新宇 审稿）

6. Jones, P. D., Raper, S. C. B. & Wigley, T. M. L. *J. clim. appl. Meteorol.* **25**, 1213-1230 (1986).

7. Jones, P. D. *J. clim.* (in the press).

8. Hansen, J. E. & Lebedeff, S. *J. Geophys. Res.* **92**, 13345-13372 (1987).

9. Wigley, T. M. L., Angell, J. K. & Jones, P. D. in *Detecting the climatic effects of increasing carbon dioxide* (eds MacCracken, M. C. & Luther, F. M.) 55-90 (US Dept of Energy, 1985).

10. Pan, Y. -H. and Oort, A. H. *Mon. Weath. Rev.* **111**, 1244-1258 (1983).

11. Yasunari, T. *J. met. Soc. Japan* **65**, 67-80 (1987).

12. Heath. D. F. *Nature* **332**, 219-227 (1988).

13. Kiehl, J. T., Boville, B. A. & Briegleb, B. P. *Nature* **332**, 501-504 (1988).

GAL4 Activates Transcription in *Drosophila*

J. A. Fischer *et al.*

Editor's Note

The GAL4-UAS system is used to study gene expression and function. It has two parts: the *gal4* gene, which encodes the transcription-activating protein GAL4, and the upstream activation sequence (UAS), which binds GAL4 to activate transcription. Here molecular biologist Mark Ptashne and colleagues demonstrate that GAL4 activates transcription in the fruit fly *Drosophila*. GAL4-activated transcription can be seen in a tissue-specific manner thanks to the inclusion of the *lacz* reporter gene, and the technique offered researchers a way to alter gene expression in specific tissue types. Although GAL4 is a yeast protein not normally found in other organisms, it can promote transcription in many other species, including humans and the model organisms *Xenopus* and zebrafish.

GAL4 is a yeast regulatory protein that binds to specific sites within a DNA sequence called UAS$_G$ (galactose upstream activating sequence) and activates transcription of linked genes[1-6]. This activation requires two functions of the protein[7,8]: a DNA binding domain located near the amino terminus[8] , and one or more "activating regions"[7-11]. The "activating regions" are highly acidic[9-11] (see also ref. 12) and can be replaced, for example, by a short peptide designed to form a negatively charged, amphipathic α-helix[13] . GAL4, as well as deletion derivatives bearing one or more "activating regions" attached to the DNA binding domain, activates transcription in cultured mammalian cells from mammalian promoters linked to a UAS$_G$ (refs 14, 15). Here we show that GAL4, when expressed in particular tissues of *Drosophila* larvae, stimulates tissue-specific transcription of a *Drosophila* promoter linked to GAL4 binding sites.

WE constructed an effector gene that expresses GAL4 in a tissue specific manner in *Drosophila*, and a reporter gene that allows the visualization of GAL4-activated transcription by a histochemical stain for β-galactosidase activity (Fig. 1). In the effector gene, expression of GAL4 is driven by a *Drosophila Adh* promoter. This promoter, when fused to the *lacz* gene of *Escherichia coli*, expresses β-galactosidase mainly in four larval tissues—fat body (fb), Malpighian tubules (mt), anterior midgut (amg) and middle midgut (mmg): expression in the hindgut (hg) and tracheae (tr) is variable (Figs 3, 4; refs 16, 34). In the reporter gene, the TATA-box and 5'-untranslated region of the *Drosophila* heat shock gene *hsp70* are fused to *lacz* (Fig. 1). This fusion gene is transcriptionally inactive (see below): the *hsp70* promoter is normally heat inducible, but sequences upstream of −43 from the *hsp70* transcription start site were deleted, thus eliminating the regulatory elements required for that induction[17-20]. We inserted four copies of a 17 base pair (bp)

在果蝇中GAL4激活转录

费希尔等

编者按

GAL4-UAS 系统用于基因表达与功能的研究。它由两部分组成：编码转录激活蛋白 GAL4 的 gal4 基因和上游激活序列（UAS），该序列通过结合 GAL4 可激活转录。在本文中，分子生物学家马克·普塔什尼和他的同事们证明了在果蝇中 GAL4 可激活转录。lazc 报告基因的引入使得研究者可以通过组织特异性的方式观察到 GAL4 激活的转录，这项技术给他们提供了在特定组织类型中改变基因表达的方法。尽管 GAL4 是一种仅在酵母内发现的蛋白，但它能够在包括人类和模式生物如非洲爪蟾和斑马鱼在内的许多其他的物种中启动转录。

GAL4 是一种酵母调节蛋白，它可与 UAS_G（半乳糖上游活化序列）上的特异性位点结合并激活连锁基因的转录 [1-6]。激活需要这种蛋白的两个功能 [7,8]：一个临近氨基末端的 DNA 结合域 [8]，以及一个或多个"激活域" [7-11]。激活域高度酸化 [9-11]（也见参考文献 12）并且可以被替换，例如它可被一段带负电的双性 α 螺旋短肽所取代 [13]。GAL4 及其包含一个或多个与 DNA 结合域相连的"激活域"的缺失衍生物，在人工培养的哺乳动物细胞中激活与 UAS_G 相连的哺乳动物启动子的转录（参考文献 14、15）。我们在本文展示的是，当 GAL4 在果蝇幼虫特定组织中表达时，可激活一个与 GAL4 结合位点相连的果蝇启动子的组织特异性转录。

我们构建了一个在果蝇体内以组织特异性的方式表达 GAL4 的效应基因和一个可以通过组织化学染色反映 β–半乳糖苷酶活性从而观察到 GAL4 激活转录的报告基因（图 1）。在效应基因中由果蝇的 Adh 启动子驱动 GAL4 的表达。该启动子与大肠杆菌的 lacz 基因融合后，主要在幼虫的以下四种组织中表达 β–半乳糖苷酶：脂肪体（fb）、马氏管（mt）、前部中肠（amg）和中部中肠（mmg）中；GAL4 在后肠（hg）和气管（tr）中的表达是变化的（图 3、4；参考文献 16、34）。在报告基因中果蝇热激基因 hsp70 的 TATA 盒和 5′ 非翻译区被融合到 lacz 中（图 1）。这个融合基因是转录失活的（见下文）：hsp70 启动子通常可被热激诱导，但将 hsp70 转录起始位点到上游 −43 位点的序列缺失后，会造成诱导所需的调节元件被删除 [17-20]。我们插入了具有 17 个碱基对（bp）的四个拷贝，即 17-mers 的 hsp70 TATA 盒上游序列：这些

sequence called the 17-mer upstream of the *hsp70* TATA-box: these 17-mers are closely related to the GAL4 binding sites in UAS$_G$ (ref. 8) and are recognized by GAL4 (ref. 15) (see legend to Fig. 1).

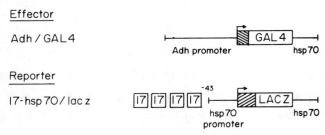

Fig. 1. Effector and reporter genes introduced into the *D. melanogaster* genome by P element transformation. The effector gene (*Adh/GAL4*) is a hybrid gene in which a *Drosophila Adh* promoter drives transcription of the yeast GAL4 coding sequences. The *Adh* promoter in the effector gene is that of the *D. mulleri Adh* –1 gene[24,25], with additional copies of its natural enhancer, BOX B[16,34] inserted upstream to increase its level of expression. The reporter gene (*17-hsp70/lacz*) is a hybrid gene in which the TATA-box of the *Drosophila hsp70* gene, with four GAL4 17-mers immediately upstream, drives transcription of the *E. coli* gene encoding β-galactosidase (*lacz*). The 17-mers are high affinity GAL4-binding sites (see below). Each gene contains transcriptional termination sequences from *hsp70*. The effector and reporter genes were separately introduced into the *D. melanogaster* genome by P element transformation[21,22].

Methods. The *Adh* promoter in the effector gene contains a *Bgl*II/*Bal*I fragment from the 5′-flanking region of the *D. mulleri Adh*–1 gene which extends from –1.5 kilobase (kb) to +58 bp from the transcription start site, immediately downstream of the ATG start codon. A *Bam*HI linker was inserted at the *Bal*I site, and three copies of an 100 bp *Sac*I-linked DNA fragment (–282 to –181 from the *Adh*–1 transcription start site) containing BOX B were cloned into the *Sna*BI site at –1.45 kb. GAL4 coding sequences were fused to the *Adh* promoter at the *Bam*HI site inserted downstream of the ATG of *Adh*–1 via a *Hin*dIII site within the untranslated leader sequence of GAL4 in pLPK-C15[26]. Site-directed mutagenesis with a mismatched primer[27] generated a "perfect" fusion of the *Adh*–1 leader sequences to the ATG start codon of GAL4. The reporter gene was constructed from an *hsp70/lacz* gene (a gift of John Lis and colleagues) containing *Drosophila hsp70* sequences from –43, 10 bp upstream of the TATA-box, to +265 (thus including the promoter and the first seven codons), fused in-frame to an *E. coli lacz* gene. Four copies of a 29 bp *Kpn*I/*Pst*I fragment of pMH100[15], containing a high affinity (Melvyn Hollis and M. Ptashne., unpublished data; see ref. 15) 17-mer GAL4 recognition site (the *Sca*I 17-mer: 5′-CGGAGTACTGTCCTCCG-3′) were cloned into the *Kpn*I site just upstream of the *hsp70/lacz* gene in pSP73lac2 (a gift of Dean Falb), which contains the *hsp70/lacz* gene cloned as a *Sal*I fragment into the *Sal*I site of pSP73 (ref. 28). A 4.8 kb *Xba*I fragment containing the effector gene and a 3.6 kb *Xba*I fragment containing the reporter gene were each cloned into the P element transformation vector C70TX (a gift of Dean Falb), in the same transcriptional orientation as the *rosy* gene. C70TX was constructed by inserting an *Xba*I linker into the *Sal*I site of C70T (a gift of John Lis and colleagues), which is a derivative of Carnegie 20 (ref. 29) containing, in the *Sal*I site, a 250 bp *Sal*I/*Xho*I fragment of *hsp70* gene terminator sequences. The P element plasmids were purified by banding in CsCl-EtBr gradients and coinjected at a concentration of 300 μg ml^{-1} with the helper plasmid pπ25.7wc[30] (70 μg ml^{-1}) into embryos of *D. melanogaster* strain *ry*[506] as described[21,22]. The effector plasmid was also injected at a concentration of 100 μg ml^{-1}, because very few embryos injected even with the lower concentration survived past the first instar larval stage. Flies from embryos that survived microinjection were individually backcrossed to *ry*[506]. Among the backcross progeny, germ-line transformants were distinguished by their wild type (*ry*$^+$) eye colour. The backcross progeny, heterozygous for the P element, were used to perform the effector × reporter crosses. All enzymatic reactions and DNA manipulations were carried out using standard conditions and techniques[31]. Flies were grown at 25 °C on standard cornmeal food.

17-mer 上游序列与 UAS_G 上的 GAL4 的结合位点非常接近（参考文献 8）并且可以被 GAL4 识别（参考文献 15）（见图 1 注）。

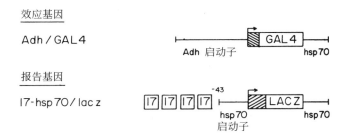

图 1. 效应基因和报告基因通过 P 因子转化转入黑腹果蝇基因组内。效应基因（*Adh/GAL4*）是一个复合基因，由果蝇的 *Adh* 启动子启动酵母 GAL4 编码序列的转录。效应基因的 *Adh* 启动子是果蝇（*D. mulleri*）*Adh*–1 基因的启动子 [24,25]，并具有其自身增强子的额外拷贝，BOX B[16,34] 插入到上游以提高其表达水平。报告基因（*17-hsp70/lacz*）也是复合基因，在果蝇 *hsp70* 基因上的 TATA 盒，携带紧邻上游的四个 GAL4 17-mer 序列，这些序列将启动大肠杆菌 β– 半乳糖苷酶编码基因（*lacz*）的转录。17-mer 序列是 GAL4 高亲和性的结合位点（见下文）。每个基因都含有来自 *hsp70* 的转录终止序列。效应基因和报告基因分别通过 P 因子转入黑腹果蝇体基因组内 [21,22]。

方法. 效应基因的 *Adh* 启动子包含一个来自果蝇 *Adh*–1 基因 5′ 侧翼区的 *Bgl*II/*Bal*I 片段，侧翼区包括自转录起始点至紧邻 ATG 起始密码子下游的 –1.5 kb 到 +58 bp 之间的区域。在 *Bal*I 位点插入一个 *Bam*HI 接头，包含 BOX B 的长度为 100 bp 的 *Sac*I 连接的 DNA 片段（*Adh*–1 转录起始位点 –282~–181 的区域）的三个拷贝被克隆到 –1.45 kb 处的 *Sna*BI 位点。GAL4 编码序列在 *Bam*HI 位点与 *Adh* 启动子融合，该 *Bam*HI 位点通过 pLPK-C15[26] 上 GAL4 非翻译引导序列内的一个 *Hind*III 位点插入在 *Adh*–1 基因的 ATG 起始密码子下游。利用错配引物造成的定点突变 [27] 产生 *Adh*–1 引导序列与 GAL4 ATG 起始密码子的"完美"融合。报告基因是由 *hsp70/lacz* 基因（约翰·利斯及同事惠赠）开始构建，该基因包含果蝇 *hsp70* 中从 –43 即 TATA 盒上游 10 bp 到 +265 的一段序列（因此包含启动子和开始的七个密码子），并以符合读码框架的形式与大肠杆菌的 *lacz* 基因融合。pMH100[15] 的 29 bp *Kpn*I/*Pst*I 片段的四个拷贝被克隆到 pSP731ac2（迪安·法尔布惠赠）中 *hsp70/lacz* 基因上游的 *Kpn*I 位点，上述片段包含高亲和性的（梅尔文·霍利斯和马克·普塔什尼，未发表数据；参考文献 15）17-mer GAL4 识别位点（*Sca*I 17-mer：5′-CGGAGTACTGTCCTCCG-3′），而 pSP731ac2 则是将 *hsp70/lacz* 基因作为一个 *Sal*I 片段克隆到 pSP73（参考文献 28）的 *Sal*I 位点。一个包含效应基因的 4.8 kb 的 *Xba*I 片段和一个包含报告基因的 3.6 kb 的 *Xba*I 片段分别以与红眼基因（*rosy*）相同的转录方向克隆到 P 因子转化载体 C70TX（迪安·法尔布惠赠）中。C70TX 是通过将一个 *Xba*I 接头插入在 C70T（约翰·利斯及同事惠赠）的 *Sal*I 位点上构建出来的，C70T 是 Carnegie 20（参考文献 29）的一个衍生物，在 *Sal*I 位点处包含 *hsp70* 基因终止序列的一个 250 bp *Sal*I/*Xho*I 片段。P 因子质粒通过氯化铯–溴化乙锭梯度分带纯化，并以 300 μg·ml⁻¹ 的浓度与辅助质粒 pπ25.7wc[30]（70 μg·ml⁻¹）共同注射到上文说过的黑腹果蝇 *ry*⁵⁰⁶ 株系的胚胎中 [21,22]。效应质粒的注射浓度为 100 μg·ml⁻¹，因为即使注射浓度再低一些也只有很少的胚胎能活过一龄幼虫期。胚胎显微注射后成活的成虫与 *ry*⁵⁰⁶ 株系果蝇回交。在回交后代中，通过野生型（*ry*⁺）眼睛颜色分辨出种系转化体。含有杂合 P 因子的回交后代被用来进行效应基因与报告基因的杂交。所有酶促反应和 DNA 操作均采用标准条件和技术进行。果蝇在 25 ℃ 用标准燕麦培养。

The effector and reporter genes were separately introduced into the *D. melanogaster* genome by P element transformation[21,22] (Fig. 1 legend). Three independent effector transformant lines were separately mated to nine independent reporter transformant lines. Twelve larval progeny of each cross were tested for expression of the reporter gene by a histochemical staining assay for β-galactosidase activity (Fig. 4 legend). The flies transformed with the effector and reporter genes were each heterozygous for the respective P elements (Fig. 1 legend), and so we expected one fourth of their larval progeny to carry one copy of each gene.

In each of the 27 crosses, we detected β-galactosidase activity in~one quarter of the larval progeny. In all of these larvae, enzyme activity was observed at high levels in the fat body and anterior midgut (Fig. 2), two of the tissues in which we expect the *Adh* promoter of the effector gene to be active. Also as expected, we detected variable levels of β-galactosidase activity in the hindgut and tracheae (Figs 2 and 3). In the middle midgut and Malpighian tubules, two other tissues in which we expect the *Adh* promoter of the effector gene to be active, we detected enzyme activity in only a small number of larvae, and then only in a few cells (data not shown); perhaps the *Adh/GAL4* transcript or GAL4 itself is particularly unstable in these two tissues. β-galactosidase activity was never detected in tissues other than those in which we expect the *Adh* promoter of the effector gene to be active (Figs 3 and 4), and no β-galactosidase activity (data not shown) nor reporter transcripts (Fig. 2) were detected in larvae transformed with the reporter gene alone. Furthermore, neither β-galactosidase activity (data not shown; see Fig. 3) nor transcripts (Fig. 2) were detected from a reporter gene lacking the 17-mers. GAL4-activated transcription of the reporter gene was initiated at the same start point as was transcription of the reporter gene activated by a *Drosophila Adh* enhancer (Fig. 2). GAL4 bound to the 17-mers stimulated transcription as efficiently as the *Drosophila* enhancer (Fig. 2 legend).

通过 P 因子转化将效应基因及报告基因分别转入到黑腹果蝇基因组内 [21,22]（图 1 注）。三个独立的效应基因转化系分别与九个独立的报告基因转化系交配。用组织化学染色法分别对每个杂交组合 12 个幼虫后代中报告基因表达的 β− 半乳糖苷酶活性进行检测（图 4 注）。转化了效应基因和报告基因的果蝇各自所含的 P 因子都是杂合的（图 1 注），因此我们预计其幼虫后代中有四分之一各含有每个基因的一个拷贝。

对 27 个杂交组合，我们检测了约四分之一幼虫后代的 β− 半乳糖苷酶活性。在所有幼虫的脂肪体和前部中肠都检测到了高水平的酶活性（图 2），我们预计这两个组织中效应基因的 Adh 启动子应处于激活状态。而在后肠和气管中我们观察到 β− 半乳糖苷酶活性水平是变化的，这也与我们的预期相符（图 2 和 3）。在我们期望的效应基因的 Adh 启动子呈激活状态的另外两个组织——中部中肠和马氏管中，我们仅在少量幼虫的少数细胞中观察到了酶活性（数据未显示），这可能是 Adh/GAL4 转录本或 GAL4 自身在这两个组织中极不稳定。除了我们预计的效应基因的 Adh 启动子呈激活状态的组织外，未在其他组织中检测到 β− 半乳糖苷酶活性（图 3 和 4），并且在报告基因单独转化的幼虫中既未检测到 β− 半乳糖苷酶活性（数据未显示）也未检测到报告基因转录本（图 2）。此外，缺少 17-mer 的报告基因转化幼虫中也均未检测到 β− 半乳糖苷酶活性（数据未显示，见图 3）和转录本（图 2）。GAL4 与果蝇 Adh 增强子激活的报告基因的转录起始点相同（图 2）。GAL4 结合到 17-mer 上激活转录的效率与果蝇增强子相同（图 2 注）。

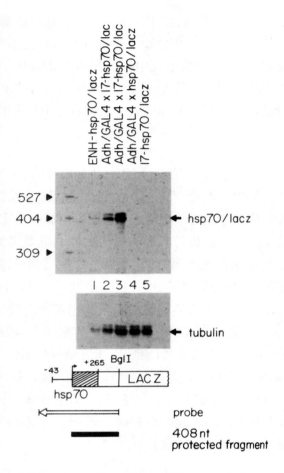

Fig. 2. Reporter gene transcripts in transformed larvae. The transcription start site of the reporter gene (*17-hsp70/lacz*) in the transformed larvae or larval progeny of the crosses indicated was assayed by quantitative RNAse protection[32] using the uniformly ^{32}P-labelled RNA probe shown, complementary to the 5′ end of the reporter transcripts, and also an RNA probe complementary to the endogenous α1-*tubulin* gene as an internal control for mRNA levels. ENH-*hsp70/lacz* (lane 1) are transformants (a gift of Dean Falb) carrying a gene like the reporter, except the enhancer of the *D. melanogaster Adh* gene's distal promoter (−660 to −128 from the distal transcription start site; Dean Falb and T.M., unpublished data) was installed upstream of the truncated *hsp70* promoter instead of the GAL4 17-mers. Two independent effector (*Adh/GAL4*) transformant lines were crossed with the same reporter (*17-hsp70/lacz*) line in lanes 2 and 3. Identical fragments of the reporter transcripts were protected by the probe in lanes 1–3. The appearance of two bands is probably an artefact of the RNAse digestion. Consistent with the β-galactosidase activity assay, no protected fragments were detected in larval progeny of a cross of the effector and a reporter with no 17-mers (*hsp70/lacz*; lane 4), or in larvae transformed with the reporter gene alone (lane 5). (Flies transformed with the *hsp70/lacz* gene, which lacks the 17-mers, were a gift of Dean Falb.) An approximation of the relative strengths of the GAL4 enhancer and the particular *Drosophila Adh* enhancer in ENH-*hsp70/lacz* was obtained by densitometry of appropriate autoradiographic exposures of the *hsp70/lacz* and tubulin protected fragments in lanes 1–3. The ratios of *hsp70/lacz* to tubulin signals were corrected for gene copy number and then normalized to the ratio obtained for lane 1, which was arbitrarily assigned the value 1.0: the results were 0.3 (lane 2) and 1.2 (lane 3). Thus, GAL4 bound to the 17-mers is comparable with the *Adh* enhancer in its ability to activate transcription of the reporter gene.

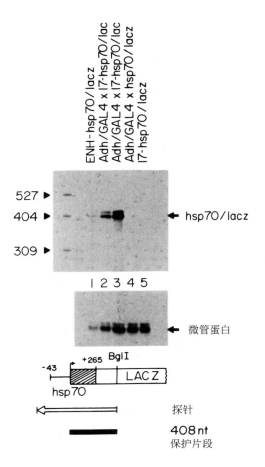

图 2. 转化幼虫中报告基因的转录产物。转化幼虫或杂交的幼虫后代中报告基因（*17-hsp70/lacz*）转录起始点通过定量 RNA 酶保护分析，用一段与报告基因转录本 5′ 末端互补的 ^{32}P 均一标记的 RNA 探针显示，还有一个与内源 α1 微管蛋白基因互补的 RNA 探针作为 mRNA 水平的内参。ENH-*hsp70/lacz*（泳道 1）是一个携带与报告基因相似的基因的转化子（迪安·法尔布赠），二者的唯一区别是将黑腹果蝇 *Adh* 基因远端启动子的增强子（远端转录起始位点 –660 到 –128 的区域；迪安·法尔布和汤姆·马尼阿蒂斯，未发表数据）而不是 GAL4 17-mer 序列安装在截短的 *hsp70* 启动子上游。泳道 2 和 3 分别显示两个独立的效应基因（*Adh/GAL4*）转化系与同一个报告基因（*17-hsp70/lacz*）转化系杂交的结果。在 1~3 泳道中，相同的报告基因转录物片段被探针保护。泳道上显示的两条带可能是 RNA 酶消化的人为效应。与 β– 半乳糖苷酶活性实验结果相一致，在效应基因和缺少 17-mer 序列的报告基因（*hsp70/lacz*，泳道 4）的杂交幼虫后代或报告基因独自转化的幼虫（泳道 5）中未检测到保护片段。（缺少 17-mer 序列的 *hsp70/lacz* 基因转化的果蝇成虫为迪安·法尔布惠赠。）通过对泳道 1~3 中的 *hsp70/lacz* 和微管蛋白保护片段适当曝光的放射自显影照片的密度计量，显示 GAL4 增强子和 ENH-*hsp70/lacz* 中果蝇的 *Adh* 增强子的相对强度接近。*hsp70/lacz* 与微管蛋白的信号比率通过基因拷贝数修正，并对泳道 1 的数据进行归一化，设定其值为 1.0 后；实验结果是 0.3（泳道 2）和 1.2（泳道 3）。因此，结合于 17-mer 序列的 GAL4 与 *Adh* 增强子在激活报告基因转录的能力上是相当的。

Methods. RNA was prepared as previously described[24,25] from actively feeding third instar larvae, or from ENH-*hsp70/lacz* adults. Two uniformly ^{32}P-labelled RNA probes were transcribed with SP6 RNA polymerase as described[33], from the plasmids SP6-αtub[25] (a gift of Vicki Corbin) and SP6-hslac. SP6-hslac was constructed by ligating a ~450 bp *Bgl*II/*Bgl*I fragment (the *Bgl*I end was treated with T4 DNA polymerase) of pSP73lac2 (see Fig. 1 legend) into pSP72 (ref. 28) digested with *Bgl*II and *Sma*I. Before transcription, SP6-hslac was digested with *Bgl*II, resulting in a ~450 nucleotide (nt) probe. The SP6-αtub probe[25] protected a 90 nt fragment of the endogenous α1-tubulin gene transcripts. As shown, the SP6-hslac probe protected a 408 nt fragment of the *hsp70/lacz* fusion gene transcripts. Five-forty μg of each RNA preparation was hybridized simultaneously with the ^{32}P-labelled RNA probes as previously described[25]. RNAse digestion conditions were also as described[25]. Samples were electrophoresed on a 6% denaturing acrylamide gel. The top portion of the gel is a longer autoradiographic exposure than the bottom portion.

	Summary of β-galactosidase Activity in Larval Tissues												
	fb	mt	amg	mmg	hg	tr	gc	pro	pmg	di	br	sg	ov/ts
Adh/lacz (6)	+	+	+	+	var	var	−	−	−	−	−	−	−
Adh/GAL4 (3) ; 17-hsp70/lacz (9)	+	+/−	+	+/−	var	var	−	−	−	−	−	−	−

Fig. 3. Tissue specificity of β-galactosidase activity in transformed larvae. The tissue specificity of β-galactosidase activity, detected by histochemical staining, in *Adh/lacz* transformant larvae or in larvae carrying both the effector (*Adh/GAL4*) and reporter (*17-hsp70/lacz*) genes is summarized. The *Adh/lacz* gene is described in the legend to Fig. 4, and the effector and reporter genes are described in Fig. 1. The numbers in parentheses indicate the number of independent transformant lines assayed. The tissues indicated are: fat body (fb), Malpighian tubules (mt), anterior midgut (amg), middle midgut (mmg), hindgut (hg), tracheae (tr), gastric caecae (gc), proventriculus (pro), posterior midgut (pmg), imaginal discs (di), brain (br), salivary glands (sg), ovaries and testes (ov/ts). +, High staining intensities in all lines. −, Staining was never seen, +/−, Staining was observed in some larvae, and only at a low level in a few cells. Variable staining is indicated as var: by variable we mean that the staining intensity varied from high to none within or between different lines or crosses. No β-galactosidase activity was detected with a reporter gene lacking 17-mers, nor in larvae transformed with the reporter gene alone (data not shown).

a

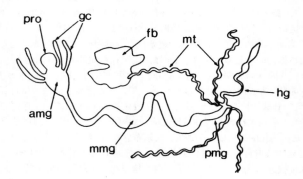

方法。RNA 来自于活跃进食的三龄幼虫或 ENH-*hsp70/lacz* 成虫，制备方法按前人描述 [24,25]。如前人描述 [33]，用 SP6 RNA 聚合酶从质粒 SP6-αtub[25]（维基·科尔宾惠赠）和 SP6-hslac 转录出两个均一 [32]P 标记的 RNA 探针。SP6-hslac 的构建是通过将 pSP73*lac2*（见图 1 注）的一个约 450 bp 的 *Bgl*II/*Bgl*I 片段（*Bgl*I 末端用 T4 DNA 聚合酶处理）连接到用 *Bgl*II 和 *Sma*I 消化的 pSP72（见参考文献 28）上完成的。转录前 SP6-hslac 用 *Bgl*II 消化，产生一段约 450 核苷酸（nt）的探针。SP6-αtub 探针 [25] 保护内源 α1-微管蛋白基因转录本的一个 90 nt 片段。如图所示，SP6-hslac 探针保护 *hsp70/lacz* 融合基因转录本的一个 408 nt 片段。如前所述，5～40 μg 的 RNA 样品与 [32]P 标记的 RNA 探针同时进行杂交 [25]。RNA 酶消化条件同样参照文献描述 [25]。样品经 6% 的变性丙烯酰胺凝胶电泳。凝胶上部曝光时间比底部略长。

在幼虫组织中β-半乳苷酶活性总结

	fb	mt	amg	mmg	hg	tr	gc	pro	pmg	di	br	sg	ov/ts
Adh/lacz (6)	+	+	+	+	var	var	−	−	−	−	−	−	−
Adh/GAL4 (3) ; 17-hsp70/lacz (9)	+	+/−	+	+/−	var	var	−	−	−	−	−	−	−

图 3. 在转化幼虫中 β- 半乳糖苷酶活性的组织特异性。通过组织化学染色观察，在 *Adh/lacz* 转化幼虫或者同时携带效应基因（*Adh/GAL4*）和报告基因（*17-hsp70/lacz*）的幼虫中 β- 半乳糖苷酶活性组织特异性总结如图 3。*Adh/lacz* 基因在图 4 注解中有描述，效应基因和报告基因在图 1 注解中有描述。括号中的数字表示检测的独立转化系数目。组织表示符号如下：脂肪体（fb）、马氏管（mt）、前部中肠（amg）、中部中肠（mmg）、后肠（hg）、气管（tr）、胃盲囊（gc）、前胃（pro）、后部中肠（pmg）、成虫盘（di）、脑（br）、唾液腺（sg）、卵巢和睾丸（ov/ts）。+，所有种系中染色强度都很高；−，从未观察到染色；+/−，只在部分幼虫中的少数细胞中观察到低强度的染色。染色变化用 var 表示：所谓染色变化是指在不同株系或杂交后代之间染色强度从高到无。在缺少 17-mer 的报告基因或报告基因单独转化的幼虫中未检测到 β- 半乳糖苷酶活性（数据未显示）。

a

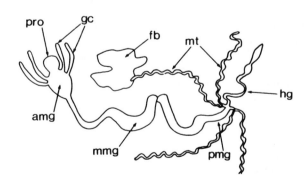

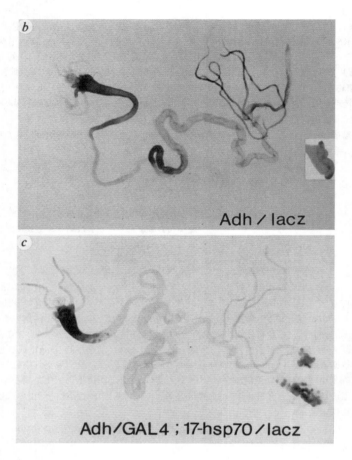

Fig. 4. β-galactosidase activity in larval tissues of P element transformants. *a*, Diagram of the larval tissues in the photographs beneath: gastric caecae (gc), proventriculus (pro), anterior midgut (amg), middle midgut (mmg), posterior midgut (pmg), Malpighian tubules (mt), fat body (fb), and hindgut (hg) are indicated. *b*, β-galactosidase activity in third instar larvae of six independent lines transformed with an *Adh/lacz* hybrid gene was visualized by a histochemical stain. The hybrid gene contains the same *Adh* promoter as in the effector gene, but here, fused in-frame to the *E. coli lacz* gene rather than to GAL4[16,34]. Blue staining is observed only in the fat body, Malpighian tubules, anterior midgut, middle midgut, and in this particular larva, also in the hindgut. Expression of β-galactosidase in the hindgut, and also in the tracheae, was variable (see refs 16, 34 and Fig. 3). *c*, A third instar larva carrying both the effector (*Adh/GAL4*) and the reporter (*17-hsp70/lacz*) genes expressed β-galactosidase in the fat body and anterior midgut. Other larvae expressed β-galactosidase in the hindgut and/or tracheae, and low levels of β-galactosidase activity were sometimes detected in a few cells of the middle midgut or Malpighian tubules (see Fig. 3).

Methods. Transformant larvae were dissected in a solution of 1% glutaraldehyde in 0.1 M $NaPO_4$ pH 7.0, 1 mM $MgCl_2$. After 15 min, the tissues were transferred to a stain solution consisting of 10 mM $NaPO_4$ pH 7.0, 150 mM NaCl, 1 mM $MgCl_2$, 3.3 mM K_4Fe $(CN)_6$ $3H_2O$, 3.3 mM K_4Fe $(CN)_4$ $3H_2O$, and 0.2% X-gal dissolved as a 2% solution in dimethylformamide (Pieter Wensink, personal communication). After staining for 15 min (*a*) or 1 h (*b*), the tissues were placed in a drop of 70% glycerol on a slide, covered with a coverslip and photographed.

We have shown that a single protein, GAL4, when expressed in a tissue specific manner, generates tissue specific gene expression in *Drosophila*. Typical tissue specific enhancers (the

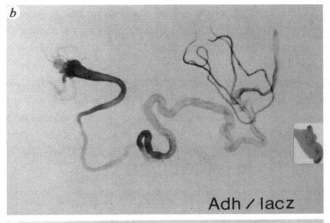

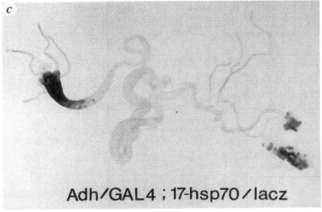

图 4. P 因子转化体幼虫组织的 β–半乳糖苷酶活性。*a*，下面照片中幼虫组织的示意图：胃肠盲囊 (gc)、前胃 (pro)、前部中肠 (amg)、中部中肠 (mmg)、后部中肠 (pmg)、马氏管 (mt)、脂肪体 (fb) 和后肠 (hg)。*b*，通过组织染色法观察到的 *Adh/lacz* 杂合基因转化的六个独立体系的三龄幼虫中 β–半乳糖苷酶活性。杂合基因包含与效应基因相同的 *Adh* 启动子，但它以符合读码框架的形式与大肠杆菌 *lacz* 基因而不是 GAL4 融合[16,34]。蓝色染料仅在脂肪体 (ft)、马氏管 (mt)、前部中肠 (amg)、中部中肠 (mmg) 观察到，在这只特定幼虫的后肠 (hg) 中也观察到。β–半乳糖苷酶在后肠 (hg) 和气管 (tr) 中的表达是变化的（见参考文献 16、34 和图 3）。*c*，同时携带效应基因 (*Adh/GAL4*) 和报告基因 (*17hsp70/ lacz*) 的三龄幼虫在脂肪体 (ft) 和前部中肠 (amg) 中表达 β–半乳糖苷酶。其他幼虫在后肠 (hg) 和（或）气管 (tr) 中表达 β–半乳糖苷酶，有时在中肠或马氏管的少数细胞中可观察到低水平的 β–半乳糖苷酶活性（见图 3）。

方法。在含 0.1 M NaPO₄ pH 7.0，1 mM MgCl₂ 的 1% 的戊二醛溶液中解剖转化体幼虫。15 分钟后，将组织转移到染液中，染液包含 10 mM NaPO₄ pH 7.0，150 mM NaCl，1 mM MgCl₂，3.3 mM K₄Fe(CN)₆·3H₂O，3.3 mM K₄Fe(CN)₄·3H₂O 及 0.2% 的半乳糖苷，半乳糖苷是在二甲基甲酰胺中溶解成 2% 的溶液（彼得·文辛克，个人交流）。分别在染色 15 分钟 (*a*) 或 1 小时后 (*b*) 将组织放在载玻片上的 70% 的甘油液滴中，盖上盖玻片并拍照。

　　我们展示了当一个 GAL4 蛋白在果蝇中以组织特异性方式表达时，可造成组织特异的基因表达。典型的组织特异性增强子（研究最清楚的是哺乳动物基因的增强

best characterized are those of mammalian genes) interact with several different proteins (ref. 23 and refs therein). Our results suggest that the apparent complexity of tissue specific enhancers is not necessary for their function as transcriptional activators. Perhaps that complexity is exploited to obtain intricate patterns of gene control from a relatively small number of regulatory proteins. The ability of GAL4 to activate mammalian and *Drosophila* promoters suggests that the protein with which DNA-bound GAL4 interacts to stimulate transcription in yeast—perhaps RNA polymerase—has a close homologue in higher eukaryotes. It seems likely that the mechanism of action of at least one class of gene activators is conserved between yeast, mammalian cells and *Drosophila*.

We thank Dean Falb for generous gifts of unpublished plasmids and transformant lines, and Gerald Rubin, Melvyn Hollis, Liam Keegan and John Lis for plasmids. This work was supported by grants from the American Cancer Society (to M.P.) and the National Institutes of Health (to T.M.).

(**332**, 853-856; 1988)

Janice A. Fischer, Edward Giniger, Tom Maniatis & Mark Ptashne
Department of Biochemistry and Molecular Biology, Harvard University, 7 Divinity Avenue, Cambridge, Massachusetts 02138, USA

Received 29 February; accepted 14 March 1988.

References:

1. Guarente, L., Yocum, R. R. & Gifford, P. *Proc. Natl. Acad. Sci. U.S.A.* **79**, 7410-7414 (1982).

2. Yocum, R. R., Hanley, S., West, R. W., Jr. & Ptashne, M. *Molec. Cell. Biol.* **4**, 1985-1998 (1984).

3. West, R. W., Jr., Yocum, R. & Ptashne, M. *Molec. Cell. Biol.* **4**, 2467-2478 (1984).

4. Johnston, M. & Davis, R. W. *Molec. Cell. Biol.* **4**, 1440-1448 (1984).

5. Bram, R. & Kornberg, R. D. *Proc. Natl. Acad. Sci. U.S.A.* **82**, 43-47 (1985).

6. Giniger, E., Varnum, S. M. & Ptashne, M. *Cell* **40**, 767-774 (1985).

7. Brent, R. & Ptashne, M. *Cell* **43**, 729-736 (1985).

8. Keegan, L., Gill, G. & Ptashne, M. *Science* **231**, 699-704 (1986).

9. Ma, J. & Ptashne, M. *Cell* **48**, 847-853 (1987).

10. Ma, J. & Ptashne, M. *Cell* **51**, 113-119 (1987).

11. Gill, G. & Ptashne, M. *Cell* **51**, 121-126 (1987).

12. Hope, I. A. & Struhl, K. *Cell* **46**, 885-894 (1986).

13. Giniger, E. & Ptashne, M. *Nature* **330**, 670-672 (1987).

14. Kakidani, H. & Ptashne, M. *Cell* **52**, 161-167 (1987).

15. Webster, N., Jin, J. R., Green, S., Hollis, M. & Chambon, P. *Cell* **52**, 169-178 (1987).

16. Fischer, J. A. thesis Harvard Univ. (1987).

17. Pelham, H. R. B. *Cell* **30**, 517-538 (1982).

18. Lis, J. T., Simon, J. A. & Sutton, C. A. *Cell* **35**, 403-410 (1983).

19. Dudler, R. & Travers, A. A. *Cell* **38**, 391-398 (1984).

20. Cohen, R. S. & Meselson, M. *Proc. Natl. Acad. Sci. U.S.A.* **81**, 5509-5513 (1984).

21. Spradling, A. C. & Rubin, G. M. *Science* **218**, 341-347 (1982).

22. Rubin, G. M. & Spradling, A. C. *Science* **218**, 348-353 (1982).

23. Maniatis, T., Goodbourn, S. & Fischer, J. A. *Science* **236**, 1237-1245 (1987).

24. Fischer, J. A. & Maniatis, T. *Nucleic Acids Res.* **13**, 6899-6917 (1985).

子）可以与几个不同的蛋白相互作用（参考文献 23 及其中的文献）。我们的实验结果表明组织特异性增强子的复杂性并不是其转录活化功能所必需的。或许这种复杂性是通过一小部分的调节蛋白的调控来达到精细的基因控制模式。GAL4 具有激活哺乳动物和果蝇启动子的能力，这提示我们，在酵母中一个与结合了 DNA 的 GAL4 相互作用的蛋白（或许是 RNA 聚合酶）可激活转录，它与高等真核生物中的 RNA 聚合酶高度同源。这表明至少有一类基因活化因子的作用机制很可能在酵母、哺乳动物细胞和果蝇之间是保守的。

我们感谢迪安·法尔布慷慨地赠予未发表的质粒和转化体系，感谢杰拉尔德·鲁宾、梅尔文·霍利斯、利亚姆·基根和约翰·利斯赠予质粒。本研究受到美国癌症协会（由马克·普塔什尼承担）和美国国家卫生研究院（由汤姆·马尼阿蒂斯承担）的资助。

（李梅 翻译；胡松年 审稿）

25. Fischer, J. A. & Maniatis, T. *EMBO J.* **5**, 1275-1289 (1986).

26. Silver, P. A., Keegan, L. P. & Ptashne, M. *Proc. Natl. Acad. Sci. U.S.A.* **81**, 5951-5955(1984).

27. Zoller, M. J. & Smith, M. *Meth. Enzym.* **100**, 469-500 (1983).

28. Krieg, P. A. & Melton, D. A. *Meth. Enzym. Recomb. DNA.* **155**, 397-415 (1987).

29. Rubin, G. M. & Spradling, A. C. *Nucleic Acids Res.* **11**, 6341-6351 (1983).

30. Karess, R. E. & Rubin, G. M. *Cell* **38**, 135-146 (1984).

31. Maniatis, T., Fritsch, E. F., Sambrook, J. *Molecular Cloning: A Laboratory Manual* (Cold Spring Harbor Laboratory, New York, 1982).

32. Zinn, K., DiMaio, D. & Maniatis, T. *Cell* **34**, 865-879 (1983).

33. Melton, D. A., Krieg, P. A., Rebagliati, M. R., Maniatis, T., Zinn, K. & Green, M. *Nucleic Acids Res.* **12**, 7035-7056.

34. Fischer, J. A. & Maniatis, T. *Cell* **53** (in the press).

Mysteries of HIV: Challenges for Therapy and Prevention

J. A. Levy

Editor's Note

Here virologist Jay Levy, who co-discovered HIV five years earlier, describes the unsolved problems in HIV research. Four key areas deserve special attention, namely the viral and cellular determinants of infection, the mechanisms generating different strains, the factors influencing progression to disease and an understanding of how HIV causes disease. Subsequent research into these areas has, as Levy correctly speculated, greatly influenced therapeutic and prophylactic design. In particular, the development and refinement of anti-retroviral drugs paved the way for combination therapy, which continues to reduce morbidity and increase quality of life in HIV-positive people. Although no cure or vaccine currently exists, research into these and other areas should prove crucial in the fight against HIV.

A number of problems still surround infection by the human immunodeficiency virus and the pathogenesis of AIDS. Solutions to the problems would provide valuable information for the development of antiviral therapy and a vaccine.

DESPITE substantial progress in our understanding of the human immunodeficiency virus (HIV), a number of mysteries remain concerning the virus, its target cells and the responses of the infected host. If a rational approach to treatment and therapy of AIDS is to be successful, solutions to the mysteries must be found. From my perspective, the four major questions are: what are the viral and cellular determinants of infection, what mechanisms generate the different HIV strains, how does HIV cause disease, and what determines the course from infection to disease?

What Governs Viral Tropism?

Recognition that the CD4 antigen on the surface of human helper T lymphocytes is a major cellular receptor for the HIV envelope protein gp120[1] led to the inference that endocytosis of the virus by cells expressing the CD4 molecule is an initial step in infection. But although mouse cells expressing human CD4 (as a result of experimental transfection) can bind HIV to the cell surface, they do not produce virus[2]. Moreover, HIV can infect cells lacking CD4, such as brain astrocyte cell lines[3] and human fibroblasts[4], and the virus is detected in endothelial[5] and epithelial[6] cells of seropositive individuals. Together, these observations strongly suggest that there are also mechanisms that do not involve CD4 by which HIV initially interacts with some cells.

Fusion of the target cell membrane with the HIV transmembrane envelope protein gp41

神秘的HIV：它的治疗和预防面临的挑战

利维

编者按

五年前共同发现HIV的病毒学家杰伊·利维描述了HIV研究中未解决的问题。四个关键的领域值得给予特殊关注：病毒与细胞感染的决定因素，不同病株的产生机制，影响疾病进展的因素和对于HIV引发疾病的理解。正如利维所说，随后对于这些领域的研究，极大地影响了治疗和预防药物的开发。特别是抗逆转录病毒药物的开发和完善为联合治疗铺平了道路，联合治疗可以持续减少发病率和提高HIV阳性患者的生活质量。尽管现在没有治愈的方法和疫苗，但是在这些领域和其他领域内的研究对抵抗HIV是至关重要的。

围绕人类免疫缺陷病毒感染和艾滋病的发病机理仍旧存在许多问题。这些问题的解决将会为抗病毒治疗和疫苗研发提供有价值的信息。

尽管我们在人类免疫缺陷病毒（HIV）的理解上已经取得了实质性的进展，但是关于 HIV 病毒还有很多未解之谜，如它的靶细胞和感染后宿主的反应。如果要寻找成功治疗 AIDS 的合理方法，那么我们必须解决这些难题。在我看来，这四个主要问题是：病毒和细胞感染的决定性因素是什么，不同 HIV 株的产生机制是什么，HIV 怎样引发疾病以及从感染到发病的过程中的决定因素是什么？

支配病毒亲嗜性的因素

我们认识到，人辅助 T 淋巴细胞表面的 CD4 抗原是 HIV 病毒包膜蛋白 gp120[1]主要的细胞受体，细胞表达 CD4 分子导致病毒通过胞吞作用进入细胞，这是感染的第一步。尽管表达人 CD4 的小鼠细胞（转染的实验结果）可以在细胞表面结合 HIV，但是它们不能产生 HIV 病毒颗粒[2]。另外，HIV 可以感染缺乏 CD4 的细胞，比如脑星形胶质细胞系[3] 和人成纤维细胞[4]，血清反应阳性的个体在内皮[5] 和上皮[6] 细胞里也发现 HIV 病毒。总之，这些观察结果有力地表明还存在另外一些机制，即在 HIV 病毒与某些细胞早期的相互作用过程中并不涉及 CD4。

靶细胞膜和 HIV 跨膜的包膜蛋白 gp41 融合可能是病毒进入细胞的一种方法。

is one possible alternative means of virus entry. It may operate alone or in concert with gp120. In support of a fusion process, infection by HIV appears to be pH-independent[7]. Moreover, part of the sequence of gp41 is similar to a sequence coding for the fusogenic glycoproteins of paramyxoviruses[8], and antibodies to the gp41 protein neutralize HIV[9]. In addition, antibody-dependent enhancement of virus infection can mediate HIV infection of cells[10]. As previously described for dengue and other viruses[11], virus-antibody complexes permit HIV infection of macrophages and T cells, most likely via the complement and/or Fc receptor.

These findings should prompt re-evaluation of the likelihood that soluble CD4 will be of major value in the prevention of HIV infection of cells and encourage the further search for methods to control the first steps in virus infection. It could be worth directing attention to the second conserved region of the viral gp120, which is not involved in CD4 attachment but is essential for early stages of infection[12].

The establishment of HIV infection requires several processes that are influenced by both viral and cellular factors. Strain variations in specific viral genes may, for example, account for the fact that, compared with blood isolates of HIV, isolates from the central nervous system replicate better in macrophages—the main HIV-expressing cell type of the brain[5]—than in T lymphocytes[13]. The properties of brain isolates may be reflected in the clinical observation of some infected individuals who have neurological defects without signs of immune deficiency[14]. Strain variations in specific viral genes such as the heterogenous *orf-B* region (see below) may also account for the lack of replication of some HIV isolates despite their efficient attachment to human $CD4^+$ T cells[15].

In other studies, cellular factors appear to determine virus replication. For instance, a single HIV isolate displays different levels of productive infection in peripheral blood mononuclear cells from various individuals[15]. Cultured mouse cells, in contrast to human cells, do not produce a substantial number of virus progeny after transfection with a biologically active DNA clone of HIV[16]. Cellular factors, such as the NF-κB protein, have been shown to interact with regulatory regions of HIV and enhance virus replication[17].

Defining the viral and cellular genes governing the host-range specificity of HIV is a major avenue of study. Experiments using recombinant HIVs, in which portions of macrophage-tropic and lymphocyte-tropic strains are combined, or using site-directed mutagenesis of biologically active DNA clones of these viruses should help clarify the viral genes involved. Assays of proteins found in selected cells or the use of somatic cell hybrids (mouse-human, for example) could uncover cellular factors influencing viral tropism. Clearly, the wide host range of HIV and the factors affecting virus replication are important variables to be defined for therapeutic strategies against viral infection of all cell types.

What Causes HIV Heterogeneity?

Biological heterogeneity of HIV is reflected by differences in host range, replicative

它可能单独起作用或者与 gp120 共同起作用。由于需要一个融合的过程，所以 HIV 的感染表现为非 pH 依赖性[7]。此外，gp41 的部分序列与副粘病毒膜融糖蛋白的编码序列相似[8]，且 gp41 蛋白的抗体可中和 HIV[9]。此外，病毒感染的抗体依赖性增强可介导 HIV 对细胞的感染[10]。就像以前报道的登革热病毒和其他病毒[11]一样，病毒–抗体复合物最有可能通过补体(和)或 Fc 受体允许 HIV 感染巨噬细胞和 T 细胞。

这些发现促进我们重新评估可溶的 CD4 扮演预防 HIV 感染细胞的主要角色的可能性，并激励我们深入寻找控制病毒感染第一步的方法。我们值得将注意力转向病毒 gp120 的第二个保守区，它没有参与 CD4 附着，但是在感染的早期是非常重要的[12]。

HIV 病毒感染的完成需要几个过程，这几个过程都受病毒和细胞因子的影响。某些病毒基因发生株变异可以说明这个事实，与从血液中分离出的 HIV 相比，从中枢神经系统分离的 HIV 病毒在巨噬细胞中——脑部主要表达 HIV 的细胞类型[5]——比在 T 淋巴细胞[13]中有更好的复制能力。这种脑部分离株的特性可以在一些有神经缺陷但是没有免疫缺陷迹象的感染者的临床观察中反映出来[14]。某些病毒基因的株变异，如 orf-B 区的异质性（如下），也可以解释某些 HIV 分离株虽然能有效地黏附人 CD4$^+$ T 细胞，但是无法复制的现象[15]。

在其他的研究中发现细胞因子对病毒的复制起到决定性作用。比如单个 HIV 分离株在不同个体的外周血单核细胞中表现出不同水平的生产性感染[15]。培养的小鼠细胞与人源细胞相比，经过具有生物活性的 HIV 的 DNA 克隆转染后，没有产生大量的病毒后代[16]。细胞因子，如 NF-κB 蛋白，已被证明可与 HIV 的调控区域相互作用，并增强病毒的复制[17]。

明确病毒和细胞基因调控 HIV 宿主范围的特异性是研究的主要途径。利用嗜巨噬细胞和嗜淋巴细胞病毒株的部分基因形成的重组 HIV 或者利用定点诱变的有生物学活性的病毒 DNA 克隆进行实验，有助于阐明所涉及的病毒基因。分析在选定的细胞或者杂交的体细胞（如小鼠和人）中发现的蛋白，可以揭示影响病毒亲嗜性的细胞因子。显然，对于所有类型细胞抗病毒感染的治疗策略来说，HIV 广泛的宿主范围和影响病毒复制的细胞因子都是需要定义的重要变量。

是什么引起了HIV的异质性？

HIV 的生物异质性反映在宿主范围、复制特性和感染细胞中的细胞病变作用的

properties and cytopathic effects in infected cells[18]. Restriction enzyme[19] and sequence analyses[20] of HIV isolates, as well as the patterns of neutralization of different isolates by antibodies,[21] also demonstrate genetic diversity, particularly in the envelope glycoprotein. (This is true not only of HIV-1 but also of the more recently identified HIV-2 subtype[22]). The mechanism responsible for generating these varying strains of virions is puzzling. One theoretical possibility is that the unintegrated proviral copies of HIV that accumulate during acute replicative infection[23] can undergo efficient genomic recombination leading to the evolution of infectious variants. The lack of genetic changes in HIV during long-term passage of the integrated virus in persistently infected cells[24] is consistent with this hypothesis.

Three explanations may account for the occurrence of envelope variants. First, the immunological reaction of the host selects specific spontaneous mutants which differ in their external envelope region. Thus far, this mechanism has only been observed with certain animal lentiviruses[25]. Second, mutations in the envelope, in contrast to other structural genes, can be tolerated during HIV replication. Third—and most speculatively—the HIV reverse transcriptase may be most error-prone when dealing with sequences for glycosylated proteins.

What Determines Pathogenesis?

An understanding of how HIV causes disease is a major research objective. As with any infectious agent, both viral and host determinants are involved.

Neuropathy. The disease in the central nervous system has been attributed by some investigators to the production by infected macrophages of cytokines that affect normal brain function[5,26]. HIV-infected brain capillary endothelial cells could compromise the maintenance of the blood–brain barrier, so permitting entry of toxic materials from the blood[5,26]. HIV also infects oligodendrocytes and astrocytes[3,5,14]. Compared with brain macrophages, only a small number of these glial cells produce viral RNA[4,5] but persistent or low replication of HIV in glial cells might affect their function. Since astrocytes maintain the integrity of the blood–brain barrier[27] and oligodendrocytes produce myelin, which is required for nerve conduction, the participation of these infected cells in AIDS neuropathy should be further evaluated. Finally, whether the neurologic disease results from long-term effects of HIV infection or specific pathogenic properties of a neurotropic strain[13,14] remains to be elucidated.

Enteropathy. HIV infection of enterochromaffin cells in the intestinal mucosa[6], perhaps by a process similar to that in the brain, could explain the chronic diarrhoea and malabsorption (particularly with duodenal involvement) observed in AIDS patients in the absence of any known bowel pathogens. These neuroendocrine cells migrate during embryogenesis from the neural crest and help regulate motility and digestive functions of the intestine. How their infection specifically accounts for the pathology is not known and the possible toxic effects of cytokines secreted by infected macrophages in the lamina propria needs to be considered.

不同 [18]，HIV 分离株的限制性内切酶 [19] 和序列分析 [20]，以及不同分离株中和抗体的模式 [21]，也证明遗传的多样性，尤其是包膜糖蛋白。（这是事实，不仅是 HIV-1，还有最近发现的 HIV-2 亚型也是如此 [22]）。产生这些不同病毒株的机制令人费解。理论上的可能性是，未整合的 HIV 前病毒的拷贝在急性复制感染期过程中累积 [23]，能发生高效的基因重组，导致有感染性的变异体的演变。在持续感染的细胞中的整合病毒在长期传代过程中，HIV 缺乏遗传变化 [24]，与这个假说一致。

三个解释可以说明包膜变异体的发生。首先，宿主免疫反应筛选特定的自发突变体，它与其他突变体的外部包膜区域不同。迄今为止，这个机制只在某些动物的慢病毒中观察到 [25]。第二，包膜的突变与其他结构基因相比，在 HIV 复制的过程中可被耐受。第三，最大胆的猜想是，处理糖基化蛋白的序列时，HIV 逆转录酶是最容易出错。

是什么决定了发病机理？

对 HIV 是如何导致疾病的理解是一个主要的研究目标。与任一感染原相同，是由病毒和宿主共同参与的。

神经病变 一些研究者将中枢神经系统疾病归因于被感染的巨噬细胞产生的细胞因子对脑正常功能的影响 [5,26]。被 HIV 感染的脑部毛细血管内皮细胞可能损害血脑屏障，使血液中的有毒物质能够进入 [5,26]。HIV 还感染少突胶质细胞和星形胶质细胞 [3,5,14]。与脑巨噬细胞相比，仅有少量的神经胶质细胞能够产生病毒 RNA [4,5]，但是 HIV 在神经胶质细胞中持续或者低水平的复制可能影响它们的功能。由于星形胶质细胞维持血脑屏障 [27] 的完整性和少突胶质细胞产生神经传导所需要的髓磷脂，因此感染细胞在艾滋病神经病变中的作用应进一步评估。最终，神经疾病是由于 HIV 感染的长期效应所引起的还是由一个嗜神经变异株的特殊病理症状所导致 [13,14]，仍有待阐明。

肠病变 HIV 感染肠黏膜中的肠嗜铬细胞 [6]，也许是通过与感染脑部相似的过程，这就可以解释在缺少任何已知的肠病原体的情况下，艾滋病人中观察到的慢性腹泻和吸收不良（尤其是十二指肠的参与）。在胚胎发生期，这些神经内分泌细胞从神经嵴中迁移出来，帮助调节肠道的蠕动和消化功能。感染的机制如何通过病理学来解释还是未知的，并且需要考虑固有层中被感染的巨噬细胞分泌的细胞因子可能的毒性作用。

Immunopathology. How HIV causes immune suppression presents the greatest enigma. The immune dysfunctions identified in HIV infection were first linked to the cytopathic effects of HIV on helper T lymphocytes that play a vital role in regulating immune function. These cells infected with HIV *in vitro* undergo syncytial formation by recruiting many uninfected cells before proceeding to cell death[1].

Several observations, however, have challenged this suggested explanation for HIV-induced immunopathology. First, despite extensive histopathological studies of infected individuals, little evidence exists for syncytial cell formation *in vivo*[28]. Second, the number of HIV-infected cells in the blood $(10^2-10^3$ per ml$)$[29] does not account for the quantity of cells lost over time in the infected host; moreover, CD4$^+$ cells infected by HIV can survive several weeks in culture[30]. Third, many HIV isolates obtained from immunologically suppressed individuals are not highly cytopathic *in vitro*[18,31] and non-cytopathic isolates of HIV have sometimes been associated with disease[22]. Finally, abnormalities of immune function are observed not only in HIV-infected helper T cells and macrophages but also in uninfected cells of the haematopoietic system (Table 1)[32].

Table 1. Immune function abnormalities in AIDS

T lymphocytes	**B lymphocytes**
(1) Decreased proliferative responses to mitogens, soluble antigens, and allogeneic cells.	(1) Polyclonal activation with hypergammaglobulinaemia and spontaneous plaque forming cells.
(2) Decreased lymphokine production (IL-2, gamma interferon) in response to antigen.	(2) Decreased humoral response to immunization.
(3) Decreased cytotoxic T lymphocyte activity against virus-infected cells.	(3) Production of autoantibodies.
Monocytes	**NK cells**
(1) Decreased chemotaxis.	(1) Decreased cytotoxic activity.
(2) Decreased IL-1 production (or production of an inhibitor of IL-1).	
(3) Decreased microbiocidal activity.	

These abnormalities appear to begin with acute depletion of T helper cells and proliferation of B cells; other defects, many revealed by *in vitro* studies, accumulate over time. Several of the immune abnormalities may result from the decrease in CD4$^+$ lymphocytes and cytokine production[32].

What other mechanisms could explain the immunological features of HIV pathogenesis (Table 2)? HIV infection is known to cause epiphenomena including decreased expression of immunological recognition sites, such as CD4 and the interleukin-2 (IL-2) receptor, and reduced production of cytokines such as IL-1, IL-2, and gamma interferon (Table 2)[32]. Loss of these molecules could have far reaching effects on other cells of the immune system. Moreover, HIV infection of progenitor cells could reduce the replenishment of circulating lymphocytes and macrophages. The disarray in immune function could generate T suppressor cells or factors[33] that further compromise the immune response. HIV envelope proteins have been found to be toxic or inhibitory to immune cells[34]. By circulating in the blood, these proteins may block the ability of lymphocytes to recognize or respond to foreign antigens and may interfere with the function of antigen-presenting cells.

免疫病理学 HIV 如何引起免疫抑制是最大的谜题。HIV 感染引起的免疫功能紊乱，首先与 HIV 对辅助 T 淋巴细胞的病变效应联系起来，该细胞在免疫功能调节中发挥重要作用。体外感染 HIV 的这些细胞在死亡之前募集未感染细胞形成合胞体[1]。

然而数个观察结果对 HIV 诱导的免疫病理学的解释提出质疑。首先，尽管有大量受感染的个体的组织病理学研究，但是很少有证据证明在体内可形成合胞体细胞[28]。第二，血液中感染 HIV 的细胞数量（每毫升 $10^2 \sim 10^3$ 个）[29]不能说明被感染宿主一段时间里丧失的细胞数量，而且被 HIV 感染的 $CD4^+$ 细胞在培养基中可以存活几周[30]。第三，在体外实验中许多从免疫抑制个体中获得的 HIV 分离株没有引起严重的细胞病变[18,31]，非细胞病变 HIV 分离株有时与疾病有关[22]。最后，免疫功能失常不仅仅在 HIV 感染的辅助 T 细胞和巨噬细胞中被观察到，在非感染的造血系统细胞中也有（表 1）[32]。

表 1. 艾滋病引起的免疫功能异常

T 淋巴细胞	B 淋巴细胞
(1) 减少有丝分裂原、可溶性抗原和异源细胞的增殖反应。 (2) 减少抗原反应产生的淋巴因子(IL-2和γ-干扰素)。 (3) 减少对病毒感染的细胞毒性T淋巴细胞的活性。	(1) 多克隆活化高γ球蛋白血症和自发空斑形成细胞。 (2) 减少体液免疫反应。 (3) 产生自身抗体。
单核细胞 (1) 趋化性下降。 (2) 减少IL-1的生成(或是生成IL-1抑制剂)。 (3) 杀菌活性下降。	**NK 细胞** (1) 细胞毒素活性下降。

这些异常似乎伴随着 T 辅助细胞的急速消耗和 B 细胞的增殖；体外实验证明其他的缺陷随着时间而积累。几个免疫异常可能由于 $CD4^+$ 淋巴细胞的减少和细胞因子产生的减少导致的[32]。

还有什么其他的机制可以解释 HIV 发病机理的免疫学特征呢（表 2）？我们已知 HIV 感染引起的附带现象包括免疫识别位点的表达的减少，如 CD4 和白细胞介素 –2 （IL-2）受体，和细胞因子产生的减少，如 IL-1、-2 和 γ 干扰素（表 2）[32]。这些分子的丧失对免疫系统其他细胞影响深远。另外，HIV 感染祖细胞能够减少外周血淋巴细胞和巨噬细胞的补充。免疫功能的紊乱能够产生 T 抑制细胞或因子[33]，它们能够进一步损害免疫应答。已发现 HIV 包膜蛋白对免疫细胞有毒害或抑制作用[34]。通过血液循环，这些蛋白可能会阻断淋巴细胞识别或应答外源抗原的能力，并且可能会干扰抗原提呈细胞的功能。

Table 2. Mechanisms of immune suppression by HIV infection

Direct mechanisms	Indirect mechanisms
(1) HIV cytocidal effect on CD4⁺ lymphocytes.	(1) Generation of suppressor T cells and/or factors.
(2) Functional defects in infected CD4⁺ cells:	(2) Toxic or inhibitory effects of viral protein.
(a) decreased expression of cell surface proteins (for example, IL-2 receptor, CD4);	(3) Immune complex formation.
(b) impaired production of lymphokines such as IL-2 or gamma interferon.	(4) Induction of autoimmune phenomena:
(3) Impaired antigen presentation and/or monokine production by infected macrophages; cell death.	(a) autoantibodies resulting from polyclonal B cell activation or antigen mimicry;
	(b) virus mediated, enhanced immunogenicity of normal cellular proteins.
	(5) Cytotoxic cell activity against viral or self proteins.

In addition, HIV is associated, often early in the infection, with a polyclonal activation of B cells resulting in hypergammaglobulinaemia[32]. Some of these antibodies form immune complexes that can be detrimental to the immune system; some react with self-proteins, leading to autoimmunity[35]. The destruction of activated helper T cells by lymphocytotoxic autoantibodies directed against a normal cellular protein (p18) has been suggested as one mechanism for the substantial loss of CD4⁺ cells in advanced disease[35]. Antibodies and/or cytotoxic cells directed against other shared antigens on immune cells can induce further abnormalities in immune function or haematopoiesis[36,37]. Finally, antibody-dependent cellular cytotoxicity reacting against envelope proteins bound to ligands on uninfected CD4⁺ cells could be a factor in the pathogenic process[38]. Clearly, multiple effects of HIV infection on the immune system, both direct and indirect, need to be fully evaluated to appreciate their potential role in the immunological abnormalities observed.

Cytopathology. A critical question surrounding HIV pathogenesis is how the virus kills the cell. In general, helper T lymphocytes are most susceptible to the cytopathic effects of HIV; in culture, they often undergo fusion before cell death. Macrophage killing by some strains of the virus has also been observed[1]. Syncytial formation by T cells, however, does not always proceed cell death; infected cells can die without undergoing fusion[39]. The viral envelope gp120, alone or through its interaction with CD4, could be responsible for cell death[34,40,43]. Direct inoculation of inactivated virus or the envelope gp120 onto peripheral blood mononuclear cells can also produce cytopathic effects[34,41]. Cell death may result from direct membrane disruption involving calcium channels[42] and/or phospholipid synthesis[43]. The accumulation of unintegrated proviral copies of HIV DNA is an attractive explanation for cytopathology since it is associated with cell death in other retrovirus systems[44]. Finally, whether the cytopathology of HIV in cell culture mirrors pathogenesis in the host awaits development of an appropriate animal model.

What Influences Progression to Disease?

Long-term follow-up studies of HIV seropositive individuals indicate that about a third will remain free of symptoms for at least seven years[45]. Moreover, some healthy seropositive individuals lose a large proportion of their CD4⁺ lymphocytes, yet do not

表 2. HIV 感染引起免疫抑制的机制

直接机制	间接机制

(1) HIV 对 CD4[+] 淋巴细胞的杀细胞效应。
(2) 被感染的 CD4[+] 细胞的功能缺失：
    (a) 细胞表面蛋白表达减少(比如 IL-2受体、CD4)；
    (b) 减少淋巴因子的产生，如 IL-2 或 γ 干扰素。
(3) 减少被感染的巨噬细胞的抗原提呈和/或者单核因子的产生；
    细胞死亡。
	(1) 产生抑制性 T 细胞和/或者因子。
	(2) 病毒蛋白的毒性或抑制效应。
	(3) 免疫复合物形成。
	(4) 诱导自身免疫现象：
	    (a) 多克隆 B 细胞激活或抗原模拟导致自身抗体的产生；
	    (b) 病毒介导、增强正常细胞蛋白的免疫原性。
	(5) 细胞毒性细胞对抗病毒或自身蛋白的活性。

另外，通常在感染初期，HIV 与多克隆 B 细胞活化导致血丙种球蛋白过多有关 [32]。有些抗体形成的免疫复合物可损害免疫系统；有些抗体与自身蛋白反应导致自身免疫性 [35]。针对正常细胞蛋白 p18 的淋巴细胞毒性自身抗体导致活化的辅助性 T 细胞的损伤，被认为是疾病发展中 CD4[+] 细胞大量丧失的一个机制 [35]。针对免疫细胞上其他共享抗原的抗体或（和）细胞毒性细胞，可进一步导致免疫功能或造血作用失常 [36,37]。最后，针对结合在未感染的 CD4[+] 细胞配体上的包膜蛋白应答的抗体依赖性细胞的细胞毒性，可能是致病过程中的一个因素 [38]。显然，HIV 感染对免疫系统的多种效应，无论直接的或是间接的都需要我们进行全面的评估，从而理解它们在观察到的免疫异常中的潜在作用。

细胞病理学 一个关于HIV发病机理的关键问题是病毒怎样杀死细胞。一般情况下，辅助 T 淋巴细胞最容易受 HIV 导致的细胞病变的影响；在培养基中，它们常常在死亡之前发生细胞融合。某些病毒株也被观测到正在杀死巨噬细胞 [1]。然而，T 细胞合胞体的形成并不总是导致细胞死亡；感染的细胞可以不经历融合而死亡 [39]。病毒包膜蛋白 gp120，可以独自或通过与 CD4 相作用，导致细胞死亡 [34,40,43]。直接接种灭活的病毒或者包膜蛋白 gp120 到外周血单核细胞也能够产生细胞病变效应 [34,41]。细胞死亡可能是由于细胞膜直接被破坏，涉及钙通道 [42]（和）或者磷脂合成 [43]。对于细胞病理学来说，未整合的 HIV 前病毒 DNA 拷贝的累积是一个有吸引力的解释，因为它与其他逆转录病毒系统中的细胞死亡有关 [44]。最后，在培养细胞中 HIV 的细胞病理学是否反映了在宿主体内的发病机理，要等待建立合适的动物模型才可以证明。

是什么影响了疾病的发展？

对 HIV 血清反应阳性者进行长期随访的研究表明，大概有三分之一的人在至少七年的时间里没有症状 [45]。此外，一些健康的血清反应阳性的个体，在丧失了大量 CD4[+] 淋巴细胞后，仍旧没有出现症状 [46]。一些艾滋病人（多数为患有波氏肉瘤）长

develop symptoms[46]. Several AIDS patients (many with Kaposi's sarcoma) have remained clinically stable for up to six years. Two patients followed at our medical center have had only 5% of their normal CD4$^+$ cell number for over a year without any new symptoms. Thus, predictions on the development of opportunistic infections or cancers based solely on a decrease in CD4$^+$ cells could be misleading; other presently unrecognized functions of the immune system may be fundamental in warding off disease.

CD8$^+$ cell activity. What determines the resistant state? Cytotoxic T lymphocytes that react with cells expressing HIV proteins[47,48] have been noted in infected individuals, but the clinical importance of this antiviral response is unknown. In our laboratory, studies of asymptomatic individuals have revealed that their peripheral blood mononuclear cells do not readily release HIV when placed in culture. Nearly all, however, yield virus when a subset of their CD8$^+$ lymphocytes is removed from the blood sample[49]. Similar observations have recently been made with the primate immune deficiency virus[50]. These CD8$^+$ cells apparently prevent HIV replication not by killing infected cells, but by producing a diffusible suppressor factor or factors. Among seropositive individuals, the level of this CD8$^+$ cell activity varies, and can be reflected in clinical status. Peripheral blood mononuclear cells cultured from many patients with disease readily produce virus and their CD8$^+$ cells show very little antiviral activity.

This variation in HIV replication in cultured cells probably mirrors the increase of viral p25 antigen in the plasma of individuals as they advance in disease[51]. Whether this observation reflects enhanced virus production or a decrease in antibodies to p25 is still not clear. Nevertheless, the information does suggest that the resistant state in infected individuals is mediated by cellular immune responses operating soon after infection; once these are reduced, renewed production of HIV can occur. The resumption of HIV replication could enhance progression to disease because of the emergence, by mutation or selection, of new HIV variants that replicate rapidly to high titre in a variety of cell types, and that are highly cytopathic[18]. This observation correlates clinically with the increased loss of CD4$^+$ cells[46] and the high levels of p25 antigenaemia[51] associated with development of disease. Nevertheless, whether the progression to disease results first from a reduced immune response or from the eventual emergence of a more pathogenic HIV strain, or from both, needs to be clarified.

Taken together, the data suggest steps in HIV infection that might explain variations in the course of the disease (Fig. 1). Levels of antiviral immune response, the inherent sensitivity of the host cell to virus replication and the relative virulence of the virus strain are major variables to be defined. What ends the resistant state (that is, triggers progression to disease) is not known, but could be a variety of factors including antilymphocyte antibodies, enhanced production of virus by activating events, progressive destruction of CD4$^+$ lymphocytes by intermittent periods of HIV replication and a decreased production by CD4$^+$ lymphocytes of cytokines required for the growth and function of antiviral CD8$^+$ cells.

达六年临床表现稳定。在我们医疗中心，有两个病人正常 CD4+ 细胞数目只有 5%，一年多没有任何新的症状。因此，仅仅以 CD4+ 细胞的减少为依据预测机会性感染或癌症的发展可能产生误导；目前其他还没有被发觉的免疫系统的功能也许是预防疾病的基础。

CD8+ 细胞活性 是什么决定了抵抗状态？人们已经注意到，在被感染个体中，细胞毒性 T 淋巴细胞可与表达 HIV 蛋白的细胞发生作用[47,48]，但是这种抗病毒反应的临床意义还是未知数。在我们实验室，对无症状个体的研究显示，当进行培养时，其外周血单核细胞不容易释放 HIV 病毒。然而从他们血液样本中分离出的 CD8+ 淋巴细胞从血液样本中分离后，几乎都产生病毒[49]。最近对灵长类免疫缺陷病毒也观察到相似的结果[50]。很显然，这些 CD8+ 细胞不是通过杀死感染的细胞来阻止 HIV 复制，而是通过产生一种或多种可扩散的抑制因子。血清反应阳性的不同个体中，CD8+ 细胞的活性水平是有差异的，并且可以反映其临床状态。提取许多患者的外周血单核细胞进行培养，很容易产生病毒，而他们的 CD8+ 细胞表现出很低的抗病毒活性。

在培养的细胞中，HIV 复制发生变异，可能反映出在感染个体血浆中随着疾病的发展[51]病毒 p25 抗原的增加。仍不清楚这个观察结果反映的是病毒复制增强还是 p25 的抗体减少。然而，这个信息确实显示，在被感染个体中，细胞免疫应答在感染以后很快介导了抵抗反应；一旦这些反应减弱，HIV 便开始重新产生了。HIV 病毒复制的重新开始可能加快了疾病的发展，因为通过突变或者选择，出现了新的 HIV 变异体，这些变异体在许多类型细胞中，都是迅速复制达到很高的滴度，并且导致高度的细胞病变[18]。这个观察结果与临床上随着疾病的发展 CD4+ 细胞[46]的缺失增加以及高水平的 p25 抗原血症[51]有关。然而，疾病的发展首先是由于免疫应答减弱还是最终高致病性 HIV 株的出现或是两者都有，仍需要进一步研究。

总之，有数据表明 HIV 感染的阶段可以解释病程的变化（图 1）。抗病毒免疫应答的水平，宿主细胞对病毒复制的内在敏感性和病毒株的相对毒性是需要明确的主要变量。现在仍不知道是什么终止了抵抗状态（即触发了疾病进展），但可能是多因素的，包括抗淋巴细胞抗体，激活事件导致病毒复制率增加，HIV 复制间歇期 CD4+ 淋巴细胞进行性的破坏以及抗病毒的 CD8+ 细胞生长和发挥作用所需的 CD4+ 淋巴细胞的细胞因子产生的减少。

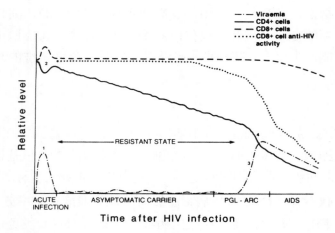

Fig. 1. A model of possible stages in the course of HIV infection. (1) Acute infection is characterized by the presence of free-virus (or its antigen) in the blood in the absence of antibodies to HIV. (2) A CD8$^+$ cells increase rapidly with a concomitant decrease in CD4$^+$ cells; thus the helper/suppressor ratio is dramatically reduced. After a short period (2–12 weeks) a resistant state develops in which CD8$^+$ cells return to above normal levels, CD4$^+$ cells decrease at a slow rate, and free virus is not readily detected in the blood, probably because it is produced episodically. Subsequently, after a variable time lag, the resistant state wanes for reasons that are not known. (3) The virus enters multiple replicative cycles during which a variant strain that can be resistant to the immune response and highly cytopathic can emerge and further compromise the antiviral state. (4) Viraemia is accompanied by enhanced destruction of CD4$^+$ cells and progression of disease.

Cofactors in pathogenesis. A major unresolved issue is whether other infectious agents can affect this asymptomatic period. Concomitant viral or parasitic infections may activate immune cells so they produce more virus, or become more sensitive to HIV infection[1]. Such events might lead to the suggested intermittent periods of HIV production. As demonstrated *in vitro*, agents such as the herpes viruses may act on the regulatory regions of HIV to enhance virus replication within the cell[52]. Continued surveillance of individuals with long asymptomatic periods, as well as studies of infected chimpanzees that have not yet shown any clinical abnormalities, should provide insight into factors influencing resistance to HIV.

Latency. A long incubation period might also be explained by a latent infection. During the latent period of retrovirus infection very little viral protein or RNA is made and no infectious progeny are produced by the infected cell[53]. When cells that have been latently infected with HIV in culture are treated with activating agents, such as halogenated pyrimidines and cytokines, virus replication begins and is then either maintained or reverts to latency[14,54].

Studies of the *orf-B* (or *3' orf*) gene of HIV suggest it could be responsible for latency. Deletion of *orf-B* leads to a 5–10 fold increase in virus replication compared with the wild-type virus[55]. Conceivably, the *orf-B* gene product (p27 protein), which has GTPase and phosphorylating properties[56], interacts with cellular factors to down-regulate virus replication (see above) in a continuum that can proceed to latency.

348

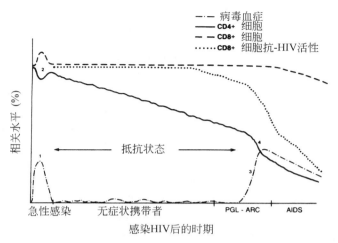

图 1. HIV 感染的过程中可能的阶段模型。（1）在缺少 HIV 抗体时, 血液中出现游离病毒（或者它的抗原）是急性感染的特征。（2）伴随着 CD4$^+$ 细胞的减少 CD8$^+$ 细胞快速增加; 从而辅助 T 细胞 / 抑制 T 细胞的比率明显下降。短期后（2~12 周）, 形成抵抗状态, 此时 CD8$^+$ 细胞恢复到正常水平以上, CD4$^+$ 细胞也以较慢的速度减少, 游离病毒在血清中不容易检测到, 可能因为它的产生是偶发的。随后, 经过一段不定的滞后时间, 不知何种原因, 抵抗状态衰退。（3）当对免疫应答有抵抗力的变异株和高度细胞病变出现后, 病毒进入多复制周期, 进一步危害抗病毒状态。（4）病毒血症的产生伴随着 CD4$^+$ 细胞的损坏增强和疾病的发展。

发病机理的辅助因素 一个重大的悬而未决的问题是其他的感染原是否影响无症状期。伴随病毒或寄生虫感染可以激活免疫细胞, 使他们产生更多病毒, 或对 HIV 更加敏感 [1]。这些事情可以导致暗示的 HIV 复制间歇期。体外研究证明, 其他传染病源如疱疹病毒可以在 HIV 的调控区域发生作用, 以提高病毒细胞内的复制 [52]。持续观察长期处于无症状时期的个体以及研究没有任何临床异常的被感染的猩猩, 能够深入了解影响 HIV 抵抗力的因素。

潜伏期 潜伏期的感染也可以解释长时间的潜伏期。在逆转录病毒感染的潜伏期, 产生很少病毒蛋白或者 RNA, 感染的细胞不产生感染性的后代 [53]。当培养被 HIV 病毒感染而处于潜伏期的细胞时, 加入激活剂, 如卤代嘧啶和细胞因子, 病毒开始复制, 然后或继续复制或回到潜伏期 [14,54]。

HIV 的 *orf-B*（或者 *3' orf*）基因的研究表明它可能与潜伏感染有关。*orf-B* 的缺失可导致病毒复制速率比野生型病毒增加5~10倍 [55]。可以想象, *orf-B* 基因的产物（p27 蛋白）具有 GTP 酶和磷酸化特性 [56], 通过与细胞因子相互作用持续下调病毒复制水平（见上文）, 从而进入潜伏期。

In rare cases, individuals who have been HIV seropositive become seronegative. In some of these individuals the presence of a latent HIV infection in peripheral mononuclear cells can be detected by means of the polymerase chain reaction; in others no HIV can be detected[57]. This potentially encouraging observation suggests that HIV infection in some individuals might be eliminated completely, but most likely the virus remains latent at other sites. Defining the factors governing latency should provide valuable information for the development of antiviral strategies. Moreover, the importance of latency to viral transmission must be assessed in "false negative" serological states.

Conclusions

Answers to many questions about the viral and host determinants of HIV pathogenesis could assist the prospects for therapy and prevention of AIDS. On current information, there are several features of HIV that need to be taken into account (Table 3). We should target antiviral drug strategies at the vulnerable sites of HIV replication, both before and after integration. In this regard, understanding how an HIV strain evolves into a more cytopathic (and potentially pathogenic) agent[18] would be valuable. We must find methods for inducing strong intracellular and cellular host responses against the virus: intracellular production of the *orf-B* protein or stimulation of the $CD8^+$ cell population responsible for suppressing HIV replication might produce long asymptomatic periods. Preventing the formation of antibodies to lymphocytes would be another promising direction. For vaccine development we need novel approaches that will define both specific epitopes of HIV and the appropriate adjuvant to elicit strong cross-reacting immune responses not generally observed in natural infection. Toward this objective, elimination of those epitopes responsible for antibody-dependent enhancement[10] would appear important. The immunized host must respond not only against free virus, but most importantly against productively and latently infected cells that can be major sources of HIV transmission[58]. Concentration on these areas of research should provide valuable information to help in the attack against HIV. In the process, we will learn a great deal more about viruses and the function of the immune system.

Table 3. Features of HIV of relevance to antiviral therapy

(1) Virus infection involves integration of the viral genome into the chromosome of the infected cell. This cell is a protective environment for the virus and a reservoir for persistent virus production.
(2) The infected cell is a major source of virus transmission and can pass HIV by cell-to-cell contact.
(3) The infected cells can remain "latent" and express very few viral antigens. Can these cells be recognized and eliminated by an antiviral response?
(4) HIV transmission occurs at specific sites in the host (such as the rectum). Prevention requires immune response at these local sites.
(5) Several independent serotypes and subtypes of HIV can be identified. Can they all be controlled by one strategy?
(6) Portions of HIV proteins resemble normal cellular proteins. Immunization may induce autoantibodies.
(7) Vaccination may induce antibodies that enhance HIV infection.

Studies conducted by the author were supported by the California State Universitywide Task Force on AIDS, the American Foundation for AIDS Research, and the National Institutes of Health. I would like to thank Drs S. Levy and J. Ziegler as well as Drs C. Cheng-Mayer, L. Evans, J. Homsy, J. Hoxie, J. Leong, M. McGrath and C. Walker for

在极少的病例中，HIV 血清反应阳性的个体会变为血清反应阴性。在一些这样的个体中，外周血单核细胞中存在的 HIV 潜伏感染可通过聚合酶链式反应检测，另外一些则检测不到 HIV 病毒[57]。这个可能令人鼓舞的观察结果表明，HIV 在一些感染的个体中可能完全被消除，但是最有可能病毒潜伏在其他位置。明确潜伏期的调节因素为抗病毒策略的发展提供了有价值的信息。此外，潜伏期对于病毒传播的重要性，须考虑假阳性这一血清学参数。

结　　论

解答在 HIV 发病机理中病毒和宿主的决定因素的问题，会为艾滋病的治疗和预防提供帮助。就目前的资料而言，我们需要考虑 HIV 的几个特点（表 3）。整合前后，我们都应该将抗病毒药物的目标定位在 HIV 复制时容易受攻击的部位。就这一点而言，了解一个 HIV 株怎样发展为一个能引发细胞病变（及潜在病变的）的病毒株[18] 会有很大的意义。我们必须寻找能诱导强的细胞内和细胞宿主抵抗病毒的方法：细胞内产生 *orf-B* 蛋白或者依靠刺激 CD8+ 细胞分裂来抑制 HIV 的复制可能产生长时间的无症状期。阻止淋巴细胞抗体的形成可能是另一种有前途的方向。对于疫苗的研制，我们需要新的方法来找到 HIV 的特定抗原表位和适当的佐剂引起免疫系统强烈的交叉反应，这在自然感染中一般是观察不到的。为了实现这个目标，消除这些抗体依赖性增强的抗原表位显得更重要[10]。免疫的宿主不仅要抵抗游离的病毒，最重要的是抵抗复制期和潜伏期的感染细胞，它们可能是主要的 HIV 传播源[58]。集中精力在这些领域进行研究，可以为攻击 HIV 提供有价值的信息。在这个过程中，我们将了解大量的关于病毒和免疫系统功能的知识。

表 3. HIV 与抗病毒治疗的相关特征

(1) 病毒感染包括病毒的基因组整合到被感染细胞的染色体中。细胞为病毒提供了一个安全的环境并成为病毒持续复制的一个储存器。
(2) 被感染细胞是病毒传播的主要源泉，病毒能够通过细胞之间的接触进行传播。
(3) 感染细胞处于潜伏状态，表达少量的病毒抗原，这些细胞能够被抗病毒应答所识别和消除吗？
(4) HIV传播发生在宿主的特定部位(如直肠)。这些部位的免疫应答可对病毒起到预防作用。
(5) 几个独立的HIV血清型和亚型能被鉴定。能通过一种方法全部控制吗？
(6) 部分HIV蛋白类似于正常的细胞蛋白，免疫自身诱导自身抗体。
(7) 疫苗可能会产生加强HIV感染的抗体。

作者进行的研究得到了加利福尼亚州立大学艾滋病研究小组、美国艾滋病研究基金会和美国国家卫生研究院的支持。我还要感谢利维、齐格勒、郑迈耶、埃文斯、霍姆西、霍克西、梁、麦格拉思和沃克博士对于这篇文章有价值的评论和贝格林

their helpful comments on this article, and C. Beglinger for its preparation.

(**333**, 519-522; 1988)

Jay A. Levy
Department of Medicine and Cancer Research Institute, University of California School of Medicine, San Francisco, California 94143-0128, USA

References:

1. Fauci, A. S. *Science* **239**, 617-622 (1988).

2. Maddon, P. J. *et al. Cell* **47**, 333-348 (1986).

3. Cheng-Mayer, C. *et al. Proc. Natl. Acad. Sci. U.S.A.* **84**, 3526-3530 (1987).

4. Tateno, M. & Levy, J. A. IV Int. Conf. AIDS, Stockholm (abstr.) (1988).

5. Wiley, C. A. *et al. Proc. Natl. Acad. Sci. U.S.A.* **88**, 7089-7093 (1986).

6. Nelson, J. A. *et al. Lancet* **i**, 259-262 (1988).

7. Stein, B. S. *et al. Cell* **49**, 659-668 (1987).

8. Gallaher, W. R. *Cell* **50**, 327-328 (1987).

9. Chanh, T. C. *et al. EMBO J.* **5**, 3065-3071 (1986).

10. Robinson, W. E. *et al. Lancet* **i**, 790-795 (1988).

11. Halstead, S. B. & O' Rourke, E. J. *J. exp. Med.* **146**, 201-217 (1977).

12. Ho, D. D. *et al. Science* **239**, 1021-1023 (1988).

13. Gartner, S *et al. Science* **233**, 215-219 (1986).

14. Levy, J. A. *et al. Ann. Inst. Pasteur* **138**, 101-111 (1987).

15. Evans, L. A. *et al. J. Immun.* **138**, 3415-3418 (1987).

16. Levy J. A. *et al. Science* **232**, 998-1001 (1986).

17. Nabel, G & Baltimore, D. *Nature* **326**, 711-713 (1987).

18. Cheng-Mayer, C. *et al. Science* **240**, 80-82 (1988).

19. Hahn, B. H. *et al. Science* **232**, 1548-1553 (1986).

20. Starcich, B. R. *et al. Cell* **45**, 637-648 (1986).

21. Weiss, R. A. *et al. Nature* **324**, 572-575 (1986).

22. Evans, L. A. *et al. Science* **240**, 1522-1525 (1988).

23. Luciw, P. A. *et al. Nature* **312**, 760-763 (1984).

24. Robert-Guroff, M. *et al. J. Immun.* **137**, 3306-3309 (1986).

25. Carpenter, S. *et al. J. Virol.* **61**, 3783-3789 (1987).

26. Price, R. W. *et al. Science* **239**, 586-592 (1988).

27. Fontana, A. *et al. Nature* **307**, 273-276 (1984).

28. Cohen, M. B. & Beckstead, J. in *AIDS: Pathogenesis and Treatment* (ed. Levy, J. A.) (Dekker, New York, in the press).

29. Harper, M. E. *et al. Proc. Natl. Acad. Sci. U.S.A.* **83**, 772-776 (1986).

30. Hoxie, J. A. *et al. Science* **229**, 1400-1402 (1985).

31. Asjo, B *et al. Lancet* **2**, 660-662 (1986).

32. Koenig, S. & Fauci, A. S. in *AIDS: Etiology, Diagnosis, Treatment and Prevention*, 2nd edn. (eds DeVita, V., Hellman, S. & Rosenberg, S.) (Lippincott, Philadelphia, in the press).

33. Laurence, J. *et al. J. clin. Invest.* **72**, 2072-2081 (1983).

34. Shalaby, M. R. *et al. Cell Immun.* **110**, 140-148 (1987).

35. Stricker, R. B. *et al. Nature* **327**, 710-713 (1987).

36. Ziegler, J. & Stites, D. P. *Clin. Immunol. Immunopathol.* **41**, 305-313 (1986).

37. Donahue, R. E. *et al. Nature* **326**, 200-203 (1987).

38. Weinhold, K. J. *et al. Lancet* **i**, 902-904 (1988).

39. Somasundaran, M. & Robinson, H. L. *J. Virol.* **61**, 3114-3119 (1987).

40. Hoxie, J. *et al. Science* **234**, 1123-1127 (1986).

41. Rasheed, S. *et al. Virology* **154**, 395-400 (1986).

42. Gupta, S. & Vayuvegula, B. *J. clin. Immun.* **7**, 486 (1987).

43. Lynn, W. S. *et al. Virology* **163**, 43-51 (1988).

44. Keshet, E. & Temin, H. M. *J. Virol.* **31**, 376-388 (1979).

格所做的准备工作。

（郑建全 翻译；孙军 审稿）

45. Rutherford, G. W. & Werdegar, D. in *AIDS: Pathogenesis and Treatment* (ed. Levy, J. A.) (Dekker, New York, in the press).

46. Lang, W. *et al.* Abstr. Int. on Conf. AIDS, Stockholm (abstr.) (1988).

47. Walker, B. *et al. Nature* **328**, 345-348 (1987).

48. Plata, F. *et al. Nature* **328**, 348-351 (1987).

49. Walker, C. M. *et al. Science* **234**, 1563-1566 (1986).

50. Kannagi, M. *et al. J. Immun.* **140**, 2237-2242 (1988).

51. Lange, J. M. A. *et al. Br. med. J.* **293**, 1459-1462 (1986).

52. Mosca, J. D. *et al. Proc. Natl. Acad. Sci. U.S.A.* **84**, 7408-7412 (1987).

53. Rojko, J. L. *et al. Nature* **298**, 385-388 (1982).

54. Folks, T. M. *et al. Science* **231**, 600-602 (1986).

55. Luciw, P. A. *et al. Proc. Natl. Acad. Sci. U.S.A.* **84**, 1434-1438 (1987).

56. Guy, B. *et al. Nature* **330**, 266-269 (1987).

57. Farzadegan, H. et *al. Ann. int. Med.* **108**, 785-790 (1988).

58. Levy, J. A. *J. Am. med. Ass.* **259**, 3037-3038 (1988).

Human Basophil Degranulation Triggered by Very Dilute Antiserum against IgE

E. Davenas *et al.*

Editor's Note

This is one of the most controversial papers *Nature* has published, reflected in the fact that its category ("Scientific paper") was never used before or since. Jacques Benveniste and his co-workers of the French medical research organization INSERM claimed to have found that antibodies remain able to trigger an immune response from a class of white blood cells called basophils even when the antibodies are diluted until no molecules should still be present in solution. This activity, they claimed, recurs in a periodic manner with increasing dilution. This appeared to offer some basis for homeopathy, which uses such ultra-dilute solutions. The study was never clearly replicated subsequently, but it gave rise to the notion that water has a "memory" of what it has dissolved.

When human polymorphonuclear basophils, a type of white blood cell with antibodies of the immunoglobulin E (IgE) type on its surface, are exposed to anti-IgE antibodies, they release histamine from their intracellular granules and change their staining properties. The latter can be demonstrated at dilutions of anti-IgE that range from 1×10^2 to 1×10^{120}; over that range, there are successive peaks of degranulation from 40 to 60% of the basophils, despite the calculated absence of any anti-IgE molecules at the highest dilutions. Since dilutions need to be accompanied by vigorous shaking for the effects to be observed, transmission of the biological information could be related to the molecular organization of water.

THE antibodies responsible for human immediate hypersensitivity belong to the IgE isotype[1]. The most salient feature of IgE is its capacity to bind to mast cell and polymorphonuclear basophil membranes through receptors with high affinity[2]. Human basophils are specifically challenged by immunological stimuli such as allergens or anti-IgE antiserum that can bridge IgE molecules in membrane[3]. This process triggers transmembrane and intracellular signals followed by granule exocytosis with the release of histamine and loss of metachromatic staining of basophil granules by a basic dye such as toluidine blue. Optical basophil degranulation is well correlated with other *in vitro* and *in vivo* procedures for the diagnosis of allergy[4-7].

In preliminary experiments, degranulation of human basophils contained in leukocyte suspensions was induced not only by the usual concentration of anti-IgE antibody (1×

356

高度稀释的抗IgE抗血清引发人嗜碱性粒细胞脱颗粒

达弗纳等

编者按

本文为《自然》发表的最有争议的文章之一，事实上，《自然》此前和此后再没有发表类似的"科学论文"。法国国家健康与医学研究院的雅克·邦弗尼斯特和他的同事们声称他们发现即使在抗体稀释到其分子不存在于溶液中的情况下，仍然可以引发一类被称为嗜碱性粒细胞的白细胞作出免疫应答。他们称，这种活性随着逐步稀释呈周期性的反复出现。这似乎为使用超稀溶液的顺势疗法提供了支持。后来该研究从来没有被清晰地重复出来，但是它给人们带来一种观念，即水对已溶解物质有"记忆"。

当人的多形核嗜碱性粒细胞————一种表面表达 E 型免疫球蛋白（IgE）抗体的白细胞，遇到抗 IgE 抗体时，它们会释放细胞内颗粒中的组胺，并改变自身的染色特性。后者可以通过使用不同稀释倍数的抗 IgE 抗体（$1 \times 10^2 \sim 1 \times 10^{120}$ 倍稀释）来证实；在这个范围里，即使最大稀释度时已经无法测算抗 IgE 分子，也可以观察到 40%~60%嗜碱性粒细胞脱颗粒的一系列峰。由于只有在伴随剧烈摇动的稀释中才能观察到这些现象，因此生物信息的传递可能与水的分子结构有关。

造成人速发型超敏反应的抗体属于 IgE 同种型 [1]。IgE 最突出的特点是它能够通过高亲和力的受体结合到肥大细胞和嗜碱性多形核粒细胞的膜上 [2]。在过敏原或抗 IgE 抗血清（可以与细胞膜上 IgE 分子结合）等免疫原的刺激下，人嗜碱性粒细胞的反应最为明显 [3]。这一过程会触发跨膜和细胞内信号，随即引起颗粒胞吐及组胺释放并导致嗜碱性颗粒对甲苯胺蓝等碱性染料的异染性消失。视检嗜碱性粒细胞脱颗粒现象与其他体内和体外的过敏诊断程序之间具有很大的关联 [4-7]。

在初步的实验中我们发现，不仅常规浓度的抗 IgE 抗血清（1×10^3 倍稀释抗 IgE 抗血清，相当于该法中有 2.2×10^{-9} M 抗 IgE 抗体）可以引起白细胞悬液中的人

10^3 dilution of anti-IgE antiserum, corresponding to 2.2×10^{-9} M anti-IgE antibody in the assay), but also by very low concentrations of this antibody ($2.2 \times 10^{-16/18}$ M), where the number of IgG anti-IgE molecules in the assay is supposedly too low to trigger the process. We then further explored this phenomenon.

Serial tenfold dilutions of goat anti-human IgE (Fc) antiserum (1 mg specific antibody per ml) were prepared in HEPES-buffered Tyrode's solution containing human serum albumin (HSA) down to 1×10^{60} dilution, corresponding to a 2.2×10^{-66} M theoretical concentration (th) in the assay (see Fig.1 legend for methods). The expected basophil degranulation, which was assessed by counting cells with metachromatical properties, was observed after exposure of leukocyte preparations to low antiserum dilutions with a maximum at $\sim 1 \times 10^3$ dilution. Successive peaks of degranulation varying between 40 and 60% were then found down to 1×10^{60} dilution, with periods of 6 to 9 tenfold dilutions (Fig. 1a). In other experiments, the antiserum was serially diluted a hundred-fold down to 1×10^{120} (to give 2.2×10^{-126} M th in the assay) and similar results were obtained (Fig. 1b). Degranulation induced by high dilutions of anti-IgE antiserum was observed in ten experiments on the full range of dilutions down to 1×10^{60}, when at least 70 similar results were obtained at one or the other part of the high dilution scale in the participating laboratories (Toronto, preliminary results). As controls, goat anti-human IgG (Fc) antiserum (Fig.1b, $n = 4$) or Tyrode's solution containing HSA ($n = 5$) were diluted down to 1×10^{120} and 1×10^{30}, respectively. Cells incubated in conditions identical to those with anti-IgE anti-serum gave no significant degranulation. The repetitive waves of anti-IgE-induced degranulation were reproducible, but the peaks of degranulation could shift by one or two dilutions with every fresh sequential dilution of anti-IgE and depended on the blood sample. The waves of basophil degranulation were also seen with substances other than anti-IgE anti-serum at high and low dilutions, such as monoclonal anti-human IgE antibodies, specific antigen in allergic patients or in peroxidase-immunized rabbits, phospholipase A_2 from bee venom or porcine pancreas, the Na^+ ionophore monensin (up to 90% degranulation at 1×10^{-30} M th) and the Ca^{2+} ionophores A23187 and ionomycin (1×10^{-38} M th). The specificity of the observed effects at high dilutions (already noted when comparing antiserum against IgE with antiserum against IgG) was further strikingly illustrated in the ionophore experiments, because removing the corresponding ion from the cellular environment blunted basophil degranulation.

嗜碱性粒细胞脱颗粒，而且极低浓度的抗体（$2.2 \times 10^{-16/18}$ M）也可以引起这一过程，通常人们认为 IgG 抗 IgE 分子的数量已经太少，不足以引发此过程。于是我们对这一现象进行了深入研究。

我们用含有人血清白蛋白（HSA）的 HEPES 缓冲蒂罗德液对羊抗人 IgE（Fc 段）抗血清（每毫升含 1 mg 特异性抗体）进行 10 倍梯度稀释，一直稀释到 1×10^{60} 倍，该法中理论浓度（th）相当于 2.2×10^{-66} M（方法参见图 1 注）。将低浓度的抗血清稀释液加入到白细胞后可以发生预期的脱颗粒现象，通过对异染性细胞计数可以计算嗜碱性粒细胞的脱颗粒程度，观察发现不超过 1×10^3 倍稀释液能刺激产生脱颗粒。而随着抗血清稀释倍数逐渐增大到 10^{60}，脱颗粒的连续峰在 40%～60% 之间波动，并且以每 10^6~10^9 倍稀释为一个周期出现一个峰值（图 1a）。在另一个实验中，我们采用 100 倍梯度稀释抗血清直到 1×10^{120} 倍（相当于 2.2×10^{-126} M th）也可以得到类似的结果（图 1b）。在稀释倍数降到 1×10^{60} 倍的全范围稀释的 10 次实验中观察到通过抗 IgE 抗血清引起的脱颗粒现象，同时在参与实验的其他实验室中（多伦多，初步结果）也观察到在高度稀释的范围中至少存在 70 个类似的实验结果。作为对照，我们将羊抗人 IgG（Fc 段）抗血清（图 1b，$n = 4$）或含 HSA 的蒂罗德液（$n = 5$）分别梯度稀释到 1×10^{120} 和 1×10^{30} 倍。发现培养的细胞在与抗 IgE 抗血清同样的条件下，并不能引发嗜碱性粒细胞显著的脱颗粒现象。由抗 IgE 引起的脱颗粒曲线的峰谷交错是可重复的，不过曲线的峰值可能会由于每次新制的抗 IgE 系列稀释液及血样的不同而偏移 1 或 2 个稀释度。除了高、低稀释度的抗 IgE 抗血清外，其他物质如单克隆抗人 IgE 抗体、过敏患者体内或过氧化物酶免疫过的兔体内的特异性抗原、蜜蜂毒液或猪胰腺中的磷脂酶 A_2、钠离子载体莫能菌素（1×10^{-30} M th 可引起超过 90% 的细胞脱颗粒）以及钙离子载体 A23187 和离子霉素（1×10^{-38} M th）都可以引起这样的嗜碱性粒细胞脱颗粒曲线。因为细胞环境中相关离子的去除钝化了嗜碱性粒细胞脱颗粒，所以高倍稀释时其作用的特异性（在比较抗 IgE 抗血清和抗 IgG 抗血清时已注明）将在离子载体实验中作进一步深入阐明。

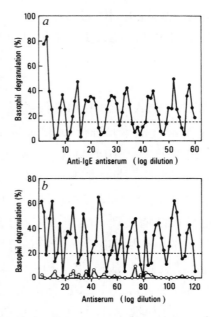

Fig. 1. Human basophil degranulation induced either by anti-IgE antiserum (●) diluted tenfold from 1×10^{2} down to 1×10^{60} (a) or hundredfold down to 1×10^{120} (b) or by anti-IgG antiserum (○) diluted hundredfold from 1×10^{2} down to 1×10^{120} (representatives of at least 10 experiments for anti-IgE and 4 experiments for anti-IgG). The significant ($P<0.05$) percentage of degranulation was 15% (a) and 20% (b). (....) relation to the number of counted basophils from control wells[15].

Methods. Goat anti-human IgE(Fc) antiserum or as a control, goat anti-human IgG (Fc) antiserum (Nordic Immunology, The Netherlands) was serially diluted as indicated above in HEPES-buffered Tyrode's solution (in g l^{-1}: NaCl, 8; KCl, 0.195; HEPES, 2.6; EDTA-Na$_4$, 1.040; glucose, 1 human serum albumin (HSA), 1.0; heparin, 5,000 U per 1; pH 7.4). Between each dilution, the solution was thoroughly mixed for 10 s using a Vortex. Given the molecular weight of IgG molecules (150,000), the 1×10^{60} and 1×10^{120} dilutions correspond in the assay to 2.2×10^{-66} M (th) and 2.2×10^{-126} M (th) respectively. Venous blood (20 ml) from healthy donors was collected using heparin (1 U per ml) and a mixture of 2.5 mM EDTA-Na$_4$/2.5 mM EDTA-Na$_2$(final concentrations) as anticoagulants and allowed to sediment. The leukocyte-rich plasma was recovered, twice washed by centrifugation ($400g$, 10 min) and finally resuspended in an aliquot of HEPES-buffered Tyrode's solution. The cell suspension (10 μl) was deposited on the bottom of each well of a microtitre plate containing 10 μl CaCl$_2$ (5 mM final) and 10 μl of either of anti-IgE or anti-IgG antiserum dilutions. To a control well were added 10 μl CaCl$_2$ and 10 μl Tyrode's but no anti-IgE or anti-IgG antiserum. Plates were then incubated at 37°C for 30 min. Staining solution (90 ml; 100 mg toluidine blue and 280 μl glacial acetic acid in 100 ml 25% ethanol, pH 3.2–3.4) was added to each well and the suspension thoroughly mixed. Specifically redstained basophils (non-degranulated basophils) were counted under a microscope using a Fuchs-Rosenthal haemocytometer. The percentage of basophil degranulation was calculated using the following formula: Basophil no. in control–basophil no. in sample/basophil no. in control $\times$ 100. Between 60 and 120 basophils were counted in cell suspensions from control wells after incubation either in the absence of anti-IgE antiserum, or in the presence of anti-IgG antiserum.

To confirm these surprising findings, four blind experiments were carried out (Table 1). In all cases the results were clear-cut, with typical bell-shaped degranulations at anti-IgE dilutions from 1×10^{32} to 1×10^{37}. The replicates were usually very close and of high significance (ANOVA test). In a fifth experiment, 7 control tubes and 3 tubes containing a dilution previously determined as active (1×10^{34}) were counted blind: basophil

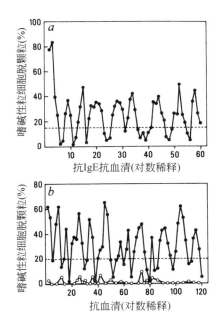

图1. 抗 IgE 抗血清（●）和抗 IgG 抗血清（○）引起的人嗜碱性粒细胞脱颗粒，抗 IgE 抗血清从 1×10^2 倍稀释液十倍梯度稀释到 1×10^{60} 倍（a）或百倍梯度稀释到 1×10^{120} 倍（b）；抗 IgG 抗血清从 1×10^2 倍稀释液百倍梯度稀释到 1×10^{120} 倍（图中的数据至少反映了使用抗 IgE 抗血清进行的 10 次实验和使用抗 IgG 抗血清进行的 4 次实验）。脱颗粒的显著（P<0.05）比例分别为 15%（a）和 20%（b）。（·····）代表对照孔中嗜碱性粒细胞的计数 [15]。

方法。将羊抗人 IgE（Fc）抗血清或作为对照的羊抗人 IgG（Fc）抗血清（荷兰诺迪克免疫公司）分别用上文所述的 HEPES 缓冲蒂罗德液（含 8 g/l NaCl；0.195 g/l KCl；2.6 g/l HEPES；1.040 g/l EDTA–Na₄；1 g/l 葡萄糖 1 g/l 人血清白蛋白（HSA）；5,000 U/l 肝素；pH 7.4）梯度稀释。在每次稀释后，使用涡旋混合器振荡 10 秒以使溶液充分混匀。假设 IgG 分子的分子量为 150,000，那么 1×10^{60} 和 1×10^{120} 倍稀释液中分别为 2.2×10^{-66} M（th）和 2.2×10^{-126} M（th）。用肝素（1 U/ml）和 2.5 mM EDTA–Na₄/2.5 mM EDTA–Na₂ 混合物（终浓度）作为抗凝血剂，从健康受试者身上采集 20 ml 静脉血，静置沉淀。两次离心收集富含白细胞的血浆（400g，10 分钟），最后用 HEPES 缓冲蒂罗德液重悬。在已加入 10 µl CaCl₂（终浓度为 5 mM）和 10 µl IgE 或 IgG 抗血清稀释液的微量滴定板的小孔底部，加入细胞悬液（10 µl）。对照孔中加入 10 µl CaCl₂ 和 10 µl 蒂罗德液，但不加抗 IgE 或抗 IgE 抗血清稀释液。将整个滴定板放置在 37℃ 孵育 30 分钟。向各孔中加入染色液（90 ml；将 100 mg 甲苯胺蓝和 280 µl 冰醋酸溶于 100 ml 25%乙醇，pH 3.2~3.4）并充分混匀。使用富–罗式血细胞计数器在显微镜下对特异性红染的嗜碱性粒细胞（未脱颗粒的嗜碱性粒细胞）计数。采用下列公式计算嗜碱性粒细胞脱颗粒的比例：（对照组中嗜碱性粒细胞的数量 – 实验组中嗜碱性粒细胞的数量）/ 对照组中嗜碱性粒细胞的数量 ×100。在对照孔中，不管是加入抗 IgG 抗血清的还是不加入抗 IgE 抗血清，都数到 60~120 个嗜碱性粒细胞。

为了进一步确认这些惊人的发现，我们又进行了 4 组双盲实验（表 1）。所有情况下结果都是明确的，在 1×10^{32} 倍到 1×10^{37} 倍的抗 IgE 稀释液间脱颗粒曲线均为典型的钟形曲线。重复实验的结果也非常相近，并具有很高的显著性（方差分析）。在第 5 次实验中，7 个对照样品和 3 个事先验证过具有活性的（1×10^{34} 倍

degranulation was $7.7\pm1.4\%$ for the controls, and 44.8, 42.8 and 45.7% for the tubes containing diluted anti-IgE. The random chance in all these experiments was 2% and therefore the cumulative results statistically confirm the measured effect.

Table 1. Basophil counts after exposure to anti-IgE antiserum at low and high dilutions

Samples	Experiment 1	Experiment 2	Experiment 3	Experiment 4
Tyrode's-HSA*	81.3±1.2†	89.0±3.1	81.7±2.2	106.7±1.8
Tyrode's-HSA	81.6±1.4	87.7±1.4	83.0±1.0	105.0±1.2
Tyrode's-HSA	80.0±1.5	88.0±2.3	81.7±1.8	105.7±0.9
aIgE 1×10^{3}*	35.5±1.8(56)‡	42.3±4.8(53)	27.7±0.7(66)	40.0±1.5(62)
aIgE 2×10^{32}	77.6±0.8(4)	87.3±1.2(3)	66.3±2.3(18)	93.7±1.9(12)
aIgE 1×10^{33}	76.0±1.1(6)	88.7±1.8(1)	77.7±1.8(4)	74.7±2.8(30)
aIgE 1×10^{34}	53.6±1.4(33)	52.7±1.4(41)	38.0±0.6(53)	48.3±2.4(55)
aIgE 1×10^{35}	45.0±0.5(44)	35.0±1.0(61)	41.3±1.8(49)	49.3±1.2(54)
aIgE 1×10^{36}	49.0±1.7(40)	50.3±0.7(44)	55.0±2.1(32)	74.3±2.3(31)
aIgE 1×10^{37}	79.0±2.3(2)	85.3±0.7(5)	73.3±1.7(10)	105.3±0.7(0)

Blind experiments: test tubes were randomly coded twice by two independent pairs of observers and assayed. The codes were simultaneously broken at the end of all experiments. Dilutions of anti-IgE antiserum were performed as described in legend to Fig. 1.

* Uncoded additional tubes for negative (Tyrode's-HSA) or positive (aIgE 1×10^{-3}) controls.

† Data represent the mean ± s.e. of basophil number actually counted in triplicate (see legend to Fig. 1 for methods).

‡ Number in parenthesis indicates percentage degranulation compared with Tyrode's-HSA.

Two further blind experiments were performed using the usual dilution procedure: of the 12 tubes used in the first experiment (Table 2), 2 tubes contained goat anti-human antiserum IgE at 1×10^{2} and 1×10^{3} dilutions, 6 tubes contained dilutions from 1×10^{32} to 1×10^{37}, and 4 tubes buffer-HSA alone. The tubes were then randomly coded twice by three parties, one of which kept the two codes. The 12 tubes were each divided into 4. Three batches of 12 tubes were lyophilized, one of which was used for gel electrophoresis, one for assay of monoclonal antibodies, and the last (with the unlyophilized sample) for gel electrophoresis and basophil degranulation. By comparing the results of the different tests it was easy to identify the tubes containing IgE at normal concentrations compared with the tubes containing highly diluted IgE and the control tubes. When the codes were broken, the actual results exactly fitted those predicted, but HSA and its aggregates were present in all solutions and complicated interpretation of the gel electrophoresis. So we performed another almost identical experiment, using 6 tubes containing unlyophilized samples and buffer without HSA. Four tubes contained antibody at 1×10^{2}, 1×10^{3}, 1×10^{35} and 1×10^{36} dilutions, and 2 contained buffer alone. These tubes were coded and assayed according to the above protocol. The decoded results were clear-cut, high basophil degranulation being obtained with 1×10^{2}, 10^{3}, 10^{35} and 10^{36} dilutions, but no anti-IgE activity or immunoglobulins were detected either in the control tubes or in assays containing the 1×10^{35} and 10^{36} dilutions (Tables 2 and 3 and Fig.2). Thus there is no doubt that there was basophil degranulation in the absence of any detectable anti-IgE molecule.

稀释)样品采取了双盲检测：对照组嗜碱性粒细胞脱颗粒的百分比为 $7.7 \pm 1.4\%$，而含有稀释抗 IgE 的样品分别为 44.8%、42.8% 和 45.7%。在所有这些实验中，随机因素的影响为 2%，因此这些结果再次从统计学上证实了上述检测结果。

表 1. 不同稀释度抗 IgE 抗血清刺激后的嗜碱性粒细胞计数

样品	实验一	实验二	实验三	实验四
蒂罗德液–HSA*	81.3 ± 1.2†	89.0 ± 3.1	81.7 ± 2.2	106.7 ± 1.8
蒂罗德液–HSA	81.6 ± 1.4	87.7 ± 1.4	83.0 ± 1.0	105.0 ± 1.2
蒂罗德液–HSA	80.0 ± 1.5	88.0 ± 2.3	81.7 ± 1.8	105.7 ± 0.9
抗IgE 1×10^3*	$35.5 \pm 1.8(56)$‡	$42.3 \pm 4.8(53)$	$27.7 \pm 0.7(66)$	$40.0 \pm 1.5(62)$
抗IgE 2×10^{32}	$77.6 \pm 0.8(4)$	$87.3 \pm 1.2(3)$	$66.3 \pm 2.3(18)$	$93.7 \pm 1.9(12)$
抗IgE 1×10^{33}	$76.0 \pm 1.1(6)$	$88.7 \pm 1.8(1)$	$77.7 \pm 1.8(4)$	$74.7 \pm 2.8(30)$
抗IgE 1×10^{34}	$53.6 \pm 1.4(33)$	$52.7 \pm 1.4(41)$	$38.0 \pm 0.6(53)$	$48.3 \pm 2.4(55)$
抗IgE 1×10^{35}	$45.0 \pm 0.5(44)$	$35.0 \pm 1.0(61)$	$41.3 \pm 1.8(49)$	$49.3 \pm 1.2(54)$
抗IgE 1×10^{36}	$49.0 \pm 1.7(40)$	$50.3 \pm 0.7(44)$	$55.0 \pm 2.1(32)$	$74.3 \pm 1.2(31)$
抗IgE 1×10^{37}	$79.0 \pm 2.3(2)$	$85.3 \pm 0.7(5)$	$73.3 \pm 1.7(10)$	$105.3 \pm 0.7(0)$

双盲实验：待测样品分别由两组独立的观察者进行两次随机编号和实验，在全部实验结束后，同时公布所有的编号。抗 IgE 抗血清的稀释方法参见图 1 注。

* 未编号的额外样品，分别为阴性对照（蒂罗德液 – HSA）和阳性（aIgE 1×10^{-3}）对照。

† 数据为 3 次重复实验对嗜碱性粒细胞计数的平均值 $\pm$ s.e.（方法参见图 1 注）。

‡ 括号中的数据为与蒂罗德液 –HSA 处理组相比脱颗粒细胞的百分比。

我们进一步使用普通的稀释程序进行了两次双盲实验：在第 1 次实验的 12 个样品中（表 2），2 个分别为羊抗人 IgE 抗血清的 1×10^2 倍和 1×10^3 倍稀释液、6 个为从 1×10^{32} 倍到 1×10^{37} 倍稀释液、4 个为只含 HSA 的缓冲液。这些样品被 3 组人员随机编号 2 次，其中一组保存 2 个编号。然后，把这 12 个样品分成 4 份，3 份冻干后，1 份用于凝胶电泳实验，1 份用于单克隆抗体实验，最后 1 份（和未冻干样品）用于凝胶电泳与嗜碱性粒细胞脱颗粒实验。通过比较这些不同实验的结果，我们很容易鉴定出正常浓度和高倍稀释的 IgE 抗血清以及对照。最后我们公布样品编号，发现实验结果与预期完全相符，不过由于 HSA 和其聚合物在所有样品中都存在，导致电泳实验的结果解释起来比较复杂。因此我们又进行了另外一个几乎完全相同的实验，用 6 个含未冻干样品和缓冲液但不含人血清白蛋白的样品进行实验。其中 4 个样品分别为抗体的 1×10^2、1×10^3、1×10^{35} 和 1×10^{36} 倍稀释液，2 个只含缓冲液。我们采用与上述实验相同的方法对这些样品进行了双盲编号和分析。结果是明确的，即 1×10^2、1×10^3、1×10^{35} 和 1×10^{36} 倍稀释液均能引发嗜碱性粒细胞高度脱颗粒，但在对照组以及 1×10^{35} 和 1×10^{36} 倍稀释液处理组中检测不到任何抗 IgE 活性和免疫球蛋白（表 2、表 3 和图 2）。因此，毫无疑问地，即使抗 IgE 抗体的浓度低到无法检测，也可以引发嗜碱性粒细胞脱颗粒。

Table 2. Comparison of basophil degranulation with the presence of immunoglobulins and
anti-IgE activity in dilutions performed in HSA-containing Tyrode's

Samples	Basophil degranulation (%)*			Gel electrophoresis†		Anti-IgE activity
	I	II	III	A	B	μ ml^{-1}
Tyrode's-HSA	0	0	0	−	−	$<1\times10^{-3}$
Tyrode's-HSA	0	0	0	−	−	$<1\times10^{-3}$
Tyrode's-HSA	0	0	0	−	−	$<1\times10^{-3}$
Tyrode's-HSA	0	0	0	−	−	$<1\times10^{-3}$
aIgE 1×10^{-2}‡	53	50	33	++§	++	ND
aIgE 1×10^{-2}	51	44	37	++	++	10.6
aIgE 1×10^{-3}	65	38	45	+?	−	1.1
aIgE 1×10^{-32}	7	26	22	−	−	$<1\times10^{-3}$
aIgE 1×10^{-33}	37	0	13	−	−	$<1\times10^{-3}$
aIgE 1×10^{-34}	45	37	20	−	−	$<1\times10^{-3}$
aIgE 1×10^{-35}	39	41	34	−	−	$<1\times10^{-3}$
aIgE 1×10^{-36}	31	29	39	−	−	$<1\times10^{-3}$
aIgE 1×10^{-37}	23	12	29	−	−	$<1\times10^{-3}$

Blind experiments and dilution protocols as in Table 1. −, Lack of strained bands. ND, not determined. A faint band corresponding to IgG appeared after reduction by 2-mercaptoethanol.

* Basophil degranulation tests I, II, III were performed using 3 different blood samples (see Fig. 1). Percentage basophil degranulation induced by aIgE, as compared to Tyrode's HSA, was calculated from duplicates.

† Electrophoresis (polyacrylamide 7–15%, revealed by silver staining) was carried out in Rehovot (A) and at INSERM U 200 (B).

‡ Uncoded additional tube for positive control.

§ ++,+ Bands correspond to IgG present in large or small amounts.

Table 3. Comparison of basophil degranulation with the presence of immunoglobulins and
anti-IgE activity in dilutions performed in Tyrode's without HSA.

Samples	Basophil degranulation (%)		Gel electrophoresis		Anti-IgE activity
	I	II	A	B	(μ ml^{-1})
Tyrode's	0	0	−	−	$<1\times10^{-3}$
Tyrode's	0	0	−	−	$<1\times10^{-3}$
aIgE 1×10^{-2}*	85	48	++	++	ND
aIgE 1×10^{-2}	81	47	++	++	32.6
aIgE 1×10^{-3}*	ND	ND	+	+	ND
aIgE 1×10^{-3}	75	53	+	+	ND
aIgE 1×10^{-35}	35	31	−	−	$<1\times10^{-3}$
aIgE 1×10^{-36}	40	35	−	−	$<1\times10^{-3}$

* Uncoded tubes for positive control of basophil degranulation and/or gel electrophoresis.
ND, not determined.

364

表 2. 在含 HSA 的蒂罗德液中比较免疫球蛋白引起的嗜碱性粒细胞脱颗粒
与稀释液的抗 IgE 活性

样品	嗜碱性粒细胞脱颗粒(%)*			凝胶电泳†		抗IgE活性
	I	II	III	A	B	μ ml^{-1}
蒂罗德液–HSA	0	0	0	–	–	$<1 \times 10^{-3}$
蒂罗德液–HSA	0	0	0	–	–	$<1 \times 10^{-3}$
蒂罗德液–HSA	0	0	0	–	–	$<1 \times 10^{-3}$
蒂罗德液–HSA	0	0	0	–	–	$<1 \times 10^{-3}$
抗IgE 1×10^{-2}‡	53	50	33	++§	++	ND
抗IgE 1×10^{-2}	51	44	37	++	++	10.6
抗IgE 1×10^{-3}	65	38	45	+?	–	1.1
抗IgE 1×10^{-32}	7	26	22	–	–	$<1 \times 10^{-3}$
抗IgE 1×10^{-33}	37	0	13	–	–	$<1 \times 10^{-3}$
抗IgE 1×10^{-34}	45	37	20	–	–	$<1 \times 10^{-3}$
抗IgE 1×10^{-35}	39	41	34	–	–	$<1 \times 10^{-3}$
抗IgE 1×10^{-36}	31	29	39	–	–	$<1 \times 10^{-3}$
抗IgE 1×10^{-37}	23	12	29	–	–	$<1 \times 10^{-3}$

双盲实验和稀释方法与表 1 同。 – ，表示无染色带。ND，表示未检出。使用 2–巯基乙醇还原后可以看见一条模糊的 IgG 的带。

* 嗜碱性粒细胞脱颗粒实验 I、II、III 分别是采用 3 个不同的血样进行的（见图 1）。与蒂罗德液 – HSA 处理相比，抗 IgE 引起的嗜碱性粒细胞脱颗粒的百分比是两次计算的平均值。

† 凝胶电泳实验（7%~15% 聚丙烯酰胺，银染）分别在雷霍沃特（A）和法国国家健康与医学研究院 U 200（B）实验室进行。

‡ 阳性对照，未进行双盲编码。

§ ++、+ 代表 IgG 条带含量的多少。

表 3. 在不含 HSA 的蒂罗德液中比较免疫球蛋白引起的嗜碱性粒细胞脱颗粒
与稀释液的抗 IgE 活性

样品	嗜碱性粒细胞脱颗粒(%)		凝胶电泳		抗IgE活性
	I	II	A	B	(μ ml^{-1})
蒂罗德液	0	0	–	–	$<1 \times 10^{-3}$
蒂罗德液	0	0	–	–	$<1 \times 10^{-3}$
抗IgE 1×10^{-2}*	85	48	++	++	ND
抗IgE 1×10^{-2}	81	47	++	++	32.6
抗IgE 1×10^{-3}*	ND	ND	+	+	ND
抗IgE 1×10^{-3}	75	53	+	+	ND
抗IgE 1×10^{-35}	35	31	–	–	$<1 \times 10^{-3}$
抗IgE 1×10^{-36}	40	35	–	–	$<1 \times 10^{-3}$

* 未进行双盲编码的阳性对照的嗜碱性粒细胞脱颗粒和（或）凝胶电泳实验。

ND，表示未检出。

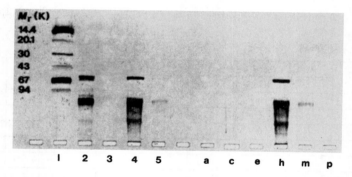

Fig. 2. Electrophoresis (polyacrylamide 7–15%, bands revealed by silver staining): samples numbered 1 to 5 are standards for the blind experiments a, c, e, h, m, p. Lane 1, Molecular weight standards for electrophoresis; lane 2, monoclonal IgG added with human serum albumin; lane 3, Tyrode's buffer without human serum albumin; lane 4, 1×10^2 anti-IgE dilution; lane 5, 1×10^3 dilution. Samples tested blind: a and c, buffer; e, 1×10^{36} anti-IgE dilution; h, 1×10^2 anti-IgE dilution; m, 1×10^3 anti-IgE dilution; p, 1×10^{35} anti-IgE dilution.

These results may be related to the recent double-blind clinical study of Reilly *et al.*[8] which showed a significant reduction of symptoms in hay-fever patients treated with a high dilution (1×10^{60}) of grass pollen versus placebo, and to our *ex vivo* experiments in the mouse[9]. We have extended these experiments to other biological systems: using the fluorescent probe fura-2, we recently demonstrated changes in intracellular Ca^{2+} levels in human platelets in the presence of the Ca^{2+} ionophore ionomycin diluted down to 1×10^{-39} M th (F.B. *et al.*, unpublished results).

Using the molecular weight of immunoglobulins and Avogadro's number, we calculate that less than one molecule of antibody is present in the assay when anti-IgE antiserum is diluted to 1×10^{14} (corresponding to 2.2×10^{-20} M). But in the experiments reported here we have detected significant basophil degranulation down to the 1×10^{120} dilution. Specific effects have also been triggered by highly diluted agents in other *in vitro* and *in vivo* biological systems[8-11], but still remain unexplained. The valid use of Avogadro's number could be questioned, but we are dealing with dilutions far below the Avogadro limit $(1 \times 10^{100}$ and below). It could be argued that our serial dilution procedure is subject to experimental error, but this is ruled out because: (1) pipette tips and glass micropipettes were discarded between each dilution (performed under laminar flow hood). (2) The c.p.m. in tubes containing serially diluted radioactive compounds decreased in proportion to the degree of dilution down to the background (data not shown). (3) Contamination would not explain the successive peaks of activity that evoke a periodic phenomenon and not a monotonous dose–effect curve, as usually observed when concentration of an agonist decreases. (4) To eliminate the possibility of contaminating molecules present in the highly diluted solutions, we carried out two series of experiments which can be summarized as follows. An Amicon membrane with molecular weight cut-off 10K retained the basophil degranulating IgG (150K) present at low dilutions $(1 \times 10^2$, $1 \times 10^3)$ in anti-IgE antiserum. By contrast, the activity present at high dilutions $(1 \times 10^{27}$, $1 \times 10^{32})$ was totally recovered in the 10K Amicon filtrate. Anion or cation exchange chromatography, according to the

366

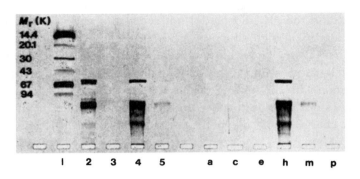

图 2. 凝胶电泳（7% ~15%聚丙烯酰胺，银染）：1~5 为双盲实验中 a、c、e、h、m、p 的比对标准。1 道为凝胶电泳的标准分子量；2 道为加了人血清白蛋白的单克隆抗体 IgG；3 道为不含人血清白蛋白的蒂罗德液；4 道为抗 IgE 的 1×10^2 倍稀释液；5 道为 1×10^3 倍稀释液。双盲测定样品：a 和 c 为蒂罗德液；e 为抗 IgE 的 1×10^{36} 倍稀释液；h 为抗 IgE 的 1×10^2 倍稀释液；m 为抗 IgE 的 1×10^3 倍稀释液；p 为抗 IgE 的 1×10^{35} 倍稀释液。

这些实验结果可能与赖利等人最近进行的临床双盲研究[8] 存在一定关系，他发现与安慰剂相比，使用高倍稀释（1×10^{60}）的草花粉治疗枯草热患者可以显著地缓解症状，与我们进行的小鼠离体实验的结果[9] 也相关。我们在其他生物学系统中进一步扩展了这些实验：使用 fura-2 作为荧光探针，我们证明了稀释到 1×10^{-39} M 的钙离子载体离子霉素可以引起人血小板中细胞内钙离子水平的改变（博韦等，未发表的结果）。

利用免疫球蛋白的分子量和阿伏伽德罗常量，我们可以计算出当抗 IgE 抗血清稀释 1×10^{14} 倍时（相当于 2.2×10^{-20} M），在前面所述的每个实验中平均只含有不到 1 个抗体分子。但是，我们的结果却表明即使稀释 1×10^{120} 倍，抗血清也可以引发显著的嗜碱性粒细胞脱颗粒。在其他体内、体外的生物系统中，人们也观察到了高倍稀释的试剂具有一些特殊的效应[8-11]，但尚不清楚其中的奥妙所在。也许在此处使用阿伏伽德罗常量是否合适尚存疑问，不过我们的稀释倍数已经远远低于阿伏伽德罗界限（1×10^{100} 甚至更低）。也许有人会怀疑我们的系列稀释方法会受到实验误差的影响，不过这个可能性已经被排除了，因为：（1）稀释用的移液器吸头和玻璃微量移液器都是一次性的（在超净台中进行）；（2）在含有放射性化合物的样品中，其放射性强度随着稀释过程相应成比例降低，直到与背景值一样（结果未显示）；（3）杂质污染无法解释脱颗粒曲线呈现周期性，而不是单一的剂量–效应曲线（通常随激动剂浓度的降低而改变）；（4）为了排除在高倍稀释的样品中含有杂质分子的可能，我们进行了下述两个系列的实验。使用截留分子量为 10K 的 Amicon 膜可以将抗 IgE 抗血清中的 IgG（分子量 150K）保留下来，从而抑制低倍数稀释液（1×10^2、1×10^3）引发嗜碱性细胞脱颗粒的能力。相反，对于高稀释倍数液（1×10^{27}、1×10^{32}）来说，使用分子量为 10K 的 Amicon 膜过滤处理并不能抑制该抗

type of resin used and the pH, did or did not retain the anti-IgE IgG at low dilutions, whereas the same activity at high dilution was always excluded from the columns and fully recovered in the first eluate. These filtration and ionexchange experiments demonstrated that the activity of the antiserum at high dilution cannot result from contamination of the highly diluted solution with the starting material. They showed, in addition, that the high-dilution activity does not present in space the steric conformation of an IgG molecule as it acts like a 150K charged molecule, but is not retained by the 10K filter or by a charged chromatography column.

We then investigated the physical chemical nature of the entity active at high dilution. Our results can be summarized as follows. (1) The importance of agitation in the transmission of information was explored by pipetting dilutions up and down ten times and comparing with the usual 10-s vortexing. Although the two processes resulted in the same dilution (degranulations at 1×10^2 and 1×10^3 were superimposable whatever the dilution process), degranulation did not occur at high dilution after pipetting. Ten-second vortexing was the minimum time required, but vortexing for longer (30 or 60 s) did not increase high-dilution activity. So transmission of the information depended on vigorous agitation, possibly inducing a submolecular organization of water or closely related liquids. (2) The latter is possible as ethanol and propanol could also support the phenomenon. In contrast, dilutions in dimethylsulphoxide did not transmit the information from one dilution to the other, but increasing the proportion of water in dimethylsulphoxide resulted in the appearance and increment of the activity at high dilutions. (3) Heating, freeze-thawing or ultrasonication suppressed the activity of highly diluted solutions, but not the activity of several active compounds at high concentrations. A striking feature was that molecules reacted to heat according to their distinctive heat sensitivity, whereas all highly diluted solutions ceased to be active between 70 and 80 °C. This result suggests a common mechanism operating at high dilution, independent of the nature of the starting molecule.

Therefore we propose that none of the starting molecules is present in the dilutions beyond the Avogadro limit and that specific information must have been transmitted during the dilution/shaking process. Water could act as a "template" for the molecule, for example by an infinite hydrogen-bonded network[12], or electric and magnetic fields[13,14]. At present we can only speculate on the nature of the specific activity present in the highly diluted solutions. We can affirm that (1) this activity was established under stringent experimental conditions, such as blind double-coded procedures involving six laboratories from four countries; (2) it is specific for the ligand first introduced, as illustrated when goat antiserum (IgG) anti-human IgE, but not goat IgG anti-human IgG supported this phenomenon. The link between high and low anti-IgE dilutions is shown as we could not detect basophil degranulation at high dilutions if it did not occur within the classical range. High dilutions of histamine, but not of its carboxylated precursor histidine, inhibited IgE-dependent basophil degranulation. Finally, ionophores at high dilution did not work when the specific ion was removed from the cell suspension (F.B., unpublished results). (3) Using six biochemical and physical probes, we demonstrated that what supports the activity at high dilutions is not a molecule. (4) Whatever its nature, it is capable of "reproducing" subtle

血清引发脱颗粒的能力。此外，不论根据树脂型号和 pH 值进行的阴离子或阳离子交换层析能或不能保留低倍稀释液中的抗 IgE 抗血清中的 IgG，但高倍稀释液在柱层析之前及其第一次洗脱之后却始终具有相同的脱颗粒活性。这些过滤和离子交换实验的结果证明高倍稀释液的血清的活性不可能是由于高倍稀释的原始样品被污染而造成的。此外，高倍稀释液的活性也与 IgG 分子空间构象的改变无关，因为它虽然表现得像 150K 带电分子，却不会被截流分子量为 10K 的滤膜和离子交换柱拦截。

我们进一步对高倍稀释液中活性实体物质的物理化学性质进行了分析。其结果如下：（1）我们分别对样品采取了抽吸 10 次或涡旋振荡 10 秒的处理，以分析搅动方式对于信息传递的重要性。尽管这两种方法都能达到相同的稀释度（两种处理方法得到的 1×10^2 倍和 1×10^3 倍稀释液分别发生相同的脱颗粒现象），但枪头抽吸处理得到的高倍稀释液却不能产生脱颗粒现象。 涡旋振荡 10 秒是混匀所需的最少时间，不过进一步延长涡旋的时间（30 秒或 60 秒）并不能增强高倍稀释液脱颗粒的活性。据此我们认为某种信息的传递依赖于剧烈摇晃，这种摇晃可能诱导水或密切相关的液体中亚分子的组装；（2）相关液体可以为乙醇和丙醇，以它们为溶剂可以支持这一现象。相反，二甲基亚砜则不能在稀释过程中传递信息，但逐渐增加二甲基亚砜中水的含量可以使高倍稀释液的活性出现并逐渐增加；（3）加热、冻融或超声都会抑制高倍稀释液的活性，但不会影响几种高浓度活性化合物的活性。令人惊奇的是，基于不同的热敏感性，分子可对热作出反应，而高倍稀释的样品在 70℃ ～ 80℃ 活性逐渐消失。这表明在高倍稀释液中存在一种共同的机制，其与初始样品的性质无关。

据此，我们认为当稀释倍数超出阿伏伽德罗界限后，已经没有初始的分子残留在溶液中，而在稀释 - 摇晃过程中则一定有某种特定信息在传递。水分子在这个过程中可能起到分子"模板"作用，比如它可以形成一个无限的氢键网络[12]或电场和磁场[13,14]。目前我们只能基于这种高倍稀释液的特殊活性进行推断。我们确认：（1）这种活性是在严格的实验条件下被发现的，例如由 4 个国家的 6 个实验室参与的双盲实验；（2）正如此前证明的只有羊抗血清（IgG）抗人 IgE 而不是羊抗血清（IgG）抗人 IgG 才能够引起这种现象，说明这种活性对首次引入的配体是特异性的。如果传统浓度范围内不能引发嗜碱性粒细胞脱颗粒，那么高倍稀释液也不行，所以高低倍抗 IgE 稀释液的活性是存在联系的。高倍稀释的组胺可以抑制 IgE 依赖的嗜碱性粒细胞脱颗粒，而其羧基化的前体组氨酸则不行。最后，当细胞悬液中的特定离子被去除后，高倍稀释液的离子载体将不能发挥作用（博韦，未发表的结果）；（3）我们使用了 6 种生物化学的和物理的探针证明高倍稀释液的活性并不是由某种

molecular variations, such as the rearrangement of the variable region of an IgG (anti-ε versus anti-γ) molecule.

The precise nature of this phenomenon remains unexplained. It was critical that we should first establish the reality of biological effects in the physical absence of molecules. The entities supporting this "metamolecular" biology can only be explored by physical investigation of agitation causing interaction between the original molecules and water, thus yielding activity capable of specifically imitating the native molecules, though any such hypothesis is unsubstantiated at present.

We thank Professor Z. Bentwich from Ruth Ben Ari Institute for supervision of experiments conducted in Rehovot. The participation of J. Geen (Univ. Toronto), B. Descours and C. Hieblot (INSERM U 200) in experiments and of V. Besso in editing is gratefully acknowledged. This work is dedicated to the late Michel Aubin, who played a decisive role in initiating it.

Editorial Reservation

Readers of this article may share the incredulity of the many referees who have commented on several versions of it during the past several months. The essence of the result is that an aqueous solution of an antibody retains its ability to evoke a biological response even when diluted to such an extent that there is a negligible chance of there being a single molecule in any sample. There is no physical basis for such an activity. With the kind collaboration of Professor Benveniste, *Nature* has therefore arranged for independent investigators to observe repetitions of the experiments. A report of this investigation will appear shortly.

(**333**, 816-818; 1988)

E. Davenas, F. Beauvais, J. Amara[*], M. Oberbaum[*], B. Robinzon[†], A. Miadonna[‡], A. Tedeschi[‡], B. Pomeranz[§], P. Fortner[§], P. Belon, J. Sainte-Laudy, B. Poitevin & J. Benveniste[||]

INSERM U 200, Université Paris-Sud, 32 rue des Carnets, 92140 Clamart, France
[*] Ruth Ben Ari Institute of Clinical Immunology, Kaplan Hospital, Rehovot 76100, Israel
[†] Department of Animal Sciences, Faculty of Agriculture, PO Box 12, The Hebrew University of Jerusalem, Rehovot 76100, Israel
[‡] Department of Internal Medicine, Infectious Diseases and Immunopathology, University of Milano, Ospedale Maggiore Policlinico, Milano, Italy
[§] Departments of Zoology and Physiology, Ramsay Wright Zoological Laboratories, University of Toronto, 25 Harbord Street, Toronto, Ontario M5S 1A1, Canada
[||] To whom correspondence should be addressed

Received 24 August 1987; accepted 13 June 1988.

References:
1. Ishizaka, K., Ishizaka, T. & Hornbrook M. M. *J. Immun.* **97**, 75-85 (1966).
2. Metzger, H. *et al. A. Rev. Immun.* **4**, 419-470 (1986).
3. Ishizaka, T., Ishizaka, K., Conrad, D. H. & Froese, A. *J. Allergy clin. Immun.* **61**, 320-330 (1978).

分子来实现的；（4）不管它的本质是什么，它具有对分子进行"再造"引入一些精细改变的能力，例如对 IgG（抗 ε 不抗 γ）分子可变区的重排。

上述现象的精确本质仍有待探索。重要的是，我们在物理上尚未发现分子存在的情况下，首先确定了这种生物功能的真实存在。支持这种"超分子"生物学的本质，只能通过物理上的探索，研究晃动引起原始分子（如抗 IgE，编者注。）和水产生的相互作用，是否使液体特异的模仿本来分子的能力而产生活性，不过对于这些假设目前尚无法证实。

我们感谢露丝本阿里学院的本特威奇教授对在雷霍沃特进行的实验的指导。衷心感谢多伦多大学的吉恩、法国国家健康与医学研究院 U 200 的德库尔和耶布洛参与实验，感谢贝索的编辑工作。把这个工作献给米歇尔·奥宾先生，他在这些工作的启动中发挥了决定性的作用。

编辑的保留

本文的读者可能会分享在过去的几个月中对几种版本做出评论的评论者所做出的多种质疑。本文结果的实质为，即使把抗体稀释到样品中不可能含有一个分子的浓度时，其水溶液仍然保持了激发生物反应的能力。这种活性不具备物理基础。在与邦弗尼斯特教授友好沟通之后，《自然》已经安排独立的调查员前去观察实验重复。调查报告将于近期公布。

（张锦彬 翻译；胡卓伟 审稿）

4. Benveniste, J. *Clin. Allergy* **11**, 1-11 (1981).

5. Camussi, G., Tetta, C., Coda, R. & Benveniste, J. *Lab. Invest.* **44**, 241-251 (1981).

6. Pirotzky, E. *et al. Lancet* i, 358-361 (1982).

7. Yeung-Laiwah, A. C., Patel, K. R., Seenan, A. K., Galloway, E. & McCulloch, W. *Clin. Allergy* **14**. 571-579 (1984).

8. Reilly, D. T., Taylor, M. A., McSharry, C. & Aitchison, T. *Lancet* ii, 881-886 (1986).

9. Davenas, E., Poitevin, B. & Benveniste, J. *Eur. J. Pharmac.* **135**, 313-319 (1987).

10. Bastide, M., Doucet-Jacoeuf, M. & Daurat, V. *Immun. Today* **6**, 234 (1985).

11. Poitevin, B., Davenas, E. & Benveniste, J. *Br. J. clin. Pharmac.* **25**, 439-444 (1988).

12. Stanley, H. E., Teixeira, J., Geiger, A. & Blumberg, R. L. *Physics* **106A**, 260-277 (1981).

13. Fröhlich, H. *Adv. Electron.* & *Electron. Phys*, **53**, 85-152 (1980).

14. Smith, C.W. & Aarholt, E. *Hlth Phys.* **43**, 929-930 (1988).

15. Petiot, J. F., Sainte-Laudy, J. & Benveniste, J. *Ann. Biol. Clin.* **39**, 355-359 (1981).

"High-Dilution" Experiments a Delusion

John Maddox *et al.*

Editor's Note

The controversy stemming from the publication in *Nature* of a paper alleging biological activity in solutions of biomolecules at "homeopathic" high dilutions was only heightened when this investigation of the research appeared a month later. *Nature*'s editor John Maddox went with "fraud debunkers" James Randi (a professional magician) and Walter Stewart to the laboratory of French immunologist Jacques Benveniste, who had made the claims, and asked him to repeat the experiments. The French scientists were unable to reproduce their results, and Maddox and colleagues made various accusations of poor technique (but not fraud). Benveniste denounced the investigation as a stunt, and continued to work on high-dilution effects until his death in 2004. But his claims were dismissed by other scientists.

The now celebrated report by Dr J. Benveniste and colleagues elsewhere is found, by a visiting *Nature* team, to be an insubstantial basis for the claims made for them.

THE remarkable claims made in *Nature* (**333**, 816; 1988) by Dr Jacques Benveniste and his associates are based chiefly on an extensive series of experiments which are statistically ill-controlled, from which no substantial effort has been made to exclude systematic error, including observer bias, and whose interpretation has been clouded by the exclusion of measurements in conflict with the claim that anti-IgE at "high dilution" will degranulate basophils. The phenomenon described is not reproducible in the ordinary meaning of that word.

We conclude that there is no substantial basis for the claim that anti-IgE at high dilution (by factors as great as 10^{120}) retains its biological effectiveness, and that the hypothesis that water can be imprinted with the memory of past solutes is as unnecessary as it is fanciful.

We use the term "high dilution" reluctantly; these solutions contain no molecules of anti-IgE, and so are not solutions in the ordinary sense. "Solute-free solution" would similarly be illogical.

Our conclusion is based on a week-long visit to Dr Benveniste's laboratory, the INSERM unit for immunopharmacology and allergy (otherwise INSERM 200) at Clamart, in the western suburbs of Paris, during the week beginning 4 July. Among other things, we were

374

高倍稀释实验的错觉

约翰·马多克斯等

编者按

发表在《自然》杂志上的一篇论文宣称"顺势疗法"似的超高倍稀释的生物分子溶液仍有生物学活性。这一论文引起的争议被一个月后的研究调查激化。《自然》杂志的编辑约翰·马多克斯与"骗局揭露者"詹姆斯·兰迪（一位职业魔术师）及沃尔特·斯图尔特去了得出此结论的法国免疫学家雅克·邦弗尼斯特的实验室，并请他重复这一实验。法国科学家不能重复他们的结果，而马多克斯和他的同事们对粗劣的实验技术（但并非造假）提出了多项指控。邦弗尼斯特指责这次调查是一场闹剧，并继续高倍稀释效应的工作，直至其 2004 年去世。但是他的观点并未得到其他科学家的理会。

一个《自然》杂志调查小组认为邦弗尼斯特博士和他的同事们在他们的著名论文中提出的观点缺乏可靠证据。

在《自然》杂志（**333**，816；1988）中，雅克·邦弗尼斯特博士和他的助手们提出了一个著名的观点，然而他们用以得出结论的大规模系列实验缺乏统计学对照，研究者也没有进行实质性的努力来排除包括实验观测者的偏好在内的系统误差。并且，他们将与"高倍稀释的抗 IgE 抗体会引发嗜碱性粒细胞脱颗粒"这一结论相矛盾的测试都予以排除，这使得他们所阐述的观点变得不太可信。此外，他们所描述的实验现象在通常情况下没有可重复性。

我们认为"高倍稀释（稀释倍数高达 10^{120}）的抗 IgE 抗体仍具有生物学效应"的说法是缺乏可靠依据的，并且关于"水可以对之前的溶质形成记忆"的假设也太过离奇。

我们勉强地使用"高倍稀释溶液"这个名词，因为在所谓的高倍稀释的溶液中，已经没有抗 IgE 抗体，因此也不再是通常意义上的溶液了。"无溶质的溶液"在逻辑上也是讲不通的。

我们的结论是基于对邦弗尼斯特博士所在的实验室——位于法国巴黎西部郊区克拉马尔的法国国家健康和医学研究院免疫药理学与过敏反应研究组（也称 INSERM 200）进行的为期一周的调查访问（始于 7 月 4 日）后作出的。我们了解到

dismayed to learn that the salaries of two of Dr Benveniste's coauthors of the published article are paid for under a contract between INSERM 200 and the French company Boiron et Cie., a supplier of pharmaceuticals and homoeopathic medicines, as were our hotel bills.

Benveniste's results are being widely interpreted as support for homoeopathic medicine. In the light of our investigation, we believe that such use amounts to misuse.

Our visit and investigation were preconditions for the publication of the original article. We acknowledge that we are an oddly constituted group. One of us (J.R.) is a professional magician (and also a MacArthur Foundation fellow) whose presence was originally thought desirable in case the remarkable results reported had been produced by trickery. Another of us (W.W.S.) has been chiefly concerned, during the past decade, in studies of errors and inconsistencies in the scientific literature and with the subject of misconduct in science. The third (J.M.) is a journalist with a background in theoretical physics. None of us has first-hand experience in the field of work at INSERM 200.

We acknowledge that we might well have found ourselves unable to get to grips with the work of the laboratory. But, on the basis of our experience, we are confident that the design of the experiments reported by INSERM 200 is inadequate as a basis for the claims made last month and that the defects we shall catalogue are a sufficient explanation of the remarkable results then reported.

We believe that experimental data have been uncritically assessed and their imperfections inadequately reported. We believe that the laboratory has fostered and then cherished a delusion about the interpretation of its data.

We are grateful to Dr Jacques Benveniste for his openness in discussing most of the questions we raised with him. He allowed us to borrow and to photocopy the relevant laboratory notebooks, which were invaluable for our investigation. We have every reason to believe that Dr Benveniste was (and, perhaps, still is) convinced of the reality of the phenomena reported in his article. We are also in the debt of several of Dr Benveniste's colleagues, especially to Dr Elisabeth Davenas. On her fell most of the burden of demonstrating the standard dilution experiments and of repeating them in a blinded protocol under our scrutiny. We know that our report will be a disappointment to the laboratory. We are sorry.

What follows is a narrative account of our visit and a summary of our conclusions.

Our investigations concentrated exclusively on the experimental system on which the publication was based. During our week in Paris, we resisted several proffered opportunities to examine other systems in which high dilution is claimed not to diminish the biological effectiveness of a molecule.

和邦弗尼斯特博士所发表论文的两名共同作者的薪水是按 INSERM 200 和一家法国公司 Boiron et Cie. 所签署的一份合同来支付的。Boiron et Cie. 公司是顺势疗法药物的供应商，它也负担了我们此次访问的住宿费用。我们对上述情况感到很不安。

邦弗尼斯特的实验结果被广泛地宣传以支持顺势疗法医学理论。经过调查，我们认为这是一种滥用。

此次访问和调查源于这篇文章的发表。我们承认这个调查小组是一个奇特的队伍。小组中的一员（詹姆斯·兰迪）是一名专业的魔术师（也是麦克阿瑟基金会的成员），邀请他的初衷是希望他能够发现这个著名的实验结果中是否含有某种欺骗性的成分。另一个成员（沃尔特·斯图尔特）在过去十年中参与研究科学论文中的错误和矛盾，以及科学界的学术不端问题。第三个成员（约翰·马多克斯）是一位具有理论物理学背景的记者。所有成员都没有 INSERM 200 相关领域的直接工作经历。

我们承认我们可能无法快速了解这个实验室的工作。但是基于经验，我们充分相信 INSERM 200 设计的实验方案不足以支持他们上个月所得出的结论，并且我们所罗列的这些实验设计的缺陷足以解释他们所观察到的实验现象。

我们相信他们对实验数据的评估不够严格，而实验数据的缺陷也没有被充分地显示。我们相信这个实验室对这些数据进行解释时形成了错觉，并一直维持着这一错觉。

我们非常感谢雅克·邦弗尼斯特在与我们讨论多数问题时的坦诚。他允许我们借出并复印相关的实验记录本，这对于我们的调查来说弥足珍贵。我们完全相信邦弗尼斯特博士确信（也许现在仍是）他的论文中所报道的实验现象的真实性。我们也对邦弗尼斯特博士的一些同事，尤其是伊丽莎白·达弗纳博士深表感谢。在我们的详细审查下，验证标准稀释实验和按双盲原则重复它们的压力都落在她的身上。我们知道我们的报告会让这个实验室失望，对此我们很遗憾。

下面是我们叙述性的访问报告以及我们结论的总结。

我们的调查完全集中在邦弗尼斯特博士的论文所依赖的实验系统上。在我们访问巴黎的一周时间内，我们多次拒绝了对方提供的检查其他系统的机会，据说在那些系统中经过高倍稀释后分子的生物学效应仍未消失。

The experimental system has evolved from a test for assessing the susceptibility of people to specific allergens. The guiding principle is that blood-borne allergens have the specific effect of interacting with the leukocytes known as basophils, causing them to degranulate—that is, to release the contents of cytoplasmic granules carrying histamine and other active substances provoking the symptoms of asthma and hay-fever.

These allergic reactions are apparently mediated at least in part by IgE molecules attached to the surfaces of basophils (in the blood) or mast cells (in tissues). Normally, degranulation is triggered by the interaction of anchored IgE molecules with an antigen, but the same effect can be brought about by the use of anti-IgE—antibody prepared by injecting human IgE into an animal of another species. (INSERM 200 uses goat anti-IgE at a concentration of 1 mg cm^{-3} sold by the Dutch company Nordic.)

The laboratory notebooks provide ample evidence that this expected degranulation is a maximum between log (dilution) 2 and 4.

Benveniste described the published procedure as a "simple experiment". A buffered solution of anti-IgE is serially diluted by a factor of 10 by transferring measured volumes from one test-tube to another. Pipette tips are discarded after each transfer. Measured volumes of resuspended white cells derived from human blood are transferred to wells in a polystyrene plate. To each of these is added a measured volume of serially diluted anti-IgE or buffer as a control. The wells are incubated for 30 minutes at 37°C. An acidic solution of toluidine blue, which stains intact but not degranulated basophils red, is added and the numbers of recognizable basophils counted on a haemocytometer slide. Anti-IgG, which does not degranulate basophils, is used as a control.

We were surprised to learn that the experiments do not always "work". There have been periods of several months at a time during which solutions at high dilution have not degranulated basophils. Indeed, the laboratory had just emerged from such a period. (Speculation at the laboratory is that the distilled water may have been contaminated, or otherwise made unsuitable.) It also appears that bloods that "do not degranulate" are often encountered; we were informed that, in this event, data are recorded but not included in analyses prepared for publication. Even so, the source of blood for the experiments is not controlled, except that an attempt is made not to use blood from people with an allergy.

We witnessed a total of seven runs of this experiment, of which three were routine repetitions of the standard procedure. For the fourth experiment, samples of diluted IgE were transferred by one of us (W.W.S.) to wells in a plastic plate in a random sequence and then read blind by Dr Davenas. All four of these experiments, the last after decoding, gave results described as positive by Benveniste, but three further sequences of counts of stained basophils in three further strictly blind experiments gave negative results (see below).

这个实验系统是从一个检测人们对特定过敏原的易感性的实验演化而来的。其指导原则是血源性过敏原可以与嗜碱性粒细胞等白细胞相互作用并发挥效应，引起这些细胞脱颗粒，释放细胞质颗粒物中的组胺和其他活性物质，从而引起哮喘和枯草热的症状。

这些过敏反应（至少部分）是由附着在嗜碱性粒细胞（血液中）或肥大细胞（组织中）表面的 IgE 分子介导的。一般来讲，脱颗粒过程由锚定于细胞表面的 IgE 分子与抗原相互作用而触发，但是抗 IgE 抗体也可以引发相同的效应。将人 IgE 分子注射到其他物种的动物中便可以得到抗 IgE 抗体。（INSERM 200 使用了荷兰 Nordic 公司出售的山羊抗人 IgE 抗体，浓度为 $1\,mg\cdot cm^{-3}$）

实验记录本提供了充分的证据表明这一脱颗粒过程在抗 IgE 抗体稀释倍数为 10^2 倍与 10^4 倍之间达到最大值。

邦弗尼斯特将发表的实验程序描述为一个"简单的实验"。将含抗 IgE 抗体的缓冲溶液分步稀释，每次把一定体积的溶液从一个试管移入另一个试管并稀释 10 倍。枪头在每次移液后都会被扔掉。一定体积的来自人血液中的白细胞重悬液被加入到聚苯乙烯板的培养孔中。实验人员将一定体积的经系列稀释的抗 IgE 抗体或作为对照的缓冲液加入到这些培养孔中。在 37℃ 孵育 30 分钟后，向孔中加入甲苯胺蓝的酸性溶液，它可以将完整但没有脱颗粒的嗜碱性粒细胞染成红色。利用血球计数板可以对可见的嗜碱性粒细胞进行计数。此外，不能够引发嗜碱性粒细胞脱颗粒的抗 IgG 抗体被用作阴性对照。

我们很惊奇地发现，这个实验并不是总能"奏效"。曾经有几个月的时间那些高倍稀释的抗血清并不能够引发嗜碱性粒细胞脱颗粒。事实上，这个实验室也刚经历过这样的时期。（对此该实验室推测可能是由于蒸馏水被污染或者其他制备方法不合适。）并且，似乎他们也经常遇到那些"不能够脱颗粒"的血液样品。我们获悉，在遇到这种情况时虽然实验数据被记录下来，但是并没有包含在用于发表的分析中。即便如此，除了尽量避免使用有过敏倾向的人的血液之外，实验中所用的血液样品的来源并没有受到人为的控制。

我们总共见证了七轮实验，其中三次是按照标准步骤按部就班的重复。在第四次实验中，稀释的抗 IgE 抗体样品由调查组的一个成员（沃尔特·斯图尔特）随机加到含有嗜碱性粒细胞的培养孔中，然后由达弗纳博士在双盲的情况下观察细胞脱颗粒的情况。所有这四次实验，其中最后一次是在揭盲后，邦弗尼斯特得出了支持自己结论的阳性结果。但是在接下来的三个严格按照双盲规定进行的实验中，染色的嗜碱性粒细胞的计数给出了阴性结果（如下）。

Figure 1 shows results gathered in the first group of experiments. The ordinate is the decrease (compared with the control) of the numbers of stained basophils at dilutions ranging from 10^{-2} to 10^{-30}. In each case, the left-most peak is that expected from the interaction between anti-IgE and IgE bound to basophils. The number of stained basophils increases to near its control value at log (dilution) of between 5 and 7 (0 percent degranulation, called "achromasie"); the unexpected phenomenon is that the graphs then reach a series of three or four further peaks with increasing dilution.

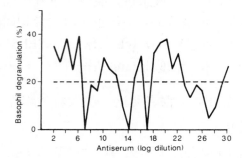

Fig. 1. A demonstration degranulation, the first of the three open experiments.

These are the successive peaks of activity said in the original article to occur in a periodic fashion, and whose position was said to be reproducible. It is clear from the four graphs that this claim is not obviously supported by this data. The laboratory notebooks confirm that the position of the peaks varies from one experiment to another.

The data in the fourth experiment appear different from those recorded earlier in the laboratory. Indeed, Benveniste volunteered that "we've not seen one like this before". The odd feature of the curve is that the activity of the diluted anti-IgE is, at its peak, identical with that of anti-IgE at log (dilution) 3—presumably the point at which the natural degranulating effect of anti-IgE is a maximum.

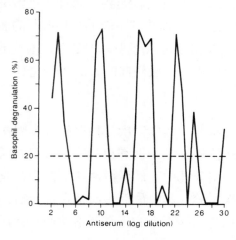

Fig. 2. The fourth demonstration experiment (read "blind") with unexpectedly high peaks (see text).

图 1 所示为第一组实验得到的结果。纵坐标是在稀释度 10^{-2}~10^{-30} 倍之间的实验组中染色的嗜碱性粒细胞减少的百分数（与对照组比较后）。最左边的峰是抗 IgE 抗体与嗜碱性粒细胞表面的 IgE 分子结合后所引起的。当稀释倍数增大到 10^5~10^7 时，实验组中染色的嗜碱性粒细胞的数量与对照组的相当（0% 脱颗粒，称为"色盲"）；出乎意料的是，在此之后，随着稀释倍数的增大，又出现了 3~4 次脱颗粒峰值。

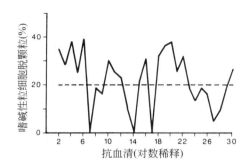

图 1. 脱颗粒实验的图示，三个公开实验中的第一次实验结果

上图即为邦弗尼斯特论文中所提到的呈周期性的连续的峰，并且这些峰值所处的位置被认为是可重复的。从本文 4 张图中我们可以清楚地看出，这些数据并不能够充分地支持这一论点。他们的实验记录也证明这些峰的位置在不同的实验中是不同的。

第四次实验的数据似乎与这个实验室之前所记录的结果有所不同。确实，邦弗尼斯特自己也说"我们以前没有看见过这样的实验结果"。这个曲线的奇怪之处在于随着抗 IgE 抗体的稀释，后续出现的各峰值与稀释 10^3 倍时的峰值一样——而我们知道，10^3 倍可能是抗 IgE 抗体引发的嗜碱性粒细胞脱颗粒的最大值的稀释倍数。

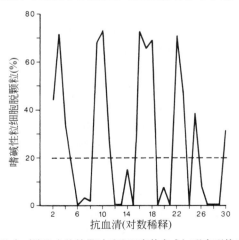

图 2. 在第四次实验中（读取实验结果时采取双盲的方式）观察到的出乎意料的高峰值（见正文）。

We raised with Dr Benveniste and his colleagues the obviously relevant question of the sampling error. We were astonished to learn, in the discussion of our conclusions at the end of our visit, that neither Dr Benveniste nor his colleagues seemed to be aware of what sampling errors are. We provided a simple explanation, complete with an account of what happens when one pulls a handful of differently coloured balls from a bag, to argue that the sampling error of any counting measurement must be of the order of the square root of the number to be counted. On several occasions, Benveniste called these "theoretical objections".

Ironically, he is himself one of the three authors of a paper published in 1981, in which just this issue had been addressed in a superficially similar situation (Petoit, J. F., Sainte-Laudy, J. & Benveniste, J. *Ann. Biol. clin.* **39**, 355; 1981), and which appears to be the justification of the dotted line drawn at about 20 percent (corresponding to two standard deviations) on the percent degranulations of intact basophils after axis.

That brief paper deals exclusively with the effect of sampling errors (not other kinds of errors) on the interpretation of measurements of intact basophils after white-cell suspensions had been allowed to react with allergens via their attached IgE molecules. Even now, at the Clamart laboratory, provision is made for the measurement of two control samples. Among other things, the paper provides a statistical test for telling when the difference between the two control values is statistically significant at the 5 percent level, in which case people using the procedure as a diagnostic test of allergy are advised to start their experiment all over again.

At INSERM 200, there seems to have grown up a less formal way of dealing with problems of this kind; when the reading of a diluted sample is greater than the control counts, the experimenter often counts the control sample again, on the grounds that the first reading "must have been wrong". This happened when Dr Davenas was counting the first of the first group of experiments.

This procedure exaggerates to some extent the amount of basophil degranulation measured with reagents at high dilution. The practice makes the control values unreliable, and is a significant pointer to the laboratory's disregard of statistical principles.

In these circumstances, it is natural that we should eagerly have accepted Benveniste's invitation to devise a blind experiment. We set out to devise a procedure that would be watertight. We asked that three samples of blood should be run. The serial dilutions would be prepared by Dr Davenas, secretly coded by us before being transferred to wells for incubation and staining by her.

In a small laboratory, procedures like this are inevitably and understandably disruptive. At INSERM 200, the sense of melodrama was further heightened by the general recognition of the importance of the trial, and by the precautions necessary to ensure that the code would not be known to others than ourselves as well as by the need that the one of us with

对此，我们向邦弗尼斯特博士和他的同事们提出了关于采样误差的疑问。在我们此次访问结束前的总结讨论中，我们很惊讶地发现，邦弗尼斯特博士和他的同事们似乎对采样误差毫不了解。我们对此进行了简单的解释，并以从一个装有各种颜色彩球的袋子中掏出一把不同颜色的球为例，排除计数方法的抽样误差，必须考虑样本量的平方根。对此，邦弗尼斯特称之为"理论上的反对意见"。

具有讽刺意味的是，他自己曾是 1981 年发表的一篇涉及相似问题的论文的三个作者之一（珀图瓦特、圣洛迪、邦弗尼斯特，《生物临床年报》第 39 卷，第 355 期，1981 年）。在这篇文章中，他们认为应在完整嗜碱性粒细胞的脱颗粒百分比的 20% 处（对应两个标准差）划一条点线作为判据，点线之下为可信的读数。

那篇文章专门研究了白细胞悬浮液通过表面 IgE 分子与抗原相互作用后，采样误差（不是别的误差）对检测脱颗粒后完整嗜碱性粒细胞的影响。即使现在，在克拉马尔实验室，也仍然规定要测量两个对照样品。此外，这篇文章还给出了用于验证两个对照值之间的差异是否具有统计学显著性（p<0.05）的检验方法。这使得那些通过观察嗜碱性粒细胞脱颗粒的情况检测过敏反应的研究人员开始重新设计他们的实验。

在 INSERM 200，对于此类问题似乎存在一个不那么正式的处理方法。当实验组的读值比对照组还要高的时候，实验员通常会以第一次读值"一定有问题"为理由而重新计算对照组的数值。这一情况在达弗纳博士统计第一组实验的第一个实验的结果时便发生了。

这种实验方法在某种程度上夸大了高倍稀释试剂中检测到的嗜碱性粒细胞脱颗粒的数量。这一行为使得对照组的数值变得不可信，这是这个实验室无视统计学原理的重要体现。

在这种情况下，我们自然热切地接受了邦弗尼斯特请我们设计一个双盲实验的邀请。我们着手设计了一个完善的实验流程。我们要求测试 3 个不同的血液样品，并且由我们对达弗纳博士系列稀释后的抗 IgE 抗体进行秘密编号，然后由她将这些样品加入到培养板中与嗜碱性粒细胞共孵育和染色。

在一个小型实验室，这样的实验流程的混乱是不可避免的，也是可以理解的。不过在 INSERM 200，由于大家都认为此次实验非常重要，同时由于我们想尽办法防止他人获知试管编号，还由于我们不让以变戏法著称的詹姆斯·兰迪接触到盛有

a reputation for sleight of hand (J.R.) could be shown to have been kept away from the test-tubes containing the serial dilutions.

This was done by arranging that Davenas should carry the diluted anti-IgE solutions in stoppered test-tubes to a separate room, where their contents would have been transferred to previously labelled tubes as determined by counters drawn at random from a bag. The coding procedure was monitored by a video camera operated by Randi, who was thereby prevented from touching anything else. (We have a record of the proceedings on an unbroken reel of tape.)

We made two last-minute changes in the planned procedure. First, we included 5 control tubes containing only buffer. Second, having been warned that homoeopathists might regard the data as invalid if solutions were decanted from one set of tubes to another, we removed the numbers written with a felt pen on the original tubes, replacing them with numbered labels which Randi assured us were tamper-proof. The code itself was eventually folded in aluminium foil, enclosed in an envelope specially sealed by Randi and then taped to the laboratory ceiling for the duration of the experiment.

We also arranged a second step of coding just before the slides were counted. One of us (W.W.S.) took responsibility for pipetting, after securing the agreement of Davenas and Benveniste that his technique was satisfactory. Both the laboratory procedures and the codes themselves were recorded on video tape. The plates containing the stained cell suspensions were stored in a box (sealed by Randi) in a cold room until read, in random order. The second plate took longer to read, partly because each well was read in duplicate by each observer (Dr Davenas and her colleague, Dr Francis Beauvais), partly because the cells of the second plate were only faintly stained and were thus difficult to read.

Whatever the three runs would provide, we were especially anxious to derive some objective estimate of the intra- and inter-observer measurement errors. We had been told at the outset, by Benveniste, that Dr Davenas was not merely exceptionally devoted to her work but the one in whose hands the experiment most often "works". He said that she usually "counts more cells" than other people. Dr Beauvais, who was also said to be exceptionally skilled, read the slides separately from Dr Davenas, but at the same time. On this occasion, the sampling errors missing from most of the laboratory records did indeed appear.

The duplicate measurements in our strictly blinded experiments were especially important. First, they show that sampling errors do indeed exist, and are not "theoretical objections". Second, they show that the two observers were counting as accurately as could be expected, which gives the lie to the later complaint that the results of the double-blind experiments might be unreliable because the observers had been exhausted by our demands.

系列稀释试剂的试管，一切变得更富戏剧性。

整个实验过程是这样的：达弗纳将稀释好的抗 IgE 抗体溶液装到一个带塞子的试管中，并拿到另一个房间；在这个房间里，我们将这些溶液转移到事先做好标记的试管中，这些试管是由计数者从一个袋子里随机取出的。整个编号的过程由兰迪使用摄像机进行记录，从而避免他触碰任何其他东西。（我们有整个编号过程的完整的录影带。）

对于上述实验流程，我们还做了两个"最后一分钟的改变"。第一，我们在样品中混入了五个只含有空白缓冲液的试管作为阴性对照。第二，为了避免"顺势疗法"论者以"溶液被从一个试管中倒入另一个试管中"为理由称此次实验数据不能说明问题，我们将原始试管上用毡笔写的数字擦去，并贴上标有数字的标签，兰迪向我们确保它们不会被做手脚。最后用铝箔把这些编号包起来，并装入信封中由兰迪进行特殊密封，用胶带贴在实验室的天花板上并在实验过程保持这种状态。

在对脱颗粒情况进行计数前，我们还安排了第二次编号的步骤。我们中的一员（沃尔特·斯图尔特）负责移取液体，他的技术已经事先得到了达弗纳和邦弗尼斯特的认可。这些实验室操作和样品编码都被摄像记录下来。在染色后，含有细胞悬液的培养板被随机放到一个盒子中（由兰迪密封）并置于冷藏室，直到读数前才取出来。第二块板读数花的时间比较长，一部分原因是每个孔都分别由达弗纳博士和她的同事弗朗西斯·博韦重复观察。之所以这样做，部分是由于第二块板染色比较模糊，不易分辨结果。

无论这三个实验会产生什么样的结果，我们非常渴望对源自观测者自身和不同观测者之间的实验误差进行客观的评价。在最开始我们便从邦弗尼斯特博士那里获知达弗纳博士不仅对她自己的工作异常投入，而且她经手的实验通常多数是"奏效"的。邦弗尼斯特博士说达弗纳博士通常会比别人"数出更多的细胞"。博韦博士也是一个技术很精湛的研究人员，她与达弗纳博士同时分别读数。在这种情况下，大多数实验记录中缺乏的采样误差确实地出现了。

在我们严格的双盲实验中，双重测量是非常重要的。第一，它们证明采样误差是确实存在的，并且不是"理论反对意见"。第二，它们显示两名观测者都在尽可能准确地计数，这也反驳了后来有些人的抱怨，他们认为实验人员被我们的各种要求弄得筋疲力尽，从而整个实验的结果是不可信的。

Others working in this field recognize the difficulty of counting basophils (roughly 1 in 100 among leukocytes), preferring instead to measure the histamine released on degranulation. This practice is not followed at INSERM 200 because, we were told, of previous failure to record histamine release (as distinct from the disappearance of stained basophils) at high dilution (whence the term "achromasie").

We began to break the codes by lunchtime on our last day, the Friday. When the slides had been matched to the wells from which their samples had derived, but before the appropriate dilutions had been assigned to them, there was a great sense of light-heartedness in the laboratory, no doubt at the prospect that the ordeal would soon be at an end. Benveniste, glancing at the half-decoded data, even offered to predict where the peaks and troughs would fall in the data. His offer was accepted. But his predictions proved to be entirely wrong.

We asked at this stage for criticisms of the conduct of the trials, but were given none. To the question what would be said if the two observers had recorded degranulation peaks, but at different high-dilution values, Benveniste said that would still constitute success.

Opening sealed envelopes is Randi's expertise. He found that the sealed flap of the envelope had detached itself at a surprisingly straight angle when the scotch tape attaching the code to the ceiling was pulled away, but inspection of the aluminium foil allowed him to pronounce himself satisfied that the code had not been read. Then came the decoding—one person singing out numbers to another.

So do the numbers make sense? Six numbers into the record of the first plate to be read, Benveniste said "that patient isn't degranulating, try another". So we did—first the parallel readings by Dr Beauvais, then the remaining two experiments. In the event, the results of all three experiments were similar. The anti-IgE at conventional dilutions caused degranulation, but at "high dilution" there was no effect. Blood from three sources in a row degranulated at ordinary dilutions but not at homoeopathic dilutions. Each of the three experiments was a failure.

Conclusions

We conclude that the claims made by Davenas *et al.* are not to be believed. Our conclusion, not based solely on the circumstance that the only strictly double-blind experiments we had itnessed proved to be failures, may be summarized as follows:

■ **The care with which the experiments reported have been carried out does not match the extraordinary character of the claims made in their interpretation.** What we found, at Clamart, was a laboratory procedure possibly suitable for the application of a well-tested

相关领域的其他人员认识到嗜碱性粒细胞的计数是一个很难的事情（100 个白细胞中约有 1 个），因此，他们更倾向于测定在脱颗粒的过程中释放出的组胺的含量。不过，在 INSERM 200 并没有采用这一方法，是因为我们被告知在先前的实验中他们在高倍稀释下（发生"色盲"）检测不到组胺的释放（显著区别于染色的嗜碱性粒细胞的消失）。

在我们访问的最后一天，也就是星期五的午餐时间，我们公布了样品的编号情况。在将稀释样品与最终脱颗粒情况对应起来之前，我们先公布了玻片上的样品与样品孔的对应关系。此时，实验室的气氛是轻松的，大家认为这个痛苦的过程总算要结束了。邦弗尼斯特瞟了一眼这个解密了一半的数据，甚至提出要预测哪里是脱颗粒曲线的波峰、哪里是波谷。大家接受了他的提议。不过事实证明他的预测是完全错误的。

这个时候我们问大家对此次实验的执行是否有疑问，不过没有得到回应。当我们问到如何看待"两名观测人员虽然都记录到了脱颗粒的峰值，但是对应的是不同的稀释倍数"这个问题时，邦弗尼斯特认为这仍证明脱颗粒实验是成功的。

打开密封的信封是兰迪的拿手好戏。在把粘在天花板上的编号的透明胶带除去时，他发现信封的封口已经自己展成了令人惊讶的直角。通过检查包在外面的铝箔，他确认编号并没有被人偷看。然后我们开始解码——一个人把编号唱给另一个人。

那么结果与预期相符合么？读取了第一块板测的 6 个样品的脱颗粒情况之后，邦弗尼斯特说"这个病人的血样不能发生脱颗粒，试试另一个"。于是我们照做了——首先是博韦博士对第一块板的平行读数，然后继续分析剩下的两个实验结果。最终大家发现，所有三个实验的结果都是相似的：正常稀释倍数的抗 IgE 抗体可以引起脱颗粒，而"高倍稀释"的则无效；三个不同来源的血液样品都可以被正常稀释的抗 IgE 抗体引发脱颗粒，但不能被所谓的"顺势疗法"的高倍稀释抗体引发。从这个意义上说，这三个实验都是"失败"的。

结　论

我们认为达弗纳等人所得出的结论是不可信的。我们所作出的结论不仅仅是基于我们所见证的那次严格的双盲实验，还包括以下方面的内容：

■ **他们所进行的实验的细致程度达不到能证明他们在论文中所阐述的那些非同寻常的结论的要求。**在克拉马尔，我们所看到的这些实验流程可能只适合用于已经被广泛认可的生物实验，而不适合在这里用于证明稀释 10^{120} 倍的抗 IgE 抗体仍能引

bioassay, but unsuitable as a basis for claiming that anti-IgE retains its biological activity even at a log (dilution) of 120. In circumstances in which the avoidance of contamination would seem crucial, no thought seemed to have been given to the possibility of contamination by misplaced test-tube stoppers, the contamination of unintended wells during the pipetting process and general laboratory contamination (the experiments we witnessed were carried out at an open bench). We have no idea what would be the effect on basophil degranulation of the organic solvents and adhesives backing the scotch tape used to seal the polystyrene wells overnight, but neither does the laboratory.

The design of the experiments hardly matches the nature of their interpretation. For example, one would have thought that counting wells at least in duplicate would have been an elementary precaution against gross errors. The second of our strictly blinded experiments seems to be one of the few in which something of this kind had been attempted.

The laboratory seems to have been curiously uncritical of the reasons why its experiments do not, on many occasions, "work". For example, we were told that the best results were obtained when cells were left in the cold room overnight before counting, but there has been no investigation of that phenomenon, or of the reports that taking a second sample from a single well gives odd results (an effect not apparent in our double-blind experiments).

■ **The phenomena described are not reproducible, but there has been no serious investigation of the reasons.** We have referred to the fact that some blood yields negative results, and that there are periods of time when no experiments work. But the laboratory notebooks show great variability in the positions at which peaks occur.

■ **The data lack errors of the magnitude that would be expected, and which are unavoidable.** This is best illustrated by Fig. 3, whose two graphs have been constructed from data recorded by Dr Davenas from samples supposedly identical with each other, usually measurements of control samples but also including some duplicate runs. The recorded values have been normalized by subtracting the mean and dividing by the square root of the mean (the expected sampling error). If the only source of error were sampling error, the standard deviation of the plotted curve should be unity (1). Other sources of error, for example, experimental variability, could only increase the standard deviation. But Fig. 3 shows that repeat observations agree more closely than would be expected from the underlying distribution. This is a well-known effect that sometimes affects duplicate readings by the same individual, but the magnitide of the effect in this case calls into question the validity of the readings. This artefact is nevertheless not apparent in the blinded duplicated readings.

发嗜碱性粒细胞脱颗粒这样的结论。很显然，排除样品污染对于证明这个结论来说非常重要。不过，他们似乎并没有考虑试管塞的错误放置，移液过程中无意造成的样品孔污染和普通的实验室污染（我们看到实验是在开放的实验台上进行的）的可能性。我们不知道有机溶剂以及用于聚丙烯微量培养板密封过夜的透明胶带背面的黏合剂会对嗜碱性粒细胞脱颗粒的影响，不过这个实验室的人员似乎也没有考虑过这个问题。

实验设计难以揭示本质现象。例如在进行细胞计数时，至少应该采取两次读数取平均值的方式以减少粗差，这是人们通常的想法。然而，似乎只有在我们进行的第二个严格的双盲实验中，他们才对这种方法进行了尝试。

这个实验室似乎对于为什么有时候他们的实验不能"奏效"这个问题缺乏思考。例如，他们告诉我们，当把细胞放在冷藏室过夜后可以获得最好的脱颗粒实验的结果，但他们对这个现象并没有进行研究，也没有去解释为什么从同一个孔中再取一个样进行测试会得到奇怪的结果（在我们的双盲实验中这种效应并不明显）。

■ **他们所描述的现象是不可重复的，但他们并没有对其中的原因进行严肃地调查**。我们在前面提到过一些血液样品总是产生阴性的结果，并且曾经有一段时期这个实验都做不出预期的结果。此外，实验记录显示脱颗粒峰值的位置在不同的实验中波动很大。

■ **实验数据缺少在合理范围内不可避免会存在误差**。这在图3中得到了很好的体现。这两个图都来自达弗纳博士的数据，这些数据被认为是完全相同的样品的测试结果，通常是对照实验的结果，也包括一些重复实验的结果。我们把实验数据减去该组实验的平均值然后再除以平均值的平方根（预期采样误差），即可将测量数据标准化。如果整个实验系统中误差的唯一来源是采样误差，那么图中曲线的标准差则应该是统一的（1）。其他的误差来源，如实验可变性，只会导致标准偏差的增大。图3的数据说明重复测量的结果比根据潜在分布做出的预期更加吻合。这是一种众所周知的效应，它会影响同一个人的重复读数。不过在这个实验中，这种效应的影响程度已经导致了读数可靠性的问题。在双盲实验中，这种人为因素造成的假象并不显著。

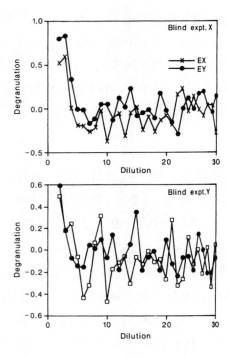

Fig. 3. Records for the first two blind experiments (5–7 inclusive). showing sampling noise only below the expected decline of degranulation with increasing dilution. Note that the ordinate extends below zero on the degranulation scale (to accommodate sampling errors above as well as below the control values).

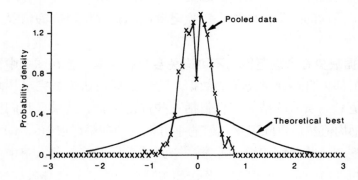

Fig. 4 . Comparison of measured departures of duplicate normalized readings from their means with the gaussian distribution expected.

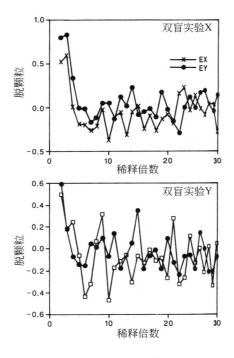

图 3. 前两个双盲实验的结果（包括 5~7）显示随着抗血清稀释倍数的增大，由采样误差导致的脱颗粒的数值仅比预期由抗血清所引发的数值略低。值得注意的是，纵坐标中细胞脱颗粒的百分比已经低于零（这是为了让这些由采样误差引起的值能够得以体现出来）。

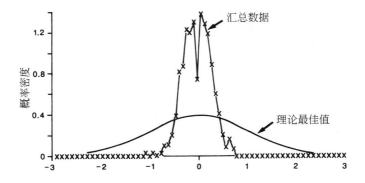

图 4. 将脱颗粒实验结果的两次读数的平均值标准化之后与预期的高斯分布进行测量偏离的比较。

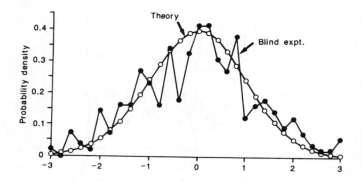

Fig. 5. Same as Fig. 4 except that data derive from duplicated readings within the blind experiments only.

■ **No serious attempt has been made to eliminate systematic errors, including observer bias.** It is true that the laboratory notebooks record experiments in which anti-IgG has been used as a control; we were surprised to find that the IgG control run reported by Davenas *et al.* (their Fig. 1*b*) was carried out at a different time from the run with IgE published in the same figure.

Most of the data recorded in the laboratory notebooks derive from experiments in which the same person has been responsible for the sequential dilution, plating out and counting. Given the shared belief at Clamart in the reality of the phenomenon reported last month, and its potential importance, it is mystifying that duplicate and blind counting is not routine.

■ **The climate of the laboratory is inimical to an objective evaluation of the exceptional data.** So much is readily apparent from the way in which experiments are described as successes and failures, by the use of the word "working" to describe experiments yielding a positive result, and by the several speculations we were offered, without experimental evidence in their support, to explain the several failures the laboratory has experienced. The folklore of high-dilution work pervades the laboratory, as epitomized by the suggestion that decanting diluted solution from one tube to another might spoil the effect and the report that the repeated serial dilution by factors of three and seven (rather than ten) always yields negative results.

Collaborations

We have not been able to pay as much attention as we would have wished to the data collected at other laboratories and cited in Davenas *et al.*, but we have examined documentary evidence available.

Supporting data were said to have come from Rehovot (Israel), Milan and Toronto. Dr Benveniste told us we could not see the Toronto data, described as preliminary, without the consent of the authors, who could not be telephoned.

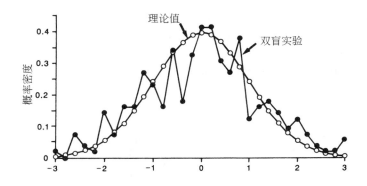

图 5. 同图 4，只是本图数据仅来自双盲实验中重复读数。

■ **他们没有认真尝试采取相关措施排除包括观测者偏好在内的系统误差。**实验室记录中确实显示研究人员使用了抗 IgG 抗血清作为实验的阴性对照，不过我们却惊奇地发现由达弗纳等人进行的 IgG 对照实验（图 1b）与发表在同一图表的 IgE 实验是在不同时间进行的。

实验记录显示，大多数实验都是由同一个人全程完成系列稀释、铺板、计数等一系列操作步骤的。考虑到克拉马尔的研究人员对"高倍稀释的抗血清可以引发嗜碱性粒细胞脱颗粒"这个实验现象真实性以及潜在的重要性都很有信心，我们对他们缺乏重复实验和双盲实验的意识而感到迷惑。

■ **这个实验室不能客观地评价实验中不支持自己假说的数据。**从实验通常被描述为"成功"的和"失败"的诸多事实已经证明了这一点。当得到阳性的结果时，人们会说这个实验"奏效"了；而对于好几次被认为"阴性"的结果，用我们提出的若干推测而非实验证据来解释。这个实验室还很流行高倍稀释效应这样的民间传说，并且还认为把稀释后的溶液从一个试管中倒入另一个试管会破坏其疗效，以及报告称先后稀释 10^3 倍和 10^7 倍（而不是 10^{10} 倍）的抗血清总是会产生阴性的结果。

合　作

虽然我们很希望能够对由其他实验室获得并被达弗纳等人引用的数据进行同样的分析，但受时间和精力所限，我们只能对其中可以获得的一些文件进行检查。

雷霍沃特（以色列）、米兰、多伦多等多个地方的实验室都参与了这项工作。邦弗尼斯特博士告诉我们：不能在没有得到作者的同意的情况下看多伦多的数据，该数据被视为最起始的数据，而作者电话打不通。

The data gathered in Israel and Milan are, apparently, significant. Figure 6 is typical of the data from Milan. Though there are no duplicate measurements and therefore no direct evidence of sampling error, there is also some evidence of degranulation at high dilution. Without knowing more about the circumstances, we are unable to comment.

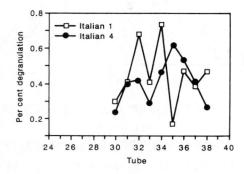

Fig. 6. Two duplicate Italian runs showing high degranulation, but discordantly.

The Israeli data are more extensive. The first trials were in March 1987, during a visit to Rehovot by Dr Davenas. The most remarkable of several successful trials was her correct identification of seven high-dilution tubes out of ten presented to her blind. Even so, the report (to Benveniste) of the trials was cautious. Later, analysis of the tubes which had tested positive in this trial revealed not merely immunoglobins but other protein contaminants apparently identical with materials in the original IgE vial. One of the participants (Professor Meir Shinitsky of the Weizmann Institute) then withdrew as a putative co-author.

Since then, there have been two developments in Israel— a series of experiments carried out independently of Benveniste's laboratory and a further blinded experiment. Data from the latter are unfortunately not available. Maitre Simart, a legal official at Clamart who held the codes, is said not to have had time to decode them.

These measurements are nevertheless, to judge from the documents we have seen, stronger evidence than any we found at Dr Benveniste's laboratory to support his claims. But we do not have the information to evaluate them.

Postscript

We presented the substance of these conclusions to Dr Benveniste and his colleagues immediately after the strictly blinded experiments were decoded. The discussion that followed was inevitably tense. Benveniste acknowledged that his experimental design may not have been "perfect", but insisted (not for the first time) that the quality of his data was no worse than that of many papers published in *Nature* and other such journals.

以色列和米兰的数据显然是很重要的。图 6 是一个具有代表性的米兰的数据。尽管他们没有对结果进行重复测量，也因此无法计算采样误差，但仍有一些证据表明在他们的实验中，高倍稀释的抗血清可以引发脱颗粒。由于无法获知更多的实验相关的信息，我们无法对此结果作出评论。

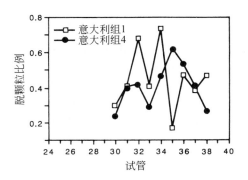

图 6. 两个来自意大利的重复实验结果，它们都显示存在很高的脱颗粒比例，但两个实验的数据并不一致。

来自以色列的结果相对更具有普遍意义。第一次实验是在 1987 年 3 月达弗纳博士到雷霍沃特访问时进行的。在几个成功的实验中，最著名的是她在单盲实验中正确地从 10 个样品中识别出了 7 个高倍稀释样品。虽然如此，她给邦弗尼斯特的报告中对这次实验的表述也是很谨慎的。后来，对该实验中盛阳性样品的试管进行分析发现，其中不仅含有免疫球蛋白，还含有与原始 IgE 样品中同样的蛋白质污染物。于是这个实验的参与者之一——魏茨曼科学研究所的梅厄·希尼特斯克伊教授放弃成为共同作者。

之后，我们又调查了在以色列进行的取得进展的另两个实验：一个是独立于邦弗尼斯特实验室的一系列实验，另外一个是进一步的双盲实验。不幸的是，我们没有拿到双盲实验的数据。克拉马尔的一位法律官员迈特尔·西马尔掌握着这些数据的密码，但据称他没有时间将它们解密。

从文件判断，以色列的这些结果比我们在邦弗尼斯特博士的实验室看见的更能支持其结论。但由于缺乏相关的信息，我们也无法对此进行评价。

后　记

在严格的双盲实验解码结束后，我们即向邦弗尼斯特和他的同事们通报了上述结果。不可避免的，接下来的讨论是非常紧张的。邦弗尼斯特承认他的实验设计或许不够"完美"，但仍然一再坚持他的实验数据的质量不比在《自然》和其他类似杂志上发表的论文差。

One of us (J.M.) said it would be best if Benveniste would withdraw the published article, or at least write to *Nature* to qualify his findings and their interpretation, in which case we would not publish this report. It was mutually agreed that nothing would be said publicly until 28 July. But Benveniste said that the laboratory would work through the weekend "and all next week" to prove the reality of the phenomenon.

Our greatest surprise (and disappointment) is that INSERM 200 seems not to have appreciated that its sensational claims could be sustained only by data of exceptional quality. Randi put the point best, during our Friday discussion, by saying: "Look, if I told you that I keep a goat in the backyard of my house in Florida, and if you happened to have a man nearby, you might ask him to look over my garden fence, when he'd say 'That man keeps a goat'. But what would you do if I said, 'I keep a unicorn in my backyard'?" We have no way of knowing whether the point was taken.

Eventually, there was no more to say. We shook hands all round, sped past the common-room filled with champagne bottles destined now not to be opened and into the lens of a news agency photographer summoned for the happier event.

(**334**, 287-290;1988)

John Maddox, James Randi & Walter W. Stewart

我们小组中的约翰·马多克斯说如果邦弗尼斯特愿意撤销已发表的论文或者至少向《自然》杂志写信对他的发现和阐述进行修改，那么我们就不发表此次调查报告。双方都同意在 7 月 28 日之前不就此事发表公开声明。但邦弗尼斯特也表示将利用这个周末以及下周的时间验证他们所发现的现象的真实性。

最令我们惊讶同时也让我们失望的是，INSERM 200 似乎并没有意识到他们宣称的轰动性结论仅仅被一些非正常的数据支持。在我们周五的讨论中，兰迪指出，"如果我告诉你我在佛罗里达州的房子的后院里面养了一只山羊，而且你恰巧有一个朋友在那里附近，你就可以请他从篱笆外面看一下，他会说'那人养了一只山羊'。但如果我说'我在后院养了一只独角兽'时，你会怎么做呢？"我们不知道他们是否理解了兰迪的意思。

最后，大家都没什么要说的了。我们和所有人握手告别，从摆满了现在无法开启的香槟酒瓶子的公共休息室中穿过，旁边是期待着捕捉圆满结局画面的新闻摄影师。

（张锦彬 翻译；秦志海 审稿）

New Semiconductor Device Physics in Polymer Diodes and Transistors

J. H. Burroughes *et al.*

Editor's Note

Carbon-based polymers (plastics) had been long regarded as electrical insulators. But in the 1970s, Japanese chemist Hideki Shirakawa discovered an electrically conducting form of polyacetylene. Here Richard Friend and his co-workers at Cambridge report transistors made from polyacetylene, offering the promise of a "plastic microelectronics" that could be cheap, robust and flexible. They show that the polymer conducts in a different way to silicon, involving electronic states called excitons associated with distortions of the molecular chains. The immense technological potential of such devices played a big part in the decision to award the 2000 Nobel Prize in Chemistry to Shirakawa, along with Alan MacDiarmid and Alan Heeger who helped develop the early field of polymer electronics.

Semiconductor devices have been made from polyacetylene, a conjugated polymeric semiconductor. The device operates in a novel way: charge is stored in localized soliton-like excitations of the polymer chain, which are introduced not by doping or photoexcitation but by the presence of a surface electric field. The formation of charged solitons changes the optical properties of the polymer, introducing optical absorption below the band gap. Combined with the processibility of the polymer, these new electro-optic effects may be exploited technologically in electro-optic modulators.

THERE is current interest in the possible use of "molecular" organic materials as the active materials in electronic or optical devices, and this field is now designated "molecular electronics". But basic questions as to whether or not it is possible (or appropriate) to make use of modes of operation familiar in inorganic semiconductor science remain largely unanswered. Conjugated polymers are "molecular" analogues of inorganic semiconductors[1], which exhibit high electronic mobilities when doped[2]. Despite the considerable progress made in the past decade towards an understanding of the electronic properties of conjugated polymers, there has been relatively little work on their use as the active component in semiconductor device structures. There are several reasons for this, the most important of which is that most conjugated polymers cannot be conveniently processed to the forms required in these devices. Most conjugated polymers are not readily soluble in easily handled solvents, and are infusible. This has severely limited the scope for construction of devices and those that have been reported in the literature show rather poor characteristics. Schottky and p-n diodes have been studied by

高分子二极管和晶体管中半导体器件物理学的新学问

伯勒斯等

编者按

碳基高分子（"塑料"）在相当长的一段时间里被认为是电绝缘材料。但 20 世纪 70 年代，日本化学家白川英树发现了聚乙炔的导电现象。本文中，剑桥大学的理查德·弗兰德和他的合作者们报道了由聚乙炔制备的晶体管，这显示出了"塑料微电子学"的发展前景，这种器件具有廉价、耐用以及柔性等特点。他们的结果表明高分子导电方式不同于硅，导电的过程涉及一种名为激子的与分子链的变形相关的电子态。这种器件巨大的技术潜力在很大程度上促使 2000 年的诺贝尔化学奖授予了艾伦·麦克迪尔米德、艾伦·黑格与白川英树这几位早期导电高分子领域的开拓者。

聚乙炔这种共轭高分子半导体已被用于制备器件。该器件以一种新颖的方式工作：电荷存储在高分子链的定域的类孤子激发中，这种激发并非由掺杂或者光激发引起，而是由于表面电场的存在所致。带电孤子的形成改变了高分子的光学性质，引起了低于带隙的光吸收。与高分子的可加工性相结合，这种新的电光效应从技术上来讲可以应用于电光调制器。

最近，人们对于使用"分子"有机材料作为光电器件的活性材料很感兴趣，这一领域现在被称为"分子电子学"。然而，一些基本的问题，例如有没有可能（或者是不是合适）在"分子电子学"中采用无机半导体学中我们所熟知的操控模式，大都还没有答案。共轭高分子是无机半导体的"分子"类似物[1]，它在掺杂之后可以表现出高的电子迁移率[2]。过去十年间对共轭高分子的电子学性质的理解获得了可观的进展，然而，将之作为有效构件用于半导体器件中的研究工作相对来说很少。造成这种状况的原因是多方面的，其中最重要的原因就是大多数共轭高分子不能方便地加工成器件所要求的形态，这是因为大多数共轭高分子不易溶于常用的溶剂，也很难熔化。这严重限制了其在器件中的应用，文献中已经报道的器件性能也都较差。有一些研究组研究过肖特基二极管和 p-n 结二极管[3-6]，报道的最大整流比（正向和

several groups[3-6], and rectification ratios ($I_{forward}/I_{reverse}$) of up to a few hundred have been reported. There are also reports of field-induced conductivity measured in MISFET (metal–insulator–semiconductor field-effect transistor) structures[7,8].

A major advance in the control of the polymer processing is in the use of a solution-processible precursor polymer which can be converted to the conjugated polymer after processing. This was first demonstrated by Edwards and Feast[9] for the preparation of polyacetylene (the Durham route) and it is polyacetylene produced by this route that we have used in the present studies. We have made thin-film devices by spin-coating the precursor polymer, poly((5,6-bis(trifluoro-methyl)-bicyclo-[2,2,2]octa-5,7-diene-2,3-diyl)-1,2-ethenediyl), in solution onto the required substrate, followed by heat treatment to convert to the polyacetylene by elimination of hexafluoro-ortho-xylene[10-15]. As we discuss later, the films of polyacetylene prepared in this way are p-doped (possibly with catalyst residues at chain ends) to a level suitable for device applications ($\sim 10^{16}$ cm^{-3}), and these dopants do not appear to be mobile under applied electric fields. We have not found it necessary, therefore, to dope the polymer further. We have investigated a range of unipolar devices: Schottky-barrier diodes, MIS (metal–insulator–semiconductor) structures and MISFETs. By careful control of the processing, with rigorous exclusion of oxygen, we have been able to get the device performance up to levels respectable enough to learn about the detailed functioning of the device. For the Schottky diodes we routinely measure rectification ratios of about 500,000, and for the MIS and MISFET structures we can demonstrate that the devices show "textbook" formation of charge accumulation, inversion and depletion layers at the polyacetylene–insulator interface.

We did not expect charge storage in these devices to be in the band states as electrons and holes. It is established that there is a structural relaxation around charges present on the polymer chains, both when charges are added to the polymer chain through chemical doping, or separated following photoexcitation. For polyacetylene, the localized states are bond alternation defects, or solitons[16,17]. Charge injected into the polyacetylene in these device structures should also be stored in soliton states. The formation of a depletion layer in polyacetylene should remove the charged solitons introduced through extrinsic doping. The formation of an accumulation or inversion layer, however, provides a new means of charging the polymer chains. The clearest evidence for the formation of solitons in polyacetylene is the appearance of additional optical absorption below the band gap, associated with the vibrational and electronic excitations of the solitons[18]. For polyacetylene prepared by the Durham route the "mid-gap" absorption feature due to transitions between the "mid-gap" levels of the solitons and the band edges is seen at ~ 1.0 eV for chemically doped samples[13], and at 0.55 eV for photoexcited charges[15]. We expect, therefore, that "charge injection" will change the optical properties of the polyacetylene in these devices; depletion should reduce the mid-gap optical absorption whereas accumulation or inversion-layer formation should introduce mid-gap states onto previously undistorted chains, increasing the mid-gap optical absorption. We find both qualitative and quantitative agreement with these theoretical predictions.

反向电流之比）可达数百。对金属－绝缘体－半导体场效应晶体管（MISFET）中测得的电场诱导的电导也有报道[7,8]。

在控制高分子加工方面的一个主要进展是可以溶液处理的高分子前驱体的使用，加工完毕后可将其再转换为共轭高分子。这种方法首见于爱德华兹和费斯特[9]制备聚乙炔（通过杜伦合成路线），本文研究中使用的聚乙炔也是采用这种方法制备的。薄膜器件制备如下：先将高分子前驱体聚（(5,6-二(三氟甲基)-双环-[2,2,2]辛-5,7-二烯-2,3-二炔基)-1,2-乙烯）的溶液旋涂在所需基底上，然后通过热处理除去六氟邻二甲苯，将前驱体转换成聚乙炔[10-15]。如下文所述，通过这种方法得到的聚乙炔薄膜是 p 型掺杂的（可能是链末端的催化剂残留造成的），掺杂水平（约为 10^{16} cm^{-3}）比较适合器件应用，在外加电场作用下这些掺杂物未表现出可迁移性。因此，我们认为不必对高分子进行进一步掺杂。我们研究了一系列单极子器件：肖特基势垒二极管，MIS（金属－绝缘体－半导体）结构和 MISFET。通过对工艺过程的精细调控，在严格排除氧气的条件下，我们可以提升器件的性能，以便研究其详细工作机理。对肖特基二极管常规测量的整流比为 500,000 左右，对 MIS 和 MISFET 结构而言，我们可以证明这些器件在聚乙炔－绝缘体界面上出现了"教科书"中所示的电荷积累层、反型层和耗尽层。

我们认为器件中的电荷并不以电子和空穴的形式存在于能带中。通常认为不论是通过化学掺杂将电荷引入到高分子链上，还是通过光激发后进行的电荷分离，高分子链上的电荷附近都会出现结构弛豫。就聚乙炔而言，定域态为键交替缺陷或者孤子[16,17]。在这些器件结构中，注入聚乙炔中的电荷也应该以孤子的形式存在。聚乙炔中耗尽层的形成应该排除非本征掺杂产生的带电孤子。然而积累层和反型层的形成为高分子链的带电提供了新的途径。聚乙炔中孤子形成的最明确的证据是伴随着孤子的振动能级和电子能级的激发，在带隙下出现了附加的光学吸收[18]。对采用杜伦路线制备的聚乙炔而言，其"中间能隙"吸收特征源于孤子的"中间能隙"能级和能带边缘间的跃迁，对于化学掺杂样品来说这个能级大约在 1.0 eV[13]，而对于光激发电荷来说大约在 0.55 eV[15]。因此，我们认为"电荷注入"会改变这些器件中聚乙炔的光学性质；耗尽层将会削弱中间能隙的光吸收，而积累层或反型层的形成将会在之前未变形的链上引入中间能隙态，从而增强中间能隙的光吸收。从定性和定量的角度，我们的发现都与这些理论预测一致。

Fabrication

Thin films of polyacetylene were formed by spin-coating films of the Durham precursor polymer from solution in 2-butanone. Transformation of the precursor polymer to the *trans* isomer of polyacetylene was achieved by heating the film to 80 °C for 12 h. By adjustment of the concentration of the precursor polymer solution and the conditions for spin-coating, fully dense, coherent films of polyacetylene with thicknesses in the range 200 Å to 1 μm were readily produced. All fabrication and measurements involving the polyacetylene were carried out with rigorous exclusion of oxygen. A variety of device structures were fabricated and examples are given below. Note that most of these are arranged to allow passage of sub-band-gap light through the layers.

Schottky diodes. The multilayer structure used was built up with a wide-field spectrosil substrate, 200 Å gold, polyacetylene film (typically 1 μm), and a top contact of 200 Å aluminium. Gold forms an ohmic contact with p-type polyacetylene, aluminium the rectifying contact.

MIS diodes. Several configurations have been used. (1) Ultrapure silicon substrate (thickness 0.3 mm, $<10^{13}$ cm^{-3} charged impurities), 4,000 Å heavily phosphorus-doped ($>10^{19}$ cm^{-3}) silicon layer, 2,000 Å silicon dioxide (insulator layer), polyacetylene (typically 200–1,200 Å) and a top contact of 200 Å gold. (2) Wide-field spectrosil substrate, 200 Å gold, 1,500 Å poly (methyl-methacrylate) (insulator layer; spin-coated from dichloromethane solution), polyacetylene film (typically 200 Å), 200 Å chromium and 100 Å gold.

MISFET structures. (1) Gold source and drain contacts: n-doped silicon substrate (distributed gate electrode), 2,000 Å silicon dioxide, gold source and drain electrodes (thickness 500 Å, channel length 0.1 mm, channel width 75 mm), polyacetylene film (typically 200 Å). Similar source and drain contacts can also be deposited by evaporation onto the MIS diode (2) above. (2) Poly n-silicon source and drain contacts: the structure used is shown as Fig. 1.

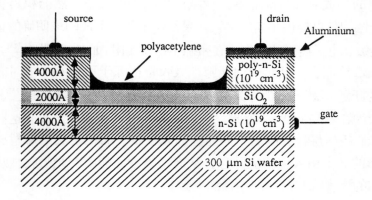

Fig. 1. Schematic diagram for a polyacetylene MISFET structure. Dimensions shown are to scale, except the channel width (20 μm) and length (1.5 m).

制　备

　　聚乙炔薄膜是通过杜伦高分子前驱体的 2-丁酮溶液旋涂制备的。将薄膜加热至80℃并保持 12 小时，就可将高分子前驱体转化为聚乙炔反式异构体。通过调整高分子前驱体溶液的浓度和旋涂的条件，可以很容易制得厚度为 200 Å 到 1 μm 的完全致密且连续的聚乙炔膜。所有涉及的聚乙炔的制备和测试过程都在严格排除氧气的条件下进行。我们制备了多种器件结构，下面会举例说明。需要指出的是，大部分器件是允许亚带隙的光通过薄膜的。

　　肖特基二极管　使用的多层结构是在宽视野、光谱纯的石英基底上分别覆盖厚度为 200 Å 的金、聚乙炔薄膜（通常 1 μm 厚）和 200 Å 厚的铝顶部接触电极构成。金与 p 型聚乙炔形成欧姆接触，铝形成整流接触。

　　MIS 二极管　我们使用了几种结构。（1）超纯硅基底（厚度为 0.3 mm，带电杂质含量低于 10^{13} cm^{-3}），厚度为 4,000 Å 的磷重掺杂（大于 10^{19} cm^{-3}）的硅层，厚度为 2,000 Å 的二氧化硅层（绝缘层），聚乙炔层（通常在 200~1,200 Å 之间），顶部接触为厚度 200 Å 的金。（2）宽视野光谱纯的石英基底，厚度为 200 Å 的金，1,500 Å 的聚甲基丙烯酸甲酯（绝缘层；二氯甲烷溶液旋涂得到），聚乙炔膜（通常 200 Å），200 Å 的铬和 100 Å 的金。

　　MISFET 结构　（1）用金作为源极和漏极：n 型掺杂硅为基底（作为分立的栅极），2,000 Å 的二氧化硅作为绝缘层，金作为源极和漏极（厚度 500 Å，沟道长 0.1 mm，宽 75 mm），聚乙炔膜（通常 200 Å）作为活性层。相似源极和漏极接触也可以通过蒸镀的方式沉积在上述的 MIS 二极管（2）上。（2）用 n 型多晶硅作为源极和漏极：使用的结构如图 1 所示。

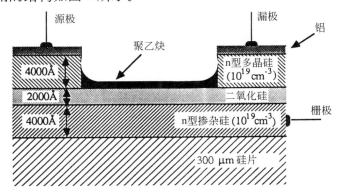

图 1. 聚乙炔 MISFET 结构示意图。除了沟道宽度为 20 μm、长度为 1.5 m 之外，图上尺寸均为标度尺寸。

Electrical Characterization

Schottky diodes. The current density versus voltage characteristics for Schottky diodes constructed as above are shown in Fig. 2, in which $\log|I|$ is plotted versus bias voltage for both forward and reverse biases. The ratio of forward to reverse current reaches a value of typically 5×10^5 at bias voltages of ~1.5 V. The usual parameterization for the variation of current density with bias voltage is $J = J_{sat} \exp(qV/nkT)$ for $V>3kT/q$, where n is the ideality factor, which for a "perfect" diode is equal to 1. As seen in Fig. 2, $n\approx1.3$ at low forward biases. At higher forward biases the current is limited by the bulk resistance. In the thermionic emission model for conduction across the junction, the saturation current density, J_{sat} is given by $J_{sat} = A^*T^2 \exp\{q\Psi/kT\}$, with A^* the effective Richardson constant (120 A K^{-2} cm^{-2} for an effective electron mass of one), and Ψ the barrier height[19]. By extrapolating from the linear region in Fig. 2, we estimate that $J_{sat} = 4.4\times10^{-13}$ A cm^{-1}, and hence $\Psi = 1.28$ eV. The reverse current does not appear to saturate, contrary to the prediction of the thermionic emission model; this is probably caused by the formation of a small interfacial layer between the polyacetylene film and the blocking contact[20]. The doping density may be obtained from the variation of the Schottky diode capacitance with reverse bias voltage, using the simple depletion model for the voltage dependence of the depletion width. In terms of the measured differential capacitance, C, this may be expressed as

$$\frac{1}{C^2} = \frac{1}{A^2}\left(\frac{2(\phi+V)}{\varepsilon_r\varepsilon_0 qN_A}\right)$$

where N_A is the acceptor concentration and ϕ is the built-in potential[19]. This relation is obeyed well for reverse bias, giving values of $N_A = 9\times10^{15}$ cm^{-3} and $\phi = 0.94$ V. We thus find that the electrical characteristics of the Schottky barrier between aluminium and polyacetylene indicate that the device is operating in the conventional way, whereby the depletion layer boundary moves under the influence of the applied bias voltage. We show later, however, that the charge depleted in the polyacetylene is stored in soliton states, rather than as holes in the valence band, in which case detailed modelling of the electrical properties using a conventional, rigid-band picture is inappropriate.

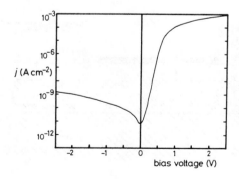

Fig. 2. Modulus of current versus voltage for a Schottky diode.

电 学 表 征

肖特基二极管 前文所述的肖特基二极管的电流密度 – 电压特性如图 2 所示，其中 log |I| 是以正向偏压和反向偏压作图的。偏压约为 1.5 V 时，正向和反向电流比的典型值达到了 5×10^5。当 $V > 3kT/q$ 时，通常对于电流密度随偏压变化采用公式 $J = J_{sat} \exp(qV/nkT)$ 来求解其参数，式中 n 为理想化参数，对一个"完美"的二极管来说，n 值为 1。由图 2 可知，在低的正向偏压时，$n \approx 1.3$。在较高的正向偏压时，电流受限于本体电阻。在描述通过结的电导的热电子发射模型中，饱和电流密度 J_{sat} 由公式 $J_{sat} = A^* T^2 \exp\{q\Psi/kT\}$ 决定，其中 A^* 为有效理查森常数（有效电子质量为 1 时，取值为 120 A · K^{-2} · cm^{-2}），Ψ 为势垒高度[19]。从图 2 的线性区域外推，我们估算出 $J_{sat} = 4.4 \times 10^{-13}$ A · cm^{-1}，因此 $\Psi = 1.28$ eV。与热电子发射模型的预测相反，反向电流并没有呈现饱和；这可能是由于聚乙炔薄膜和阻挡电极之间形成了一个小的界面层[20]。利用简单的耗尽模型中耗尽层宽度对电压的依赖性，掺杂密度可以通过肖特基二极管的电容随反向偏压的变化得到。利用测得的微分电容 C，这可以表示为：

$$\frac{1}{C^2} = \frac{1}{A^2}\left(\frac{2(\phi+V)}{\varepsilon_r \varepsilon_0 q N_A}\right)$$

式中 N_A 是受体浓度，ϕ 为内建电势[19]。这一关系在反向偏压时满足得很好，此时 $N_A = 9 \times 10^{15}$ cm^{-3}，$\phi = 0.94$ V。由此我们发现铝和聚乙炔之间肖特基势垒的电子学特性表明这种器件是按照常规的方式运行的，耗尽层的边界在外加偏压的影响下会发生移动。然而，正如我们后面要指出的那样，聚乙炔中耗尽的电荷是以孤子的形式存在的，而不是以价带中的空穴的形式存在，因此，采用常用的刚性能带模型来描述其电学特征是不合适的。

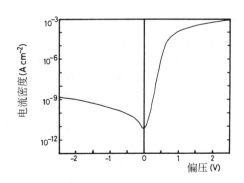

图 2. 肖特基二极管的电流密度绝对值随电压的变化图。

MIS structures. The MIS structure allows the possibility of band bending at the insulator–semiconductor interface through the Fermi level to produce a surface-charge layer which may be of the same carrier sign as the majority carriers (accumulation layer) or as the minority carriers (inversion layer)[21]. The formation of accumulation, depletion and inversion layers may be demonstrated through the relationship between the device capacitance and the bias voltage. The measured capacitance, C, is that of the series combination of the insulator capacitance, C_i, and the capacitance of the active region of the semiconductor, C_d, and is given by $C = C_i C_d/(C_i + C_d)$. Because C_d is large for the accumulation and inversion layers, C is equal to the geometric capacitance of the insulating layer, but falls to a lower value if the depletion layer moves. The capacitance versus bias voltage curve for a polyacetylene MIS structure is shown in Fig. 3. As expected, for negative gate voltages the capacitance tends to the geometric capacitance of the insulator, indicating the formation of an accumulation layer. The decrease in measured capacitance for positive voltages reveals the formation of a depletion layer. Saturation of the capacitance sets in for large positive biases, when the depletion layer extends across the polyacetylene film (estimated to be ~1,200 Å in thickness for this device).

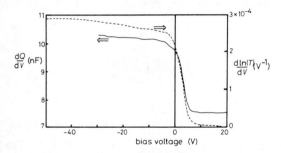

Fig. 3. The differential optical transmission, $\partial \ln(T)/\partial V$ at 0.8 eV (dashed), and differential capacitance, $\partial Q/\partial V$ (solid) versus bias voltage for the MIS structure. Measurements were made at 500 Hz and with an a. c. modulation of 0.25 eV.

MISFETs. A MISFET structure demonstrates that the charges at the polyacetylene–insulator interface in the MIS structure are mobile: source and drain contacts allow measurement of the conductance of the surface charge layer. Figure 4a shows results for a MISFET fabricated with gold source and drain contacts, for which the channel current, I_{DS}, is plotted against drain voltage, V_{DS}, for different gate voltages, V_{GS}. The channel current increases with negative gate voltage and saturates for large V_{DS} because of pinch-off of the channel near the drain electrode. Since the source and drain electrodes form ohmic contacts with the polyacetylene, we expect majority carrier injection from the electrodes into the polymer. The device is thus operating by modulation of the accumulation layer at the semiconductor–insulator interface. The channel conductivity for this structure could be modulated by a factor of about 2,000, from extreme depletion (full thickness of polyacetylene depleted) at $V_{GS} = +5$ V to accumulation at $V_{GS} = -30$ V. Formation of an inversion layer for large positive gate voltages is not expected to increase the channel conductance since the gold source and drain contacts are expected to form blocking contacts to the n-polyacetylene layer.

MIS 结构 在 MIS 结构中，能带在绝缘体 – 半导体的界面上发生弯曲，穿过费米能级，产生一个表面电荷层。如果这个表面电荷层带有与多数载流子相同的电荷，称为积累层；反之，如果带有与少数载流子相同的电荷，则称为反型层[21]。电荷积累层、耗尽层和反型层的形成可以通过器件的电容与偏压之间的关系得到验证。测得的电容 C 是绝缘体电容 C_i 和半导体活性区域的电容 C_d 的串联组合，由公式 $C = C_iC_d/(C_i + C_d)$ 决定。对于积累层和反型层，C_d 很大，C 等于绝缘层的几何电容，但如果耗尽层发生移动，C 值会变小。聚乙炔 MIS 结构的电容随偏压变化的曲线如图 3 所示。与预测类似，在负的栅压下电容趋向于绝缘体的几何电容，这意味着电荷积累层的形成。正电压下测得的电容减小表明形成了耗尽层。在大的正偏压下，当耗尽层扩展穿过聚乙炔薄膜（对这个器件来说，其厚度估计在 1,200 Å 左右）的时候，电容开始饱和。

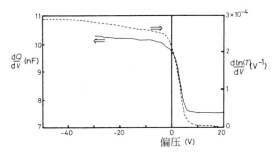

图 3. MIS 结构中 0.8 eV 处的微分光学透过率 $\partial\ln(T)/\partial V$（虚线）和微分电容 $\partial Q/\partial V$（实线）随偏压的变化。测量以 500 Hz 进行，交流调制信号为 0.25 eV。

MISFETs MISFET 的结构表明，MIS 结构中位于聚乙炔 – 绝缘体界面上的电荷是可移动的：利用源极和漏极可以测量这个表面电荷层的电导。图 4a 显示了以金为源漏电极的 MISFET 器件的测量结果，图中曲线为不同栅压 V_{GS} 下沟道电流 I_{DS} 随漏电压 V_{DS} 的变化。随着栅压的负移，沟道电流增大，在大的 V_{DS} 下达到饱和，因为沟道在漏电极附近发生了夹断。因为源漏电极与聚乙炔形成了欧姆接触，我们认为多数载流子从电极注入了高分子。因此，器件是通过调制半导体 – 绝缘体界面的电荷积累层来运行的。从 V_{GS} = +5 V 的极端耗尽（厚度为整个聚乙炔层）到 V_{GS} = −30 V 的电荷积累，器件的沟道电导可以变化 2,000 倍。由于金的源极和漏极接触会对 n 型聚乙炔层产生阻挡接触，因此在大的正栅压下反型层的形成不会增加沟道电导。

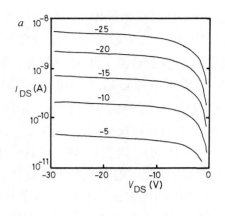

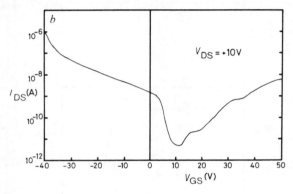

Fig. 4. *a*, I_{DS} versus V_{DS} at values of V_{GS} from −5 to −25 V, for a MISFET with gold source and drain contacts. *b*, I_{DS} versus V_{GS} at constant V_{DS} (+10 V) for a MISFET with poly n-silicon source and drain contacts, as shown in Fig. 1.

The MISFET shown in Fig. 1 is constructed with n-silicon source and drain contacts, which are expected to make ohmic contacts to the n-polyacetylene layer. We thus expect to find enhanced channel conductance by formation of an n-type inversion layer for positive gate voltages. Figure 4*b* shows the variation of I_{DS} with V_{GS} at constant V_{DS}. The channel conductance has a minimum at V_{GS} = +10 V (full depletion) and rises for gate voltages both more positive (inversion layer) and more negative (accumulation layer), with a maximum on/off ratio for this structure of 100,000 (V_{GS} = −40 V to +10 V). We see, therefore, the behaviour expected for positive bias, although the strong enhancement of the conductivity for negative bias indicates that the accumulation layer is still able to make good contact to the source and drain electrodes.

The MISFET structure provides a very convenient means of controlling the charge carrier concentration in the surface layer of the semiconductor. We have determined the carrier mobility from conductance measurements as a function of gate voltage, and find low values, typically 10^{-4} cm^2 V^{-1} s^{-1}. Similar mobilities are estimated for photogenerated carriers and for the extrinsic carriers in Durham polyacetylene (P. D. Townsend and R. H.

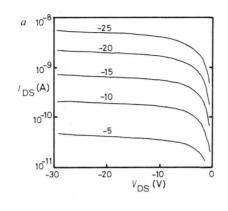

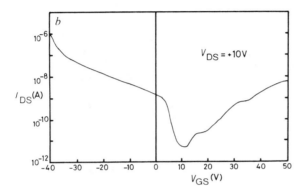

图 4. a，使用金作为源极和漏极的 MISFET 器件，V_{GS} 在 –5 V 到 –25 V 范围内 I_{DS} 随 V_{DS} 的变化。b，使用 n 型多晶硅作为源极和漏极的 MISFET 器件，结构如图 1 所示，V_{DS} 为 +10 V 时，I_{DS} 随 V_{GS} 的变化。

图 1 所示的 MISFET 结构由 n 型硅作为源极和漏极，可以预期它们与 n 型聚乙炔层会形成欧姆接触。因此我们预计在正的栅压下由于 n 型反型层的形成会导致沟道电导增加。图 4b 显示了在固定的 V_{DS} 下 I_{DS} 随 V_{GS} 的变化。沟道电导在 V_{GS} = +10 V 时达到最小值（完全耗尽），从该点开始无论栅压变得更正（反型层）还是更负（积累层），沟道电导都会增加，这一结构最大的开 / 关比可达 100,000（V_{GS} 从 –40 V 变化到 +10 V）。由此我们看到了正偏压下预期的结果，尽管负偏压下电导的强烈增加表明积累层仍然能够与源极和漏极形成良好的接触。

MISFET 结构提供了一种非常简便的控制半导体表面层电荷载流子浓度的方法。我们通过测量出的电导与栅压之间的函数关系计算出了载流子的迁移率，该值较低，通常为 10^{-4} cm^2 · V^{-1} · s^{-1}。对于杜伦聚乙炔（汤森和弗兰德，即将发表）中的光生载流子和非本征载流子迁移率的估算与上述数值类似；我们认为迁移的限制过程是链

Friend, to be published); we consider that the mobility-limiting process is the transfer of charge between chains.

Optical Properties

As discussed earlier, charge in polyacetylene is stored in "soliton" localized states, which are associated with non-bonding p_z mid-gap states. As a result, we expect to see a modulation in the optical properties of the active semiconductor region of these devices with applied bias voltage. The formation of a pair of negatively-charged solitons on a polyacetylene chain is shown schematically in Fig. 5.

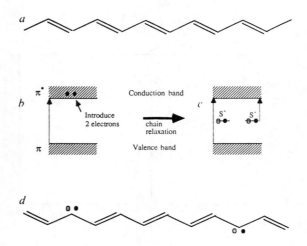

Fig. 5. Schematic representation of the formation of a pair of solitons on a polyacetylene chain. *a*, Undistorted chain; *b*, associated band scheme. The interband π–π^* optical transition is shown as a dotted arrow. If two electrons are introduced into the conduction band of the chain as shown in *b*, the chain relaxes to the form shown in *d*, with a reversed sense of bond alternation in the centre of the chain separated by two solitons. Associated with the two solitons are non-bonding π states in the gap, created from one (doubly occupied) valence and one (empty) conduction band state. These two states (S) are doubly occupied, as shown in *c*, and each carries a negative charge. New optical transitions from the soliton level to the conduction band are indicated with a dotted arrow; the oscillator strength for the interband transition is weakened through the loss of the band states. A complementary picture holds for positive charge, which is accommodated as unoccupied solitons levels.

Schottky diodes. An increase in the width of the depletion layer should remove charged soliton states thereby reducing absorption within the gap and increasing the absorption in the region of the π–π^* transitions above 1.4 eV. The voltage-modulated transmission (VMT) spectrum between 0.4 and 1.8 eV is shown in Fig. 6. The positive signal for energies less than 1.4 eV shows that the transmission does increase for reverse bias voltages. The position of the electro-bleaching peak at 0.55 eV is in general agreement with photo-induced absorption experiments[15] on spin-coated Durham polyacetylene. The periodic structure in the modulated transmission spectrum below the band gap is due to the formation of interference fringes (modulation of the finesse of the Fabry-Perot etalon formed by the polyacetylene film). Electro-absorption is seen at energies greater than 1.4 eV, as expected if extra π- and π^*-band states are created at the expense of soliton states.

间的电荷转移。

光 学 性 质

正如之前所讨论的，聚乙炔中的电荷存储在"孤子"的局域态中，它与非成键的 p_z 轨道中间能隙态相关。因而，我们期待观察到外加偏压对这些器件的活性半导体区域的光学性质的调制。在聚乙炔链上形成一对带负电荷的孤子的机制如图 5 所示。

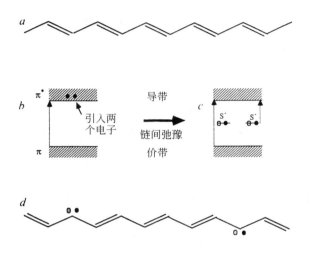

图 5. 聚乙炔链上孤子对的形成示意图。a，未变形的分子链；b，相应的能带结构示意。带间 π–π^* 光跃迁用虚线箭头表示。如果两个电子被引入 b 中所示的链的导带中，链会弛豫到 d 中所示的形态，同时伴随着被两个孤子分开的链中间键的反方向交替变化。而相应的两个孤子是带隙中的非键 π 态，由一个价带（双重占据）态和一个导带（空）态组合产生。图 c 所示的两个态（S）都处于双重占据态，而每一个态携带一个负电荷。从孤子能级到导带的新的光学跃迁用虚线箭头表示；由于能带状态的损耗，带间跃迁的振荡强度减弱。互补的物理图像也适用于正电荷，它对应于未被占据的孤子能级。

肖特基二极管 耗尽层宽度的增加会移除带电孤子态，从而减小带隙内的吸收、增加 1.4 eV 以上的 π–π^* 跃迁区域的吸收。0.4~1.8 eV 之间的电压调制透射（VMT）光谱如图 6 所示。能量小于 1.4 eV 时的正信号表明透射确实随着反向偏压而增加。对应 0.55 eV 的电漂白峰的位置通常与旋涂杜伦聚乙炔的光致吸收实验[15]相一致。调制透射光谱在低于带隙处的周期结构是因为干涉条纹（对聚乙炔薄膜制成的法布里–珀罗标准器精细常数的调制）的形成所致。能量高于 1.4 eV 时能够观察到电吸收，正如预测的消耗孤子态会产生额外的 π 和 π^* 能带状态。

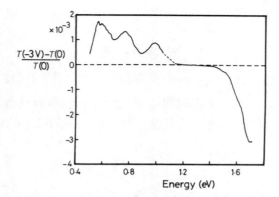

Fig. 6. Voltage-modulated transmission for a Schottky diode, $[T(V) - T(0)]/T(0)$, versus photon energy (E_p), with $V = -3$ V with respect to the blocking contact.

MIS and MISFET structures. For these structures we expect a decrease in the device transmission below the band-edge as the device is driven towards accumulation and new charged solitons are introduced onto the polyacetylene chains at the interface with the insulator. The VMT spectrum between 0.4 and 1.2 eV (Fig. 7a) shows a decrease in the transmission through the device for negative bias. The peak value of $\Delta T/T$, at 0.8 eV, is ~0.64%. If all the charge at the polymer–insulator interface is stored in soliton-like states then the VMT signal, $\partial \ln(T)/\partial V$, should scale with $\partial Q/\partial V$, the differential capacitance, as the bias voltage is varied. This is shown to be the case in Fig. 3, where $\partial \ln(T)/\partial V$ and the differential capacitance are both plotted against bias voltage. We have investigated the VMT response in a variety of structures, including the MISFET shown in Fig. 1. For this structure we find results similar to those in Fig. 7a, that is, the VMT response expected for both accumulation and inversion. It should be noted that the optical path for the MISFET is between the source and drain contacts, and that there is no "back" electrode.

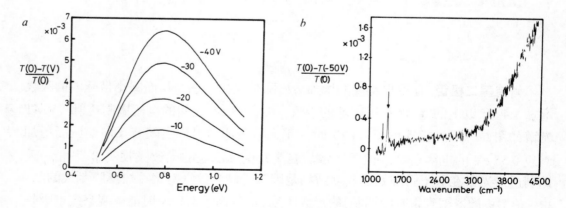

Fig. 7. a, Voltage-modulated transmission for a MIS diode, $[T(0)-T(V)]/T(0)$, versus photon energy, for various values of V (all negative with respect to the gate). b, Voltage-modulated transmission for a MIS diode, $[T(0)-T(-50 \text{ V})]/T(0)$, in the spectral range 1,000–4,500 cm^{-1}.

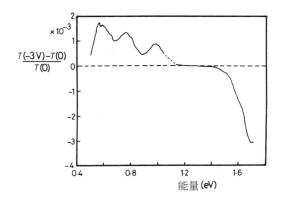

图 6. 肖特基二极管电压调制的透过率 $[T(V) - T(0)]/T(0)$ 随光子能量 (E_p) 的变化，其中 $V = -3$ V 是相对于阻挡接触而言的。

MIS 和 MISFET 结构　对于这一类的结构我们预期低于能带边缘处器件的透过率会降低，原因是在器件驱动时，随着积累层的形成，新的带电孤子被引入到位于绝缘体界面处的聚乙炔链上。0.4 eV 至 1.2 eV 的 VMT 光谱（图 7a）表明负偏压下器件的透过率会降低。在 0.8 eV 处，$\Delta T/T$ 的峰值大约为 0.64%。如果所有位于高分子 – 绝缘体界面处的电荷都以类孤子的形式存在，那么在偏压发生变化的时候，VMT 信号 $\partial \ln(T)/\partial V$ 应该与微分电容 $\partial Q/\partial V$ 成比例。这种情况如图 3 所示，图中为 $\partial \ln(T)/\partial V$ 和微分电容关于偏压的图像。我们研究了包括图 1 所示的 MISFET 在内的多种结构的 VMT 响应。就这一器件结构而言，我们发现结果同图 7a 中的结果类似，即在电荷积累和反型过程中 VMT 光谱产生了预期响应。需要指出的是，对 MISFET 器件来说，光通路位于源极和漏极之间，没有"背"电极。

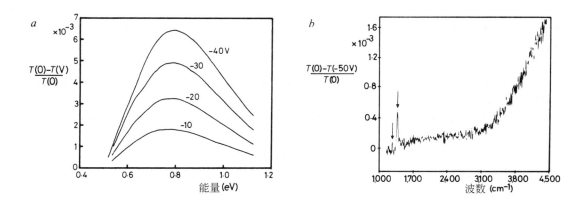

图 7. a，不同 V 值(相对栅压为负)下，MIS 二极管的电压调制透过率 $[T(0) - T(V)]/T(0)$ 随光子能量的变化。
b，光谱范围 1,000~4,500 cm^{-1} 内 MIS 二极管的电压调制透过率 $[T(0) - T(-50V)]/T(0)$。

413

For the low areal soliton concentrations, N^a, found in the device structures, the modulation in transmission, $\Delta T/T$, can be expressed as σN^a, where σ is the optical cross-section for the dopant-induced mid-gap absorption. The determination of N^a is particularly simple for the MIS device driven into accumulation, for which $N^a = \varepsilon_r \varepsilon_0 V/qd$, where V is the bias voltage and d the insulator thickness. The value for $\partial \ln(T)/\partial V$ becomes constant for negative bias voltages (Fig. 3), as expected in this simple model. Typical results, such as those shown in Fig. 7a, give the magnitude of the optical cross-section at the peak in the mid-gap absorption as 1.2×10^{-15} cm^2, in very close agreement with the value measured from dopant-induced absorption[18]. We obtain similar agreement from analysis of optical modulation in the Schottky diode. Note that the maximum depth of optical modulation is fixed by the maximum value for N^a, which is determined for the MIS structure by the product $\varepsilon_r E_{max}$ for the insulator, where E_{max} is the dielectric breakdown field. For silicon oxide, the maximum value for N^a is $\sim 2 \times 10^{13}$ cm^{-2}, and the maximum value for $\Delta T/T$ is thus $\sim 2.4\%$.

Besides the electronic transitions associated with the soliton state, there is extra infrared activity from new vibrational modes that couple to motion of the charged soliton along the polymer chain[22]. These are seen in both doping[13] and photoexcitation[15] experiments on unoriented Durham polyacetylene. Figure 7b shows the results from an FTIR experiment on an MIS structure, showing the difference in transmission for the MIS device biased between 0 and -50 V with respect to the gate. There are three peaks: an absorption above 4,000 cm^{-1} (this is the low-energy side of the electronic absorption, as in Fig. 7a) and two sharp vibrational features at 1,379 and 1,281 cm^{-1}. We identify these as the two higher-frequency translation modes of the soliton. The value of 1,379 cm^{-1} lies between that measured for photo-induced charges, 1,373 cm^{-1} (ref. 15), and for dopant-induced charges, 1,410 cm^{-1} (ref. 13), and provides information about the chain conformation and degree of conjugation. We were not able to measure the VMT spectrum below 1,000 cm^{-1} because of a very large absorption peak from SiO$_2$, and we were thus unable to observe the lowest-frequency, "pinned" translational mode.

The results presented above are all obtained on structures with silicon dioxide as the insulator layer. It is important to demonstrate that these effects can be achieved with other insulators, and we have investigated several organic systems that can be readily formed as thin coherent films. Results on polyacetylene MIS structures, with spin-coated poly(methylmethacrylate) serving as the insulator, show similar behaviour, with an absorption band below the band gap, although the peak in absorption is at a lower energy, 0.55 eV.

Discussion

The formation of depletion, inversion and accumulation charge layers in a semiconductor device is restricted to semiconductors that are free of defects with energy levels within the semiconductor gap. Polymeric semiconductors are not obvious candidates since the structure is inherently disordered, with a large number of conformation defects (bends, twists) on the chains. But there are two principles common to conjugated polymers which run in their favour. First, there are no unsatisfied chemical bonds at the surface of

当器件中的孤子浓度 N^a 较低时，透过率的调制 $\Delta T/T$ 可以表达为 σN^a，式中 σ 是掺杂剂诱导中间能隙吸收的光学截面。对于积累模式的 MIS 器件，N^a 的确定非常简单，$N^a = \varepsilon_r \varepsilon_0 V/qd$，式中 V 为偏压，d 为绝缘层的厚度。正如在这一简单模型中预料的那样，在负偏压下 $\partial \ln(T)/\partial V$ 为常数（图 3）。典型的结果如图 7a 中所示，中间能隙吸收的峰值处光学截面的大小为 1.2×10^{-15} cm^2，与通过掺杂剂诱导吸收所测得的值高度一致[18]。这个值与我们分析肖特基二极管中光学调制时所得到的结果也非常吻合。我们注意到光学调制的最大深度是由 N^a 的最大值确定的，而在 MIS 结构中对绝缘体而言，N^a 是由乘积 $\varepsilon_r E_{\max}$ 决定的，其中 $E_{\max}$ 为电介质的击穿电场。对二氧化硅而言，N^a 的最大值约为 2×10^{13} cm^{-2}，从而 $\Delta T/T$ 的最大值应为 2.4% 左右。

除了与孤子态相关的电子跃迁外，与带电孤子沿高分子链的运动耦合的新的振动模式也会带来额外的红外活性[22]。这些在非取向的杜伦聚乙炔的掺杂[13]和光激发[15]实验中都观察到过。图 7b 来自一次 MIS 结构的傅里叶变换红外实验的结果，显示出了相对于栅压，MIS 器件偏压为 0 V 和 –50 V 时透过率的不同。图中有 3 个峰：一个大于 4,000 cm^{-1} 的吸收峰（这是电子吸收的低能端，参见图 7a）和两个位于 1,379 cm^{-1} 和 1,281 cm^{-1} 处的明显的振动特征峰。我们将其归属于孤子的两个高频平动模式。1,379 cm^{-1} 介于光生电荷的测量数值（1,373 cm^{-1}）（参考文献 15）和掺杂剂诱导的电荷的测量数值（1,410 cm^{-1}）（参考文献 13）之间，为链的构象和链的共轭程度提供了信息。由于一个巨大的二氧化硅吸收峰的存在，我们无法测量低于 1,000 cm^{-1} 的 VMT 光谱，因而我们无法观测到对应于最低频率的"受缚"平动模式。

上述结果都在以二氧化硅为绝缘层的器件结构中获得。这些效应能否在其他的绝缘体中得到，证实这一点非常重要。我们研究了几个可以很容易形成连续薄膜的有机体系。在聚乙炔的 MIS 结构中，通过旋涂聚甲基丙烯酸甲酯作为绝缘层，得到了类似的实验结果，在低于带隙处有一个吸收带，尽管这个吸收峰位于更低的能量处（0.55 eV）。

讨　论

半导体器件中，耗尽层、反型层和积累层的形成只能是在这样的半导体中，即其没有能级位于半导体能带中的缺陷。由于结构的固有无序、并且链上具有大量的构型缺陷（弯曲和扭转），高分子半导体并不是一个很好的选择。但是共轭高分子具有两个突出的优点：首先，高分子的表面没有不饱和化学键，如果在干净、无氧的条件下制备高分子与金属（肖特基二极管）或者与绝缘体（MIS 结构）的界面，

the polymer, and we can expect that if the interface with the metal (Schottky diode) or insulator (MIS structures) is prepared in clean, oxygen-free conditions, we should avoid the problems with surface states well known for inorganic semiconductors. Second, defects on the polymer chain tend naturally to weaken the degree of π electron delocalization, and therefore to increase the π–π^* gap at the defect[11,13,15]. The electronic levels associated with the defect are thus removed from the semiconductor gap and play no active part in the device operation. This principle is of particular importance here since the unoriented films of Durham polyacetylene we have used are known to have straight-chain sequences of no more than 20 or so carbon-carbon bonds[10-15].

Optical spectroscopy reveals that charge storage in depletion, inversion or accumulation layers in these polyacetylene devices is not in band states (as with conventional semiconductors) but in soliton-like mid-gap states. For the depletion layer the chain deformation associated with these states is achieved by extrinsic doping. For accumulation and inversion layers, however, we have demonstrated a new means of putting charge onto the chains, in which the presence of the surface field forces charged soliton–antisoliton pairs onto previously undistorted chains, as shown schematically in Fig. 5.

Modulation of the optical properties by control of the charged-soliton density with the voltage applied across the device provides a new and powerful spectroscopy for investigating the electronic structure of the active region in these semiconductor devices. By comparison of the variation of differential transmission at mid-gap ($\partial \ln(T)/\partial V$) and the differential capacitance ($\partial Q/\partial V$) with bias voltage, we have shown that there is a direct correspondence between the two quantities and that therefore all charges at the interface are accommodated on polyacetylene chains in soliton-like states. From the spectrally resolved electronic and vibrational absorption features, we can also learn much about the detailed electronic structure of those polymer chains at the interface on which the charge is stored; we will report on this elsewhere.

The electro-optic effects we have demonstrated here are large, and there are obvious areas of technology in which these devices may be exploited. Modulation depths, measured here for a single pass of the light beam through the device, can be readily enhanced, either in multiple-reflection structures (Fabry-Perot etalon) or in wave-guided structures in which the light is guided parallel to the active surface of the semiconductor.

We thank British Petroleum PLC for financial support for this work.

(**335**, 137-141; 1988)

416

我们能够避免无机半导体中广为人知的表面态的问题；其次，高分子链上的缺陷会弱化 π 电子离域，从而增加了缺陷处的 π–π* 带隙[11,13,15]。与缺陷相关的电子能级由此从半导体的带隙中移除并且不会在器件的运行中发挥作用。这一点非常重要，因为我们使用的杜伦聚乙炔非取向膜中含有不超过 20 个左右的碳碳键构成的直链单元[10-15]。

光谱表明聚乙炔器件中耗尽层、反型层和积累层中电荷的存储不同于传统的半导体，不是存储于能带中而是存储于类孤子中间能隙中。对于耗尽层来说，与这些态相关的链的变形可以通过非本征掺杂来得到。但是，对电荷积累层和反型层，我们证实了一种新的方法将电荷引入高分子链中，即通过表面电场形成带电孤子 – 反孤子对进入到原先未变形的链中，如图 5 所示。

通过器件的外加电压控制带电孤子的密度，从而实现对其光学性质的调制。这为我们提供了一个新的、强有力的光谱方法用以研究半导体器件中活性区的电子结构。通过对比中间能隙处的微分透过率（$\partial \ln(T)/\partial V$）和微分电容（$\partial Q/\partial V$）随偏压的变化，我们发现这两个量是直接对应的，因此所有的位于界面处的电荷都以类孤子态积累于聚乙炔链上。根据光谱分辨的电子和振动吸收特征，我们可以知道这些高分子链在荷电界面上的详细的电子结构，这些结果我们将随后发表。

我们在这里所证实的电光效应是比较强的，基于这些器件的技术也具有潜在的应用前景和开发价值。光束单次通过器件所测得的调制深度无论是采用多次反射结构（法布里 – 珀罗标准器）或者是波导结构（光被诱导沿着平行于半导体活性面的方向传播）都可以得到增强。

我们感谢英国石油公司为本项研究提供经费支持。

（李琦 翻译；胡文平 审稿）

J. H. Burroughes, C. A. Jones & R. H. Friend
Cavendish Laboratory, Madingley Road, Cambridge CB3 0HE, UK

Received 6 July; accepted 10 August 1988.

References:

1. *Handbook on Conducting Polymers* (ed. Skotheim, T. J.) (Dekker, New York, 1986).

2. Basescu, N. *et al. Nature* **327**, 403-405 (1987).

3. Grant, P. M., Tani, T., Gill, W. D., Krounbi, M. & Clarke, T. C. *J. appl. Phys.* **52**, 869-873 (1980).

4. Kanicki, J. in *Handbook on Conducting Polymers* (ed. Skotheim, T. J.) 544-660 (Dekker, New York, 1986).

5. Garnier, F. & Horowitz, G. *Synthetic Metals* **18**, 693-698 (1987).

6. Tomozawa, H., Braun, D., Phillips, S., Heeger, A. J. & Kroemer, H. *Synthetic Metals* **22**, 63-69 (1987).

7. Ebisawa, E., Kurokawa, T. & Nara, S. *J. appl. Phys.* **54**, 3255-3260 (1983).

8. Koezuka, H., Tsumura, A. & Ando, T. *Synthetic Metals* **18**, 699-704 (1987).

9. Edwards, J. H. & Feast, W. J. *Polymer Commun.* **21**, 595-597 (1980).

10. Friend, R. H. *et al. Trans. R. Soc.* A**314**, 37-49 (1985).

11. Friend, R. H. *et al. Synthetic Metals* **13**, 101-112 (1986).

12. Bott, D. C. *et al. Synthetic Metals* **14**, 245-269 (1986).

13. Friend, R. H., Bradley, D. D. C., Townsend, P. D. & Bott, D. C. *Synthetic Metals* **17**, 267-272 (1987).

14. Friend, R. H., Bradley, D. D. C. & Townsend, P. D. *J. Phys.* D**20**, 1367-1384 (1987).

15. Friend, R. H., Schaffer, H. E., Heeger, A. J. & Bott, D. C. *J. Phys.* C**20**, 6013-6023 (1987).

16. Su, W. P., Schrieffer, J. R. & Heeger, A. J. *Phys. Rev. Lett.* **42**, 1698-1701 (1979); B**22**, 2099-2111 (1980); erratum, B**28**, 1138 (1983).

17. Rice, M. J. *Phys. Lett.* **71**A, 152-154 (1979).

18. Orenstein, J. in *Handbook on Conducting Polymers* (ed. Skotheim, T. J.) 1297 (Dekker, New York, 1986).

19. Sze, S. M. *Physics of Semiconductor Devices*, 2*nd* edn (Wiley-Interscience, New York, 1981).

20. Rhoderick, E. M. *Metal-Semiconductor Contacts* (Clarendon Press, Oxford, 1978).

21. Ando, T., Fowler, A. B. & Stern, F. *Rev. mod. Phys.* **54**, 437-672 (1982).

22. Horovitz, B. *Solid St. Commun.* **41**, 729-734 (1982).

418

Resolution of Quantitative Traits into Mendelian Factors by Using a Complete Linkage Map of Restriction Fragment Length Polymorphisms

A. H. Paterson *et al.*

Editor's Note

Genetic mapping has proved a powerful approach for identifying genes and biological processes underlying inheritance-influenced traits. Its simplest form, linkage analysis, uses the meiotic recombination of "linked" genes to work out the location of a gene relative to a known sequence or "marker". But the genetic regions underlying complex traits were at this time hard to map, because the inheritance of an entire genome could not be studied with genetic markers. Here geneticist Eric Lander and colleagues show that complex quantitative traits can be resolved into discrete inheritable (Mendelian) factors. They achieve this by using a complete linkage map of restriction fragment length polymorphisms (RFLPs), DNA variations that become detectable when enzymatically cleaved fragments are analysed on a gel.

The conflict between the Mendelian theory of particulate inheritance[1] and the observation of continuous variation for most traits in nature was resolved in the early 1900s by the concept that quantitative traits can result from segregation of multiple genes, modified by environmental effects[2-5]. Although pioneering experiments[6-9] showed that linkage could occasionally be detected to such quantitative trait loci (QTLs), accurate and systematic mapping of QTLs has not been possible because the inheritance of an entire genome could not be studied with genetic markers[7]. The use of restriction fragment length polymorphisms[10] (RFLPs) has made such investigations possible, at least in principle. Here, we report the first use of a complete RFLP linkage map to resolve quantitative traits into discrete Mendelian factors, in an interspecific back-cross of tomato. Applying new analytical methods, we mapped at least six QTLs controlling fruit mass, four QTLs for the concentration of soluble solids and five QTLs for fruit pH. This approach is broadly applicable to the genetic dissection of quantitative inheritance of physiological, morphological and behavioural traits in any higher plant or animal.

The parents for the back-cross were the domestic tomato *Lycopersicon esculentum* cv. UC82B (denoted E) and a wild South American green-fruited tomato *L. chmielewskii*[11] accession LA1028 (denoted CL). These strains have very different fruit masses (E~65 g; CL~5 g) and concentrations of soluble solids[12] (E~5%; CL~10%)—traits of agricultural importance, because they jointly determine the yield of tomato paste. In addition, the

通过限制性酶切片段长度多态性的完整连锁图对孟德尔因子数量性状的解析

佩特森等

编者按

遗传作图已被证明是用于识别基因和遗传性状背后的生物学过程的有力工具。连锁分析，是遗传作图最简单的形式，它通过利用"连锁"基因的减数分裂重组来定位一个基因相对于一段已知序列或"标记"的位置。但由于仅通过遗传标记无法研究整个基因组的遗传，故对决定复杂性状的遗传区域的定位成为一大难题。本文中遗传学家埃里克·兰德及其同事的工作表明，复杂的数量性状可被分解为独立的遗传因子（孟德尔因子）。通过对限制性酶切片段长度多态性完整连锁图的分析可得出以上结论，DNA 变异可以通过酶切片段的凝胶电泳分析来检测。

孟德尔的颗粒遗传理论和自然界生物的大部分性状中所观察到的连续变异之间存在矛盾，这一矛盾在二十世纪初期通过一个关键观点的提出而得到解决，即经环境因素修饰的多基因的分离产生了数量性状 [2-5]。尽管早期一些开拓性的实验 [6-9] 已经表明偶尔能够测到这些数量性状基因座（QTLs）的连锁，但是对其更加准确和系统地作图却还不能实现，因为只通过一些基因遗传标记无法对整个基因组的遗传进行研究 [7]。限制性酶切片段长度多态性（RFLPs）[10] 的应用使得这一研究成为可能，至少在理论上此方法是可行的。在此，我们首次在番茄的种间回交实验中用完整的 RFLP 连锁图谱将数量性状分解为孟德尔遗传因子来研究。采用这种新的分析方法，我们鉴定出了六个控制果实质量的 QTL、四个控制可溶性固形物含量的 QTL 以及五个控制果实 pH 的 QTL。此方法也可广泛地应用于其他高等动植物的生理学特征、形态学特征和行为学特征数量性状的遗传学研究中。

回交品种的亲本是驯养品种番茄 *Lycopersicon esculentum* cv.UC82B(标注为 E) 和野生的南美绿果番茄 *L. chmielewskii*[11] accession LA1028(标注为 CL)。这些品种在果实质量（E 约为 65 克，CL 约为 5 克）和可溶性固形物含量 [12]（E 约为 5%；CL 约为 10%）方面有很大差异，而这两个性状体现在作物的农业价值上是很重要的，

strains are known to be polymorphic for genes affecting fruit pH, which is important for the optimal preservation of tomato products[13]; the difference in pH between the parental strains is, however, small.

A total of 237 back-cross plants, with E as the recurrent parent, were grown in the field at Davis, California. Between five and 20 fruit from each plant were assayed[13] for fruit mass, soluble-solids concentration (°Brix; see Fig. 1 legend for definition) and pH, each of which showed continuous variation (Fig. 1). Soluble-solids concentration correlated negatively with fruit mass ($r = -0.42$) and positively with pH ($r = +0.33$).

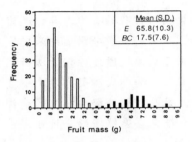 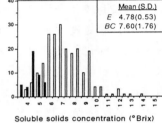 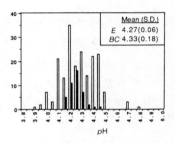

Fig. 1. Frequency distribution for fruit mass, soluble-solids concentration (°Brix, a standard refractometric measure primarily detecting reducing sugars, but also affected by other soluble constituents; 1°Brix is approximately 1% w/w) and pH in the E parental strain and in the back-cross (BC) progeny. The tomatoes were grown in the field at Davis, California, in a completely randomized design including 237 BC plants (with E as the recurrent pistillate parent), as well as E, CL and the F_1 as controls. Neither CL nor the F_1 progeny matured completely, as is typical in the central valley of California. Among the BC plants, six failed to mature and 12 produced too few fruit to assay reliably for quantitative traits. The absence of quantitative trait data for these few progeny should yield at most a slight bias in our analyses. Means and standard deviations for the distributions of the E parental strain (*E* filled bars) and the BC progeny (*BC* open bars) appear in the upper right of each histogram. The distributions for soluble-solids concentration and pH are approximately normal. The distribution of the BC progeny for fruit weight is clearly skewed; $\log_{10}$ (fruit mass) was studied throughout to achieve approximate normality (see ref. 5; $E = 1.81 \pm 0.07$; *BC* = 1.20 ± 0.19). The proportion of variance due to environment was estimated to be the square of the ratio of the standard deviations (E/BC), for log-mass, solids and pH.

We had previously constructed a genetic linkage map of tomato[14] with over 300 RFLPs and 20 isozyme markers, by analysing 46 F_2 individuals derived from *L. esculentum* cv. VF36 ×*L. pennellii* accession LA716 (E×P). The map is essentially complete: it has linkage groups covering all 12 tomato chromosomes with an average spacing of 5 cM between markers (1 cM is the distance along the chromosome which gives a recombination frequency of one percent). For QTL mapping, we selected a subset of markers spaced at approximately 20 cM intervals and displaying polymorphism between the E and CL strains. These included 63 RFLPs and five isozyme markers. In addition, the E and CL strains differ in two easily-scored, simply-inherited morphological traits: determinacy (described below) and uniform ripening, controlled by the *sp* and *u* genes, respectively. Although a few distal regions did not contain appropriate markers, we estimate that about 95% of the tomato genome was detectably linked to the markers used.

因为它们共同决定了番茄酱的产量。并且影响果实 pH 值的基因在这两个品种中呈现多态性，果实 pH 值对于番茄制品的优化保存是很重要的 [13]；而亲本品种的 pH 值差异很小。

以 E 作为轮回亲本，在加利福尼亚州戴维斯的试验田中一共种植了 237 株回交品种植株，然后分析了每个植株上 5~20 个不等的果实 [13]，得到了这些植株的果实质量、可溶性固形物含量 (单位为白利度，见图 1 注中对其的定义) 和 pH 值性状指标，每一个性状都表现出连续变异的特点（见图 1）。可溶性固形物含量与果实质量（$r = -0.42$）呈负相关，而与果实的 pH（$r = +0.33$）呈正相关。

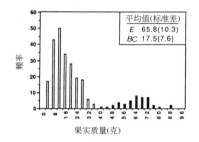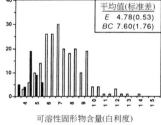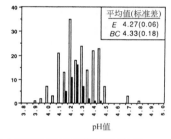

图 1. E 亲本和回交 (BC) 后代中果实质量、可溶性固形物含量（白利度是主要用于测定还原糖的标准折射率测定法，但也会受到其他可溶性成分的影响。1 白利度约等于 1% 质量浓度）和 pH 的频率分布。番茄以完全随机的方式种植于加利福尼亚州戴维斯的试验田里，包括 237 株 BC 植株，（以 E 作为雌性轮回亲本），以 E、CL 和 F$_1$ 作为对照组。由于是生长在加利福尼亚的中央谷中，CL 和 F$_1$ 子代没有完全成熟。在所采集的 BC 植株中，有 6 个未成熟，有 12 个所产果实由于量过少以至于不能准确分析其数量性状。这些少数样本的数量性状数据的缺失对我们的数据分析影响并不大。每个柱状图的右上方显示了 E 亲本（实心柱所示）和 BC 子代（空心柱所示）频率分布的平均值和标准差。可溶性固形物含量和 pH 的频率分布近似正态分布，但 BC 子代的果实质量的频率分布发生了明显的偏移。将果实质量进行对数作图以求其近似正态分布性（详见参考文献 5，$E = 1.81 \pm 0.07$，$BC = 1.20 \pm 0.19$），通过计算标准差（E/BC）的平方评估了环境所引起的果实质量对数、可溶性固形物含量和 pH 值这些性状比例的变化。

在此之前，我们已经通过分析 46 株 *L. esculentum* cv. VF36 × *L. pennellii* accession LA716（E × P）的 F$_2$ 代植株，绘制出了番茄的基因连锁图谱，其中包括超过 300 个 RFLP 和 20 个同工酶标记。所得遗传图谱基本完整，包含的连锁群覆盖了所有 12 条番茄染色体，其上遗传标记之间的平均遗传距离为 5 厘摩（1 厘摩为同一染色体上重组率为百分之一的两位点的距离）。在定位 QTL 时，我们选择了遗传距离在 20 厘摩左右、并且在 E 和 CL 品种中呈现多态性的一组遗传标记。所选的这些遗传标记包括了 63 个 RFLP 和 5 个同工酶标记。另外，E 和 CL 这两个品种在生长习性（见下文解释）和成熟度上存在明显差异，这两个分别由 *sp* 和 *u* 基因控制的形态性状比较容易评价且遗传行为简单。尽管一些基因组远端区域没有合适的遗传标记，但我们推测番茄基因组中约 95% 的基因可利用我们设计的生物遗传标记检测到。

These 70 genetic markers were scored for each of the 237 E×CL back-cross progeny (as described in ref. 13), and a linkage map was constructed *de novo* using MAPMAKER[15]. The map covers all 12 chromosomes with an average spacing of 14.3 cM. Although the linear order of markers inferred from the E×CL cross essentially agreed with that inferred from the E×P cross (but see Fig. 3 legend), genetic distances differed markedly in certain intervals (for example, 51 cM in E×P and 11 cM in E×CL, for the distance between the 45S ribosomal repeat and *TG1B* on chromosome 2). In total, the markers scored in both crosses span 852 cM in the E×CL map versus 1,103 cM in the E×P map, a highly significant ($P<0.01$) difference. Skewed segregation ($P<0.05$) was detected for 48 of the 70 markers, comprising 21 distinct regions distributed over all 12 chromosomes. The heterozygote (E/CL) was overabundant in 12 cases, whereas in nine cases the homozygote (E/E) was favoured. Overall, the effects of skewing approximately cancelled each other out: on average, the back-cross contained the expected 75% E genome (Fig. 2).

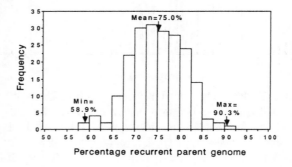

Fig. 2. Distribution of percentage of recurrent parent (E) genotype in the 237 back-cross progeny, estimated on the basis of the marker genotypes and their relative distances. Determination of marker genotypes was as previously described[13]. Estimates of the percentage of recurrent parent genome were produced by the recently developed computer program HyperGene™ (N. D. Young, A.H.P. and S.D.T., unpublished results). Although the average agreed closely with the Mendelian expectation of 75% for a back-cross, values for individual plants ranged from 59% to over 90%. The distribution of the proportion of recurrent-parent genome agrees with the mathematical expectation[35,36]. The individual with >90% E appears to carry only five fragments from CL (ranging from 9 to 47 map units in length) and could be returned to essentially 100% *E* with two additional back-crosses of fewer than 100 plants each, or one additional back-cross of about 550 plants. This is far more rapid than the 6–8 back-crosses routinely used to eliminate donor genome in the absence of markers.

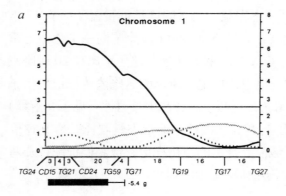

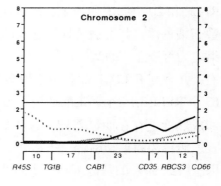

　　分别对 237 个 E×CL 回交子代（如参考文献 13 所述）的 70 个遗传标记进行遗传距离测定，并用 MAPMAKER[15] 从头构建连锁图。此连锁图覆盖了番茄的全部 12 条染色体，平均遗传距离为 14.3 厘摩。尽管从 E×CL 杂交种中推测出来的所有遗传标记的线性顺序与 E×P 杂交种中的顺序基本一致（见图 3 注），但是某些区间的遗传距离却有很大的差别（例如，45S 核糖体重复序列与 2 号染色体上 *TG1B* 之间的遗传距离在 E×P 和 E×CL 中分别为 51 厘摩和 11 厘摩）。总之，在两次杂交实验中，这些遗传标记在 E×CL 图谱中跨越了 852 厘摩，而在 E×P 图谱中跨越了 1,103 厘摩，统计检验表明这一差异高度显著（$P<0.01$）。经卡方检验，70 个遗传标记中，48 个发生了偏分离（$P<0.05$），这 48 个标记分布于所有 12 条染色体，包含 21 个不同的区域。杂合体（E/CL）在 12 例中丰度较高，而在 9 例中纯合体（E/E）较占优势。回交种中平均携带了预期的 75% 的 E 基因组,总体上,偏移的影响基本上可以被相互抵消(图2)。

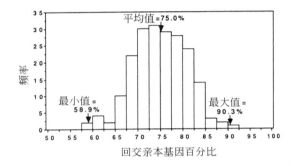

图 2. 根据遗传标记的基因型和它们之间的相对距离，评估轮回亲本 E 基因型在 237 株回交子代中所占百分比的分布情况。对于检测遗传标记基因型的方法如前所述 [13]。在计算轮回亲本基因组所占比例时采用了近期新研发的计算机程序—HyperGene ™（扬、佩特森和坦克斯利未发表结果）。尽管对整个回交子代来讲所计算百分比的平均值与孟德尔遗传规律所期望的 75% 很接近，但是对个体的植株来说此百分比则介于 59% 至 90% 以上。轮回亲本基因组在子代中所占百分比的分布情况与数学期望一致[35,36]。携带有超过 90% 亲本 E 基因组的个体似乎只携带了五个来自 CL 的片段（在长度上介于 9 到 47 染色体图距单位），这些个体通过两代（每代不超过 100 株植株）的回交或一次约 550 株植株的回交就可以基本恢复到携带 100% E 亲本基因组。在缺少标记的情况下，这与通常需要 6 至 8 代回交才能消除供体基因组相比快了很多。

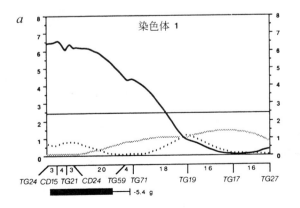

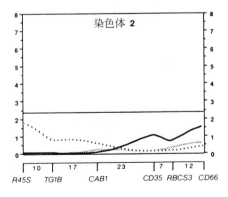

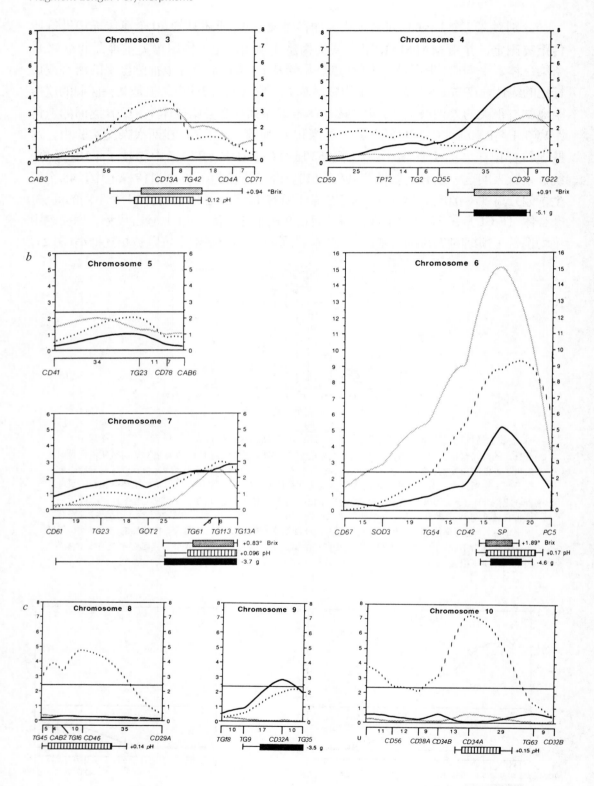

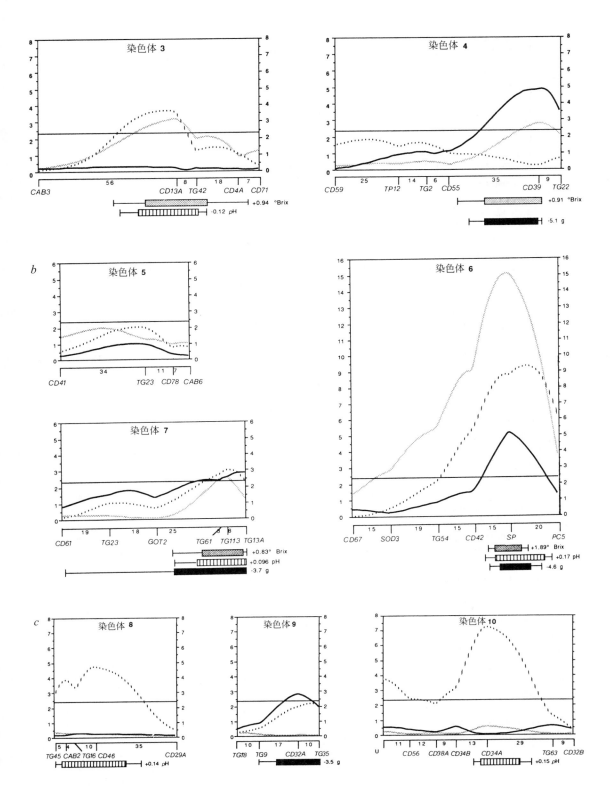

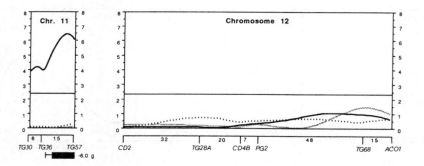

Fig. 3. QTL likelihood maps indicating lod scores for fruit mass (solid lines and bars), soluble-solids concentration (dotted lines and bars) and pH (hatched lines and bars), throughout the 862 cM spanned by the 70 genetic markers. The RFLP linkage map used in the analysis is presented along the abscissa, in Kosambi[37] cM. (The order of the markers agrees with the previously published map[14] of the E×P cross, except for three inversions of adjacent markers: (*TG24-CD15*), (*TG63-CD32B*) and (*TG30-TG36*). In the first case, re-analysis of the E×P data with MAPMAKER[15] indicates that the order shown here is the more likely in both E×P and E×CL. For the other two, the orders shown here are more likely in E×CL by odds of $10^4:1$ and $10^7:1$, but the inverse is more likely in E×P by $11:1$ and $8:1$ odds. These differences will be investigated in a larger E×P population.) Soluble-solids concentration and pH were analysed in °Brix and pH units, respectively; allele effects on fruit mass are presented in g; log-transformation of fruit mass was used in all analyses to achieve approximate normality. The maximum likelihood effect of a putative QTL, as well as the lod score in favour of the existence of such a QTL, have been determined at points spaced every 1 cM throughout the genome, according to Lander and Botstein[16] and a smooth curve plotted through the points. The height of the curve indicates the strength of the evidence ($\log_{10}$ of the odds ratio) for the presence of a QTL at each location—not the magnitude of the inferred allelic effect. The horizontal line at a height of 2.4 indicates the stringent threshold that the lod score must cross to allow the presence of a QTL to be inferred (see text). Information about the likely position of the QTL can also be inferred from the curve. The maximum likelihood position of the QTL is the highest point on the curve. Bars below each graph indicate a $10:1$ likelihood support interval[16] for the position of the QTL (the range outside which the likelihood falls by a lod score of 1.0), whereas the lines extending out from the bars indicate a $100:1$ support interval. Phenotypic effects indicated beside the bars are the inferred effect of substituting a single CL allele for one of the two E alleles at the QTL. Several regions show sub-threshold effects on one or more traits (chromosome one near *TG19*, chromosome five near *TG32* and chromosome 12 near *TG68*) which may represent QTLs but this requires additional testing. The region near *TG68* may be particularly interesting, as it is the only instance found where the CL allele seems to decrease soluble-solids concentration (by about 0.7 °Brix). In the case of chromosome 10, the lod score for pH crosses the significance threshold in two places. Controlling for the presence of a QTL near *CD34A*, we tested for the presence of a second QTL near *u* (by comparing the maximum lod scores assuming the presence of only the first QTL to the maximum lod score assuming the presence of two QTLs). Allowing for a QTL in the region of *CD34A*, the residual lod score near *u* falls below the required threshold. Thus, the evidence is not yet sufficient to support the presence of a QTL near *u*.

Methods. The lod score and the maximum likelihood estimate (MLE) of the phenotypic effect at any point in the genome is computed assuming that the distribution of phenotypes in the BC progeny represents a mixture of two normal distributions (of equal variance) with means depending on the genotype at a putative QTL at the given position. (Note that QTLs are considered individually and thus we did not assume that different QTL effects can be added—except in studying the possibility of two QTLs on chromosome 10 affecting pH.) Specifically, at a given position in the genome, the likelihood function for individual i with quantitative phenotype Φ_i is given by $L_i(\alpha, \sigma) = (2\pi\sigma^2)^{-1/2}\{p_1 \exp(-\Phi_i)^2 / 2\sigma^2 + p_2 \exp(-(\Phi_i) - \alpha)^2 / 2\sigma^2\}$, where α is the effect of substituting a CL allele for an E allele at a putative QTL in the given position, σ^2 is the phenotypic variance not attributable to the QTL and p_1 and p_2 are the probabilities that individual i has genotype E/E and E/CL, respectively, at the QTL (which

428

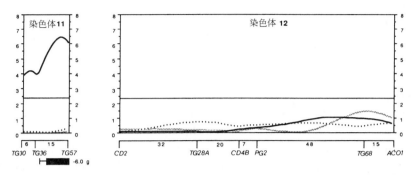

图 3. QTL 似然图谱显示了跨越 862 厘摩遗传距离的 70 个遗传标记在果实质量（实线和实线柱）、可溶性固形物含量（点线和点线柱）和 pH 值（阴影线和阴影柱）上的对数优势比。横坐标为 RFLP 连锁图谱，单位为 Kosambi cM[37]。（遗传标记的顺序与之前发表的 E×P 杂交品种的图谱[14] 一致，但例外的是 (TG24-CD15)、(TG63-CD32B) 和 (TG30-TG36) 这三个相邻的倒位遗传标记。在第一种情况下，用 MAPMARKER[15] 重新分析 E×P 的数据，结果表明这里显示的顺序更可能同时存在于 E×P 和 E×CL 两种情况中。而对于另外两种情况，其顺序则在 E×CL 中的概率为 $10^4:1$ 和 $10^7:1$，但是其反向顺序在 E×P 中的概率则为 11:1 和 8:1。这些差异仍需研究更大的 E×P 种群。）可溶性固形物含量、pH 值分别以白利度和 pH 为单位进行分析；等位基因对果实质量的影响以克表示；为获得近似的正态分布，在所有分析中将果实质量进行对数转换。假定的 QTL 的最大似然效应和这一 QTL 存在的对数优势比已在整个基因组上每 1 厘摩距离的位点中确定，此计算是基于兰德和博特斯坦的方法[16] 和这些点拟合后的平滑曲线完成的。曲线的高度代表了每个位置存在 QTL 的证据的强度（优势比以 10 为底的对数值），而不是推测的等位基因效应强度。图中 2.4 位置处的水平线是所设定的严格阈值，只有高于这个阈值时，才认定存在 QTL（详见正文）。根据曲线也可以推测出 QTL 可能的位置信息，曲线上的最高点代表了 QTL 的最大似然位置。每个图下方的横柱显示了 QTL 所在位置的 10:1 似然支持区间[16]（范围以外的似然值下降了 1.0 个对数优势比），而从横柱延伸出的线段则代表了 100:1 的支持区间。除了根据横柱估计，还推测出由单个 CL 等位基因替代 QTL 处的两个 E 等位基因中的一个后引起的表型效应。若干区域在一个或多个性状上表现出了亚阈值效应（1 号染色体靠近 TG19 的区域、5 号染色体上靠近 TG32 的区域和 12 号染色体上靠近 TG68 的区域），这些性状可能说明了 QTL 的存在，但需要进一步检验。靠近 TG68 的区域尤其值得关注，因为它是仅有的 CL 等位基因可能减少可溶性固形物含量的例子（减幅约为 0.7 白利度）。10 号染色体中，pH 性状的对数优势比曲线有两处都高于显著性阈值。控制 CD34A 附近存在的 QTL，我们检验了 u 附近存在另一个 QTL 的可能性（通过比较只存在一个 QTL 时的最大优势比与两个 QTL 都存在的最大优势比）。若在 CD34A 区域存在一个 QTL 时，u 附近区域其余的优势比则低于要求阈值。因此，目前的证据还不能充分证明 u 附近区域存在 QTL。

方法。 假设回交子代中表型效应的分布代表了两个混合的正态分布（具有相等方差），其平均值与给定位置处所假定的 QTL 的基因型相关。然后计算基因组中任何位点上表型影响的对数优势比和最大似然估计（MLE）。（注意：在此 QTL 是作为单独个体来研究的，因此，除研究 10 号染色体上两个 QTL 对 pH 值的影响外，我们并没有假设不同 QTL 引起的效应是可以相加的。）尤其是在基因组的给定位点，对于有数量性状表型 Φ_i 的个体 i，其似然函数为 $L_i(\alpha,\sigma)=(2\pi\sigma^2)^{-1/2}\{p_1\exp(-\Phi_i)^2/2\sigma^2+p_2\exp(-(\Phi_i)-\alpha)^2/2\sigma^2\}$，其中 α 是在给定位置的假定 QTL 上由一个 CL 等位基因代替 E 等位基因后的效应。σ^2 是非数量性状位点引起的表型差异。p_1 和 p_2 分别是个体 i 在 QTL 处（QTL 位置可以通过侧翼遗传标记的基因型和 QTL 与标记的距离计算得到）拥有 E/E 和 E/CL 基因型的概率。整个种群的似然函数为 $L=\prod L_i$。同样，α^* 和 σ^* 表示 MLE 所允许出现 QTL 的可能性（最大值为 L），σ^{**} 表示 σ 的 MLE，即限定无连锁的 QTL（$\alpha=0$）。对数优势比为 $\log_{10}\{L(\alpha^*,\sigma^*)/L(0,\sigma^{**})\}$。此方法在数量性状位点图谱绘制上的发展在参考文献 16 中有更充分的展示。

429

can be computed on the basis of the genotypes at the flanking markers and the distance to the flanking markers). The likelihood function for the entire population is $L = \Pi \, L_i$. Also α^* and σ^* denote the MLEs allowing the possibility of a QTL at the location (the values which maximize L) and σ^{**} denotes the MLE of σ, subject to the constraint that no QTL is linked ($\alpha = 0$). The lod score is then given by $\log_{10}\{L(\alpha^*, \sigma^*) / L(0, \sigma^{**})\}$. This method for QTL mapping is developed more fully in ref. 16.

We then turned to the question of mapping the Mendelian factors that underly continuous variation in fruit mass, soluble-solids concentration and pH. The method of maximum likelihood and lod scores, commonly used in human linkage analysis[17], has recently been adapted[16] to allow interval mapping of QTLs. At each position in the genome, one computes the "most likely" phenotypic effect of a putative QTL affecting a trait (the effect which maximizes the likelihood of the observed data arising) and the odds ratio (the chance that the data would arise from a QTL with this effect divided by the chance that it would arise given no linked QTL). The lod score, defined as the $\log_{10}$ of the odds ratio, summarizes the strength of evidence in favour of the existence of a QTL with this effect at this position; if the lod score exceeds a pre-determined threshold, the presence of a QTL is inferred. The traditional approach[8,9] to mapping QTLs involves standard linear regression, which accurately measures the effect of QTLs falling at marker loci only, underestimating the effects of other loci in proportion to the amount of recombination between marker and QTL. In contrast, interval mapping allows inference about points throughout the entire genome and avoids confounding phenotypic effects with recombination, by using information from flanking genetic markers. In the special case when a QTL falls exactly at a marker locus, interval mapping reduces to linear regression. A computer program, MAPMAKER-QTL, was written (S.E.L. and E.S.L., unpublished) to implement interval mapping.

Due to the large number of markers tested, an extremely high lod score threshold must be adopted to avoid false positives. Given the genetic length of the tomato genome and the density of markers used, a threshold of 2.4 gives a probability of less than 5% that even a single false positive will occur anywhere in the genome[16]. This is approximately equivalent to requiring the significance level for any single test to be 0.001.

QTL likelihood maps, showing how lod scores for fruit mass, soluble-solids concentration and pH change as one moves along the genome, reveal multiple QTLs for each trait and estimate their location to within 20–30 cM (Fig. 3).

(1) Factors for fruit mass were found on six chromosomes (1, 4, 6, 7, 9 and 11). In each case, CL alleles decrease fruit mass (by 3.5 to 6.0 g), adding to a total reduction of 28.1 g inferred for back-cross progeny carrying a CL allele at all six loci. This accounts for about half of the approximately 60 g difference between E and CL.

(2) Factors for soluble-solids concentration were found on four chromosomes (3, 4, 6 and 7). In each case, CL alleles elevate soluble-solids concentration (by 0.83 to 1.89 °Brix), adding to a total of 4.57 °Brix (versus a difference of ~5 °Brix between the parental strains). This

我们再回到最初的问题上，如何定位果实质量、可溶性固形物含量和pH值这三个连续变异背后的孟德尔遗传因子呢？最大似然法和对数优势比通常被用于人的遗传连锁分析[17]，最近这些方法也被用于数量性状位点（QTL）的区间作图[16]。在基因组的每一个位置计算出 QTL 影响性状的"最大可能"表型效应（此效应将所观测到数据的似然最大化）和优势比（数据来自与此效应相关的 QTL 的概率除以与此效应无关的 QTL 概率的比值）。对数优势比定义为以 10 为底优势比的对数值，它代表了在某一位置存在与表型效应相关的 QTL 的证据的强度，假如对数优势比超过了预设的阈值，则认为存在 QTL。作为定位 QTL 的传统方法[8,9]之一，标准线性回归精确地测量了仅位于遗传标记位点的 QTL 所产生的效应，却低估了与基因标记和 QTL 重组相关的其他位点所产生的效应。但区间作图运用了侧翼遗传标记的信息，从而可以推测出贯穿整个基因组的位点，并且能够避免混淆重组造成的表型效应。在特殊情况下，当 QTL 严格地位于遗传标记位点时，间距图谱可以归纳为线性回归。MAPMAKER-QTL 是一个专门为区间作图而编写的计算机程序（兰德和林肯，尚未发表）。

由于检验了较大数量的遗传标记，所以需要设定一个极高的对数优势比的阈值以避免得到假阳性结果。鉴于番茄基因组的遗传学长度和使用的遗传标记的密度，当预设的阈值为 2.4 时，出现假阳性的概率不到 5%，即使这样也意味着单个假阳性会出现在基因组的任何位置[16]。这相当于在任何单次检验中其显著性水平都需要为 0.001。

QTL 的似然图谱显示了每一性状的多个 QTL 及其在 20~30 厘摩遗传距离范围内的定位（图 3），能够让我们看出在整个基因组水平上针对果实质量、可溶性固形物含量和 pH 值的对数优势比是怎样变化的。

（1）我们在六条染色体（1、4、6、7、9 和 11）上发现了能够影响果实质量的因子。在每一个位点，CL 的等位基因都能降低果实质量（减少量从 3.5~6 克不等），推测在携带所有 6 个 CL 等位基因的回交子代中果实质量总减少量达 28.1 克。这也许能解释为什么 E 和 CL 的果实质量存在的约 30 克的差距。

（2）在四条染色体（3、4、6 和 7）上发现了能够影响可溶性固形物含量的因子。每一个位点上，CL 等位基因都能够提高可溶性固形物的含量（从 0.83~1.89 白利度不等），增加量总和为 4.57 白利度（与亲本品种之间存在的约 5 白利度的差异相对应）。

large effect in the back-cross is consistent with previous reports that high soluble-solids concentration exhibits dominance[12] and overdominance[13]. The QTL alleles for both fruit mass and soluble-solids concentration all produce effects in the direction predicted by the difference between the parental strains.

(3) Factors for pH were found on five chromosomes (3, 6, 7, 8 and 10). In addition, the lod score for a putative QTL on chromosome 9 fell just below our threshold. Because the parental strains do not differ greatly in pH, we suspected that CL alleles might not all produce effects in the same direction. In fact, pH was increased by four QTLs and decreased by two, including the likely QTL on chromosome 9. This provides a genetic explanation for the observation that many back-cross progeny exhibited more extreme phenotypes than the parental strains (Fig. 1), a phenomenon known as transgression[18].

Together, the QTLs identified for fruit mass, soluble solids and pH account for 58%, 44% and 48%, respectively, of the phenotypic variance among the back-cross progeny, with another 13%, 9% and 11% attributable to environment.

The numbers of QTLs reported for each trait must be considered a minimum estimate. Because an extremely stringent threshold was used to avoid any false positives, some sub-threshold effects probably represent real QTLs. For example, the regions near *TG19* on chromosome 1, *CD41* on chromosome 5 and *TG68* on chromosome 12 may affect soluble-solids concentration and merit further attention in larger populations. Similarly, the region near the *u* locus on chromosome 10 may contain an additional QTL affecting pH (see Fig. 3 legend). Moreover, we cannot rule out the presence of many additional QTLs with tiny phenotypic effects—postulated in evolutionary theory[19] and supported by some experimental evidence[20]. Also, it is conceivable that some of our apparent QTLs actually represent several closely-linked QTLs, each with small phenotypic effects in the same direction—a phenomenon that might arise particularly in regions of genetic map compression. Finally, we should emphasize that the QTL mapping here strictly applies only to the specific environment tested and to heterozygosity for CL alleles. In principle, homozygosity for CL alleles could have been studied by using an F_2 self between E and CL, but in practice too many of the progeny are sterile.

Some regions of the genome clearly exert effects on more than one trait (for example, chromosome 6; Fig. 3), providing a genetic explanation for at least some of the correlation between the traits. Although the present data are insufficient to distinguish between pleiotropic effects of a single gene and independent effects of tightly-linked loci, the frequent coincidence of QTL locations for different traits makes it likely that at least some of the effects are due to pleiotropy.

The region near *sp* on chromosome 6 has the largest effects on soluble solids and pH, as well as a substantial effect on fruit mass. The *sp* gene affects plant-growth habit: the dominant CL allele causes continuous apical growth (indeterminate habit), whereas the recessive E allele causes termination in an inflorescence ("determinate" or "self-pruning"

在回交品种中产生如此巨大的影响，这与之前关于可溶性固形物的高含量呈显性[12]或超显性[13]的报导相一致。控制果实质量和可溶性固形物含量的 QTL 等位基因产生的影响都与根据亲本品系之间差异所预期的影响一致。

（3）发现控制 pH 的位点存在于五条染色体（3、6、7、8 和 10）上，此外 9 号染色体上一个假定的 QTL 对数优势比恰好低于我们所设定的阈值。因为在亲本中 pH 差异就很小，所以我们推测 CL 等位基因并没有都朝同一个方向起作用。事实上，包括存在于 9 号染色体上疑似的 QTL 在内，有四个 QTL 引起 pH 值的升高，两个位点造成 pH 值的降低。这在遗传学角度上解释了为什么许多回交子代与亲代相比具有更加极端的表型（图 1），也就是所谓的越亲现象[18]。

总体上，在鉴定出的回交子代的果实质量、可溶性固形物含量和 pH 值表型变异中，各有 58%、44% 和 48% 受到 QTL 的控制，而其他各 13%、9% 和 11% 的变异则归因于环境因素。

对控制每个性状的 QTL 数目必须有个最小估算。为了避免任何假阳性，设置了极端严格的对数优势比阈值，但一些真正的 QTL 产生的效应也可能是亚阈值。例如，1 号染色体上靠近 *TG19* 的区域、5 号染色体 *CD41* 附近的区域和 12 号染色体 *TG68* 附近的区域可能影响了可溶性固形物含量，值得在更大的种群范围内更深入地关注。相似的情况还有 10 号染色体上靠近 *u* 基因座区域可能存在一个影响 pH 值的额外 QTL（见图 3 注）。我们不能否认，那些仅产生细微表型变化的数量性状位点的存在是进化论[19]的推论，而且可以得到实验证据[20]的支持。可想而知，一些我们认为显著的 QTL 事实上代表了若干紧密连锁的位点，每一个位点都产生细微的同一趋势的表型效应，特别是在遗传图谱位点基因密集区会出现这样的现象。最后还要特别强调的是这里的 QTL 遗传图谱只能严格应用于特定环境下的检测和 CL 等位基因杂合子的情形。理论上，CL 等位基因纯合子能够通过 E 和 CL 的 F_2 自交后代来研究，但实际上非常多的子二代是不育的。

我们已经很清楚，基因组上的一些区域能够影响不止一种性状（如图 3 所示的 6 号染色体），这给出了性状之间至少存在某种关联的遗传学解释。尽管现有的数据还不足以区分单个基因的多效性和紧密连锁的多个基因座各自独立的效应，但是同一位置的 QTL 时常影响着不同的遗传性状，说明可能至少某些效应是基因多效性造成的。

6 号染色体上接近 *sp* 基因的区域对可溶性固形物和 pH 值能够造成最显著的影响，对果实质量也能产生巨大的影响。*sp* 基因能够影响植物的生长习性，其显性 CL 等位基因能够导致连续性的顶端生长（无限生长习性），而隐性 E 等位基因会终

habit)[21]. Although indeterminacy has been reported previously[22] to elevate both fruit mass and soluble-solids concentration within *L. esculentum*, we associated it with reduced fruit mass in both E×CL and another interspecific cross (E×*L. cheesmanii*; A.H.P., S. Damon, J.D.H. and S.D.T., unpublished data). These differing results might be due to a second, tightly-linked locus or to unlinked modifier genes.

Overall, pairwise epistatic interactions between intervals were not common (about 5% of two-way analysis-of-variance tests were significant at 0.05). An interesting exception was the region near *TG16* on chromosome 8, at which the CL allele significantly enhanced the effect of three of the four QTLs for soluble-solids concentration. *TG16* also showed the most extreme segregation distortion of any marker scored (about 4 : 1 in favour of the E/E homozygote) and is in a region known to exhibit skewed segregation in back-crosses to other green-fruited tomato species[23,24]. The unusual properties of this region of CL clearly merit further study.

The QTLs identified here may well differ from those that would be fixed by repeated back-crossing with continuing selection for a trait, a classical method for introgressing quantitative traits. Work on LA1563, a strain with increased soluble solids produced[12] through back-crossing a different strain of E to CL has provided some suggestive evidence. By surveying RFLPs, Tanksley and Hewitt[13] recently found that LA1563 has maintained three separate regions from CL: near *CD56* on chromosome 10, near *Got2* on chromosome 7 and near *TG13* on chromosome 7. Here, we detected above-threshold effects in the last of these three regions only (which, interestingly, failed to show effects on soluble solids in a single-environment test by Tanksley and Hewitt[13]). Moreover, we detected QTLs affecting soluble-solids concentration in regions that did *not* seem to be retained. Unfortunately, the results of the two experiments are not directly comparable due to the use of a different E strain by Rick, possible environmental differences between the experiments, the possibility that small CL fragments containing QTLs went undetected in LA1563, the possibility that the region near *TG13* retained in LA1563 may not contain the QTL we detected here and the possibility that some of our sub-threshold effects are real. Although more detailed studies are clearly needed, it is interesting to speculate about why repeated back-crossing may fix a narrower class of QTLs than found by QTL mapping. Because such breeding programs[12] demand horticultural acceptability, they are likely to select against otherwise-desirable QTLs which are closely linked to undesirable effects from the wild parent. If such QTLs can first be identified by mapping, it may be feasible to remove linked deleterious effects by recombination.

Having mapped several QTLs with relatively large effects, we are now making crosses to isolate them in near-isogenic lines. These lines will be used to characterize the QTLs in various dosages, genetic backgrounds, environments and combinations. By re-assembling selected CL alleles in an otherwise E genotype, we hope to engineer an agriculturally-

止花序的顶端生长（有限生长或自修剪习性）[21]。尽管之前的研究认为无限生长能够提高 *L. esculentum* 品种中果实的质量和可溶性固形物的含量，但是我们发现它与 E×CL 杂交品种和其他一些种间杂交品种(E×*L. cheesmanii* 杂交品种；佩特森、戴蒙、约翰和坦克斯利，未发表的数据）的果实质量的降低有关。此差异可能是由另一个与基因座紧密连锁的基因或者不连锁的修饰基因造成的。

总的来说，位点之间成对的上位相互作用并不是很普遍（约 5% 的双向方差分析检验的显著度是 0.05）。一个有趣的特例是在 8 号染色体上靠近 *TG16* 的区域，CL 等位基因能够显著地增强四个影响可溶性固形物含量的 QTL 中三个的效应。*TG16* 也显示出与任何遗传标记的极端偏分离（E/E 纯合子中约 4∶1），*TG16* 所在的区域在与其他绿果番茄品种回交时显示出偏分离[23,24]。所以 CL 基因组中这个非同寻常的区域是值得进一步研究的。

我们所鉴定的 QTL 与传统经典的方法获得的 QTL 有很大不同，因为传统的鉴定基因渗入的数量性状是通过反复回交连续筛选同一性状。LA1563 是一个可溶性固形物含量增加了的品种，它是通过 E 的另一个种系回交 CL 得到的，对 LA1563 的研究为我们提供了一些提示性证据。坦克斯利和休伊特最近通过观察 LA1563 的 RFLP 发现 LA1563 保留了三个来自 CL 的独立区域，分别是 10 号染色体上靠近 *CD56* 的区域、7 号染色体上靠近 *Got2* 的区域、7 号染色体上靠近 *TG13* 的区域。在此我们仅在这三个区域中的最后一个中检测到超出临界阈值的效应（有意思的是坦克斯利和休伊特并未在单一环境检验中检测到这一区域对可溶性固形物浓度的影响）。并且我们又检测了那些看似不能保留下来的影响可溶性固形物含量的 QTL。然而这两个实验的结果并不能直接进行比较。因为以下几方面原因：第一，里克用了 E 的另外一个不同的种系；第二，两实验的实验环境也可能不一样；第三，一些含有 QTL 的 CL 基因组的小片段在 LA1563 中可能是检测不到的；第四，也许我们所检测的保留在 LA1563 中的 *TG13* 附近的区域是不含 QTL 的；第五，一些亚阈值效应的 QTL 也许是存在的。尽管需要更多的详细研究，但有趣的是，仍可以推测为什么反复回交鉴定的 QTL 的类别要少于绘制 QTL 图谱所鉴定出来的位点的原因。因为这种反复回交的育种方案要求有园艺学上的可接受性，需要筛选掉其他一些野生亲本中与非期望效应紧密连锁的 QTL。假如这种遗传作图的方法能在最初就鉴定出这些 QTL，它将有望通过重组消除不利的连锁效应。

由于已经定位了若干引起相对显著效应的 QTL，我们正在通过杂交从近等基因系中分离出这些位点。这些近等基因系可用于在不同的剂量水平、遗传背景、环境因素以及上述各种影响因素组合的背景下鉴定 QTL。我们希望通过从其他 E 基因型中重组

useful tomato with a higher yield of soluble solids.

The general approach of QTL mapping is broadly applicable to a wide range of biological endeavours. In agriculture, it might be desirable to transfer to domestic strains many quantitative traits harboured in wild species, including resistance to diseases and pests, tolerance to drought, heat, cold and other adverse conditions, efficient use of resources and high nutritional quality[25,26]. In mammalian physiology, selective breeding has generated rodent strains which differ greatly in quantitative traits such as hypertension, atherosclerosis, diabetes, predispositions to cancer, drug sensitivities and various behavioural patterns; information on the number, location and nature of these QTLs would be of value in medicine[16,27]. In evolutionary biology, the process of speciation can be investigated by studying the number and nature of genes underlying reproductive isolation[28].

The availability of detailed RFLP linkage maps[14,29-34] makes it possible to dissect quantitative traits into discrete genetic factors (QTLs): all regions of a genome can be assayed and accurate estimates of phenotypic effects and genetic position derived from interval analysis[16]. Once QTLs are mapped, RFLP markers permit genetic manipulations such as rapid construction of near-isogenic lines: flanking markers may be used to retain the QTL and the study of the remaining markers may be used to speed progress by identifying individuals with a fortuitously high proportion of the desired genetic background[38] (Fig. 2 legend). Using isogenic lines, the fundamental tools of genetics and molecular biology may be brought to bear on the study of QTLs—including testing of complementation, dominance and epistasis; characterization of physiological and biochemical differences between isogenic lines; isolation of additional alleles by mutagenesis (at least in favourable systems); and, eventually, physical mapping and molecular cloning of genetic factors underlying quantitative traits.

We thank Janice Chen, Mark Daly, Gerald Dickinson and Mitzi Aguirre for technical assistance. We thank our colleagues and the referees for comments on the manuscript. This work was supported in part by grants from the NSF (to E.S.L. and to S.D.T.), from the System Development Foundation (to E.S.L.), and from the US Department of Agriculture (to S.D.T.).

(**335**,721-726;1988)

Andrew H. Paterson*, Eric S. Lander†‡, John D. Hewitt§, Susan Peterson*, Stephen E. Lincoln† & Steven D. Tanksley*
* Department of Plant Breeding and Biometry, Cornell University, Ithaca, New York 14853, USA
† Whitehead Institute for Biomedical Research, 9 Cambridge Center, Cambridge, Massachusetts 02142, USA
‡ Harvard University, Cambridge, Massachusetts 02138, USA
§ Department of Vegetable Crops, University of California, Davis, California 95616, USA

Received 8 July; accepted 9 September 1988.

筛选 CL 等位基因从而构建出具有农用价值的可溶性固形物产量更高的番茄品种。

QTL 定位的一般方法可以在诸多生物领域有广泛的应用。在农业上，可以将一些野生品种中特有的 QTL 转移到驯化品种中来，包括对疫病和害虫的抗性、对干旱、热、冷等逆境条件的耐受能力，以及对资源的高效利用能力和高营养价值 [25,26]。在哺乳动物生理学中，选择育种已经能够培育出数量性状差异很大的啮齿类动物品种。这些数量性状包括高血压、动脉粥样硬化、糖尿病、癌症易感体质、药物敏感性和各种行为模式等方面的差异。这些 QTL 的数量、位置以及性质方面的信息具有一定的医学价值。在进化生物学中，可以通过研究造成生殖隔离的基因的数目和性质来研究物种形成的过程 [28]。

精细的 RFLP 遗传连锁图谱 [14,29-34] 的获得使我们能够将数量性状分解成很多离散的遗传因子（QTL）来研究。这样就可以分析基因组中所有的区域，通过区间分析 [16] 准确地估算表型效应和基因位置。一旦 QTL 被定位，就能利用 RFLP 遗传标记进行一些遗传操作，例如快速构建近等基因系：侧翼遗传标记可用于保持 QTL，对保留下来的遗传标记的研究可以用来加速对具有罕见高比例的期望遗传背景的个体识别进程 [38]（图 2 注）。作为遗传学和分子生物学的基本工具，等基因系可用于QTL 的研究，包括基因互补作用、显性和上位效应、等基因系之间生理生化特性差异的鉴定、利用基因突变对其他等位基因的分离（至少是在良好的体系中的突变）以及最终对这些决定数量性状的遗传因子进行物理定位和分子克隆。

在此，我们要感谢贾尼丝·陈、马克·戴利、杰拉尔德·迪金森和米蒂兹·阿吉雷在技术上的帮助。还要感谢我们的同事和审稿人对稿件提出的宝贵意见。本工作得到了美国国家科学基金会、系统发育基金和农业部的部分资助。

（周晓明 翻译；方向东 审稿）

Resolution of Quantitative Traits into Mendelian Factors by Using a Complete Linkage Map of Restriction Fragment Length Polymorphisms

References:

1. Mendel, G. *Verh. naturf. Ver. in Brunn.* **4**, (1868).

2. Johannsen, W. *Elemente der exakten Erblichkeitsllehre* (Fischer, Jena, 1909).

3. Nilsson-Ehle, H. *Kreuzunguntersuchungen an Hafer und Weizen* (Lund, 1909).

4. East, E. M. *Genetics* **1**, 164-176 (1915).

5. Wright, S. *Evolution and the Genetics of Populations* (University of Chicago Press, 1968).

6. Sax, K. *Genetics* **8**, 552-556 (1923).

7. Thoday, J. M. *Nature* **191**, 368-369 (1961).

8. Tanksley, S. D., Medina-Filho, H. & Rick, C. *Heredity* **49**, 11-25 (1982).

9. Edwards, M. D., Stuber, C. W. & Wendel, J. F. *Genetics* **116**, 113-125 (1987).

10. Botstein, D., White, R. L., Skolnick, M. & Davis, R. W. *Am. J. Hum. Genet.* **32**, 314-331 (1980).

11. Chmielewski, T. *Genet. pol.* **9**, 97-124 (1968).

12. Rick, C. M. *Hilgardia* **42**, 493-510 (1974).

13. Tanksley, S. D. & Hewitt, J. *Theor. appl. Genet.* **75**, 811-823 (1988).

14. Tanksley, S. D., Miller, J., Paterson, A. & Bernatzky, R. *Proc. 18th Stadler Genet. Symp.* (in the press).

15. Lander, E. S. *et al. Genomics* **1**, 174-181 (1987).

16. Lander, E. S. & Botstein, D. *Genetics* (in the press).

17. Ott, J. *Analysis of Human Genetic Linkage* (Johns Hopkins, Baltimore, 1985).

18. Simmonds, N. W. *Principles of Crop Improvement*, 82-85 (Longman, New York, 1981).

19. Lande, R. *Heredity* **50**, 47-65 (1983).

20. Shrimpton, A. E. & Robertson, A. *Genetics* **11**, 445-459 (1988).

21. Yeager, A. F. *J. Hered.* **18**, 263-265 (1927).

22. Emery, G. C. & Munger, H. M. *J. Am. Soc. Hort. Sci.* **95**, 410-412 (1966).

23. Zamir, D. & Tadmor, Y. *Bot. Gaz.* **147**, 355-358 (1986).

24. Tanksley, S. D. in *Isozymes in Plant Genetics and Breeding* (eds Tanksley, S. D. & Orton, T. J.) 331-338 (Elsevier, Amsterdam, 1983).

25. Rick, C. M. in *Genes, Enzymes and Populations* (ed. A. M. Srb) 255-268 (Plenum, New York, 1973).

26. Harlan, J. R. *Crop Sci.* **16**, 329-333 (1976).

27. Festing, M. F. W. *Inbred Strains in Biomedical Research* (Oxford, New York, 1979).

28. Coyne, J. A. & Charlesworth, B. *Heredity* **57**, 243-246 (1986).

29. Helentjaris, T. *Trends Genet.* **3**, 217-221 (1987).

30. Landry, B. S., Kessell, R., Leung, H. & Michelmore, R. W. *Theor. appl. Genet.* **74**, 646-653 (1987).

31. Burr, B., Burr, F. A., Thompson, K. H., Albertsen, M. C. & Stuber, C. W. *Genetics* **118**, 519-526 (1988).

32. Chang, C., Bowman, J. L., DeJohn, A. W., Lander, E. S. & Meyerowitz, E. M. *Proc. Natl. Acad. Sci. U.S.A.* **68**, 6856-6860.

33. McCouch, S. R. *et al. Theor. appl. Genet.* (in the press).

34. Bonierbale, M. W., Plaisted, R. L. & Tanksley, S. D. *Genetics* (in the press).

35. Franklin, I. A. *Theor. Populat. Biol.* **11**, 60-80 (1977).

36. Stam, P. *Genet. Res.* **25**, 131-155 (1980).

37. Kosambi, D. D. *Ann. Eugen.* **12**, 172-175 (1944).

38. Tanksley, S. D. & Rick, C. M. *Theor. appl. Genet.* **57**, 161-170 (1980).

Observation of Cold Nuclear Fusion in Condensed Matter

S. E. Jones *et al.*

Editor's Note

In 1989, two groups of researchers working in Utah believed they had found evidence that electrolysis of heavy water using palladium electrodes could trigger nuclear fusion of the deuterium atoms, offering vast amounts of energy in a simple benchtop process. Both groups submitted their results to *Nature*. After questions raised by referees, one team—Martin Fleischmann, Stanley Pons and their student Marvin Hawkins at the University of Utah—withdrew their paper and published it elsewhere. This is the other paper, by Steven Jones and colleagues at Brigham Young University. The controversial claim of cold fusion spurred worldwide activity to replicate the results, but no such vindication was ever found, and electrolytic "cold fusion" is now almost universally discredited.

When a current is passed through palladium or titanium electrodes immersed in an electrolyte of deuterated water and various metal salts, a small but significant flux of neutrons is detected. Fusion of deuterons within the metal lattice may be the explanation.

FUSION of the nuclei of isotopes of hydrogen is the principal means of energy production in the high-temperature interiors of stars. In relatively cold terrestrial conditions, the nuclei are surrounded by electrons and can approach one another no more closely than is allowed by the molecular Coulomb barrier. The rate of nuclear fusion in molecular hydrogen is then governed by quantum-mechanical tunnelling through that barrier, or equivalently, the probability of finding the two nuclei at zero separation. In a deuterium molecule, where the equilibrium separation between deuterons (d) is 0.74 Å, the d–d fusion rate is exceedingly slow, about 10^{-74} per D_2 molecule per second[1].

By replacing the electron in a hydrogen molecular ion with a more massive charged particle, the fusion rate is greatly increased. In muon-catalysed fusion, the internuclear separation is reduced by a factor of ~200 (the ratio of the muon to electron mass), and the nuclear fusion rate correspondingly increases by about eighty orders of magnitude. Muon-catalysed fusion has been shown to be an effective means of rapidly inducing fusion reactions in low-temperature mixtures of hydrogen isotopes[2,3].

A hypothetical quasi-particle a few times as massive as the electron would increase the cold fusion rate to readily measurable levels of ~10^{-20} fusions per d–d molecule per

凝聚态物质中观察到的冷核聚变

琼斯等

编者按

1989 年，犹他州的两个研究小组认为他们已经找到了证据证明，在一个简单的桌面装置中，用钯电极电解重水会引发氘原子核聚变，释放巨大的能量。这两组都把他们的结果投到了《自然》。在审稿人提出问题之后，其中的一组——犹他大学的马丁·弗莱施曼，斯坦利·庞斯和他们的学生马尔温·霍金斯——撤回了他们的论文并在别处发表。本文则是另一篇论文，由杨百翰大学的史蒂文·琼斯及其同事们所作。冷核聚变的提出颇具争议，激励着世界范围内的研究行动来重复该结果，但是一直没有得到证实，如今，由电解产生的"冷核聚变"受到人们的普遍质疑。

当电流通过浸没在由氘化水和各种金属盐组成的电解质中的钯或钛电极时，我们探测到了一个微弱却意义重大的中子流。对于该现象，金属晶格中的氘核聚变或许可以做出解释。

在高温的恒星内部，氢同位素的核聚变是能量产生的主要途径。而在相对寒冷的陆地环境中，原子核被电子包围着，并且彼此间的距离不会比分子库仑势垒所允许的距离更小。因此，氢气分子的核聚变率受穿过势垒的量子力学隧道效应的控制，相当于受两核间距为零的现象发生概率的控制。在氘分子中，氘核（即 d）间的平衡距离为 0.74 Å，d–d 聚变率非常小，大约每秒钟每个氘气分子中发生 10^{-74} 次聚变[1]。

用一个更大的带电粒子来替代氢分子离子中的电子，聚变率会大大提高。在 μ 子催化聚变中，核间距会缩小约 200 倍（即 μ 子与电子质量之比），相应地核聚变率也会提升约 80 个数量级。μ 子催化聚变已经被证实为能够在氢同位素低温混合物中迅速引起聚变反应的一个有效途径[2,3]。

一个假定的比电子大几倍的准粒子会将冷核聚变率增加到易于测量到的水平，即每秒钟每个氘核对中约 10^{-20} 次聚变[1]。本文报告的结果表明，在特定条件下将氢

second[1]. The results reported here imply that a comparable distortion of the internuclear wavefunction can be realized when hydrogen isotope nuclei are loaded into metals under certain conditions. We have discovered a means of inducing nuclear fusion without the use of either high temperatures or radioactive muons.

Indirect Evidence

Observations of naturally occurring ^{3}He in the Earth suggested to us new directions for laboratory investigations of nuclear fusion in condensed matter. ^{3}He is produced by the following fusion reactions:

$$p + d \rightarrow {}^3He + \gamma(5.4 \text{ MeV}) \tag{1}$$

$$d + d \rightarrow {}^3He(0.82 \text{ MeV}) + n(2.45 \text{ MeV}) \tag{2a}$$

$$\rightarrow t(1.01 \text{ MeV}) + p(3.02 \text{ MeV}) \tag{2b}$$

Tritium (t) decays with a 12.4-yr half-life to produce ^{3}He. The well established high ^{3}He/^{4}He ratio in solids, liquids and gases associated with volcanoes and other areas of high heat flow[4-6] suggests fusion as a possible source for the ^{3}He.

To estimate a possible rate of fusion in the Earth, we assume a simple, steady-state model in which the known flux of ^{3}He out of the mantle, 2×10^{19} ^{3}He atoms per second[7], arises from p–d fusion occurring uniformly in the mantle water reservoir, taken as $\sim 1.4 \times 10^{24}$ g (R. Poreda, personal communication). Note that if the Earth contains "primordial" ^{3}He, our calculated rate will be an upper limit; on the other hand, if fusion-produced ^{3}He is stored in the mantle (so that the outward flux does not equal the production rate), our value will be a lower limit. As each p–d fusion produces one ^{3}He atom, and as the isotopic abundance of deuterium in water is $\sim 1.5 \times 10^{-4}$ deuterons per proton, we infer a geological fusion rate constant, λ_f, of

$$\lambda_f \approx \frac{2 \times 10^{19} \text{ }^3He \text{ atoms s}^{-1}}{1.4 \times 10^{43} \text{ deuterons}}$$

$$\approx 10^{-24} \text{ fusions d}^{-1} \text{ s}^{-1} \tag{3}$$

This rate is fifty orders of magnitude larger than that expected in an isolated HD molecule, and fusion at this rate could be detected if reproduced in the laboratory.

Cold nuclear fusion may be important in celestial bodies other than the Earth. Jupiter, for example, radiates about twice as much heat as it receives from the Sun. It is interesting to consider whether cold nuclear fusion in the core of Jupiter, which is probably metallic hydrogen plus iron silicate, could account for its excess heat. Heat is radiated at an approximate rate of 10^{18} watts, which could be produced by p–d fusions occurring at a rate of 10^{30} s^{-1}[1]. Assuming a core of radius 4.6×10^9 cm, containing mostly hydrogen, with density ~ 10 g cm^{-3} and a deuteron/proton ratio of $\sim 10^{-4}$, we deduce a required p–d fusion rate of $\lambda_f \approx 10^{-19}$ fusions d^{-1} s^{-1} if all the heat derives from fusion. Catalysed nuclear

同位素原子核注入到金属中，可以实现原子核间波函数相应的变化。我们已经发现了一种在既不要求高温也不使用放射性 μ 子的情况下实现核聚变的方法。

间 接 证 据

对地球上自然产生的 ^{3}He 的观测，为我们在实验室条件下研究凝聚态物质中的核聚变指明了新的方向。^{3}He 在下列聚变反应中产生：

$$p + d \rightarrow {}^3He + \gamma(5.4 \text{ MeV}) \tag{1}$$

$$d + d \rightarrow {}^3He(0.82 \text{ MeV}) + n(2.45 \text{ MeV}) \tag{2a}$$

$$\rightarrow t(1.01 \text{ MeV}) + p(3.02 \text{ MeV}) \tag{2b}$$

氚（即 t）以 12.4 年的半衰期衰变产生 ^{3}He。与火山爆发和其他高温热流相关的固体、液体、气体中存在的已经确定的 ^{3}He/^{4}He 的高比值[4-6]表明，聚变是 ^{3}He 的一个可能来源。

为估算地球中的可能聚变率，我们假设一个简单的稳态模型，在该模型中，已知从地幔中流出的 ^{3}He 流为每秒钟 2×10^{19} 个 ^{3}He 原子[7]，是由在地幔储水层（约 1.4×10^{24} g）中均匀发生的 p–d 聚变引起的（波雷达，个人交流）。需要注意的是，一方面，如果地球含有"原始"^{3}He，那么我们计算出的上述聚变率就是上限；另一方面，如果核聚变产生的 ^{3}He 是储藏在地幔中的（这样一来，向外流出的量就与产生率不相等），那么我们的计算值就是下限。由于每次 p–d 聚变产生一个 ^{3}He 原子且水中氘的同位素丰度约为每个质子对应 1.5×10^{-4} 个氘核，我们推断出一个地球的聚变率常数 λ_f：

$$\lambda_f \approx \frac{2 \times 10^{19} \text{ }^3He \text{ 原子 / 秒}}{1.4 \times 10^{43} \text{ 氘核}}$$

$$\approx 10^{-24} \text{ 聚变 / （氘核·秒）} \tag{3}$$

这个聚变率要比孤立 HD 分子中的预期聚变率高出 50 个数量级，如果在实验室条件下重现该过程，处于这种聚变率的聚变是可以被探测到的。

与地球不同，天体中的冷核聚变或许是很重要的。例如木星，它辐射出的热量大约是其从太阳那里吸收的热量的两倍。那么，发生在可能由金属氢加铁硅酸盐组成的木星核心处的冷核聚变能否为多余的热量做出解释呢？这是一个很有趣的问题。热量辐射率大约为 10^{18} W，而该热量可以由聚变率为 10^{30} s^{-1} 的 p–d 聚变产生[1]。假设有这样一个核心，其半径为 4.6×10^9 cm，主要由氢组成，密度约为 10 g·cm^{-3}，氘核与质子之比约为 10^{-4}，且如果所有的热量全部来自聚变，那么我们推断出 p–d 聚变率 λ_f 必须为每秒钟每个氘核中约 10^{-19} 次聚变。处于这个聚变率的催化核聚变在

fusion at this rate could be readily measured in the laboratory.

Further evidence for cold nuclear fusion in condensed matter comes from studies of ^{3}He and ^{4}He in metals. There have been several reports of high ^{3}He concentrations in metal crucibles and foils (H. Craig, R. Poreda, A. Nier, personal communications), consistent with *in situ* formation by cold fusion. In particular, Mamyrin *et al.*[8] report the occurrence of patchy, high concentrations of ^{3}He in a number of metal foils. Electrolytic refining of the metals could have provided the appropriate conditions for the cold nuclear fusion reactions (1) and possibly (2). Among several possible explanations for the observations, the authors suggest an analogue of muon catalysis[8].

Detection of Cold-fusion Neutrons

The considerations outlined above led to laboratory experiments performed at Brigham Young University to determine whether cold nuclear fusion can actually occur in condensed matter. We now report the observation of deuteron–deuteron fusion at room temperature during low-voltage electrolytic infusion of deuterons into metallic titanium or palladium electrodes. The fusion reaction (2a) is apparently catalysed by the deposition of d$^+$ and metal ions from the electrolyte at (and into) the negative electrode. Neutrons with an energy of ~2.5 MeV are clearly detected with a sensitive neutron spectrometer. The experimental layout is shown in Fig. 1.

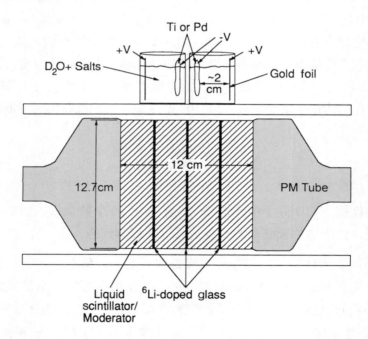

Fig. 1. Schematic diagram of the experiment. Electrolytic cells are shown on top of the neutron spectrometer.

实验室条件下可以很容易地被探测到。

关于凝聚态物质中冷核聚变的进一步证据来源于对金属中的 ^3He 和 ^4He 的研究。目前已经有一些关于金属坩埚和金属箔中的高浓度 ^3He 的报道（克雷格，波雷达，尼尔，个人交流），且与冷核聚变在原位形成相一致。特别是，马梅林等人声称在许多金属箔中观察到了分布不均匀的高浓度 ^3He[8]。金属的电解精炼可能为冷核聚变反应（1），甚至可能包括反应（2）提供了适宜的条件。在对该现象的一些可能的解释中，作者比较赞同类似于 μ 子的催化作用的解释[8]。

冷核聚变中子的探测

鉴于上面概述的种种考虑，在杨百翰大学进行了实验以验证冷核聚变能否在凝聚态物质中发生。我们在这里报道了室温下将氘核向金属钛或钯电极低压电解注入期间的 d–d 聚变。聚变反应（2a）显然受到了负电极处（及其内部）电解质中的 d^+ 和金属离子沉积的催化。灵敏的中子谱仪也明显探测到能量约为 2.5 MeV 的中子。实验装置如图 1 所示。

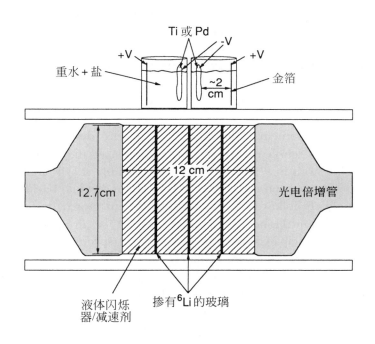

图 1. 实验装置简图。在中子谱仪上放置的是电解池。

The neutron spectrometer, developed at Brigham Young University over the past few years (ref. 9 and manuscript in preparation) has been crucial to the identification of this cold fusion process. The detector consists of a liquid organic scintillator (BC-505) contained in a glass cylinder 12.5 cm in diameter, in which three glass scintillator plates doped with lithium-6 are embedded. Neutrons deposit energy in the liquid scintillator through multiple collisions, and the resulting light output yields energy information. As their energy decreases, the neutrons are scavenged by ^{6}Li nuclei, and the reaction n + ^{6}Li→t + ^{4}He results in scintillations in the glass. Pulse shapes and amplitudes from the two scintillators differ; the two distinct signals are registered by two photomultiplier tubes, whose signals are summed. A coincidence of identified signals from the two media within 20 μs identifies an incoming neutron that has stopped in the detector.

The spectrometer was calibrated using 2.9- and 5.2-MeV neutrons generated by deuteron –deuteron interactions at 90° and 0°, respectively, with respect to a deuteron beam from a Van de Graaff accelerator. The observed energy spectra show broad structures which imply that 2.45-MeV neutrons should appear in the multichannel analyser spectrum in channels 45-150. The stability of the detector system was checked between data runs by measuring the counting rate for fission neutrons from a broad-spectrum californium-252 source.

We have performed extensive tests to verify that the neutron spectrometer does not respond preferentially in this pulse height range to other sources of radiation such as thermal neutrons. In particular, we made unsuccessful efforts to generate false 2.5-MeV neutron "signals" by using various γ-ray and neutron sources and by turning auxiliary equipment on and off. Neutron-producing machines such as the Van de Graaff accelerators were off during all foreground and background runs.

Many background runs were made using operating cells (described below) containing standard electrodes and electrolytes, except that H_2O replaced the D_2O; other background runs were made using both new and previously used standard cells containing D_2O plus the usual electrolyte but with no electrical current. The individual background runs were all featureless and closely followed the pattern of the integrated background shown in Fig. 2. Background rates in the neutron counter are $\sim 10^{-3}$ s^{-1} in the energy region where 2.5-MeV neutrons are anticipated. By comparing energy spectra from γ-ray and neutron sources we have determined that approximately one-fourth of the observed background events arise from accidental coincidences of γ-rays and three-fourths from ambient neutrons. The γ-ray background comes mainly from radioactive radium and potassium in the surrounding materials. We attribute the ambient neutrons to cosmic-ray sources. Although the typical neutron evaporation spectrum (at birth) has a broad maximum near 2.5 MeV (ref. 10), Monte Carlo calculations show that moderation in the source medium (predominantly the shielding surrounding the detector) will wash out this structure and produce a smoothly decreasing background spectrum above 0.5 MeV, as observed.

杨百翰大学在过去几年中发展的中子谱仪（参考文献 9 及处于准备阶段的稿件）对于识别这种冷核聚变过程是非常重要的。探测器包括一个放置在直径为 12.5 cm 的玻璃圆筒中的液体有机闪烁器（BC–505），该圆筒内嵌着三个掺杂有 Li–6 的玻璃闪烁器平板。中子通过多次碰撞将能量存积在液体闪烁器中，然后生成的光输出产生能量信息。由于能量减少了，中子就会被 ^6Li 核全部吸收，并且该反应 n + ^6Li → t + ^4He 会在玻璃中引起闪烁。来自两个闪烁器的脉冲波形和振幅不相同；这两个不同的信号会被两个光电倍增管记录下来，并把倍增管的信号相加。在 20 μs 内来自两个倍增管的可分辨的一致信号就能够识别出一个停在探测器内的入射中子。

用 d–d 反应产生的，能量分别为 2.9 MeV 和 5.2 MeV 的中子来校准谱仪，这些中子相对于范德格拉夫加速器氘核束流的方向在 90° 和 0° 方向射出。观测到的能谱比较宽，这意味着 2.45 MeV 中子应该出现在多道分析器的第 45 到第 150 道之间。通过对锎–252 广谱源裂变中子计数率的多次测量，检验了探测系统的稳定性。

我们已做了大量的测试证实，在这种脉冲高度范围内，中子谱仪不会对像热中子这样的其他辐射源优先响应。特别是，我们企图通过使用多种 γ 射线、中子源和开 / 关辅助设备来产生赝 2.5 MeV 中子"信号"的努力都失败了。在所有的信号和本底运行中，我们关闭了像范德格拉夫加速器这样的中子产生装置。

许多本底运行是用含标准电极和电解质的正在运行的电解池（下文将介绍）完成的，只是将其中的 D_2O 换成了 H_2O；而其他的本底运行是用新的和之前用过的包含 D_2O 和平常电解质的无电流标准电解池完成。单个的本底运行是毫无特征的，且与图 2 所示的整体本底模式高度一致。在预期的 2.5 MeV 中子出现的能量范围内，中子计数器的本底率约为 10^{-3} s^{-1}。通过对比 γ 射线和中子源的能谱，我们已经确定，在观测到的本底事件中，大约 1/4 是由于 γ 射线的偶然重叠，3/4 由周边环境中的中子引起。γ 射线本底主要来源于周围材料中的放射性镭和钾。我们将环境中的中子归因于宇宙射线源。尽管典型的中子的发射谱（初生的）在接近 2.5 MeV 处有一个很宽的峰（参考文献 10），但蒙特卡罗计算表明，由于源介质的小曼化（主要是对探测器周围的屏蔽层引起）将消除这种结构，并产生一个在 0.5 MeV 以上的平滑递减的本底谱，这和观测结果一致。

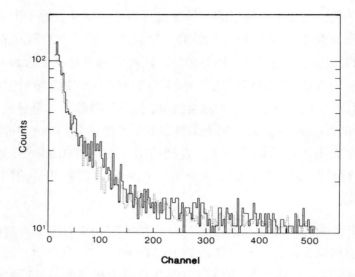

Fig. 2. Foreground (solid) and background (dashed) counts as a function of pulse height (corresponding to neutron energy) in the neutron spectrometer. Ten counts have been added to each three-channel bin for clarity of presentation.

The predicted and measured absence of structure in the spectrum of cosmic-ray-produced neutrons will not be influenced by the relatively small temporal variations that may occur in the cosmic-ray flux, such as the observed decreases that may accompany solar flares. This means that the observed peak at 2.5 MeV cannot be accounted for by ambient-neutron background variations, because, as explained below, the analysis is based on the shape of the spectra and not simply on rates. Low-energy cosmic-ray muons would be rapidly scavenged by nuclei with high atomic number, so as to reduce muon-catalysed d–d fusion to a negligible level[2,3]. Considering volume and solid angle, the rate of production of neutrons by muons absorbed by carbon nuclei in the detector exceeds that from muons absorbed by oxygen nuclei in the electrolytic cells by a factor of ~60. Thus, the presence or absence of electrolytic cells is an unimportant perturbation in the background.

During the search for suitable catalytic materials, the following (unoptimized) prescription for the electrolytic cells evolved. It began with salts typical of volcanic hot springs and included electrode-metal ions. The electrolyte is typically a mixture of ~160 g D_2O plus various metal salts in ~0.1 g amounts each: $FeSO_4 \cdot 7H_2O$, $NiCl_2 \cdot 6H_2O$, $PdCl_2$, $CaCO_3$, $Li_2SO_4 \cdot H_2O$, $Na_2SO_4 \cdot 10H_2O$, $CaH_4(PO_4)_2 \cdot H_2O$, $TiOSO_4 \cdot H_2SO_4 \cdot 8H_2O$, and a very small amount of AuCN. The pH is adjusted to $\leqslant 3$ with HNO_3. All 14 runs reported here began with this basic electrolyte.

Titanium and palladium, initially selected because of their large capacities for holding hydrogen and forming hydrides, were found to be effective negative electrodes. Individual electrodes consisted of ~1 g purified "fused" titanium in pellet form, or 0.05 g of 0.025-mm-thick palladium foils, or 5 g of mossy palladium. Typically 4–8 cells were used simultaneously. The palladium pieces were sometimes re-used after cleaning and

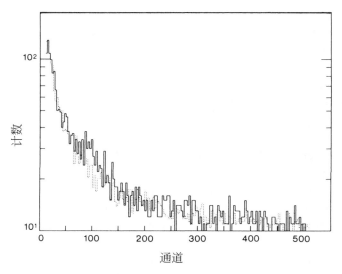

图 2. 信号（实线）和本底（虚线）计数关于中子谱仪中脉冲高度（对应于中子能量）的函数。为了表述清楚，我们在每 3 通道中加入 10 个计数。

预期和测到的宇宙射线产生的中子谱中的这种结构的缺失，不会受宇宙射线流中可能发生的相对微小而短暂的变化（如可观测到的与太阳耀斑相伴出现的减小）的影响。这就意味着，周边环境中子本底的变化不能对 2.5 MeV 处所观测到的峰作出解释，因为，正像下文解释的那样，分析是基于谱的形状而不是简单地依据比率得出的。低能宇宙射线 μ 子应该被具有较高原子序数的原子核迅速清除掉，以便将 μ 子催化的 d–d 聚变降到可以忽略的水平上[2,3]。考虑到体积和立体角，由检测器中碳核吸收的 μ 子产生中子的速率比在电解池中氧核吸收的 μ 子产生中子的速率要快近 60 倍。因此，电解池存在与否对本底的影响并不大。

在寻找合适的催化剂材料的过程中，逐渐形成了下面对电解池的配方（非最优化的）。它从火山温泉中典型的盐类化合物开始，并要包含电极－金属离子。典型的电解质是一种混合物，包含约 160 g D_2O 与多种金属盐，每种金属盐的总量约为 0.1 g，其中包括：$FeSO_4 \cdot 7H_2O$、$NiCl_2 \cdot 6H_2O$、$PdCl_2$、$CaCO_3$、$Li_2SO_4 \cdot H_2O$、$Na_2SO_4 \cdot 10H_2O$、$CaH_4(PO_4)_2 \cdot H_2O$、$TiOSO_4 \cdot H_2SO_4 \cdot 8H_2O$ 以及极少量的 AuCN。用 HNO_3 将 pH 值调整到 ≤3。本文中所报道的这 14 次运行均从这一基础的电解质开始。

最初选择钛和钯是由于它们能够大量储存氢并形成氢化物，结果发现它们还是有效的负电极。单个电极是由约 1 g 纯化的小球形状的"熔融"钛组成，或者由 0.05 g 厚度为 0.025 mm 的钯箔组成，也可以由 5 g 表面粗糙的钯组成。通常会同时使用 4~8 个电解池。有时我们用稀释过的酸或磨蚀材料对钯箔的表面进行清洗、粗化，

roughening the surfaces with dilute acid or abrasives. Hydrogen bubbles were observed to form on the Pd foils only after several minutes of electrolysis, suggesting the rapid absorption of deuterons into the foil; oxygen bubbles formed at the anode immediately. Gold foil was used for the positive electrodes. Direct-current power supplies provided 3–25 volts across each cell at currents of 10–500 mA. Correlations between fusion yield and voltage, current density, or surface characteristics of the metallic cathode have not yet been established.

Small jars, ~4 cm high and 4 cm in diameter, held ~20 ml of electrolyte solution each. The electrolytic cells were placed on or alongside the neutron counter, as shown in Fig. 1. The present cells are simple and undoubtedly far from optimum. Nevertheless, the present combination of our cells with the neutron spectrometer is sufficient to establish the phenomenon of cold nuclear fusion during electrolytic infusion of deuterium into metals.

Figure 2 shows the energy spectrum obtained under the conditions described above, juxtaposed with the (scaled) background spectrum. We acquired about twice as much background data as foreground data. Assuming conservatively that all deviations from background are statistical fluctuations, we scale the background counts by a factor of 0.46 to match the total number of foreground counts over the entire energy range shown in Fig. 2. A feature in channels 45–150 rises above background by nearly four standard deviations. This implies that our assumption is too conservative and that this structure represents a real physical effect. After re-scaling the background by a factor of 0.44 to match the foreground levels in regions just below and just above this feature, the difference plot (Fig. 3) is obtained. It shows a robust signal centred near channel 100, with a statistical significance of almost five standard deviations. A gaussian fit to this peak yields a centroid at channel 101 with a standard deviation of 28 channels, and an amplitude of 23.2 ± 4.5 counts. Both the position and width of this feature correspond to those expected for 2.5-MeV neutrons, according to the spectrometer calibration. The fact that a significant signal appears above background with the correct energy for d–d fusion neutrons (~2.5 MeV) provides strong evidence that room-temperature nuclear fusion is occurring at a low rate in the electrolytic catalysis cells.

之后将其回收利用。仅仅在电解发生的几分钟之后，我们就观察到钯箔上形成了氢气泡，这说明氘核已经被迅速吸收进箔里；氧气泡也在阳极迅速形成。阳极材料为金箔。直流电源对每个电解池提供了 3~25 V 电压和 10~500 mA 电流。但是，聚变产额与电压、电流密度或金属阴极的表面特征间的关联还不确定。

在每个高和直径均约为 4 cm 的小广口瓶中盛有约 20 ml 的电解质溶液。如图 1 所示，我们将电解池放在中子计数器的上面或旁边。无疑，目前的电解池非常简单，而且远远未达到最佳效果。但对于证实在氘电解注入金属期间的冷核聚变现象而言，这种带有中子谱仪的电解池组合已经足够了。

图 2 给出了在上述条件下得到的能谱，且并列给出本底谱（已定标）。我们取得的本底数据大约是信号数据的两倍。保守地假设来自于本底的所有偏差都是统计涨落，我们用大小为 0.46 的因子来定标本底计数，使它与图 2 所示的整个能量范围内的信号计数相匹配。在 45~150 道之间的一个特征峰高出本底将近 4 个标准偏差。这意味着，我们的假设太过保守，且这个结构显示了真实的物理效应。在以大小为 0.44 的因子对本底进行重新定标之后，我们得到了二者的差分图（图 3），重新定标旨在使本底计数在稍低于和稍高于该特征峰的区域内与信号水平相匹配。该图展示了一个集中于 100 道附近的强烈信号，其统计显著性几乎是 5 个标准偏差。高斯拟合后，有一个峰，其中心在 101 道附近，其标准偏差是 28 个通道，幅度为 23.2±4.5 个计数。根据光谱仪校准，该特征峰的位置和宽度对应于 2.5 MeV 中子的期望值。在本底之上出现的显著信号对应的能量恰为 d–d 聚变的中子能量（约 2.5 MeV），这一事实为电解质催化电解池中存在反应率很低的核聚变提供了强有力的证据。

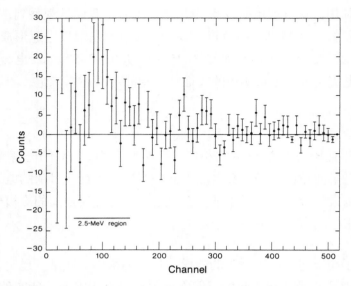

Fig. 3. Difference spectrum obtained by substracting scaled background from the foreground. Statistical errors ($\pm 1\sigma$) are shown for each eight-channel bin.

Fusion Rate Determination

It is instructive to examine the fourteen individual runs which enter into the combined data discussed above. These runs were performed over the period 31 December 1988 to 6 March 1989. Figure 4 displays, for each run, the ratio of foreground count rate in the 2.5-MeV energy region to the background rate obtained for each run. Electronic changes were made in the apparatus during the course of the experiment which altered the observed background rates, so we plot the data in terms of foreground-to-background ratios rather than absolute rates. In one set of data (runs 1 to 8) for which the system was kept as untouched as possible to avoid changes in background rates, the measured rate of detection of 2.5-MeV neutrons was $(6.2\pm1.3)\times10^{-4}$ s^{-1} above background. For this set of data, the background and foreground rates for all energies above ~3 MeV (that is, for all channels from 190 to 512) are equal, at $(1.4\pm0.1)\times10^{-3}$ s^{-1}.

Run 6 is particularly noteworthy, with a statistical significance of approximately five standard deviations above background. Fused titanium pellets were used as the negative electrode, with a total mass of ~3 g. The neutron production rate increased after about one hour of electrolysis. After about eight hours, the rate dropped dramatically, as shown in the follow-on run 7. At this time, the surfaces of the titanium electrodes showed a dark grey coating. An analysis using electron microscopy with a microprobe showed that the surface coating was mostly iron, deposited with deuterons at the cathode. The same phenomenon of a decrease in the neutron signal after about eight hours of operation appears in run 13 followed by run 14. Runs 13 and 14 use the same eight electrochemical cells, and again the negative electrodes developed coatings after a few hours of electrolysis. These observations suggest the importance of surface conditions for the cold fusion process. Variations in surface conditions and electrolyte composition are anticipated

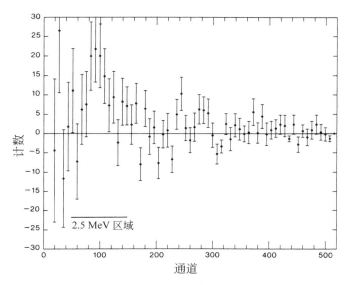

图 3. 通过从信号中减去定标的本底得到的差分谱图。图中给出每 8 个通道的统计误差（±1σ）。

测定聚变率

对列入上文讨论的综合数据中的那 14 次运行分别进行考查是有益的。这些运行是在 1988 年 12 月 31 日至 1989 年 3 月 6 日期间完成的。图 4 给出了每一次运行在 2.5 MeV 的能量区域内的信号计数率与本底计数率之比。在改变观察到的本底率的实验过程中，仪器中存在电子学的变化，所以我们根据信号/本底计数率的比值而非绝对计数率来绘制数据。在一组数据中（运行 1 到 8），我们尽量使系统不受影响以避免本底率的改变，对 2.5 MeV 中子探测的测量率高出本底 $(6.2 \pm 1.3) \times 10^{-4}$ s^{-1}。在这组数据中，本底率和信号率对于所有约 3 MeV 以上（即 190 道到 512 道之间的所有道）的能量来说都是相等的，为 $(1.4 \pm 0.1) \times 10^{-3}$ s^{-1}。

特别值得注意的是运行 6，其在本底之上的统计显著性为将近 5 个标准偏差。我们将质量约为 3 g 的熔融钛小球作为负极。在电解开始一个小时之后，中子产率增加了。约 8 个小时之后，中子产率却急剧地降低了，这点可以从后续的运行 7 看出。此时，在钛电极表面出现了一个深灰色的涂层。使用电子显微镜上的微探针进行分析后发现，该表面涂层主要是铁，而氘核在阴极沉积。同样的现象，即电解进行约 8 个小时之后中子信号减弱，也发生在运行 13 及其后的运行 14 中。运行 13 和运行 14 用的是相同的 8 个电解池，并且在电解开始的几个小时之后涂层又出现在了阴极上。这些观察结果揭示了表面状况对于冷核聚变过程的重要性。由于物质会从溶液中析出，所以每次测试运行中表面状况及电解质成分的变化是可以预料到的；

453

during each test run because materials plate out of solution; the solution pH also changes significantly during a run. These 14 runs represent two choices of electrode material plus various operating currents. These variations may account for the fluctuations in the signal level that are evident in Fig. 4. As these runs represent a total of only ~200 signal neutrons at an average rate of ~2 per hour, it was difficult to optimize experimental conditions. This is a task for future research.

The observed "turning off" of the signal after about eight hours may account for low signal-to-background ratios in runs 1 and 3, in that a signal that lasted for only a few hours may have been overwhelmed after a long (~20-hour) running time. When run 10 started with rates substantially above background, we stopped the run and removed half of the electrochemical cells as a test. The neutron production rate dropped off as expected (run 11). In determining the statistical significance of the data, we included runs 1, 3, 7, 11 and 14, even though we see a systematic reason for their low foreground-to-background ratios as explained above. Run 8, shown in Fig. 4, was inadvertently lost from the magnetic storage device and could not be included in Figs 2 and 3. This does not change our conclusions.

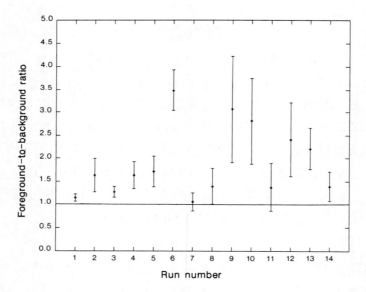

Fig. 4. Ratio of foreground rate to background rate for each run, in the 2.5-MeV energy region of the pulse-height spectrum. Statistical errors (±1σ) are shown.

We can estimate the rate for the neutron-production branch of d–d fusion during electrolysis, specifically for run 6, as follows:

$$\text{Fusions per deuteron pair per second} = \frac{R / \varepsilon}{M \times \frac{d}{2M}} \tag{4}$$

where the observed rate of neutron detection, $R = (4.1 \pm 0.8) \times 10^{-3} \text{ s}^{-1}$, is based on

并且溶液的 pH 值在一个运行过程中也会显著地变化。这 14 次运行展示了对于电极材料和多种工作电流的两个选择。这些变化或许可以解释图 4 中信号电平的明显波动。鉴于这些运行展示了总量只有约 200 个的信号中子，其平均产生率约为每小时 2 个，优化该实验条件是非常困难的。这是未来研究的一项任务。

　　实验观察到的约 8 小时之后出现的信号"中断"或许可以解释运行 1 和 3 中的信号 / 本底的低比值，因为信号只能持续几个小时，在一个较长的运行时间（约 20 小时）之后，该信号可能早就被覆盖掉了。当运行 10 以明显高于本底的速率开始后，作为测试，我们停止该运行，并撤去一半的电解池。正如我们所料，中子产生率逐渐减少（运行 11）。在检测数据的统计显著性时，我们将运行 1、3、7、11 和 14 包括进来，尽管我们看到了造成上文提到的它们较低的信号 / 本底之比的系统性原因。图 4 中所示的运行 8 从磁存储器中不幸丢失，因而在图 2 和图 3 中未显示出来，但这并不影响我们的结论。

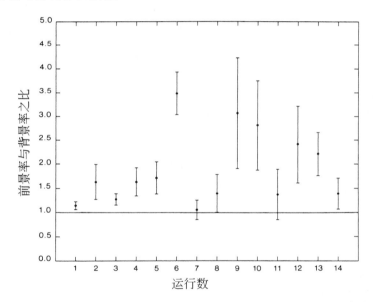

图 4. 在脉冲高度谱的 2.5 MeV 能区内，每个运行的信号率与本底率之比。图中给出统计误差（±1σ）。

　　特别是对于运行 6，我们可以用以下公式估计电解过程中 d–d 聚变产生中子分支的产率：

$$每秒钟每个氘核对的聚变次数 = \frac{R/\varepsilon}{M \times \dfrac{d}{2M}} \tag{4}$$

其中，观测到的中子探测率 $R = (4.1 \pm 0.8) \times 10^{-3} \text{ s}^{-1}$ 是基于 45~150 道间的信号计数

foreground minus corresponding background counts in channels 45–150; the neutron detection efficiency, including geometrical acceptance, is calculated using a Monte Carlo neutron–photon transport code[11] to be $\varepsilon = (1.0\pm0.3)\%$; $M \approx 4\times10^{22}$ titanium atoms for 3 g of titanium; and the ratio of deuteron pairs to metal ions, $d/2M \approx 1$, is based on the assumption that nearly all tetrahedral sites in the titanium lattice are occupied, forming the γ-TiD$_2$ hydride. Then the estimated cold nuclear fusion rate for the neutron-production branch, by equation (4), is $\lambda_f \approx 10^{-23}$ fusions per deuteron pair per second. If most fusions take place near the surface, or if the titanium lattice is far from saturated with deuterons, or if conditions favouring fusion occur intermittently, then the inferred fusion rate must be much larger, perhaps 10^{-20} fusions per deuteron pair per second.

We note that such a fusion rate could be achieved by "squeezing" the deuterons to about half their normal (0.74-Å) separation in molecules. That such rates are now observed in condensed matter suggests catalysed "piezonuclear" fusion as the explanation[1]. A possible cause is that quasi-electrons form in the deuterated metal lattice, with an effective mass a few times that of a free electron. Isotopes of hydrogen are known to accumulate at imperfections in metal lattices[12], and a local high concentration of hydrogen ions might be conducive to piezonuclear fusion. Because we have not seen any evidence for fusion in equilibrated, deuterated metals or compounds such as methylamine-d$_2$ deuteriochloride or ammonium-d$_4$ chloride, we conclude that non-equilibrium conditions are essential. Electrolysis is one way to produce conditions that are far from equilibrium.

It may seem remarkable that one might influence the effective rate of fusion by varying external parameters such as pressure, temperature and electromagnetic fields, but just such effects are seen in another form of cold nuclear fusion, muon-catalysed fusion[13].

Conclusions

The correlation of ideas regarding cold piezonuclear fusion[1] with observations of excess ^{3}He in metals and in geothermal areas of the Earth led to our experimental studies of fusion in electrochemical cells, which began in May 1986. Our electrolyte compositions evolved from geochemical considerations, and changed as results were observed. The presence of a fusion neutron signal was consistently reproduced, although the rate varied widely. Now that our exploratory searches have disclosed a small piezonuclear fusion effect, it remains to disentangle the factors that influence the fusion rate.

The need for off-equilibrium conditions is clearly implied by our data, and suggests that techniques other than electrochemistry may also be successful. We have begun to explore the use of ion implantation and of elevated pressures and temperatures, mimicking geological conditions. Cold nuclear fusion in condensed matter may be of interest as a novel probe of metal-hydrogen systems, including geological ones, and as a source of monoenergetic neutrons. If deuteron–deuteron fusion can be catalysed, then the d–t fusion reaction is possibly favoured because of its much larger nuclear cross-section. Although the fusion rates observed so far are small, the discovery of cold nuclear fusion in condensed

减去相应的本底计数得出的；用蒙特卡罗中子 – 光子传输编码[11]计算出的中子探测效率（包括几何接受角）是 $\varepsilon = (1.0 \pm 0.3)\%$；而 3 g 钛中含 $M \approx 4 \times 10^{22}$ 个钛原子；基于钛晶格中几乎所有的四面体位点均被占据的假设，氘核对与金属离子之比 $d/2M \approx 1$，形成 γ–TiD$_2$ 氢化物。利用方程（4），对产生中子分支的冷核聚变率的估算值 λ_f 为每秒钟每个氘核对内约 10^{-23} 次聚变。如果大多数聚变发生在表面附近，或者钛晶格远远没有被氘核占据，又或者利于聚变产生的条件间歇性出现，那么推断出的聚变率一定会大很多，大概是每秒钟每个氘核对 10^{-20} 次聚变。

我们注意到，这样的聚变率可以通过将分子中的氘核间距"挤压"至其正常值（0.74 Å）的一半来得到。这样的聚变率如今可以在凝聚态物质中观察到，表明可以用催化的"压核"聚变来解释[1]。一个可能的原因是，在氘化金属晶格中形成了准电子，其有效质量是一个自由电子的几倍。众所周知，氢的同位素一般积聚在金属晶格的缺陷中[12]，而局部的高浓度氢离子可能有利于压核聚变。因为在平衡氘化金属或混合物（比如甲胺–d$_2$ 氘化氯化物或铵–d$_4$ 氯化物）中，我们没有发现任何聚变发生的证据，所以我们推断非平衡条件是必需的。电解就是一种产生远离平衡态的条件的方法。

通过改变诸如压强、温度和电磁场等外部参数，或许可以影响聚变的有效率，但是这种影响被看作是冷核聚变的另一种形式，即 μ 子催化聚变[13]。

结　　论

关于冷压核聚变[1]的有关想法以及对存在于金属和地球地热区中的过量 ³He 的观测，促使我们对电解池中的聚变进行了实验研究，该研究始于 1986 年 5 月。我们的电解质成分演变发端于地球化学的考虑，并且随着观测到结果而逐渐加以改变。虽然产生率波动很大，但聚变中子信号的出现一再被重现出来。既然我们的探索性研究已经揭露了一个小的压核聚变效应，接下来就要弄清影响聚变率的各种因素。

我们的数据清楚地表明了需要远离平衡态条件的要求，并且该要求提示那些不同于电化学的方法也许同样可行。我们已经开始探索离子注入、增大压强和提高温度的作用，这些操作是为了模拟相应的地质条件。将凝聚态物质中的冷核聚变作为一种包括地质系统在内的金属氢系统的新型探测手段，以及作为一种单能中子源，或许是非常有用的。如果 d–d 聚变能够被催化，那么 d–t 聚变反应可能会更受青睐，因其核截面要大得多。尽管目前观测到的聚变率很低，但凝聚态物质中冷核聚变的

matter opens the possibility, at least, of a new path to fusion energy.

(**338**, 737-740; 1989)

S. E. Jones[*], E. P. Palmer[*], J. B. Czirr[*], D. L. Decker[*], G. L. Jensen[*], J. M. Thorne[*], S. F. Taylor[*] & J. Rafelski[†]

[*] Departments of Physics and Chemistry, Brigham Young University Provo, Utah 84602, USA

[†] Department of Physics, University of Arizona, Tucson, Arizona 85721, USA

Received 24 March; accepted 14 April 1989.

References:

1. Van Siclen, C. D. & Jones, S. E. *J. Phys.* G. **12**, 213-221 (1986).

2. Jones, S. E. *Nature* **321**, 127-133 (1986).

3. Rafelski, J. & Jones, S. E. *Scient. Am.* **257**, 84-89 (July 1987).

4. Craig, H., Lupton, J. E., Welhan, J. A. & Poreda, R. *Geophys. Res. Lett.* **5**, 897-900 (1978).

5. Lupton, J. E. & Craig, H. *Science* **214**, 13-18 (1981).

6. Mamyrin, B. A. & Tolstikhin, L. N. *Helium Isotopes in Nature* (Elsevier, Amsterdam, 1984).

7. Craig, H. & Lupton, J. E. in *The Sea* Vol. 7 (ed. Emiliani, C.) Ch. 11 (Wiley, New York, 1981).

8. Mamyrin, B. A., Khabarin, L. V. & Yudenich, V. S. *Soviet Phys. Dokl.* **23**, 581-583 (1978).

9. Jensen, G. L., Dixon, D. R., Bruening, K. & Czirr, J. B. *Nucl. Instrum. Meth.* **220**, 406-408 (1984).

10. Hess, W. N., Patterson, H. W. & Wallace, R. *Phys. Rev.* **116**, 445-457 (1959).

11. *MCNP: Monte Carlo Neutron and Photon Transport Code*, CCC-200 (Version 3) (Radiation Shielding Information Center, Oak Ridge Natn. Lab., 1983).

12. Bowman, R. C. Jr in *Metal Hydrides* (ed. Bambakides, G.) 109-144 (Plenum, New York, 1981).

13. Jones, S. E. *et al. Phys. Rev. Lett.* **51**, 1757-1760 (1983).

Acknowledgements. We acknowledge valuable contributions of James Baer, David Mince, Rodney Price, Lawrence Rees, Eugene Sheely and J. C. Wang of Brigham Young University, and of Mike Danos, Fraser Goff, Berndt Müller, Albert Nier, Göte Ostlund and Clinton Van Siclen. We especially thank Alan Anderson for advice on the data analysis and Harmon Craig for continuing encouragement. This research is supported by the Advanced Energy Projects Division of the US Department of Energy.

发现至少为一条通往聚变能的新途径提供了可能性。

（牛慧冲 翻译；李兴中 审稿）

Problems with the γ-Ray Spectrum in the Fleischmann *et al.* Experiments

R. D. Petrasso *et al.*

Editor's Note

The claim by electrochemists Martin Fleischmann and Stanley Pons to have conducted "cold" nuclear fusion by electrolysis led to attempts worldwide to replicate the findings. Others focused on whether Fleischmann and Pons' evidence supported their claims. A key argument was that they detected the neutrons and gamma-rays expected to be emitted, at well-defined energies, from the fusion reaction and its by-products. Here fusion expert Richard Petrasso of MIT and his colleagues investigate a gamma-ray spectrum shown on US television by Fleischmann and Pons (the only time they revealed it), and show that the alleged gamma-ray peak is in the wrong place. This challenge led to the first suspicions of fraud, rather than poor experimentation, in the cold-fusion claims.

SIR—Fleischmann, Pons and Hawkins[1] recently announced the observation of significant heating in their cold-fusion experiments, a result that they attribute to copious fusion reactions. As compelling evidence that fusion had occurred, they reported the observation of the 2.22-MeV γ-ray line that originates from neutron capture by hydrogen nuclei[2,3]

$$n + p \rightarrow d + \gamma \ (2.22 \ \text{MeV}) \tag{1}$$

(Here d represents a deuteron.) They contend that the neutron in reaction (1) is generated by the reaction

$$d + d \rightarrow n + {}^3\text{He} \tag{2}$$

and conclude, therefore, first that the 2.22-MeV γ-ray confirms that the fusion process (2) is occurring, and second that a neutron production rate of the order of 4×10^4 neutrons s^{-1} is derivable from their γ-ray signal rate. They further state that most of the heat generation occurs not through process (2), but through a hitherto unknown nuclear-fusion process.

Here we focus solely on the identity of the reported γ-ray line, which we shall henceforth call the signal line. We argue that the claim of Fleischmann *et al.* to have observed the 2.22-MeV line characteristic of reaction (1) is unfounded. We do so on the basis of three quantitative considerations: (1) that the linewidth is a factor of two smaller than their instrumental resolution would allow; (2) that a clearly defined Compton edge[4], which

弗莱施曼等人实验中 γ 射线谱的问题

佩特拉索等

编者按

电化学家马丁·弗莱施曼和斯坦利·庞斯宣称通过电解实现了"冷"核聚变，这引发了世界范围内去重复这一发现的尝试。而另一些人则关注弗莱施曼和庞斯的证据是否能够支持他们的结论。争论的关键在于他们是否在聚变反应和它的副产物中观测到了预期中的具有特定能量的中子和 γ 射线发射。麻省理工学院的核聚变专家理查德·佩特拉索和他的合作者研究了弗莱施曼和庞斯在美国的电视节目上演示的 γ 射线谱（这是他们唯一一次展示该图谱），并指出他们所声称的 γ 射线峰处于错误的位置。这一质疑引发了人们对冷核聚变的报告中存在欺诈的首次怀疑，而不仅仅只是对简陋实验的质疑。

弗莱施曼、庞斯和霍金斯[1]最近宣称在他们的冷核聚变实验中观察到了明显的放热现象，他们将这一结果归因于大量的聚变反应。作为核聚变发生的强有力的证据，他们在报道中说发现了 2.22 MeV 的 γ 射线，该射线源于氢原子核对中子的捕获[2,3]

$$n + p \rightarrow d + \gamma \ (2.22 \text{ MeV}) \tag{1}$$

（其中 d 代表一个氘核。）他们认为反应 (1) 中的中子产生于下述反应

$$d + d \rightarrow n + {}^3\text{He} \tag{2}$$

由此得出如下结论：首先，2.22 MeV 的 γ 射线证实了核聚变过程 (2) 的发生；其次，量级为每秒 4×10^4 个中子的中子产生速率可以由他们的 γ 射线信号的产生速率推导而来；他们进一步声明大多数热量的产生并非通过过程 (2)，而是通过一个迄今为止并不清楚的核聚变过程。

我们在本文中主要关注如何识别报道的那条 γ 射线，本文中我们将称之为信号线。我们认为弗莱施曼等人所声称的反应 (1) 中观察到的 2.22 MeV 的特征谱线其实并未被找到。我们这么认为主要基于以下三个定量的考虑：(1) 谱线宽度是他们的仪器所允许的分辨率的一半；(2) 在他们发表的数据中本应位于 1.99 MeV 的清晰可辨

should be evident in their published data at 1.99 MeV, is not in fact present; and (3) that their estimated neutron production rate is too large by a factor of 50. In addition, from a consideration of the terrestrial γ-ray background, we argue that their purported γ-ray line actually resides at 2.5 MeV rather than 2.22 MeV. These conclusions are, in part, based on our studies of neutron capture by hydrogen, using a neutron source submerged in water. These measurements allow us to compare the results of Fleischmann *et al.* directly with a controlled experiment.

We measured terrestrial γ-ray background spectra in order to compare our detector characteristics with those of Fleischmann *et al.* Figure 1*a* shows a typical terrestrial γ-ray background spectrum obtained with a 3 in. × 3 in. NaI(Tl) crystal spectrometer system (see ref. 5 for details). The main features of the background spectrum are quite similar throughout the terrestrial environment[6,7]. Fleischmann *et al.* showed a similar γ-ray spectrum on television (Fig. 1*b*). (We believe that we have viewed all the cold-fusion γ-ray spectra that have been shown on KSL-TV (Utah) up to 19 April. This information was obtained from Utah News Clips, Inc., Utah. As far as we can tell, all spectra are identical to that of Fig. 1*b*.) This spectrum was obtained in the course of the Fleischmann *et al.* experiments (M. Hawkins, personal communication). Their spectrometer system consisted of a Nuclear Data ND-6 portable analyser with a 3 in. × 3 in. NaI (Tl) crystal (ref. 1 and M. Hawkins and R. Hoffmann, personal communications). A $\frac{3}{8}$-in.-thick Pb annulus encompassed the scintillator. It is clear from Fig. 1*a* and *b*, and particularly from the ^{40}K (1.46 MeV) and ^{208}Tl (2.61 MeV) lines, that our resolution is comparable to or better than that of the spectrometer used by Fleischmann *et al.*, a point to which we return later.

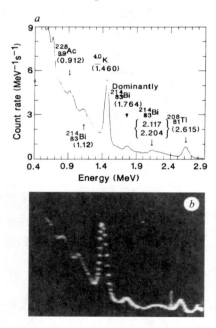

Fig. 1. *a*, The γ-ray background spectrum measured with a 3 in. × 3 in. NaI(Tl) detector at MIT. Some important terrestrial γ-ray lines have been identified in this figure[6,7,12]. (As explained in ref. 12, the

的康普顿边 [4]，却没有出现；(3) 他们估算的中子产率大了 50 倍。更进一步地说，考虑到地面的 γ 射线本底，我们怀疑他们所声称的 γ 射线实际上位于 2.5 MeV 处，而非 2.22 MeV 处。这些结论部分基于我们对氢捕获中子的研究，该研究通过将中子源浸没在水中进行。这些测量使得我们可以将弗莱施曼等人的结果与对照实验进行直接对比。

为了比较我们与弗莱施曼等人的探测器的特性，我们测量了地面的本底 γ 射线谱。图 1a 显示了一个典型的地面本底 γ 射线谱，该光谱由 3 in×3 in 碘化钠（铊）晶体光谱仪系统（详见参考文献 5）测得。在整个地面环境中 γ 射线本底谱的主要特征都非常相似 [6,7]。弗莱施曼等人在电视上展示了一个类似的 γ 射线谱（图 1b）。（我们相信我们看到了截止到 4 月 19 日在 KSL 电视台（犹他州）播出的所有的冷核聚变的 γ 射线谱。此信息从犹他州的犹他新闻剪影公司获得。在我们所能分辨的范围内，所有的光谱都与图 1b 所示的相同。）这个 γ 谱是从弗莱施曼等人的实验中获得的（霍金斯，个人交流）。他们的光谱仪系统由一个装有 3 in×3 in 碘化钠（铊）晶体的 ND-6 型便携式核数据分析仪组成（参考文献 1 以及与霍金斯和霍夫曼的个人交流）。一个 3/8 in 厚的铅圆筒包裹着闪烁体。从图 1a 和 1b 中，尤其是 [40]K（1.46 MeV）和 [208]Tl（2.61 MeV）的谱线中看得非常清楚，我们的分辨率与之相当或者优于弗莱施曼等人的 γ 谱仪，这一点我们后面还会谈到。

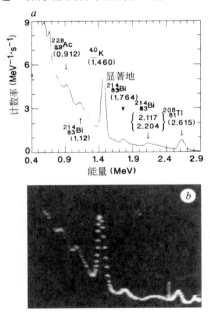

图 1. a，用一个 3 in×3 in 碘化钠（铊）探测器在麻省理工学院测得的 γ 射线本底谱。一些重要的地面 γ 射线谱线在图中被标示出来 [6,7,12]。（正如参考文献 12 中所解释的那样，最终衰变产物的瞬态母核是可

immediate parent of the final decay product is identified. For example, ^{40}K β^+ decays into an excited nuclear state of ^{40}Ar, which actually then emits the 1.460-MeV photon discussed in the text.) The spectrum is averaged over an 84-hour run. *b*, the γ-ray spectrum shown on television by Fleischmann *et al.* The main characteristics of the two spectra are similar; one can also tell that the two detectors have comparable spectral resolution. In *b*, note the curious structure at about 2.5 MeV and that beyond the ^{208}Tl peak (2.61 MeV), which appear to be artefacts. (The spectrum can also be obtained from KSL-TV in Utah (M. Hawkins, personal communication).)

In the interval 1.46–2.61 MeV, the energy resolution of a NaI(Tl) spectrometer, which determines the γ-ray linewidth, can be well described by the formula[8,9]

$$R(E) = \frac{\Delta E}{E} \approx R(E_n) \sqrt{E_n/E} \tag{3}$$

Here ΔE is the full width at half maximum (FWHM) of the line, E is the energy of the photon and $R(E_n)$ is the measured "reference" resolution at energy E_n. $R(E_n)$ can be accurately determined using a ^{60}Co source (that is, the ^{60}Co line at 1.33 MeV), or it can be fairly well approximated by the ^{40}K decay line at 1.46 MeV. (From Fig. 1*b*, the ^{40}K decay line allows one to estimate Fleischmann *et al.*'s resolution as ~8%.) Table 1 lists the resolution data for our detectors and for that of Fleischmann *et al.*.

Table 1. Comparison of energy resolutions of the γ-ray spectrometers

(a) Resolution of MIT spectrometers					
Energy (MeV)	1.17 ^{60}Co	1.33 ^{60}Co	1.46 ^{40}K	2.22 n(p, γ)d	2.61 ^{208}Tl
origin					
Natural background			0.055		0.043 (0.041)
^{60}Co	0.056	0.051			
Pu/Be neutron source				0.05 (0.045)	
(b) Resolution of the Fleischmann *et al.* spectrometer[1]					
Energy (MeV)		1.33 ^{60}Co	1.46 ^{40}K	2.22 n(p, γ)d	2.61 ^{208}Tl
Reference					
Hoffman*		0.056	0.065		
TV news†			~0.08		~0.05 (0.049)
Ref. 1 (errata)				0.025 (0.053)	

The resolution is defined as the full width at half maximum (FWHM) divided by the peak energy. Numbers in parentheses are predicted values based on the detector resolution at 1.46 MeV (see text). In *b*, the prediction is based on the resolution value (0.065 at 1.46 MeV) provided by R. Hoffman (personal communication)
*R. Hoffman (personal communication).
† Derived from images of the televised news broadcasts.

We now compare the signal line of Fleischmann *et al.* (Fig. 1*a* of ref. 1 (errata), shown as Fig. 2 here) with our measured spectrum obtained from the experiments on neutron capture by hydrogen (Fig. 3 here, and Fig. 4 of ref. 5). In these experiments, a Pu/Be

以辨认的。例如，^{40}K 经 β^+ 衰变后转变为处于核激发态的 ^{40}Ar，其实这个核然后会放射出文章中讨论的 1.460 MeV 的光子。）γ 谱是经过 84 小时测量后所取的平均值。b，弗莱施曼等人在电视上展示的 γ 射线谱。两张 γ 谱的主要特征是相似的；两个探测器具有相当的 γ 谱分辨率。b 中，注意在大约 2.5 MeV 处和超出 ^{208}Tl 峰（2.61 MeV）处的奇异结构，看上去像是伪造的。（γ 谱也可从犹他州的 KSL 电视台获得（霍金斯，个人交流）。）

在 1.46~2.61 MeV 区间内，决定 γ 射线线宽的碘化钠（铊）γ 谱仪能量分辨率可以由下式描述 [8,9]

$$R(E) = \frac{\Delta E}{E} \approx R(E_n) \sqrt{E_n/E} \tag{3}$$

其中 ΔE 是 γ 谱线的半高宽（FWHM），E 是光子的能量，$R(E_n)$ 为能量 E_n 处测量的"参考"分辨率。$R(E_n)$ 可以使用 ^{60}Co 源（即在 1.33 MeV 处 ^{60}Co 的谱线）进行准确的测定，或者通过 ^{40}K 在 1.46 MeV 处的衰变谱线进行相对准确的估算。（通过图 1b 中 ^{40}K 的衰变谱线可以估算出弗莱施曼等人的 γ 谱仪分辨率约为 8%。）表 1 列出了我们和弗莱施曼等人的探测器的分辨率数据。

表 1．两组 γ 射线谱仪能量分辨率的对比

(a) 麻省理工学院 γ 谱仪的分辨率					
能量(MeV)	1.17 ^{60}Co	1.33 ^{60}Co	1.46 ^{40}K	2.22 n(p,γ)d	2.61 ^{208}Tl
源					
自然本底			0.055		0.043 (0.041)
^{60}Co	0.056	0.051			
钚/铍中子源				0.05 (0.045)	
(b) 弗莱施曼等人的 γ 谱仪的分辨率[1]					
能量(MeV)		1.33 ^{60}Co	1.46 ^{40}K	2.22 n(p,γ)d	2.61 ^{208}Tl
参考					
霍夫曼*		0.056	0.065		
电视新闻†			~0.08		~0.05 (0.049)
参考文献 1（勘误）				0.025 (0.053)	

本分辨率定义为半高宽（FWHM）除以峰值的能量。括号中的数字为基于探测器在 1.46 MeV 处的分辨率预测的数值（见文中）。在 b 中，预测值是基于霍夫曼（个人交流）提供的分辨率数值（1.46 MeV 处为 0.065）得出的。
* 霍夫曼（个人交流）。
† 从电视新闻节目的图像获得。

我们现在将弗莱施曼等人的信号线（参考文献 1（勘误）中的图 1a，即本文所示的图 2）与我们在氢捕获中子的实验中测量的 γ 谱（本文的图 3 和参考文献 5 的图 4）来进行对比。在这些实验中，一个钚 / 铍的中子源被放置在水槽中。$^{239}_{94}$Pu neutron source was placed in a water tank. $^{239}_{94}$Pu emits energetic α-particles, which produce neutrons through (α, n) reactions with Be (refs 4,9). The neutrons are thermalized in water, and we observe the emitted neutron-capture γ-rays with our spectrometers. The measured resolution at 2.22 MeV is ~5% (Table 1a), and is reasonably well predicted by equation (3). As a consequence, this calls into immediate question the identity of Fleischmann *et al.*'s signal line as a γ-ray line. Specifically, Fig. 2 shows the signal line to have a resolution of 2.5%. This is about a factor of two smaller than that predicted by equation (3) on the basis of the known resolution (Table 1b) from either the ^{40}K decay line (1.46 MeV) or from the ^{60}Co source (1.33 MeV) (R. Hoffman, personal communication). But we know from Table 1 that the spectrometer used by Fleischmann *et al.* has a resolution that is at best comparable to our own for the entire region from 1.46 to 2.61 MeV (see also Fig. 1), so it is inconsistent that their linewidth at 2.22 MeV is a factor of two below the predicted value.

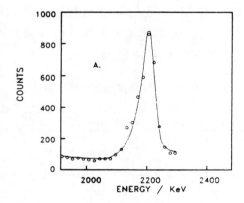

Fig. 2. A reproduction of the purported 2.22-MeV γ-ray signal line of Fleischmann *et al.* (Fig. 1a of errata to ref. 1). The resolution, based on the linewidth, is about 2.5%. With such resolution, one would expect to see a clearly defined Compton edge at 1.99 MeV. No edge is evident. Also, a resolution of 2.5% is inconsistent with their spectral resolution. Furthermore, we argue that the signal line may reside at 2.5 MeV, not at 2.22 MeV as is claimed by Fleischmann *et al.* and depicted here.

There is a second crucial inconsistency with the published signal line (Fig. 2). If we assume a resolution of 2.5% at 2.22 MeV, then there should be a clearly defined Compton edge[4] at 1.99 MeV. For example, in Fig. 3 the Compton edge is evident even for our measured resolution of only 5%. For a resolution of 2.5%, the definition of the Compton edge would be distinctly sharper. The lack of a Compton edge at 1.99 MeV for the signal line therefore negates the conclusion of Fleischmann *et al.* that they have observed the 2.22-MeV γ-rays from neutron capture by hydrogen.

放射出具有一定能量的 α 粒子，α 粒子与铍通过（α，n）反应产生中子（参考文献4、9）。中子在水中达到热平衡，我们通过我们的 γ 谱仪对产生的中子捕获 γ 射线进行观测。测量的分辨率在 2.22 MeV 处约为 5%（表 1a），这一分辨率可以通过方程（3）合理地预测出来。因而，这立即引出了弗莱施曼等人的信号线作为 γ 射线峰的验证问题。具体来说，图 2 表明信号线具有 2.5% 的分辨率。这是在从 ⁴⁰K 的衰变谱峰（1.46 MeV）或者 ⁶⁰Co 源（1.33 MeV）获知的分辨率（表 1b）的基础上根据方程（3）计算出的分辨率的二分之一（霍夫曼，个人交流）。但是我们从表 1 知道，弗莱施曼等人使用的 γ 谱仪分辨率在 1.46 MeV 到 2.61 MeV 的整个范围内至多与我们的仪器相当（见图 1），而这与他们在 2.22 MeV 处的线宽只有推算值的二分之一不相符。

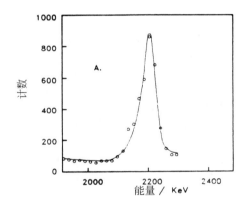

图 2. 弗莱施曼等人所声称的 2.22 MeV 的 γ 射线信号线的重复实验（参考文献 1 的勘误中的图 1a）。基于线宽，分辨率约为 2.5%。在这样的分辨率下，预期可以在 1.99 MeV 处看到清晰可辨的康普顿边。可是显然没有康普顿边。另外，2.5% 的分辨率与他们的 γ 谱分辨率不符。进一步说，我们怀疑那个信号线可能位于 2.5 MeV 处，而不是弗莱施曼等人所声称的以及这里所展示的 2.22 MeV 处。

发表出来的信号线（图 2）还有第二个严重的矛盾。如果我们假设 2.22 MeV 处的分辨率为 2.5%，那么在 1.99 MeV 处应该有一个清晰可辨的康普顿边[4]。比如，即使对于我们的测量分辨率仅有 5% 的结果而言，图 3 中的康普顿边也非常明显。对于 2.5% 的分辨率而言，康普顿边的轮廓应该更锐利。信号线在 1.99 MeV 处康普顿边的缺失否定了弗莱施曼等人观察到的氢捕获中子产生 2.22 MeV 的 γ 射线的结论。

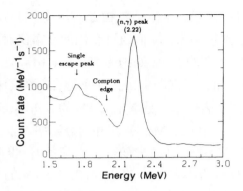

Fig. 3. The γ-ray spectrum measured by a 3 in. × 3 in. NaI(Tl) spectrometer during a neutron-capture-by-hydrogen experiment using a (Pu/Be) neutron source submerged in water. Because of the finite size of the crystal (which is identical to that of Fleischmann *et al.*[1]), we also see an escape peak[2-4] and, of particular importance here, the Compton edge[4]. In this figure, the digitization energy width is 0.024 MeV per channel. The full Pu/Be and background spectra are shown in Fig. 4 of ref. 5.

We also point out that in our (Pu/Be) neutron-capture experiments, a conspicuous e^+–e^- annihilation single-escape peak exists at 1.71 MeV (Fig. 3), as well as a double-escape peak at 1.20 MeV. (The full spectrum from the Pu/Be experiment, as well as the background spectrum, can be found in ref. 5.) Such features unambiguously identify the primary γ-rays as having an energy of 2.22 MeV, and are a necessary consequence of the physical processes of detection of γ-rays in a finite-sized NaI scintillator.

Based independently on both their γ-ray and neutron measurements, Fleischmann *et al.* claim to have observed a neutron production rate of ∼ 4×10^4 neutrons s^{-1} (ref. 1). This claim is clearly inconsistent with their γ-ray signal line, for the following quantitative reasons. The Pu/Be neutron source used in our experiment is absolutely calibrated to within 10% of 1.5×10^6 neutrons s^{-1} (ref. 10 and MIT Reactor Radiation Protection Office). In obtaining the data in Fig. 3, we used an experimental setup similar to that of Fleischmann *et al.* (ref. 1; televised broadcasts; and M. Hawkins and R. Hoffman, personal communications). Our Pu/Be source was submerged 6 in. into a large water tank. The rate at the 2.22-MeV peak, after subtracting the background continuum, is about 1.4×10^3 MeV^{-1} s^{-1} (see Fig. 3). Scaling this rate to a neutron source of 4×10^4 neutrons s^{-1} (the level given by Fleischmann *et al.*), and integrating over the linewidth, gives a total 2.22-MeV γ-ray rate of about 4.5 counts per second. This value is a factor of 50 times higher than the rate that would be calculated on the basis of the results in Fig. 1*a* (that is, 0.081 counts per second). (Fleischmann *et al.* state that their neutron count rate is measured with a BF$_3$ neutron counter over a 0.4 mm × 10 cm Pd cell, and that the γ-ray measurement is over a 0.8 mm × 10 cm Pd cell[1]. If the total reaction rate is proportional to the volume of Pd rod, as they state, the inconsistency in the reported neutron rate is by a factor of 200 rather than 50.) While differences in rates of a factor of two might possibly be explained by geometrical considerations, a factor of 50 is inexplicable.

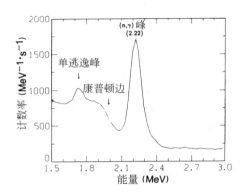

图 3. 在使用浸入水中的（钚 / 铍）中子源进行的氢捕获中子的实验中，通过一个 3 in × 3 in 碘化钠（铊）γ 谱仪测得的 γ 射线谱。因为晶体的有限尺寸（与弗莱施曼等人[1] 使用的完全相同），我们也看到了逃逸峰[2-4]，尤其重要的是，我们看到了康普顿边[4]。本图中，数字化能量的宽度为每通道 0.024 MeV。钚 / 铍以及本底的全谱示于参考文献 5 中的图 4。

我们也要指出，在我们的（钚 / 铍）中子捕获实验中，一个明显的正负电子湮灭的单逃逸峰出现在 1.71 MeV 处（图 3），在 1.20 MeV 处也存在一个双逃逸峰。（钚 / 铍实验中的全谱以及本底光谱都可以在参考文献 5 中找到。）这些特征毫无疑问地确认了初始的 γ 射线具有 2.22 MeV 的能量，这也是用一个有限尺寸的碘化钠闪烁体探测 γ 射线的物理过程的必然结果。

分别基于他们的 γ 射线和中子测量的结果，弗莱施曼等人声称观察到了约为每秒 4×10^4 个中子的中子产生速率（参考文献 1）。基于下述的几个定量分析，这一结论与他们的 γ 射线信号线明显不符。我们实验中使用的钚 / 铍中子源经过了校准，中子产率为每秒 1.5×10^6 个中子，该值的校准精度为 10%（参考文献 10 和麻省理工学院反应堆辐射防护办公室）。在获得图 3 的数据的过程中，我们使用的实验装置与弗莱施曼等人所使用的装置类似（参考文献 1；电视广播；与霍金斯和霍夫曼的个人交流）。我们的钚 / 铍中子源被浸入水槽中的水下 6 in 处。对应于 2.22 MeV 的峰的中子产生速率在扣除连续的本底之后大约为每 MeV 每秒 1.4×10^3 个中子（见图 3）。将这个速率放大到每秒 4×10^4 个中子（弗莱施曼等人所给出的水平），对整个线宽进行积分，得出整个 2.22 MeV 的 γ 射线的产生速率为每秒 4.5 个中子。这一数值是根据图 1a 中的结果计算出来的速率（即每秒 0.081 个中子）的 50 倍。（弗莱施曼等人指出，他们的中子计数速率是用一个三氟化硼中子计数器在一个 0.4 mm × 10 cm 的钯电解池上测得的，而 γ 射线的测量是在一个 0.8 mm × 10 cm 的钯电解池上进行的[1]。如果整个反应的速率如他们所说的正比于钯棒的体积，那么报道的中子产生速率的差别将达到 200 倍而不是 50 倍。）反应速率存在两倍的差异也许可以从几何尺寸方面给予解释，但相差 50 倍的原因就无法解释了。

A further point concerning the identification of the signal line is the precise value of the energy at which the peak occurred. From Fig. 2, the background in the neighbourhood of the peak is seen to be ~ 80 counts per channel, a level that corresponds to ~ 400 counts per channel for a 48-hour accumulation time (the data in Fig. 2 were accumulated for a period of 10 hours[1]). On the other hand, in the Utah measurements of terrestrial γ-ray background, the level in the vicinity of the 2.22-MeV feature was found to be ~ 4,000 counts per channel (R. Hoffman, personal communication). The only relevant part of the entire γ-ray spectrum (between 1.46 and 2.61 MeV) in which the background was as low as 400 counts was at an energy in the vicinity of 2.5 MeV (R. Hoffman, personal communication). Thus, we argue that the peak in the spectrum shown in Fig. 2 may be at 2.5 MeV, not at 2.22 MeV.

The importance of properly identifying the energy of the feature claimed by Fleischmann *et al.* can hardly be overemphasized. Thus, it is extremely unfortunate that they chose to display only the energy range 1.9-2.3 MeV in their published Fig. 1*a*, thereby not providing the supporting evidence of the ^{40}K (1.46-MeV) and ^{208}Tl (2.61-MeV) features which must be present in their spectra in order for their identification to be correct.

Therefore, although Fleischmann *et al.* may have observed a change in their γ-ray spectra that bears some relation to detector location, we conclude that it is unrelated to the 2.22-MeV neutron-capture γ-rays, and that it is also unrelated to the background $^{214}_{83}Bi$ line (2.20 MeV; Fig. 1*a*), as has been suggested elsewhere[11]. We can offer no plausible explanation for the feature other than it is possibly an instrumental artefact, with no relation to a γ-ray interaction.

(**339**, 183-185; 1989)

R. D. Petrasso, X. Chen, K. W. Wenzel, R. R. Parker, C. K. Li and C. Fiore
Plasma Fusion Center, Massachusetts Institute of Technology, Cambridge, Massachusetts 02139, USA

References:
1. Fleischmann, M., Pons, S. & Hawkins, M. *J. electroanalyt. Chem.* **261**, 301-308 (1989); and errata.
2. Hamermesh, B. & Culp, R. J. *Phys. Rev.* **92**, 211 (1953).
3. Greenwood, R. C. & Black, W. W. *Phys. Lett.* **6**, 702 (1966).
4. Knoll, G. F. *Radiation Detection and Measurements* (Wiley, New York, 1979).
5. Petrasso, R. D. *et al.* MIT Plasma Fusion Center Report PFC/JA-89-24 Rev. (1989).
6. Eisenbud, M. *Envir. Radioactivity* (Academic, New York, 1973).
7. Adams, J. A. S. & Lowder, W. M. *The Natural Radiation Environment* (Univ. of Chicago Press, 1964).
8. *Harshaw Radiation Detectors Scintillation Counting Principles*, Solon, Ohio, 44139 (1984).
9. Crouthamel, C. E. *Applied Gamma-Ray Spectrometry* 2nd edn (eds Adam, F. & Dams, R.) (Pergamon, Oxford, 1970).
10. Reilly, W. F. thesis, Massachusetts Institute of Technology (1959).
11. Koonin, S. E., Bailey, D. C. *Am. phys. Soc. Meet.* Special Session on Cold Fusion, Baltimore, Maryland, 1-2 May (1989).
12. Lederer, M. C., Hollander, J. M. & Perlman, I. *Table of Isotopes* 6th edn (Wiley, New York, 1967).

Acknowledgements. We thank V. Kurz, J. S. Machuzak, F. F. McWilliams and Dr S. C. Luckhardt. For the use of a spectrometer system, we thank Professor G. W. Clark. For discussions, we thank M. Hawkins and R. Hoffman of the University of Utah. For suggestions and criticisms, we are grateful to Dr G. R. Ricker Jr and Professor D. J. Sigmar. We are indebted to J. K. Anderson for assembling this document. For locating important references, we thank K. A. Powers. Supported in part by the US Department of Energy.

关于信号线的确认更进一步的问题是谱峰出现位置的能量的准确值。从图 2 中，临近谱峰的本底看上去约为 80 计数 / 通道，这个量级与累计 48 小时约 400 计数 / 通道的值是相对应的（图 2 中的数据累计了 10 小时 [1]）。另一方面，在犹他州测量的地面 γ 射线本底中，在 2.22 MeV 特征峰附近的本底数量级约为 4,000 计数 / 通道（霍夫曼，个人交流）。而整个 γ 射线谱（1.46~2.61 MeV）的本底都低至 400 计数，其中唯一与之相当的部分就是在能量 2.5 MeV 附近（霍夫曼，个人交流）。因此，我们质疑图 2 中 γ 谱的谱峰可能位于 2.5 MeV 处而不是在 2.22 MeV 处。

对弗莱施曼等人声称的特征峰进行正确分辨的重要性再怎么强调都不为过。然而，非常遗憾的是在他们发表的图 1a 中仅展示了 1.9 ~2.3 MeV 的能量范围，却没有提供 ^{40}K（1.46 MeV）和 ^{208}Tl（2.61 MeV）的特征峰作为支持的证据，而为了证实他们的观点是正确的，这些峰本应出现在他们的谱图中。

因此，尽管弗莱施曼等人可能在他们的 γ 射线光谱中观察到了某种由探测器位置改变所造成的变化，但正如之前人们所提出的那样 [11]，我们认为那与 2.22 MeV 的中子捕获 γ 射线并无关联，也与本底的 $^{214}_{83}$Bi 谱线（2.20 MeV；图 1a）无关。除了认为可能是仪器出错，而与 γ 射线的作用无关以外，我们不能够为这个现象提供其他可信的解释。

（李琦 翻译；李兴中 审稿）

DNA Fingerprinting on Trial

E. S. Lander

Editor's Note

DNA fingerprinting, the forensic technique used to analyse DNA from crime scenes, was developed by British geneticist Alec Jeffreys in the mid 1980s. It quickly caught on, and by 1989 had already been used in more than 80 criminal trials in the United States. But here US geneticist Eric Lander cautions against its hasty introduction to the courts. Lander, who had acted as an advisor to the defence on recent murder trials, is concerned that appropriate controls are sometimes lacking and that interpretation of results is not standardized. Here he calls for the scientific community to agree on clear guidelines for procedures and standards in order that the true power of DNA fingerprinting for forensic identification be realized.

In the rush to use the tremendous power of DNA fingerprinting as a forensic tool, the need for standards has been overlooked.

WITH the exception of identical twins, no human beings have identical DNA sequences. Of the 3,000 million nucleotides which we inherit from each parent, about 1 in 1,000 is a site of variation, or polymorphism, in the population. These DNA polymorphisms are most conveniently detected when they alter the length of the DNA fragments produced by the action of restriction enzymes, giving rise to restriction fragment length polymorphisms (RFLPs). In standard practice, the length of the fragments is measured by the rate at which they move in an electrophoresis gel.

More than 3,000 RFLPs have been identified to date, including some 100 highly polymorphic loci at which dozens of variant alleles are present in the population. By using RFLPs to trace the inheritance of chromosomal regions in families afflicted with genetic disorders, human geneticists have been able to pinpoint the location of the genes causing diseases such as Huntington's disease, cystic fibrosis and others—in the process spawning the field of DNA diagnostics.

Forensic science has more recently latched onto RFLPs, but with a different purpose: to identify the individual origin of blood or semen samples found in criminal investigations based on their distinctive RFLP patterns. In the United States, forensic RFLP testing has been pioneered by two private laboratories—Lifecodes Corporation of Valhalla, New York and Cellmark Diagnostics of Germantown, Maryland—and is also used by the Federal Bureau of Investigation, which began testing earlier this year.

DNA指纹图谱技术在庭审中的应用

兰德

编者按

DNA 指纹图谱是一种用于分析来自犯罪现场 DNA 的法医学技术，于 20 世纪 80 年代中期由英国遗传学家亚历克·杰弗里斯建立。这种技术迅速流行，截至 1989 年在美国已经有超过 80 起刑事案件的审理应用了此项技术。但是在本文中，美国遗传学家埃里克·兰德警告说这项技术引入庭审有些草率。作为近期几起谋杀案庭审的辩方顾问，兰德注意到该技术有时缺少合适的对照并且对检测结果的解释也没有标准化。他呼吁科学界就操作方法和标准建立清晰的指导原则，以发挥 DNA 指纹图谱技术在法医学鉴定中的真正威力。

人们忙于将 DNA 指纹图谱技术作为强有力的法医学工具进行使用，却忽视了建立相关标准的需求。

除了同卵双胞胎以外，没有人和其他人拥有一模一样的 DNA 序列。就整个人群而言，在我们从父母那里遗传而来的三十亿核苷酸中，大约每一千个中就会有一个变异位点，也称为多态性。当 DNA 被限制性酶切割时，由于某些位点发生变异使酶切产生的片段长度发生变化，从而形成限制性酶切片段长度多态性（RFLPs），这种 DNA 的多态性最容易被检测出来。标准的检测手段是通过电泳凝胶中 DNA 片段的迁移速率来区分它们的长度。

迄今为止，人们已经鉴定出 3000 多种 RFLP，其中包括 100 个高度多态性的位点。这些位点分布在人群中已经发现的几十个变异的等位基因上。随着 DNA 诊断学的蓬勃发展，通过 RFLP 对患有遗传疾病的家族进行染色体区域的遗传追踪，人类遗传学家已经可以精确定位导致亨廷顿病以及囊性纤维化等遗传疾病的基因。

出于另外一个目的，即基于每个人所独有的 RFLP 图谱，可以鉴定在刑事侦查中发现的血液或精液样本来自何人，法医学如今也与 RFLP 更加紧密联系起来。在美国，法医学 RFLP 检测由两家私人实验室（位于纽约瓦尔哈拉的生命密码公司和位于马里兰州日耳曼敦的细胞标记诊断公司）率先开创。联邦调查局也于今年早些时候开始了此项检验。

Since the first use of DNA "fingerprinting" in a trial in Florida in 1988, DNA "fingerprint" evidence has already been used in more than 80 criminal trials in the United States. Applying the legal standard for the admissibility of novel scientific evidence defined in *United States v. Frye* in 1923, trial judges have raced to admit DNA fingerprinting as evidence on the grounds that the methods are "generally accepted in the scientific community", citing the application of RFLPs in DNA diagnostics and accepting claims that false positives are virtually impossible.

With due respect, the courts have been too hasty. Although DNA fingerprinting clearly offers tremendous potential as a forensic tool, the rush to court has obscured two critical points: first, DNA fingerprinting is far more technically demanding than DNA diagnostics; and second, the scientific community has not yet agreed on standards that ensure the reliability of the evidence.

DNA diagnostics requires simply identifying whether each parent has passed to a child the RFLP pattern inherited from his or her mother or father. Because the four discrete patterns are known in advance, these investigations have built-in consistency checks which guard against many errors and artefacts.

DNA fingerprinting, by contrast, is more like analytical biochemistry: one must determine whether two completely unknown samples are identical. Because hypervariable RFLP loci often involve 50–100 alleles yielding restriction fragments of very similar lengths, reliably recognizing a match is technically demanding. At one commonly used locus, for example, most alleles lie within a mere 2 percent of the length of the gel.

Few molecular geneticists, in such circumstances, would declare a match without performing a mixing experiment, in which a 50:50 mixture of the two samples is shown to yield the same pattern as each sample separately. In the rare event that a mixing experiment could not be carried out, most molecular geneticists would at least insist on using internal controls—probes which detect non-polymorphic DNA fragments within each lane—to verify that the lanes have run at equal speeds and to provide standards against which fragment sizes can be measured precisely.

Yet the DNA fingerprinting results now being introduced into the US criminal courts are often based on much flimsier evidence. Not only are mixing experiments and internal controls often omitted, but some laboratories use no objective standards whatsoever for declaring a match.

Unlike DNA diagnostics, DNA fingerprinting also depends on inferences about the frequency with which matching RFLP patterns will be found by chance, which in turn rest on simplifying assumptions about population genetics whose accuracy has not yet been rigorously tested for highly polymorphic RFLP loci. For example, it is assumed without convincing proof that Caucasians, Blacks and Hispanics can each be regarded as homogeneously mixed populations, without significant subgroups, even when considering

自从 1988 年佛罗里达州第一次将 DNA "指纹图谱"用于案件审理以来，在美国已经有超过 80 起刑事案件的审理中用到 DNA "指纹图谱"证据。根据 1923 年弗赖伊案中定义的允许采纳新科学证据的法律标准，法官们争先恐后地采用 DNA 指纹图谱作为证据。因为该技术是"在科学界被普遍接受的"，并以 RFLP 在 DNA 诊断学上的应用为引证，接受了假阳性几乎是不可能的这一观点。

冒昧地说，法院的这个做法太草率了。虽然 DNA 指纹图谱技术作为法医学工具有着巨大的潜力，但是法院的仓促决定忽视了非常关键的两点：第一，DNA 指纹图谱的技术要求比 DNA 诊断要高得多；第二，科学界尚未就如何确保该证据的可靠性达成统一的标准。

DNA 诊断只需要简单的鉴定父母双亲是否将他们从自己父母那里继承的 RFLP 图谱遗传给他们的子女。由于四个独立的样本图谱已经预先得知，这些检查可以通过一致性检验来防止许多可能的错误和假象。

相反地，DNA 指纹图谱技术更像是分析生物化学。它必须要确定两个完全未知的样品是否一模一样。由于高度变异的 RFLP 位点通常与 50~100 个等位基因相关，这些等位基因产生的限制性酶切片段长度非常相似，准确地识别一对匹配样品对技术的要求很高。举例来说，针对一个经常用到的位点，大部分等位基因都分布在仅占凝胶总长度 2% 的范围内。

在这样的情况下几乎不会有分子遗传学家不做混合实验就宣布样品是匹配的。混合实验是指将两种样品按 50 : 50 的比例混合，查看混合样品是否能获得与两种样品分别单独电泳相同的图谱。在很罕见的情况下，混合实验不能进行，这时大部分分子遗传学家至少会坚持用内参——即在每条泳道中用来检测非多态性 DNA 片段的探针——来确定每条泳道中样品的迁移速率一致，并提供精确测量片段大小的标准。

然而，目前美国刑事法庭所采纳的 DNA 指纹图谱结果都基于非常薄弱的实验证据。不仅这些证据常常省略了混合实验和内参，甚至有些实验室没有定义判断匹配与否的客观标准。

与 DNA 诊断不同，DNA 指纹图谱技术还依赖于对 RFLP 图谱随机匹配发生频率的推测。相反地，这一推测则基于简化的群体遗传学假定，而这些假设在高多态性的 RFLP 位点的精确性并未得到严格检验。例如，在没有令人信服的证据的情况下，即使考虑那些从群体遗传学的角度看来形成相对较晚的大部分等位基因位点，

loci at which most alleles are relatively young from the perspectives of population genetics.

Yet despite such fundamental uncertainties, forensic labaratories blithely cite breathtaking frequencies: a recent report based on the study of only four RFLPs announced that the chance of an alleged match occurring at random was 1 in 738,000,000,000,000.

It is my belief that we, the scientific community, have failed to set rigorous standards to which courts, attorneys and forensic-testing laboratories can look for guidance—with the result that some of the conclusions presented to courts are quite unreliable.

My concern is not merely academic: during the past five months, I have been an advisor for the defence and given six days of testimony in what has turned out to be the longest and most searching pretrial Frye hearing in the United States on the admissibility of DNA evidence—a murder case in the Bronx, one of the boroughs of New York City. I have also had occasion to investigate several other DNA fingerprinting cases in the course of preparing a report at the request of the US Office of Technology Assessment, to be delivered later this summer. (My own field is medical genetics: both projects arose as unintended consequences of accepting an invitation to a conference on DNA forensics at Cold Spring Harbor's Banbury Center in late 1988.)

It is my contention that DNA forensics sorely lacks adequate guidelines for the *interpretation* of results—both in molecular biology and in population genetics. To illustrate this, I will draw examples from cases with which I am personally familiar. I should emphasize that the focus on specific cases is not intended to criticize particular testing laboratories: with scientific consensus lacking, similar disagreements about interpretation would surely arise in many other cases involving other laboratories.

The Castro Case

On 5 February 1987, Vilma Ponce and her 2-year-old daughter were stabbed to death in their Bronx apartment. Acting on a tip, police interrogated a neighbourhood handyman, Jose Castro. Detectives noticed a small bloodstain on Castro's watch, which was sent for analysis to Lifecodes. Company scientists extracted about 0.5 μg of DNA from the bloodstain, which they compared with DNA from the two victims.

The DNA was digested with the restriction enzyme *Pst*1, size-fractionated on an agarose gel, and transferred onto a Southern blot. The blot was then hybridized with probes for three RFLP loci; DXYS14, D2S44 and D17S79, as well as a probe for a Y-chromosome locus to identify sex. (Human loci detected by random DNA probes are named according to chromosome and order of discovery.) On 22 July 1987, Lifecodes issued a formal report[1] to the district attorney (Table 1) stating that the DNA patterns on the watch and the mother matched, and reporting the frequency of the pattern to be about 1 in 100,000,000 in the Hispanic population. The report indicated no difficulties or ambiguities. Yet there are several fundamental difficulties, as follows:

高加索人、黑人和西班牙裔仍分别被看作是没有显著亚群体特征的同种混合的种群。

然而很多法医学实验室无视这些基本的不确定因素，满怀喜悦地引用着激动人心的数据：最近一项仅仅基于四种 RFLP 的研究宣称，那些被宣布匹配的样本是随机匹配的可能性仅为七百三十八万亿分之一。

我相信科学界还没有建立起可供法庭、律师和法医鉴定实验室寻求指导的严格标准，因此一些呈送给法庭的结论是非常不可信的。

我的担心并不仅仅是学术上的：在过去的五个月里，我在弗赖伊预审听证会上作为辩方顾问用六天时间向法庭提供了证词，这是美国历史上最长也是最深入的关于 DNA 证据可采纳性的预审听证会——关于一起发生在纽约市布朗克斯区的谋杀案。应美国技术评估办公室之邀，我也有机会参与了其他几个 DNA 指纹图谱相关案件的调查，调查报告预计于今年夏天交付。（我个人的研究领域是医学遗传学：上述两个项目都是我接受 1988 年底在冷泉港的班伯里中心举行的 DNA 法医学会议邀请的意外结果。）

我的观点是，从分子生物学和群体遗传学的角度来讲，DNA 法医学都极度缺乏适宜的准则来对测试结果进行解释。为了阐述这一观点，我将用几个我熟悉的案件来举例说明。我需要强调的是，聚焦于特定的案件并不是要批评某些参与测试的实验室：因为缺少科学性的共识，其他实验室对其他案件的解释也会引发相似的分歧。

卡斯特罗案

1987 年 2 月 5 日，比尔马·庞塞与其两岁的女儿被刺死在她们位于布朗克斯的公寓里。根据线报，警察审问了隔壁的勤杂工——乔斯·卡斯特罗。侦探们注意到卡斯特罗的手表上有滴很小的血迹，就将其送往生命密码公司进行分析。公司的科学家从血迹中提取出了 0.5 微克的 DNA，并用这些 DNA 与两名受害者的 DNA 进行了比较。

科学家用限制性酶 *Pst*1 对 DNA 进行酶切，用琼脂糖凝胶进行 DNA 片段分离，然后转膜进行 DNA 印迹。之后将膜上印迹的 DNA 与三个 RFLP 位点的探针进行杂交。这三个位点分别是：DXYS14、D2S44 和 D17S79，以及用于检测性别的 Y 染色体位点的探针。（被随机 DNA 探针检测到的人类 RFLP 位点是根据其所在的染色体以及发现顺序命名的。）1987 年 7 月 22 日，生命密码公司向地方检察官出具了一份正式报告（表 1），指出手表上发现的 DNA 与受害母亲的 DNA 图谱匹配，并称该种图谱在西班牙裔中出现的频率约为一亿分之一。该报告没有指出任何困难或者不清楚的地方。然而，这份报告的确存在着以下几个基本的难点：

Table 1. Reported fragment sizes (in kilobases) at three RFLPs in *New York v. Castro,* as given in Lifecodes' formal report to the district attorney

	D2S44	D17S79		DXYS14		
Blood from watch	10.25	3.87	3.50	4.83	3.00	1.94
Deceased mother	10.25	3.87	3.50	4.83	3.00	1.94
Deceased daughter	ND	3.87	3.50	4.83	—	1.94

DXYS14: Identifying bands. Contrary to the forensic report (Table 1), the only autoradiogram involving DXYS14 shows five bands in the watch lane and only three bands in the mother's (Fig. 1). In his testimony, Michael Baird, Lifecodes' director of paternity and forensics, agreed that the watch lane showed two additional non-matching bands, but he asserted that these bands could be discounted as being contaminants "of a non-human origin that we have not been able to identify".

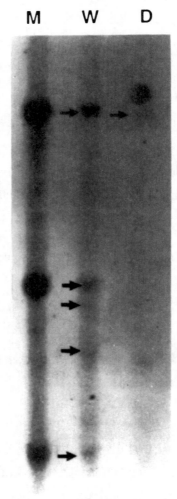

Fig. 1. Hybridization of probe 29C1 for the locus DXYS14 to *Pst*1-digested DNA from deceased mother (M), blood speck from defendant's watch (W) and deceased daughter (D), performed by Lifecodes in *New*

表1. 纽约卡斯特罗案中报告的三个RFLP的片段大小(以千碱基对计)。数据来自生命密码公司向地方检察官提交的正式报告。

	D2S44	D17S79		DXYS14		
手表上的血迹	10.25	3.87	3.50	4.83	3.00	1.94
已故的母亲	10.25	3.87	3.50	4.83	3.00	1.94
已故的女儿	未检出	3.87	3.50	4.83	-	1.94

DXYS14: 条带的鉴定。 与法医报告（表 1）相矛盾的是，和 DXYS14 有关的唯一一张放射性自显影照片显示在手表上的血迹样品的泳道里有五条条带，而母亲样品的泳道中却只有三条（图 1）。在生命密码公司亲子关系与法医学部门负责人迈克尔·贝尔德的证词中，他承认手表上的血迹样品的泳道中多出了两条没有匹配的条带，但他坚称这些多出的条带是"一种我们无法鉴定的非人类来源的污染物"因而不予考虑。

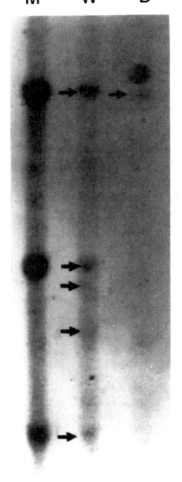

图 1. 纽约卡斯特罗案中已故的母亲（M），被告手表上的血迹（W）和已故的女儿（D）的 DNA 在 *Pst*1 消化后所得片段与检测 DXYS14 位点的探针 29C1 杂交的结果。实验由生命密码公司完成。尽管放射性

York v. Castro. Although the autoradiogram shows three bands in lane M, five bands in lane W and one band in lane D, Lifecodes recorded three bands in identical positions in all three lanes. The autoradiogram is an overnight exposure; no further exposures or hybridizations involving this probe were performed.

In my opinion, it is impossible to know whether the bands are non-human without demonstrating that they are absent when the experiment is repeated with an uncontaminated probe. How then did Lifecodes reach its judgment? Baird stated that, in his experience, DXYS14 should exhibit a pattern of fragments whose intensities decrease in proportion to their length: the extra bands could be ignored because their intensities were "not in the proportion I would expect to see".

In fact, the published scientific literature shows that DXYS14 actually yields patterns (ranging from one to more than six polymorphic fragments) whose intensities obey no ironclad rule. Ironically, the prosecution itself had put into evidence the very article which proved the point: the original paper[2] defining DXYS14, by Howard Cooke of the Medical Research Council in Edinburgh, containing photographs of *Pst*1 Southern blots showing lanes in which hybridization intensity and fragment length are clearly uncorrelated (Figs 6*c* and 7*a* in ref. 2).

David Page of the Whitehead Institute later introduced *Pst*1 blots from his laboratory showing arbitary patterns of intensities at DXYS14. Finally, Cooke himself, who had provided the probe to Lifecodes, testified that the DXYS14 autoradiogram had to be considered to exclude the defendant in the absence of any experiments to explain away the non-matching bands.

Lifecodes' discounting of the two non-matching bands in the watch lane suggests that its identification of bands may have been influenced by making direct comparisons between lanes containing different DNA samples, rather than by considering each lane in its own right. Additional support for this hypothesis is provided by two further examples:

(1) In the dead daughter's pattern at DXYS14, all other expert witnesses for the prosecution and the defence identified only a single band (Fig. 1). However, Lifecodes' laboratory records show that it recorded three bands in this lane—in precisely the same positions as those recorded for the mother and the watch. (For reasons I do not know, the forensic report listed only two of these bands.)

(2) Although D17S79 is expected to yield at most two bands, the dead daughter's lane exhibited four bands in the appropriate size range (not shown) in the only hybridization with the probe completed before the forensic report was issued. The report listed only two of these four bands—the two in the same position as in the mother and the watch.

The tendency to use lane-to-lane comparison to distinguish between bands and artefacts is perfectly natural; such comparison can be quite helpful in certain experiments. However, in my opinion, it is inappropriate in DNA fingerprinting analysis of unknown samples—as

自显影照片显示 M 泳道有 3 条条带，W 泳道有 5 条条带，D 泳道有 1 条条带，生命密码公司却记录说在三条泳道的同一位置都有三条条带。放射性自显影照片曝光过夜；后续没有用该探针进行其他杂交或曝光实验。

我认为，除非证明这些多余的条带在使用未被污染的探针进行重复实验后消失，否则就无法得知这些条带是否为非人类来源。生命密码公司是如何做出他们的判断的呢？贝尔德声称在他的经验中，DXYS14 应该呈现一种随片段长度减少而信号强度逐渐递减的模式，而那些多余的条带之所以被忽略，是因为它们的强度"没有呈现出我所预计的比例"。

事实上，已发表的科学文献显示，DXYS14 图谱（可以是从 1 条到 6 条以上的多态性片段）的信号强度模式并没有一定之规。讽刺的是，检方自己将证明如下观点的文章列为了证据：在爱丁堡医学研究理事会的霍华德·库克定义 DXYS14 的原始文献中，有用 *Pst*1 酶切后做的 DNA 印迹的图片，上面显示杂交的信号强度与片段的长度明显不具有相关性（见参考文献 2 中的图 6*c* 和 7*a*）。

怀特黑德研究所的戴维·佩奇从库克的实验室引进了 *Pst*1 印迹法，并用此法显示了 DXYS14 的强度模式是无规可循的。最终，向生命密码公司提供探针的库克自己作证说 DXYS14 的放射性自显影照片在缺乏实验来解释不匹配条带的情况下，只能认为被告的嫌疑被排除。

生命密码公司对手表上的血迹样品中两条不匹配的条带不予考虑，暗示了影响条带鉴定的因素可能是对载有不同 DNA 样本的泳道进行直接比较，而不是从每条泳道自身考虑。为了进一步支持这个假说，我们另外再举两个例子：

(1) 在死去的女儿的 DXYS14 图谱中，所有控方和辩方的其他专家都确认只有一条条带（图 1）。然而，生命密码公司的实验室记录显示这条泳道中有三条条带——恰好精准的位于与母亲和手表上的血迹样品中同样的位置上。（出于我所不知道的原因，法医学报告中仅列出了其中的两条条带。）

(2) 尽管 D17S79 被预计为最多出现两条条带，但死去的女儿的泳道中却在大小合适的位置上出现了四条条带（未显示），这一结果出现在法医报告出具以前完成的唯一一次该探针的杂交实验中。报告最终只列出了四条条带中的两条——两条与母亲和手表上的血迹样品在同一位置的条带。

用泳道之间的对比来区分条带与假象是非常自然的事情，这种方法在特定的实验中非常有用。然而我认为，这种方法并不适用于对未知样品的 DNA 指纹图谱进

one runs the risk of discounting precisely those differences that would exonerate an innocent defendant. Forensic laboratories should be required to use objective criteria for identifying the bands in each lane, and to use experiments to rule out proposed artefacts.

When a result is reported to have an error rate of 1 in 100,000,000, it seems essential that the underlying data are not left as a matter of subjective opinion.

D2S44 and D17S79: declaring a match. To obtain objective measurements of a band's position, Lifecodes uses a computer-digitizing apparatus[3-5]. The approach is reported to be highly accurate: when identical fragments are electrophoresed in different lanes, the difference between their positions is reported to show a standard deviation (s.d.) equal to 0.6 percent of molecular weight[3,5]. Based on these experiments, Lifecodes defined a formal matching rule: two fragments are said to match when their positions differ by less than 3 s.d.s. The matching rule was explicitly stated in a recent population study[5] ("two DNA fragments were considered to be of different size if their values differed by more than 3 s.d.s") and in the formal forensic reports[1] in the Castro case ("fragments with measurements that are within [3 s.d.s] of each other … are considered indistinguishable and their average size reported".)

Because the fragments at D2S44 and D17S79 did not appear to match perfectly, the defence examined Lifecodes' computer measurements. In fact, the bands fell outside the declared matching rule; as shown in Table 2, the bands at D2S44 differ by 3.06 s.d.s and the lower bands at D17S79 differ by 3.66 s.d.s. Under the objective matching rule, the bands were non-matches.

Table 2. Measured fragment sizes (in base pairs) at three RFLPs in *New York v. Castro,* as shown in Lifecodes' records from its computer-digitizing apparatus produced in response to subpoena

	DS244	D17S79		DXYS14		
Blood from watch	10,350	3,877	3,541	4,858	2,995	1,957
Deceased mother	10,162	3,869	3,464	4,855	2,999	1,946
Difference (percent of average size)	1.83	0.21	2.20	0.06	0.13	0.56
Difference in number of s.d.s	3.06*	0.34	3.66*	0.10	0.22	0.94

According to Lifecodes' published papers[3,5] and its formal reports to district attorney[1], the difference between two identical bands in different lanes shows an s.d. equal to 0.6 percent of fragment size. Asterisks, bands differing by > 3 s.d.s.

Why then was a match declared? Lifecodes stated that it did not actually use the objective threshold of 3 s.d.s. for declaring a forensic match: its decisions were based on subjective visual comparison. Agreeing that the explicit statements in the forensic report implied that the objective criterion had been used, Baird allowed that the statement "may not be the best explanation" of the company's actual procedures. As far as I can see, there is also no mention of the use of visual matching in the company's scientific papers or forensic reports. Clearly, there has been a significant misunderstanding about the matching rule which Lifecodes has been using.

行分析——它会带来无视某些差异的风险，而那些差异本可以让无辜的被告无罪开释。法医学实验室应该使用客观的标准来鉴定泳道里的每一条条带，并用实验来排除那些预测出的假象。

作为一个重要的前提，当一个结果被报告为有着一亿分之一的错误率时，一些潜在的数据可能不会由于主观原因未被记录下来。

D2S44 和 D17S79：匹配的认定。 为了获得条带的客观测量位置，生命密码公司使用了计算机数字化设备[3-5]。据报告，这项技术是高度精确的：当相同的片段在不同的泳道进行电泳时，它们之间位置差异的标准差（s.d.）相当于分子量的0.6%[3,5]。基于上述实验，生命密码公司定义了正式的匹配规则：当两个片段的位置差异小于3个标准差时，就认为这两个片段是匹配的。该匹配原则在一份最近的种群研究[5]（"当两个DNA片段之间的值差异超过3个标准差时就认为这两个片段大小不同"）以及卡斯特罗案正式的法医报告中[1]（"片段之间测量值差异小于[3个标准差]……被认为无法区分并按它们的平均大小进行报告"）都有明确的陈述。

由于D2S44和D17S79的片段看上去并不完全匹配，辩护方检查了生命密码公司的计算机测量结果。事实上，这些条带不符合他们声明的匹配规则：如表2中所示，D2S44的条带之间差了3.06个标准差，D17S79中较低的条带相差3.66个标准差。按客观的匹配规则来看，这些条带是不匹配的。

表2. 纽约卡斯特罗案中测量的三个RFLP的片段大小（以碱基对计）。数据来自生命密码应法庭传讯所出示的计算机数字化设备记录。

	D2S44	D17S79		DXYS14		
手表上的血迹	10,350	3,877	3,541	4,858	2,995	1,957
已故的母亲	10,162	3,869	3,464	4,855	2,999	1,946
差异（占平均片段大小的百分比）	1.83	0.21	2.20	0.06	0.13	0.56
差异与标准差的倍数比	3.06*	0.34	3.66*	0.10	0.22	0.94

根据生命密码公司发表的文章[3,5]及其向地方检察官提供的正式报告[1]，在不同泳道中的相同条带之间差异的标准差（s.d.）相当于片段大小的0.6%。星号表示条带差异大于3个标准差。

那为什么还要宣称这些条带是匹配的呢？生命密码公司陈述说他们实际上并不是用3个标准差这一客观阈值来确定条带是否在法医学上匹配：他们的结果是基于主观的肉眼比较来决定的。法医学报告中明确的陈述暗示客观标准已被使用，贝尔德同意这一观点，同时他承认那份陈述"可能不是"公司实际操作的"最好解释"。就我看来，不管是在公司的科学文献还是法医学报告中，都没有提到过用肉眼识别匹配。很明显，人们对生命密码公司使用的匹配原则存在着非常明显的误解。

In my opinion, visual matching is inappropriate in DNA fingerprinting, inasmuch as (1) many alleles have very similar sizes; (2) the accuracy of the measurement process is reported to be known; and (3) without an objective definition of a match, there is no meaningful way to determine the probability that a declared match might have arisen by chance (see below).

DYZ1: Use of controls. The DYZ1 locus provides a convenient method of identifying the sex of a sample: the locus is repeated about 2,000 times on the distal long arm of the Y chromosome, giving rise to an intense 3.7-kilobase (kb) *Pst*1 band in males and no such band in females. Based on a hybridization with a probe for DYZ1, the blood on the watch was said to have come from a female.

Indeed, the mother, daughter and watch DNAs showed no male-specific band. But neither did the lane marked control. Who was the control?

(1) Initially, Baird testified that the control DNA came from the female-derived HeLa cell line.

(2) Two weeks later, however, the technician who actually performed the experiments testified that the control DNA came not from HeLa cells but rather, he recalled, from a male scientist.

(3) Baird then explained the absence of a positive signal in the now-male control lane by telling the court that the male scientist has a "short" Y chromosome which "does not react with this repeat sequence", a condition which is "fairly rare, but it does happen". In conventional genetic terminology, the individual was a genetic mutant deleted for the region.

(4) I then testified that the population frequency of such complete deletions is about 1 in 10^3–10^4, with most causing phenotypic abnormalities usually including complete sterility (D. Page, H. Cooke and K. Smith, personal communication). A normal male with such a deletion would be so rare as to be publishable.

(5) Baird then reported that the control DNA came not from the male scientist, but from a female technician. Although no precise record had been kept of which DNA preparation had been used, he said that he had managed to identify the source of the control lane by studying its RFLP pattern—an unforeseen use of DNA fingerprinting.

The confusion had probably resulted from faulty recollections (by Baird and the technician) and faulty inferences (about the male scientist), but it underscored the need for meticulous record-keeping in DNA forensics, which may not originally have been as clear.

Leaving aside the identity of the control DNA, there is a more important question: should

鉴于以下原因，我认为肉眼识别匹配对 DNA 指纹图谱技术是不适合的：（1）许多等位基因的大小非常相似；（2）测量过程的精确性是已知的；（3）没有对匹配的客观定义，就没有有意义的方法来计算所谓的匹配偶然发生的概率（见下文）。

DYZ1：对照组的使用。DYZ1 位点提供了鉴定样本性别的简便方法：在男性中，这个位点在 Y 染色体长臂远端重复了约 2,000 次，在 *Pst*1 酶切后产生了一条 3.7 千碱基对的强信号条带，女性没有该条带。基于与 DYZ1 探针的杂交结果，手表上的血液被认为是来自女性。

母亲、女儿和手表上的 DNA 都确定没有男性特异性的条带。但是没有一条泳道被标记为对照组。谁是对照组呢？

（1）最初，贝尔德作证说对照组 DNA 来自于女性来源的海拉细胞系。

（2）然而两周后，实际操作这个实验的实验员却作证说，根据他的回忆，对照组 DNA 来源于一位男性科学家，而不是海拉细胞。

（3）贝尔德随后向法庭解释了这个现在是男性的对照组泳道里为什么没有阳性信号。他说这位男性科学家有一个"短的"Y 染色体，因而"不能对该重复序列产生反应"，这个情况"虽然罕见，但是的确发生了"。用传统遗传学的术语来说，该个体是该区域缺失的遗传突变体。

（4）我随即证实，人群中发生这种完全缺失的频率大约是 1/1,000~1/10,000。并且大多数情况下该突变会导致异常表型，通常包括完全不育（与戴维·佩奇，霍华德·库克及史密斯进行的个人交流）。一个正常的男性有这样的缺失是非常罕见的，如果有的话一定会被发表出来。

（5）之后贝尔德又报告说对照组 DNA 并非是来源于那位男性科学家，而是来源于一名女性实验员。尽管没有准确的记录表明使用了哪份 DNA 样品，贝尔德却说他通过研究该样品的 RFLP 图谱设法鉴定了对照组的来源——这真是 DNA 指纹图谱的意外用法。

这些困惑可能是源于错误的回忆（来自贝尔德和实验员）和错误的推断（关于那名男性科学家），但是它们却强调了 DNA 法医学对严谨的实验记录的要求，而这种要求可能并不是一开始就很清楚。

撇开对照组 DNA 的来源不谈，我们还有一个更重要的问题：放射性自显影照片中

a sex test be considered reliable without seeing a positive control on the autoradiogram to prove that the experiment had worked correctly? Baird testified that such a result could be considered "reliable". I would vigorously disagree.

D2S44: Analysis of degraded DNA. Based on seeing only a single band in the watch DNA, the sample was reported to be homozygous for a 10.25-kilobase (kb) band at the D2S44 locus. Although the conclusion may seem reasonable at face value, there is a serious problem: the small quantity of DNA on the watch was clearly degraded, and nearly 90 percent of alleles in the Hispanic population lie above 10.25 kb.

How can one be sure that the sample was not a heterozygote, with a higher band undetected due to degradation? Estimating the extent of degradation by eye, Baird stated that the photographs of the ethidium bromide stain of the gel "gives you some indication that there is enough material present to be able to get a signal" in the 12–15-kb range", but that "I['d] hate to bet the ranch" on it.

Wouldn't a probe detecting a non-polymorphic single-copy band at about 15 kb have provided a definitive positive control? He replied as follows:

"If you are making a decision based only on a single locus, whether or not a pattern you saw was homozygous or whether or not you are missing a band, you'd have to have some way to absolutely be sure that you were seeing everything that was there and the control that you mentioned would be very helpful to do that.

"Now, in addition to the D2S44 locus, we also looked at two additional loci, D17S79 and DXYS14. By looking at the combination of loci, and seeing whether or not there was a pattern that matched or not, allowed us to determine or help[ed] us to determine that the pattern that we saw with the D2S44 locus is [a] homozygote."

Personally, I do not understand how the presence of matches at D17S79 and DXYS14 has any bearing on the determination of a match at D2S44: each test must be evaluated independently, especially as the individual probabilities of a match for each locus are multiplied together at the end (see below).

Probe contamination. To explain various artefacts, Lifecodes invoked four separate instances of probe contamination: human probes were said to be contaminated with bacterial sequences, and bacterial and plasmid probes were said to be contaminated with human sequences. Moreover, Baird testified that the company continued to use probes even after learning that they were contaminated, while apparently keeping no precise record of when such probes had been used.

Although the use of contaminated probes may be permissible in some types of experiment, it is, in my opinion, inappropriate in DNA forensics. Because the samples are

没有出现一个可以证明实验正确运行的阳性对照组。在这种情况下，性别测试还能被认为是可信的吗？贝尔德作证说这样的结果可以被认为是"可信的"。我对此表示强烈反对。

D2S44：对降解的 DNA 的分析。由于在手表上的血迹样品的 DNA 中只看到了单一条带，因此报告称该样品在 D2S44 位点上是一个含有 10.25 千碱基对的纯合子。尽管表面上看这个结论是合理的，但实际上存在一个很严重的问题：手表上的少量 DNA 很明显被降解了，因为在西班牙裔人群中近 90% 的这种等位基因的酶切片段都大于 10.25 千碱基对。

如果在更高处有条带却因为降解而未被检测到，又怎能确定这个样品不是杂合子呢？通过肉眼观察对降解的程度进行估测，贝尔德声称在溴化乙锭染色的胶图中"有迹象表明在 12~15 千碱基对范围内有足够的 DNA 信号"，但是"我并不打包票"。

在 15 千碱基对处被探针检测到的非多态性单拷贝条带不是正好提供了明确的阳性对照吗？对此他是这样回应的：

"如果你仅基于一个单一位点来决定你所见的图谱是否是纯合子，或者你是否遗失了一条条带，你必须采取一些手段来确保你看见了图谱上所有的东西，在这种情况下你所提到的对照组会非常有用。

"现在，除了 D2S44 位点，我们还查看了其他两个位点：D17S79 和 DXYS14。综合观察这些位点，并且查看图谱是否存在匹配，可以让我们判定或者帮助我们判定在 D2S44 位点看见的图谱是纯合子。"

从个人角度来说，我并不理解在 D17S79 和 DXYS14 位点出现的匹配与判定 D2S44 位点上匹配与否之间有任何关系：每一个测试都必须独立地进行评估，尤其在每个位点独立匹配的概率最终要相乘的情况下（见下文）。

探针污染。为了解释各种假象，生命密码公司列举了四个不同的探针污染的例子：据称被细菌序列污染的人类探针，以及据称被人类序列污染的细菌和质粒探针。此外，贝尔德作证说公司在得知这些探针被污染后依然继续使用，同时显然对这些探针何时被使用也没有准确的记录。

尽管在一些类型的实验中允许使用被污染的探针，然而在我看来，这样做在 DNA 法医学中是不合适的。因为样品的来源未知并且经常被污染，（使用污染过的

of unknown origin and often contaminated, false matches can result but may be hard to recognize.

Population genetics. After declaring a forensic match, testing laboratories apply a three-step procedure to calculate the probability that the match might have arisen by chance in the population: (1) for each allele, one counts the frequency with which matching bands occur in a previously-drawn population sample (Lifecodes used a database[5] of US Hispanics in the Castro case); (2) for each locus, one then computes the probability of observing a matching genotype by applying the classical Hardy–Weinberg equations[5,6], under the assumption that population is freely intermixing and thus contains no heterogeneous subgroups; and (3) for the complete RFLP pattern, one then multiplies the three single-locus probabilities, under the assumption that the genotypes at the loci are in linkage equilibrium (are uncorrelated). In fact, none of these steps stood up to scientific scrutiny in the Castro case.

Probability of a match: inconsistent matching rules. Whatever matching rule is used to declare a forensic match, it is axiomatic that the same matching rule must then be used for counting the matches occurring in the population database. In fact, Lifecodes' calculations did not use the same matching rule.

■ To declare a forensic match with a given band, Lifecodes' published matching rule calls for examining a range of ±3 s.d.s around the band. Obviously, the chance of a match arising at random is just the proportion of bands in this range.

■ To calculate the probability of a matching band occurring by chance, however, Lifecodes uses a completely different approach: the reported probability is essentially the frequency of bands occurring in a window of size ±2/3 s.d.s. More exactly, as described in an as-yet-unpublished paper[8], it is a weighted-average of frequencies corresponding to such intervals, with the terms weighted according to a gaussian distribution centred on the estimated allele size.

Because the method involves averaging frequencies corresponding to intervals that are 4.5-fold smaller than those allowed for declaring a forensic match, the probability reported for each allele will typically be too small by a factor of about 4.5. Because each RFLP involves two alleles, the probability may thus be understated by a factor of about $(4.5)^2$, or about 20, for each locus. For a three-locus genotype, the error may thus be about 8,000-fold. (Of course, these calculations assume that one uses the 3 s.d. matching threshold. If the less stringent standard of visual matching is used, the discrepancy may be even greater.) Such a statistical procedure is like catching a match with a 10-foot-wide butterfly net, but then attempting to prove the difficulty of the feat by showing how hard it is to catch matches with a 6-inch-wide butterfly net.

探针）很可能导致假匹配并且很难被识别出来。

群体遗传学。在宣布一个法医学上的匹配以后，测试的实验室会计算该匹配在人群中偶然发生的概率，该程序分三个步骤：（1）对每对检测的等位基因，都要计算匹配条带在已统计的人口样本（在卡斯特罗案中，生命密码公司使用了一个美国西班牙裔数据库 [5]）中的发生频率；（2）对每个位点，都通过经典的哈迪-温伯格方程计算观测到匹配的基因型的概率 [5,6]。该方程基于人群是自由混合并且没有异质性亚群这一假设；（3）根据位点基因型的连锁平衡（无关联）假设，对于完整的 RFLP 图谱，要将三个单基因位点各自的概率相乘。事实上，在卡斯特罗案中，上述的任何一个步骤都禁不起严格的科学检验。

匹配的概率：矛盾的匹配原则。无论使用什么样的匹配规则来宣布一个法医学上的匹配，都必须使用相同的规则对群体数据库中的匹配进行计数，这一点无疑是不言自明的。而实际上，生命密码公司的计算并没有使用同一个匹配规则。

■ 为了报告给定条带的法医学匹配结果，生命密码公司公布了一种匹配规则。该规则需要检测条带附近 3 个标准差的范围。显然，随机匹配发生的概率仅和该范围内条带所占的比例有关。

■ 然而，为了计算条带匹配偶然发生的概率，生命密码公司采用了完全不同的方法：报告中的概率基本上是条带在 ±2/3 个标准差范围内出现的频率。更准确地说，正如一篇尚未发表的论文中所描述的那样 [8]，它是以某一区间内频率的加权平均值来计算的。这个区间通过以等位基因大小预估值为中心的高斯分布来加权获得。

因为该方法用来计算平均频率的区间比用于宣布法医学匹配的区间小了 4.5 倍，所以每个等位基因在报告中的概率也都小了 4.5 倍。因为每个 RFLP 都包含两个等位基因，所以每个位点的概率可能都因此被低估了 4.5 的平方倍，或者说大概 20 倍左右。对于一个包含三个位点的基因型，这个误差可能有大约 8,000 倍。（当然，这些计算都假设他们用了 3 个标准差作为匹配阈值。如果他们用到了肉眼判断匹配这样更不严格的标准，差异可能会更大。）这样的统计法就好比用 10 英尺宽的捕蝶网来抓住一只匹配的蝴蝶，却又试图通过展示用 6 英寸宽的捕蝶网抓住匹配的蝴蝶的困难程度来证明前一项技艺的困难。

How does Lifecodes justify its approach? Once a forensic match is declared between two bands, Lifecodes apparently considers the average fragment size to represent the allele present in the sample. It then estimates the population frequency of this allele, essentially by counting the bands within a range so narrow that it may not even include either of the two actual measurements. This approach substantially underestimates the true chance of a forensic match occurring at random, as it takes no account of the actual threshold used for declaring matches.

Heterogeneity within the Hispanic population. To justify applying the classical formulas of population genetics in the Castro case, the Hispanic population must be in Hardy–Weinberg equilibrium. In fact, Lifecodes' own data show that it is not. The classical test for Hardy–Weinberg equilibrium is based on Wahlund's principle[7,9] that the rate of homozygosity in a population containing distinct subgroups will be higher than would be expected under the assumption of random mating. Applying this test to the Hispanic sample, one finds spectacular deviations from Hardy–Weinberg equilibrium: 17 percent observed homozygotes at D2S44 and 13 percent observed homozygotes at D17S79 compared with only 4 percent expected at each locus, indicating, perhaps not surprisingly, the presence of genetically distinct subgroups within the Hispanic sample. (The expected 4 percent frequency of homozygotes is based on the empirical probability of randomly drawing two alleles from the population sample that are either identical or so close together as to be scored as a single band; the minimum size difference needed to discriminate between one versus two bands in Lifecodes' experiments was stated explicitly in testimony and in a paper[8].)

Once a population is known to be heterogeneous, one also cannot assume linkage equilibrium even for loci on different chromosomes: if an individual possesses an allele common among Puerto Ricans at one locus, it is more likely that he will do so at a second locus as well.

In fact, Lifecodes' population study[5] is scientifically valuable. From an evolutionary point of view, highly polymorphic loci contain many young alleles which may not be uniformly distributed within the Caucasian, Black or Hispanic populations. Studies of RFLP frequencies can reveal the detailed substructure of the human population, shedding light on migrations and trading patterns.

Such complexities, however, can undermine the use of simplified calculations in DNA forensics. Without the assumption of Hardy–Weinberg equilibrium and linkage equilibrium, there is no reliable way to convert allele frequencies into overall genotype frequencies: applying the classical equations can lead to spuriously low probabilities of a match. Possible solutions include empirical studies to identify ethnic subgroups that are in Hardy–Weinberg equilibrium and theoretical studies to derive appropriate correction factors for heterogeneity.

生命密码公司怎样证明这一方法是合理的呢？一旦两条条带被宣布为法医学匹配，生命密码公司很明显就会考虑用这些片段的平均大小来代表样品中出现的等位基因。然后他们就通过对这些条带计数来估计等位基因在人群中出现的频率，而这些条带值的范围是如此之窄以至于它们很可能不包括一对等位基因的任何实际测量值。因为没有考虑到宣布匹配实际用到的阈值，这样的方法本质上低估了法医学匹配随机发生的真实概率。

西班牙裔群体中的异质性。在卡斯特罗案中，为了证明使用群体遗传学经典方程的合理性，西班牙裔群体必须符合哈迪－温伯格平衡。实际上，生命密码公司自己的数据显示事实并非如此。对哈迪－温伯格平衡的经典检验基于瓦隆德原理[7,9]，即一个含有不同的亚群体的种群，在随机交配的假设下，其纯合子的比率要高于预期值。将这一检验应用于西班牙裔样本中，我们发现这一样本与哈迪－温伯格平衡有着惊人的差异：17% 的人在 D2S44 上是纯合子，13% 的人在 D17S79 上是纯合子。而相比较之下，这两个位点都是纯合子的预期值仅有 4%。这一结果提示我们一个也许并不奇怪的结论，那就是在西班牙裔样本中存在着在遗传学上不同的亚群体。（纯合子为 4% 这一预期值是基于经验概率，即从种群样本中随机抽取两个等位基因，它们完全一致或者相似到不能区分的概率；在生命密码公司的实验中，区分一条条带还是两条条带的最小差异在其证词和一篇文章中已经被明确阐述[8]。）

一旦一个群体被确定是异质性的，那么即使是对不同染色体上的位点，也不能假设它们是连锁平衡的：如果一个人在某个位点上拥有一个在波多黎各人中常见的等位基因，那么他很可能在另一个位点上也是如此。

事实上，生命密码公司的种群研究[5]在科学上是很有价值的。从进化的角度来看，那些高度多态性的位点包含许多可能并没有在高加索人、黑人或西班牙裔中均匀分布的新基因。研究 RFLP 的频率可以揭示人类种群微观结构，从而有助于人们阐明人类迁徙和流动的模式。

然而这样的复杂性会损害简化计算在 DNA 法医学上的应用。除了基于哈迪－温伯格平衡和连锁平衡的假设，并没有一个可靠的方法将等位基因频率转换为所有基因型的频率。但是应用这些经典方程又会大大降低匹配的概率。可能的解决方法包括通过经验研究的方法鉴定符合哈迪－温伯格平衡的亚种群，以及用理论研究的方法得到适用于异质群体的关联因子。

The Experts' Statement

After stepping down from the witness stand in late April, I attended the next day a Cold Spring Harbor conference on genome mapping co-organized by Richard Roberts, who had been the prosecution's lead witness when the Castro case had begun in mid-February. As Roberts explained, his testimony had been intended simply to provide the court with a primer on DNA analysis. Concerned about the issues that had come to light, Roberts conceived a novel plan: a joint scientific meeting of the experts who had testified for either side to review the evidence.

At the meeting, held on 11 May, the experts agreed upon a consensus statement declaring that "the DNA data in this case are not scientifically reliable enough to support the assertion that the samples ... do or do not match. If these data were submitted to a peer-reviewed journal in support of a conclusion, they would not be accepted. Further experimentation would be required". In particular, the statement cited the inappropriateness of (1) discounting the extra bands at DXYS14; (2) declaring a match between bands at D2S44 and D17S79 whose measured positions differed by more than Lifecodes' announced threshold of 3 s.d.s; and (3) using a less-strict matching rule when declaring forensic matches than when searching the population database. (Baird was unable to attend the experts' meeting because of a prior engagement.)

At first, the prosecution indicated that it would withdraw the DNA evidence based on the advice of its own scientific experts. Eventually, however, the district attorney decided to press ahead.

The hearing then resumed, with former prosecution witnesses testifying now for the defence. The prosecution's efforts to mount a rebuttal case fizzled:

■ To rebut the non-matching bands at D2S44 and D17S79, the prosecution stated that the use of a new measurement system now reportedly showed that the bands actually lay within 3 s.d.s. The judge ruled this evidence inadmissible, however, calling a last-minute switch of methodology "highly unscientific".

■ To rebut the problem with degradation above 10 kb, Lifecodes probed the Southern blot with the human *Alu* repeat sequence and determined that it showed hybridization up to the 23-kb molecular mass marker. In my opinion, the experiment itself was meaningless (because the ability to detect a sequence repeated 300,000 times in the genome has no bearing on the ability to detect single-copy sequences), but it was unnecessary to explain this to the court. Defence attorney Peter Neufeld, by now a veteran reader of autoradiograms, noticed that someone had accidentally misread the size markers: the *Alu* hybridization actually extended only to the 9.8-kb marker.

■ To rebut the population-genetic issues, the prosecution made eleventh hour phone calls to various scientists, but they refused to testify for the state.

专 家 声 明

四月底出庭作证后的第二天，我参加了在冷泉港举行的关于基因组作图的会议。会议的组织者之一——理查德·罗伯茨曾在二月中旬卡斯特罗案开始时出任检方的首席证人。罗伯茨解释说，他出庭作证只是想向法庭提供一种用于 DNA 分析的引物。考虑到已经暴露出来的问题，罗伯茨提出了一个新的计划：召开一个由控辩双方专家共同参加的联合科学会议来审查证据。

在 5 月 11 日举行的会议上，专家们达成共识并发表声明，宣布"本案中 DNA 数据在科学上的可信度不足以支持这些样品匹配与否的论断。如果这些数据被提交至一份同行评审的刊物用以支持某个结论，它们是不会被接受的，而是会被要求进一步实验"。声明中特别引出了如下的不恰当之处：（1）未将 DXYS14 中多出的条带计算在内；（2）在位置差异大于生命密码公司公布的 3 个标准差阈值的情况下，仍然宣称 D2S44 和 D17S79 的条带是匹配的；（3）用于证明法医学匹配的原则比搜索种群数据库时所用原则的严格度低。（贝尔德由于之前另有安排，未能参加此次专家会议。）

最初检方表明，基于他们自己的科学家给出的建议，他们将收回这些 DNA 证据。然而最终，地方检察官却决定继续使用。

听证会继续召开，之前的检方证人现在开始为辩方作证。检方发起反驳的努力失败了：

■ 为了反驳 D2S44 和 D17S79 条带不匹配的说法，检方声明使用一种新的检测系统后，两条条带落在了 3 个标准差的范围内。然而法官判定该证据不被采纳，原因是最后关头换用方法是"非常不科学的"。

■ 为了反驳 10 千碱基对以上降解的问题，生命密码公司用探针对人类 *Alu* 重复序列进行 DNA 印迹，并判定在高达 23 千碱基对分子量标记处 DNA 仍有杂交。在我看来，这个实验本身就没有意义（因为检测一个在基因组中重复 30 万次的序列的能力和检测一个单拷贝序列的能力根本就没有关系），不过没有必要向法庭解释这些。辩方律师彼得·诺伊费尔德现在已经是个阅读放射自显影照片的老手了，他发现有人偶然地误读了分子量大小标记：*Alu* 杂交事实上只延伸到了 9.8 千碱基对标记处。

■ 为了反驳群体遗传学上的问题，检方最后向多位科学家打电话，但他们都拒绝在这一问题上作证。

In the end, the prosecution's rebuttal case consisted only of the contention that the DYZ1 sex-test hybridization had actually worked correctly—based on the fact that Lifecodes had located another experiment done on the same day which showed a male-specific band in a rape suspect. (This would be an adequate, if unorthodox, control if it could be proved that both hybridizations had been carried out in the same plastic bag.)

The hearing concluded on 26 May, about 15 weeks after it began. Lawyers for both sides are now preparing briefs. Justice Gerald Sheindlin is expected to issue a decision in July. Sometime thereafter, the murder trial itself will commence—with or without the DNA evidence.

Other Illustrative Cases

The general issues of interpretation are unique neither to the Castro case nor to Lifecodes, as the following examples show.

Georgia v. Caldwell. In a death-penalty case currently in progress in Atlanta, James Caldwell stands accused of raping and killing his daughter Sarah. According to the forensic report, Caldwell's blood matches semen samples from the crime with 67,500,000,000:1 odds against the match arising at random. Testifying at the Frye hearing, Lifecodes scientist Kevin McElfresh described the process of declaring a match as a "very simple straight-forward operation", asserting that "there are no objective standards about making a visual match. Either it matches or it doesn't. It's like if you walk into the parking lot and see two blue Fords parked next to each other. That's the situation here."

In fact, the patterns clearly do not match by eye (Fig. 2). McElfresh agreed, but asserted that "There is, however, a consistent non-alignment of the bands throughout the test, telling us there's a match." In other words, McElfresh contended that the differences were due to one lane having run faster than the other, although Lifecodes presented no internal controls to support this explanation.

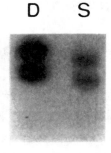

Fig. 2. Hybridization of probe pAC256 for the locus D17S79 to *Pst*1-digested DNA from defendant (D) and semen sample (S), performed by *Lifecodes in Georgia v. Caldwell*.

Although the hearing had been expected to last only a week, prosecutors asked for a month-long delay to prepare their rebuttal. Observers speculated that Lifecodes might use

最终，检方的反驳理由只剩下了 DYZ1 的性别检验杂交事实上是正确的这一个观点。这一观点的根据是生命密码公司在同一天做的另一个实验，在一个强奸嫌疑人的样品中显示了一条男性特异性的条带。（如果能证明两个杂交是在同一个塑料袋中进行的，那么这就是一个不那么正统但是差强人意的对照组。）

在开始了 15 周后，听证会于 5 月 26 日结束。双方律师正在准备辩护状，法官杰拉尔德·沙因德林预计于 7 月作出判决。在这之后，将会开始这件谋杀案的审理——使用或者不使用 DNA 证据。

其 他 案 例

大部分案件的解读与卡斯特罗案以及生命密码公司没有什么不同，如下例所示。

佐治亚州考德威尔案。 正在亚特兰大审理的一桩死刑案中，詹姆斯·考德威尔被控强奸并杀害了他的女儿萨拉。根据法医学报告，考德威尔的血液与犯罪现场提取的精液样品匹配，该匹配随机发生的概率为 675 亿分之一。在弗赖伊听证会的证言中，生命密码公司的科学家凯文·麦克尔弗雷休描述判断匹配的过程是一个"非常简单直接的操作"，并断言"没有关于视觉判断匹配的客观标准。条带要么匹配要么不匹配，这就像你走进一个停车场看见两辆蓝色的福特汽车并排停在一起一样，情况就是这样的。"

事实上，凭肉眼就能看出这两条条带的模式明显不匹配（图 2）。麦克尔弗莱希同意这种说法，但是他断言"然而整个实验过程中，有很一致的条带没有对齐的现象，这告诉我们这是匹配的。"换言之，麦克尔弗莱希主张这些差异是由于一条泳道比另一条泳道跑得快，尽管生命密码公司没有提供任何内参来支持这一解释。

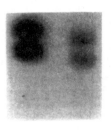

图 2. 佐治亚州考德威尔案中被告（D）与精液样品（S）中的 DNA 经 *Pst*1 消化后，与检测 D17S79 位点的 pAC256 探针杂交的结果。该实验由生命密码公司完成。

尽管听证会预期只进行一个星期，检方还是申请了一个月的延期来准备他们的反证。观察员推测说生命密码公司可能利用这段时间来测试他们的内参。如果是这

the time to test an internal control. If so, it would raise the question of whether Frye hearings are becoming a substitute for having generally accepted laboratory protocols in the first place.

New York v. Neysmith. In a Bronx case in 1987, Hamilton Neysmith was charged with rape based on the victim's identification. Asserting his innocence, Neysmith hired Lifecodes to compare his blood with semen samples from the assailant: the laboratory declared an exclusion. Protesting that the defendant may not have sent his own blood, prosecutors obtained a court order to compel a second blood sample: Lifecodes reported in August 1988 that the two blood samples came from different people. Based on this evidence, Bronx assistant district attorney Karen Yaremko asked the court to revoke Neysmith's bail, planning to charge him with obstruction of justice. The judge declined to revoke bail and the defendant, rather than leaving town, maintained his innocence, and demanded a third blood sample. After Yaremko pressed Lifecodes, she said, the company determined that an error had indeed occurred. Having come close to losing his liberty over inaccurate DNA results, Neysmith was finally exonerated after blood and semen samples were sent to Cellmark Diagnostics which confirmed the original exclusion. (Lifecodes declined last week to comment about the incident, which may have been nothing more than the sort of sample mix-up that can occur in any clinical laboratory. In view of the infallibility with which many jurors regard DNA fingerprinting, however, it may be that even stricter sample-handling procedures should be required.)

In *New York v. McNamara* in November 1988, another Bronx defendant sought to prove his innocence with DNA fingerprinting. Assistant district attorney Renee Myatt opposed the request, telling the court, "the office policy in dealing with a particular agency that does testing with respect to DNA [is] that their testing has been inaccurate, and therefore, unreliable." Notwithstanding this policy, the same District Attorney's office sought to introduce DNA evidence three months later in *New York v. Castro*.

Texas v. Hicks. In this rape–murder, the odds of the declared match occurring at random were reported to be 1 in 96,000,000. Apart from the issue of the matching rule used for searching the database, the population-genetic analysis took no account of the fact that the crime occurred in a small, inbred Texas town founded by a handful of families. The defendant was convicted and sentenced to death.

The case of the abandoned baby. When the president of an insurance agency in Ocean City, Maryland left her car to be towed for repairs to a garage in February 1988, the mechanic claimed that he had discovered a dead infant in the back seat. Although the woman insisted and a detailed medical examination confirmed that she had not been pregnant, Cellmark Diagnostics reported that its DNA analysis showed that she was the mother. (The evidence consisted of one hybridization with a mixture of four RFLP probes in which the woman shared four of eight bands with the child, as well as two hybridizations using probes detecting certain multi-locus repeats.) Local papers reported the sensational news. No murder charges were filed, however, after the state medical examiner determined that the baby had been stillborn on about 4 February.

样，那么就引出了这样一个问题：弗赖伊听证会是否正在取代被普遍接受的实验流程成为首要规则？

纽约内史密斯案。在 1987 年布朗克斯区的一桩案件中，基于受害者的指证，汉密尔顿·内史密斯被控犯有强奸罪。内史密斯坚称自己是清白的，并雇佣生命密码公司将他的血液与袭击者的精液样品进行比较：结果实验室宣布内史密斯的嫌疑被排除。为防止被告没有提供其本人的血液样本，检方得到了法庭的命令，强制获得了第二份血样。生命密码在 1988 年 8 月报告说这两份血样来自不同的人。基于这个证据，布朗克斯区助理地方检察官卡伦·亚列姆科请求法庭撤销内史密斯的保释，并准备起诉他妨碍司法公正。法官拒绝撤销保释，被告在不离开本市的情况下依然无罪，并要求获取第三份血样。亚列姆科在向生命密码公司施压后说，该公司承认的确犯了个错误。内史密斯由于错误的 DNA 检测结果而险些失去自由，在其血液和精液样品被送至细胞标记诊断公司，证实了最初内史密斯的嫌疑被排除的结论后，他最终被判定无罪。（生命密码公司上周拒绝就此次事件做出评论。即使评论，也很可能就是些将样品搞混了之类的每个临床实验室都可能发生的事情。然而，鉴于许多陪审员都认为 DNA 指纹图谱是绝对可靠的，样品处理流程应该需要更严格的规定。）

在 1988 年 11 月的纽约麦克纳马拉案中，另一位布朗克斯区的被告试图通过 DNA 指纹图谱技术来证明自己的清白。地区助理检察官勒妮·米亚特反对该请求，并告诉法庭："负责处理该案的有关部门的确检测了关于 DNA 的一些项目，但是他们的检测结果是不准确的，因而是不可信的。"尽管如此，同一个地方检察院在三个月后的纽约卡斯特罗案中还是引入了 DNA 证据。

得克萨斯州希克斯案。在这个奸杀案中，匹配来源于随机匹配的概率被宣称为 9,600 万分之一。且不论用于搜索数据库的匹配原则，在群体遗传分析中根本没有考虑到这个案件发生在得克萨斯州一个在几户人家基础上建立起来的近亲繁殖的小镇上。被告被宣布有罪并判处死刑。

弃婴案。1988 年 2 月，马里兰州大洋城一家保险代理公司的董事长的车被拖去车库修理。机械师声称他在车的后座发现了一个死婴。尽管这个女人坚称自己没有怀孕，细致的医学检查也证实了这一点，但细胞标记诊断公司仍报告说 DNA 分析显示她就是婴儿的母亲。（证据包括一次用四个 RFLP 混合探针做的杂交，显示在小孩的八条条带中，该女子有四条相同。另外还包括两次与用于检测某多位点重复序列的探针进行的杂交。）当地报纸报道了这则轰动性的新闻。然而在州验尸官确认这名婴儿在 2 月 4 日出生时已经夭折后，未提出谋杀指控。

As it happens, the woman later gave birth to a full-term baby girl on October 24—conceived on about January 29, according to sonograms carried out by her obstetrician. In view of the apparent contradiction, Cellmark last week invited a group of outside scientists to reanalyse remaining DNA samples from the baby.

Setting Standards

Readers should not conclude from this article that DNA fingerprinting is not a powerful tool for forensic identification or that current testing labs are not competent: as in the early stages of any new technology, some difficulties are to be expected. Rather, there is an urgent need for the scientific community to agree on clear guidelines for the procedures and standards needed to ensure reliable DNA fingerprinting. Legislators should also consider whether licensing and proficiency testing should be required in forensics. At present, forensic science is virtually unregulated—with the paradoxical result that clinical laboratories must meet higher standards to be allowed to diagnose strep throat than forensic labs must meet to put a defendant on death row.

An appropriate start would be a US National Academy of Sciences committee, charged with preparing a report on guidelines for DNA fingerprinting. There is ample precedent: when voice-print evidence began to be introduced in the 1970s, the academy convened such a group to examine the technology. An academy study on DNA fingerprinting had been planned for last year, but was postponed indefinitely when the National Institute of Justice would not finance it. As one justice official told me, the study was unwelcome: scientists had done their part by discovering DNA; it was not their job to tell forensic labs how to use it.

(339, 501-505; 1989)

Eric S. Lander is in the Whitehead Institute for Biomedical Research, Nine Cambridge Center, Cambridge, Massachusetts 02142, USA.

References:

1. *Lifecodes' formal reports to District Attorney* (22 July 1987, 12 August 1988 and 6 February 1989).

2. Cooke, H. *Nature* 317, 687-692 (1985).

3. Baird, M. *et al. Am. J. Hum. Genet.* 39, 489-501 (1986).

4. Baird, M. *et al. Adv. forens. Haemogenet.* 2, 396-402 (1988).

5. Balasz, I., Baird, M., Clyne, M. & Meade, E. *Am. J. Hum. Genet.* 44, 182-190 (1989).

6. Cavalli-Sforza, L. L. & Bodmer, W. F. *The Genetics of Human Populations* (Sinauer, Sunderland, Mass., 1989).

7. Hartl, D. L. & Clark, A. G. *Principles of Population Genetics* (Sinauer, Sunderland, Massachusetts, 1989).

8. Morris, J. W., Sanda, A. I. & Glassberg, J. *J. forens. Sci.* (in the press).

9. Wahlund, S. *Hereditas* 11, 65-106 (1928).

Acknowledgements. The Castro defence was a joint effort with my colleagues Howard Cooke, Lorraine Flaherty, Conrad Gilliam, Philip Green and David Page, together with attorneys Peter Neufeld and Barry Scheck. I also thank Richard Roberts for his efforts to help resolve this hearing and Carl Dobkin for participating in the experts' meeting. I am grateful to Susan Lee and Stephen Lincoln for technical assistance.

碰巧的是，这名女子后来在 10 月 24 日生下了一名足月的女婴——根据她的产科医生扫描的超声波图，她在 1 月 29 日就已怀孕。考虑到明显的前后不一致，细胞标记诊断公司上周邀请了一组第三方的科学家对婴儿剩余的 DNA 样品进行重新检测。

建 立 标 准

读者们不应从这篇文章得出结论说 DNA 指纹图谱技术不是法医学鉴定的有力工具，或者现在的测试实验室不能胜任：任何新技术发展的最初阶段，出现困难都是预料之中的。更确切地说，现在迫切需要科学界就所需的操作步骤和实验标准达成明确一致的准则，以确保 DNA 指纹图谱的可靠性。立法者也应考虑在法医中是否需要颁发执照和进行能力测试。目前，法医科学实际上是不规范的——矛盾的是，临床实验室诊断脓毒性咽喉炎所需达到的标准都比法医学实验室把被告扔进死囚牢里所需的标准高。

由美国国家科学委员会负责起草关于 DNA 指纹图谱的指导原则是一个良好的开端。有大量这样的先例：当声纹证据最初在 20 世纪 70 年代被引入时，科学委员会就召集了这样一个小组来检测该技术。一项关于 DNA 指纹图谱技术的学术研究本来计划在去年进行，但是由于美国国家司法研究所不予资助而无限期延后。一位司法官员告诉我，这项研究不受欢迎：科学家做好自己发现 DNA 的本职工作就好了，告诉法医学实验室怎么使用它不属于他们的职责范畴。

（周晓明 翻译；肖景发 审稿）

Stratospheric Clouds and Ozone Depletion in the Arctic during January 1989

D. J. Hofmann *et al.*

Editor's Note

The prediction that human-made chlorofluorocarbons (CFCs) released into the atmosphere could destroy ozone in the stratosphere, exposing the Earth's surface to greater intensities of harmful ultraviolet rays, was verified by observations in the Antarctic in 1985. The atmospheric conditions are particularly conducive to ozone destruction there, owing to the cold and the isolation of air circulation in a vortex. The Arctic does not have such a steady vortex, but it was suspected that ozone depletion might nevertheless happen there—less extensively, but much closer to regions of dense population. Here atmospheric scientist David Hofmann and co-workers report the first confirmation of that, from observations made the previous winter. Arctic ozone depletion was regularly seen in subsequent years.

Stratospheric clouds, believed to be necessary for springtime polar ozone depletion to take place, were detected with balloon-borne sensors at Kiruna, Sweden during January 1989, the coldest January in the north polar stratosphere for at least 25 years. Comparison of the ozone profile in the region of the clouds with those obtained during the past three austral spring seasons at McMurdo Station in Antarctica suggests the beginning of ozone depletion at a height of 22–26 km.

THE role of stratospheric clouds in springtime polar ozone depletion has been recognized in the Antarctic but not, so far, in the Arctic. Here we describe measurements made from two instrumented balloons in January 1989 with which we have been able to establish both the appearance of Arctic stratospheric clouds and the signature of the onset of ozone depletion at or around the altitude of these clouds.

The Arctic polar stratosphere during the winter of 1988–89 was unusually cold with no stratospheric sudden warmings until February[1]. The polar vortex was relatively stable throughout January, giving rise to conditions similar to those in the Antarctic winter stratosphere. The January average North Pole 30-hPa (~22-km altitude) height and temperature were the lowest ever measured. The average temperature at 30 hPa for January was as much as 12 °C below the 20-year mean over large areas of the polar region. Figure 1 shows the 30-hPa heights and temperatures on 23 and 24 January and on 30 and 31 January, periods covering the two balloon flights to be discussed here. Before 23 January, the vortex was centred near the North Pole. Intensification of the Aleutian high-pressure system began a shift of the vortex towards Scandinavia on 24 January which

500

1989年1月北极上空的平流层云与臭氧亏损

霍夫曼等

编者按

1985年南极的观测结果证实了释放到大气中的人为产生的氯氟烃（CFCs）破坏平流层中臭氧，使地球表面暴露于更强的有害紫外线辐射中的预测。由于寒冷和极涡中大气环流的隔离，那里的大气条件容易导致臭氧破坏。北极并不存在如此稳定的极涡，然而有人怀疑臭氧亏损仍可能发生在那里——范围更小，但更接近于人口密集的区域。本文中大气科学家戴维·霍夫曼和他的同事们通过前一个冬季的观测结果首次证实了北极臭氧亏损。在随后几年中，北极臭氧亏损定期出现。

平流层云被认为是春季极地臭氧亏损发生的必要条件，1989年1月我们利用气球运载的探测仪探测了瑞典基律纳地区的平流层云，这个1月是至少25年来北极平流层最冷的1月份。对比南极地区麦克默多站上过去三年的春季臭氧廓线与云层所在区域的臭氧廓线，我们认为臭氧亏损的起点位于海拔22~26 km处。

在南极地区，平流层云在春季臭氧亏损中的作用已经得到公认，但到目前为止，它在北极地区的作用仍尚未明确。本文中我们介绍了1989年1月利用载有仪器的气球进行的观测，以此得以确定北极平流层云的出现及其对应海拔高度处臭氧亏损出现的信号。

1988~1989年冬季，北极平流层异常寒冷，直到2月都没有出现平流层爆发性增温现象[1]。整个1月极涡相对稳定，从而形成了与南极冬季平流层相似的条件。1989年1月北极30 hPa处（海拔约22 km）平均高度和平均温度均是有史以来测到的最低值。北极大部分地区1月30 hPa处平均温度比20年的平均值低了12℃。图1所示为1月23日、24日和1月30日、31日30 hPa处的高度和温度值，本文所讨论的两个气球探测航次正是在这两个时期内进行。1月23日之前，极涡中心位于北极附近。阿留申高压系统的增强使得极涡从1月24日开始向斯堪的纳维亚移动，并

was eventually followed by a major stratospheric warming on about 10 February (K. Labitzke, personal communication). Before the major warming, however, temperatures as low as −92 °C were observed on 1 February at 30 hPa over southern Scandinavia. Temperatures below −85 °C in the 20–25-km region were responsible for the frequent displays of nacreous or "mother of pearl" clouds (stratospheric water-ice crystals) observed at Kiruna, Sweden (68° N, 20° E).

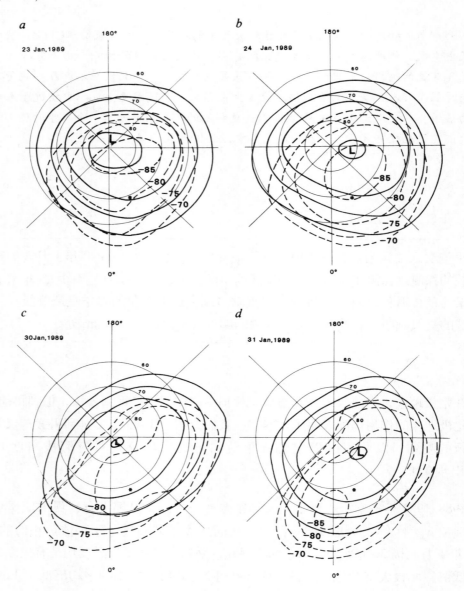

Fig. 1. Temperature (dashed) and height (full) contours at 30 hPa in the Arctic for 00:00 GMT on 23 January (a), 24 (b), 30 (c) and 31 (d), 1989, from the Berlin analysis (K. Labitzke, personal communication). The height contour of the north polar low is 21.5 km and the contour interval is 0.5 km. Temperatures are in °C. The location of Kiruna is marked by a star. Balloon flights at Kiruna occurred from 14:30 to 17:30 GMT, 23 January, and 11:30 to 14:30 GMT, 30 January.

最终导致平流层从 2 月 10 日左右开始明显变暖（拉比茨克，个人交流）。不过在明显变暖之前，2 月 1 日在斯堪的纳维亚南部上空 30 hPa 处测到的温度仍低达 –92℃。海拔 20~25 km 处的温度低于 –85℃，因此，瑞典基律纳（68°N，20°E）观测到贝母云或"珠母"云（平流层水 – 冰晶）频繁出现。

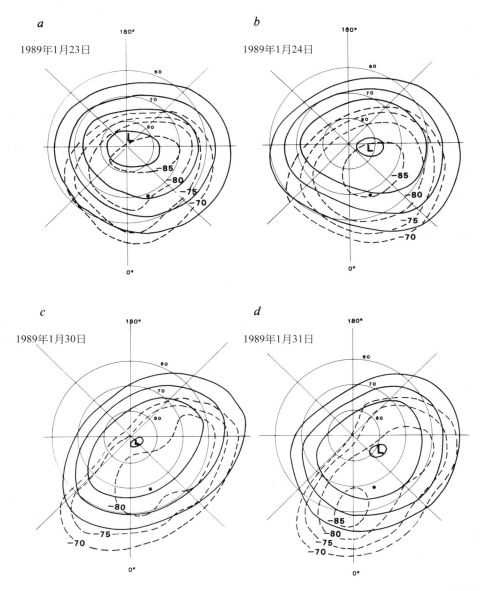

图 1. 由柏林分析得到的 1989 年 1 月 23 日 (a)、24 日 (b)、30 日 (c)、31 日 (d) 00:00 GMT（译者注：格林尼治标准时间）北极地区 30 hPa 处的温度（虚线）和高度（实线）等值线（拉比茨克，个人交流）。北极的最低等高线为 21.5 km，等值线间隔为 0.5 km。温度的单位为℃。基律纳的位置以星号标出。在基律纳，气球飞行的时间分别为 1 月 23 日 14:30~17:30 GMT 和 1 月 30 日 11:30~14:30 GMT。

Stratospheric clouds are thought to be important in converting hydrochloric acid and chlorine nitrate into active chlorine and in stratospheric denitrification through the condensation of HNO_3 vapour, thus removing odd nitrogen from the gas phase which would otherwise prevent the destruction of ozone by the active chlorine[2]. The observation of extensive stratospheric clouds in the Arctic in January 1989 is therefore important in assessing ozone depletion under perhaps the most favourable conditions for this to occur since at least 1957. Before 1957 there was insufficient chlorine in the stratosphere to cause ozone depletion even with extensive clouds.

At a pressure of 30 hPa and for a typical stratospheric water-vapour mixing ratio of 5 p.p.m.v., a temperature of $\sim -87.5\,°C$ is required to condense the vapour and form ice clouds (the "frost point" temperature). However, studies of the nitric acid trihydrate (NAT) solid in the laboratory[3] indicate that this crystalline phase will form at a temperature of $-80\,°C$ (10 parts per 10^9 by volume (p.p.b.v.) HNO_3) to $-81°C$ (5 p.p.b.v. HNO_3) for 5 p.p.m.v. water vapour at 30 hPa. A predominant NAT composition of Antarctic stratospheric clouds was proposed earlier from theoretical considerations[4,5] and has been identified in *in situ* measurements in Antarctica[6]. Thus, it appears that extensive NAT clouds and more local nacreous (water-ice) clouds should have formed in the Arctic stratosphere above ~20 km during January 1989. Because sunlight is also required to destroy ozone, the question of Arctic ozone depletion hinges on the amount of time that the air, which has been heterogeneously processed by stratospheric clouds, has spent in sunlight. As the Arctic polar vortex generally breaks down before sufficient sunlight reaches the near-polar regions, the most probable location for the detection of ozone depletion in the Arctic is near the Arctic circle during unusually cold years. For example, Kiruna experienced ~8 hours of sunlight per day on 23 January at 21 km where temperatures as low as $-86.7\,°C$ were observed. Owing to the effects of the Aleutian high, the vortex and the coldest regions are generally displaced towards Scandinavia (see Fig. 1) so that locations such as Kiruna are quite favourable. Here we report observations of polar stratospheric clouds and ozone during balloon flights on 23 and 30 January at Esrange, near Kiruna.

Cloud Particle Measurements

The data were obtained with University of Wyoming balloon-borne particle counters as used on many occasions in Antarctica[7]. The optical counter has an air-sample flow rate of ~200 cm^3 s^{-1}, capable of resolving low concentrations ($\sim10^{-3}$ cm^{-3}) as associated with ice-crystal formation. The instrument measured in seven size ranges, radius $r\geqslant0.20$, 0.25, 0.30, 1.0, 2.0, 3.0 and 5.0 µm, for spherical particles or slightly non-spherical particles of equivalent volume. A condensation-nuclei detector sensitive to particles with $r\geqslant0.01$ µm was added for the second flight on 30 January to obtain the total aerosol concentration profile and to determine the fraction of condensation sites taking part in cloud-particle growth.

Figure 2 shows the temperature and $r\geqslant0.20$ µm aerosol profiles measured during balloon ascent for the two flights. For the flight of 23 January, temperatures were $<-80\,°C$ between

一般认为，平流层云在盐酸和硝酸氯转化为活性氯以及平流层脱氮过程中均发挥着重要作用。在脱氮过程中，平流层云通过 HNO_3 蒸气凝结，进而从气相中脱去奇氮加速了活性氯对臭氧的破坏[2]。因此，1989 年 1 月对北极大范围的平流层云做的观测对于评估此次臭氧亏损有着重要意义，这次臭氧亏损事件是自至少 1957 年以来最有利条件下的产物。1957 年以前，平流层中虽然有大量云层，但其中的氯含量并不足以引起臭氧亏损。

当气压为 30 hPa、平流层中的水汽混合比为 5 ppmv 这一典型值时，要使水汽凝结形成冰晶云，温度需达到 –87.5℃ 左右（"霜点"温度）。然而，对固态三水合硝酸（NAT）的实验室研究[3] 表明，在 30 hPa、水汽混合比为 5 ppmv 时该结晶相的形成温度为 –80℃（HNO_3 为 10 ppbv，ppbv：按体积计算的十亿分之一）到 –81℃（HNO_3 为 5 ppbv）。理论研究[4,5] 很早就推断南极平流层云中的主要成分为 NAT，并且已在南极就地测量中得到证实[6]。因此，1989 年 1 月期间，似乎会有大量 NAT 云和更多的局部贝母云（水–冰晶）应该会在北极地区 20 km 以上的平流层中形成。由于破坏臭氧还需要阳光的参与，因此，北极地区臭氧亏损的问题取决于平流层云非均相过程产生的空气接受光照的时间长短。由于北极极涡通常在足够的阳光照射到极地附近之前就已消亡，因此探测北极臭氧亏损的最佳位置是在异常寒冷年份的北极圈附近。例如，基律纳在 1 月 23 日每天接受约 8 小时光照，其上空 21 km 处所观测到的温度低达 –86.7℃。由于阿留申高压的影响，极涡及最冷地区通常会向斯堪的纳维亚移动（见图 1），因此，像基律纳这样的位置是非常有利的观测地点。本文中，我们将报道 1 月 23 日和 30 日在基律纳附近的雅斯兰吉航天中心进行的气球飞行对北极平流层云和臭氧的观测。

云粒子测量

本文所用数据均由怀俄明大学气球运载的粒子计数器采集，该类计数器已在南极被使用过多次[7]。光学计数器的空气采样流速约为 200 cm³·s⁻¹，足以分辨出冰晶形成时的低浓度值（约 10^{-3} cm⁻³）。该设备测量了 7 个尺寸范围：粒径 $r \geqslant 0.20$ μm、0.25 μm、0.30 μm、1.0 μm、2.0 μm、3.0 μm 和 5.0 μm 的球形粒子或等效体积的略呈非球形的粒子。在 1 月 30 日进行的第二次飞行中增加了凝结核探测器，它可以探测到粒径 $r \geqslant 0.01$ μm 的粒子，以获取总气溶胶浓度廓线，并确定云粒子生长过程中凝结核所占的比例。

图 2 给出了两次飞行中气球上升期间获得的温度及 $r \geqslant 0.20$ μm 的气溶胶廓线。1 月 23 日探测到，海拔 18.5~27 km 的温度低于 –80℃，20.2~21.3 km 温度低于 –85℃，

altitudes of 18.5 and 27 km and below −85 °C between 20.2 and 21.3 km, and reached −85 °C briefly several times between 23 and 25 km. Because the balloons encountered very low temperatures, the rise rate was generally kept low (1–2 m s⁻¹) with occasional short periods of float before ballasting. This may have resulted in inadequate ventilation of the temperature sensor and could account for some of the unusual temperature increases observed above ~20 km. This would not affect the particle counter or ozone sensors because they are aspirated by pumps. Some of the temperature structure seen during both flights may be related to orographic waves originating from the mountain ranges west of Kiruna which appeared to be responsible for the generation of nacreous clouds during the measurement period. Westerly wind speeds in the stratosphere were very high (in excess of 50 m s⁻¹) and a minimum temperature during the balloon ascent on 23 January of −86.7 °C was reached in the cold layer between 20 and 21 km. The second flight, on 30 January, did not experience such low temperatures, with a minimum of −82.7 °C at ~25 km.

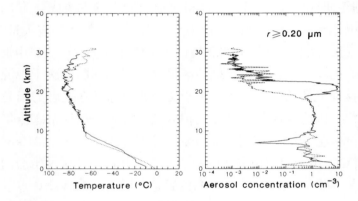

Fig. 2. Temperature and aerosol ($r \geqslant 0.20$ μm) profiles measured during balloon ascent at Kiruna, Sweden on 23 January (full lines) and 30 January (dashed lines) 1989.

The aerosol profiles in Fig. 2 indicate a normal sulphate layer between ~10 and 18 km with concentrations similar to those observed in Antarctica in September 1988[8]. These aerosols represent the global background sulphuric acid layer, there having been no major volcanic eruptions since EI Chichón in 1982 which increased the atmospheric sulphate concentration by nearly an order of magnitude[9]. In the cold layer at 19–22 km on 23 January we see a large increase in $r \geqslant 0.20$ μm particles, reaching a concentration of 8 cm⁻³ or more than 50% of the concentration of condensation nuclei in this region. The condensation-nuclei or total-aerosol profile was measured on the second flight and is reasonably constant in the absence of homogeneous nucleation of new particles. The particle enhancement on 23 January actually extends uniformly at lower concentrations to at least 26 km.

The large particles ($r \geqslant 1.0$ μm) were also enhanced but only to the extent of ~1 in 10⁴ of the available condensation nuclei. Very few particles having radii >2 μm and no large ice crystals ($r \geqslant 5$ μm) were observed in the layer. Thus it appears that pure water did not

在 23~25 km 温度也几次达到 –85℃。由于气球所处的温度极低，因此其上升速度也比较缓慢（1~2 m·s⁻¹），并在压舱之前偶尔出现短暂的漂移。这些都可能导致温度仪通风不足，或许可以解释在约 20 km 以上观测到某些温度异常升高的现象。粒子计数器和臭氧探测仪并不受影响，因为它们采用了气泵送气。两航次期间观测到的一些温度结构可能与基律纳西部山脉造成的地形波有关，测量期间珠母云的形成可能也与之有关。平流层中的西风风速很高（超过 50 m·s⁻¹），1 月 23 日气球上升期间遇到的最低温度为 –86.7℃，出现在 20~21 km 的寒冷层段。1 月 30 日的第二次飞行中未遇到如此低的温度，遇到的最低温度为 –82.7℃，在 25 km 附近。

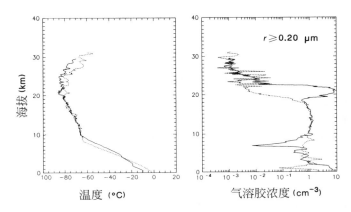

图 2. 1989 年 1 月 23 日（实线）和 1 月 30 日（虚线），在瑞典基律纳气球上升过程中测到的温度和气溶胶（$r \geqslant 0.20$ μm）廓线。

图 2 中的气溶胶廓线显示，约 10~18 km 处存在一个正常硫酸盐层，其浓度值类似于 1988 年 9 月在南极观测到的硫酸盐层[8]。此类气溶胶代表着全球背景下的硫酸盐层，自 1982 年的埃尔奇琼火山喷发至今未发生过大规模的火山喷发，而那次火山喷发使大气中硫酸盐的浓度升高了约 1 个数量级[9]。1 月 23 日，在 19~22 km 的冷层中，我们观测到 $r \geqslant 0.20$ μm 的粒子明显增多，其浓度达到了 8 cm⁻³，比该区的凝结核浓度高出 50%。第二次飞行中测定了凝结核的浓度和总气溶胶廓线，在无新粒子的均质核化作用时变化很小。1 月 23 日粒子的增加实际上均匀地扩展到至少 26km 处的更低浓度区域。

大粒子（$r \geqslant 1.0$ μm）也有所增加，不过也仅达到可利用凝结核的万分之一左右。该层中半径 >2 μm 的粒子极少，且没有观测到大的冰晶（$r \geqslant 5$ μm）。因此纯水在云

condense in this cloud, indicating a frost point temperature below −87°C at 36 hPa or a water-vapour mixing ratio of ⩽4.5 p.p.m.v. No large ice crystals were detected at any other altitude and the balloon therefore did not penetrate any nacreous clouds which may have been present at the time. Overcast skies prevented the observation of such clouds on the day of the flight. Stratospheric clouds, however, were visible nearly every day when observing conditions allowed, on some occasions to solar zenith angles of 96°, indicating altitudes in excess of 20 km, throughout the period 23 January to 2 February. Very low values of column NO_2 were measured by the PEL (Physics and Engineering Laboratory, Lauder, New Zealand) group at the Swedish Institute of Space Physics Observatory in Kiruna during the measurement period. These low values are essential for the chlorine chemistry detailed in ref. 3 to occur. The second flight on 30 January, at somewhat warmer temperatures, observed numerous thin (100–300-m-thick) particle layers between 18 and 26 km. In contrast to the 23 January cloud, the particles in these thin layers were mainly in the 2–3-μm radius size range at concentrations of $<10^{-2}$ cm^{-3} suggesting preferential growth on the largest ($r \geqslant 0.30$ μm) sulphate aerosol as observed previously in Antarctica[7]. It is quite likely that the 18–26-km region contained such tenuous layers of large cloud particles throughout the period 23–30 January.

Ozone Observations

Ozone profiles were measured with the Service d'Aeronomie chemiluminescent detector[10] on the 23 January flight, the University of Houston (NASA-JSC) ultraviolet photometer[11] on the 30 January flight and the University of Wyoming digital electrochemical detector[12] on both flights. Figure 3 shows the ozone partial pressure and mixing-ratio profiles measured by these instruments during the two flights. Agreement between the different techniques on both flights is generally good, although the electrochemical instrument is known to have uncertainties owing to the pump efficiency, especially at high altitude[13]. The pumps on these instruments were calibrated before flight. In addition, the response time is longer (20–30 s) for the electrochemical sensor as compared to the other two. This may explain slight displacements of some of the peaks, especially on 30 January when the balloon rise rate was considerably faster. In addition, each ozone sensor had its own ambient pressure sensor, and some small differences may therefore be expected. Integration of the partial pressure profiles resulted in ~325 Dobson units (DU) of total column ozone on both days. Column measurements of total ozone by the PEL group at Kiruna indicate a value of 330±25 DU on 23 January. The total ozone mapping spectrometer (TOMS) satellite instrument gave values of ~270 DU and 235 DU near Kiruna on the two days (A. Krueger, personal communication). 23 January was the first day for which TOMS had sufficient sunlight to determine a value. Past experience at McMurdo in Antarctica indicates that TOMS values are ~10% lower than those calculated from ozonesonde data during the first days of sunlight in early September but then generally agree to within a few percent thereafter[13]. The large fluctuations in ozone between 12 and 18 km are similar to those observed in association with quasi-horizontal advection, possibly from other latitudes[14]. However, the reductions in ozone in the 22–26-km range of ~25% on 23 January and ~10% on 30 January seem unusual. As discussed below, this apparent ozone deficit is very similar to the initial stages of ozone depletion in early September in Antarctica.

中看起来不会凝结，说明 36 hPa 处的霜点温度低于 –87℃，或水汽混合比 ≤4.5 ppmv。其他高度上也未检测到大的冰晶，因此气球未曾穿过当时可能存在的贝母云。观测当天阴暗的天空阻碍了对此类云层的观测。然而，1 月 23 日至 2 月 2 日期间，只要条件合适，几乎每天都能看到平流层云，有时太阳天顶角可达 96°，意味着高度超过了 20 km。在该测量期间，PEL（位于新西兰劳德的物理与工程实验室）研究小组在基律纳的瑞典空间物理研究所天文台测得的 NO_2 气柱值极低。这样的低值是参考文献 3 介绍的氯化学反应发生的必要条件。1 月 30 日的第二次观测中，温度略有升高，在 18~26 km 处观测到了大量薄（厚度为 100~300 m）粒子层。与 1 月 23 日观测到的云层不同，这些薄层中粒子的半径大部分在 2~3 μm，浓度 <10^{-2} cm^{-3}，说明就像之前在南极所观测到的一样，最大的硫酸盐气溶胶粒子（$r \geqslant 0.30$ μm）会优先生长[7]。1 月 23 日到 30 日，18~26 km 的区域都极有可能含有这种大的云粒子的稀薄层。

臭 氧 观 测

臭氧廓线的观测在 1 月 23 日使用的是高层大气物理学部门的化学发光检测仪[10]，在 1 月 30 日使用休斯敦大学（美国国家航空航天局约翰逊航天中心）的紫外分光光度计[11]，两次观测都使用了怀俄明大学的数字电化学探测仪[12]。图 3 所示为两次观测过程中，利用上述仪器测得的臭氧分压及混合比廓线。虽然气泵的效率可导致电化学仪器具有不确定性，尤其是海拔较高时[13]，但两次观测中不同仪器观测结果的一致性较好。所有仪器使用的气泵在观测之前均作过校正。此外，与其他两种仪器相比，电化学仪的响应时间较长（20~30 s）。这可能可以解释有些峰值出现微弱的位移，特别是在 1 月 30 日气球上升速度明显加快的时候。另外，每个臭氧仪都有自己的环境压力探测仪，这使得测定结果也会存在微弱的差异。积分分压廓线可以得到这两天的臭氧柱总量约为 325 个多布森单位（DU）。PEL 研究小组在基律纳测定的臭氧柱总量显示，1 月 23 日的值为（330±25）DU。装载于卫星上的臭氧总量测量仪（TOMS）给出的基律纳附近这两天的值分别约为 270 DU 和 235 DU（克鲁格，个人交流）。1 月 23 日是 TOMS 受到足够的阳光照射，进而给出观测值的第一天。根据过去在南极麦克默多的经验，9 月初，在受到阳光照射的第一天，TOMS 的观测值要比臭氧无线电探测仪数据计算出的值低 10% 左右，之后会接近到百分之几以内[13]。12~18 km 处臭氧的大幅波动类似于观测到的准水平平流，这些平流可能来自于其他纬度[14]。然而，从 1 月 23 日到 1 月 30 日，22~26 km 处的臭氧减少量由 25% 左右下降到了 10% 左右，这似乎有些异常。这种明显的臭氧亏损与南极 9 月初臭氧亏损的起始阶段极为相似，下文将进行讨论。

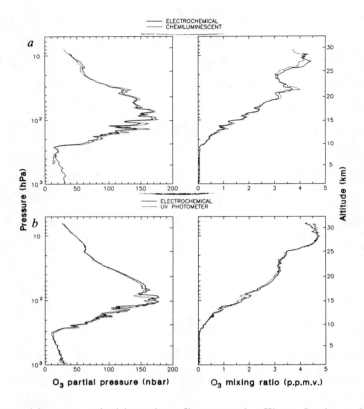

Fig. 3. Ozone partial pressure and mixing ratio profiles measured at Kiruna, Sweden on 23 January (*a*) and 30 January (*b*), 1989.

Discussion

The question of denitrification, necessary for ozone depletion to take place, can be addressed from cloud particle observations on the assumption that they are composed of NAT. Conversion of the particle-size distribution to a mass concentration, or the determination of the condensation temperature, can be used to estimate the amount of HNO_3 vapour present in the cloud.

Some information on the condensation temperature may be obtained by comparing data during balloon ascent and parachute descent, which occurred ~1 h after passing through the cloud at 21 km on 23 January. Winds were from the north-west at a relatively constant speed of 50 m s⁻¹ above 20 km so that the cloud observed on ascent probably should have also been observed on descent if it persisted. The ascent and parachute descent profiles of temperature and aerosol concentration are compared in Fig. 4. The descent temperature profile has less structure because of the rapid descent rate in the stratosphere. Small fluctuations in the sulphate layer at 14 km, reproduced in the descent profile, further suggest little differential motion of the balloon and the 15–20-km stratospheric air mass. The descent profile indicates the lowest temperature to be ~ −87 °C at 24 km. It should be noted that the temperature sensor on the particle counter, mounted on top of

510

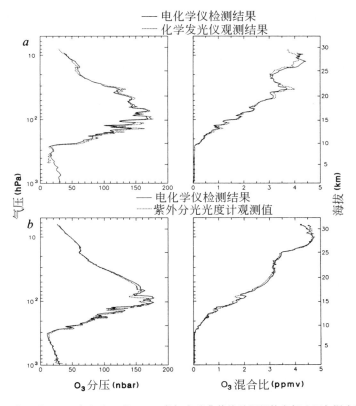

—— 电化学仪检测结果
········ 化学发光仪观测结果

—— 电化学仪检测结果
········ 紫外分光光度计观测值

图 3. 1989 年 1 月 23 日 （*a*）和 1 月 30 日 （*b*）在瑞典基律纳测得的臭氧分压与混合比廓线。

讨　论

假设云层粒子是由 NAT 组成，那么脱氮作用的问题可通过云层粒子观测结果来回答，该作用是臭氧亏损发生的必要条件。将粒子大小的分布转化为质量浓度，或对凝结温度进行确定，可用来估算云层中 HNO_3 蒸气的含量。

通过对比气球上升和降落伞下降时的数据可以获得凝结温度，其中下降过程是在 1 月 23 日穿过 21 km 处的云层约 1 小时后发生。风来自西北方向，在 20 km 之上风速相对维持在 50 m · s^{-1}，因此，如果云层一直存在，那么上升与下降期间观测到的云层应该是相同的。气球上升和降落伞下降过程中的温度及气溶胶浓度廓线对比见图 4。由于平流层中下降速度很快，因此下降温度廓线的波动较少。在 14 km 处硫酸盐层的小波动在下降廓线中也有重现，进一步说明气球及 15~20 km 的平流层气团几乎没有相对运动。下降廓线显示，在 24 km 处最低温度达 –87℃ 左右。值得注意的是，在快速下降初期，安装于吊舱顶部的粒子计数器上的温度仪并不是测定温度

the gondola, was not ideal for measuring temperatures during the initial rapid descent. A side-mounted thermistor of the Nagoya group, which gave similar results on ascent, gave a temperature of $\sim -90\,°C$ at 24 km. In this very cold region another particle layer, not present on ascent, was observed. The 19–22-km particle layer, observed on ascent at a concentration of ~8 cm^{-3}, was again present at a temperature of $\sim -84\,°C$ (on both sensors) and a reduced concentration of 2–3 cm^{-3}. One can probably conclude that some evaporation of the cloud observed on ascent had occurred at the higher temperature and that a new cloud had formed or was forming at 24–25 km, suggesting a condensation-evaporation temperature of $\sim -84\,°C$.

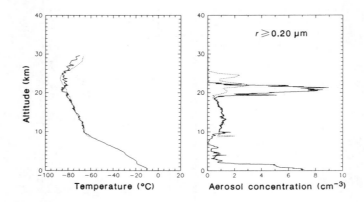

Fig. 4. Temperature and aerosol ($r \geqslant 0.20$ µm) profiles measured during balloon ascent (full lines) and parachute descent (dashed) at Kiruna, Sweden on 23 January 1989.

A condensation temperature of $-84\,°C$ for NAT is somewhat lower than expected and suggests either substantial denitrification had already taken place in this air parcel or that it was undergoing rapid cooling, in which case the vapour may have been supersaturated. For 5 p.p.m.v. water vapour at 36 hPa (the centre of the cloud) and a NAT condensation temperature of $-84\,°C$, laboratory measurements[3] suggest a HNO$_3$ mixing ratio of ~0.25 p.p.b.v. or nearly complete denitrification. On the other hand, if the actual HNO$_3$ mixing ratio was as high as 10 p.p.b.v., as measured in the 20–25-km region at Kiruna on 1 February 1988 (ref. 15), a very high degree of supersaturation would have had to exist. It is quite likely that neither of these conclusions is correct by itself but that this air parcel had been somewhat denitrified and that the cold layer at 21 km was caused by a recent rapid cooling.

To address this issue further, we may estimate the mass in the cloud-particle distribution. The measured integral size distributions can be fitted with differential log-normal distributions to facilitate calculation of mass and particle surface-area density[7]. The aerosol mass can be converted to a condensed vapour mass for an assumed NAT composition. Table 1 summarizes these calculations for the small and large particle mode in the 21-km layer on 23 January. Mass estimates for the thin layers of large particles observed on 30 January are not included here because of uncertainties in the size owing to the unknown shape of these larger particles. However, if composed of NAT and if the 2–3-µm-radius

的理想工具。名古屋研究小组利用安装在一侧的热敏电阻，在上升时可获得相似的结果，此时在 24 km 处测得的温度为 –90 ℃ 左右。在这个极其寒冷的区域还观测到了另一个粒子层，这在上升过程中是没有的。上升过程中观测到位于 19~22 km 的粒子层，其浓度约为 8 cm⁻³，该层同样也出现在下降过程中，温度约为 –84 ℃（两个探测仪均是），而浓度减小为 2~3 cm⁻³。由此可以得出结论，上升过程中观测到的云层的某些蒸发发生于较高的温度上，并且在 24~25 km 处有新的云层已经或正在形成，这表明凝结 – 蒸发温度约为 –84 ℃。

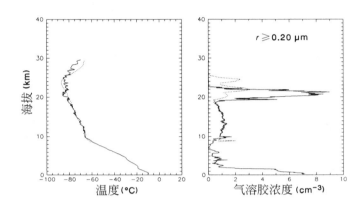

图 4. 1989 年 1 月 23 日，在瑞典基律纳气球上升（实线）和降落伞下降（虚线）过程中测得的温度与气溶胶（r ≥ 0.20 μm）廓线。

对 NAT 来说，–84 ℃ 的凝结温度比预期略低，这说明该气团中已发生显著的脱氮作用，或者该气团正经历着快速降温从而导致气体达到过饱和状态。36 hPa 条件下水汽为 5 ppmv（云层中心）且 NAT 凝结温度为 –84 ℃ 时，实验室测定结果[3] 显示，HNO₃ 的混合比约为 0.25 ppbv，即近乎完全脱氮。另一方面，倘若实际的 HNO₃ 混合比高达 10 ppbv，如 1988 年 2 月 1 日在基律纳上空 20~25 km 测得的值（参考文献 15），则必定存在极高的过饱和度。上述结论本身很可能都是错误的，但该气团中极有可能发生了某种程度的脱氮，并且 21 km 处的冷层也极有可能是由近期的快速降温形成的。

为了进一步说明这一问题，我们评估了云层粒子的质量分布。所测粒子大小的积分分布符合微分对数正态分布，可更容易地计算出质量和粒子表面积密度[7]。在假定组分为 NAT 的前提下，气溶胶的质量可以转化为冷凝气体的质量。表 1 概括了 1 月 23 日 21 km 处大小粒子模态计算结果。由于不清楚较大的粒子的形状而引起的粒子尺寸的不确定性，这里并未包含 1 月 30 日观测到的大粒子薄层中的质量估算。不过，倘若粒子均由 NAT 组成，并且 2~3 μm 的半径估计值还近似正确，那么沉降

estimate is even approximately correct, then some degree of denitrification through sedimentation could have occurred. Further cooling below the water frost point for only a short period could result in considerable denitrification without substantial dehydration[16]. Size determination, and therefore estimation of mass, is much more accurate for the small particle mode which comprised most of the mass in the 23 January layer. The implied HNO_3 mass of ~5 p.p.b.v. incorporated in the aerosol suggests that if the cloud observed on 23 January was indeed composed of NAT, then the air in the cloud was probably not completely denitrified. Although the small particles are inefficient for denitrification, as indicated in Table 1, they dominate the surface-area density, the parameter important for heterogeneous chemistry. This was also observed in Antarctic polar stratospheric clouds at lower altitude[8].

Table 1. Polar stratospheric cloud mass and area on 23 January at a height of 21 km

Particle Size mode	N_0 (cm^{-3})	σ	r_0 (μm)	Mass† (p.p.b.v.)	Area (μm^2 cm^{-3})
Small	15	1.36	0.20	4.7	9.1
Large	0.002	1.59	1.5	0.4	0.09
Total				5.1	9.2

N_0, σ and r_0 are respectively the total number concentration, the distribution width and the mode radius of a log-normal size distribution.
† HNO_3 vapour mass from assumed nitric acid trihydrate composition, density=1.62 g cm^{-3}.

We now turn to the issue of possible ozone depletion in the 22–26-km region, where the mixing ratio was seen to be depressed (see Fig. 3). Transport of ozone-poor air from other latitudes is not expected here owing to the strength and containment properties of the vortex at these altitudes. One cannot entirely rule out the possibility that the depression is a permanent feature of the Arctic ozone distribution; however, similar depressions are not observed in Antarctica before the beginning of ozone depletion in late August. The 30 January ozone reduction might be interpreted as having been due to a major vertical motion between about 20 and 26 km, because the ozone mixing ratio is relatively constant over this region; however, the temperature profile does not appear to vary adiabatically over this interval as might be expected. On the other hand, the reduction in ozone mixing ratio with altitude between 21 and 24 km on 23 January suggests a true ozone sink. The altitude of the ozone deficit does not coincide exactly with the large increase in small particles seen on 23 January but does coincide with the region of lower concentrations of larger, probably aged, particles as seen both on 23 and 30 January. The numerous small particles at 19 to 22 km on 23 January are believed to have been created recently through rapid cooling by vertical motions, possibly a lee-wave event, which resulted in the very low temperature in the 21-km region as discussed earlier. Thus, this cloud was probably not old enough to have a measurable effect on ozone chemistry.

As mentioned earlier, although stratospheric sunlight in late January is insufficient for the photochemistry required for ozone depletion over much of the Arctic, this is not the

过程中可能发生了某种程度的脱氮作用。由水的霜点起再继续降温一小段时间就会引起明显的脱氮作用，并且不发生大量脱水[16]。小粒子模态下，粒子尺寸的确定以及由此估算的质量则准确得多，这种小粒子模态正是1月23日云层的主要质量组分。气溶胶中隐含硝酸的质量约为5 ppbv，说明倘若1月23日观测到的云层确实由NAT组成，那么云层中的空气很可能并未完全脱氮。虽然小粒子在脱氮作用方面效率较低，如表1所示，但它们在比表面积密度中却占有主导地位，这一参数对于非均相化学作用是非常重要的。在较低高度的南极平流层云中也观测到了同样的现象[8]。

表 1. 1 月 23 日 21 km 高度处极地平流层云的质量和面积

粒子尺寸模态	N_0 (cm^{-3})	σ	r_0 (μm)	质量† (ppbv)	面积 (μm^2·cm^{-3})
小	15	1.36	0.20	4.7	9.1
大	0.002	1.59	1.5	0.4	0.09
总和				5.1	9.2

N_0、σ 和 r_0 分别为总数量浓度、分布宽度以及呈对数正态分布的粒子大小的模态半径。
† HNO_3 气体的质量由假定的三水合硝酸组分得出，密度 = 1.62 g·cm^{-3}。

现在我们转向 22~26 km 区域可能存在臭氧亏损的问题上，这一区域上混合比有所降低（见图 3）。鉴于这一高度上极涡的强度和组成性质，我们认为不存在其他纬度地区的贫臭氧空气的输送。尽管在南极地区，当 8 月末臭氧开始亏损之前并未观测到类似低值，但并不能排除低值是北极臭氧分布的永久性特征的可能性。1 月 30 日出现的臭氧减少有可能是 20 km 和 26 km 之间主要的垂直运动的结果，因为该区臭氧的混合比相对比较稳定；但温度廓线看上去并不是如预期那样在该高度段上呈绝热变化的。另一方面，1 月 23 日在 21~24 km 处的臭氧混合比例随高度升高而降低，表明该段是一个天然臭氧吸收汇。臭氧出现亏损的高度与 1 月 23 日观测到的小粒子大幅度增加的高度并不完全一致，但与在 1 月 23 日和 30 日都曾观测到的低浓度的、大的、可能老化的粒子所在区域却是一致的。1 月 23 日观测到的 19~22 km 处的无数小粒子被认为是在近期内由垂直运动引起的快速降温形成的，而这个垂直运动很可能是一个背风波事件，它会使 21 km 附近区域的温度变得极低，这一点前文已讨论过。所以，该云层可能还比较年轻，不足以对臭氧化学过程产生较大的影响。

如前所述，虽然 1 月末北极大部地区平流层接受到的阳光不足以引起致使臭氧亏损的光化学作用，但位于北极圈附近的基律纳却另当别论，尤其是在轻微的非纬

case at Kiruna, near the Arctic circle, especially if slightly non-zonal flow increases the time air parcels spend in sunlight, as was the case in late January 1989. For example, from the Berlin analysis of Northern hemisphere 30-hPa heights, winds and temperatures (K. Labitzke, personal communication), simple isobaric trajectory estimates suggest that an air parcel may have been in sunlight for as much as half of the time. The temperature extremes along this approximate trajectory are large owing to the fact that the height and temperature contours were not concentric (see Fig. 1) with variations from −57 to −86°C. It thus appears that the air sampled over Kiruna in late January may have been subjected to the required conditions for ozone depletion, that is, temperatures sufficiently low for denitrification through the formation of polar stratospheric clouds and also sufficient sunlight. However, as the timescale for the onset and relaxation of chemical ozone depletion may be the order of a week or more, such air-parcel history estimates may not be definitive in determining the ultimate extent of ozone depletion.

It has been shown[12-14] that ozone depletion begins at McMurdo Station, Antarctica (78° S) in the 22-km region during the last week in August and then progresses rapidly to lower altitude, as stratospheric illumination rapidly increases, terminating in the 12-km region. There are some interesting similarities in the apparent deficit in ozone mixing ratio observed at high altitude in the Arctic and that observed in Antarctica. The 20-km region experienced ~8 h of sunlight per day at Kiruna on 23 January and ~9 h on 30 January. Similar illumination periods exist at McMurdo in late August and early September. There are some slight differences at these times as the Sun rises several degrees higher in the sky at local noon at Kiruna than at McMurdo whereas the daily increase of sunlight hours is slightly faster at McMurdo than at Kiruna.

Figure 5 shows ozone partial pressure and mixing-ratio profiles covering this period at McMurdo in 1986, 1987 and 1988. McMurdo was in a favourable position well within the polar vortex during the last week of August and the first half of September in each of these years so that temperature histories above 20 km are comparable. The general nature of the ozone mixing-ratio depression is strikingly similar to that observed at Kiruna except that it is in the 18–22-km region, varying slightly from year to year, or ~4 km lower than in the Arctic. Thus, it is quite likely that we are witnessing the onset of a phenomenon identical to that which takes place in the Antarctic stratosphere except at higher altitude in the Arctic. In Antarctica the depletion generally continues throughout September and October, reaching altitudes as low as 12 km because these regions are very cold and clouds form throughout the winter, a situation which does not exist in the Arctic. For example, the 30-hPa average polar temperature in January 1989 was 2–3 °C colder than at 50 hPa (about 19 km altitude) and ~8 °C colder than at 100 hPa (~15 km altitude). The latter temperatures were too high for cloud formation (−75 °C minimum) whereas temperatures of −80 to −85 °C are common at 15 km in the Antarctic winter and spring. Thus, the low temperatures required for ozone depletion are at higher altitude in the Arctic, where there is much less ozone than in the 12–22-km Antarctic depletion range.

向气流使气团接受光照的时间延长的情况下，1989 年 1 月末正是如此。例如，根据北半球 30 hPa 的高度场、风场和温度场的柏林分析结果（拉比茨克，个人交流），简单的等压轨迹分析表明一个气团可能有一半的时间都能接受到阳光。该轨迹上的温度极值很大，基本上归因于高度和温度等值线是非同心的（见图 1），温度的变化范围为 –57℃到 –86℃。由此看来，1 月末在基律纳上空采集到的空气样本可能满足了臭氧亏损的必需条件，也就是说，这里不仅温度低到足以通过形成平流层云而发生脱氮作用，而且还具备充足的阳光。然而，由于化学过程臭氧亏损启动和松弛的持续时间可能为一周或者更长，此类气团的历史估计值并不能确定出臭氧亏损的最终程度。

已有研究证明[12-14]，臭氧亏损始于南极麦克默多站（78°S）的 22 km 区域，于 8 月的最后一周开始，之后迅速向低海拔延伸，并且随着平流层光照度的快速升高，在 12 km 附近终止。在北极高海拔处观测到的臭氧混合比的明显亏损中，与南极的观测结果存在许多有趣的相似之处。1 月 23 日基律纳地区上空 20 km 区域的日光照时间约为 8 小时，1 月 30 日约为 9 小时。8 月末和 9 月初麦克默多站也存在相似的光照时间长度。由于当地正午时分太阳在基律纳要比在麦克默多高出几度，而在麦克默多地区光照时间的日增速要略快于基律纳，所以两地情况在这些时候会有些不同。

图 5 所示为 1986 年、1987 年和 1988 年麦克默多站在这一时段的臭氧分压与混合比廓线。上述三年中 8 月的最后一周和 9 月的前半个月，麦克默多站恰好位于极涡内的有利位置，因此，20 km 以上高度的温度变化具有可比性。臭氧混合比低值的总体特征与基律纳的观测结果极为相似，不同只是出现在 18~22 km 处，或者比北极低 4 km 左右，此高度在各年份间存在微弱差异。因此，除北极较高海拔以外，我们所观测到的极有可能是类似于南极平流层中发生现象的起始阶段。在南极地区臭氧亏损通常会持续整个 9 月和 10 月，影响范围可低至海拔 12 km 处，这是因为这些地区的温度都很低并且整个冬季都有云层形成，但北极并不存在这种情况。例如，1989 年 1 月极地地区 30 hPa 处的平均温度要比 50 hPa 处（海拔约 19 km）低 2~3℃，比 100 hPa 处（海拔约 15 km）低 8℃左右。对于云层的形成（最低 –75℃）来说，后两个温度就太高了；而在南极，冬春两季时 15 km 高度上 –80℃到 –85℃的气温是很常见的。所以，在北极地区臭氧亏损必需的低温只有在较高的海拔上才能达到，而这里的臭氧量要远远少于南极地区 12~22 km 的亏损区间。

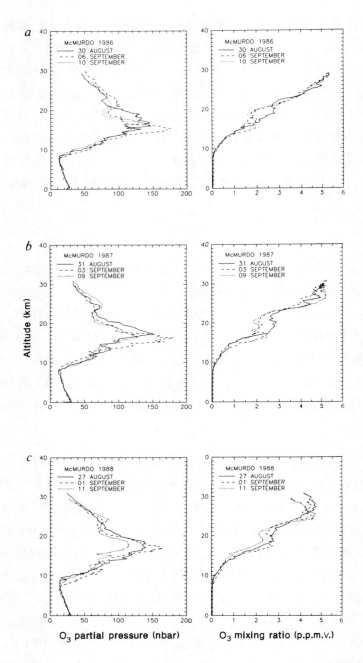

Fig. 5. Ozone partial pressure and mixing-ratio profiles measured at McMurdo Station, Antarctica during the early phases of springtime ozone depletion in 1986 (*a*), 1987 (*b*) and 1988 (*c*).

The amount of the apparent ozone deficit observed in the Arctic is very small. If the mixing-ratio curve on 23 January is filled in so that the depression between 22 and 26 km does not exist, and the total ozone is then calculated, a value only 10 DU, or ~3%, higher is obtained. In more normal, relatively cloud-free years, one would expect even smaller

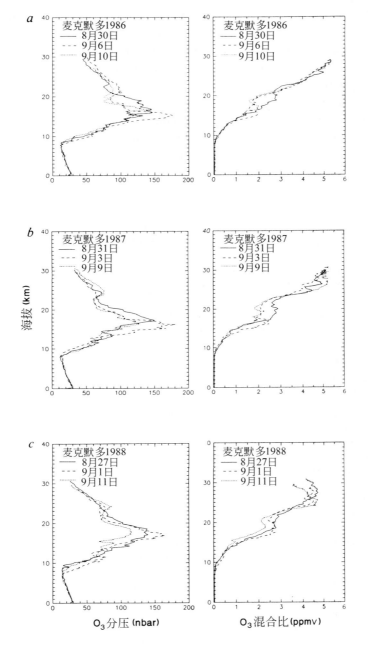

图 5. 1986 年 (*a*)、1987 年 (*b*) 和 1988 年 (*c*) 春季臭氧亏损早期，在南极麦克默多站测得的臭氧分压和混合比廓线。

在北极观测到的明显臭氧亏损量不多。倘若将 1 月 23 日的混合比廓线填满，22~26 km 处的低值区将消失，由此就可计算出臭氧总量仅为 10 DU，或更高一些，即 3% 左右。在正常情况下，相对无云的年份里，这种降低应该更小。因此，虽然

reductions. Thus, although 1989 was an unusually cold winter, the major warming and breakdown of the polar vortex in early February probably terminated any possibility for ozone depletion of sufficient magnitude for surface or satellite measurements to detect easily. The warming ended the cloud formation process and cloud evaporation reintroduces nitrogen to the gas phase, reducing any ozone depletion that may have been occurring. Some irreversible loss of odd nitrogen, through cloud-particle sedimentation during the winter, may have occurred. If the cold regions had persisted into February or March, a larger depletion could have resulted, but in any case could not have exceeded removal of most of the ozone between about 18 and 26 km, the cloud formation region, which is at most 25% of the total.

(**340**, 117-121; 1989)

D. J. Hofmann[*], T. L. Deshler[*], P. Aimedieu[†], W. A. Matthews[‡], P. V. Johnston[‡], Y. Kondo[§], W. R. Sheldon[||], G. J. Byrne[||] & J. R. Benbrook[||]

[*] Department of Physics and Astronomy, University of Wyoming, Laramie, Wyoming 82071, USA
[†] Service d'Aeronomie, CNRS, 91371 Verrieres le Buisson, France
[‡] DSIR/PEL Lauder, Central Otago, New Zealand
[§] Research Institute of Atmospherics, Nagoya University, Toyokawa, Japan
[||] Department of Physics, University of Houston, Houston, Texas 77204, USA

Received 2 March; accepted 2 June 1989.

References:

1. Kuhlbarsch, T. & Naujokat, B. *Beilage zur Berliner Wetterkarte* 25/89 Institute for Meteorology, Free University of Berlin (1989).

2. Solomon, S. *Rev. Geophys.* **26**, 131-148 (1988).

3. Hanson, D. & Mauersberger, K. *Geophys. Res. Lett.* **15**, 855-858 (1988).

4. Toon, O. B., Hamill, P., Turco, R. P. & Pinto, J. *Geophys. Res. Lett.* **13**, 1284-1287 (1986).

5. Crutzen, P. J. & Arnold, F. *Nature* **324**, 651-655 (1986).

6. Fahey, D. W. *et al. J. Geophys. Res.* **94**, 11299-11315(1989).

7. Hofmann, D. J., Rosen, J. M., Harder, J. W. & Hereford, J. V. *J. geophys. Res.* **94**, 11253-11269(1989).

8. Hofmann, D. J. *Nature* **337**, 447-449 (1989).

9. Hofmann, D. J. *Rev. Geophys.* **25**, 743-759 (1987).

10. Aimedieu, P. & Barat, J. *Rev. Sci. Instr.* **52**, 432 (1981).

11. Robbins, D. E. in *Atmospheric Ozone* (eds Zerefos, C. S. & Ghazi, A.) 460-464 (Reidel, Dordrecht, 1985).

12. Hofmann, D. J., Harder, J. W., Rolf, S. R. & Rosen, J. M. *Nature* **326**, 59-62 (1987).

13. Hofmann, D. J., Harder, J. W., Rosen, J. M., Hereford, J. V. & Carpenter, J. R. *J. Geophys. Res.* **94**, 16527-16536(1989).

14. Hofmann, D. J., Rosen, J. M. & Harder, J. W. *J. Geophys. Res.* **93**, 665-676 (1988).

15. Arnold, F. & Knop, G. *Nature* **333**, 746-749 (1989).

16. Salawitch, R. J., Gobbi, G. P., Wofsy, S. C. & McElroy, M. B. *Nature* **339**, 525-527 (1989).

Acknowledgements. We acknowledge the financial and technical support given to this research by the Centre National d'Etudes Spatiales (CNES). The support of the Centre National de la Recherche Scientifique (CNRS), the NSF Division of Atmospheric Chemistry and Division of Polar programs, NASA, the Chemical Manufacturers Association, the Texas Higher Education Coordinating Board, The Scandinavia-Japan Sasakawa Foundation, Esrange and the Swedish Institute of Space Physics is also gratefully acknowledged. We wish to thank the Stratospheric Group of the Institute for Meteorology of the Free University of Berlin for providing the 30-hPa analyses. D.J.H. acknowledges the support provided by the A. v. Humboldt Foundation and the Institute for Atmospheric Environmental Research, Garmisch-Partenkirchen, FRG while on leave there.

1989 年的冬季异常寒冷，但 2 月初天气变暖，极涡被破坏，使得臭氧亏损值很小时就被终止，导致地面或卫星测量都很难测到这种亏损。天气的变暖结束了云层的形成过程，而云层的蒸发将氮再次转化为气相，从而导致可能发生的臭氧亏损减少。冬季时，因云粒子的沉积作用可能会导致部分奇氮的不可逆损失。倘若寒冷区域可持续到 2 月或 3 月，那么臭氧亏损将大得多，但无论如何也不会将 18~26 km 的大部分臭氧都去除掉，在云层形成区域最多也只能达到总量的 25%。

（齐红艳 翻译；安俊岭 审稿）

A Membrane-Targeting Signal in the Amino Terminus of the Neuronal Protein GAP-43

M. X. Zuber *et al.*

Editor's Note

Growth-associated protein 43 (GAP-43) is a neuronal protein expressed in high levels in growth cones, specialized structures found at the end of growing nerve fibres that help guide them to their destination. Research had suggested that the protein's amino terminus might be important for binding the otherwise cytoplasmic protein to the growth cone membrane. Here Mauricio Zuber and colleagues use mutational analysis and confocal microscopy to confirm the hypothesis. They show that the first ten amino acids of the molecule act as membrane-targeting signals. GAP-43, also called neuromodulin, is now known to guide developing axons during development —mice lacking the protein die shortly after birth due to axon path-finding defects. GAP-43 is also involved in regeneration and plasticity.

Neurons and other cells, such as those of epithelia, accumulate particular proteins in spatially discrete domains of the plasma membrane. This enrichment is probably important for localization of function, but it is not clear how it is accomplished. One proposal for epithelial cells is that proteins contain targeting signals which guide preferential accumulation in basal or apical membranes[1]. The growth-cone membrane of a neuron serves as a specialized transduction system, which helps to convert cues from its environment into regulated growth. Because it can be physically separated from the cell soma, it has been possible to show that the growth-cone membrane contains a restricted set of total cellular proteins[2], although, to our knowledge, no proteins are limited to that structure. One of the most prominent proteins in the growth-cone membrane is GAP-43 (refs 3–5; for reviews see refs 6 and 7). Basi *et al.* have suggested that the N-terminus of GAP-43 might be important for the binding of GAP-43 to the growth-cone membrane[8]. Skene and Virag[9] recently found that the cysteines in the N-terminus are fatty-acylated and that this post-translational modification correlates with membrane-binding ability. We investigated the binding of GAP-43 to the growth-cone membrane by mutational analysis and by laser-scanning confocal microscopy of fusion proteins that included regions of GAP-43 and chloram-phenicol acetyltransferase (CAT). We found that a short stretch of the GAP-43 N-terminus suffices to direct accumulation in growth-cone membranes, especially in the filopodia. This supports a previous proposal[8,9] for the importance of this region of GAP-43 in determining the membrane distribution of GAP-43.

神经元蛋白GAP-43氨基末端中的膜导向信号

朱伯等

编者按

生长相关蛋白43（GAP-43）是一种神经元生长锥中高表达的蛋白，生长锥是在正在生长的神经纤维末端发现的特殊结构，有助于指引这些纤维到达它们的目的地。研究揭示，此蛋白的氨基末端可能对于使本来分布于细胞质的蛋白质分子结合到生长锥膜是重要的。在这里毛里西奥·朱伯和他的同事运用突变分析和共聚焦显微技术来证实上述假说。他们的结果显示，此分子的前10个氨基酸起到了膜导向信号的作用。GAP-43，也被称为神经调制蛋白，现在已知它在发育过程中指引正在发育的轴突——缺乏此蛋白的小鼠在出生后很快死亡，因为轴突的路径寻找功能存在缺陷。GAP-43在神经再生和可塑性中也有作用。

神经元和其他细胞，例如上皮细胞，在原生质膜上不同的区域中积累特定的蛋白。这一蛋白富集可能对于功能定位来说是重要的，但并不清楚此过程是如何实现的。一个关于上皮细胞的设想是：蛋白质分子具有在细胞膜的基部或顶端优先积累的导向信号 [1]。神经元的生长锥膜作为特化的信号转导系统，有助于将来自周围环境的信号转化为受调控的生长。生长锥与细胞体空间上分隔，已经发现生长锥膜含有细胞总蛋白有限的一部分 [2]，尽管据我们所知，没有蛋白仅仅分布于这一结构内。在生长锥膜上，最引人注目的蛋白之一就是 GAP-43（参考文献3~5；综述见参考文献6和7）。巴锡等人指出，GAP-43 的 N 端可能对于使它与生长锥膜结合来说是重要的 [8]。斯基恩和维拉格 [9] 最近发现，N 端中的半胱氨酸是脂肪酸酰基化的，并且这一翻译后修饰与膜结合活性相关。通过突变分析和激光扫描共聚焦显微镜对 GAP-43 部分区域与氯霉素乙酰转移酶（CAT）的融合蛋白的分析，我们研究了 GAP-43 与生长锥膜的结合。我们发现，GAP-43 N 端的一小段序列足够指导该分子在生长锥膜，特别是丝状伪足中的积累。这支持以前的设想 [8,9]，即 GAP-43 的这一区域在决定 GAP-43 膜分布中具有重要意义。

ALTHOUGH GAP-43 lacks the hydrophobic amino-acid sequences that are characteristic of integral membrane proteins[9,10], it resists dissociation by agents that usually remove peripheral membrane proteins[9,11-14]. Hence, the mechanism of membrane binding is not clear. We have found that transfected GAP-43 binds to the membrane in COS cells and other non-neuronal cells[15]. The high level of GAP-43 expression in COS cells permitted preliminary screening to determine which regions were important in membrane association. Whereas membrane binding persists after deletion of a large internal segment (residues 41–189 out of 226 residues), or after deletion of the C-terminal eight amino acids and substitution of an unrelated dodecapeptide, the deletion of amino acids 2–5 markedly diminishes membrane binding (data not shown). Contained in the N-terminus are the only two cysteines in GAP-43, at positions 3 and 4, and it seemed reasonable that this unusual structure of adjacent sulphydryl groups might contribute to membrane binding. As shown in Fig. 1, in which cytosolic and membrane cell-fractions are compared, GAP-43 binds predominantly to the membranes, whereas replacement of Cys 3 or Cys 4, or both, by threonine, causes most of the protein to remain cytosolic. These two cysteines are palmitylated and this correlates with membrane association in brain[14]. Thus, the N-terminus of GAP-43, especially its N-terminal cysteine residues, seem to be necessary for the binding of GAP-43 to membranes.

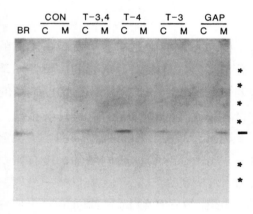

Fig. 1. GAP-43 N-terminal mutations prevent membrane association. COS cells were transfected with the expression vector pGAP (GAP) or with plasmids containing point mutations (Cys to Thr) at position 3 (T-3), position 4 (T-4) or position 3 and 4 (T-3, 4). Immunoblots of membrane (M)- and cystosolic (C) fractions stained with anti-GAP antibody show that GAP-43 immunoreactivity co-migrated with purified GAP-43 protein (bar on right) and was greatly enriched in the membrane fraction. By contrast, the mutant GAP proteins were all more concentrated in the cytosol. Non-specific staining by the antibody was negligible in control fractions from CDM8-transfected COS cells (CON). A crude membrane fraction from rat brain (BR) shows immunostaining at a band corresponding to the same relative molecular mass (M_r) as the band for the GAP-transfected COS cells. The migration positions of protein standards with M_rs of 116,000 (116K), 84K, 58K, 48.5K, 36.5K and 26.6K are indicated by the asterisks.

Methods. Point mutations in GAP-43 were generated from single-stranded DNA made from pGAP and used to alter the cysteines to threonines. The oligonucleotides GGCATGCTGACCTGTATG, ATGCTGTGCACTATGAGA, and GCAGGCATGCTGACCACTATGAGAAGAACC were used to mutate Cys 3 to Thr, Cys 4 to Thr, and Cys 3, 4 to Thr, respectively. After mutagenesis, a 200-base pair (bp) fragment containing the mutation was subcloned into a non-mutated plasmid. The sequence was confirmed after mutagenesis by dideoxy chain-termination sequencing. Other procedures are as described in Fig. 2.

虽然 GAP-43 缺乏作为整合型膜蛋白[9,10]特征的疏水氨基酸序列，但是它可以耐受由通常能移除外周膜蛋白[9,11-14]的试剂造成的质膜解离。因此其膜结合的机制尚不清楚。我们已经发现，在 COS 细胞和其他非神经元细胞[15]中，转染的 GAP-43 与膜结合。GAP-43 在 COS 细胞中的高度表达使我们得以初步筛选决定哪一区域对膜结合是重要的。在一个大片段（226 个残基中的 41~189 位残基）被删除后，或在 C 端 8 个氨基酸被删除，并被某一无关的十二肽所取代后，膜结合依然存在。而第 2~5 位的氨基酸残基删除则显著减少了膜结合（数据未展示）。GAP-43 仅有的 2 个半胱氨酸在 N 端第 3 位和第 4 位，而这种相邻巯基团的不寻常结构可能有助于膜结合，这看上去是合理的。如图 1 所示，将胞浆和膜组分做比较，GAP-43 主要与膜结合，然而用苏氨酸替换第 3 位或第 4 位半胱氨酸，或者二者都被替换为苏氨酸，使此蛋白多数保留在胞浆中。这两个半胱氨酸是棕榈酰化的，而且这与大脑[14]中的膜结合是对应的。因此，GAP-43 的 N 端，特别是它的 N 端半胱氨酸残基，看上去对于 GAP-43 与膜的结合来说是必要的。

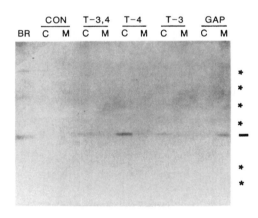

图 1. GAP-43 N 端突变阻断膜结合。用 pGAP (GAP) 表达载体或含有点突变（半胱氨酸突变为苏氨酸）的质粒转染 COS 细胞，质粒点突变的位置在第 3 位（T-3）或第 4 位（T-4）或第 3 位和第 4 位（T-3,4）。用抗 GAP 抗体染细胞膜（M）和细胞质（C）组分的免疫印迹实验显示，GAP-43 的免疫反应性与纯化的 GAP-43 蛋白共迁移（由右侧横线显示），并且在膜组分中极大富集。作为对比，突变 GAP 蛋白在胞质更集中。在来自 CDM8 转染的 COS 细胞（CON）的对比组分中，抗体的非特异染色可以忽略。来自大鼠大脑（BR）的细胞膜粗提取物显示，有一条带的免疫染色与 GAP 转染 COS 细胞的条带具有相同的相对分子量（M_r）。星号指明了蛋白分子量标记的迁移位置，分子量分别为 116K、84K、58K、48.5K、36.5K 和 26.6K。

方法。GAP-43 中的点突变产生于 pGAP 制造的单链 DNA，并用来将半胱氨酸转化为苏氨酸。寡核苷酸链 GGCATGCTGACCTGTATG、ATGCTGTGCACTATGAGA 和 GCAGGCATGCTGACCACTATG-AGAAGAACC 被分别用来使第 3 位半胱氨酸突变为苏氨酸，使第 4 位半胱氨酸突变为苏氨酸，以及使第 3 位和第 4 位半胱氨酸突变为苏氨酸。突变形成后，一个含有突变的长 200 碱基对（bp）的片段被亚克隆加入一个非突变质粒。突变发生后通过双脱氧链终止测序确定序列。其他过程如图 2 中所述。

To determine whether the N-terminus is sufficient to confer on GAP-43 the ability to bind to membranes, we made constructs that encoded differing amounts of the GAP-43 N-terminus fused to a reporter peptide, and expressed them in COS and PC12 cells. We chose chloramphenicol acetyltransferase (CAT) as the reporter peptide because it is cytosolic when expressed in eukaryotic cells and is very stable. We constructed plasmids that encode fusion proteins containing either the first 10 amino acids of GAP-43, Met-Leu-Cys-Cys-Met-Arg-Arg-Thr-Lys-Gln, fused to the N-terminus of the complete CAT protein ($GAP_{10}CAT$), or the first 40 amino acids of GAP-43 fused to CAT ($GAP_{40}CAT$). As shown by immunoblotting, the CAT that was expressed in COS cells (Fig. 2a) or PC12 cells (Fig. 2b) was present only in the cytosolic fraction. By contrast, the chimaeric proteins $GAP_{10}CAT$ and $GAP_{40}CAT$ were membrane-associated. We were able to extract the fusion protein with detergent, but not with sodium chloride, calcium chloride or EGTA (data not shown). Thus, the nature of this membrane binding was similar to that of native GAP-43 in rat brain[11-14].

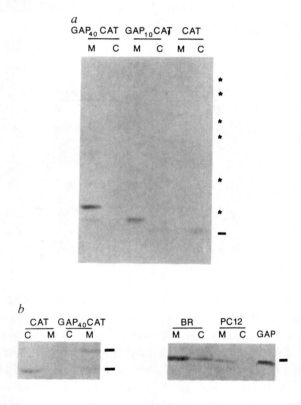

Fig. 2. Membrane association of GAP-43 and GAP-CAT fusion proteins. *a*. Chimaeric proteins with the N-terminus of GAP-43 fused to CAT associate with COS cell membranes. The constructs CAT, $GAP_{10}CAT$ and $GAP_{40}CAT$ were transiently expressed in COS cells. Immunoblots of membrane (M)- and cytosolic (C) fractions from each transfection were prepared using anti-CAT antibody. Note that in the CAT-transfected cells, immunoreactivity was found only in the cytosolic fraction and co-migrated with purified CAT protein (indicated by the bar). In the $GAP_{40}CAT$- and $GAP_{10}CAT$-transfected cells, nearly all of the immunoreactivity was membrane-associated and migrated more slowly than that for CAT-transfected cells, as expected for fusion proteins with an M_r of 4K or 10K greater than CAT. Protein

为了确定 N 端是否足够赋予 GAP-43 与膜结合的能力，我们构建了不同长度的 GAP-43 N 端与报告多肽融合蛋白的表达载体，并使它们在 COS 和 PC12 细胞中表达。我们选择氯霉素乙酰基转移酶（CAT）作为报告多肽，因为它在真核细胞胞浆中表达，并且非常稳定。我们构建编码融合蛋白的质粒，该融合蛋白或者将 GAP-43 的前 10 个氨基酸，甲硫氨酸–亮氨酸–半胱氨酸–半胱氨酸–甲硫氨酸–精氨酸–精氨酸–苏氨酸–赖氨酸–谷氨酰胺，融合到完整 CAT 蛋白的 N 端（GAP$_{10}$CAT），或者是 GAP-43 的前 40 个氨基酸融合到 CAT（GAP$_{40}$CAT）。如免疫印迹所示，在 COS 细胞中（图 2a）或 PC12 细胞中（图 2b）表达的 CAT 只存在于可溶性胞质组分中。与此相对照，嵌合蛋白 GAP$_{10}$CAT 和 GAP$_{40}$CAT 与膜相关。我们能够用去垢剂，而不是用氯化钠、氯化钙或 EGTA（数据未展示）提取融合蛋白。因此，此蛋白的膜结合属性与大鼠脑[11-14]中的天然 GAP-43 类似。

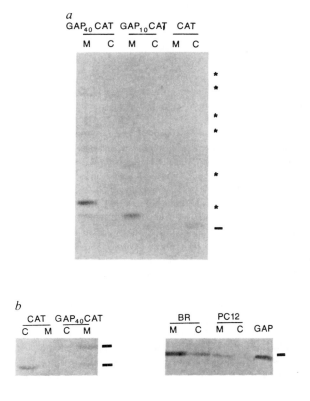

图 2. GAP-43 及 GAP-CAT 融合蛋白的膜结合。a. GAP-43 N 端与 CAT 融合形成的嵌合蛋白与 COS 细胞膜结合。CAT、GAP$_{10}$CAT 和 GAP$_{40}$CAT 载体都在 COS 细胞中瞬时表达。使用免疫印迹的方法通过抗 CAT 抗体检测来自每一转染的膜（M）和胞质（C）组分。在 CAT 转染细胞中，免疫反应性只存在于胞质组分中，并且与纯化的 CAT 蛋白共迁移（由横线显示）。在 GAP$_{40}$CAT 和 GAP$_{10}$CAT 转染细胞中，几乎所有的免疫反应性都在膜组分中，并且比 CAT 转染的细胞迁移得更慢。正如预期的那样，融合蛋白的分子量比 CAT 大 4K 或 10K。星号所示蛋白标准的分子量为 116K、84K、58K、48.5K、36.5K 和

standards with M_rs of 116K, 84K, 58K, 48.5K, 36.5K and 26.6K migrated as indicated by the asterisks. *b*. Membrane association of GAP and GAP$_{40}$CAT in PC12 cells. Stably transfected PC12 cells expressing CAT, GAP$_{40}$CAT or GAP were selected as described below. Immunoblots of membrane (M)-and cytosolic (C) fractions were stained with anti-CAT antibodies (left panel) or anti-GAP (right panel) antibodies. CAT-transfected cells (CAT) contained immunoreactivity in the cytosolic, but not in the membrane fraction, and this immunoreactive CAT co-migrated with purified CAT (lower bar to right of left panel). In contrast, GAP$_{40}$CAT transfected cells contained membrane-associated CAT immunoreactivity, which migrated more slowly (upper bar). Fractions from rat brain (BR) demonstrate that most, but not all, endogenous GAP-43 immunoreactivity was membrane-associated. In transfected PC12 cells over-expressing GAP-43 (PC12), nearly all of the GAP-immunoreactivity was membrane-associated and co-migrated with purified GAP-43 (GAP; indicated by far-right bar).

Methods. In the GAP-43-expression plasmid, pGAP, the GAP-43-coding sequence replaced the stuffer region at the *Xba*I sites of the CDM8 plasmid described by Seed[25]. The inserted GAP-43 sequence included the entire coding sequence of rat GAP-43, from the *Nla*III site at the start of translation to the *Sau*3AI site 68 bp downstream from the termination codon[8]. For the CAT expression plasmid, pCAT, the *Hind*III-*Bam*HI fragment containing the CAT-coding sequence and polyadenylation site from pSV2CAT[26] replaced the *Hind*III-*Bam*HI fragment of CDM8 containing the stuffer region and polyadenylation site. Plasmids pGAP$_{40}$CAT and pGAP$_{10}$CAT included sequences encoding the first 40 or 10 amino acids of GAP-43, respectively, fused in-frame with *CAT* in pCAT by the use of polylinkers. For transient transfection of COS cells we used DEAE-dextran and chloroquine as described[27]. For stable transfection of PC12 cells we used a neomycin-resistance plasmid co-transfected with the plasmid of interest on a 1:10 ratio as described[15]. During selection of PC12 cells, 400 µg ml^{-1} of active Geneticin (GIBCO) were used. Transient transfection of PC12 cells was by electroporation with the BioRad electroporation system using 300 V and 960 µF. After 8 h the medium was changed. Twenty-four hours after electroporation the cells were plated on poly-D-lysine-coated coverslips in the presence of 50 ng ml^{-1} NGF and analysed 24 h later. For immunochemical assays, rabbit anti-GAP-43 antibodies were made by immunizing rabbits against four peptides including amino-acid residues 1–24, 35–53, 53–69, and 212–228 of rat GAP-43. Anti-GAP-43 antibody was affinity-purified on GAP peptide agarose. Anti-GAP antibody was bound to a resin which contained 10 mg ml^{-1} of each peptide coupled to agarose by the cyanogen bromide method, and the antibody was eluted at pH 3.5. Rabbit anti-CAT antibodies were obtained from 5 Prime-3 Prime Inc. Secondary antibodies were obtained from Organon Teknika, Jackson Immunologicals and Vector Labs. For cell fractionation, COS or PC12 cells were scraped from 100-mm confluent Petri dishes and pelleted at 2,000*g* for 10 min. The pelleted cells were homogenized by Polytron in 10 mM Tris-HCl, 1 mM EDTA, pH 7.6 (300 µl per dish) and centrifuged at 250,000*g* for 30 min at 4°C. The supernatant was collected as the cytosolic fraction. The pellet was washed by homogenization and centrifugation in the same buffer, and then resuspended to the same volume as the cytosol fraction. Rat brain was obtained from 3-day-old rats and homogenized by Polytron in 10 mM Tris-HCl, 1 mM EDTA, pH 7.6 (10 ml per gram of wet-weight tissue). The cytosolic and washed-membrane fractions were prepared by centrifugation as described for the cell extracts. GAP-43 protein was purified from rat brain by a modification of the method of Andreasen *et al.*[28] and used as a positive control for immunostaining. The same volume of cytosolic or membrane fraction (usually 100 µl) was electrophoresed on polyacrylamide gels[29]. Proteins were electrophoretically transferred to nitrocellulose and excess sites were blocked with 4% BSA. Membranes were then incubated for 24 h at 4°C with 40 µg ml^{-1} affinity-purified anti-GAP, or a 1:1,000 dilution of anti-CAT antibodies. Bound antibody was detected using anti-rabbit horseradish-peroxidase method (Vectastain) according to the manufacturer's instructions. Tetramethyl benzidine (Kirkegaard and Perry, Gaithersburg, Maryland) was used as peroxidase substrate.

We investigated the cellular distribution of GAP-43 and the GAP-CAT chimaeric proteins in nerve growth factor (NGF)-treated transfectants of PC12 cells by confocal microscopy to determine whether the N-terminus accounts for the growth-cone enrichment of GAP-43 in neuronal cells. In this assay, CAT remained cytosolic (Fig. 3*a*), whereas GAP-43 was distributed in a punctate pattern with notable enrichment in many growth cones (Fig. 3*b*), a pattern similar to that of native GAP-43 in neurons. The N-terminus of GAP-43, which

26.6K。*b*. PC12 细胞中 GAP 和 GAP$_{40}$CAT 与膜结合，按如下所述选择 CAT、GAP$_{40}$CAT 或 GAP 表达稳定的转染 PC12 细胞。使用免疫印迹的方法通过抗 CAT 抗体（左图）或抗 GAP 抗体（右图）检测膜（M）和胞质（C）组分。CAT 转染细胞（CAT）含有的免疫反应性在胞质中而非膜中，而且这一具免疫反应性的 CAT 与纯化的 CAT（左图右下横线）共迁移。与此形成对比的是 GAP$_{40}$CAT 转染细胞在膜组分中具有 CAT 免疫反应性，并且迁移得更慢（上部横线）。来自大鼠脑（BR）的组分显示大部分但非所有内源 GAP-43 的免疫反应性在膜组分中。在转染的 PC12 细胞中过表达的 GAP-43（PC12），几乎所有免疫反应性都在膜中，并且与纯化的 GAP-43（GAP；如最右侧横线所示）共迁移。

方法。 在 GAP-43 表达质粒 pGAP 中，GAP-43 编码序列取代了位于锡德[25]所述 CDM8 质粒的 *Xba*I 位点的填充区域。插入的 GAP-43 序列包括大鼠 GAP-43 的全编码序列，从位于翻译起点的 *Nla*Ⅲ位点直到距离下游终止密码子[8]68 个碱基对的 *Sau*3AI 位点。CAT 表达质粒 pCAT 用含有 CAT 编码序列的 *Hind*Ⅲ-*Bam*HI 片段和来自 pSV2CAT[26]的聚腺苷酸化位点取代含有填充区域和聚腺苷酸化位点的 CDM8 的 *Hind* Ⅲ -*Bam*HI 片段。质粒 pGAP$_{40}$CAT 和 pGAP$_{10}$CAT 分别包括编码 GAP-43 的前 40 或前 10 个氨基酸的序列，通过含多克隆位点的接头在同一阅读框中与 pCAT 中的 *CAT* 融合。如同以前描述[27]的那样，我们使用了 DEAE 葡聚糖和氯喹对 COS 细胞进行瞬时转染。至于 PC12 细胞的稳定转染，如同以前描述[15]的那样，我们使用按 1∶10 比例混合的具有新霉素抗性质粒和感兴趣的质粒共同转染细胞。在 PC12 细胞的筛选过程中，使用了 400 μg·ml⁻¹ 的活性遗传霉素（GLBCO）。用 BioRad 电穿孔系统，通过电穿孔（300 V，960 μF）转染 PC12 细胞。8 小时后换培养基。电穿孔 24 小时后，将细胞置于多聚赖氨酸包被的盖玻片上，培养液中 NGF 浓度为 50 ng·ml⁻¹，并在 24 小时后分析。为了进行免疫组化实验，用包含大鼠 GAP-43 的氨基酸残基 1~24、35~53、53~69 以及 212~228 的 4 个肽段免疫兔子，以制备兔源抗 GAP-43 抗体。在 GAP 肽琼脂糖上亲和纯化抗 GAP-43 抗体。通过溴化氰方法使含有 10 mg·ml⁻¹ 的每一多肽的树脂与琼脂糖偶联，再使抗 GAP 抗体结合到这一树脂，并在 pH 3.5 的条件下洗脱抗体。从 5 Prime-3 Prime 公司获得兔源抗 CAT 抗体。从欧加农泰尼克，杰克逊免疫学和载体实验室获得二级抗体。为了提取细胞各种组分，从长满细胞的直径 100 mm 培养皿上刮下 COS 或 PC12 细胞，2,000g 离心 10 分钟。在包含 10 mM Tris-HCl 和 1 mM EDTA 且 pH 7.6（每个培养皿 300 μl）缓冲液中用 Polytron 对离心获得的细胞进行匀浆，并于 4℃ 250,000g 离心 30 分钟。收集上清作为胞质可溶性组分。剩下的沉淀在同一缓冲溶液中匀浆和离心，然后重新悬浮达到与胞质组分相同体积。取 3 日龄大鼠的大脑，并在包含 10 mM Tris-HCl 和 1 mM EDTA 且 pH 7.6 溶液中（每克湿重组织用 10 ml 溶液）用 Polytron 匀浆。像描述的那样，通过离心制备可溶性胞质和洗脱过的膜组分。使用安德烈亚森等所提出的修订后的方法[28]来纯化大鼠脑的 GAP-43 蛋白。并以此作为免疫染色的阳性对照。在聚丙烯酰胺胶[29]上电泳分离相同体积的可溶性胞质或膜组分（通常是 100 μl）。电转蛋白到硝酸纤维膜上，并用 4%BSA 封闭过量位点。用 40 μg·ml⁻¹ 亲和纯化的抗 GAP 抗体或 1∶1000 稀释的抗 CAT 抗体在 4℃ 条件下孵育膜 24 小时。使用抗兔辣根过氧化物酶方法（Vectastain 试剂盒），遵照厂商的使用说明检测结合抗体。使用四甲基联苯胺（马里兰州盖瑟斯堡的柯克加德和佩里实验室）作为过氧化物酶的底物。

我们用共聚焦显微技术研究了 GAP-43 和 GAP-CAT 融合蛋白在神经生长因子（NGF）处理过的转染 PC12 细胞中的分布，以确定 N 端是否在 GAP-43 在神经细胞生长锥富集过程中起作用。在这一实验中，CAT 保留在可溶性胞质中（图 3*a*），而 GAP-43 呈点状分布并明显富集在很多生长锥中（图 3*b*），与神经元中的天然

was fused to CAT, caused the resulting fusion protein to acquire a distribution that closely resembled that of GAP-43 itself (Fig. 3c, d). Perinuclear labelling for both GAP-43 and the chimaeric protein was detected at a low level, and may have been due to localization to the Golgi, as has been observed for native GAP-43[16]. Glutaraldehyde fixation provided better histological preservation of the finer processes of the growth cones, and revealed that the chimaeric protein accumulated especially within filopodia (Fig. 4).

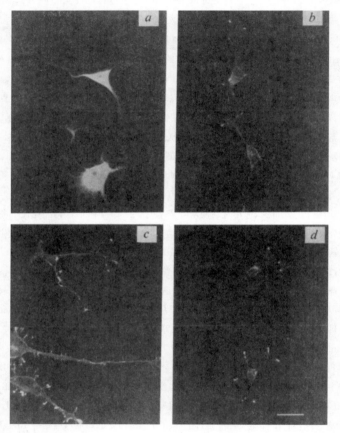

Fig. 3. Subcellular localization of CAT, GAP-43 and fusion proteins in transfected PC12 cells. Confocal immunofluorescence of CAT (a), GAP-43 (b), GAP$_{40}$CAT (c), and GAP$_{10}$CAT (d) in PC12 cells. Two representative fields of cells transfected with each plasmid are shown. CAT labelling is diffuse and cytosolic, whereas GAP-43 is localized to the membrane in a punctate fashion with some enrichment in the growth cones. When either the N-terminal 40 amino acids (GAP$_{40}$CAT) or 10 amino acids (GAP$_{10}$CAT) were fused to CAT, the immunofluorescent distribution resembled that for GAP-43, including enrichment in growth cones. All cells were treated with NGF for 24 h before fixation. Anti-CAT antibody was used for a, c, and d, whereas anti-GAP-43 antibody was used for b. Control PC12 cells of this variant expressed undetectable levels of GAP-43 and CAT immunoreactivity. Scale bar, 25 μm.

Methods. PC12 cells were transferred to poly-D-lysine-coated coverslips 24 h before immunofluorescence in the presence of 50 μg ml^{-1} NGF, fixed with 3.7% formaldehyde for 7 min, and made permeable with 0.1% Triton X-100 for 3 min. The samples were blocked with 4% BSA in PBS for 1 h, incubated for 1 h in primary antibody, rinsed with PBS, incubated in 0.3% H$_2$O$_2$ in PBS for 15 min (to reduce background), rinsed again and incubated for 1 h in secondary antibody. After washing with PBS several times, coverslips were rinsed with water and mounted with Gelvatol containing 0.4% n-propyl gallate to decrease bleaching. Immunofluorescence was not detectable above background when cells did not contain specific antigens or when the primary or secondary antibodies were omitted.

GAP-43 类似。GAP-43 N 端与 CAT 融合，使融合蛋白获得了非常类似 GAP-43 自身的分布（图 3c、d）。检测到 GAP-43 和融合蛋白在细胞核周围标记水平都很低，这可能因为它们和观察到的天然 GAP-43[16] 一样定位到高尔基体。戊二醛固定对生长锥的精细突起形态保存更好，并揭示了融合蛋白的积累，尤其是在丝状伪足中（图 4）。

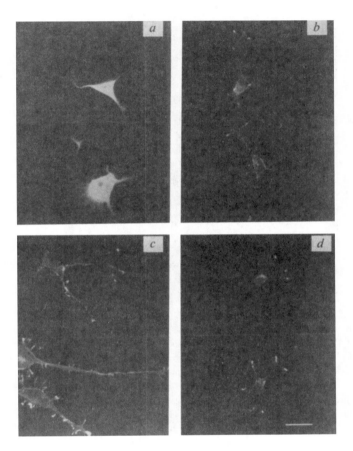

图 3. CAT、GAP-43 和融合蛋白在被转染的 PC12 细胞中的亚细胞定位。在 PC12 细胞中的 CAT（a）、GAP-43（b）、GAP$_{40}$CAT（c）以及 GAP$_{10}$CAT（d）的共聚焦免疫荧光结果。图片显示了用每一质粒转染的两个典型视野。CAT 标记是弥散的，并且分布在可溶性胞质中，而 GAP-43 位于膜上，呈点状分布，在生长锥中有一些富集。当 N 端的 40 个氨基酸（GAP$_{40}$CAT）或 10 个氨基酸（GAP$_{10}$CAT）与 CAT 融合，免疫荧光的分布类似 GAP-43 的结果，包括在生长锥中富集。所有细胞在固定前用 NGF 处理 24 小时。对 a、c 以及 d 使用抗 CAT 抗体，而对 b 使用抗 GAP-43 抗体。作为对照的 PC12 细胞表达的 GAP-43 和 CAT 的免疫反应性在可检测水平以下。比例尺为 25 μm。

方法。将 PC12 细胞转移到多聚赖氨酸覆盖的盖玻片上，用 50 μg·ml^{-1} NGF 培养液培养 24 小时后进行免疫荧光实验，用 3.7% 甲醛溶液固定 7 分钟，0.1% Triton X-100 处理 3 分钟，使细胞变得通透。用含 4%BSA 的 PBS 封闭 1 小时，加一抗孵育 1 小时，用 PBS 冲洗，在含 0.3%H$_2$O$_2$ 的 PBS 溶液中孵育 15 分钟（以降低背景），再次冲洗，然后加二抗孵育 1 小时。在用 PBS 洗涤数次后，用水冲洗盖玻片，然后加含 0.4% 3,4,5- 三羟基苯甲酸正丙酯的 Gelvatol 以减少褪色。当细胞不含有特异性抗原或忽略一抗二抗时，背景上的免疫荧光是检测不到的。

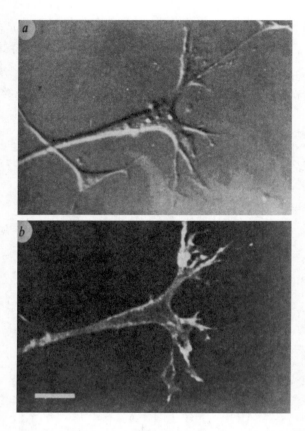

Fig. 4. Localization of $GAP_{40}CAT$ in the growth cone of a PC12 cell. A high power comparison of PC12 cells expressing $GAP_{40}CAT$ viewed with Nomarski optics (top) and scanning confocal immunofluorescence, labelled with anti-CAT antibodies (bottom). Cells had been treated with NGF for 7 days. One growth cone is brightly labelled, but the smaller one is not. Unequal labelling of different growth cones, even of the same cells, occurs for native GAP-43 in neurons[30] and did for the cells here. Comparison of the two images shows that filopodia are especially labelled. Similar results were seen for $GAP_{10}CAT$ (data not shown). Scale bar, 5 μm.

Methods. For high resolution confocal microscopy, the cells were fixed with freshly made 4% paraformaldehyde and 0.5% glutaraldehyde, which was essential to preserve the fine structure of the filopodia, and then with 0.1% Triton X-100 for 3 min and 2 mg ml⁻¹ sodium borohydrate in PBS for 10 min. Confocal analysis used a BioRad MRC-500 scanning confocal imaging system and a Zeiss Axioplan microscope.

Thus, the first 10 amino acids of GAP-43 suffice to direct the cellular distribution of GAP-43. We are not aware of other proteins that have a sequence closely related to the GAP-43 N-terminus, although at least one other non-integral membrane protein that accumulates in growth-cone membranes, SCG 10 (ref. 17) has two cysteines in close proximity (at positions 22 and 24). In polarized epithelial cells, different proteins accumulate in the apical and basolateral plasma membranes[1,18,19], a process believed to depend on sorting signals in the protein, similar to the signals that direct traffic of membrane- and secreted proteins to their particular destinations[20-22]. For epithelial cells, such signals would also

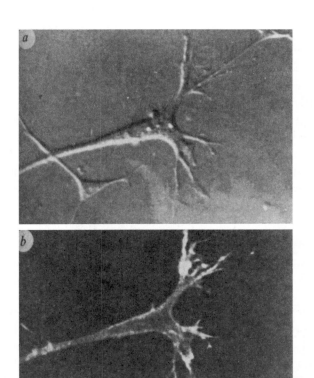

图 4. GAP$_{40}$CAT 在 PC12 细胞生长锥中的定位。表达 GAP$_{40}$CAT 的 PC12 细胞在高倍下诺马斯基光学图像（顶部）与用抗 CAT 抗体染色的免疫荧光共聚焦扫描结果（底部）比较。细胞用 NGF 处理了 7 天。一个生长锥被染得很亮，但是稍小一点的生长锥不是这样。不同生长锥标记程度不同，甚至同一细胞的生长锥染色也不相同，这种情况发生于神经元[30] 中的天然 GAP-43，而这里的细胞也是如此。两幅图的比较显示，特别是丝状伪足被染色。类似的结果也见于 GAP$_{10}$CAT（数据未展示）。比例尺为 5 μm。

方法。为进行高分辨率共聚焦显微分析，用新鲜配制的 4% 多聚甲醛和 0.5% 戊二醛固定细胞，后者对于保存丝状伪足的精细结构来说是必需的，然后用 0.1% Triton X-100 处理 3 分钟，并用含 2 mg·ml^{-1} 硼氢化钠的 PBS 溶液处理 10 分钟。使用 BioRad MRC-500 扫描共聚焦成像系统和蔡司 Axioplan 显微镜做共聚焦分析。

因此，GAP-43 的前 10 个氨基酸足以指导它在细胞中的分布。虽然至少有一个在生长锥膜中积累的非整合蛋白，SCG10（参考文献 17）有两个邻近的半胱氨酸（在位置 22 和 24），但我们没有发现含有 GAP-43 N 端序列相似序列的其他蛋白。在极化的上皮细胞中，不同的蛋白在细胞膜顶部和底部[1,18,19] 积累，此过程被认为依赖于蛋白中的分选信号，类似于指导膜蛋白以及分泌型蛋白运输到它们特定目的地的信号[20-22]。对于上皮细胞，这样的信号也会识别细胞膜的顶部和底部。在神经元中，

recognize different regions of the plasma membrane as apical or basolateral. In neurons, the growth-cone membrane is also distinctive, although not unique, in its protein make-up. One interesting possibility is that the growth-cone membrane has binding sites that recognize and enhance the binding of the palmitylated N-terminus of GAP-43. Although possible, it seems less likely that the palmitylated residues interact with the lipid bilayer directly, because that would probably cause a more uniform membrane distribution for GAP-43. Along these lines, the fatty acid moiety of another acylated protein, N-myristylated VP4 of the poliovirus, has been shown by X-ray diffraction to interact with specific amino-acid residues of other viral proteins and not with the lipid bilayer[23, 24]. Because GAP-43 and GAP-CAT fusion proteins bind to the membrane of non-neuronal cells, similar or identical binding sites must be present in other cells types. However, because GAP-43 is neuron-specific, these sites would presumably be targets for different proteins in non-neuronal cells. Sorting and selective transport, however, are as likely to account for growth-cone accumulation[31] as is the existence of specialized membrane binding-sites.

It is notable that the sorting domain of GAP-43 caused enrichment especially in many filopodia. This is the normal location of GAP-43 in these cells, as shown by electron microscopy[16]. Given the previous observation that transfected GAP-43 can enhance the propensity of non-neuronal cells to extend filopodia[15], it will be of interest to correlate GAP-43 location with the motile activity of particular filopodia. Finally, the sequence described here may be useful in the delivery of histological markers or other agents to the growth-cone membrane.

(**341**, 345-348; 1989)

Mauricio X. Zuber, Stephen M. Strittmatter & Mark C. Fishman
Developmental Biology Laboratory of the Massachusetts General Hospital Cancer Center, Departments of Medicine and Neurology of Harvard Medical School, and the Howard Hughes Medical Institute, Wellman 4, Massachusetts General Hospital, Boston, Massachusetts 02114, USA

Received 12 June; accepted 14 August 1989.

References:
1. Matlin, K. S. *J. Cell Biol.* **103**, 2565-2568 (1986).
2. Ellis, L., Wallace, I., Abreu, E. & Pfeninger K. H. *J. Cell Biol.* **101**, 1977-1989 (1985).
3. Meiri, K. F., Pfenninger, K. H. & Willard, M. B. *Proc. Natl. Acad. Sci. U.S.A.* **83**, 3537-3541 (1986).
4. Skene, J. H. E. *et al. Science* **233**, 783-786 (1986).
5. De Graan, P. N. E. *et al. Neurosci. Lett.* **61**, 235-241 (1985).
6. Benowitz, L. I. & Routtenberg, A. *Trends Neurosci.* **10**, 527-532 (1987).
7. Skene, J. H. P. A. *Rev. Neurosci.* **12**, 127-156 (1989).
8. Basi, G. S., Jacobson, R. D., Virag, I., Schilling, J. & Skene, J. H. P. *Cell* **49**, 785-791 (1987).
9. Skene, J. H. P. & Virag, I. *J. Cell Biol.* **108**, 613-624 (1989).
10. Karns, L. R., Ng, S.-C., Freeman, J. A. & Fishman, M. C. *Science* **236**, 597-600 (1987).
11. Cimler, B. M., Andreasen, T. J., Andreasen, K. I. & Storm, D. R. *J. Biol. Chem.* **260**, 10784-10788 (1985).
12. Perrone-Bizzozero, N. I., Weiner, D., Hauser, G. & Benowitz, L. I. *J. Neurosci. Res.* **20**, 346-350 (1988).
13. Oestreicher, A. B., Van Dongen, C. J., Zwiers, H. & Gispen, W. H. *J. Neurochem.* **41**, 331-340 (1983).
14. Chan, S. Y., Murakami, K. & Routtenberg, A. *J. Neurosci.* **6**, 3618-3627 (1986).

生长锥膜的蛋白组成也是有特点的，虽然并非独一无二。一个有趣的可能性是，生长锥膜具有能够识别并增强与 GAP-43 的棕榈酰化 N 端结合的结合位点。虽然可能，但棕榈酰化的残基直接与脂质双分子层相互作用的可能性不大，因为可能会引起 GAP-43 更均匀的膜分布。同理，X 射线衍射显示另一乙酰化蛋白，脊髓灰质炎病毒的 N- 十四烷基化的 VP4 蛋白质分子的脂肪酸部分与其他病毒蛋白的特异氨基酸残基相互作用，而并不与脂质双分子层相互作用 [23,24]。由于 GAP-43 和 GAP-CAT 融合蛋白与非神经元细胞的细胞膜结合，类似或相同结合位点必然存在于其他细胞类型中。尽管如此，因为 GAP-43 是神经元特异性的，所以在非神经元细胞中，这些位点大概是其他蛋白的结合靶点。虽然如此，分选和选择性转运就像特化的膜结合位点一样，可能对其生长锥中的积累 [31] 起作用。

很明显，GAP-43 的分选结构域造成了蛋白质的富集，特别是在很多丝状伪足中。如电子显微镜结果所示，在这类细胞中，这是 GAP-43 的正常定位 [16]。根据此前的观察结果，转染的 GAP-43 能够增强非神经元细胞延伸丝状伪足的倾向 [15]，这揭示 GAP-43 的定位与某些丝状伪足的运动活性之间的关系值得研究。最后，这里描述的氨基酸序列可能有助于将组织学标记或其他蛋白质分子定向转运到生长锥膜。

（周平博 翻译；刘佳佳 审稿）

15. Zuber, M. X., Goodman, D. W., Karns, L. R. & Fishman, M. C. *Science* **244**, 1193-1195 (1989).

16. Van Hooff, C. O. M. *et al. J. Cell Biol.* **108**, 1115-1125 (1989).

17. Stein, R., Mori, N., Matthews, K., Lo. L.-C. & Anderson, D. J. *Neuron* **1**, 463-476 (1988).

18. Rodriguez-Boulan, E. J. & Sabatini, D.D. *Proc. Natl. Acad. Sci. U.S.A.* **75**, 5071-5075 (1978).

19. Simmons, K. & Fuller, S. D. *Ann. Rev. Cell Biol.* **1**, 243-288 (1985).

20. Wickner, W. T. & Lodish, H. F. *Science* **230**, 400-407 (1985).

21. Verner, K. & Schatz, G. *Science* **241**, 1307-1313 (1988).

22. Pfeffer, S. R. & Rothman, J. E. *Ann. Rev. Biochem.* **56**, 829-852 (1987).

23. Schultz, A. M., Henderson, L. E. & Oroszlan, S. *A. Rev. Cell Biol.* **4**, 611-647 (1988).

24. Chow, M. *et al. Nature* **327**, 482-486 (1987).

25. Seed, B. *Nature* **329**, 840-846 (1987).

26. Gorman, C. M., Moffat, L. F. & Howard, B. H. *Molec. Cell. Biol.* **2**, 1044-1051 (1982).

27. Zuber, M. X., Simpson, E. R. & Waterman, M. R. *Science* **234**, 1258-1261 (1986).

28. Andreasen, T. J., Leutje, C. W., Heideman, W. & Storm, D. R. *Biochemistry* **22**, 4615-4618 (1983).

29. Laemmli, U. K. *Nature* **227**, 680-685 (1970).

30. Goslin, K., Schreyer, D. J., Skene, J. H. P. & Banker, G. *Nature* **336**, 672-674 (1988).

31. Sargent, P. B. *Trends Neurosci.* **12**, 203-205 (1989).

Acknowledgements. We thank D. Goodman and L. Karns for help with plasmid construction, D. Rosenzweig and A. Pack for technical assistance, J. Garriga, R. Horvitz, P. Matsudaira and M. Shafel from MIT and J. White from the MRC for assistance with and access to confocal microscopy , and J. Jackson for preparation of the manuscript. M.X.Z. is the recipient of a postdoctoral fellowship from the American Cancer Society.

536

Rescue of *bicoid* Mutant *Drosophila* Embryos by Bicoid Fusion Proteins Containing Heterologous Activating Sequences

Wolfgang Driever *et al.*

Editor's Note

The patterning and fate of cells in developing embryos is influenced by so-called "morphogen gradients" of diffusible molecules. German biologists Wolfgang Driever and Christiane Nüsslein-Volhard had previously shown that the transcription factor Bicoid (Bcd) exists along a concentration gradient in *Drosophila* embryos, which in turn influences the expression pattern of other body-patterning genes. Here they team up with molecular biologists Mark Ptashne and Jun Ma to investigate the morphogenetic properties of Bcd. Mutants lacking the *bicoid* (*bcd*) gene develop duplicate posterior structures but lack heads and thoraces. But the embryos can be rescued by injecting them with mRNA encoding fusion proteins consisting of acidic transcriptional activating sequences—peptides that trigger transcription in many eukaryotes—and the *bicoid* DNA-binding domain.

The maternal gene *bicoid* (*bcd*) determines pattern in the anterior half of the *Drosophila* embryo. It is reported here that the injection of *bcd⁻* mutant embryos with messenger RNAs that encode proteins consisting of heterologous acidic transcriptional activating sequences fused to the DNA-binding portion of the *bcd* gene product, can completely restore the anterior pattern of the embryo.

THE *bcd* gene organizes development in the anterior half (head and thorax) of the *Drosophila* embryo[1]. The molecular basis for this morphogen function is a concentration gradient of Bcd protein spanning the anterior two thirds of the syncytial blastoderm stage embryo[2]. The Bcd protein is synthesized from *bcd* mRNA that is localized at the anterior tip of the embryo[3,4], and the concentration of Bcd protein determines positional values along the anterio-posterior axis[5]. Genetic analyses indicate that the zygotic expression of *hunchback* (*hb*), a gap gene that is expressed early in a distinct domain in the anterior 45% of the embryo, is regulated by the Bcd protein[6-9]. Recent experiments demonstrate that Bcd protein binds specifically to the *hb* promoter region and induces the expression of *hb* in both *Drosophila* Schneider cells and the embryo[10]. The binding of Bcd protein to multiple copies of Bcd-binding sites in the upstream region of fusion genes is sufficient to generate an *hb*-like expression pattern in the early embryo[11].

通过含异源激活序列的Bicoid融合蛋白拯救
*bicoid*突变果蝇胚胎

沃尔夫冈·德里费尔等

编者按

胚胎发育过程中细胞的模式建成与命运受到可扩散分子形成的所谓"形态发生素梯度"的影响。德国生物学家沃尔夫冈·德里费尔和克里斯蒂安娜·福尔哈德早前已经揭示转录因子 Bicoid（Bcd）在果蝇胚胎中以浓度梯度的形式存在，此梯度反过来影响其他身体形态建成相关基因的表达模式。本文中他们与分子生物学家马克·普塔什尼和马俊合作研究 Bcd 在形态发生方面的特性。缺失 *bicoid*（*bcd*）基因的突变体发育出重复的后部结构但是缺少头部和胸部。但是这些胚胎可以通过注射某种信使 RNA 获得拯救，这种信使 RNA 编码一种融合蛋白，这种蛋白包含酸性转录激活序列（在许多真核生物中启动转录的多肽）和 *bicoid* 的 DNA 结合域。

母体基因 *bicoid*（*bcd*）决定果蝇胚胎前半部的发育模式。本文报道，将融合蛋白的信使 RNA（mRNA）注入 *bcd⁻* 突变胚胎中，该信使 RNA 编码一个蛋白，该蛋白由异源酸性转录激活序列与 *bcd* 基因产物的 DNA 结合域融合而成，可以完全恢复胚胎前部的构造。

bcd 基因决定果蝇胚胎前半部（头和胸）的发育 [1]。这种形成发生素功能的分子基础是横跨合胞体胚盘期胚胎前三分之二区域的 Bcd 蛋白浓度梯度 [2]。Bcd 蛋白由定位于胚胎前端的 *bcd* mRNA 合成 [3,4]，Bcd 蛋白的浓度决定胚胎前后轴的位置信息 [5]。遗传分析表明一个合子表达的驼背基因（*hb*），是一种早期在胚胎前部 45% 的特定区域内表达的裂隙基因，受 Bcd 蛋白的调控 [6-9]。最近的实验表明 Bcd 蛋白与 *hb* 启动子区特异性结合，并诱导 *hb* 在果蝇的施耐德细胞和胚胎中表达 [10]。早期胚胎中，Bcd 蛋白与融合基因上游多拷贝的 Bcd 结合位点结合足以产生类似 *hb* 的表达模式 [11]。

The N-terminal portion of the 489-amino-acid Bcd protein[4] contains a homoeodomain (residues 92–151), a protein sequence which is conserved among many gene products participating in embryonic pattern formation[12-14], and which is believed to direct specific DNA binding[15-18]. Recent experiments indicate that at least several of the homoeodomain proteins involved in *Drosophila* embryonic pattern formation are transcriptional regulatory proteins[19-21]. Near the N-terminal end of the Bcd protein there is a repeat that is found in the *paired* gene product[3]; this repeat is a sequence of ~30 amino acids, rich in histidine and proline, which is also present in other gene products in *Drosophila*. The function of this repeat, however, is unknown. The C-terminal part of the Bcd protein contains an acidic region (residues 347–414, with 16 acidic and 5 basic residues) as well as a glutamine-rich region (M- or opa-repeat; residues 256–289)[12]. The Bcd protein is also rich in hydroxyl amino acids (37 serines, 27 threonines and 19 tyrosines). In *Drosophila* Schneider cells, and most probably in the embryo, the Bcd protein is phosphorylated at several sites[10]. Wild-type Bcd protein, as well as certain other homoeodomain-containing proteins in *Drosophila*, activate transcription in yeast[18,22], and the protein product of several mutant *bcd* alleles have been analysed for their transcriptional function in yeast[22].

Recent studies on yeast transcriptional activators indicate that a typical activator contains two separable functions: one that directs the activator to specific DNA sequences and another that interacts with some component of the transcriptional machinery[23-26]. For example, the yeast transcriptional activators GAL4 and GCN4, which are involved in galactose metabolism and amino-acid synthesis, respectively, contain acidic activating sequences that interact with the transcriptional machinery[27,28]. The activating sequences of GAL4 can be functionally replaced either by acidic peptides encoded by *Escherichia coli* DNA, or by an acidic peptide designed to form an amphiphilic α-helix[29,30]. Not all acidic peptides function as activating sequences; some aspect of structure, perhaps an α-helix, is required[30]. GAL4, or its derivatives that contain one or more acidic activating sequences fused to the DNA-binding portion of GAL4, also stimulate gene expression in mammalian, insect and plant cells, provided that the sequence to which GAL4 binds is inserted near the promoter of the test gene[31-34]. Other classes of activating sequences have been described[35,36]; none of these, to our knowledge, has been shown to function in many different eukaryotic cells as do the acidic sequences, and some of them have been shown to work only in restricted cell types[36].

Here we describe experiments that show that the Bcd protein activates transcription from the Bcd-binding sites in three different systems—yeast cells, *Drosophila* Schneider cells, and *Drosophila* embryos. We also report that the N-terminal half of the Bcd protein (residues 1–246), which contains the DNA-binding function, has little transcriptional activation function in all three systems. When tested in *Drosophila* embryos by injecting the corresponding mRNA, residues 1–246 of Bcd only partially rescues the mutant *bcd⁻* phenotype, whereas fusion proteins consisting of residues 1–246 of Bcd attached to heterologous acidic activating sequences fully rescue the *bcd⁻* phenotype.

含 489 个氨基酸的 Bcd 蛋白 N 末端 [4] 包含一个同源异型结构域（第 92~151 位残基），这个同源域在许多参与胚胎构造形成的基因产物中都是保守的 [12-14]，可以认为指导特异性的 DNA 结合 [15-18]。最近的实验表明参与果蝇胚胎构造形成的同源异型结构域蛋白中至少有几个是转录调控蛋白 [19-21]。Bcd 蛋白 N 末端附近有一段在 prd 基因产物中发现的重复序列 [3]，这个重复序列约含 30 个氨基酸，富含组氨酸和脯氨酸，该重复序列在果蝇其他基因产物也存在。然而这个重复序列的功能尚未知。Bcd 蛋白的 C 末端含一个酸性区（第 347~414 位残基，有 16 个酸性残基和 5 个碱性残基）和一个富含谷氨酰胺的区域（甲硫氨酸或 opa 重复；第 256~289 位残基）[12]。Bcd 蛋白也富含羟基氨基酸（37 个丝氨酸、27 个苏氨酸和 19 个酪氨酸）。在果蝇的施耐德细胞中并且最可能在胚胎中，Bcd 蛋白几个位点是磷酸化的 [10]。研究人员已经分析了若干 bcd 突变等位基因的蛋白产物在酵母中的转录功能 [22]，发现果蝇的野生型 Bcd 蛋白及其他某些含同源域的蛋白，可在酵母中激活转录 [18, 22]。

最近对酵母转录激活子的研究表明一个典型的激活子包含两个独立的功能：一个是介导激活子结合到特异 DNA 序列上，另一个是与转录机器的某些组件相互作用 [23-26]。例如，酵母转录激活子 GAL4 和 GCN4，分别参与半乳糖代谢和氨基酸合成，它们包含与转录机器相互作用的酸性激活序列 [27,28]。GAL4 激活序列功能可被大肠杆菌 DNA 编码的酸性多肽或可形成两性 α 螺旋结构的酸性多肽所取代。并不是所有酸性多肽都具有激活序列的功能；某种特定的结构，可能是一个 α 螺旋，是必需的 [30]。GAL4 或它的衍生物包含一个或多个与其 DNA 结合域融合的酸性活性序列，也能在哺乳动物、昆虫和植物细胞中激活基因表达，只要与 GAL4 结合的序列插入在检测基因的启动子附近 [31-34]。其他类型的激活序列也有过报道 [35, 36]；据我们所知，它们都不能像酸性序列一样在许多不同的真核细胞中起作用，其中有一些仅在有限的细胞类型中起作用 [36]。

本文描述的实验证明在三种不同体系——酵母细胞、果蝇施耐德细胞和果蝇胚胎中，Bcd 蛋白通过 Bcd 结合位点激活转录。我们也报道了一半的有 DNA 结合功能的 Bcd 蛋白 N 末端（第 1~246 位残基）在上述三种体系中很少有转录激活功能。通过向果蝇胚胎注射相应的 mRNA 做检测时，Bcd 的 1~246 位残基只能部分拯救突变体 bcd⁻ 的突变表型，而 Bcd 1~246 位残基与异源酸性激活序列的融合蛋白则能完全拯救突变体 bcd⁻ 的表型。

Transcriptional Activation by Bcd Derivatives

Transcriptional activity in yeast was measured in cells bearing an integrated *GAL1–lacZ* fusion gene[37] containing three strong Bcd-binding sites[10,11]. These yeast cells also contained plasmids expressing, from the yeast *ADH1* promoter[38], genes encoding the *Drosophila* Bcd protein or one of its C-terminal deletion derivatives. The activities of Bcd derivatives in *Drosophila* Schneider cells were measured by co-transfecting the cells with a reporter plasmid containing the gene for chloramphenicol acetyl transferase (CAT) fused to the *hb* gene, and effector plasmids expressing the Bcd protein or one of its derivatives. For the assay in embryos, mRNAs encoding the Bcd protein or one of its derivatives were synthesized *in vitro*. These were then co-microinjected with a plasmid containing the reporter gene *hb-298CAT* into the anterior half of pre-polecell stage embryos from females homozygous for *bcd^El*, a strong *bcd* allele bearing a large deletion[1,4,22]. The injected mRNA is efficiently translated, as revealed by immunohistological stainings of the injected embryos for Bcd protein (data not shown). The reporter DNA might enter the nuclei during the rapid syncytial nuclear divisions and the *hb-CAT* fusion gene is transcribed under the control of the Bcd protein[10]. About 3 h after injection, at the onset of gastrulation, CAT enzyme activity was measured in extracts prepared from the injected embryos (Table 1).

Table 1. Activities of Bcd protein and its deletion derivatives

Effector	Yeast	*Drosophila* Schneider cells	*Drosophila* embryos	
	β-gal activities (hb-GAL1–lacZ)	CAT activities (hb–298CAT)	CAT activities (hb–298CAT)	Rescue of *bcd⁻* mutant phenotype
Wt Bcd (1–489)	125	45	40	complete
Bcd (1–396)	12	36	35	complete
Bcd (1–348)	12	9*	19	complete
Bcd (1–246)	13	8	8	partial
Bcd (1–111)	<1	2	2	none
None	<1	2	2	—

The stimulatory effect of Bcd protein on *hb* transcription was assayed in yeast, *Drosophila* Schneider cells and *Drosophila* embryos. Yeast—plasmids expressing Bcd or its deletion derivatives were transformed into a yeast strain (GGY1:: MA630R) containing an integrated *GAL1–lacZ* fusion gene; the *hb* promoter element bearing the Bcd protein binding sites[10] was located upstream of the *GAL1* gene. *Drosophila* Schneider cells—the effector plasmids, which express from the *Drosophila* metallothionein promoter various Bcd deletion derivatives, were transfected into Schneider cells together with the reporter plasmid hbCAT-289 which expresses the *E. coli CAT* gene from the *hb* promoter bearing the Bcd-protein-binding sites. CAT activities (percent acetylated forms of total chloramphenicol) are shown.* In Schneider cells, instead of Bcd (1–348), the derivative Bcd (1–338) was used. *Drosophila* embryos—*in vitro* transcribed mRNAs encoding Bcd protein and its deletion derivatives were co-injected with the reporter plasmid hbCAT-298 into the anterior half of pre-pole cell stage embryos derived from females homozygous for *bcd^El*. CAT activities were determined at the onset of gastrulation. The rescue of the *bcd⁻* mutant phenotype is described in detail in Fig. 2 and Table 3a.

The yeast strain used in these experiments is derived from GGY1 (*ura3, leu2, his3, Δgal4, Δgal80*) (ref. 46) by integrating at the *URA3* locus a modified *GAL1–lacZ* fusion gene. The plasmid pMA630R, which was used to generate GGY1:: MA630R, was constructed by inserting the *Hind*III–*Mlu*I fragment from the plasmid hbCAT-298 (ref. 10) into the *Xho*I site of LR1Δ1Δ2μ(ref. 37). The plasmids expressing Bcd deletion proteins were constructed in two steps. First, the *Xba*I linker (5'-CTAGTCTAGACTAG-3'), which contains translational stop codons in all three reading frames,

由 Bcd 衍生物引起的转录激活

在含有整合的 *GAL1–lacZ* 融合基因[37]的细胞中检测酵母中的转录活性，该基因含三个强 Bcd 结合位点[10,11]。这些酵母细胞也包含质粒，这些质粒通过酵母 *ADH1* 启动子[38]表达编码果蝇 Bcd 蛋白或它的一个 C 端缺失衍生物的基因。果蝇施耐德细胞中 Bcd 衍生物的活性是通过将细胞与一个报告基因质粒和一个效应基因质粒共同转染测定的，报告基因质粒中氯霉素乙酰转移酶（CAT）与 *hb* 基因融合，而效应基因质粒表达 Bcd 蛋白或它的一个衍生物。在胚胎实验中编码 Bcd 蛋白或其衍生物的 mRNA 在体外合成。然后与含报告基因 *hb-298CAT* 的质粒共同显微注射到 *bcd^{E1}* 雌性纯合子的前极细胞期胚胎的前半部，*bcd^{E1}* 是 *bcd* 一个大片段缺失的强等位基因[1,4,22]。在注射过的胚胎中用胚胎免疫组织学染色检测 Bcd 蛋白（数据未显示），结果显示注射的 mRNA 被有效地翻译了。报告基因的 DNA 可能在快速合胞体核分裂期间进入核中，并且 *hb-CAT* 融合基因在 Bcd 蛋白控制下转录[10]。注射约 3 小时后，在原肠胚形成初期，注射胚胎的提取物中检测到 CAT 酶活性（表 1）。

表 1. Bcd 蛋白及其缺失衍生物的活性

效应基因	酵母	果蝇施耐德细胞	果蝇胚胎	
	β–半乳糖苷酶活性（hb-GAL1–lacZ）	CAT活性(hb–298CAT)	CAT活性(hb–298CAT)	*bcd^-*突变表型的拯救
野生型Bcd(1~489)	125	45	40	完全
Bcd(1~396)	12	36	35	完全
Bcd(1~348)	12	9 *	19	完全
Bcd(1~246)	13	8	8	部分
Bcd(1~111)	<1	2	2	无
无	<1	2	2	—

在酵母、果蝇施耐德细胞和果蝇胚胎中检验 Bcd 蛋白对 *hb* 转录的激活效应。酵母——将表达 Bcd 或其缺失衍生物的质粒转化到一个酵母菌株（GGY1∷MA630R）中，这个菌株包含整合的 *GAL1–lacZ* 融合基因；含有 Bcd 蛋白结合位点[10]的 *hb* 启动子元件位于 *GAL1* 基因的上游。果蝇施耐德细胞——效应基因质粒通过果蝇金属硫蛋白启动子表达各种 Bcd 缺失衍生物，与报告基因质粒 hbCAT-289 一起转入施耐德细胞，这种报告基因质粒通过具有 Bcd 蛋白结合位点的 *hb* 启动子表达大肠杆菌 *CAT* 基因。CAT 活性（总氯霉素乙酰化形式的百分比）如表所示。* 在施耐德细胞中用的不是 Bcd（1~348），而是衍生 Bcd（1~338）。果蝇胚胎—体外转录的编码 Bcd 蛋白及其缺失衍生物与报告基因质粒 hbCAT-298 一起注射到 *bcd^{E1}* 雌性纯合子产生的前极细胞期胚胎前半部分。在原肠胚形成初期测定 CAT 活性。对 *bcd^-* 突变表型拯救的详细描述见图 2 和表 3*a*。

这些实验中用的酵母菌株是通过在 GGY1（*ura3*、*leu2*、*his3*、*Δgal4*、*Δgal80*）（参考文献46）的 *URA3* 位点整合一个修饰过的 *GAL1–lacZ* 融合基因得到的。用于产生 GGY1∷MA630R 的质粒 pMA630R 是通过将质粒 hbCAT-298（参考文献 10）的 *HindIII–MluI* 片段插入到 LR1Δ1Δ2μ（参考文献 37）的 *XhoI* 位点构建起来的。构建表达 Bcd 缺失蛋白的质粒分两步。第一，将在所有三个阅读框中包含转录终止密码子的 *XbaI* 接头

was inserted at different positions in the *bcd* gene in the plasmid pTN3bcd, an expression vector (Sp6 promoter) for the Bcd-encoding region with the frog globin mRNA leader[39]. Then, either the intact or modified Bcd encoding regions were inserted into the *Hin*dIII site of the yeast plasmid AAH5 containing the yeast *ADH1* promoter[38]. The *Xba*I linker was inserted at the following positions: *Pst*I site (at residue 111), *Sal*I site (at residue 246), *Acc*I site (at residue 348) and *Bgl*II site (at residues 396). The β-galactosidase (β-gal) activities were measured in yeast cells grown in synthetic minimal medium lacking leucine with glycerol and ethanol as carbon sources[47]. For Schneider cells, modified Bcd encoding regions containing stop codons at various positions were inserted into plasmid pRmHa-3, a *Drosophila* expression vector bearing the metallothionein promoter[48]. Unlike the Bcd (1–348) protein, which was generated by inserting the stop codon linker at the *Acc*I site, we used Bcd (1–338) in Schneider cells, the stop linker being inserted at the *Ava*I site. The procedures for Schneider-cell transfection, the reporter plasmid hbCAT-298 and CAT assay were as described previously[10,49]. Twelve hours after transfection, the culture medium was replaced by the medium containing 1 mM $CuCl_2$ to induce the metallothionein promoter, and the CAT activities were assayed 24 h later. The transfection efficiency was normalized by the β-gal activity expressed from the third transfected plasmid pPAclacZ (ref. 10). For the assays in yeast and Schneider cells, synthesis of the various Bcd proteins was tested by immunoblotting analysis (Fig. 1). For *Drosophila* embryos, mRNAs coding for Bcd protein or its deletion derivatives were transcribed *in vitro* by Sp6 RNA polymerase[50] from plasmid pTN3bcd and its derivatives (see above). The mRNAs (0.5 μg μl^{-1}) were co-injected with the reporter plasmid phbCAT-298(1 μg μl^{-1}) into the anterior half of pre-pole cell stage embryos from females homozygous for *bcd*[51]. At the onset of gastrulation, extracts were prepared and CAT activities were determined as described previously[10]. All assays described above were done in quadruplicate. For assays in yeast and Schneider cells, the standard error of the mean (s. e. m.) was normally <20%; for assays in *Drosophila* embryos the s. e. m. was 20% (for wild-type (wt) Bcd), 26% (for Bcd1–396) and 50–60% (for the shorter truncations).

Table 1 describes transcriptional activation by the Bcd protein and various deletion derivatives in the three assays, as well as the results of experiments measuring rescue of *bcd*⁻ embryos (see later). Wild-type Bcd protein activates transcription in all three systems. Deletion of 83 C-terminal residues from the Bcd protein creates a derivative containing residues 1–396, Bcd (1–396), which activates transcription only 10% as efficiently in yeast as does the wild-type Bcd protein, but 80% as efficiently as does the wild-type protein in *Drosophila* cells and embryos. Derivative Bcd (1–338) has lost most of its ability to activate transcription in Schneider cells, but activates ~50% as efficiently as wild-type Bcd protein in *Drosophila* embryos. Derivative Bcd (1–246) activates transcription only slightly in all three systems, and Bcd (1–111), which contains only a third of the homoeodomain, is inactive. Figure 1 shows that proteins of the expected size are synthesized in yeast and Schneider cells. However, the results are obscured somewhat by our lack of knowledge of protein levels in the three test systems but, when taken with the results of the following section, indicate a correlation between the ability of a Bcd derivative to activate transcription in the embryo and its biological function as a morphogen. The fragment Bcd (1–396) has lost part of the acidic sequence of the Bcd protein, and Bcd (1–348) has lost all of it; thus this acidic sequence is not required for all of the transcriptional activation function of the Bcd protein in the embryo.

(5'-CTAGTCTAGACTAG-3'), 插入到质粒 pTN3bcd 中 bcd 基因的不同位置, pTN3bcd 是一个表达 Bcd 编码区的载体 (Sp6 启动子), 它带有蛙珠蛋白 mRNA 前导序列 [39]。然后, 将完整的或修饰过的 Bcd 编码区插入到含酵母 ADH1 启动子的酵母质粒 AAH5 的 HindIII 位点 [38]。将 XbaI 接头插入到以下位置: PstI 位点 (位于 111 位残基)、SalI 位点 (位于 246 位残基)、AccI 位点 (位于 348 位残基)、BglII 位点 (位于 396 位残基)。β-半乳糖苷酶活性以在丙三醇和乙醇作碳源且缺少亮氨酸的合成基本培养基上培养的酵母细胞中测定 [47]。对施耐德细胞, 将修饰过的含有位于不同位置的终止子 Bcd 编码区插入到质粒 pRmHa-3 中, pRmHa-3 是具有金属硫蛋白启动子的果蝇表达载体 [48]。不像将终止密码子接头插入 AccI 位点得到 Bcd (1~348) 蛋白, 在施耐德细胞中我们用 Bcd (1~338), 是将终止密码子接头插在 AvaI 位点。施耐德细胞的转染策略, 报告基因质粒 hbCAT-298 和 CAT 检测已有描述 [10,49]。转染后 12 小时, 将培养基换为含 1mM 氯化铜的培养基, 以诱导金属硫蛋白启动子, 并在 24 小时后检测 CAT 活性。转染效率通过第三个转化质粒 pPAclacZ (参考文献 10) 表达的 β-半乳糖苷酶的活性校正。在酵母和施耐德细胞实验中, 各种 Bcd 蛋白的合成通过免疫印迹分析检测 (图 1)。果蝇胚胎实验中, Bcd 蛋白或其缺失衍生物的 mRNA 在体外通过 Sp6 RNA 聚合酶由 pTN3bcd 和它的衍生物转录而来 (见上文)。mRNA (0.5 μg·μl⁻¹) 与报告基因质粒 phbCAT-298 (1 μg·μl⁻¹) 一起注射到 bcd^{EI} 雌性纯合子的极细胞前期胚胎的前半部。在原肠胚形成初期, 按以前的描述制备提取物和测定 CAT 活性 [10]。上述所有实验都做了四次。酵母和施耐德细胞实验的平均标准误差 (s.e.m.) 通常 < 20%; 果蝇胚胎实验的平均标准误差是 20% (野生型 (wt) Bcd)、26% (Bcd1~396) 及 50%~60% (更短片段)。

表 1 描述了在三个实验中 Bcd 蛋白及其各种缺失衍生物的转录激活, 及拯救 bcd⁻ 胚胎的实验检测结果 (见后文)。野生型 Bcd 蛋白在三种实验体系中都激活转录。Bcd 蛋白缺失 C 末端 83 个残基产生一个 1~396 个残基的衍生物, Bcd (1~396), 它在酵母中激活转录的效率只有野生型 Bcd 蛋白的 10%, 但在施耐德细胞和果蝇胚胎中的效率为野生型蛋白的 80%。衍生物 Bcd (1~338) 在施耐德细胞中丢失了大部分转录激活功能, 但在果蝇胚胎中的转录激活效率为野生型 Bcd 的 50%。衍生物 (1~246) 在三种体系中只能微弱地激活转录, Bcd (1~111) 只包含三分之一的同源异型结构域, 无活性。图 1 显示了在酵母和施耐德细胞中预期大小的蛋白的合成。然而, 由于我们缺乏这三个检测系统的蛋白质水平的知识, 这些结果有些不明朗, 但当此结果与随后的部分结合, 则表明一种 Bcd 衍生物在胚胎中激活转录的能力与它作为形态发生素的生物学功能之间的相互关系。片段 Bcd (1~396) 缺失 Bcd 蛋白酸性序列的一部分, Bcd (1~348) 缺失了所有酸性序列; 因此这个酸性序列不是胚胎中 Bcd 蛋白所有转录激活功能所必需的。

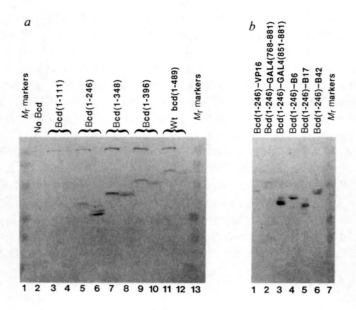

Fig. 1. Immunoblotting assays. *a*, The intact Bcd protein and deletion derivatives synthesized in yeast (lanes 4, 6, 8, 10 and 12; lane 2, yeast extracts without Bcd protein) and *Drosophila* Schneider cells (lanes 3, 5, 7, 9 and 11). The predicted relative molecular masses (M_r) are ($M_r \times 10^{-3}$): wild-type Bcd, 54 (ref. 4); Bcd (1–396), 44; Bcd (1–348), 39; Bcd (1–246), 28; and Bcd (1–111), 13. The monoclonal antibody does not react with Bcd (1–111). The apparent M_r of the proteins including wild-type Bcd protein are higher than predicted. The electrophoretic mobilities of the proteins synthesized in yeast are relatively higher than those of the proteins from Schneider cells; the possible effect of different post-translational modifications in yeast and Schneider cells is discussed in the text. *b*, The Bcd fusion proteins synthesized in yeast. The predicted M_r of the fusion proteins are ($M_r \times 10^{-3}$): Bcd (1–246) –VP16 (326 amino acids), 36; Bcd (1–246) –GAL4 (768–881) (361 amino acids), 40; Bcd (1–246) –GAL4 (851–881) (278 amino acids), 31; Bcd (1–246) –B6 (334 amino acids), 37; Bcd (1–246) –B17 (278 amino acids), 31; and Bcd (1–246)–B42 (337 amino acids), 37. Apparently, the fusion protein Bcd (1–246) –B6 synthesized in yeast migrates faster than expected, and it is possible that most of this protein is degraded; this result may be related to the observation that Bcd (1–246) –B6 is not very active in yeast cells (see Table 2). The sizes of M_r markers (from BioRad) are ($M_r \times 10^{-3}$): 130, 75, 50, 39, 27 and 17.

Methods. Procedures of preparing proteins from yeast and Schneider cells were as previously described[10,51]. For the yeast proteins in *a*, the yeast cells were grown in 10 ml synthetic minimal medium (lacking leucine) with glycerol and ethanol (optical density at 600 nm (OD_{600}) at 0.8–1.1), and for Bcd fusion proteins in *b*, the yeast cells were grown in 5 ml synthetic minimal medium with glucose (OD_{600} at 1.0–1.7). The amount of protein samples loaded on the protein gel was normalized by the density of the yeast cultures (OD_{600}). Proteins from Schneider cells were expressed from the *Drosophila* metallothionein promoter as described in the legend to Table 1. The derivative Bcd (1–348) in Schneider cells should be Bcd (1–338) (see legend to Table 1 for details). A 12% SDS gel was used to separate the proteins. The first antibody (mouse anti-Bcd)[2] was diluted 1:1,000 and the second antibody (alkaline phosphatase conjugated rabbit anti-mouse IgG) was diluted 1:1,500. Staining procedure was according to the manufacturer's instructions (BRL)

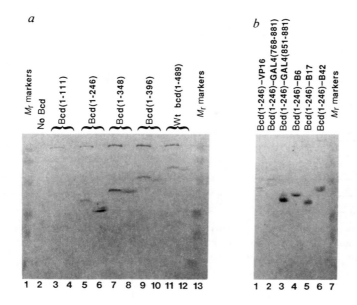

图 1. 免疫印迹实验。*a*，酵母（泳道 4、6、8、10 和 12；泳道 2 是不含 Bcd 蛋白的酵母提取物）和果蝇施耐德细胞（泳道 3、5、7、9 和 11）中合成的完整 Bcd 蛋白和缺失衍生物。预测相对分子量（M_r）为（$M_r \times 10^{-3}$）：野生型 Bcd，54（参考文献 4）；Bcd（1~396），44；Bcd（1~348），39；Bcd（1~246），28 和 Bcd（1~111），13。单克隆抗体不与 Bcd（1~111）作用。包括野生型 Bcd 蛋白，这些蛋白表观相对分子量比预测的大。酵母中合成的蛋白电泳迁移率与施耐德细胞合成的相比较高；可能是酵母细胞和施耐德细胞中不同的翻译后修饰引起的，下文对此进行了讨论。*b*，酵母中合成的 Bcd 融合蛋白。融合蛋白的预测相对分子量为（$M_r \times 10^{-3}$）：Bcd（1~246）–VP16（326 个氨基酸），36；Bcd（1~246）–GAL4（768~881）（361 个氨基酸），40；Bcd（1~246）–GAL4（851~881）（278 个氨基酸）31；Bcd（1~246）–B6（334 个氨基酸），37；Bcd（1~246）–B17（278 个氨基酸），31；Bcd（1~246）–B42（337 个氨基酸），37。显然地，酵母中合成的 Bcd（1~246）–B6 迁移速度比预测快，可能是这个蛋白的大部分降解了，这个结果可能与观察到的 Bcd（1~246）–B6 在酵母细胞中不很活跃有关（见表 2）。相对分子量标记（购自伯乐公司）的大小为（$M_r \times 10^{-3}$）：130、75、50、39、27 和 17。

方法。从酵母和施耐德细胞制备蛋白的步骤参照以前的描述[10,51]。对 *a* 中的酵母蛋白，酵母细胞在 10 ml 含丙三醇和乙醇的人工基本培养基（缺亮氨酸）中培养（600 nm 光密度（OD_{600}）0.8~1.1），对于 *b* 中的 Bcd 融合蛋白，酵母细胞在 5 ml 含葡萄糖的人工基本培养基中培养（OD_{600} 为 1.0~1.7）。蛋白凝胶的蛋白上样量通过酵母培养物 600 nm 处光密度（OD_{600}）归一化。施耐德细胞的蛋白由果蝇金属硫蛋白启动子表达，在表 1 注中描述过了。衍生物 Bcd（1~348）在施耐德细胞中应为 Bcd（1~338）（详细说明见表 1 注）。用 12% 的 SDS 凝胶分离蛋白质。一抗（鼠抗 Bcd）[2] 按 1∶1,000 稀释，二抗（碱性磷酸酶结合的兔抗鼠球蛋白 IgG）按 1∶1,500 稀释。染色步骤按产品操作说明（BRL 公司）。图中出现的单词 M_r Marker：分子量标记；No Bcd：无 Bcd 蛋白。

Table 2. Activities of Bcd fusion proteins

Effector	Yeast β-gal activities (hb–GAL1–lacZ)	*Drosophila* embryos Rescue of *bcd⁻* mutant phenotype
Wt Bcd	125	complete
Bcd (1–246)	13	partial
Bcd (1–246) –VP16	1,307	lethal
Bcd (1–246) –GAL4 (768–881)	953	lethal
Bcd (1–246) –GAL4 (851–881)	342	complete
Bcd (1–246) –B6	43	complete
Bcd (1–246) –B17	105	complete
Bcd (1–246) –B42	367	lethal
None	<1	—

Yeast—plasmids expressing Bcd fusion proteins were transformed into a yeast strain, and β-gal activities measured. See legend to Table 1 for further details. *Drosophila* embryos—the rescue of the *bcd⁻* mutant phenotype by injection of *in vitro* transcribed mRNAs coding for Bcd protein derivatives is described in detail in Fig. 2 and Table 3*b*. Various activating sequences were fused to the *bcd* gene in the plasmid pTN3bcd; these plasmids were also used to synthesize the mRNAs for the assays in *Drosophila* embryos. The activating sequences were obtained from the *Hin*dIII-*Sal*I fragment of the plasmid β58dTX for VP16, and the *Eco*RI-*Sal*I fragments for all the others[28,29]. Then, these *bcd* fusion genes were inserted into the *Hin*dIII site of the yeast expression vector AAH5 (ref. 38). The yeast strain used was GGY1:: MA630R. The assays were done in quadruplicate and the standard error was normally <20%.

Morphogenetic Activities

We tested the morphogenetic activity of the Bcd deletion derivatives by injecting small mounts of corresponding *in vitro*-synthesized mRNAs into the anterior tip of embryos obtained from *bcd^{E1}* mutant females and analysing the cuticle phenotype after one day of development (Tables 1 and 3*a*; Fig. 2). Embryos not injected do not develop heads and thoraces, but instead form duplications of posterior structures anteriorly (Fig. 2*a*). Depending on the concentration, injection of mRNA coding for wild-type Bcd protein can completely rescue the mutant phenotype, and larvae frequently hatch, giving rise to adult flies[39]. Of the deletion derivatives, both Bcd (1–396) and Bcd (1–348) are also able to rescue the mutant phenotype completely. By contrast, Bcd (1–111) does not rescue any aspect of the *bcd⁻* mutant phenotype. The derivative Bcd (1–246) only partially restores the wild-type pattern: it suppresses the formation of posterior structures at the anterior, and induces with high frequency thoracic structures, and more rarely, structures of the segmented region of the head, the labial, maxillary or mandibular segment. But even when the mRNA coding for the derivative Bcd (1–246) is injected at high concentration (5 μg μl⁻¹; Table 3*a*), the embryos never hatch (see Fig. 2*d*). Embryos injected with mRNA encoding the fragment Bcd (1–246) resemble those from females that are homozygous for two of the weak *bcd* alleles, *bcd^{E5}* and *bcd^{111}* (ref.1), which are caused by amber mutations at amino acids 259 and 257, respectively[22]. Thus our data indicate that the C-terminal third of the protein, containing the acidic region (residues 347–414), is not essential for the ability of the protein to rescue the mutant phenotype. Our results also indicate that only those forms of Bcd that activate transcription in the embryo—wild type, Bcd (1–396) and Bcd (1–348)—can completely rescue *bcd⁻* embryos. We now show that Bcd (1–246), a

表 2. Bcd 融合蛋白活性

效应基因	酵母 β–半乳糖苷酶活性(hb–GAL1–lacZ)	果蝇胚胎拯救*bcd⁻*突变表型
野生型Bcd	125	完全
Bcd（1~246）	13	部分
Bcd（1~246）–VP16	1,307	致死
Bcd（1~246）–GAL4（768~881）	953	致死
Bcd（1~246）–GAL4（851~881）	342	完全
Bcd（1~246）–B6	43	完全
Bcd（1~246）–B17	105	完全
Bcd（1~246）–B42	367	致死
无	<1	—

酵母——将表达 Bcd 融合蛋白的质粒转入酵母菌株，并测定 β–半乳糖苷酶活性。其他细节见表 1 注。**果蝇胚胎**——注射体外转录的 Bcd 蛋白衍生物 mRNA 拯救 *bcd⁻* 突变表型，详细描述见图 2 和表 3*b*。在质粒 pNT3bcd 中各种激活序列被融合到 *bcd* 基因上；这些质粒用来合成果蝇胚胎实验所用的 mRNA。VP16 的激活序列从质粒 β58dTX 的 *Hind*III-*Sal*I 片段而来，其他的激活序列从 *Eco*RI-*Sal*I 片段而来[28,29]。然后，将这些 *bcd* 融合基因插入到酵母表达载体 AAH5 的 *Hind*III 位点（参考文献 38）。所用酵母菌株为 GGY1：：MA630R。所有实验重复四次，标准误差通常小于 20%。

形态发生活性

我们检测了 Bcd 缺失衍生物的形态发生活性，通过向 *bcd^E1* 突变母体产生的胚胎前端注射少量相应的体外合成的 mRNA，发育一天后分析表皮表型（表 1 和 3*a*；图 2）。未注射胚胎没有发育出头部和胸部，而是形成了后部结构向前的重复（图 2*a*）。依赖于 mRNA 浓度，注射编码野生型 Bcd 蛋白的 mRNA 可以完全拯救突变表型，大部分幼虫孵化，并发育为成虫[39]。在缺失衍生物中 Bcd（1~396）和 Bcd（1~348）也可以完全拯救突变表型。相反，Bcd（1~111）不能在任何方面拯救 *bcd⁻* 突变表型。衍生物 Bcd（1~246）只能部分修复野生型模式：它抑制后部结构在前部的形成，高频率地诱导胸部结构发生，但很少出现头、唇、上颌或下颌的体节结构。但即使以高浓度注射（5 μg·μl⁻¹；表 3*a*）衍生物 Bcd（1~246）的 mRNA，胚胎也从不孵化（见图 2*d*）。用片段 Bcd（1~246）mRNA 注射的胚胎类似于两个含纯合的弱 *bcd* 等位基因 *bcd^E5* 和 *bcd^111*（参考文献 1）的雌性产生的胚胎，它们分别由 259 位氨基酸和 257 位氨基酸的琥珀型突变引起[22]。因此，我们的数据表明这个蛋白靠近 C 末端的三分之一，包括酸性区域（347~414 位残基）不是它拯救突变表型的能力所必需的。我们的结果还表明只有在胚胎中激活转录的几种 Bcd——野生型、Bcd（1~396）和 Bcd（1~348）——可以完全拯救 *bcd⁻* 胚胎。我们现在展示的 Bcd（1~246），是一个在三个体系中都能微弱地激活转录的衍生物，当它与异源酸性激活序列融合

derivative that activates transcription poorly in all three systems, can rescue bcd^- mutant embryos when fused to heterologous acidic activating sequences.

Table 3a. Rescue of bcd^- embryos by Bcd and its deletion derivatives

	Bcd(1–111)				Bcd(1–246)					Bcd(1–348)				Bcd(1–396)				Wild-type Bcd			
RNA concentration (µg µl⁻¹)	1.20	0.40	0.10	0.02	5.00	1.20	0.40	0.10	0.02	1.20	0.40	0.10	0.02	1.20	0.40	0.10	0.02	1.20	0.40	0.10	0.02
Phenotype n	31	16	34	21	33	56	62	60	63	65	47	56	39	84	61	59	55	58	71	54	65
1. Anterior not developed	3	6	0	0	48	38	15	5	0	25	15	14	8	25	18	5	4	26	7	13	2
2. bcd^- mutant	97	94	100	100	3	9	58	93	100	0	4	27	85	1	18	88	96	2	9	41	97
3. Partial rescue	0	0	0	0	9	5	18	2	0	28	38	52	8	35	36	7	0	21	32	37	2
4. Partial rescue (anterior open)	0	0	0	0	40	48	7	0	0	29	19	7	0	20	21	0	0	29	18	9	0
5. Head and thorax completely rescued	0	0	0	0	0	0	0	0	0	18	23	0	0	19	7	0	0	22	35	0	0

Table 3b. Rescue of bcd^- embryos by Bcd and Bcd fusion proteins

	Bcd(1–246)–VP16				Bcd(1–246)–GAL4 (768–881)				Bcd(1–246)–GAL4 (851–881)				Bcd(1–246)–B6				Bcd(1–246)–B17				Bcd(1–246)–B42			
RNA concentration (µg µl⁻¹)	1.20	0.40	0.10	0.02	1.20	0.40	0.10	0.02	1.20	0.40	0.10	0.02	1.20	0.40	0.10	0.02	1.20	0.40	0.10	0.02	1.20	0.40	0.10	0.02
Phenotype n	19	59	52	33	24	73	64	43	46	34	73	51	29	57	64	38	25	45	72	54	40	35	56	67
1. Anterior not developed	95	92	96	55	58	18	28	14	13	3	21	2	10	5	23	5	12	0	18	30	63	12	60	28
2. bcd^- mutant	5	7	4	45	0	5	13	65	2	26	10	98	7	2	17	95	0	2	11	20	5	14	5	34
3. Partial rescue	0	0	0	0	0	60	56	21	6	29	38	0	7	32	30	0	20	40	50	50	5	43	20	37
4. Partial rescue (anterior open)	0	0	0	0	42	15	3	0	59	29	22	0	60	25	28	0	64	35	11	0	27	31	14	0
5. Head and thorax completely rescued	0	0	0	0	0	0	0	0	19	12	10	0	17	37	3	0	4	20	11	0	0	0	0	0

Shown are the results of micro-injections of mRNAs encoding different Bcd derivatives into embryos that were obtained from homozygous bcd^{E1} females[1]. The cuticles of the developed embryos were analysed and the phenotypes classified (on the left of each Table) as described in Fig. 2. The mRNAs encoding various Bcd derivatives are shown at the top of each Table; concentrations as indicated. n, Number of cuticles analysed that developed from 100 injected embryos. The phenotypic classes are specified as a percentage of total embryos analysed. See legend to Fig. 2 for details of experiments. To test the statistical significance of the data obtained, several series of injections were repeated and the average difference between two injection series were <50%; different phenotypic classes were never obtained.

时能拯救 bcd^- 突变胚胎。

表3a. Bcd 及其缺失衍生物拯救 bcd^- 胚胎

RNA浓度 ($\mu g \cdot \mu l^{-1}$) / 表型	Bcd(1~111)				Bcd(1~246)					Bcd(1~348)				Bcd(1~396)				野生型Bcd			
	1.20	0.40	0.10	0.02	5.00	1.20	0.40	0.10	0.02	1.20	0.40	0.10	0.02	1.20	0.40	0.10	0.02	1.20	0.40	0.10	0.02
n	31	16	34	21	33	56	62	60	63	65	47	56	39	84	61	59	55	58	71	54	65
1. 前部未发育	3	6	0	0	48	38	15	5	0	25	15	14	8	25	18	5	4	26	7	13	2
2. bcd^-突变	97	94	100	100	3	9	58	93	100	0	4	27	85	1	18	88	96	2	9	41	97
3. 部分拯救	0	0	0	0	9	5	18	2	0	28	38	52	8	35	36	7	0	21	32	37	2
4. 部分拯救(前部开放)	0	0	0	0	40	48	7	0		29	19	7	0	20	21	0	0	29	18	9	0
5. 头和胸完全拯救	0	0	0	0	0	0	0	0	0	18	23	0	0	19	7	0	0	22	35	0	0

表3b. Bcd 及 Bcd 融合蛋白拯救 bcd^- 胚胎

RNA浓度 ($\mu g \cdot \mu l^{-1}$) / 表型	Bcd(1~246)-VP16				Bcd(1~246)-GAL4 (768~881)				Bcd(1~246)-GAL4 (851~881)				Bcd(1~246)-B6				Bcd(1~246)-B17				Bcd(1~246)-B42			
	1.20	0.40	0.10	0.02	1.20	0.40	0.10	0.02	1.20	0.40	0.10	0.02	1.20	0.40	0.10	0.02	1.20	0.40	0.10	0.02	1.20	0.40	0.10	0.02
n	19	59	52	33	24	73	64	43	46	34	73	51	29	57	64	38	25	45	72	54	40	35	56	67
1. 前部未发育	95	92	96	55	58	18	28	14	13	3	21	2	10	5	23	5	12	0	18	30	63	12	60	28
2. bcd^-突变体	5	7	4	45	0	5	13	65	2	26	10	98	7	2	17	95	0	2	11	20	5	14	5	34
3. 部分拯救	0	0	0	0	0	60	56	21	6	29	38	0	7	32	30	0	20	40	50	50	5	43	20	37
4. 部分拯救(前部开放)	0	0	0	0	42	15	3	0	59	29	22	0	60	25	28	0	64	35	11	0	27	31	14	0
5. 头和胸完全拯救	0	0	0	0	0	0	0	0	19	12	10	0	17	37	3	0	4	20	11	0	0	0	0	0

表中为向 bcd^{E1} 雌性纯合子产生的胚胎进行不同 Bcd 衍生物 mRNA 的显微注射的结果 [1]。对发育后胚胎表皮的分析和表型分类（在每个表的左侧）在图 2 中有描述。编码各种 Bcd 衍生物的 mRNA 标注在每个表的顶部，浓度也在表内标明。n，从 100 个注射过的胚胎发育来的已分析的表皮数目。每种表型标明了其占已分析的全部胚胎的百分数。实验细节见图 2 附注。为检验所获数据的统计显著性，重复了几个系列的注射，两个注射系列之间的平均差异 < 50%；未得到不同类型的表型。

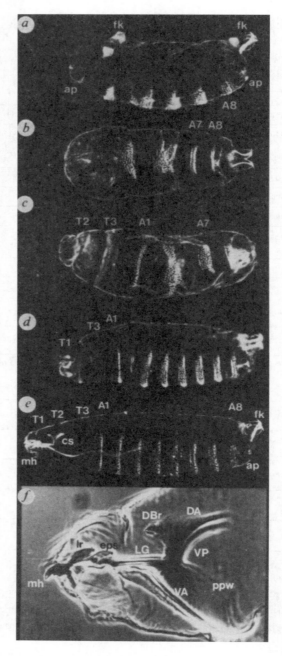

Fig. 2. Rescue of *bcd⁻* mutant *Drosophila* embryos by Bcd-acid-sequence fusion proteins. Shown are
cuticular preparations of *bcd⁻* embryos injected with *in vitro* synthesized mRNAs encoding Bcd derivatives.
The phenotypes of these embryos are grouped into five classes (also see legend to Table 3*a, b*). *a*, Strong
bcd⁻ phenotype (class 2 in Table 3*a, b*). Heads and thoraces of the embryos are replaced by a duplication
of posterior telson structures (for example, filzkörper, and anal plates)[1]. All embryos containing filzkörper
structures anteriorly are classified as *bcd⁻* mutant, including a few embryos that form thoracic structures as
well as filzkörper anteriorly. *b*, Anterior structures not developed (class 1). Neither anterior nor posterior
structures develop at the anterior of the embryo, and the anterior-most identifiable structures are the

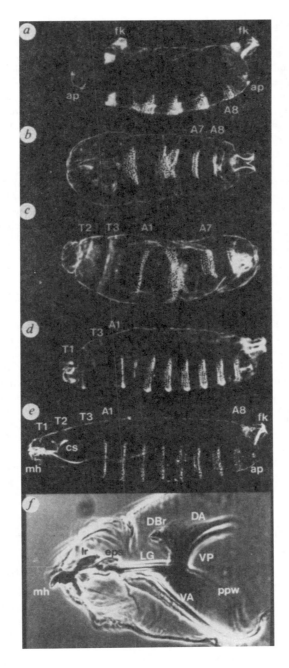

图 2. Bcd 酸性序列融合蛋白拯救 bcd⁻ 突变胚胎。图中是注射体外合成 Bcd 衍生物 mRNA 的 bcd⁻ 胚胎的表皮标本。将这些胚胎的表型分为五类（也见表 3a, b 注）。a，强 bcd⁻ 表型（表 3a, b 第 2 类）。头和胸被重复的尾节结构取代（例如，filzkörper 和肛板）[1]。所有前部包含 filzkörper 结构的都归为 bcd 突变体，包括少量前部形成胸和 filzkörper 的胚胎。b，前部结构未发育（第 1 类）。胚胎前部既不发育前部结构也不发育后部结构，近前部可识别结构是第三或第四腹齿带。虽然有些个体前部是封闭的，但通常表皮的前端都有一个大洞。c，带有开放前端的部分拯救（第 4 类）。胚胎发育具有高的可变性，发

third or fourth abdominal denticle belt. Usually the cuticles have a large hole at the anterior end, though in some cases (as shown) the anterior end is closed. *c*, Partial rescue with open anterior ends (class 4). The embryos develop, with a high variability, one to three thoracic denticle bands, an antennal sense organ, a maxillary sense organ, and/or mouth hooks, but they never develop a complete head skeleton. The cuticles have a hole of varying size at the anterior. Frequently some of the abdominal segments are fused or deleted. Embryos of this class form headfolds shifted towards the posterior of the embryos. Thus, the abdominal anlagen are obviously compressed and the segmentation distorted, whereas the head region is vastly expanded and can no longer be involuted—a possible cause for the hole at the anterior end. *d*, Partial rescue (class 3), The phenotype of this class resembles those of weak *bcd⁻* mutants (for example, bcd^{E5})[1]. Thoracic and gnathal structures but no structures derived from the anterio-most 20% of the blastoderm fate map, for example, the labrum, are formed. *e*, Complete rescue (class 5). Such embryos develop complete head and thorax including the anterior-most structure, the labrum. In a few cases the proportioning of the head skeleton deviates slightly from the wild-type form, and distortions of the abdominal segmentation appear frequently. After rescue by either wild-type Bcd protein or Bcd fusion proteins, 30–50% of the larvae in this class hatch, and some develop into adult flies. *f*, Higher magnification of the head region of a rescued *bcd⁻* mutant embryo. All the structures present in wild-type embryos can be identified here.

Methods. See legends to Table 1 and Table 2 for a description of the expression vectors used in our study. The mRNAs, synthesized *in vitro* by Sp6 RNA polymerase[50], were extracted with phenol-chloroform and chloroform, precipitated with ethanol, washed with 70% ethanol, and diluted in diethyl-pyrocarbonate-treated water to different concentrations. The mRNAs obtained were tested in an *in vitro* wheat-germ translation extract (Amersham) in the presence of [³⁵S] methionine. Measurement of ³⁵S incorporation into the proteins showed that all the mRNAs were of similar quality, and SDS-PAGE revealed proteins of the expected M_r (data not shown). The mRNAs were then injected into the anterior tips of the pre-pole-cell stage embryos obtained from homozygous mutant bcd^{E1} females according to standard procedures[1]. Embryos developed for 40 h at 18°C and the cuticles were prepared as previously described[1]. The anterior is always at the left and dorsal at top when lateral views are shown (*a*, *d–f*); *b* and *c* show ventral views. The mRNAs injected were (in μg μl⁻¹): Bcd (1–246) –GAL4 (851–881), 0.1 (*a*); Bcd (1–246) –VP16, 1.2 (*b*); Bcd (1–246) –GAL4 (768–881), 1.2 (*c*) ; Bcd (1–396), 0.8 (*d*); Bcd (1–246) –B17, 0.4 (*e*); Bcd (1–246) –B6, 0.4 (*f*). A1–A8, Ventral abdominal dentical bands; ap, anal plates; cs, cephalopharyngeal skeleton; DBr, dorsal bridge; DA, dorsal arm; eps, epistomal sclerite; fk, filzkörper; LG, lateralgräte; lr, labrum; mh, mouth hook; ppw, wall of pharynx posterior to ventral arm; T1–T3, thoracic denticle bands; VA, ventral arm; VP, vertical plate[52].

Bcd Fusion Proteins

We attached Bcd (1–246) fragments to (1) the acidic activating sequences of the herpes vital activator VP16 (residues 411–491) [40,41]; (2) the acidic activating region II of GAL4 (residues 768–881) [28]; (3) part of region II of GAL4 (residues 851–881) [28]; or (4) the *E. coli*-derived acidic activating sequences B6, B17, and B42 (ref. 29) (Fig. 1). As expected, each of these fusion proteins activates transcription in yeast cells more efficiently than does the N-terminal fragment of Bcd alone (Table 2).

We tested the morphogenetic activity of the Bcd fusion proteins by injecting the respective mRNAs synthesized *in vitro* into the anterior tip of embryos obtained from mutant females homozygous for bcd^{E1}. Three of these mRNAs, at appropriate concentrations, can completely rescue the *bcd⁻* mutant phenotype (Table 3*b*). The phenotypes obtained are described in detail in the legend to Fig. 2 and are discussed below. A complete rescue of head and thorax was obtained when the embryos were injected with mRNAs encoding fusion proteins of fragment Bcd (1–246) attached to either GAL4 (851–881) or the *E. coli* DNA-derived activating sequences B6 and B17. Up to 19%, 37% and 20% of the

育出一至三个胸齿带、一个触角感觉器官、一个上颌感觉器官和（或）口钩，但从没发育出完整的头部骨骼。在前部表皮上有一个尺寸不一的洞。一些腹部体节经常融合或缺失。这类胚胎形成头褶并向胚胎后部移动。因此腹部原基显著压缩且体节扭曲，而头部极度延伸并不向内卷—可能是前端形成洞的一个原因。*d*，部分拯救（第3类）。这类表型类似弱 *bcd⁻* 突变体（如，*bcd^E5*）[1]。形成胸和颚结构，但胚盘囊胚发育图前20%的结构都没形成，例如上唇。*e*，完全拯救（第5类）。这些胚胎发育出完整的头和胸，包括近前部结构，上唇。在一些个体中头部骨骼比例与野生型相比发生细微地偏离，腹部体节扭曲频繁出现。经野生 Bcd 蛋白或融合 Bcd 蛋白拯救后，这类幼虫中有 30%~50% 孵化出来，有一些发育为成蝇。*f*，一个拯救的 *bcd⁻* 突变胚胎头部的高倍放大。野生型胚胎中出现的所有结构在这里都能识别。

方法。我们研究用的表达载体的详细描述见表1注和表2注。通过 Sp6 RNA 聚合酶[50] 在体外合成的 mRNA 用酚－氯仿和氯仿抽提，乙醇沉淀，70% 的乙醇洗涤，用焦碳酸二乙酯处理的水稀释到不同浓度。得到的 mRNA 在体外含 [S³⁵] 甲硫氨酸的麦胚翻译提取物（安玛西亚公司）中检测。³⁵S 结合蛋白的测量显示所有 mRNA 质量相似，SDS 聚丙烯酰胺凝胶电泳反映蛋白的预测分子量（数据未显示）。然后根据标准步骤，将 mRNA 注射到突变 *bcd^E1* 雌性纯合子产生的前极细胞期胚胎的前端[1]。胚胎在 18℃ 发育 40 小时，按以前的方法制备表皮[1]。前部总是在左，侧视展示时背部在上（*a, d~f*）；*b* 和 *c* 展示腹面观。注射的 mRNA（单位为 μg·μl⁻¹）：Bcd(1~246)–GAL4(851~881)，0.1（*a*）；Bcd(1~246)–VP16，1.2（*b*）；Bcd(1~246)–GAL4(768~881)，1.2（*c*）；Bcd(1~396)，0.8（*d*）；Bcd(1~246)–B17，0.4（*e*）；Bcd(1~246)–B6，0.4（*f*）。A1–A8，腹侧腹齿带；ap，肛板；cs，头咽骨；DBr，背桥；DA，背腕；eps，额唇骨片；fk，filzkörper；LG，lateralgräte；lr，上唇；mh，口钩；ppw，后咽壁到腹腕；T1–T3，胸齿带；VA，腹腕，VP，垂直面[52]。

Bcd 融合蛋白

我们将 Bcd 片段（1~246）结合到（1）疱疹病毒重要的激活子 VP16 的酸性激活序列（411~491 位残基）[40,41]；（2）GAL4 的酸性激活域 II（768~881 位残基）[28]；（3）GAL4 激活域 II 的一部分（851~881 位残基）[28]；（4）源于大肠杆菌的酸性激活序列 B6、B17 和 B42（参考文献 29）（图 1）。与预期相同，在酵母细胞中这些融合蛋白激活转录的效率比单独的 Bcd N 末端片段高（表 2）。

通过将体外合成的 mRNA 分别注射到 *bcd^E1* 突变雌性纯合子产生的胚胎前端，检测 Bcd 融合蛋白的形态发生活性。其中的三种 mRNA，在浓度适当时可完全拯救 *bcd⁻* 的突变表型（表 3b）。获得的表型在图 2 注中有详细的描述，并在下文进行了讨论。当用片段 Bcd（1~246）与 GAL4（851~881）或源于大肠杆菌的酸性活性序列 B6、B17 的融合蛋白的 mRNA 注射胚胎时，头和胸得到完全恢复。通过这些激活子，拯救胚胎发育的比率分别达到 19%、37% 和 20%。在每个案例中，就像注射

developing embryos were rescued, respectively, by each of these activators. In each case, as is the case when wild-type *bcd* mRNA was injected, the frequency of hatching larvae was ~30% of the number of embryos with morphologically normal heads.

With the exception of the three potent activators described below, the phenotypes obtained by injecting mRNAs encoding the various fusion proteins and deletion derivatives can, depending on the concentration, result in embryos with phenotypes mimicking those of various *bcd* alleles. These phenotypes include that of wild-type flies (complete rescue; class 5 in Table 3, and Fig. 2*e*, *f*), the phenotype of weak alleles (partial rescue; class 3 and Fig. 2*d*), and the phenotype of strong alleles (no rescue; class 2 and Fig. 2*a*). In addition, a novel phenotype is observed in embryos that are injected with these mRNAs at high concentrations. In some cases, abdominal segmentation is distorted (seen in embryo of classes 3, 4 and 5), whereas in severe cases, in addition to defective abdominal development, the head anlagen are apparently shifted so far towards the posterior that head involution cannot occur, and embryos are generated bearing a hole in the cuticle anterior to the thorax (class 4). The latter phenotype can be explained by a Bcd protein gradient with a much higher overall concentration throughout the embryo than that of the wild-type Bcd protein gradient. As Bcd protein determines positions along the anterio–posterior axis in a concentration-dependent manner[5], overall higher concentrations of Bcd would result in a shift of the blastoderm anlagen towards the posterior.

The injection of mRNAs that encode potent Bcd fusion proteins bearing VP16, GAL4 (768–881) or B42 cause another novel phenotype (class 1, see Fig. 2*b*). In these embryos, neither anterior nor posterior structures form anteriorly, but development is suppressed, resulting in embryos with a partial abdominal pattern and an open anterior end. By injecting the latter two mRNAs at lower concentrations, at least a partial rescue is obtained, whereas the most potent activator, the Bcd (1–246) –VP16 fusion protein, has a deleterious effect on the anterior development even when its mRNA is injected at a very low concentration (Table 3*b*). These three potent Bcd fusion proteins could cause the toxic effects by: (1) activating the Bcd-protein target gene(s) to some intolerable level; (2) activating some otherwise non-target genes because of single Bcd-binding sites that may be randomly distributed in the *Drosophila* genome; or (3) having the general inhibitory effect on gene expression called "squelching"(refs 42, 43).

Discussion

Here we have described experiments in which we assayed the morphogenetic properties of Bcd and various Bcd derivatives by injecting mRNAs into embryos derived from *bcd⁻* mutant females. We have also described the transcriptional activating properties of Bcd and various Bcd derivatives in yeast, *Drosophila* Schneider cells and *Drosophila* embryos. Our results with the Bcd (1–246) derivative are particularly indicative. This fragment, which contains the DNA-binding homoeodomain, has a weak transcriptional activation function as assayed in all systems, compared with wild-type Bcd protein, and can only partially rescue *bcd⁻* mutant embryos. However, when fused to certain acidic activating sequences—

野生型 *bcd* 的 mRNA 一样，头部形态正常的胚胎孵化成幼虫的频率约为 30%。

除下面描述的三种有效的激活子外，以一定浓度注射各种融合蛋白和缺失衍生物的 mRNA 可以产生与各种 *bcd* 等位基因表型相似的胚胎。这些表型包括野生型果蝇（完全恢复；图 3 第 5 类和图 2*e*, *f*）、弱等位基因表型（部分恢复；第 3 类和图 2*d*）和强等位基因表型（未恢复；第 2 类和图 2*a*）。此外，在高浓度注射这些 mRNA 时，在胚胎中观察到一种新表型。在一些情况下，腹部体节扭曲（见第 3、4、5 类胚胎），然而在一些极端的案例中，除腹部发育缺陷外，头部原基显著后移以致头部不能发育，产生的胚胎在胸前部的表皮上有一个洞（第 4 类）。整个胚胎中，Bcd 蛋白梯度的总体浓度比野生型 Bcd 蛋白梯度的浓度高可解释后者表型。由于 Bcd 蛋白以浓度依赖方式决定果蝇前后轴的位置信息[5]，整体较高的 Bcd 浓度会导致腹部原基向后移。

注射含 VP16、GAL4（768~881）或 B42 的有效的 Bcd 融合蛋白的 mRNA 可产生另一种新表型（第 1 类，见图 2*b*）。在这些胚胎前部中既没形成前部结构也没形成后部结构，但是发育受抑制，产生的胚胎有部分腹部模式并且前端开放。低浓度注射后两种 mRNA，至少得到部分拯救，而最有效的激活子 Bcd（1~246）–VP16 融合蛋白即使以很低浓度 mRNA 注射也对前部发育有害（表 3*b*）。这三种有效的 Bcd 融合蛋白可产生毒性效果：（1）过度激活 Bcd 蛋白靶基因；（2）因为单个 Bcd 结合位点可能随机分布在果蝇基因组中，激活其他一些非靶标基因；（3）对基因表达有普遍的抑制效果，称为"噪音抑制"（参考文献 42 和 43）。

讨　论

通过向 *bcd*⁻ 突变雌性产生的胚胎注射 mRNA，我们分析了 Bcd 和各种 Bcd 衍生物的形态发生特性。我们也描述了在酵母、果蝇施耐德细胞和果蝇胚胎中 Bcd 和各种 Bcd 衍生物的转录激活特性。这对 Bcd（1~246）衍生物的结果尤其有指示意义。这个片段包含 DNA 结合同源域，与野生型相比在三种实验体系中只有微弱的转录激活功能，只能部分拯救 *bcd*⁻ 突变胚胎。然而，当与特定的酸性激活序列——已知在很多真核生物中激活转录的多肽——融合时，Bcd（1~246）可完全拯救 *bcd*⁻ 突变胚胎。

peptides known to confer transcriptional activation in many eukaryotes—Bcd (1–246) fully rescues *bcd*⁻ mutant embryos.

Our results with Bcd deletion derivatives also indicate a correlation between the ability of a given *bcd* allele to activate transcription as assayed in the embryo, and its ability to rescue the *bcd*⁻ mutant phenotype. Thus, for example, of the derivatives tested, three (wild type, Bcd (1–396) and Bcd (1–348)) rescued the wild-type phenotype, and these derivatives stimulated transcription most efficiently in the embryo. We note that two of these proteins (Bcd (1–396) and Bcd (1–348)) are severely impaired in the activation function as assayed in yeast. These results are consistent with the idea that the fragments Bcd (1–396) and Bcd (1–348) are modified in the embryo, perhaps by phosphorylation, to potentiate or to acquire an activating function. It is also possible that, for example, the sequence of residues 247–348, which is rich in Gln, functions as an activating sequence in the embryo, but not in Schneider cells or in yeast.

The results of the mRNA injection experiments also allowed us to begin to analyse the effects of activating strengths and concentrations of the Bcd protein derivatives on embryonic development.

First, the concentration of the activators can vary within a certain range to allow normal embryonic development. For example, the Bcd fusion proteins bearing GAL4 (851–881), B6 or B17 fragments can rescue the *bcd*⁻ mutant phenotype when their mRNAs are injected at concentrations differing by a factor of > 10 (Table 3*b*), although injection of mRNAs at high concentration tends to distort abdominal development. This observation is consistent with previous genetic data showing that the embryos from females bearing as many as six copies of the *bcd* gene show normal development, but when there are eight copies of the *bcd* gene in the female, the abdominal segmentation frequently is abnormal and the embryos may die (refs 4 and 5; T. Berleth and W.D., unpublished results). The "posteriorward" shift of position on the fate map with increased concentrations seems to be largely independent of the activator strength, because the weak activator Bcd (1–246) also shows this effect (data not shown).

Second, the activities of the Bcd derivatives can also vary within a certain range, and still allow the development of normal larvae. For example, both Bcd (1–348) and wild-type Bcd protein can completely rescue the *bcd*⁻ mutant phenotype, although their transcriptional stimulatory activities, as determined in *Drosophila* embryos, differ by a factor of two (Table 1).

Our experiments demonstrating that Bcd protein activates transcription in yeast cells from the *hb* upstream element further support the idea that one function of Bcd protein during development is to stimulate the expression of *hb* gene by directly binding to the sites located upstream of the *hb* gene promoter. In addition to activating the target gene(s), the maternal Bcd protein could have other functions during early development of *Drosophila* embryos. For example, Bcd protein could inhibit the translation of the maternal *caudal* gene mRNA (refs 2 and 44), and Bcd protein would be required to define the domain of

我们关于 Bcd 缺失衍生物的实验结果也表明在胚胎中检测到的给定 *bcd* 等位基因激活转录的能力和拯救 *bcd⁻* 突变表型的能力之间有相关性。因此，举例来讲，在检测过的衍生物中，有三个（野生型、Bcd（1~396）和 Bcd（1~348））修复了野生型表型，这些衍生物可在胚胎中最有效地激活转录。在酵母的实验中我们注意到其中两个蛋白 Bcd（1~396）和 Bcd（1~348）的激活功能严重受损。这些结果与片段 Bcd（1~396）和 Bcd（1~348）在胚胎中可能被磷酸化修饰而增强或获得激活功能的观点一致。也可能，例如，富含谷氨酰胺的 247~348 位残基的序列，在胚胎中起到激活序列的作用，而在施耐德细胞或酵母中不能。

mRNA 注射实验的结果也使得我们能够分析激活强度和 Bcd 蛋白衍生物的浓度对胚胎发育的影响。

首先，激活子的浓度可以在一个区间内变化，使胚胎正常发育。例如，当含 GAL4（851~881）、B6 或 B17 片段的 Bcd 融合蛋白的 mRNA 以大于 10 倍的浓度变化（表 3b）注射时可以拯救 *bcd⁻* 突变表型，尽管高浓度注射容易扭曲腹部发育。这些观察结果与以前的遗传学数据相符：母体含 6 拷贝 *bcd* 基因时产生的胚胎发育正常，但母体含 8 拷贝 *bcd* 基因时其胚胎腹部体节往往不正常并且胚胎会死亡。（参考文献 4 和 5；T. Berleth 和沃尔夫冈·德里费尔，未发表结果）。浓度升高导致囊胚发育图上的位置后移似乎与激活子强度没多大关系，因为弱激活子 Bcd（1~246）也产生这个效果（数据未显示）。

第二，Bcd 衍生物的活性也可在一个特定范围内变化，并使胚胎发育为正常幼虫。例如，Bcd（1~348）和野生型 Bcd 蛋白，虽然它们的转录激活活性有 2 倍的差异（表 1），如在果蝇胚胎中确定的，但它们都可完全拯救 *bcd⁻* 突变表型。

我们的研究证明了 Bcd 蛋白在酵母细胞中通过 *hb* 上游元件激活转录，进一步支持了这样的观点，即 Bcd 蛋白在发育过程中的一个功能是通过直接结合到位于 *hb* 基因启动子上游的位点激活 *hb* 基因的表达。除激活靶基因外，母性 Bcd 蛋白在果蝇胚胎早期发育中还有其他功能。例如，Bcd 蛋白可抑制母源尾部基因 mRNA 的翻译（参考文献 2 和 44），并且 Bcd 蛋白可能是决定与 *hb* 无关的另一个间隔基因（跛

expression of another gap gene (*Krüppel*) independent of *hb* (ref. 45). Our results indicate that if these effects of Bcd protein are direct and if they are essential to the development of *Drosophila* embryos, they must be specified by the N-terminal portion (residues 1–246) of Bcd which is present in the Bcd fusion proteins that are able to rescue the *bcd⁻* mutant phenotype.

(**342**,149-154;1989)

Wolfgang Driever[*], **Jun Ma**[†], **Christiane Nüsslein-Volhard**[*] & **Mark Ptashne**[†]

[*] Max-Planck-Institut für Entwicklungsbiologie, Abteilung Genetik, Spemannstrasse 35/III, D-7400 Tübingen, FRG

[†] Department of Biochemistry and Molecular Biology, Harvard University, 7 Divinity Avenue, Cambridge, Massachusetts 02138, USA

Received 3 May; accepted 5 September 1989.

References:

1. Frohnhöfer, H. G. & Nüsslein-Volhard, C. *Nature* 324, 120-125 (1986).
2. Driever, W. & Nüsslein-Volhard, C. *Cell* 54, 83-93 (1988).
3. Frigerio, G., Burri, M., Bopp, D., Baumgartner, S. & Noll, M. *Cell* 47, 735-746 (1986).
4. Berleth, T. *et al. EMBO J.* 7, 1749-1756 (1988).
5. Driever, W. & Nüsslein-Volhard, C. *Cell* 54, 95-104 (1988).
6. Tautz, D. *Nature* 332, 281-284 (1988).
7. Schröder, C. *et al. EMBO J.* 7, 2881-2888 (1988).
8. Lehmann, R. & Nüsslein-Volhard, C. *Devl. Biol.* 119, 402-417 (1987).
9. Tautz, D. *et al. Nature* 327, 383-389 (1987).
10. Driever, W. & Nüsslein-Volhard, C. *Nature* 337, 138-143 (1989).
11. Driever, W., Thoma, G. & Nüsslein-Volhard, C. *Nature* 340, 363-367 (1989).
12. McGinnis, W. *et al. Nature* 308, 428-433 (1984).
13. Laughon, A. & Scott, M. P. *Nature* 310, 25-31 (1984).
14. Gehring, W. J. *Science* 236, 1245-1252 (1987).
15. Desplan, C., Theis, J. & O'Farrell, P. *Nature* 318, 630-635 (1985).
16. Hoey, T. & Levine, M. *Nature* 332, 858-861 (1988).
17. Desplan, C., Theis, J. & O'Farrell, P. *Cell* 54, 1081-1090 (1988).
18. Hanes, S. & Brent, R. *Cell* 57, 1275-1283 (1989).
19. Jaynes, J. & O'Farrell, P. *Nature* 336, 744-749 (1988).
20. Fitzpatrick, D. & Ingles, J. *Nature* 337, 666-668 (1989).
21. Han, K., Levine, M. & Manley, J. *Cell* 56, 573-583 (1989).
22. Struhl, G., Struhl, K. & Macdonald, P. *Cell* 57, 1259-1273 (1989).
23. Brent, R. & Ptashne, M. *Cell* 43, 729-736 (1985).
24. Keegan, L., Gill, G. & Ptashne, M. *Science* 231, 699-704 (1986).
25. Ptashne, M. *Nature* 322, 697-701 (1986).
26. Struhl, K. *Cell* 49, 295-297 (1987).
27. Hope, I. & Struhl, K. *Cell* 46, 885-894 (1986).
28. Ma, J. & Ptashne, M. *Cell* 48, 847-853 (1987).
29. Ma, J. & Ptashne, M. *Cell* 51, 113-119 (1987).
30. Giniger, E. & Ptashne, M. *Nature* 330, 670-672 (1987).
31. Kakidani, H. & Ptashne, M. *Cell* 52, 161-167 (1988).
32. Webster, N., Jin, J. R., Green, S., Hollis, M. & Chambon, P. *Cell* 52, 169-178 (1988).
33. Fisher, J., Giniger, E., Ptashne, M. & Maniatis, T. *Nature* 332, 853-856 (1988).
34. Ma, J., Przibilla, E., Hu, J., Bogorad, L. & Ptashne, M. *Nature* 334, 631-633 (1988).
35. Courey, A. & Tjian, R. *Cell* 55, 887-898 (1988).
36. Tora, L. *et al. Cell* (in the press).

子）表达区域所必需的（参考文献45）。我们的结果暗示，如果 Bcd 蛋白的这些效应是直接的，而且如果它们是果蝇胚胎发育必需的，那么很可能它们的 N 末端部分（1~246 位残基）起决定作用，它们存在于 Bcd 融合蛋白中，能完全拯救 bcd^- 突变表型。

（李梅 翻译；沈杰 审稿）

37. West, R., Yocum, R. & Ptashne, M. *Molec. Cell. Biol.* 4, 2467-2478 (1984).

38. Ammerer, G. *Meth. Enzymol.* 101, 192-201 (1983).

39. Driever, W., Siegel, V. & Nüsslein-Volhard, C. *Science* (in the press).

40. Triezenberg, S., Kingsbury, R. & McKnight, S. *Genes Dev.* 2, 718-729 (1988).

41. Sadowski, I., Ma, J., Triezenberg, S. & Ptashne, M. *Nature* 335, 563-564 (1988).

42. Gill, G. & Ptashne, M. *Nature* 334, 721-724 (1988).

43. Ptashne, M. *Nature* 335, 683-689 (1988).

44. Mlodzik, M. & Gehring, W. *Development* 101, 421-435 (1987).

45. Gaul, U. & Jäckle, H. *Cell* 51, 549-555 (1987).

46. Gill, G. & Ptashne. M. *Cell* 51, 121-126 (1987).

47. Yocum, R., West, R. & Ptashne, M. *Molec. Cell. Biol.* 4, 1985-1998 (1984).

48. Bunch, T. A., Grinblat, Y. & Goldstein, L. S. B. *Nucleic Acids Res.* 16, 1043-1061 (1988).

49. Rio, D. C. & Rubin, G. M. *Molec. Cell. Biol.* 5, 1833-1838 (1985).

50. Melton, D. A. *et al. Nucleic Acids Res.* 12, 7035-7056 (1984).

51. Silver, P., Chiang, A. & Sadler, J. *Genes Dev.* 2, 707-717 (1988).

52. Jürgens, G. *et al. Wilhelm Roux's Arc. dev. Biol.* 196, 141-157 (1986)

Acknowledgements. We thank our colleagues in both MPI and Harvard, especially V. Siegel, S. Roth, M. Klingler, L. Stevens, T. Goto, L. Keegan and H. Himmelfarb, as well as P. O'Farrell at UCSF, for discussions and comments on the manuscript; G. Thoma for technical assistance; T. Berleth and D. Ruden for communicating unpublished results; and V. Siegel, T. Bunch, D. Melton and S. McKnight for plasmids. This work was supported by the DFG (Leipnitz Programm) and the NIH.

562

通过含异源激活序列的Bicoid融合蛋白拯救bicoid突变果蝇胚胎

High-Latitude Ozone Loss Outside the Antarctic Ozone Hole

M. H. Proffitt *et al.*

Editor's Note

Until this paper, observations of the destruction of stratospheric ozone, caused by human-made chlorofluorocarbons (CFCs) in the atmosphere, was restricted to the polar regions, where the atmospheric conditions were favourable for it. But Michael Proffitt and co-workers in Boulder, Colorado, here describe measurements of ozone loss outside the Antarctic "hole" at a monitoring station in Chile in 1987. They cannot say for sure whether CFCs or some natural process is responsible, but they demonstrate that the destruction is caused by a chemical process rather than simply dilution by ozone-depleted air transported from the Antarctic. These findings showed that ozone depletion was a problem not confined to the uninhabited poles.

Data taken during the 1987 Antarctic Airborne Ozone Experiment based in Punta Arenas, Chile, are used to show that from mid-August until the end of the mission in late September there was a high-latitude ozone loss outside the Antarctic ozone hole. Therefore, not only is the geographic extent of the ozone loss larger than that generally identified as chemically perturbed, but ozone is lost earlier in the year than previously reported. These results, when compared with long-term temporal trends of column ozone, indicate a possible anthropogenic component for this loss.

MEASUREMENTS from the past few years have shown that stratospheric ozone decreases substantially over Antarctica during September and October and that these decreases have intensified dramatically during the past decade. The intensification has been attributed to man's release of certain chlorine-containing compounds, primarily chlorofluorocarbons. The region of very high ozone decrease, usually referred to as the ozone hole, approximately covers the Antarctic continent, and is coincident with what is commonly called the polar vortex. Horizontally, the polar vortex is roughly defined by its perimeter, the polar night jet, a circumpolar wind belt in the stratosphere that seems to restrict exchange of air through the perimeter. The seasonal period of low ozone values is observed to terminate with the annual dissipation of the Antarctic vortex during the spring warming, at which time the air within the vortex is no longer restricted but allowed to mix freely with ozone-rich air from other latitudes. Transport towards the Equator and mixing of ozone-poor air with air at lower latitudes result in localized decreases of ozone[1]. The extent and intensity of these decreases are of global concern.

南极臭氧洞外高纬度地区臭氧的亏损

普罗菲特等

编者按

在本文发表之前，对于由人类排放氯氟烃 (CFCs) 所引起的平流层臭氧破坏的观测仅限于极地地区，因为该区域的大气条件有利于观测。但本文中，科罗拉多州博尔德的迈克尔·普罗菲特及其合作者描述了在南极"臭氧洞"范围之外进行的臭氧亏损观测，这项观测于 1987 年在智利的一个观测站进行。他们并未确切给出氯氟烃或某些自然过程是否与这一地区的臭氧亏损有关，但是他们指出，这种亏损是由化学过程，而不是简单的由来自南极的臭氧含量稀少的空气稀释引起。这些发现表明，臭氧的耗损并不仅仅局限于无人居住的极地地区。

本文利用 1987 年在智利蓬塔阿雷纳斯地区进行的南极臭氧空中实验中获得的数据，证明从 8 月中旬直到 9 月底任务完成时，在南极臭氧洞范围以外的高纬地区存在臭氧亏损。因此，臭氧亏损的地理范围比通常所认定的化学扰动区的范围要广，而且一年中臭氧开始亏损的时间也比之前报道的要早。将上述结果与臭氧柱总量长期趋势相比较可以发现，这种亏损可能有人为因素的影响。

根据过去几年的测定结果，每年 9 月到 10 月期间，南极上空平流层臭氧含量总会大幅下降，并且，在过去十年中这种下降趋势急剧增强。这种增强作用是由人类向大气中释放某些含氯化合物（主要为氯氟烃）造成的。臭氧大量减少非常明显的地区一般被称为臭氧洞，基本上覆盖了整个南极大陆，并与通常所称的极涡范围一致。极涡的水平范围大致取决于其周长，极夜急流是平流层中的一个绕极风带，它会限制周边空气的交换。季节性的低臭氧值周期随着每年春季变暖时南极涡旋的消散而终结，因为此时涡旋中的空气不再受限制，能够与其他纬度地区富含臭氧的空气自由混合。缺乏臭氧的空气向赤道运移并与低纬地区的空气相混合，导致臭氧含量局部降低 [1]。这种降低的范围和强度引起了全球关注。

The seasonal decrease in ozone is large enough to provide an unequivocal signature of loss that is easily distinguished from natural short-term dynamical variability, and has been verified from the ground, aircraft, balloons and satellites. In this paper "ozone loss" is used to identify a change in ozone due to chemical mechanisms (rather than dynamical processes) that is not predicted within standard gas-phase photochemistry models. We do not intend to imply the loss is necessarily due solely to chlorine. Measurements of total column ozone (total number of ozone molecules vertically above some area of the Earth) made from the ground and from a single station first identified ozone loss over Antarctica[2]. Satellite column measurements then verified that it was not just a local phenomenon[3]. Measurements obtained from balloons provided snapshots of the vertical distribution of ozone at a few Antarctic locations and presented striking accounts of large ozone decreases when comparing profiles from August with those from October[4,5]. But the changes observed were not simply a gradual deterioration of the ozone layer, but included a substantial day-to-day variability and frequent horizontal layering. This means that the region of decreased ozone is neither vertically nor horizontally homogeneous, and that quantification of the altitude-dependent decrease of ozone requires good temporal and geographic coverage. Although satellite measurements of total column ozone are frequently available, they cannot identify the altitude dependence of the ozone loss. *In situ* aircraft measurements can provide vertical profiles and extended horizontal coverage, but they are still insufficient to sample the entire geographic extent of the vortex frequently.

Here we present a different approach to estimating the ozone (O_3) loss inside and, more interestingly, outside the ozone hole—one that completely avoids the problems of sampling an inhomogeneous air mass. As standard gas-phase photochemistry is very slow in the region of this analysis (that is, during high-latitude winter in the lower stratosphere where O_3 has a photochemical replacement time of more than a year[6,7]), O_3 can be used effectively as a conservative tracer. The sum of the reactive nitrogen species (abbreviated as NO_y and including in that sum NO, NO_2, NO_3, HNO_3, N_2O_5 and $ClONO_2$) and nitrous oxide (N_2O) are also conserved in this environment. By combining *in situ* measurements of these tracers with empirically derived formulations that are supported by two-dimensional atmospheric models, minimum reference values for unperturbed O_3 can be estimated for any air parcel sampled. This reference value for O_3 can then be compared with the measured value, and the difference is a deviation from conservative behaviour that can be interpreted as a chemically induced change not within the standard gas-phase photochemistry. The formulations presented are first applied outside the region usually referred to as chemically perturbed. Then the analysis is used in a different manner, but this time both outside and inside. It is assumed for the analysis that there has been sufficient simultaneous sampling of the trace constituents NO_y, N_2O and O_3, spatially and temporally, to determine reliable reference formulations.

To discuss accurately the morphology of the ozone hole, the concept of the boundary of the chemically perturbed region is used as introduced and developed by Proffitt *et al.*[8] from data taken during the 1987 Antarctic Airborne Ozone Experiment (AAOE). The boundary, defined by a level of chlorine monoxide (ClO = 130 p.p.t.v. (parts per 10^{12} by

臭氧含量的季节性降低足以引起明显的亏损，使之很容易与短期的自然动力变化区分开来，这一点已分别在地面、飞机、气球和卫星上得到了验证。本文中，"臭氧亏损"是指由于标准气相光化学模型中未知的化学机制（而非动力过程）引起的臭氧变化。我们并不是说臭氧的亏损一定只是由氯引起的。我们在地面以及首先发现南极上空臭氧亏损的一个站点上[2]，对臭氧柱总量（垂直于地球表面的一定面积之上臭氧分子的总数）进行了测定。随后的卫星柱浓度观测表明这并不是一种局部现象[3]。利用气球获得的测定结果，使人们对几个南极站点上臭氧的垂直分布有了一个总体的了解，并且将 8 月份的曲线与 10 月份相比较时可以发现臭氧大量减少[4,5]。但所观测到的变化并不是单纯的臭氧层的逐渐破坏过程，而是包含着较大的日变化以及频繁的水平分层。这说明，臭氧含量降低的地区在垂直方向和水平方向上都是不均一的，而且对臭氧随高度减少的量化也要求有较好的时空覆盖范围。尽管通常情况下都可以得到臭氧柱总量的卫星测定结果，但并不能从中区别出由海拔高度的变化引起的臭氧亏损情况。现场航空测定结果可以提供垂直廓线并可扩大水平测定范围，然而，这种方法仍不足以在整个涡旋的地理范围内获取足够高的取样频率。

在这里我们采用一种不同的方法来估算臭氧洞内、外的臭氧亏损——可以完全避开不均匀气团的取样问题。由于在所分析地区标准气相光化学反应非常慢（即高纬度地区冬季平流层低层 O_3 的光化学置换时间大于 1 年[6,7]），O_3 可看作是一种有效的保守示踪剂。活性含氮化合物总量（NO_y 的简称，包括 NO、NO_2、NO_3、HNO_3、N_2O_5 以及 $ClONO_2$）及一氧化二氮（N_2O）在该环境中也是守恒的。结合这些示踪剂的现场测定结果和利用二维大气模型所支持的经验公式，可以估算出任何采样气团中无扰动臭氧的最小参考值。然后可将臭氧的该参考值与测定值相比较，两者的差值即为对保守行为的偏离值，可以解释为非标准气相光化学反应中由化学作用引起的变化。所给出的公式首先在通常认为是化学扰动的区域外部应用。然后，同样的分析以不同的方式同时用于内部和外部。在该分析中，假定空间和时间上都存在足够多的同时取样的痕量组分 NO_y、N_2O 和 O_3，以保证所得参考公式的可靠性。

为了准确地描述臭氧洞的形态，我们需要使用化学扰动区域边界的概念，该概念由普罗菲特等[8]根据 1987 年南极臭氧空中实验(AAOE)所得到的数据引入并发展。这一边界是根据一氧化氯的水平（$ClO=130$ pptv（按体积计算的万亿分之一））来确

volume)), effectively locates where this critical component in the catalytic destruction of O_3 by chlorine has a sharp poleward increase. It was found that there were also dramatic poleward decreases in NO_y and H_2O at this boundary, hence the basis for describing the interior region as chemically perturbed. We shall refine this description slightly by referring to this region as "high chemically perturbed", and thereby not exclude a possible lesser degree of chemical perturbation outside the boundary. Proffitt *et al.* have shown that this boundary is slightly poleward of the peak wind speeds of the polar night jet and that it coincides with the latitude of the strong poleward decrease in total column O_3 as measured by satellite. In addition, the boundary locates the perimeter of the large isentropic temporal O_3 decrease (ozone hole) to within at least 1° of latitude (~111 km).

Danielsen and Houben[9] give heuristic arguments for wintertime diabatic cooling over Antarctica persisting into early spring, carrying ozone-rich mid-latitude air downward and poleward into the polar vortex. Proffitt *et al.*[10] have presented supporting evidence from AAOE indicating a slow progression of diabatically cooling and descending lower stratospheric air advectively spiralling poleward as it crosses the polar jet into the ozone hole. This view can be compared with that of Tuck[11], who also concludes that there is a significant mass flow through the vortex, but argues that it is the downward diabatic motion within and outside the vortex that is important. With either view, the region near and within the ozone hole is being slowly replenished with mid-latitude ozone-rich stratospheric air during the period of O_3 decrease through diabatic descent. If this is the case, temporal trends in measured O_3 will not indicate the total loss of O_3 in a particular parcel of air unless the time series begins before there is any loss and the measurements follow the descending parcel throughout the time interval of the trend[10]. This is a difficult, if not impossible, sampling requirement, even with precise knowledge of a parcel's descent path. Possible mixing of air parcels of dissimilar origin during or following the O_3 destruction process further complicates the sampling problem.

The analysis presented is based entirely on the *in situ* data taken during AAOE from the high-altitude ER-2 aircraft. During the mission the average latitude of the boundary was 66° S, but varied from 59° S to 71° S, its position responding to synoptic-scale meteorological forcing of the polar vortex. The data are generally restricted vertically to the two levels of 425 ± 10 K and 450 ± 10 K in potential temperature (corresponding to geometric altitudes ~17.5 km and 19 km respectively over Antarctica) and horizontally from 53° S to 72° S latitude at ~65° W longitude. The longitudinal coverage is quite restricted, extending only from the southern tip of South America to the region over or near the Antarctic Peninsula. Also, data were collected during the transit flights between Moffett Field, California (37° N) and Punta Arenas, Chile (53° S), where the twelve ER-2 Antarctic flights originated.

Lower Limit for Unperturbed Ozone

The stratospheric source for NO_y is the very unreactive species N_2O. The primary destruction mechanism for N_2O is ultraviolet radiation at wavelengths $\leqslant 225$ nm, has N_2 and $O(^1D)$ as principal products, and occurs primarily in the middle of the stratosphere above 30 km. A secondary loss occurs also in the middle stratosphere where NO is created

定的，可以有效地找出在 O_3 的氯催化损耗过程中起关键作用的这种成分是在哪里发生了向极地一侧的急剧增加。研究发现，在该边界上，NO_y 和 H_2O 也表现为向极地急剧减少，此即为将内部区域称为化学扰动区的基础。我们应该对这一概念略作修改，将该区称为"高化学扰动区"，这样，就不排除在边界之外也有可能存在程度较低的化学扰动了。普罗菲特等已证明，当极夜急流达峰值风速时，该边界略向极地偏移，这与利用卫星测得的臭氧柱总量在纬向上向极地急剧减少是一致的。此外，臭氧沿等熵面随时间减少（臭氧洞）的边缘至少在一个纬度（约 111 km）以内。

丹尼尔森和霍本[9] 提出的观点具有启发意义，他们认为，冬季南极上空的非绝热冷却过程可持续至早春，并将富含臭氧的中纬度大气向下和向极地输送，进入极地涡旋。普罗菲特等[10] 也从 AAOE 的实验数据中获得了支持这一论点的证据，即非绝热冷却过程非常缓慢，并且，当下行的平流层低层大气穿过极地急流进入臭氧洞时会向极地作平流螺旋运动。该观点与塔克[11] 的观点有些类似，塔克也认为穿过极涡存在一个重要的质量流，但他认为起重要作用的是极涡内外向下的非绝热运动。无论从哪种观点来看，由于非绝热作用向下运动而使臭氧减少期间，中纬度富含臭氧的大气对臭氧洞周围及其内部区域的补偿非常缓慢。倘使如此，除非选择的时间序列是开始于亏损发生之前，并且在整个时间段内一直随气团的下降进行测定，否则，所测定的 O_3 随时间的变化趋势将不能表示某些特定气团中 O_3 的亏损总量[10]。即使知道气团块的确切下降路径，要想达到这样的采样要求，虽然不能说完全不可能但也非常困难。O_3 损耗过程中或损耗完以后，不同成因的气团还可能发生混合，从而使得取样问题更加复杂。

上述分析完全是基于 AAOE 期间利用高纬度 ER-2 型飞机现场采集的数据得出的。实验期间，边界的平均纬度为 66°S，在 59°~71°S 之间变化，其位置受极涡在天气尺度上气象强迫的影响。一般情况下，在垂直上，所得数据仅限于位温为 425 ± 10 K 和 452 ± 10 K（对应的海拔高度分别约为南极上空 17.5 km 和 19 km）的两个高度上，而水平方向上则为 65°W 附近，53°~72°S 之间。经向的覆盖范围相当有限，仅限于从南美洲南端到南极半岛或将近南极半岛的地区。同时，还航测了由加利福尼亚的莫菲特场（37°N）到智利的蓬塔阿雷纳斯（53°S）经过时的数据，12 次 ER-2 型飞机的南极航行正是从那里起飞的。

无扰动臭氧层的下限

平流层中 NO_y 的来源是惰性非常高的 N_2O。N_2O 的主要损耗机制是波长 ≤ 225 nm 的紫外线辐射，主要产物为 N_2 和 $O(^1D)$，并且主要发生于 30 km 以上的平流层中部。在平流层中部还可能发生二次亏损，即 $O(^1D)$ 与 N_2O 反应生成 NO， in the reaction of $O(^1D)$ with N_2O, providing the primary source of NO_y. Plots of N_2O against NO_y outside the boundary show them to be linearly related (Fig. 1). These data are from the two flight levels of 425 K and 450 K of potential temperature and were analysed separately by averaging within 1°-latitude bins with respect to the boundary and over a one-month period. The data in Fig. 1 labelled as within the boundary (corresponding to $N_2O \lesssim 140$ p.p.b.v. (parts per 10^9 by volume)) are known to be from within the highly chemically perturbed region. Linear least-squares fits are shown for the data outside this region and it is apparent that the straight line that fits the data at the lower altitude (or potential temperature) also fits the data at the upper altitude rather well. The linear fit to all of the points in Fig. 1 outside the boundary is given by

$$[NO_y] = 20,800 - (69.8 \times [N_2O]) \tag{1}$$

where the mixing ratio for NO_y is in p.p.t.v and for N_2O is in p.p.b.v.[10,12,13]. It is noteworthy that data taken during the flights from Punta Arenas to Moffett Field, where minimum values for N_2O of 210 p.p.b.v. were observed, also fall on the same straight line[10]. There are few further data available to verify the persistence of the linear relationship at other seasons, latitudes and altitudes, although the mid-latitude Southern Hemisphere balloon data taken by Galbally et al.[14] up to 30 km have the same characteristic. This persistent linear relationship and lack of curvature results from a balance of photochemistry, transport and mixing. The N_2O intercept and slope are probably determined in the tropics where upper tropospheric and lower stratospheric air with N_2O of ~ 300 p.p.b.v. and NO_y < 0.5 p.p.b.v. (intercept) rises into the tropical middle stratosphere where NO_y is produced from N_2O apparently with an average efficiency of $\sim 7\%$ (slope). Mixing, as the middle stratospheric air proceeds poleward, probably contributes to the observed small variability from linearity observed at high latitudes.

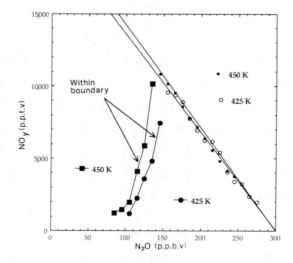

Fig. 1. NO_y against N_2O from 1987 AAOE for the 425-K and 450-K flight levels and averaged for the seven flights where data are available over intervals of 1° latitude. Data taken within clouds were excluded to obtain only gas-phase NO_y. Linear least-squares fits to the data outside the boundary are shown for each flight level.

从而成为 NO_y 的主要来源。边界外，N_2O 相对于 NO_y 的变化曲线表现为线性相关（图 1）。图中数据均来自位温为 425 K 和 450 K 的高度上，并且通过对边界一个月内的 1 个纬度的面元数据做平均来进行独立分析。已知图 1 中标记"边界内"（对应于 $N_2O \leqslant 140$ ppbv（体积的十亿分之一））的数据均来自高化学扰动区。对该区以外的数据进行最小二乘法线性拟合，结果显示，低海拔（或位温）地区数据拟合的直线与较高海拔上的数据同样拟合得很好。图 1 中所有边界外的点的线性拟合结果可以表示为

$$[NO_y] = 20,800 - (69.8 \times [N_2O]) \tag{1}$$

其中，NO_y 的体积混合比的单位为 pptv，而 N_2O 则为 ppbv[10,12,13]。值得注意的是，从蓬塔阿雷纳斯飞往莫菲特场获得的数据也都落在同一条直线上[10]，其中所观测到的 N_2O 的最小值为 210 ppbv。能够用来证明在其他季节、纬度或高度条件下可维持这种线性关系的其他数据很少，尽管盖勃利等[14]利用气球在南半球中纬度地区 30 km 高空采集到的数据也具有同样特征。光化学作用、输送作用和混合作用之间的平衡产生了这种持续的线性关系而没有弯曲。N_2O 的截距和斜率可能由热带地区决定，因为在那里对流层上部和平流层下部空气中 N_2O 和 NO_y 的含量分别为约 300 ppbv 和少于 0.5 ppbv（截距），它们会上升到热带的平流层中部，在那里 N_2O 生成 NO_y 的平均效率约为 7%（斜率）。随着中部平流层大气向极地输送，混合作用有可能导致在高纬地区观测到的数据相对于直线出现小的偏移。

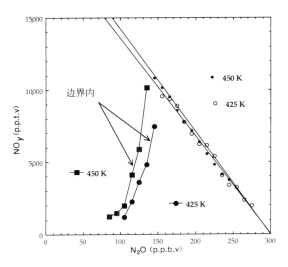

图 1. 1987 年 AAOE 期间获得的 NO_y 相对于 N_2O 的变化关系。飞行高度分别为 425 K 和 450 K，所采用值为 7 个航次的平均值，数据采集间隔均为 1° 纬度。为了保证采集样品均为气相 NO_y，剔除了在云中采集到的数据。图中还给出了每个航行高度上对边界外数据的最小二乘线性拟合结果。

The ratio of O_3 to NO_y (O_3/NO_y) can now be used to bring O_3 into the analysis. Figure 2a is a plot of O_3/NO_y against latitude taken at the start of the mission and includes data taken in transit from Moffett Field to Punta Arenas. The ratio is >300 over a wide range in latitudes, but decreases at the most southerly latitudes. Figure 2b is a similar latitude survey including the last Antarctic flight and the transit flight data during the return to Moffett Field at the end of the mission. Still lower values at the southernmost latitudes and a few data points below 300 at about 35° N are the primary differences between the two surveys. Both figures are restricted to pressure altitudes from between 18 km and 21 km, and all data within the boundary are excluded. In both plots O_3/NO_y >300 at all latitudes north of ~55° S, except on the flight of 3 October over California, where a few values as low as 260 are found. Both surveys also show an enhanced ratio in the tropics where, at 20 km, stratospheric air is apparently encountered that had recent O_3 production without the equivalent NO_y production required for the usual ratio found at mid-latitudes. Other latitude surveys of ER-2 data taken during the Stratosphere Troposphere Exchange Project in January and February 1987 from 40° N to 30° S have been analysed (D. M. Murphy et al., manuscript in preparation) and show a minimum for the ratio of 280 when restricting the data to potential temperatures >430 K. Also presented by Murphy et al. are two-dimensional model calculations[15,16] and satellite data[17] in the tropics and mid-latitudes covering pressures down to 7.5 mbar. Both the models and the data show that the O_3/NO_y ratio is >300 in the lower stratosphere and indicate either no vertical change or a slight decrease with altitude. Qualitatively these observations are consistent with the well-known mid-latitude mixing ratio maximum for O_3 and NO_y at 30–35 km with the maximum for NO_y a few kilometers higher than the O_3 maximum. These maxima correspond to N_2O values of 30–100 p.p.b.v., values much less than those measured outside the boundary and, as seen in Fig. 1, generally less than any data from AAOE.

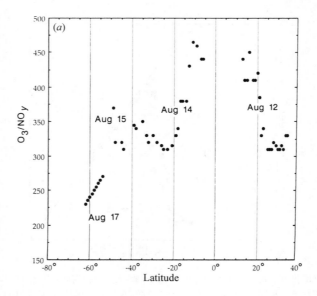

现在我们可以利用 O_3 与 NO_y 的比值(O_3/NO_y)来对 O_3 进行分析。图 2a 为 O_3/NO_y 随纬度的变化情况，所用数据是从任务一开始就采集的，并且包含从莫菲特场到蓬塔阿雷纳斯途中采集的数据。该比值在很大的纬度范围内都大于 300，但在最南部的纬度上有所下降。图 2b 也是相似纬度的航测情况，其中包括任务末期最后一次的南极飞行以及返回莫菲特场的过境飞行期间得到的数据。最南部纬度的值较低，并且在 35°N 附近有多个值低于 300，这两点是两种航测的主要区别所在。两组数据均限于 18 km 到 21 km 之间的气压高度，并且都未包含边界以内的数据。两图中在大约 55°S 以北的所有纬度上 O_3/NO_y 都大于 300，只有 10 月 3 日在加利福尼亚上空的航测中出现了几次较低值，低至 260。在热带地区两种航测也都表现为比值的增大，因为在热带地区 20 km 高空上，显然会遭遇平流层大气，而其中 O_3 刚刚形成，又没有相应量的 NO_y 生成，达不到通常在中纬度地区见到的比例所要求的量。也有学者对 1987 年 1 月和 2 月的平流层对流层交换项目期间在 40°N ~ 30°S 之间利用 ER-2 型飞机航测得到的数据作了分析（墨菲等，初稿准备中），结果表明，对于位温大于 430 K 时得到的数据，其比值最小为 280。墨菲等还给出了气压低至 7.5 毫巴的热带和中纬度地区的二维模型的计算结果[15,16]以及卫星数据[17]。模型结果与卫星数据均表明，在平流层低层 O_3/NO_y 的比值大于 300，并且既不发生垂直方向的变化也没有随高度的增加而有丝毫降低。定性地来说，在海拔 30~35 km 处，这些观测与大家所熟知的 O_3 与 NO_y 中纬度最大混合比一致，其中 NO_y 的最大值出现的位置要比 O_3 高几千米。上述最大值对应的 N_2O 含量为 30 ~100 ppbv,远远小于边界之外测得的值，如图 1 所示，并且普遍比 AAOE 期间得到的数据小。

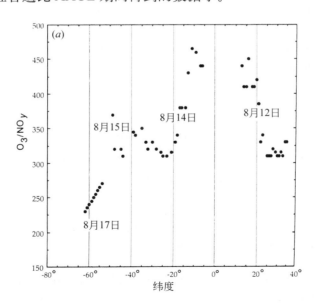

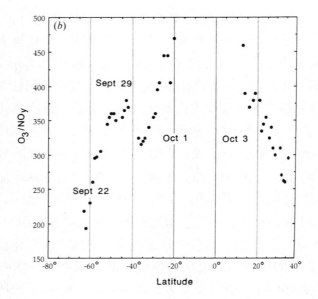

Fig. 2. O_3/NO_y latitude survey from *a*, 12 August to 17 August, 1987 and *b*, 22 September to 3 October, 1987.

From the observations made during ER-2 latitude surveys it is reasonable to assert that if NO_y and O_3 are given in identical units (such as p.p.b.v.) the inequality

$$[O_3]/[NO_y] \geqslant 270 \tag{2}$$

is representative of late winter in the Southern Hemisphere north of the boundary. The data and model calculations indicate that a larger value of 300 for the minimum ratio could be justified. But there is no established record of simultaneous measurements of NO_y and O_3 covering all latitudes, seasons and altitudes of interest from which unequivocal formulations relating O_3 to NO_y could be derived. So the conservative approach taken here is appropriate, although it may underestimate the O_3 losses that have occurred.

Ozone Losses

On 17 August between $54°\,S$ and $63°\,S$ (Fig. 2*a*), there was a significant difference between the expected O_3/NO_y ratio (inequality (2)) and its measured value. As NO_y was not perturbed and O_3/NO_y is less than our reference level of 270, an O_3 loss is indicated in that region. The value for O_3/NO_y of 230 at $63°$ S yields a 15% loss of O_3 outside the highly chemically perturbed region on 17 August. Data from the flight of 23 August also indicates a 15% loss outside the boundary, and the flights of 28 August and 22 September show a larger loss of 30%. But rather than giving flight-by-flight analysis, Fig. 3 shows averages for the period 23 August to 22 September to summarize the results and demonstrate that the O_3 losses are not isolated events found on certain flights, but were prevalent throughout the period and clearly seen in the averages. This is achieved

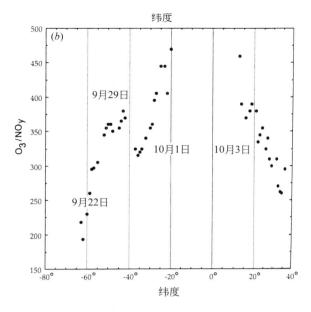

图 2. O_3/NO_y 随纬度的变化，其中 a 和 b 分别为 1987 年 8 月 12 ~17 日和 1987 年 9 月 22 日 ~10 月 3 日期间的观测结果。

从 ER-2 纬度航测得到的结果可以推断，如果 NO_y 和 O_3 采用同一单位（如：ppbv），则不等式：

$$[O_3]/[NO_y] \geqslant 270 \tag{2}$$

是边界以北南半球在冬末时期的典型代表值。卫星数据与模拟结果表明，最小比值可以为 300 这一较大值。不过，目前还没有覆盖所有我们感兴趣的纬度、季节以及高度上的 NO_y 和 O_3 的同步测定值记录，我们无法从中得到 O_3 和 NO_y 之间的明确的关系式。因此，这里所采用的保守方法尽管有可能低估 O_3 的已亏损值，但还是比较妥当的。

臭 氧 亏 损

8 月 17 日在 54°S 到 63°S 之间（图 2a），所预计的 O_3/NO_y 比值（不等式（2））与实测值差距较大。由于 NO_y 并未受到扰动，而 O_3/NO_y 的比值要小于我们的参考值 270，表明该地区存在 O_3 亏损。8 月 17 日在 63°S 处 O_3/NO_y 的比值为 230，这说明高化学扰动区外部 O_3 亏损了 15%。8 月 23 日飞行航次得到的数据同样表明边界外部存在 15% 的亏损量，而 8 月 28 日和 9 月 22 日的数据则显示了更大的亏损量，达 30%。不过图 3 并未对数据逐航次地分析，而是给出了 8 月 23 日至 9 月 22 日之间的平均值来概括地表示这一结果，从而证明 O_3 的亏损并不是特定航次中发生的孤立事件，而是在整个阶段都很普遍，并且通过平均值可以清晰地反映出来。该平均

by referencing the flight-leg data for NO_y and O_3 relative to the boundary, and then averaging the O_3/NO_y ratio over bins of 1° latitude. Only data for which NO_y is believed not to be enhanced by particles (as indicated by simultaneous particle measurements) have been plotted. This averaging procedure is done independently for both of the flight levels. The vertical bars represent the sample standard deviation and indicate how flight-by-flight variability affects the results.

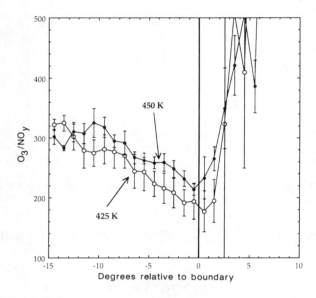

Fig. 3. O_3/NO_y against latitude relative to the boundary (heavy vertical line) for the 425-K and 450-K flight levels and averaged for the seven flights where data are available over intervals of 1° latitude. Data taken within clouds were excluded to obtain only gas-phase NO_y. Sample standard deviations are given as vertical bars.

The abrupt increase south of the boundary is due to the high degree of denitrification within the highly chemically perturbed region[13] and provides little information on the O_3 loss. We deal below with this region in a different way. However, outside the boundary where the NO_y is known to be unperturbed relative to N_2O, there are depressed ratios even below 200 near the boundary. These low ratios correspond to an average minimum O_3 loss of 15–30% in the first 5° of latitude outside the highly chemically perturbed region at these levels. It should be noted that the averaging over the one-month period is in a region where diabatic descent is believed to be taking place. An important feature in Fig. 3 is that outside the boundary the ratios at the 450-K level are ~20% higher than those at the 425-K level. This is not what would be expected from the model calculations and satellite data mentioned above, which show either no change in O_3/NO_y with altitude or a decrease. The implication is that the lowest values seen near but outside the boundary could not have come simply from vertical descent in this region. Proffitt *et al.*[10] show that within the averaging procedure used for Fig. 1, <10% of the air outside the boundary had come recently from the highly chemically perturbed region. Thus, if these results are accepted (that is, ongoing diabatic descent and little outward mixing at these potential

值是根据 NO$_y$ 和 O$_3$ 相对于边界的航段数据，将每 1 个纬度面元上的 O$_3$/NO$_y$ 比值作平均得到的。图中仅画出了那些被认为没有受颗粒影响而增大的 NO$_y$ 数据（据同步的颗粒测定结果）。两个飞行高度上的平均过程是分别独立进行的。图中垂直条代表样本的标准偏差，可以揭示各航次差异对结果的影响。

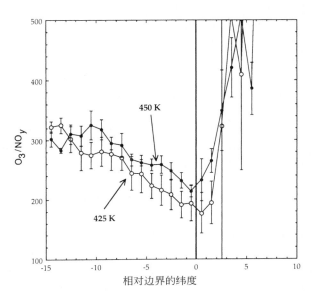

图 3. O$_3$/NO$_y$ 与相对于边界（垂直粗线）的纬度值的变化关系。两组数据的航行高度分别为 425 K 和 450 K，所用数据均为 7 个航次的平均值，数据间隔为 1 个纬度。为了保证采集样品均为气相 NO$_y$，剔除了在云中采集到的数据。垂直条表示样本的标准偏差。

比值在南部边界的突然增加是由高化学扰动区内的高度脱氮作用引起的[13]，对于 O$_3$ 的亏损不能提供多少信息。因此下面我们将采用不同的方法来处理该区数据。不过在边界以外，NO$_y$ 相对于 N$_2$O 不受扰动的地区，其比值较低，在边界附近甚至小于 200。在上述海拔位置，高化学扰动区之外的 5° 以内，这些较低比值对应的平均最小 O$_3$ 亏损量约为 15%~30%。应该注意的是，这一个月内的平均值是在被认为存在非绝热冷却的区域内得到的。图 3 有一个重要特征，即在边界以外，位温为 450 K 高度上的比值要比 425 K 高度上的比值高 20% 左右。前面提到的模拟计算和卫星数据结果都未料到这一点，之前的结果显示 O$_3$/NO$_y$ 不随高度变化或减小。这说明，该区在边界附近但处于边界之外所见到的最小值并不是简单地由垂直下降引起的。普罗菲特等[10] 证明，在图 1 所采用的平均过程中，边界外仅有不到 10% 的空气新近来自高化学扰动区。倘若认可这一结果（即，在上述位温条件下，一直存在着非绝热冷却过程并且很少发生向外混合作用）以及不等式（2），那么，从北侧向

temperatures) along with inequality (2), the decrease in the O_3/NO_y ratio, seen as the boundary is approached from the north, cannot be due to transport or mixing of air vertically nor horizontally, and therefore must be caused by some chemical mechanism operating at these levels outside the highly chemically perturbed region.

The isentropic temporal changes in O_3 outside the boundary during this one-month period are small in comparison with those inside, and in general are not significantly different from zero[18]. As discussed in the introduction, losses of O_3 in a parcel of air undergoing diabatic descent will not be represented accurately by a temporal trend calculated at a constant potential temperature, because the losses will be masked by the usual vertical gradient in O_3. Therefore the lack of a significant isentropic temporal trend outside the boundary in no way indicates that no loss of O_3 is occurring there.

To extend our analysis into the ozone hole and provide a check for consistency between two methods, equation (1) and inequality (2) are now combined into an inequality relating unperturbed O_3 directly to N_2O. If O_3 and N_2O are both in p.p.b.v.

$$[O_3] \geqslant 5,616 - (18.85 \times [N_2O]) \tag{3}$$

provides a minimum value for unperturbed O_3. First note that this formula is based on measured data and may reflect systematic errors in the measurements. In this regard, the O_3 measurement used here was generally within 2% of an independent measurement of O_3 made simultaneously on the ER-2[19,20]. There was no independent check of the NO_y measurements except as they related to the O_3 data over a long history of more than 50 ER-2 flights, but they are reported to be accurate to within ±20% and repeatable (precise) to within at least 0.1 p.p.b.v.[13]. The values used for N_2O are from the ATLAS instrument[21,22] and include a recent recalibration of the data that was not included in earlier papers[8,10-13,21,22]. The reported accuracy of the N_2O measurements is ±10%.

There is more uncertainty in applying inequality (3) inside the boundary where $N_2O < 140$ p.p.b.v. (see Fig. 1), stemming from our lack of information to support equation (1) and inequality (2) at these more southerly latitudes. Outside the boundary, equation (1) was used to test where NO_y was perturbed, then inequality (2) was used to predict O_3. By extending the application of inequality (3) to 72° S with its lower values for N_2O it is assumed that equation (1) remains linear and inequality (2) is still representative of O_3/NO_y. The use of equation (1) at lower values of N_2O is supported by noting that the linear relationship between NO_y and N_2O is predicted to persist at mid-latitudes to at least 14 p.p.b.v. of NO_y in both a one-dimensional radiative convective photochemical model[23] and a two-dimensional model[16]. Furthermore, the model calculations discussed earlier indicate that inequality (2) is satisfied at flight altitudes throughout our latitude range. Therefore all information available supports inequality (3) for these low values of N_2O. Implicit in the above discussion is that the formulations do have limits of applicability, the most obvious one being that they do not apply at altitudes above the maximum stratospheric mixing ratios for O_3. For at such altitudes, N_2O and O_3 are both decreasing with altitude but

边界接近时，O_3/NO_y 比值逐渐降低的现象不可能是由大气的垂直或水平输送与混合作用引起的，而必定是由这些高度上高化学扰动区外起作用的某些化学机制造成的。

在这一个月内边界外 O_3 沿等熵面随时间的变化小于边界内部，且一般位于零附近 [18]。正如在引言中所说，在恒定位温下计算出的时间趋势无法精确地表示处于非绝热冷却状态的单个气团中 O_3 的亏损量，因为臭氧的亏损可能会被 O_3 的垂直梯度所遮蔽。所以，边界外缺乏明显等熵时间趋势绝不代表那里没有发生 O_3 亏损。

为了将我们的分析扩展至臭氧洞，从而检验两种方法的一致性，现在将等式（1）和不等式（2）合并为一个不等式，以将不受扰动的 O_3 与 N_2O 直接联系起来。假定 O_3 和 N_2O 的单位均为 ppbv，则：

$$[O_3] \geqslant 5{,}616 - (18.85 \times [N_2O]) \tag{3}$$

可以得出不受扰动的 O_3 的最小值。首先需要注意，该项公式是基于测定数据得到的，可能会存在测定值的系统误差。有鉴于此，所采用的 O_3 测定值的误差一般在 ER-2 同步独立测定的 O_3 值的 2% 以内 [19,20]。我们没有对 NO_y 的测定值进行独立检验，只知道它们在多于 50 个 ER-2 航次的长时期内与 O_3 数据相关，不过有研究表明其准确度在 ±20% 以内，且至少在 0.1 ppbv 以内具有可重复性（精确度）[13]。所采用的 N_2O 值均由阿特拉斯(ATLAS)公司生产的设备测定 [21,22]，并新近对数据进行了再校准，这在之前的论文中是没有的 [8,10-13,21,22]。据报告，N_2O 测定的准确度为 ±10%。

对于 N_2O 含量小于 140 ppbv 的边界内区域（见图 1），要应用不等式（3）则存在更多的不确定性，这是因为我们缺少能支持等式（1）和不等式（2）的更南部纬度地区的有关资料。在边界外，可利用等式（1）来检测 NO_y 在何处受扰动，而不等式（2）则用来预测 O_3 值。当将不等式（3）的应用范围扩展至 72°S 时，由于那里的 N_2O 含量较低，可以认为等式（1）仍为线性，并且不等式（2）仍旧代表 O_3/NO_y 的比值。我们注意到，在中纬度地区当 NO_y 的含量至少为 14 ppbv 时，利用一维辐射对流光化学模型 [23] 和二维模型 [16] 得到的预测结果都表明 NO_y 和 N_2O 之间的线性关系继续存在。因此，当 N_2O 含量较低时，等式（1）仍可应用。而且，早先讨论的模拟计算结果表明，在我们的整个纬度范围内所飞行的高度上都满足不等式（2）。所以，所有可用的信息都支持不等式（3）在这些 N_2O 较低值时的应用。上述讨论说明这些公式在应用上确实存在一定的局限性，最明显的一点就是，在平流层中 O_3 达到最大混合比的海拔高度之上不适用。因为在该海拔高度之上，N_2O 和 O_3

inequality (3) implies that as N_2O decreases, O_3 increases. With this reservation a lower-limit estimate for unperturbed O_3 both outside and with increased reservation inside the boundary can now be calculated. Figure 4*a, b* shows measured O_3 against latitude with respect to the boundary where O_3 is averaged over all ten flights from 23 August to 22 September at both flight levels. Otherwise data are treated as in Fig. 3 for O_3/NO_y. Also plotted is the corresponding minimum value of unperturbed O_3 calculated from inequality (3). Figure 4*c* shows the O_3 loss with respect to the boundary, calculated as the percentage decrease in O_3 and based on Fig. 4*a, b*. The loss outside the boundary is typically 20–25% at 425 K for the first 5° with a maximum value indicated of ~30%. From Fig. 3 we obtained a maximum value of 30% O_3 loss outside the boundary, which is virtually identical to the loss shown in Fig. 4*c*, although the analysis of Fig. 3 includes only seven of the ten flights included in Fig. 4. This difference in number of flights is because particle-free NO_y data are available only from seven flights. Both analyses indicate that the loss is greater at the lower level, which is consistent with diabatic descent and a simultaneous chemical loss of O_3.

This analysis can also be applied to individual flights rather than averages of flights. For example, from data taken on 23 August, the first day that a flight clearly penetrated the boundary, we calculate a 40% loss in O_3 inside the boundary. On the last mission flight date, 22 September, still two weeks before the minimum column O_3 was measured in 1987 (ref. 24), there was a 70–80% loss within the boundary in the layer between 17.5 km and 19 km. This is substantially more than the 53% isentropic temporal decrease observed in the same region from 23 August to 22 September[18].

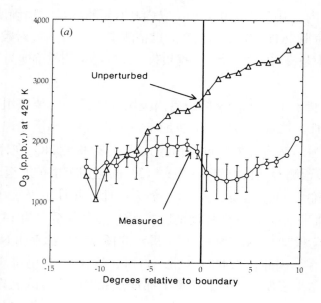

都随海拔高度而降低，而不等式（3）表明随着 N_2O 减少，O_3 增加。根据这些限制条件就可以估算出边界外更小的无扰动的 O_3 的下限，而根据更多的限制条件也可估算出边界内不受扰动的 O_3 的下限。图 4a，b 所示为 O_3 随相对边界的纬度差的变化而变化的情况，其中 O_3 分别为两飞行高度上 8 月 23 日到 9 月 22 日期间 10 个航次的平均值。其他有关 O_3/NO_y 比值的数据处理同图 3。图中还画出了利用不等式（3）得到的对应的不受扰动的 O_3 的最小值。图 4c 为 O_3 亏损量随着距边界纬度差的变化，即根据图 4a，b 得到的 O_3 减少的百分含量。在 425 K 高度上边界外 5°以内的亏损量一般为 20%~25%，最大值约为 30%。由图 3，我们得到的边界外 O_3 亏损的最大值亦为 30%，实际上与图 4c 所显示的亏损量一致，只不过图 3 仅分析了图 4 所包含的 10 个航次中的 7 个。航次数量之所以有差别，是因为仅有 7 个航次的不含颗粒物的 NO_y 数据是可用的。两图的分析都表明，高度较低时亏损量较大，这与非绝热冷却及 O_3 的同步化学亏损是一致的。

除了航次的平均值，本分析还适用于单个航次结果。比如，从 8 月 23 日，即第一天穿过边界飞行得到的数据中，我们计算出边界内 O_3 的亏损量为 40%。而在最后一次飞行任务的那天，即 9 月 22 日，离 1987 年测到 O_3 柱总量最低值的日子（参考文献 24）还有两周，17.5 km 到 19 km 之间这一层边界内的亏损量为 70%~80%。该值明显大于 8 月 23 日至 9 月 22 日期间在同一地区观测到的沿等熵面的 53% 的降低值[18]。

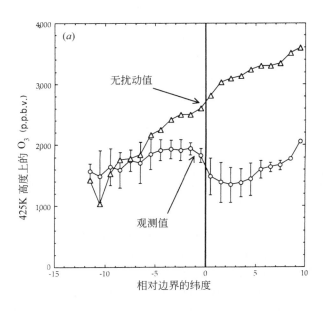

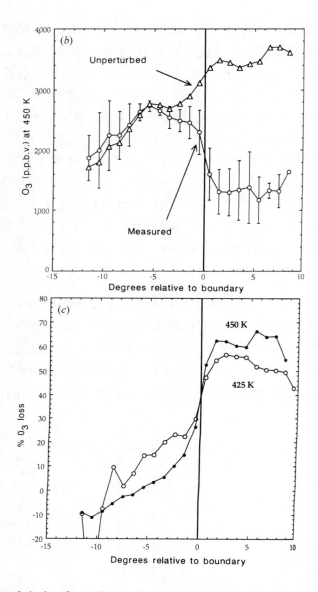

Fig. 4. *a*, O$_3$ against latitude referenced to the boundary (heavy vertical line) for the 425-K flight level. Data are averaged over intervals of 1° latitude and over all ten flights from 23 August to 22 September 1987. *b*, As in *a* except at 450-K flight level. *c*, Average percent O$_3$ loss over 30 days derived from *a* and *b*.

Discussion and Conclusions

Since the ozone hole was first identified in 1985 it has been considered to be a recurring springtime event with a nearly monotonic increase of intensity over its history of ~10–15 years[25]. Here we have presented strong evidence of significant O$_3$ loss occurring as early as mid-August both inside and outside the highly chemically perturbed region, and that this loss is chemical in origin rather than a result of atmospheric dynamics. Although the mechanism for the chemical loss outside the boundary cannot be inferred from this approach, there is evidence of a temporal column O$_3$ decrease over the past decade in this

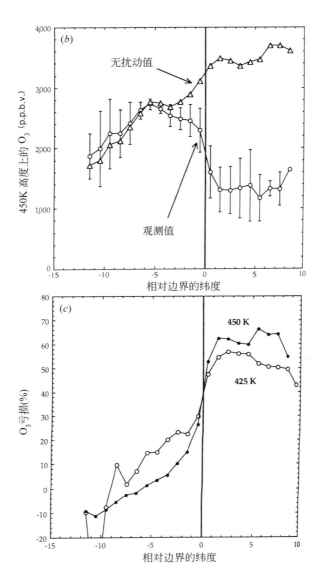

图 4. *a*，425 K 高度上 O₃ 随着相对于边界（垂直粗线）的纬度值的变化关系。图中数据为以 1 个纬度为间隔取的 1987 年 8 月 23 日到 9 月 22 日期间所有 10 个航次的平均值。*b*，为 450 K 高度上的情况。*c*，为由 *a*，*b* 得到的 30 天中 O₃ 亏损的平均百分比。

讨论与结论

臭氧洞最早于 1985 年发现，人们一直认为它是春季时期的一种循环事件，在近 10 年到 15 年的时间里其强度近于单调增加[25]。本文给出了早在 8 月中旬 O₃ 就显著亏损的有力证据，高化学扰动区内外都有，并指出该亏损的成因是化学作用而非大气动力作用的结果。虽然边界外亏损的化学机制无法根据此方法推断出，但有证据表明该区过去十年中 O₃ 柱总量是随时间降低的，这就说明我们所报道的化学亏

region, therefore indicating that the chemical loss that we report has an anthropogenic component. In particular, ref. 26 shows, by comparing satellite data from 1979–80 with 1986–87, a nine-year temporal decrease from 6% to 18% in column O_3 between 60° S and 66° S during August and September, a region near, but on the average outside, the boundary during AAOE. In ref. 27 the data were analysed with a linear fit of the yearly data, starting with 1978 and ending with 1988. This analysis produced virtually identical trends from 60° S to 66° S from mid-August through September. Both studies also show a long-term temporal decrease of more than 10%, poleward of 66° S during August. These analyses present a consistent picture of mid-August O_3 decreases, both inside and outside the vortex, that have intensified during the past ten years. The results we have presented co-locate a region of chemical O_3 loss with these long-term temporal decreases in O_3, suggesting that at least part of the loss has an anthropogenic origin.

The cause of the O_3 loss outside the boundary, where the measured ClO is only 5–10% of the level measured inside the boundary, is not known, and more experimental investigation is warranted. But it has been suggested by Tuck[11] that O_3 losses may occur near the boundary and outside the highly chemically perturbed region during June, July and August as long as there is sunlight. Such losses would be due to reactive chlorine, as is the case within the ozone hole itself. Support for this conclusion comes from photochemical model studies made along isentropic trajectories outside the boundary[28]. These studies point out that the discrepancy between observed and measured values of ClO and NO indicates significantly perturbed photochemistry in this region without substantial denitrification. In sunlight the formation of polar stratospheric clouds (PSCs) outside the boundary can perturb chlorine and nitrogen chemistry, initiating catalytic destruction cycles. Observed temperatures are above the frost point on average, but low enough for PSCs to form that contain nitric acid, a component of NO_y[13,29]. The NO_y measurements indicate that PSC formation does not generally lead to denitrification. The maximum frequency of PSC formation over the continent and inside the vortex occur to the east of the ER-2 flight tracks over the Weddell Sea[30], downwind from the ER-2 flight track. The perturbed levels of reactive chlorine initiated by the PSCs cannot be long-lived because of the lack of denitrification. In sunlight, nitric acid will gradually photolyse to produce NO_2, and this will reduce ClO levels to near unperturbed values. With such intermittent chemical perturbations, this region may contain sufficient recurrent enhancements in ClO to destroy O_3 to the extent indicated in our analysis.

Obtaining values for unperturbed O_3 in the Antarctic from other species must carry with it some uncertainty, but the analysis presented here has been conservative. In particular, if the value of 300 had been chosen for O_3/NO_y as is indicated by the Southern Hemisphere data, the analysis would have produced somewhat larger O_3 losses. The negative O_3 loss 10–15° outside the boundary (Figs 3 and 4c) shows that the choice of 270 for the ratio is conservative. Nevertheless, the method is more reliable than the simple "before and after" comparisons of O_3 profiles which we strongly caution against when analyzing losses of O_3 at high latitudes unless the losses are very large, as within the Antarctic ozone hole.

损有一定的人为因素的影响。特别地，根据参考文献 26，通过比较 1979~1980 年和 1986~1987 年的卫星资料，可以发现 8 月到 9 月里 60°S 至 66°S 之间 O_3 柱浓度的下降值在这 9 年间从 6% 变到了 18%。该区在 AAOE 实验期间位于边界附近，但平均来说是在外部。参考文献 27 对 1978 年到 1988 年间每一年的数据进行了线性拟合分析。该项分析得到的是几乎相同的趋势，同样是在 8 月中旬至整个 9 月期间 60°S 至 66°S 之间的地区。两项研究还发现，8 月从 66°S 到南极地区，O_3 随时间变化有一个高于 10% 的长期减少趋势。这些分析均表明，位于极涡内外的 O_3 含量在 8 月中旬减少，并且在过去十年间 O_3 减少量也是加强的。我们给出的上述结果显示 O_3 的化学亏损区与 O_3 随时间的长期下降区是一致的，说明至少部分亏损是由人为原因造成的。

在边界外所测定的 ClO 含量仅为边界内测定值的 5%~10%，而边界外 O_3 亏损的因素尚不清楚，有待于更多的实验研究。不过塔克[11]认为，6、7、8 月期间，在边界附近及高化学扰动区外部，只要有阳光就可能发生 O_3 亏损。此类亏损是由活性氯引起的，正如臭氧洞内发生的情况一样。支持该结论的证据来自沿边界外的等熵线进行的光化学模拟研究[28]。这些研究指出，ClO 与 NO 的观测值与测定值之间的差异说明，该区在未发生明显的脱氮作用的情况下发生了显著的光化学扰动作用。在阳光照耀下，边界外极地平流层云（PSCs）的形成会使氯元素和氮元素化学过程受到扰动，引发催化损耗循环。虽然所观测到的温度平均值均在霜点之上，但已经足以形成含有硝酸的极地平流层云，而硝酸是 NO_y 的组分[13,29]。NO_y 的测定结果表明，极地平流层云的形成一般不会引起脱氮作用。陆地上和极涡内，极地平流层云的最大生成频率发生于威德尔海上空 ER-2 航线的东侧[30]，处于 ER-2 航线的下风向。由于缺少脱氮作用，极地平流层云所引起的活性氯的扰动水平寿命不会很长。在阳光下，硝酸会逐渐被光解，生成 NO_2，这又会促使 ClO 含量降低至非扰动值附近。在这种间歇性化学扰动作用下，该区内就可以形成足够多的 ClO 循环增量，促使 O_3 的破坏程度达到我们所分析的水平。

在南极地区，根据其他方法获得的无扰动 O_3 值必定存在某些不确定性，然而本文提出的分析方法是较保守的。特别地，如南半球数据所显示的那样，当 O_3/NO_y 的比值选为 300 时，本分析方法得出的 O_3 亏损值可能会大些。边界外 10° 到 15° 范围内负的 O_3 亏损值（图 3 和图 4c）说明，270 是一个保守的比值。无论如何，在高纬度地区，除在 O_3 亏损量非常大的地区，比如在南极臭氧洞内，本方法相对于利用简单的"前后" O_3 曲线的简单对比来说更可靠一些，在分析 O_3 亏损时我们强烈反对采用后者。

We have analysed winter-time high-latitude O_3 changes in a region where O_3 is considered under dynamical control and standard gas-phase photochemistry is extremely slow. We have estimated a reference state for O_3 in this region from other conserved trace species and compared this with measured values to determine a minimum loss in ozone. In this context we can summarize the important conclusions as follows: (1) There is a substantial O_3 loss by mid-August both inside and outside the highly chemically perturbed region; (2) For the first 5° outside the boundary, the average O_3 loss from 23 August to 22 September was at least 15–30% at 17.5 km and 4–25% at 19 km; (3) The O_3 loss found outside the boundary is chemical in origin and did not occur within the highly chemically perturbed region. An anthropogenic component cannot be ruled out; (4) For the first 5° inside the boundary and in the layer between 17.5 and 19 km the air observed on 23 August had an O_3 loss of about 40%. By 22 September there was an O_3 loss of at least 75%, much larger than the average isentropic temporal decrease of 53% from 23 August to 22 September.

(**342**, 233-237; 1989)

M. H. Proffitt[*†], D. W. Fahey[*], K. K. Kelly[*] & A. F. Tuck[*]
[*] NOAA Aeronomy Laboratory, 325 Broadway, Boulder, Colorado 80303, USA
[†] CIRES, University of Colorado, Boulder, Colorado 80309, USA

Received 9 June; accepted 22 September 1989.

References:
1. Atkinson, R. J., Matthews, W. A., Newman, P. A. & Plumb, R. A. *Nature* **340**, 290-294 (1989).
2. Farman, J. C., Gardiner, B. G. & Shanklin, J. D. *Nature* **315**, 207-210 (1985).
3. Stolarski, R. S. *et al. Nature* **322**, 808-811 (1986).
4. Hofmann, D. J., Harder, J. W., Rolf, S. R. & Rosen, J. R. *Nature* **326**, 59-62 (1987).
5. Komhyr, W. D., Oltmans, S. J. & Grass, R. D. *J. Geophys. Res.* **93**, 5167-5184 (1988).
6. Solomon, S., Garcia, R. R. & Stordal, F. *J. Geophys. Res.* **90**, 12981-12989 (1985).
7. Garcia, R. R. & Solomon, S. *J. Geophys. Res.* **90**, 3850-3868 (1985).
8. Proffitt, M. H. *et al. J. Geophys. Res.* **94**, 11437-11448 (1989).
9. Danielsen, E. F. & Houben, H. *Anthropogene Beeinflüssung der Ozonschicht*, 191-242 (DECHEMA, Frankfurt am Main, 1988).
10. Proffitt, M. H. *et al. J. Geophys. Res.* (in the press).
11. Tuck, A. F. *J. Geophys. Res.* **94**, 11687-11737 (1989).
12. Kelly, K. K. *et al. J. Geophys. Res.* **94**, 11317-11357 (1989).
13. Fahey, D. W. *et al. J. Geophys. Res.* (in the press).
14. Galbally, I. E. *et al. Q. Jl R. Met. Soc.* **112**, 775-809 (1986).
15. Ko, M. K. W., McElroy, M. B., Weisenstein, D. K. & Sze, N. D. *J. Geophys. Res.* **91**, 5395-5404 (1986).
16. Solomon, S. & Garcia, R. R. *J. Geophys. Res.* **89**, 11633-11644 (1984).
17. Russell, J. M. III *et al. J. Geophys. Res.* **93**, 1718-1736 (1988).
18. Proffitt, M. H. *et al. J. Geophys. Res.* (in the press).
19. Starr, W. L. & Vedder, J. F. *J. Geophys. Res.* **94**, 11449-11463 (1989).
20. Margitan, J. J. *et al. J. Geophys. Res.* (in the press).
21. Loewenstein, M., Podolske, J. R., Chan, K. R. & Strahan, S. E. *J. Geophys. Res.* **94**, 11589-11598 (1989).
22. Podolske, J. R., Loewentstein, M., Strahan, S. E. & Chan, K. R. *J. Geophys. Res.* (in the press).
23. Brasseur, G. & Solomon, S. *Aeronomy of the Middle Atmosphere,* 2nd edn (Reidel, Dordrecht, 1986).
24. Krueger, A. J. *et al. The 1987 Airborne Antarctic Ozone Experiment: The Nimbus-7 TOMS Data Atlas* (NASA Ref. Publ., NASA RF-1201, Goddard Space Flight Center, 1988).
25. Solomon, S. *Rev. Geophys.* **26**, 131-148 (1988).

有些地区，O_3 的亏损受动力作用控制，且其标准气相光化学作用非常缓慢，我们已对这种高纬度地区内冬季时 O_3 含量的变化进行了分析。我们利用其他保守痕量气体估算了该区 O_3 含量的参考状态，然后将其与测定值相比较，以此来确定臭氧亏损的最小值。综上所述，我们可以将重要结论总结如下：(1) 到 8 月中旬，高化学扰动区内外就已存在明显的 O_3 亏损；(2) 从 8 月 23 日到 9 月 22 日，边界外 5°以内 O_3 亏损的平均值在 17.5 km 处至少为 15%~30%，在 19 km 处至少为 4%~25%；(3) 边界外发现的 O_3 亏损是由化学作用引起的，并且未发生于高化学扰动区内，不能排除人为因素的影响；(4) 对于 8 月 23 日所观测到的、边界内 5°以内 17.5~19 km 之间的大气，其 O_3 亏损量约为 40%。到 9 月 22 日，O_3 的亏损量至少达 75%，该值远远大于 8 月 23 到 9 月 22 日期间 O_3 沿等熵面随时间 53% 的平均降低值。

（齐红艳 翻译；安俊岭 审稿）

26. *International Ozone Trends Panel Report: 1988* (WMO Report No. 18, in the press).

27. UNEP/WMO *Stratospheric Assessment of Stratospheric Ozone: 1989* (UNEP/WMO Report, in the press).

28. Jones, R. L. *et al. J. Geophys. Res.* **94**, 11529-11558 (1989).

29. Chan, K. R., Scott, S. G., Bui, T. P., Bowen, S. W. & Day, J. *J. Geophys. Res.* **94**, 11573-11587 (1989).

30. Watterson, I. G. & Tuck, A. F. *J. Geophys. Res.* (in the press).

Acknowledgements. We thank J. Margitan, S. Solomon and R. Jones for their comments. We thank The Chemical Manufacturers Association and NASA for funding.

Upper Bounds on "Cold Fusion" in Electrolytic Cells

D. E. Williams *et al.*

Editor's note

When electrochemists Martin Fleischmann and Stanley Pons claimed to have found evidence of "cold" nuclear fusion happening in a small flask of salty heavy water undergoing electrolysis, conflicting reports of verification or failure quickly came from all over the world. This paper by chemist David Williams and his co-workers in England was one of the first to turn the tide of opinion towards the idea that cold fusion is an illusion. It reports a very comprehensive attempt to replicate the results of Fleischmann and Pons, and finds no evidence of excess heat, neutron emission or the formation of tritium—the last two being diagnostic of deuterium fusion.

Experiments using three different calorimeter designs and high-efficiency neutron and γ-ray detection on a wide range of materials fail to sustain the recent claims of cold fusion made by Fleischmann *et al.*[1] and Jones *et al.*[2]. Spurious effects which, undetected, could have led to claims of cold fusion, include noise from neutron counters, cosmic-ray background variations, calibration errors in simple calorimeters and variable electrolytic enrichment of tritium.

RECENT publications[1,2] reporting electrochemically induced nuclear fusion, at room temperature, have aroused great interest. The signatures reported are excess heat output, neutron emission and tritium generation from cells with palladium cathodes[1], and neutron emission alone at a much lower level from cells with titanium cathodes[2]. Conventional nuclear physics predicts that fusion between light nuclei requires either very high temperature (as in a tokamak) or unusually close proximity of the two nuclei (as in muon-catalysed fusion). The calculated fusion rate at the internuclear separation in the deuterium molecule (0.74 Å) is $\sim 3 \times 10^{-64}\,\text{s}^{-1}$ (ref. 3), so the rates reported in ref. 2 ($\sim 10^{-23}$ d-d-pair^{-1} s^{-1}; d is deuteron) are not easy to understand in the context of the known interstitial-site separations (~ 3 Å), even more so when it is realized that this rate is a severe underestimate because of incomplete deuterium loading in titanium (see Materials characterization section). The reaction rates reported in ref. 1 are even more difficult to understand[4], and the existence, despite strong arguments to the contrary (ref. 5, for example), of an unknown mechanism, which results both in an extraordinary enhancement of the reaction rate and a suppression of the normal nuclear-reaction channels, has been postulated.

电解池中"冷核聚变"的上限

威廉斯等

编者按

当电化学家马丁·弗莱施曼和斯坦利·庞斯宣称他们在小瓶的电解含盐重水中发现了"冷"核聚变的证据时，世界各地很快出现了一些证实其成功或失败的相矛盾的报告。这篇来自英国化学家戴维·威廉斯和他的合作者的文章是首篇将流行观点转向认为冷核聚变只是错觉的文章之一。文章报告了对弗莱施曼和庞斯实验结果的一次非常全面的重复尝试，结果发现没有"过热"、中子发射或者氚生成的证据，而后两者被认为是氘发生聚变的判据。

使用三种不同设计的量热计、高效率的中子和 γ 射线探测装置对多种材料进行研究的实验未能支持最近弗莱施曼等人[1]和琼斯等人[2]关于冷核聚变的宣称。可能是一些未探测到的虚假效应导致了这一关于冷核聚变的断言，其中包括中子计数器的噪声、宇宙射线本底的变化、简易量热计的标定误差和可变的氚的电解富集。

最近发表的论文[1,2]报道了室温下电化学引发的核聚变，该结果引起了极大的关注。报道中发生核聚变的鲜明特征是配有钯阴极的电解池中过剩的热量输出、中子（即 n）发射和氚（即 t）的产生[1]，以及配有钛阴极的电解池中仅有很低水平的中子发射[2]。传统核物理预测轻核之间的聚变需要非常高的温度（如在托卡马克装置中那样）或者两个核异常接近（如在 μ 子催化核聚变中那样）。根据氘（即 d）分子的核间距（0.74 Å）计算出的核聚变速率约为 3×10^{-64} s^{-1}（参考文献 3），所以在已知间隙位间距（约为 3 Å）的情况下，很难理解参考文献 2 报道的反应速率（每对氘核每秒约产生 10^{-23} 次聚变效应），如果考虑到氘在钛中并未完全充满（参见材料表征部分），这一速率（约为 3×10^{-64} s^{-1}）还是被大大低估了，参考文献 2 中的速率就更不易理解了。而参考文献 1 中报道的反应速率甚至更难理解[4]，尽管有强大的反对意见（如参考文献 5），他们还是假定存在一种未知的机理，可以使反应速率异常增加，并抑制正常的核反应通道。

591

In the first reports of the electrolytic cold fusion effect it was stated that the effect is not consistently reproducible, and that it both takes some time to appear and that it may subsequently disappear. Because electrochemical phenomena can be sensitively affected by the state of the surface, some irreproducibility is not, in itself, surprising, and other recent reports (refs 6–8, for example) give well documented accounts of failures as well as successes (R. A. Huggins and A. J. Appleby, Workshop on Cold Fusion, Santa Fe, May 1989) in observing the claimed effects. The clear lack of reproducibility necessitates significant replication, with controls at least equal in number to the number of tests, if positive results are to be viewed with confidence, and exploration of many different, well characterized, material and electrolyte combinations. Particularly, the timescales and achievable concentrations for electrolytic loading of deuterium into palladium and titanium, the quantities of hydrogen "impurity", and the species detectable by surface analysis of used cathodes ought to be determined.

Calorimetry

We used three types of calorimeter. First, we built calorimeters of size and design similar to those used by Fleischmann et al. (ref. 1 and M. Fleischmann, personal communication) (Fig. 1). We found these to be inaccurate instruments with some very subtle sources of error which it is necessary to appreciate and analyse in detail. We used sixteen such cells, containing different-size cathodes (1-, 2-, 4- or 6-mm Pd rods) and different electrolytes (0.1 M LiOD, 0.1 M LiOH, 0.1 M NaOD or 0.1 M NaOH). Figure 2a, b shows the results obtained for a typical cell. An immediately evident characteristic is the sloping baseline, with the sawtooth pattern a consequence of the regular refilling of the cell. The baseline slope can be quantitatively accounted for by a variation of the calibration constant, k, with the level of liquid in the cell. This is a result of radiative losses through the vacuum jacket[9] and conduction of the glass inner wall of the cell[10] (see Fig. 2 legend). A consequence of the sloping baseline is that any calibration is only valid for a particular liquid level. We regularly refilled these cells to a reference level at which the calibration had been performed. We calibrated the cells with the heaters before the electrolysis was started and again much later in the run, during the electrolysis, as is evident in Fig. 2a (see Fig. 1 legend for details of the calibration procedure). There was no statistically significant difference between the different calibration sets, so all data were combined.

第一批电解冷核聚变效应的报道指出，该效应并非自始至终都是可重复的，它耗时少许才出现并可能随后消失。因为电化学现象对表面状态非常敏感，一些不可重复性本身并不令人惊奇，最近其他的报道（如参考文献 6~8）在观察所谓的冷核聚变效应时给出了失败和成功的完备记录（哈金斯和阿普尔比，冷核聚变专题讨论会，圣菲，1989 年 5 月）。重复性的明显缺乏使得效果显著的重复实验变得很有必要，要想使结果具有较高的置信水平，对照实验至少在数目上应该与之前的实验相当，同时要探究许多不同的、特性明确的材料和电解液组合。尤其是钯电极和钛电极电解法充氘的时间尺度、可达到的浓度、氢"杂质"的量化，以及在用过的阴极上通过表面分析可以检测到的各种物质都应该测定。

量 热 法

我们使用了三种量热计。首先，我们构建了与弗莱施曼等人所用的（参考文献 1；弗莱施曼，个人交流）尺寸和设计相似的量热计（图 1）。我们发现这种量热计是不精准的装置，具有一些不太容易被发现的误差来源，很有必要对其进行仔细研究和分析。我们使用了 16 个这样的电解池，包括不同尺寸的阴极（1 mm、2 mm、4 mm 和 6 mm 的钯棒）和不同的电解液（0.1 M LiOD, 0.1 M LiOH, 0.1 M NaOD 或者 0.1 MNaOH）。图 2a 和 2b 显示了其中一个典型的电解池获得的结果。一个直接的明显特征是具有锯齿状形式的倾斜基线，这是电解池定期地添加电解液的结果。基线的斜率可以通过仪器常数 k 随电解池中液面水平的变化定量地求出。这是由杜瓦瓶内的真空夹层的热辐射损失 [9] 和电解池玻璃内壁的热传导 [10] 产生的结果（见图 2 的图注）。基线倾斜的结果就是任何标定只有针对特定的液面水平才是有效的。我们定期将这些电解池重新灌注到进行标定时的参考水平。在电解开始前，我们用加热器对电解池进行标定，电解期间，运行了相当一段时间后再标定一次，如图 2a 所示（标定过程的细节见图 1 的图注）。两种标定设置没有统计学上的显著差异，所以我们将所有的数据都结合起来了。

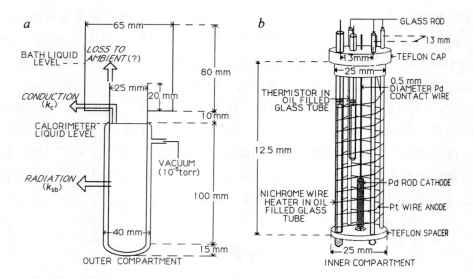

Fig. 1. Schematic diagram of the FPH-type heat-flow calorimeter used here. Heat flow paths are indicated here and discussed further in Fig. 2 legend.

METHODS. As well as the Fleischmann, Pons and Hawkins (FPH) type, we used[10] two other calorimeter types—an improved heat-flow calorimeter (IHF) and an isothermal calorimeter. The IHF calorimeters differed from the FPH type in three important ways. First, they were larger: a 500-ml-capacity cylindrical vessel constituted the cell, with anode-cathode spacing ~2 cm. Second, the electrolysis vessel was inserted, using a film of oil for thermal contact, into a tightly fitting aluminium can which was itself packed around with insulating material and placed in a Dewar flask. Whereas the temperature of the cell contents in the FPH calorimeter was determined using a glass-clad thermistor immersed in the cell itself, in the IHF design the temperature of the aluminium can was measured: the can defined an isothermal surface for conduction of heat away from the cell and its use as the temperature measurement surface eliminated the sloping-baseline problem of the FPH design. Third, the space within the Dewar flask above the electrolysis vessel was filled with a polystyrene cap extending well above the Dewar flask, with the aim of significantly reducing unquantified heat losses to the atmosphere. The two types of heat-flow calorimeter were operated in water baths held at a constant temperature of 20 °C(±0.08 °C). The tops of the water baths were covered with a polystyrene lid. In both cases the cells comprised a spirally wound Pt wire anode (0.25 mm) and a central Pd cathode (Johnson Matthey). For the FPH cells we prepared the different electrolytes using either conductivity water (H_2O cells) or slightly tritiated D_2O (specific activity 13 kBq ml^{-1}) of isotopic purity initially >99.9%. We used 0.1M LiOD (D_2O from Aldrich, measured >99.9% initial isotopic purity) as the electrolyte in the IHF calorimeters. The Pt and Pd contact wire was shrouded in glass tubing in the IHF cells to prevent any possible catalytic recombination of the electrolysis products. In later experiments with the FPH cells we also used screened electrode contacts, but this had no effect on the results obtained. The IHF cells contained a Pd wire electrode insulated to the very tip, which was positioned about three-quarters of the way up the cell. This was used to define the internal liquid level during filling, or refilling, of the cell. The larger volume of electrolyte in the IHF cells (300 ml) meant that refilling was required only occasionally, but the large thermal mass meant that the response was slow (time constant ~12 h): thus they were not sensitive to small bursts of heat. We calibrated the heat-flow calorimeters using a nichrome wire heater placed in an oil-filled glass tube which was in contact with the cell contents. The calibration procedure involved operating the heater, either without electrolytic current, or with a current significantly less (0.2–0.4 times) than the normal electrolysis current, until a steady-state temperature was attained. With the FPH cells, use of a lower electrolysis current ensured continued stirring while diminishing the errors arising from the baseline drift; before each individual calibration the cells were refilled. An empirical calibration curve was thus obtained by fitting the observed thermistor resistance, R, to a range of applied powers, P, using the equation $P = a - b(\log R) + c(\log R)^2$, where a, b and c are the fitted parameters. The

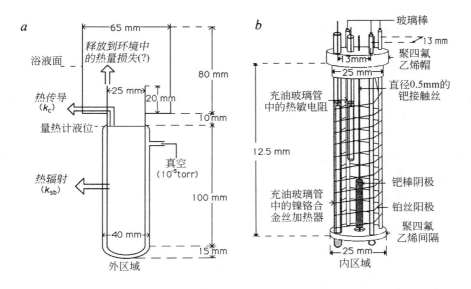

图1. 本文使用的FPH型热流量热计示意图。在图中标出了热流的路径，更进一步的讨论如图2的图注所示。

方法：除了弗莱施曼、庞斯和霍金斯（FPH）型的量热计之外，我们还使用了[10]两种其他类型的量热计——改进的热流量热计（IHF）和等温式量热计。IHF量热计与FPH量热计的不同主要表现在三个方面。首先，IHF量热计更大：500 ml容积的柱状容器构成了电解池，其中阳极–阴极间距约为2 cm。其次，电解容器被塞进一个紧密贴合的铝罐中，用一层油膜保证热接触，铝罐被隔热材料包裹起来并放入一个杜瓦瓶中。FPH量热计中电解池的温度是通过浸入电解池内的、由玻璃保护的热敏电阻进行测量的，而在IHF结构中，测量的是铝罐的温度；对于将电解池中的热量传导出去的过程而言，罐体可以被认为是一个恒温的表面，将它作为温度测量表面解决了FPH结构中基线倾斜的问题。第三，将杜瓦瓶中电解容器上方的空间用一个高高地伸展到杜瓦瓶上方的聚苯乙烯盖子填满，这样做的目的是显著减小未知的释放到大气中的热量损失。两种类型的热流量热计都在水浴中运行，水浴控制在恒定的温度20 ℃（±0.08 ℃）。水浴的顶部用一个聚苯乙烯的盖子盖住。在两种量热计中，电解池均包括一个弯成螺旋形的铂丝阳极（0.25 mm）和一个中央的钯阴极（庄信万丰公司）。对FPH电解池我们制备了不同的电解液，它们由电导水（H_2O电解池）或者初始同位素纯度大于99.9%轻微氚化了的D_2O（比活性为13 kBq·ml^{-1}）制成。我们用0.1 M LiOD（D_2O购自奥德里奇公司，测得初始同位素纯度大于99.9%）作为IHF量热计中的电解液。在IHF电解池中，铂和钯的接触丝被封装在玻璃管中，以避免电解产物任何可能的催化复合过程。在后面使用FPH电解池的实验中我们也使用了屏蔽的电极接触丝，但是这对获得的结果没有任何影响。IHF电解池包含一根用绝缘套管覆盖到顶端的钯丝电极，它被放置于距电解池底端四分之三处。这是在向电解池添加或者重复添加液体时用来规定内部液面水平的参照。IHF电解池中更大的电解液体积（300 ml）意味着重复添加仅需要偶尔进行，但是较大的热质则意味着响应会比较慢（时间常数约为12小时）；因此他们对热量的少量释放并不敏感。我们用置于填满油的玻璃管中的镍铬合金丝加热器对热流量热计进行了标定，该玻璃管与电解池的内容物相接触。标定的过程包括运行加热器，不施加电解电流或者施加显著小于（0.2~0.4倍）通常电解所需的电流，直到体系获得一个稳态的温度。对于FPH电解池，使用较小的电解电流旨在确保持续搅拌的同时减小由于基线漂移带来的误差；在每次单独的标定之前电解池都要再添加一次电解液。利用方程$P = a - b(\log R) + c(\log R)^2$将得到的热敏电阻的阻值$R$在应用的功率$P$的范围内对$P$进行拟合，其中$a$，$b$和$c$是拟合参数，这样一条经

standard error of estimate on the fitted curve varied from 10 to as much as 70 mW with the FPH cells, largely reflecting the error in extrapolation to the reference level. Neutron counting was performed in conjunction with the operation of the FPH cells, using two independent banks of counters mounted above the cells, on top of the water-bath cover[10]. Detection sensitivity above background was 3 event s^{-1} in the cell. We never observed a signal above background. The isothermal calorimeter (J. A. Mason, R. W. Wilde, J. C. Vickery, B. W. Hooton and G. M. Wells, Proc. 29th A. Meet. Inst. Nuclear Materials Management, Las Vegas, Nevada, June 1988) comprises three concentric aluminium cylinders each separated by a heat transfer medium with a relatively low thermal conductivity. The cylinder temperatures are maintained by electrical heaters wound as helical coils around each cylinder. Temperature control is achieved by resistance thermometers on each cylinder which are used in conjunction with classical control software and the cylinder heaters. The rate of thermal energy evolution in the measurement chamber (12.5-cm diameter, 26-cm high) is determined by measuring precisely the electrical power supplied to the chamber. We operated the calorimeter at a measurement-chamber temperature of $42\pm0.001\,°C$. The measurement-chamber power resolution is <5 mW for an operating power of 20 W. The electrolytic cell contained ~1 L 0.1M LiOD. The cathode was contained in a perforated glass canopy to prevent the evolved gases from mixing inside the measurement chamber. The anode was a Pt foil cylinder 3 cm high and 12 cm in diameter surrounding the cathode. The cell was thermally coupled to the calorimeter measurement chamber by conducting oil. Measurements using Pt cathodes and also using nichrome wire heaters showed that there was a small systematic error in the calorimeter, an apparent power excess that varied linearly with the input power up to 100 mW for an input of 15 W. A linear fit to these measurements (12 points, standard error of estimate 8.8 mW) was therefore used to apply a correction to the apparent excess measured for the Pd cathodes. The measured output power of both the isothermal and IHF cells was corrected for the power loss that is due to evaporation of the electrolyte, assuming that the electrolysis gases were saturated in water vapour as they passed out of the cell (25.0 mW A^{-1} at 42 °C): $q_v = (p_v/p_0)(1.5)\Delta H_v I/(2F)$ where q_v is the power loss, p_v denotes the saturation vapour pressure and ΔH_v the latent heat of evaporation of the electrolyte, p_0 is the atmospheric pressure, F is the Faraday constant and I is the current (assumes ideal gases).

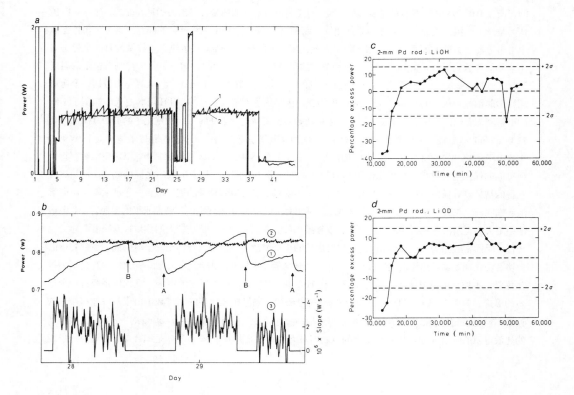

验的标定曲线就得到了。对拟合曲线估算出的 FPH 电解池的标准误差在 10 mW 到高达 70 mW 之间变化，这主要反映了外推到参考水平时的误差。中子计数使用了安装在电解池上方、水浴盖顶部[10]的两个独立的计数管组合体，是与 FPH 电解池的运行同时进行的。高于本底的探测灵敏度在电解池中为每秒 3 个计数。我们没有观察到任何高于本底的信号。等温式量热计（梅森、怀尔德、维克里、胡顿和韦尔斯，第 29 届核材料管理协会年度会议录，拉斯维加斯，内华达州，1988 年 6 月）包括三个同轴的铝筒，相互之间用一种较低热导率的导热介质隔开。圆筒的温度通过螺旋缠绕在各圆筒上的电加热器来维持。温度通过每个圆筒上的电阻式温度计来控制，该温度计与经典控制软件和圆筒加热器连接在一起。测量室（直径 12.5 cm，高 26 cm）中的热能产生速率可以通过精确测量供给测量室的电能来确定。我们在测量室温度为 42±0.001℃ 的条件下运行量热计。运行功率为 20 W 时，测量室的功率分辨率小于 5mW。电解池中含有约 1 L 0.1 M 的 LiOD。阴极置于一个打孔的盖状玻璃中，以阻止产生的气体在测量室中混合。阳极是一个绕着阴极的高 3 cm、直径 12 cm 的铂箔圆筒。电解池与量热计的测量室通过导热油进行热耦合。使用铂阴极以及镍铬铁合金丝加热器测量，测量结果显示量热计中存在一个小的系统误差，表观的功率过剩随输入功率呈线性变化，输入功率为 15 W 时，功率过剩高达 100 mW。将这些测量值（12 个点，估计值的标准误差为 8.8 mW）的线性拟合用于对钯阴极所测表观过剩的校正。再对等温式和 IHF 电解池所测的输出功率进行功率损失校正，功率损失是由于电解液的挥发造成的，假设当电解气体流出电解池（42℃时为 25.0 mW·A^{-1}）时电解气体在水蒸气中已达到饱和：$q_v = (p_v/p_0)(1.5)$ $\Delta H_v I/(2F)$，其中 q_v 为功率损失，p_v 代表饱和蒸气压，ΔH_v 为电解液挥发的相变潜热，p_0 为大气压，F 为法拉第常数，I 为电流（假设为理想气体）。

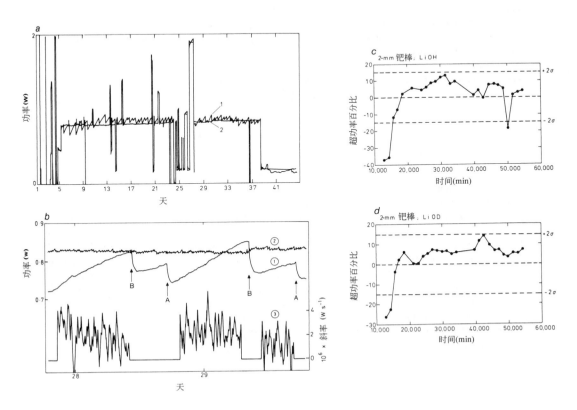

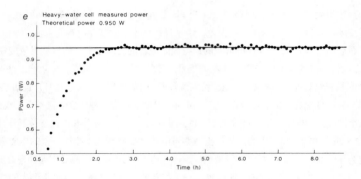

Fig. 2. *a*, Raw data from FPH-type calorimeter containing a 4-mm Pd rod (1.5 cm long, Johnson Matthey "specpure", drawn from sintered stock) in LiOH elctrolyte. Line 1 represents the output power calculated from the thermistor reading and line 2 represents the Joule input power to the cell, $P_{in} = I(V - V_0)$ where $V_0 = \Delta H_d / 2F$ (1.527 V for D_2O and 1.481 V for H_2O, ΔH_d being the enthalpy of dissociation, for example, $D_2O(l) \rightarrow D_2(g) + \frac{1}{2}O_2(g)$). The large step variations are calibrations. *b*, An expanded region of *a*, which emphasizes the sloping baseline. Lines 1 and 2 are as in *a*. Line 3 is the gradient of the apparent output power calculated by differentiation of the data using a seven-point Savitzky–Golay routine[23], stepping one point at a time. At points A the calorimeter was topped up to the reference mark with H_2O pre-warmed to the cell temperature. At points B a volume of liquid estimated from the electrolysis rate was added. *c* and *d*. Results for the *c* and *d*, Results for the two most consistently exothermic FPH calorimeters—0.2×3-cm Pd rod in (1) LiOD and (2) LiOH—in the form of percentage excess of apparent output power over the Joule input power. The error bars represent the control limits ±2σ calculated from the results obtained for all the different cells (see text). *e*, Raw data obtained using the isothermal calorimeter (20×2-mm diameter Pd cathode), immediately following the application of the input power, with the line representing the Joule input power and the dots the observed cell power. The response time of this calorimeter is governed by the time to obtain thermal mixing of the cell contents, and is faster than that of the simple calorimeters, despite the large solution volume.

Sloping baseline. The response of the "simple" FPH calorimeter can be modelled by[10]

$$P_{in} = k\Delta T = (k_{sb} + k_c)\Delta T \tag{3}$$

where[9],

$$k_{sb} = \sigma A_1[T_i^4 - T_0^4]/\Delta T \approx 4\sigma A_1 T_0^3[1 + 3\Delta T/(2T_0)] = k_{sb,0}(1 + 3\Delta T/(2T_0)) \tag{4}$$

and[10]

$$k_c \approx \kappa A_2/l = \kappa A_2/(l_0 + IV_m\delta t/(2F\pi r_i^2)) \approx k_{c,0}(1 - \alpha\delta t)$$

(P_{in} is the Joule input power, k is the calorimeter constant, k_{sb} and k_c are the contributions to the calorimeter constant of radiative losses through the vacuum jacket and conduction up the glass inner wall respectively, σ is the Stefan–Boltzmann constant, A_1 is the contact area of the solution with the wall of the cell, T_0 is the bath temperature, T_i is the cell temperature, $\Delta T = T_i - T_0$, κ is the thermal conductivity of the glass, l is the distance from the liquid to the point where the inner glass wall comes into contact with the bath and its initial value is l_0, A_2 is the cross-sectional area of the inner glass wall, I is the cell current (300 mA), V_m is the molar volume of cell solution, δt is the elapsed time after refilling the cell, r_i is the internal radius of the glass vessel and $\alpha = IV_m/(2F\pi r_i^2 l_0)$). We measured the calorimeter constant for the cells to be ~0.1 W K^{-1}, with the calculation using equation (4) indicating roughly equal contributions from k_{sb} and k_c. A more complete description of the calorimeter should also take into account the effects of the solution loss on the heat capacity of the calorimeter. It can be shown however that the contribution of this to the sloping baseline is insignificant[10].

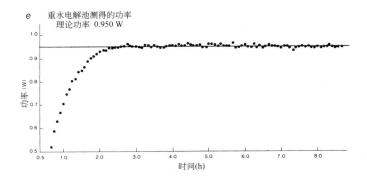

图 2. a, 从 LiOH 电解液中带有一个 4 mm 钯棒 (1.5 cm 长, 庄信万丰公司的"光谱纯"样品, 从熔融态得到) 的 FPH 型量热计得到的原始数据。线 1 表示根据温度计读数计算出的输出功率, 线 2 表示电解池的焦耳输入功率, $P_{in} = I(V - V_0)$, 其中 $V_0 = \Delta H_d/2F$ (对于 D_2O 为 1.527 V, H_2O 为 1.481 V, ΔH_d 为解离焓, 例如, $D_2O(l) \rightarrow D_2(g) + \frac{1}{2}O_2(g)$)。大的台阶式变化为标定值。b, a 的一个放大区域, 突出了倾斜的基线。线 1 和线 2 与 a 中相同。线 3 是使用七点赛威特斯基－高勒程序 [23] 对数据取微分计算出的表观输出功率的斜率, 一步一个点。在点 A, 将预热到电解池温度的水添加到量热计的参考标记处。在点 B, 添加进根据电解速率估算的一定体积的液体。c 和 d, 两个最为一致的 FPH 型量热计的结果—— 0.2 cm $\times$ 3 cm 的钯棒在 (1) LiOD 和 (2) LiOH 中——以表观输出功率超出焦耳输入功率的百分比形式表示。误差棒代表从所有不同的电解池中所得的结果计算出的控制极限 $\pm 2\sigma$ (见正文)。e, 使用等温式量热计 (20 mm $\times$ 2 mm 直径的钯阴极) 得到原始数据, 应用输入功率后立即开始测量, 曲线代表焦耳输入功率, 点代表观察到的电解池功率。这个量热计的响应时间由电解池内容物取得热量混合的时间决定, 尽管具有较大的溶液体积, 它仍快于简单量热计的响应时间。

倾斜的基线 "简易的" FPH 型量热计的响应可以模型化为 [10]

$$P_{in} = k\Delta T = (k_{sb} + k_c) \Delta T \tag{3}$$

其中 [9]

$$k_{sb} = \sigma A_1 [T_i^4 - T_0^4]/\Delta T \approx 4\sigma A_1 T_0^3 [1 + 3\Delta T/(2T_0)] = k_{sb,0}(1 + 3\Delta T/(2T_0)) \tag{4}$$

同时 [10]

$$k_c \approx \kappa A_2/l = \kappa A_2/(l_0 + IV_m\delta t/(2F\pi r_i^2)) \approx k_{c,0}(1 - \alpha\delta t)$$

(其中 P_{in} 是焦耳输入功率, k 是量热计常数, k_{sb} 和 k_c 分别为通过杜瓦瓶内的真空夹层的辐射损失和沿玻璃内壁的传导对量热计常数的贡献, σ 为斯特凡—波尔兹曼常数, A_1 为溶液与电解池壁的接触面积, T_0 为水浴温度, T_i 为电解池的温度, $\Delta T = T_i - T_0$, κ 为玻璃的热导率, l 为液体到玻璃内壁与水浴的接触点间的距离, 它的初始值为 l_0, A_2 为玻璃内壁的横截面积, I 为电解池电流 (300 mA), V_m 为电解池溶液的摩尔体积, δt 是从添加电解液后算起的时间, r_i 为玻璃容器的内半径, $\alpha = IV_m/(2F\pi r_i^2 l_0)$)。我们测量的电解池的量热计常数约为 0.1 W·K^{-1}, 是通过方程 (4) 计算的, 这表明 k_{sb} 和 k_c 的贡献大致相当。要对量热计进行更完整的描述就必须考虑溶液损失对量热计热容的影响。然而, 可以证明这对倾斜基线的影响是无足轻重的 [10]。

599

Fig. 2c shows results for two of the calorimeters at the calibrated liquid level, in the form of percentage excess of apparent output power over the Joule input power. There was apparently an endothermic period at the beginning of the run, whose duration increased with cathode diameter. We speculate that this was due in part to poor stirring of the solution during hydrogen uptake by the cathode which caused a temperature gradient in the cell (gas is not at first evolved at the cathode and the larger diameter cathodes were shorter, to keep a constant surface area). An analogous effect at the start of the electrolysis was reported by Lewis et al.[8], who showed that the apparent heating coefficient of a similar cell varied during the first part of a run. Because of this effect, we excluded the first 10,000 minutes of data from each cell when calculating the statistics. Table 1a shows the mean absolute power deviation for each cell and the standard deviation in this value. The standard deviation for all of the H_2O cells was not significantly different from that of the D_2O cells (F test, 1% level) so that the data from all of the cells can be used to estimate the error: $\sigma = 0.048$ W (that is ±5–10%). A more detailed analysis of this error[10] showed it to be largely determined by the variability in the liquid level after refilling the cell, but also with a contribution from unquantified variations in the heat loss by conduction up the calorimeter wall to the air above the water bath. Compared with these errors, effects that resulted from temperature gradients inside the cells were minor. The design used here varied from that in ref. 1 in that the glass sleeve that supported the calorimeter and which was in direct contact with the inner wall, provided a large area of thermal contact with the water bath, and thus reduced the effect of the ambient temperature variations.

Table 1. Calorimetry results

(a) FPH Calorimeters: current 300 mA, current density 80–110 mA cm⁻², 0.1 M LiOH, NaOH, LiOD, NaOD						
Pd[a]			H_2O Cells		D_2O Cells[b]	
Diameter	Volume	Cation	Mean Joule input[c] (mW)	Excess[d,e] (mW)	Mean Joule input[c] (mW)	Excess[d,e] (mW)
Surface area	Charging time					
6 mm	0.28 cm³	Li	820	−45±50	960	12±57
3.9 cm²	870 h	Na	590	14±71	980	57±44
4 mm	0.19 cm³	Li	800	−19±28	960	−20±29
3.5 cm²	810 h	Na	610	−55±53	960	−11±49
2 mm	0.094 cm³	Li	780	40±53	930	61±26
3.1 cm²	740 h	Na	620	−12±38	940	36±40
1 mm	0.071 cm³	Li	830	−46±64	980	43±64
2.8 cm²	670 h	Na	620	−18±60	980	−4±35
Mean excess	$\pm(\sigma/\sqrt{n})$ (mW)[f]			−18±4 (n = 143)		+21±4 (n = 146)

图 2c 显示了两个量热计的液面水平都在同一个标定面时的结果，以表观输出功率超过焦耳输入功率的百分比表示。实验开始时有一个明显的吸热反应阶段，这个阶段随阴极直径变大而延长。我们推测在阴极吸氢过程中搅拌不充分是原因之一，因为它在电解池中造成了一个温度梯度（电解开始时并无气体从阴极放出，为了保持表面积不变，直径较大的阴极更短一些）。电解开始时一个类似的效应由刘易斯等人[8]报道过，他们指出类似的电解池的表观传热系数在实验的初始阶段会变化。由于这个效应，我们在进行统计计算时排除了每个电解池开始运行的前 10,000 分钟的数据。表 1a 显示了每个电解池的平均绝对功率偏差值和这个值的标准偏差。所有 H_2O 电解池的标准偏差同 D_2O 电解池的没有明显差异（F 检验，1% 的水平），所以所有电解池的数据都可以用于估算误差：$\sigma = 0.048$ W（即 $\pm 5\% \sim 10\%$）。对这个误差进行更加详细的分析[10]，揭示了它主要由重新灌注电解池后液面水平的变化决定，也有由量热计壁向水浴上方空气传导造成的热量损失这一未经量化的变化量的贡献。与这些误差相比，电解池内的温度梯度产生的影响很小。本文中使用的设计不同于参考文献 1，我们用玻璃套筒来支撑量热计，而且玻璃套筒与内壁直接接触，由此玻璃套筒就可与水浴有较大面积的热接触，进而减小了室温变化的影响。

表 1. 量热法结果

(a) FPH 量热计：电流 300 mA，电流密度 80~110 mA·cm^{-2}，0.1 M LiOH、NaOH、LiOD、NaOD						
Pd^a			H_2O电解池		D_2O电解池^b	
直径 表面积	体积 运行时间	阳离子	平均焦耳输入^c (mW)	过剩^{d,e} (mW)	平均焦耳输入^c (mW)	过剩^{d,e} (mW)
6 mm 3.9 cm^2	0.28 cm^3 870 h	Li Na	820 590	-45 ± 50 14 ± 71	960 980	12 ± 57 57 ± 44
4 mm 3.5 cm^2	0.19 cm^3 810 h	Li Na	800 610	-19 ± 28 -55 ± 53	960 960	-20 ± 29 -11 ± 49
2 mm 3.1 cm^2	0.094 cm^3 740 h	Li Na	780 620	40 ± 53 -12 ± 38	930 940	61 ± 26 36 ± 40
1 mm 2.8 cm^2	0.071 cm^3 670 h	Li Na	830 620	-46 ± 64 -18 ± 60	980 980	43 ± 64 -4 ± 35
平均过剩	$\pm(\sigma/\sqrt{n})$(mW)^f			-18 ± 4 ($n = 143$)		$+21 \pm 4$ ($n = 146$)

Continued

Calorimeter type	Pd Type / Surface area	Total charging time / Volume	Current (mA cm⁻²)	Time (h)	Joule input[c] (W)	Excess[d] (mW)
IHF	2-mm rod[a] / 3.1 cm²	797 h[l] / 0.16 cm³	156	231	2.341	78±77[m]
			156	206	2.380	27±48
			219	187	3.842	−1±58
			279	173	5.188	−55±101
	Cast[g] / 14 cm²	797 h[l] / 0.88 cm³	35	236	2.172	100±40
			36	201	2.219	47±36
			49	187	3.489	−31±51
			62	173	4.863	−120±86
Isothermal	2-mm rod[a] / 1.3 cm²	284 h[b] / 0.063 cm³	159	284	0.925[o]	−10±12[n]
	Cast beads[h] / 5 cm²	355 h[b] / 0.5 cm³	50	7	0.985	33±12
			30	15	0.415	11±11
			70	7.8	1.796	5±12
			20	15	0.214	10±11
			100	8.6	3.405	−5±12
			120	270	4.825	2±13
			40	8.1	0.675	7±12
			80	5.7	2.311	9±12
			200	4.8	12.314	−10±12
			160	4.1	8.140	−17±12
			220	4.8	14.675	−9±12
	Melt-spun-ribbon[i] / 74 cm²	74 h[l] / 0.35 cm³	14	74	8.991	64±17
	2-mm rod[j] / 1.3 cm²	323 h[l] / 0.066 cm³	152	70	1.091	7±11
			530	253	10.358	15±14
	8-mm bar[k] / 28 cm²	520 h[l] / 1.5 cm³	30	520	8.974	36±15

[a] Johnson Matthey (JM) "Specpure"; drawn from sintered stock prepared from high-purity powder.

[b] D_2O from Harwell reference stock, contains 13 kBq ml⁻¹ tritium.

[c] Mean Joule input power supplied to cell (see Fig. 2 legend). Values for IHF and isothermal calorimeters have been corrected for heat loss that is due to evaporation (see Fig. 1 legend).

[d] Excess power = measured cell output power − calculated Joule input power.

[e] (Mean±1σ) of values calculated after each refilling to the reference level, excluding first 10,000 minutes of polarization (see text).

[f] Mean and standard deviation of the mean calculated for all H_2O data points and all D_2O data points.

[g] Specially produced material supplied by JM—prepared from cast Pd stock that was argon-arc melted into rod form using a gravity casting process. The rods were subsequently sliced and bent to decrease the loading time required (maximum distance from bulk to surface ~1 mm). The sample was cleaned using acetone, 10% HCl and distilled water.

续表

(b) IHF 型和等温式量热计：0.1 M LiOD						
量热计类型	Pd		电流 (mA·cm^{-2})	时间 (h)	焦耳输入[c] (W)	过剩[d] (mW)
	种类	总运行时间				
	表面积	体积				
IHF	直径 2 mm 的钯棒[a]	797 h[l]	156	231	2.341	78 ± 77[m]
			156	206	2.380	27 ± 48
	3.1 cm^2	0.16 cm^3	219	187	3.842	−1 ± 58
			279	173	5.188	−55 ± 101
	铸造[g]	797 h[l]	35	236	2.172	100 ± 40
			36	201	2.219	47 ± 36
	14 cm^2	0.88 cm^3	49	187	3.489	−31 ± 51
			62	173	4.863	−120 ± 86
等温式	直径 2 mm 的钯棒[a]	284 h[b]	159	284	0.925[o]	−10 ± 12[n]
	1.3 cm^2	0.063 cm^3				
	铸造的颗粒[h]	355 h[b]	50	7	0.985	33 ± 12
			30	15	0.415	11 ± 11
			70	7.8	1.796	5 ± 12
			20	15	0.214	10 ± 11
			100	8.6	3.405	−5 ± 12
			120	270	4.825	2 ± 13
	5 cm^2	0.5 cm^3	40	8.1	0.675	7 ± 12
			80	5.7	2.311	9 ± 12
			200	4.8	12.314	−10 ± 12
			160	4.1	8.140	−17 ± 12
			220	4.8	14.675	−9 ± 12
	熔体快淬带[i]	74 h[l]	14	74	8.991	64 ± 17
	74 cm^2	0.35 cm^3				
	直径2 mm 的钯棒[j]	323 h[l]	152	70	1.091	7 ± 11
	1.3 cm^2	0.066 cm^3	530	253	10.358	15 ± 14
	直径8 mm 的钯棒[k]	520 h[l]	30	520	8.974	36 ± 15
	28 cm^2	1.5 cm^3				

[a] 庄信万丰公司（JM）的"光谱纯"；由高纯粉末制备的烧结块料拉制而成。

[b] 购自哈尔公司的 D_2O，含 13 kBq·ml^{-1} 的氚。

[c] 提供给电解池的平均焦耳功率（参见图 2 的图注）。IHF 和等温式量热计的数值都就蒸发产生的热量损失进行了校正（参见图 1 的图注）。

[d] 过剩功率＝测量的电解池输出功率 − 计算的焦耳输入功率。

[e] 在每一次将液面加至参考液面时算出的数值（平均值 ±1σ），排除了开始 10,000 分钟极化过程的数据（见正文）。

[f] 所有 H_2O 和 D_2O 数据点的平均值和平均值的标准偏差。

[g] 由 JM 提供的特制材料——从库存的铸造钯制备得到，使用一种重力铸造工艺通过氩弧将之熔化成棒状。棒随后被切成片，并弯曲以减少所需的吸附时间（从体相到表面的最大距离约 1 mm）。样品用丙酮、10% 的盐酸和蒸馏水清洗。

[h] "Specpure" Pd arc melted three times under argon on a water-cooled copper hearth.

[i] A variety of ribbons prepared (JM) by melt spinning of cast or sintered Pd. A proportion of the ribbons were heat treated (JM) for 20 min at 100 °C under 10% H_2/N_2. Ribbon thickness, 125 µm.

[j] Type [a] that was subsequently vacuum degassed at 1,200 °C, and loaded with deuterium at a pressure of 40 bar. The sample was cooled to liquid-nitrogen temperature before transferring to the calorimeter to minimize loss of D_2.

[k] Sintered high-purity bar, sliced and bent to decrease the loading time required (maximum distance from surface to bulk ~1 mm).

[l] D_2O from Aldrich Chemical Co., contains ~15 kBq ml^{-1} tritium.

[m] Mean and standard deviation of all data points after temperature stabilization: data point every 3 min.

[n] Standard deviation given by $\sigma = \sqrt{\sigma_b^2 + \sigma_y^2 + \sigma_c^2}$ where σ_b is the standard deviation of the baseline measurement, σ_y that of the power measurement with the cell running and σ_c is the standard error of estimate of the correction line (see Fig. 1 legend). σ_b and σ_y were typically 6 mW, σ_c was 8.8 mW.

[o] Small error in this particular measurement gave rise to the apparent small endotherm.

As we expected, occasional points from both H_2O and D_2O cells lay outside the "control limits" of ±2σ (Fig. 2c). No points lay outside ±3σ. No cell showed two or more consecutive points outside ±2σ, and the number of points lying above the control limit in the D_2O-cell experiments was no different from that in the H_2O-cell experiments. Therefore, we conclude that, within the experimental error, there was no significant anomaly in the behaviour of the D_2O cells compared with that of the H_2O cells. If, however, the mean power deviation (Table 1a) for all eight of the D_2O cells (+9.91±0.47% or 0.021±0.004 W; mean Joule input 0.96 W) is tested against that for all eight of the H_2O cells (−2.46±0.72% or −0.018±0.004 W, mean Joule input 0.81 W for LiOH cells and 0.61 W for NaOH cells), it is clearly highly significant. Because no sequence of individual points lay outside the control limits established above, we suspect that there is another, unknown source of error that scales with the input power. This, of course, could be the postulated "fusion effect", but the magnitude of the effect is commensurate with the errors. The only reliable way of checking this is to construct calorimeters that are free of major sources of errors, and in particular, do not have a sloping baseline. We therefore also used both isothermal and steady state (heat flow) calorimeters which satisfy this criterion.

We have also analysed in detail the slope of the output curve[10] to look for momentary power pulses on timescales shorter than the interval between calibrated points. If the Joule input remains constant then this slope should not vary. Any sudden or momentary extra power input, q_c, would change the slope by approximately $(k_{sb} + k_{c,0}) q_c/M_0$ (M_0 is the water equivalent of the calorimeter, other symbols defined in Fig. 2 legend). The number of significant deviations from the mean slope was found to be roughly the same for both the H_2O and the D_2O cells. For the whole data set, the largest power excursion for a D_2O cell (6-mm rod) was ~45 mW and for an H_2O cell (6-mm rod) ~40 mW. These are small compared with the input power. It is certainly clear that no unusually large power pulses occurred. Given the difficulties in operating these calorimeters, very occasional occurrences of small fluctuations cannot be considered as support for a "fusion" hypothesis.

The other two types of calorimeters used in this study are described in Fig. 1 legend and results are given in Table 1b. We explored a range of different preparations of palladium and of current density, up to nearly 600 mA cm^{-2}. With the improved heat-

h "光谱纯"的钯在一个水冷的铜炉床上，在氩气保护下用电弧熔融三次。

i 由铸造或者烧结的钯通过熔体快淬制备得到（JM）的各种快淬带。一部分带经过了在含氢 10% 的氮气下 20 分钟 100 ℃ 的热处理。带的厚度为 125 μm。

j a 型随后在 1,200 ℃ 下进行真空除气处理，在 40 巴的气压下吸附氘。转移到量热计之前样品被冷却至液氮的温度，以减少 D_2 的流失。

k 烧结的高纯度钯棒被切成片并弯曲，以减小所需的吸附时间（表面到体相的最大距离为约 1 mm）。

l 购自奥尔德里奇化学品公司的 D_2O，约含 15 kBq·ml^{-1} 的氚。

m 所有数据点的平均值和标准偏差都在温度稳定后采集：每 3 分钟采集一个数据。

n 标准偏差由公式 $\sigma = \sqrt{\sigma_b^2 + \sigma_y^2 + \sigma_c^2}$ 计算，其中 σ_b 为基线测量的标准偏差，σ_y 为电解池运行时功率测量值的标准偏差，σ_c 为根据校正曲线估算的标准误差（见图 1 的图注）。σ_b 和 σ_y 的典型值为 6 mW，σ_c 为 8.8 mW。

o 这次测量中产生表观少量吸热的小的误差。

正如我们所预期，H_2O 和 D_2O 电解池给出的数据点都有少量处于 ±2σ 的"控制界限"之外（图 2c）。没有数据点是在 ±3σ 之外的。所有电解池都没有两个或者更多的连续数据点处于 ±2σ 之外，D_2O 电解池实验中超出控制界限的数据点的数目与 H_2O 电解池实验并无不同。因此，我们得出结论，在实验误差范围内，D_2O 电解池的特性与 H_2O 电解池相比没有明显的异常。然而，如果根据表 1a，将所有 8 个 D_2O 电解池（+9.91%±0.47% 或者 0.021±0.004 W；平均焦耳输入 0.96 W）与所有 8 个 H_2O 电解池的平均功率偏差（−2.46%±0.72% 或者 −0.018±0.004 W，LiOH 电解池的平均焦耳输入为 0.81 W 而 NaOH 电解池的为 0.61 W）进行对比的话，其差别是十分明显的。因为没有一系列的独立数据点处于上述的控制界限之外，我们认为有另外一个未知的误差来源，与输入功率成比例。当然，这可以是假设的"核聚变效应"，但是这个效应的数量级与误差相同。检验这个假设的唯一可信赖的方法就是构建不受主要误差来源影响的量热计，尤其是不倾斜的基线。我们因此也使用了满足这一准则的等温式量热计和稳态（热流）量热计。

我们也仔细分析了输出曲线的斜率[10]，以寻找时间尺度上短于校准点间隔的瞬时功率脉冲。如果焦耳输入保持恒定，则斜率应该不变。任何突然或瞬间额外功率 q_c 的输入，都会将斜率改变大约 $(k_{sb} + k_{c,0})q_c/M_0$（$M_0$ 为与量热计等效的水的量，其他符号沿用图 2 的图注中的定义）。H_2O 和 D_2O 电解池中与平均斜率明显偏离的数目大体相同。就所有数据而言，D_2O 电解池（6 mm 的棒）最大的功率偏移约为 45 mW，而 H_2O 电解池（6 mm 的棒）约为 40 mW。这些值与输入功率相比较小。很显然没有异常大的功率脉冲出现。鉴于控制量热计的难度，不能将非常偶然的小波动的出现视为是支持"核聚变"假说的证据。

本研究中使用的另外两种量热计在图 1 的图注中进行了描述，结果列于表 1b 中。我们尝试了一系列不同的钯制备方法和最大值接近 600 mA·cm^{-2} 的一系列电流密度。使用改进的热流量热计（IHF），功率过剩的符号和数量级随焦耳输入功率而

flow calorimeters (IHF), the sign and magnitude of the power excess varied with Joule input power, but was always <5%. Expressed in terms of the volume of the palladium cathode, this sets a limit of 100–500 mW cm^{-3}. The most accurate calorimeter used was the isothermal calorimeter (minimum-detectable power change ~10 mW; minimum-detectable energy in any brief burst ~40 J). We analysed these results at four-hour intervals by averaging both the Joule input power and the measured output power over a period of ~20 min. Inspection of the data collected every four minutes between the regions of analysis showed no obvious signs of any short heat "bursts" and we found no trend with time of the measured output power under any of the conditions used. Table 1b shows that we obtained thermal balance to better than 20 mW (24–240 mW cm^{-3} Pd). We observed slight thermal excesses (30–60 mW) during the initial charging period of the palladium beads, and during runs with high-surface-area cathodes at high current: it can reasonably be assumed that a small amount of recombination (4% at most) was responsible for this effect.

Neutron Counting

We investigated the emission of neutrons from a wide range of cells using three different detector systems (Table 2). The large, high-efficiency detector with which most of the neutron measurements were made is an oil-moderated assembly of 56 ^{10}BF$_3$ proportional counters configured as 5 concentric rings[11,12]. The total efficiency for 2.45-MeV d-d neutrons is 44%. We built an automatic cell shuttle mechanism to exchange regularly two nominally identical cells, only one of which was powered. This enabled the background (which is due mostly to cosmic rays, there being no anti-coincidence counter arrangements) and any signal to be counted virtually simultaneously. In operation the cells were exchanged every 5 min, and the data from the 5 rings were recorded separately. Data from a typical run are shown in Fig. 3 as differences in the count rate between the powered and unpowered cell. Although in the particular example shown, two spikes can be seen in the count rate differences from the detector as a whole, it is clear that these spikes are due entirely to the misbehaviour of ring 4, and are therefore spurious.

Table 2. Measured neutron and γ-ray emission rates for cold fusion electrolytic cells

(a) Neutron emission rates

Cathode			Electrolyte	Anode	Details of electrolysis			Measured neutron yield[w] (n s^{-1})
Material	Mass (g)	Surface area (cm^2)			Current (mA)	Typical voltage	Duration (h)	
Pd rod 2mm[a]	3.4	5.7	0.1 M LiOD	Pt wire	360	5	914	These cells monitored initially
Pd wire 1 mm[a]	0.94	3.1	0.1 M LiOD	Pt wire	200[r]	4	916	by low-efficiency n-detectors
Pd wire 1 mm[b]	0.94	3.1	0.1 M LiOD	Pt wire	200	4	916	with lower detection limit
Pd wire 1 mm[b]	1.4	4.7	0.1 M LiOD	Pt wire	300[s]	5	917	of ~100 s^{-1}. Later moved to
Pd wire 1 mm[c]	0.47	1.6	0.1 M LiOD	Pt wire	750	11	856	a dual-cavity neutron
Pd plate 1 mm[d]	7.5	13.5	1 M LiOD	Pt sheet	2,000	10	307	detector[10] with lower
Pd foil	0.5	8.0	0.1 M LiOD	Vitreous C	400–120[t]	4–20	142	detection limit ~2 s^{-1}.
Pd/22Ag[e]	1.6	3.8	0.1 M LiOD	Pt wire	380	5	859	No detected n-emission.
Pd/22Ag[e]	1.6	3.8	0.1 M LiOD	Pt wire	380[u]	5	547	

变化，但总是小于 5%。用钯阴极的体积表示，这个值的范围在 $100\sim500\ mW\cdot cm^{-3}$ 之间。最精确的量热计是等温式量热计（可探测的最小功率变化约为 $10\ mW$；可探测的任何最小猝发能量约为 $40\ J$）。我们分析这些以 4 小时为间隔的结果，每约 20 分钟将焦耳输入功率和测量的输出功率作平均。对分析区域每 4 分钟获得的数据进行的研究显示，没有任何短时热量"猝发"的明显迹象，而且我们发现在任何我们使用的条件下，测得的输出功率没有随着时间变化的趋势。表 1b 显示我们获得的热平衡优于 $20\ mW$（对钯而言为 $24\sim240\ mW\cdot cm^{-3}$）。在最初的钯电极充电期间以及高表面积阴极在大电流条件下运行的过程中，我们观察到了少量的热量过剩（$30\sim60\ mW$）；可以合理地假设是少量的复合过程（至多 4%）产生了此效应。

中 子 计 数

我们使用三种不同的检测系统研究了来自多种电解池的中子发射（表 2）。我们用大而高效的探测器来进行大部分的中子测量，它是一个由 56 个 $^{10}BF_3$ 正比计数器排布成的、由 5 个同心圆环阵列[11,12] 所组成的装置。$2.45\ MeV$ 的 d-d 中子总效率为 44%。我们构造了一个自动电解池滑梭装置来定期调换两个形式上完全相同的电解池，只有其中一个是通电的。这使得本底（本底主要来自宇宙射线，没有布置反符合计数管）和任何信号可以实质上同时计数。操作时，电解池每隔 5 分钟调换一次，5 个圆环上的数据分别被记录下来。从一次典型实验中得到的数据如图 3 所示，它们是通电和不通电的电解池的计数率之差。尽管在所展示的特例中，从探测器整体的计数率之差可以看到两个尖峰信号，但是这些尖峰信号显然完全是由于环 4 的错误响应引起的，因而是假象。

表 2. 所测的各冷核聚变电解池的中子和 γ 射线发射速率

(a)中子发射速率								
阴极			电解液	阳极	电解细节			测得的中子产率^w （个/秒）
材料	质量(g)	表面积(cm^2)			电流(mA)	典型电压	时长(h)	
2 mm 的钯棒^a	3.4	5.7	0.1 M LiOD	铂丝	360	5	914	这些电解池最初使用具有较低检测限（约100 s^{-1}）的低效率中子探测器进行检测。后来又使用一个具有更低检测限（约 2 s^{-1}）的双腔中子探测器[10]。
1 mm 的钯丝^a	0.94	3.1	0.1 M LiOD	铂丝	200^r	4	916	
1 mm 的钯丝^b	0.94	3.1	0.1 M LiOD	铂丝	200	4	916	
1 mm 的钯丝^b	1.4	4.7	0.1 M LiOD	铂丝	300^s	5	917	
1 mm 的钯丝^c	0.47	1.6	0.1 M LiOD	铂丝	750	11	856	
1 mm 的钯盘^d	7.5	13.5	1 M LiOD	铂片	2,000	10	307	
钯箔	0.5	8.0	0.1 M LiOD	玻碳	400~120^t	4~20	142	
钯银 22 合金^e	1.6	3.8	0.1 M LiOD	铂丝	380	5	859	未检测到中子发射
钯银 22 合金^e	1.6	3.8	0.1 M LiOD	铂丝	380^u	5	547	

Continued

(a) Neutron emission rates

Cathode					Details of electrolysis			Measured neutron yield[w]
Material	Mass (g)	Surface area (cm²)	Electrolyte	Anode	Current (mA)	Typical voltage	Duration (h)	(n s⁻¹)
Pd foil[f]	0.075	1.0	0.1 M LiOD	Pt wire	30	3	87	−0.019±0.042
Pd foil[g]	0.075	1.0	0.1 M LiOD	Pt wire	250	7	6	0.00±0.08
Pd foil[h]	0.075	1.0	0.1 M LiOD +17 mM Na₂S	Pt wire	250	7	16	0.04±0.11
Pd foil[i]	0.075	1.0	0.1M LiOD	Pt wire	250	8	16	0.005±0.063
Pd foil[j]	0.075	1.0	0.1 M LiOD	Pt wire	250	8	16	0.051±0.061
Pd foil[k]	0.075	1.0	0.1 M LiOD	Pt wire	1,000	15	56	0.068±0.061
Pd foil	0.63	8.0	0.1 M LiOD	Pt foil	1,000	14	17	−0.110±0.082
Pd foil	0.63	8.0	0.1 M LiOD	Pd foil	1,000	18	22	0.012±0.079
Pd ribbon[l]	0.45	0.92	0.1 M LiOD	Pd foil	600[e]	15	110	−0.063±0.096
Pd foil	0.60	8.0	0.1 M LiOD	Au wire	1,000	12	43	0.068±0.058
Pd pellet[m]	3.0	2	0.1 M LiOD	Pt foil	650	18	68	0.007±0.042
Pd pieces[n]	4.4		0.1 M LiOD	Pd foil	500	8	88	0.012±0.033
Pd pieces	4.4		0.1 M LiOD	Pd foil	500	15	88	0.003±0.046[x]
Ti foil	0.038	1.0	0.1 M D₂SO₄	Au wire	250	5	34	−0.091±0.054
Ti foil	0.038	1.0	0.1 M D₂SO₄	Au foil	1,000	5	3	−0.22±0.12[y]
(continued)			0.1 M D₂SO₄ +0.02M PdCl₂		1,000	5	4	−0.22±0.12[y]
Ti rod	2.2	4.3	Jones[q]	Au foil	100	4	3	−0.06±0.15[y]
(continued)					500	6	2	−0.42±0.21[y]
Ti granules[o]	0.5		0.1 M D₂SO₄	Pt wire	250	7	22	0.00±0.072
Ti granules	0.5		0.1 M D₂SO₄ +3 mM Na₄P₂O₇	Pt wire	250	7	66	0.044±0.054
Ti granules	40		0.1 M D₂SO₄	Pt wire	250	25	22	−0.009±0.058
Ti granules	40		0.1 M D₂SO₄ +3 mM Na₄P₂O₇	Pt foil	250	25	22	−0.010±0.060
Ti granules	17		Jones	Au foil	500	26	24	0.021±0.054
Ti granules								
Ti/6Al/4V	2.8	15.0	0.1 M D₂SO₄	Pt wire	670	5	87	−0.003±0.031[x]
Ti/6Al/4V[p]	2.7	14.3	0.1 M D₂SO₄	Pt wire	660	5	19	0.031±0.044[x]
TiFe granules	1		0.1 M D₂SO₄	Pt foil	250	8	24	0.12±0.06
CeAl₂ granules	11		0.1 M LiOD	Pt foil	500	22	22	−0.051±0.056
UPt₃ granules	57		0.1 M LiOD	Pt foil	500	20	94	0.10±0.06

(b) γ-ray emission rates

Cathode					Details of electrolysis			Measured 5,488-keV γ-ray
Material	Mass (g)	Surface area (cm²)	Electrolyte[z]	Anode	Current (mA)	Typical voltage	Duration (h)	yield[aa] (γ s⁻¹)
Pd foil	0.58	7.5	0.1 M LiOH	Pt foil	450	9	45	(−4.9±7.43)×10⁻³
Pd foil	0.74	9.5	0.1 M LiOH	Pt foil	510	9	164	−0.011±0.004
Pd sheet	7.7	12.9	0.1 M LiOH*	Pt foil	200	4.6	50	−0.017±0.012
Pd rod	3.1	2.3	0.1 M LiOH	Au foil	1,000	26	17	0.008±0.011

(a)中子发射速率

| 阴极 | | | 电解液 | 阳极 | 电解细节 | | | 测得的中子产率[w]（个/秒） |
材料	质量(g)	表面积(cm²)			电流(mA)	典型电压	时长(h)	
钯箔[f]	0.075	1.0	0.1 M LiOD	铂丝	30	3	87	-0.019 ± 0.042
钯箔[g]	0.075	1.0	0.1 M LiOD	铂丝	250	7	6	0.00 ± 0.08
钯箔[h]	0.075	1.0	0.1 M LiOD +17 mM Na₂S	铂丝	250	7	16	0.04 ± 0.11
钯箔[i]	0.075	1.0	0.1 M LiOD	铂丝	250	8	16	0.005 ± 0.063
钯箔[j]	0.075	1.0	0.1 M LiOD	铂丝	250	8	16	0.051 ± 0.061
钯箔[k]	0.075	1.0	0.1 M LiOD	铂丝	1,000	15	56	0.068 ± 0.061
钯箔	0.63	8.0	0.1 M LiOD	钯箔	1,000	14	17	-0.110 ± 0.082
钯箔	0.63	8.0	0.1 M LiOD	钯箔	1,000	18	22	0.012 ± 0.079
钯带[l]	0.45	0.92	0.1 M LiOD	钯箔	600[v]	15	110	-0.063 ± 0.096
钯箔	0.60	8.0	0.1 M LiOD	金丝	1,000	12	43	0.068 ± 0.058
钯颗粒[m]	3.0	2	0.1 M LiOD	铂丝	650	18	68	0.007 ± 0.042
钯片[n]	4.4		0.1 M LiOD	钯箔	500	8	88	0.012 ± 0.033
钯片	4.4		0.1 M LiOD	钯箔	500	15	88	0.003 ± 0.046^{x}
钛箔	0.038	1.0	0.1 M D₂SO₄	金丝	250	5	34	-0.091 ± 0.054
钛箔	0.038	1.0	0.1 M D₂SO₄	金丝	1,000	5	3	-0.22 ± 0.12^{y}
（续）			0.1 M D₂SO₄ +0.02 M PdCl₂		1,000	5	4	-0.22 ± 0.12^{y}
钛棒	2.2	4.3	琼斯[q]	金箔	100	4	3	-0.06 ± 0.15^{y}
（续）					500	6	2	-0.42 ± 0.21^{y}
钛颗粒[o]	0.5		0.1 M D₂SO₄	铂丝	250	7	22	0.00 ± 0.072
钛颗粒	0.5		0.1 M D₂SO₄ +3 mM Na₄P₂O₇	铂丝	250	7	66	0.044 ± 0.054
钛颗粒	40		0.1 M D₂SO₄	铂丝	250	25	22	-0.009 ± 0.058
钛颗粒	40		0.1 M D₂SO₄ +3 mM Na₄P₂O₇	铂箔	250	25	22	-0.010 ± 0.060
钛颗粒	17		琼斯	金箔	500	26	24	0.021 ± 0.054
钛颗粒								
Ti/6Al/4V合金	2.8	15.0	0.1 M D₂SO₄	铂丝	670	5	87	-0.003 ± 0.031^{x}
Ti/6Al/4V合金[p]	2.7	14.3	0.1 M D₂SO₄	铂丝	660	5	19	0.031 ± 0.044^{x}
TiFe 颗粒	1		0.1 M D₂SO₄	铂箔	250	8	24	0.12 ± 0.06
CeAl₂ 合金颗粒	11		0.1 M LiOD	铂箔	500	22	22	-0.051 ± 0.056
UPt₃ 颗粒	57		0.1 M LiOD	铂箔	500	20	94	0.10 ± 0.06

(b) γ射线发射速率

| 阴极 | | | 电解液[z] | 阳极 | 电解细节 | | | 测得的5,488 keV 的γ射线的产率[aa]（γ射线/秒） |
材料	质量(g)	表面积(cm²)			电流(mA)	典型电压	时长(h)	
钯箔	0.58	7.5	0.1 M LiOH	铂箔	450	9	45	$(-4.9 \pm 7.43) \times 10^{-3}$
钯箔	0.74	9.5	0.1 M LiOH	铂箔	510	9	164	-0.011 ± 0.004
钯片	7.7	12.9	0.1 M LiOH*	铂箔	200	4.6	50	-0.017 ± 0.012
钯棒	3.1	2.3	0.1 M LiOH	金箔	1,000	26	17	0.008 ± 0.011

Continued

(b) γ-ray emission rates								
Cathode			Electrolyte[z]	Anode	Details of electrolysis			Measured 5,488-keV γ-ray yield[aa] (γ s^{-1})
Material	Mass (g)	Surface area (cm^2)			Current (mA)	Typical voltage	Duration (h)	
Ti foil	0.089	2.0	Jones*	Au foil	320	5	42	−0.022±0.011
Ti foil	2.2	32	Jones	Au foil	1,000	4	12	−0.015±0.034
Ti foil	2.2	32	Jones	Au foil	1,000	4	6	0.012±0.007
Ti granules	25		Jones	Au foil	710	13	8	0.032±0.036
Ti granules	25		0.1 M H$_2$SO$_4$	Au foil	400	20	25	−0.019±0.018
Ti granules	25		0.1 M H$_2$SO$_4$	Au foil	765	16	16	0.017±0.022
UPt$_3$ granules	42		0.1 M LiOH	Pt foil	300	31	166	(3.1±6.0)×10^{-3}

[a] Cells provided by M. Fleischmann. Cathodes analysed for H, D after use—results H/Pd: 0.01, 0.02 D/Pd: 0.84, 0.72.

[b] Cathode wound into a tight spiral. Examined initially in the large n-detector, without shuttle, for 147 h with estimated detection limit 1 n s^{-1} and a further 5 h with detection limit 0.2 n s^{-1}. Surface of cathode then rubbed with S before further use.

[c] Cathode cleaned with emery paper after 300 h.

[d] Cathode examined initially in the large n-detector, without shuttle, in 0.1 M LiOD for 183 h; estimated detection limit 1 n s^{-1}. Abraded with 400-grit SiC paper before use.

[e] Tubes from D storage system for Tokamak.

[f] Cathode analysed for H, D after use—results: H/Pd: 0.03 D/Pd: 0.80.

[g] Electrolyte of the above run reused.

[h] Cathode and electrolyte of the above run reused; Na$_2$S added as concentrated aqueous solution.

[i] Foil vacuum degassed 1,000 °C before use. Analysed for H, D after use—results: H/Pd: 0.02 D/Pd: 0.83.

[j] Foil dipped in Na$_2$S (concentrated solution) before use. Analysed for H, D after use—results: H/Pd: 0.05 D/Pd: 0.80.

[k] Cathode cut in half and analysed for H, D after use—results: H/Pd: 0.02, 0.02 D/Pd: 0.85, 0.78.

[l] Melt-spun ribbon provided by Johnson-Matthey Technology Centre.

[m] Arc remelted twice; electrolytically charged for 1 month in 0.1 M LiOD then frozen in liquid nitrogen, dipped in concentrated Na$_2$S solution and transferred to n-counting cell.

[n] Four 1–2-mm-thick discs of different types of Pd (Johnson-Matthey) spot welded to Pd wires plus strained Pd Wire.

[o] Electrolyte reused after a previous run with a Ti cathode and Pt anode.

[p] Material heated to 900 °C then quenched in water before use.

[q] AuCN in Jones electrolyte replaced with NaAuCl$_4$.

[r] Current on for 36 h then changed between 200 mA and 20 mA every hour.

[s] Current on for 36 h then changed between 300 mA and 30 mA every 5 min.

[t] Current changed slowly over range shown during electrolysis period as anode disintegrated.

[u] Current on for 36 h then cycled off for 10 h and on for 2 h for period of 270 h. Then 5,000 s at 380 mA cathodic and 4,000 s at 10 mA anodic for rest of period.

[v] Current cycled on/off every 2 h. Neutron yield is for "on" cycle.

[w] The errors assigned (1σ, calculated over full run duration) vary somewhat because in an attempt (mostly in the earlier stages of the programme) to cover as wide a range of cell configurations as possible, pairs of unpowered + unpowered and powered + unpowered runs were not always carried out, and consequently allowance has to made for slight differences in overall cosmic-ray neutron detection efficiencies caused by slight differences between the two nominally identical cells.

[x] These data were obtained using a different data acquisition system to drive the shuttle and accumulate data, set up to look for neutron bursts[10].

[y] Cells exchanged every 5 min by hand.

[z] All electrolytes used for γ-ray work were 50:50 H$_2$O:D$_2$O except * which were 41:59 H$_2$O:D$_2$O.

[aa] For the present measurements, the system was calibrated with a set of standard γ-ray sources and a ^{238}Pu/^{13}C (α, nγ) source emitting 6,129-keV γ-rays. The cells were positioned such that their cathodes were as close as possible to the detector crystal, and the detection efficiencies were calculated by integrating previously measured[21] point efficiency functions over the cathode volume. Peaks were searched for at 5,488, 4,977 and 4,466 keV corresponding to the expected location of the full energy, single-escape and double-escape peaks using the method recommended in ref. 22.

(b) γ 射线发射速率								
阴极			电解液[z]	阳极	电解细节			测得的5,488 keV的γ射线的产率[aa]（γ射线/秒）
材料	质量(g)	表面积(cm²)			电流(mA)	典型电压	时长(h)	
钛箔	0.089	2.0	琼斯*	金箔	320	5	42	−0.022 ± 0.011
钛箔	2.2	32	琼斯	金箔	1,000	4	12	−0.015 ± 0.034
钛箔	2.2	32	琼斯	金箔	1,000	4	6	0.012 ± 0.007
钛颗粒	25		琼斯	金箔	710	13	8	0.032 ± 0.036
钛颗粒	25		0.1 M H₂SO₄	金箔	400	20	25	−0.019 ± 0.018
钛颗粒	25		0.1 M H₂SO₄	金箔	765	16	16	0.017 ± 0.022
UPt₃颗粒	42		0.1 M LiOH	铂箔	300	31	166	$(3.1 ± 6.0) × 10^{-3}$

[a] 弗莱施曼提供的电解池。使用之后分析了阴极的氢和氘——结果 H/Pd 为 0.01、0.02，D/Pd 为 0.84、0.72。

[b] 阴极绕成一个紧密的螺旋状。初始阶段在大型中子检测器中进行监测，没有滑梭，持续了 147 小时，估算的检测限为 $1\,n \cdot s^{-1}$，之后的 5 小时检测限为 $0.2\,n \cdot s^{-1}$。再次使用之前阴极的表面用硫擦过。

[c] 300 小时后用砂纸清洁阴极。

[d] 初始阶段阴极在大的中子检测器中进行监测，没有滑梭，在 0.1 M LiOD 中进行了 183 小时；估算的检测限为 $1\,n \cdot s^{-1}$。使用之前用 400 目的金刚砂纸打磨。

[e] 管材来自托卡马克装置中的氚存储系统。

[f] 使用后分析了阴极中的氢和氘——结果：H/Pd 为 0.03，D/Pd 为 0.80。

[g] 上面实验中的电解液重复使用。

[h] 上面实验中的电解液和阴极重复使用；Na₂S 以高浓度水溶液的形式加入。

[i] 使用前在 1,000 ℃ 真空下对箔进行了除气。使用后分析了氢和氘——结果：H/Pd 为 0.02，D/Pd 为 0.83。

[j] 使用之前将箔浸入 Na₂S（浓溶液）中。使用后分析了氢和氘——结果：H/Pd 为 0.05，D/Pd 为 0.80。

[k] 将阴极切掉一半，使用后分析了氢和氘——结果：H/Pd 为 0.02、0.02，D/Pd 为 0.85、0.78。

[l] 熔体快淬带，由庄信万丰工程中心提供。

[m] 电弧熔化两次；在 0.1 M LiOD 溶液中电化学充氘一个月，然后在液氮中冷冻，浸入浓的 Na₂S 溶液并转移到中子计数电解池。

[n] 包括点焊在钯丝上的四个厚度为 1~2mm、不同型号的圆形钯片（庄信万丰公司）以及受到应力的钯丝。

[o] 之前实验的电解液重复使用，使用钛阴极和铂阳极。

[p] 使用之前将材料加热到 900 ℃ 然后在水中淬火。

[q] 将琼斯使用的电解液中的 AuCN 用 NaAuCl₄ 替代。

[r] 电流开启 36 小时，然后每小时在 200 mA 和 20 mA 之间变换一次。

[s] 电流开启 36 小时，然后每 5 分钟在 300 mA 和 30 mA 之间变换一次。

[t] 由于电解期间阳极的分解，电流在所示范围内缓慢变化。

[u] 电流开启 36 小时，然后关闭 10 小时、开启 2 小时并循环这一过程 270 小时。然后余下的时间中 5,000 秒为 380 mA 的阴极电流，4,000 秒为 10 mA 的阳极电流。

[v] 电流每 2 小时开启或者关闭，依次循环。中子产率指的是"开启"期间的。

[w] 给定的误差（1σ，由整个实验期间计算而来）多少会有些变化，因为为了涵盖尽可能多的电解池的设置（主要是在规划的早期阶段），并不总是能够成对地开展未通电＋未通电和通电＋未通电的实验，从而使得整个宇宙射线中子的探测效率存在少许差异，这是由于两个形式上相同的电解池存在少许差异造成的。

[x] 采集这些数据时使用了一个不同的数据采集系统驱动滑梭和累计数据，旨在探寻猝发中子[10]。

[y] 电解池每过 5 分钟进行手动交换。

[z] 进行 γ 射线研究的所有电解液中 H₂O：D₂O 都为 50：50，标 * 的 H₂O：D₂O 为 41：59。

[aa] 当前测量中，用一系列标准的 γ 射线源和一个放射出 6,129 keV γ 射线的 ²³⁸Pu/¹³C（α，nγ）源对系统进行了校准。放置各个电解池时它们的阴极应尽可能地靠近探测晶体，探测效率通过将之前测量[21]的点效率函数对阴极体积进行积分计算出来。在预期的全能峰、单逃逸峰和双逃逸峰的位置（5,488 keV、4,977 keV 和 4,466 keV）处寻找峰，这些位置是用参考文献 22 中推荐的方法预测的。

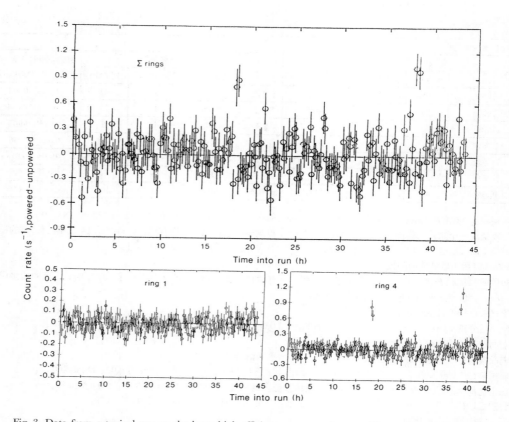

Fig. 3. Data from a typical run on the large high-efficiency neutron detector. These show the differences between count rates for powered and unpowered cells resulting from successive alternate shuttle positions for 40 g of titanium granules in 0.1 M D_2SO_4. The errors shown are 1σ errors for each five-minute counting period. In addition to results from the detector as a whole, results from two of the five rings of 2-inch diameter 107-cm active length $^{10}BF_3$ proportional counters are also shown. The counts in rings 2, 3 and 5 (not shown) were very similar to those in ring 1. The apparent bursts were seen only in ring 4 and are therefore a spurious effect. A tube (90-mm inner diameter) passes through the centre of the detector, and the shielding consists of 6 inches of borated resin, 1 mm of cadmium and 2 inches of lead. The neutron detection efficiency is high and is largely independent of neutron energy, varying from 48% for 0.5-MeV (Am/Li) neutrons to 40% for 4.2-MeV (Am/Be) neutrons. The background count rate is 4–5 count s^{-1}, and most neutrons are from cosmic rays. Each of the five rings of counters has its own independent pre-amplifier, pulse-shaping amplifier and discriminator, and the mean energy of neutrons counted can be obtained from the ratio of counts in the outermost ring of counters (ring 5) to counts in the innermost (ring 1). Because neutron counts are distributed over five rings, and because of the 135-μs-mean time to capture, neutrons emitted simultaneously from a source as a burst are counted separately (as seen with the ^{252}Cf source, for example). The pre-amplifiers, high voltage components and insulators are all contained within a desiccated electrically screened box, and we eliminate earth loops and induced electromagnetic pick-up ("aerial") effects from external coaxialcable runs to the PDP-11/45 data-acquisition computer by using isolating high-frequency pulse transformers and by winding the coaxial cables many times around ferrite rings. The neutron detector and its immediately associated electronics are located in a temperature-controlled air-conditioned blockhouse with two-foot-thick concrete walls and roof.

The details of the cells and results of the measurements are given in Table 2. The lowest limits (2σ) on neutron emission derivable from Table 2 for palladium are 1.5×10^{-2} n $s^{-1}g^{-1}$

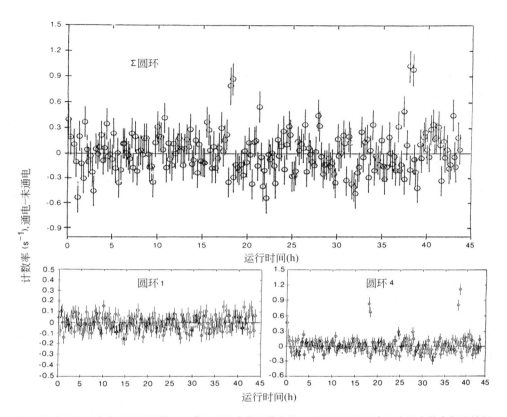

图 3. 从大型高效率中子探测器的一次典型实验中获取的数据。它们展示了通电和未通电的电解池计数率的差异，这是通过持续地变换滑梭位置实现的，具有 0.1 M D_2SO_4 的电解池中含有 40 g 钛颗粒。显示的误差为每 5 分钟计数区间的 1σ 误差。除了将探测器作为一个整体得到的结果之外，还显示了五个圆环中的两个获得的结果，组成圆环的 $^{10}BF_3$ 正比计数器直径为 2 in，活性长度为 107 cm。圆环 2、3 和 5（未显示）的计数与圆环 1 的非常相似。只在圆环 4 中观察到了明显的猝发，因此这是一个假信号。一只管（内直径 90 mm）穿过探测器的中心，屏蔽设备包括 6 in 的硼酸树脂、1 mm 的镉和 2 in 的铅。中子探测效率比较高，并且与中子能量无关，在 0.5 MeV 中子（Am/Li）的 48% 到 4.2 MeV 中子（Am/Be）的 40% 之间变化。本底计数率为每秒 4~5 个计数，大部分中子来自宇宙射线。五个圆环计数器中的每一个都有自己独立的前置放大器、脉冲形状放大器和甄别器，计数的中子的平均能量通过最外侧的环形计数器（环 5）的计数与最内侧的（环 1）计数之比得到。因为中子计数分布于五个环上，也因为平均捕获时间为 135 微秒，从一个源中同时猝发的多个中子可以被分别计数（例如，就像 ^{252}Cf 源一样）。前置放大器、高压部件和绝缘体都被囊括在一个干燥的电屏蔽箱中，我们消除了运行于 PDP-11/45 型数据采集计算机上同轴电缆的接地回路和诱发的电磁捕获（"天线"）效应，这是通过使用隔离的高频脉冲转换器并将同轴电缆在铁氧体环上缠绕多次实现的。中子探测器和与之相连的电子器件被置于一个控温的空调房中，这个空调房有两英尺厚的混凝土墙壁和屋顶。

电解池细节和测量结果列在表 2 中。如果在整个运行过程中中子持续发射，则从表 2 中推导出钯的中子发射的最低限（2σ）为 $1.5 \times 10^{-2}\,\mathrm{n \cdot s^{-1} \cdot g^{-1}}$ 或

or 1.5×10^{-2} n s^{-1} cm^{-2}, if the emission were sustained over the whole run. For titanium, the values are 3×10^{-3} n s^{-1} g^{-1} and 4×10^{-3} n s^{-1} cm^{-2}, although the latter limit is too high because it does not apply to the runs using granules having a large and indeterminate surface area. If we assume the emission to be sustained over only a one-hour period at most, then the limits are, for palladium: 7×10^{-2} n s^{-1} g^{-1} or 4×10^{-2} n s^{-1} cm^{-2}, and for titanium: 8×10^{-3} n s^{-1} g^{-1} or 2×10^{-2} n s^{-1} cm^{-2} (much less in the runs with granules). The neutron-emission rate limits are several orders of magnitude below the rates of $\sim 10^{4}$ s^{-1} reported in ref. 1 and about one order of magnitude below the rate of ~ 0.4 s^{-1} reported in ref. 2. It is significant that the limits in our work were also obtained for cells in which cold fusion could be expected to be enhanced, in particular by using titanium cathodes in the form of a large (40 g) mass of porous granules to increase both the reaction volume and the surface area, and an electrolyte specifically chosen to promote deuterium loading into the cathode[13] (see Fig. 3). As discussed later, we have not expressed the results in terms of the number of deuterium pairs within metal lattices.

Because the net count rates given in Table 2 are differences between much larger background rates, runs were undertaken with a calibrated ^{252}Cf source (0.024 ± 0.003 fissions s^{-1}) emitting 0.09 ± 0.01 n s^{-1} and a physically identical blank. The result was 0.14 ± 0.05 n s^{-1}, in satisfactory agreement. Furthermore, the expected neutron output of the unpowered UPt$_3$ cell, which is due to spontaneous fission of ^{238}U, was 0.22 s^{-1}. The value measured in comparison with an empty cell was 0.20 ± 0.06 s^{-1}. Our confidence in the results of the shuttle differences seems justified. Measurements on CeAl$_2$ and UPt$_3$ cells were included in the hope that high effective electron masses corresponding to these metal crystal lattices would mimic in some way the fusion enhancement effect of "heavy electrons" such as muons in binding the deuterium nuclei closer together. The palladium ribbon run with the cell power switched on and off every two hours (which was about eight times the characteristic diffusion time in the ribbon) was undertaken to enhance the appearance of non-equilibrium effects, and results (negative) are given in Fig. 4.

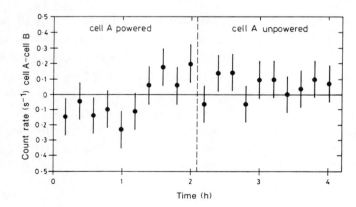

Fig. 4. Time dependence of neutron emission from an electrolytic cell with melt-spun Pd ribbon cathode and Pd foil anode, with power alternately turned on for deuterium loading and off for relaxation every 2 h by the data-acquisition computer: see Table 2 footnote l. The total length of the run was 110 h, and the sums of the "on" and "off" data are shown. After 90 h of running, we added 1 μM Pb^{2+} (to poison

1.5×10^{-2} n·s⁻¹·cm⁻²。就钛而言，这个数值为 3×10^{-3} n·s⁻¹·g⁻¹ 或 4×10^{-3} n·s⁻¹·cm⁻²，然而后面的限值太高了，因为它并不适用于所用颗粒表面积大而不确定的实验。如果我们假设发射至多持续了一个小时的时间，那么限值为，钯：7×10^{-2} n·s⁻¹·g⁻¹ 或 4×10^{-2} n·s⁻¹·cm⁻²，钛：8×10^{-3} n·s⁻¹·g⁻¹ 或 2×10^{-2} n·s⁻¹·cm⁻²（比用小颗粒的实验小得多）。中子发射速率限值比参考文献 1 报告的约 10^4 s⁻¹ 低数个数量级，比参考文献 2 报告的约 0.4 s⁻¹ 低一个数量级。值得注意的是，我们研究的限值也可以在那些冷核聚变可能会增强的电解池中得到，尤其是使用钛阴极，以大质量（40 g）的多孔颗粒来提高反应体积和表面积，而且特意选择能够促使氘吸附到阴极的电解液[13]（见图 3）。正如后面讨论的，我们没有展示氘在金属晶格中数目的结果。

由于表 2 给出的纯计数率是大得多的本底速率之间的差值，我们使用发射速率为 0.09 ± 0.01 n·s⁻¹ 的校准过的 ²⁵²Cf 源（每秒 0.024 ± 0.003 次裂变）和一个物理上一样的空白进行了实验。结果为 0.14 ± 0.05 n·s⁻¹，其一致性令人满意。而且，由于 ²³⁸U 的自发裂变，不通电的 UPt₃ 电解池预期的中子输出为 0.22 s⁻¹。与一个空电解池对比后测量值为 0.20 ± 0.06 s⁻¹。我们对滑梭差异这一结果的信心似乎得到了验证。在 CeAl₂ 和 UPt₃ 电解池中进行了测试，以期源自那些金属晶格的大的有效电子质量可以以某种方式模拟"重电子"对核聚变的增强效应，就像 μ 子将两个氘核束缚得非常接近时一样。将钯带实验电解池的电源开关每隔两个小时（约八倍于带中的特征扩散时间）转换一次，以增强非平衡效应的表现，结果（负结果）如图 4 所示。

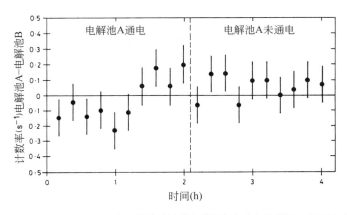

图 4. 电解池中子发射随时间的变化，使用熔体快淬的钯带状阴极和钯箔阳极，以两个小时为周期，轮换着打开电源使氘吸附、关上电源使之弛豫，这通过数据采集的计算机来实现：见表 2 的注脚 *l*。总的运行时长为 110 小时，"打开"和"关闭"数据的总和如图所示。运行 90 小时以后，我们向溶液中添加了 1 μM 的 Pb²⁺ 离子（通过铅的沉积使表面中毒）。有或者没有 Pb²⁺ 离子的数据之间没有差异，所

the surface by Pb deposition) to the solution. There was no difference between the data in the presence and absence of Pb^{2+}, and so data for the whole run was combined. This run was undertaken to enhance the appearance of the non-equilibrium effects discussed in the text. It is assumed that the ribbon would have had a high density of grain boundaries, dislocations and other lattice defects. Because the "on" and "off" periods were several times the characteristic diffusion time for the ribbon, it is assumed that the composition was cycling in the β-phase region between the fully loaded condition (D/Pd ≈ 0.83) and the limit of the (α + β) phase field (D/Pd ≈ 0.65).

γ-ray Counting

As it has been shown that cold proton-deuteron (p-d) fusion is expected to proceed at rates greater by ~8.5 orders of magnitude than d-d fusion[3], we carried out an alternative investigation of electrolytic enhancement of hydrogen-isotope fusion by looking for the D(p, γ)^{3}He 5,488-keV γ-rays from p-d fusion. We used a lead-shielded 113-cm^3 n-type high-purity germanium (HPGe) crystal γ-ray spectrometer to search for any γ-rays in the energy range 0.1–7 MeV emitted by a variety of cold-fusion cells operating with a mixture of light and heavy water. The results, also given in Table 2, are consistent with no γ-ray emission. The lowest limits (2σ) on γ-emission derivable from Table 2 are, for palladium, 7×10^{-3} γ s^{-1} g^{-1} or 1×10^{-3} γ s^{-1} cm^{-2}, and for titanium 1.4×10^{-3} γ s^{-1} g^{-1} or 4×10^{-4} γ s^{-1} cm^{-2}, if we assume that the emission is sustained over the whole run. Jones et al.[2] report that the fusion activity may last for only 4–8 h and begin ~1 h after the cell is powered, and in these circumstances typical values for the standard deviation in the γ-ray emission rates are ~0.05 s^{-1} and the 2σ limits for titanium are 4×10^{-3} γ s^{-1} g^{-1} or 3×10^{-3} γ s^{-1} cm^{-2}. Post-run analysis of the hydrogen isotopes taken up by the palladium cathodes with the mixed light and heavy-water electrolytes used gave very satisfactory D:H ratios, lying in the range 1.5–2.5. We note that if the proposed enhancement of the fusion process is as valid for p-d as for d-d fusion then, because of the enhanced tunnelling in the lighter d-p system[3], the γ-ray measurements actually provide a much more stringent limit on the cold fusion process than do the neutron measurements. The interpretation of the results from some of these cells was complicated by the dissolution of gold anodes and the consequent gold deposition onto the cathode: this also would have affected the original work[2].

Tritium Enrichment

Fleischmann et al.[1] claimed a tritium production rate of ~10^4 atom s^{-1}, commensurate with their reported neutron emission rate. They used a differential technique in which the tritium accumulation in a cell with a palladium cathode was compared with that in a cell with a platinum cathode. They took samples for analysis at regular intervals and maintained a constant total electrolyte volume by the addition of fresh D_2O.

Electrolytic enrichment is widely used to increase the concentration of tritium in water before analysis[14]. Reproducible results require careful control of the electrolysis, as the enrichment factor can vary widely (refs 15, 16 and R. L. Otlet, personal communication): important effects are seen with change of electrode materials, with variation in the condition (activity) of the electrode surface, with the current density (overvoltage) and with the temperature. Without precautions, the variations in enrichment factor can be more than a factor of two[16]. The claims therefore need to be assessed against this known

以将整个运行期间的数据都结合起来了。这次运行目的在于增强文中讨论的非平衡效应的表现。假设钯带具有高密度的晶界、位错和其他的晶格缺陷。因为"打开"和"关闭"的区间是钯带特征扩散时间的几倍，所以假设钯带的组成在完全充氘的条件（$D/Pd \approx 0.83$）和（$\alpha + \beta$）相区域的限制值（$D/Pd \approx 0.65$）之间的 β 相区域循环。

γ 射线计数

由于已经表明质子 - 氘核冷核聚变预计进行的速率比氘核 - 氘核核聚变要快约 8.5 个数量级[3]，我们通过寻找质子 - 氘核核聚变产生的 $D(p, \gamma)^3He$ 5,488 keV 的 γ 射线对氢 - 同位素核聚变的电解增强进行了研究。我们使用了一个 113 cm³ 的铅防护 n 型高纯锗晶体 γ 射线谱仪，在内有轻水和重水混合物的多种冷核聚变电解池中探寻一切能量范围在 0.1~7 MeV 的 γ 射线。结果也在表 2 中列出，它们一致表明没有 γ 射线放出。如果我们假设放射在整个运行过程中得以维持的话，那么由表 2 中可获得的 γ 放射值的最低限（2σ），钯为 7×10^{-3} γ·s⁻¹·g⁻¹ 或 1×10^{-3} γ·s⁻¹·cm⁻²，钛为 1.4×10^{-3} γ·s⁻¹·g⁻¹ 或 4×10^{-4} γ·s⁻¹·cm⁻²。琼斯等人[2] 报道核聚变的活性仅可保持 4~8 小时，而且始于电解开始后约 1 小时，在这样的条件下 γ 射线放射速率的标准偏差典型值约为 0.05 s⁻¹ 而 2σ 值对钛而言为 4×10^{-3} γ·s⁻¹·g⁻¹ 或 3×10^{-3} γ·s⁻¹·cm⁻²。运行后对钯阴极的吸附物及所用的轻水和重水混合物电解液的氢同位素进行分析，给出了令人满意的氘和氢的比值，在 1.5~2.5 的范围内。我们注意到，如果假定的核聚变过程的增强对质子 - 氘核核聚变像对氘核 - 氘核核聚变一样有效的话，那么，因为在更轻的氘核 - 质子核系统中的隧道效应增强[3]，γ 射线测量对冷核聚变过程实际能提供比中子测量更加严格的限值。由于金阳极上有金的溶解且在阴极上有相应的金的沉积，对从一些电解池获得的结果的解释变得较为复杂：这也影响了最初的工作[2]。

氚 的 富 集

弗莱施曼等人[1] 宣称氚产生速率约为每秒 10⁴ 个原子，与他们报道的中子发射速率相等。他们使用了一种差分技术，这种技术是将钯阴极电解池中氚的累积与另一个铂阴极电解池中氚的累积进行比较。他们以规定的时间间隔取样分析，同时添加新的重水以保持总电解液体积不变。

电解富集被广泛用于分析前增大水中氚的浓度[14]。要实现可重复的结果需要仔细控制电解，因为富集因子变化很大（参考文献 15、16；奥特莱，个人交流）：改变电极材料、电极表面状态（活性）、电流密度（过电压）和温度的改变都会造成巨大的影响。如果不加注意，富集因子的变化可以超过两倍[16]。因此只有考虑这个已知的可变电解富集因素才能对弗莱施曼等人的宣称作出评估。令人惊异的是，弗莱施

variable electrolytic enrichment. Surprisingly, Fleischmann et al.[1] claimed that there was no electrolytic enrichment in their platinum cell.

If the rates of electrolytic evolution of hydrogen isotopes are written as follows

$$D_2O \rightarrow D_2 + \tfrac{1}{2}O_2 \qquad \text{rate} = r$$

$$DTO \rightarrow DT + \tfrac{1}{2}O_2 \qquad \text{rate} = XSr$$

where r denotes the electrolysis rate, S the tritium-deuterium separation factor and X the mole fraction of tritium, T, in the solution, then the tritium accumulation is given by[10]

$$\frac{X}{X_0} = \frac{1}{(S+\alpha+\gamma)} \left\{ 1+\alpha+\gamma-(1-S)\exp\left[-\frac{(S+\alpha+\gamma)rt}{N_0}\right] \right\} \tag{1}$$

where the total solution volume is maintained constant by the addition of fresh D_2O (containing a mole fraction X_0 of tritium, directly proportional to the disintegration rate), the ratio of the sampling rate of the solution to the electrolysis rate is α and γ denotes the ratio of the rate of evaporation of the solution to the electrolysis rate—a small correction that may be calculated assuming that the electrolysis gases passing out of the cell are saturated with water vapour. On the timescales of interest, variability in S would give a variable enrichment

$$\delta\left(\frac{X}{X_0}\right) = -\frac{rt}{N_0}\delta S \tag{2}$$

If the solution becomes contaminated by hydrogen absorption from the atmosphere, then if S_{obs} denotes the apparent DT enrichment factor derived from the application of equation (1), $S_{obs} = S/[0.5(1+f)]$, where $f = (1-X_H)/(1+X_H(S_{HD}-1))$ with X_H denoting the mole fraction of hydrogen and S_{HD} the HD separation factor (relative rate of reaction of HDO and D_2O). Therefore, as well as the inherent variability from one electrode to another, it is evident that any variability in the amount of hydrogen pickup will give a variation in the apparent enrichment factor:

$$\frac{dS_{obs}}{dX_H} = \frac{S_{HD}}{2[1+X_H(S_{HD}-1)^2]}$$

We found that, unless exceptional precautions were taken (and we believe that we used experimental procedures very similar to those used in ref. 1 (M. Fleischmann, personal communication)), values of $X_H \approx 0.07$ were common. Under these conditions, a change of X_H of only 0.01 would give a change in S_{obs} of 0.02, which could be significant given the smallness of the claimed effect.

Any assessment of whether differential enrichment can be considered to account for the results in ref. 1 depends critically on the value of X_0, which was not reported. Using values[1] of r (1.24×10^{18} atom s^{-1}) and N_0 (14.6×10^{23} atom) we calculate from equation (2)

曼等人[1]宣称他们的铂电解池中没有电解富集。

如果氢同位素的电解过程速率表述如下

$$D_2O \rightarrow D_2 + \tfrac{1}{2}O_2 \qquad \text{反应速率为} r$$
$$DTO \rightarrow DT + \tfrac{1}{2}O_2 \qquad \text{反应速率为} XSr$$

其中 r 代表电解反应速率，S 为氘–氚分配系数，X 为氚（T）在溶液中的摩尔分数，那么氚的累积可以表示为[10]

$$\frac{X}{X_0} = \frac{1}{(S+\alpha+\gamma)}\left\{1+\alpha+\gamma-(1-S)\exp\left[-\frac{(S+\alpha+\gamma)rt}{N_0}\right]\right\} \tag{1}$$

其中通过添加新的重水（包含一定量摩尔分数为 X_0 的氚，与衰变速率成正比）保持溶液总体积不变，溶液取样速率与电解速率之比为 α，γ 代表溶液蒸发的速率与电解速率之比——需要进行一个小的纠正，可以假设从电解池中溢出的电解气体在水蒸气中是饱和的。在目标时间尺度上，S 的变化可以给出富集情况的变化

$$\delta\left(\frac{X}{X_0}\right) = -\frac{rt}{N_0}\delta S \tag{2}$$

如果溶液被大气中吸附而来的氢污染了，那么如果 S_{obs} 代表由方程（1）推导的表观 DT 富集系数，则 $S_{obs} = S / [0.5(1+f)]$，其中 $f = (1-X_H)/(1+X_H(S_{HD}-1))$，$X_H$ 代表氢的摩尔分数，S_{HD} 代表 HD 的分配系数（HDO 和 D_2O 反应的相对速率）。因此，除了一个电极到另一个电极的固有变化之外，很显然任何吸附氢的量变化都将会表现出表观富集系数的变化：

$$\frac{dS_{obs}}{dX_H} = \frac{S_{HD}}{2[1+X_H(S_{HD}-1)^2]}$$

我们发现除非采取非常严格的预防措施（而且我们相信我们采用的实验步骤与参考文献 1 中所用的是非常相似的（弗莱施曼，个人交流）），$X_H \approx 0.07$ 这样的值是常见的。在这些条件下，X_H 仅 0.01 的变化将会使 S_{obs} 变化 0.02，鉴于所宣称的效应很小，这个变化是非常显著的。

关于差分富集是否能够用来说明参考文献 1 的结果，任何这样的评价关键取决于 X_0 的值，这个值未曾被报告过。使用 r（1.24×10^{18} 原子/秒）和 N_0（14.6×10^{23} 个原子）的值[1]，我们从方程（2）计算出，如果 X_0 处于商用 D_2O 范围的极低端

that if X_0 were at the extreme low end of the range for commercial D_2O (3 Bq ml^{-1}), a value of $\delta S = 0.46$ would be required; if it were moderate (10–15 Bq ml^{-1}) a value $\delta S \approx 0.1$ would be needed; if it were high (80 Bq ml^{-1}) $\delta S \approx 0.02$ would suffice.

The applicability of equation (1) was confirmed experimentally, on both platinum and palladium cathodes, in conjunction with calorimetric and neutron-counting experiments (see Fig. 5 legend) using D_2O with an initial tritium content of 13 kBq ml^{-1} (efficiency corrected). The fit of this equation to all the experimental data (Fig. 5) gave, for palladium, $S_{obs} = 0.59$, and for platinum, $S_{obs} = 0.61$. Correction for the uptake of hydrogen, using $S_{HD} = 6$ (ref. 16), gave $S \approx 0.48$, in agreement with previous work and theoretical expectations ($S = 0.46\pm0.02$, (refs 14, 15 and D. S. Rawson and R. L. Otlet, personal communication)). For individual electrodes, S_{obs} for palladium varied from 0.46 to 0.65 (corrected S from 0.42 to 0.58), whereas S_{obs} for platinum varied from 0.56 to 0.85 (corrected S from 0.43 to 0.69)—a total range for individual electrodes of $\delta S_{obs} = 0.4$, which is enough to account for the results of Fleischmann et al.[1].

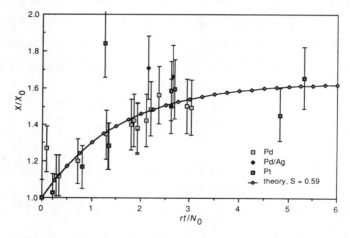

Fig. 5. Tritium enrichment by electrolysis in open cells at constant volume, with both Pd and Pt cathodes: relative count rate X/X_0 against amount of electrolysis rt/N_0 (symbols defined in the text). Initial count rate (efficiency corrected) was 13.0 ± 0.6 kBq ml^{-1}. Errors are 1σ. The Pd cells were the FPH calorimeters, sampled after 490–660 h, the cells in the first section of Table 2 (footnotes a–e) sampled at the end of the run and one cell from the high-efficiency neutron detector—footnote k in Table 2. The line is the fit to equation (1).

It is clear from these results and discussion that more evidence needs to be presented before the tritium accumulation reported[1] can be considered as experimentally reliable evidence for the occurrence of a fusion process.

Materials Characterization

With 125-μm palladium foils, hydrogen loadings (determined[10] by hot-extraction mass spectrometry of specimens frozen in liquid nitrogen, and independently by electrochemical extraction) of $H/Pd = 0.95 \pm 0.05$ were achieved in ~1 h at 100 mA cm^{-2} in 0.1 M

（3 Bq·ml⁻¹），需要 $\delta S = 0.46$；如果它属于中等（10~15 Bq·ml⁻¹），需要 $\delta S \approx 0.1$；如果它比较高（80 Bq·ml⁻¹），$\delta S \approx 0.02$ 就足够了。

方程（1）在铂和钯阴极上的适用性都经过了实验的验证，是同量热和中子计数实验联合进行的（见图5的图注），使用氚初始含量为 13 kBq·ml⁻¹ 的 D_2O（效率经过了校正）。用这个方程拟合所有给出的实验数据（图5），对钯而言，$S_{obs} = 0.59$，对于铂，$S_{obs} = 0.61$。对氢吸附量做校正，采用 $S_{HD} = 6$（参考文献16），得出 $S \approx 0.48$，与之前的工作和理论预期一致（$S = 0.46 \pm 0.02$，（参考文献14、15；罗森和奥特莱，个人交流））。对于单独的电极，钯的 S_{obs} 在 0.46 到 0.65 之间变化（校正后在 0.42 到 0.58 之间），而铂的 S_{obs} 在 0.56 到 0.85 之间变化（校正后在 0.43 到 0.69 之间）——对于单独电极的总范围 $\delta S_{obs} = 0.4$，这足以对弗莱施曼等人的结果[1]给予解释。

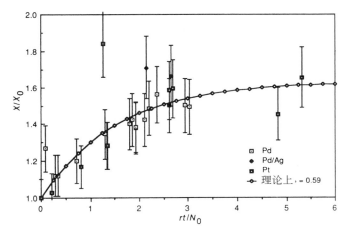

图5. 一定体积的开放电解池中氚的电解富集，使用钯和铂阳极：相对计数率 X/X_0 相对于电解量 rt/N_0 的关系（符号在文中进行了定义）。初始的计数率（经过了效率校正）为 13.0 ± 0.6 kBq·ml⁻¹。误差为 1σ。钯电解池是 FPH 量热计，490~660 小时后取样，表2中第一部分的电解池（脚注 a~e）在运行结束的时候取样，一个电解池通过高效中子探测器取样——表2的脚注 k。曲线是对方程（1）的拟合。

从这些结果和讨论中可以很清楚地看到，要证明所报告的氚的累积[1]是发生核聚变的可靠的实验证据，还需要更多的证据。

材 料 表 征

使用 125 μm 厚的钯箔，在 0.1 M 的 LiOH 溶液中以铂为阳极、电流密度为 100 mA·cm⁻² 的条件下，充氢率（通过冷冻在液氮中样品的热萃取质谱和独立的

LiOH solution with a platinum anode. The limit of deuterium loading in 0.1 M LiOD was lower (0.84±0.03). Rods (1- and 2-mm diameter) polarized for extended periods in neutron counting and calorimetry experiments showed D/Pd = 0.76±0.06. It is well known[17] that the equilibrium pressure for a given deuterium loading is higher than that for the same hydrogen loading. Current-interruption methods confirmed that overpotentials in the range 0.8–1 V (ref. 1) were being obtained. From an initial composition >99.9% D_2O, the solutions degraded to ~98.5% in 24 h and to 88–98% (analysis by infrared spectrometry) following electrolysis for many weeks. The resulting ratio H/D in the palladium was 0.02–0.04.

During electrolysis, all of the palladium cathodes became covered with a layer that varied in appearance from a dull tarnish to a dense jet black. In the latter case, loose black material was also formed, which in extreme cases came off during electrolysis, resulting in quite heavy erosion of the cathode. The layer itself evidently represented a modification of the morphology of the cathode at the surface. The formation of a thick black layer was enhanced at high current density, at high temperature, on smaller diameter wire and by frequent abrupt alterations of the current density repeated over a long period. The layer was more noticeable on the outside of a spiral-wound cathode than on the inside. The layer was also more noticeable on cathodes polarized in D_2O than on those polarized in H_2O (perhaps this is related to the greater equilibrium gas pressure for equivalent composition in the Pd–D system), and was different in appearance on materials from different sources. These observations may be explained by the old idea[17] that microfissures, or rifts, develop in palladium to release the mechanical strains resulting from the heavy loading of hydrogen, together with the assumption that any such effect would depend on the stress state of the metal surface and its microstructure.

Lithium was present in the surface layer on cathodes used in LiOD, and analysis by secondary-ion mass spectrometry (SIMS) apparently showed a concentration profile extending about 1 μm into the metal. SIMS images showed that the lithium was not uniformly distributed, however, and it seemed likely that it was trapped in microfissures in the surface layer.

Surface analysis showed a number of other species on and in the surface layer, notably small quantities of platinum and traces of copper, zinc, iron, lead and silicon: platinum would have originated from the anode and silicon from the glass container. No doubt the majority of the other contamination would have come from the solution: the levels found (a few atom percent, confined to the surface layers) were consistent with deposition by extended electrolysis from a solution of concentration around 10^{-9}–10^{-10} M. One possible criticism is that low levels of such deposition could poison any essential catalytic activity: we therefore used pre-electrolysis in several experiments, in an attempt to lower the surface contamination. We either made repeat experiments on the same solution, simply changing the cathode, or treated the solution beforehand in a separate cell.

Because of claims that an unusual mechanism might lead to nuclear reactions proceeding predominantly non-radiatively to ^{4}He, four cathodes (Table 2, first four entries) were

电化学萃取获得 [10]）达到 H/Pd = 0.95 ± 0.05 约耗时 1 小时。在 0.1 M LiOD 中充氘率的上限更低（0.84 ± 0.03）。在中子计数和量热实验中极化时间更长的钯棒（直径 1 mm 和 2 mm）显示 D/Pd = 0.76 ± 0.06。对于给定的充氘率，其平衡压力要高于同样充氢率的平衡压力，这是众所周知的 [17]。用中断电流的方法确定了所得到的过电压在 0.8~1 V 的范围内（参考文献 1）。D_2O 从初始的 99.9%，24 小时内降为约 98.5%，继续电解数个星期降为 88%~98%（通过红外光谱进行分析）。导致钯中 H/D 的比值变为 0.02~0.04。

电解期间，所有的钯阴极都会覆盖上一层从暗无光泽到致密黑色这样外观不同的物质。在后面的实例中，也发现过疏松的黑色物质，在一些极端的情况下它会在电解进行期间掉落，结果导致阴极的严重腐蚀。该层本身清楚反映了阴极表面形态的改变。在高电流密度、高温、较小直径的棒上以及在长期频繁的阶跃式改变电流密度的条件下，容易生成厚的黑色层。该层在螺旋状阴极的外侧要比内侧更容易观察到，而且在 D_2O 中极化过的阴极上也比在 H_2O 中极化过的阴极上更容易观察到（这可能与相同含量情况下 Pd–D 体系有更高的平衡气压有关），而且在不同来源的材料上其外观也不相同。这一发现可以用已有的理论 [17] 给予解释：由于充氢率很高，钯中将出现微裂缝和裂缝以释放掉由此而来的机械应力，同时也有假说认为这种效应依赖于金属表面的应力状态和它的微结构。

在 LiOD 中使用的阴极表面层含有锂，通过二次离子质谱（SIMS）分析表明锂的浓度分布已经深入金属内 1 μm。SIMS 图像显示锂并不是规则分布的，而是看起来像被捕获在表面层中的微裂缝里。

表面分析表明有一定数目的其他元素位于表面层之上或者其中，有极少量的铂，痕量的铜、锌、铁、铅和硅：铂可能来源于阳极，而硅来自玻璃容器。毫无疑问，主要的其他污染物应该来自溶液：我们发现的数量级（按原子数计算是百分之几，限于表面层）与在浓度为 10^{-9}~10^{-10} M 的溶液中长时间电解后的沉积物是一致的。可能有人批评，低水平的沉积物会使潜在的催化活性中毒：因此我们在一些实验中使用了电解预处理，以期减少表面的污染物。我们通过在同一溶液中重复实验，简单地改变阴极，或者事先将溶液在一个分开的电解池中进行处理。

因为有报告声称有一种非同寻常的机制导致核反应进行过程中优先生成非辐射性的 ^4He，我们用真空熔融 / 质谱仪对四个阴极（表 2 中的前 4 组）进行了分析。由

analysed by vacuum fusion/mass spectrometry. The high vapour pressure of palladium at the melting point caused difficulties, so internal standards were prepared by ion implantation of 10^{13} and 10^{15} atoms of ^4He into samples cut from the cathodes. Detection limits for ^3He and ^4He determined in this way were $\sim 8 \times 10^{10}$ atoms per sample— $(1-10) \times 10^{11}$ atom g^{-1}. We found no ^3He or ^4He. The expected level, if fusion had been occurring at the rate reported in ref. 1, was $\sim 10^{16}$ atom g^{-1}.

Evolution of hydrogen at a titanium cathode resulted, as is well known[13], in a dense network of hydride precipitates, observable by standard metallographic methods, penetrating below the surface. In 0.1 M D_2SO_4 electrolyte at 100 mA cm^{-2}, the network penetrated ~ 30 μm in 1 h. Precious-metal deposition inhibited the electrolytic uptake, presumably by lowering the overvoltage and promoting gas evolution. Electrolysis in the "brew" used by Jones *et al.*[2] resulted in hydride precipitates confined to the grain boundaries; other experiments showed that the presence of $PdCl_2$ in the electrolyte caused this effect, presumably as a consequence of palladium plating on the cathode. It is clear that expressions of the fusion rate that assume that the cathode has composition TiD_2 are completely misleading: metallography shows that the number of deuterium pairs is far fewer, hence the claimed fusion rate per deuterium pair is far higher than the figure given, and so the results are even more difficult to reconcile with expectations than had been implied[2].

Discussion

The interest in cold fusion has generated a large number of neutron counting experiments. It is well known that, in general, it is inadvisable to measure the signal + background and background of counting measurements at different times and in different physical locations (as in ref. 1), because of unexpected systematic variations. This is especially true for low-count-rate experiments. Compensating for variation of the background rate and assessing appropriate errors for the procedure chosen are particular problems. The work of Jones *et al.*[2] can be criticized for such errors[18]. It is notable that in ref. 2, only one run in fourteen showed a significant effect and then only because this particular run was assigned a smaller counting error than the others. Here we have attempted to minimize, by the shuttle procedure, uncertainty about background and counter variability and about error calculation. Given some of the more spectacular claims that have been made, we note that further caution is advisable because of the notorious sensitivity of $^{10}BF_3$ and ^3He proportional counters to humidity and of counter-amplifier systems to earth loops. In our work the neutron detectors were segmented, and the relationship between signals from the segments was well known, so spurious effects giving inconsistent signals from the segments could be identified.

Failure to reproduce the effects has been attributed by some to the need for rigorous exclusion of hydrogen and claims have been made that palladium electrodes must be cast and carefully degassed before use, to remove all traces of carbon and hydrogen impurity which might decorate dislocations or other high-energy sites (ref. 19 and R. A.

于钯在熔点处的高蒸气压导致实验发生困难，所以内部标样是用离子注入法向阴极上切下的样品注入 10^{13} 和 10^{15} 个 ^{4}He 原子而得到的。这种确定 ^{3}He 和 ^{4}He 的方法的检测限约为每份样品 8×10^{10} 个原子，即每克 $(1 \sim 10) \times 10^{11}$ 个原子。我们没有发现 ^{3}He 和 ^{4}He。如果核聚变以参考文献 1 中所报告的速率发生，预期的测量值应约为每克 10^{16} 个原子。

众所周知[13]，氢在钛阴极上析出得到的是一个致密的网状氢化物沉淀，该氢化物可以采用标准的金相学方法进行观察，它会渗入到表面以下。在 0.1 M D_2SO_4 电解液中，$100 \, \text{mA} \cdot \text{cm}^{-2}$ 的电流密度下，网状物 1 小时渗入约 30 μm。贵金属的沉积会阻止电解液的吸附，这可能是通过降低过电压和促进气体产生造成的。琼斯等人[2]采用的在"啤酒"（译者注：此处有调侃琼斯等人使用的多种盐混合物溶液的意思）中电解得到的氢化物沉淀局限于颗粒边界；其他实验表明电解液中 $PdCl_2$ 的存在会导致这一效应，可能是钯在阴极电镀的结果。很清楚的是，假设含有化合物 TiD_2 阴极的核聚变速率表达式完全是误导人的：金相学表明成对氘的数目非常少，因此，所声称的每个氘对的核聚变速率远高于给出的数值，所以相比之前的解释[2]，这一结果更难与预期的相符。

讨　论

对冷核聚变的兴趣催生了大量中子计数实验。众所周知，通常情况下，由于不可预期的系统变化，在不同的时间和位置对信号＋本底和本底的计数测量（如参考文献 1 所为）是不可取的。对于低计数率实验尤为如此。对本底速率变化的补偿和选定过程的误差评估都很成问题。琼斯等人的工作[2]存在这些错误[18]，是应该被批评的。在参考文献 2 中需要注意的是，十四次实验只有一次显示出明显的效应，而且仅仅是因为给这一次特殊的实验赋予了比其他实验小的计数误差。这篇文章中我们试图用滑棭的办法来减小本底和计数器的变化以及误差计算的不确定性。对一些更加惊人的声称进行思考时，我们注意到，因为人所共知的 $^{10}BF_3$ 和 ^{3}He 正比计数器对湿度的敏感性，以及计数器放大器系统对接地回路的敏感性，因此更加的谨慎是明智的。在我们的研究中，中子计数器被分成几部分，而且从不同部分得来的信号之间的关系是已知的，所以不同部分给出不一致的信号而产生的假信息是可以分辨出来的。

重现这些效应之所以失败，是由于严格除氢的需要造成的，已经有结论指出钯电极在使用前必须经过铸造并小心地除气，以除去所有痕量的碳和杂质氢（译者注：氢在此被看作杂质是相对于氘而言），它们可能存在于位错点或者其他的一些高能位

Huggins, Workshop on Cold Fusion, Santa Fe, May 1989): this is however inconsistent with the postulate of a "fusion" origin for the effect because, at low energies, p-d fusion is expected to be significantly faster than d-d fusion[3]. Furthermore, the original reports[1,2] did not mention any special precautions to exclude atmospheric water vapour apart from careful covering of the electrolytic cells. We followed similar procedures, and found that degradation of the heavy water by exchange with atmospheric moisture occurred quite rapidly. Alternatively, it is claimed that it is essential to maintain a high current density for a considerable period (A. J. Appleby, Workshop on Cold Fusion, Santa Fe, May 1989) although it is not completely clear whether these latter claims are in fact reproductions of the effect reported in ref. 1 or are something different. In our neutron counting experiments, fresh dislocations were introduced by plastic deformation, some counting experiments were carried out at current density as high as 1 A cm^{-2} (Table 2) and in one experiment in the isothermal calorimeter a high current density was maintained for a considerable period (Table 1). Trace deposition of platinum on the cathode, supposedly causing a lowering of the overpotential for deuterium evolution and hence a lowering of the attainable deuterium level in the cathode, has also been suggested as an explanation for irreproducibility (M. Fleischmann, personal communication). We observed no effect when we used palladium anodes in our neutron counting experiments.

Timescales for hydrogen and deuterium loading consistent with the expected diffusion time (x^2/D where the diffusion coefficient, $D = 10^{-7}$ cm^2 s^{-1} and x is the radius or half-thickness of the specimen) were measured[10] and nuclear counting and calorimetric experiments were always conducted over periods much longer than this. Furthermore, in the process of electrolytic loading of palladium, there will clearly be a concentration gradient, a moving phase boundary and the outer atomic layers of the metal will be saturated (possibly supersaturated) with deuterium[17]. It might be expected, therefore, that sufficiently sensitive equipment would detect any fusion process well before the material is completely loaded. Because our neutron detection sensitivity was $\sim 10^5$–10^6 times greater than that of Fleischmann et al.[1], it seems unlikely that any greatly enhanced fusion process associated with the absorption of deuterium into palladium, giving rise to neutron emission, is occurring. We are, of course, aware that it is always possible to construct essentially untestable theories involving hypothetical special conditions of the metal or of its surface. Careful characterization of materials for which positive results are claimed is therefore of great importance.

It has been argued that the neutron branch of the d-d reaction might be completely suppressed in favour of the $(t + p)$ branch and it has been further argued (S. Pons, personal communication) that the tritium produced as a result of a nuclear process inside the electrode need not necessarily exchange with the electrolyte and might not therefore be detected. However, the other product of such a nuclear process, a high-energy proton, should be detectable by its interaction with the lattice, including neutron emission: we estimate, knowing the rate of energy loss of the protons and by comparison with (p, n) reaction cross-sections for neighbouring elements, a yield of $\sim 10^{-6}$ neutron per proton, implying a neutron yield in our counting experiments of as much as 10^4 s^{-1} if fusion at the

点上（参考文献 19；哈金斯在 1989 年 5 月圣菲举行的冷核聚变专题讨论会上的报告）：然而这与该效应"核聚变"起源的假定不符，因为在低能量范围，质子 – 氘核核聚变明显快于氘核–氘核核聚变[3]。而且，最初的报告[1,2]除了小心盖好电解池以外，并没有指出任何特殊预防措施以排除空气中的水蒸气。我们沿用类似的步骤，发现重水与空气中的水汽交换而退化的现象迅速发生。另外，有人指出在相当的一段时期内维持一个高的电流密度是必需的（见阿普尔比在 1989 年 5 月圣菲举行的冷核聚变专题研讨会上的报告），尽管我们并不完全清楚后面的这个结论是对参考文献 1 所报道现象的重现还是有所不同。在我们的中子计数实验中，新形成的位错是通过塑性形变产生的，一些计数实验是在高达 $1 \, A \cdot cm^{-2}$ 的电流密度下进行的（表 2），在使用等温量热计的一个实验中，其高电流密度保持了相当长的一段时间（表 1）。痕量的铂在阴极上沉积，假设这会导致氘析出的过电压降低，从而降低阴极中氘可达到的浓度水平，也被认为是对不可重复性的一种解释（弗莱施曼，个人交流）。当我们在我们的中子计数实验中使用钯阳极时，并没有观测到任何效应。

充氢和充氘的时间与预期的扩散时间一致 (x^2/D，其中扩散系数 $D = 10^{-7} \, cm^{-2} \cdot s^{-1}$，$x$ 为样品的半径或其厚度的一半)[10]，并且核计数和量热实验进行的时间也总是远大于这一时间尺度。此外，在钯的电解充氘（氢）过程中，显然会有一个浓度梯度，一个移动的相边界，并且金属外表面的原子层会被氘所饱和[17]（也可能过饱和）。因此，可以预期，足够灵敏的设备可以在这种材料完全充氘以前检测到核聚变过程。因为我们的中子探测实验的灵敏度是弗莱施曼等人[1]的约 $10^5 \sim 10^6$ 倍，看上去似乎不太可能发生任何伴随着钯充氘的大大增强的核聚变并产生中子发射。当然，我们注意到总是有可能构建一个实质上尚难检验的理论，该理论涉及金属或其表面假定的特殊情况。因此，仔细表征具有正结果的材料是非常重要的。

氘核 – 氘核反应的中子分支会被完全抑制掉而代之以（t+p）分支，这一观点已得到一些论证，进一步的论证指出（庞斯，个人交流）在电极内部作为核过程产物的氚并不一定与电解液发生交换，因而也就可能检测不到。然而，这样一个核过程的其他的产物——高能质子在与晶格相互作用的时候应该能被检测到，产物中还应包括中子发射：我们估计，已知质子损失能量的速率，通过与相邻元素 (p, n) 反应截面的比较，产率约为每质子 10^{-6} 个中子，如果核聚变以参考文献 1 中所报道的速率

rate reported in ref. 1 were to proceed entirely through the (t + p) branch.

In view of the rather large d-d separations in both PdD and TiD$_2$, it might be argued that fusion requires some non-equilibrium state in the lattice—perhaps at the α/β phase boundary in palladium or at the tips of the growing TiD$_2$ needles or at a lattice defect—where the d-d or p-d separation could be greatly reduced. Here we created non-equilibrium situations by pulsing the current but we detected no neutron emission (Fig. 4).

Some explanations of the apparent excess heat production have emphasized recombination processes at catalytic metal surfaces[20]: apart from occasional explosions, however, which did not result in any detectable neutron emission, we found, by comparison of the volume of water added to maintain the cell volume with the electrolysis charge passed, that this was not a significant effect (in agreement with others[9]). Recombination in the gas space above the liquid, either on exposed cathode surface or catalysed by colloidal metal particles eroded from the cathode, might however account for some of the observations of bursts of heat recently reported (M. Fleischmann and S. Pons, Electrochemical Society Meeting, Los Angeles, May 1989). In discussing the claims in ref. 1, we prefer to focus on characteristics of the "simple" Fleischman, Pons and Hawkins (FPH) calorimeters, because we have only observed small effects (at the level of the inherent uncertainties), which might mistakenly be claimed as arising from cold fusion, in the one type of calorimeter (FPH type) that has major calibration difficulties. Cells using the same electrode and electrolyte materials operated in calorimeters that did not have these problems exhibited none of these effects.

There are two points regarding the calibration that could have a profound effect on the apparent results obtained with FPH-type calorimeters: the first concerns when the calibration is performed and the second how it is performed. Concerning the first point, it seems from our work and that of Lewis et al.[8] that a calibration performed during the first 10,000 min of electrolysis could be seriously in error and lead to an erroneous conclusion that subsequently, rather than being in balance, the cells were exothermic. Concerning the second point, Fleischmann et al.[1] describe calibration using the internal-resistance heater, by measurement of Newton's-law-of-cooling losses. Typically, this procedure might involve the application of power to the heater while electrolysis was occurring, following the temperature-time trace until a steady state was obtained, then switching the heater off and following the cooling curve. This procedure gives an approximation to the differential calorimeter constant, $k_d = d(\Delta P)/d(\Delta T)$ (where P is power and T is temperature) at the operating temperature of the cell and can give rise to errors in two ways. First, because any calibration sequence would require 5–10 h, extrapolation would be required to obtain the correct value at the reference liquid level: an estimated error of 20% or more could result. Furthermore, because the evaporation of the cell contents increases markedly with increasing temperature, the baseline slope would increase with increasing temperature and the effects of this sort of error would become correspondingly more marked: the claimed effects were indeed greatest in the cells run at the highest input power. Second, these calorimeters are nonlinear (equation (3), Fig. 2 legend), with the effect being significant

完全通过（t+p）分支进行的话，我们的计数实验可以产生的中子产率为 10^4 s^{-1}。

由于在 PdD 和 TiD$_2$ 中都存在相对较大的氘核－氘核间距，可能有争论说核聚变需要一些晶格中的非平衡状态——也许在钯的 α/β 相边界，或者在生长中的 TiD$_2$ 针状物的尖端，又或者在一个晶格缺陷上，在这些地方，也许氘核－氘核或者质子－氘核的间距会大大减小。本文中，我们通过脉冲电流创造了一个非平衡的状态，但是仍没有检测到中子发射（图 4）。

一些对产生表观"过热"现象的解释强调的是在具有催化性的金属表面的复合[20]；然而除了偶尔的突然爆发，它不会导致任何可观测的中子发射，通过比较为了维持电解池的体积而加入的水的体积与通过电解池的电荷数量，我们发现，这并不是一个重要的效应（与其他研究者的结论一致[9]）。在液体上方的气体空间复合，不是发生在暴露的阴极表面，就是被从阴极上腐蚀下来的胶体金属颗粒所催化，但是，这仅能解释最近报道的所观察到放热实验中的一些现象（见弗莱施曼和庞斯在 1989 年 5 月于洛杉矶举行的电化学会议上的报告）。在讨论参考文献 1 的结论时，我们倾向于关注"简易的"弗莱施曼、庞斯和霍金斯（FPH）量热计的特征，因为我们只观测到了一些小的效应（在固有的不确定性的水平上），在一种标定很困难的量热计（FPH 型）上，这些效应可能被错误地认为是来源于冷核聚变。使用同样的电极和电解液材料并利用没有这些问题的量热计，发现这样的电解池并未显示出这些效应。

有两点关于标定的问题可能对于 FPH 型量热计所获得的表观结果产生重大的影响：首先是标定何时进行，其次是标定如何进行。关于第一点，从我们和刘易斯等人[8]的工作来看，似乎在电解进行的前 10,000 分钟进行的标定是非常错误的，这将会导致错误的结论，即把处在平衡态的电解池误认作处在放热状态。关于第二点，弗莱施曼等人[1]对使用内部的电阻加热器、通过测量牛顿冷却定律的损失来进行标定的方法进行了描述。通常情况下，这一过程包括了在电解出现时给加热器施加功率，紧接着跟踪温度－时间轨迹，直到达到稳定状态，然后把加热器关掉，记录冷却曲线。这个过程可以算出工作温度下一个电解池的微分量热计常数的估计值，$k_d = \mathrm{d}(\Delta P) / \mathrm{d}(\Delta T)$（其中 P 为功率，T 为温度），有两方面的因素会造成这个值的误差变大。首先，因为任何的标定程序都需要 5~10 小时，要得到参考液面处的正确数值，需要进行外推：这估计会对结果造成 20% 或更大的误差。此外，因为电解池的蒸发量会随着温度的升高而明显增大，随着温度的升高，基线斜率也会增大，这种错误所产生的效应相应的会更加明显：声称的效应实际上在电解池以最高的输入功率运行时是最大的。第二，这种量热计是非线性的（方程（3），图 2 的图注），当温

when the temperature gradient is large: they cannot be described by a simple Newton's law-of-cooling constant. If a differential calorimeter constant is used to derive the input power, the calculated output would be (from Fig. 2 legend, equation (3))

$$P_{app} = k_d \Delta T = (k_{sb,0} + k_c)\, \Delta T + 3(k_{sb,0}/T_0)\,(\Delta T)^2$$

so that, in comparison with the correct output (equation (3))

$$P_{app} - P = 3k_{sb,0}(\Delta T)^2/2T_0$$

If the power applied to the heater is significant compared with the electrolysis power then this error will be even greater. Back calculation from the data given in ref. 1 shows that the claimed effects were largest for Joule input powers on the order of 6 W. For our FPH-type calorimeters, this would have given $\Delta T \approx 50$–$60°C$. Therefore, had these cells been calibrated in this way, an apparent heat excess on the order of 0.8–1 W would have been observed. Our method of calibration (see Fig. 1 caption) considerably reduced the effect of these sources of error. The original report[1] was clearly preliminary in nature, and it is evident from the above that the claims made therein cannot be assessed in the absence of a detailed description of the experimental procedure used and of the methods used to compensate for the systematic errors inherent in the use of a simple calorimeter.

We feel that our work has served to establish clear bounds for the non-observance of cold fusion in electrolysis cells, under carefully controlled and well understood experimental conditions and using well characterized materials. Further details are given in ref. 10. Claims of observations of cold fusion ought now to meet similar standards of data analysis and materials characterization so that a proper assessment can be made.

(**342**, 375-384; 1989)

D. E. Williams[*], D. J. S. Findlay[†], D. H. Craston[*], M. R. Sené[†], M. Bailey[†], S. Croft[†], B. W. Hooton[‡], C. P. Jones[*], A. R. J. Kucernak[*], J. A. Mason[§] & R. I. Taylor[*]

[*] Materials Development Division, [†] Nuclear Physics and Instrumentation Division and [‡] Nuclear Materials Control Office, Harwell Laboratory, UK Atomic Energy Authority, Didcot, Oxfordshire, OX11 ORA, UK
[§] Reactor Centre and Centre for Fusion Studies, Imperial College, Silwood Park, Ascot SL5 7PY, UK

Received 8 August; accepted 16 October 1989.

References:

1. Fleischmann, M., Pons, S. & Hawkins, M. *J. electroanal. Chem.* **261**, 301-308 (1989); erratum **263**, 187 (1989).

2. Jones, S. E. *et al. Nature* **338**, 737-740 (1989).

3. Koonin, S. E. & Nauenberg, M. *Nature* **339**, 690-691 (1989).

4. Sun, Z. & Tomanek, D. *Phys. Rev. Lett.* **63**, 59-61 (1989).

5. Leggett, A. J. & Baym, G. *Nature* **340**, 45-46 (1989).

6. Gai, M. *et al. Nature* **340**, 29-34 (1989).

7. Zeigler, J. F. *et al. Phys. Rev. Lett.* **62**, 2929-2932 (1989).

8. Lewis, N. *et al. Nature* **340**, 525-530 (1989).

9. Cunnane, V. J., Scannell, R. A. & Schiffrin, D. J. *J. electroanal. Chem.* **269**, 163-174 (1989).

度梯度较大时，非线性效应比较明显：它们不能用简单的牛顿冷却定律来描述。如果一个微分量热计常数通过输入功率来导出，计算出的输出功率应该为（来自图 2 的图注中的，方程（3））

$$P_{\text{app}} = k_{\text{d}} \Delta T = (k_{\text{sb},0} + k_{\text{c}}) \, \Delta T + 3(k_{\text{sb},0}/T_0) \, (\Delta T)^2$$

与正确的输出功率（方程（3））进行比较，则有

$$P_{\text{app}} - P = 3k_{\text{sb},0}(\Delta T)^2/2T_0$$

如果与电解功率相比，施加在加热器上的功率很大，那么这个误差会更大。从参考文献 1 给出的数据进行反演计算表明，声称的效应在焦耳输入功率为 6 W 的数量级时最大。对我们的 FPH 型量热计而言，这将得出 $\Delta T \approx 50{\sim}60 \, ^\circ\!C$。因此，如果这些电解池经过这种方法进行标定，将能观察到 0.8~1 W 量级的表观过热。我们的标定方法（见图 1 的图注）显著地减小了这种来源的误差。最原始的报告[1]实质上很明显是初步的，而且从上面的证据来看，在没有详细描述所采用的实验步骤和用于抵消使用一个简单量热计带来的系统误差的方法之前，最初的报告[1]中的宣称是难以评估的。

在仔细控制、很好理解实验条件并使用完备表征材料的条件下，我们认为我们的工作为电解池中尚未观察到冷核聚变建立了清晰的界限。更进一步的细节参见参考文献 10。现在对观察到冷核聚变的宣称应该符合类似的数据分析和材料表征标准，这样才能对其作出适当的评估。

（李琦 翻译；李兴中 审稿）

10. Williams, D. E. *et al. Harwell Report AERE R*-13606 (HMSO, London, 1989).

11. Edwards, G., Findlay, D. J. S. & Lees, E. W. *Ann. Nucl. Energy* **9**, 127-135 (1989).

12. Lees, E. W., Patrick, B. H. & Bowey, E. M. *Nucl. Instrum. Meth.* **171**, 29-41 (1980).

13. Fouroulis, Z. A. *J. electrochem. Soc.* **128**, 219-221 (1981).

14. Östlund, H. G. & Werner, E. in *Tritium in the Physical and Biological Sciences* Vol. **1**, 95-104 (Int. Atomic Energy Agency, Vienna, 1962).

15. Kaufmann, S. & Libby, W. F. *Phys. Rev.* **93**, 1334-1337 (1954).

16. von Buttlar, H., Vielstich, W. & Barth, H. *Ber. Bunsenges phys. Chem.* **67**, 650-657 (1963).

17. Smith, D. P. *Hydrogen in Metals* (University of Chicago Press, 1948).

18. Carpenter, J. M. *Nature* **338**, 711 (1989).

19. Gittus, J. & Bockris, J. *Nature* **339**, 105 (1989).

20. Kreysa, G., Marx, G. & Plieth, W. *J. electroanal. Chem.* **266**, 437-441 (1989).

21. Croft, S. *Nucl. Instrum. Meth. Phys. Res.* A**281**, 103 (1989).

22. Anicin, I. V. & Yap, C. T. *Nucl. Instrum. Meth. Phys. Res.* A**259**, 525-528 (1987).

23. Savitzky, A. & Golay, M. J. E. *Anal. Chem.* **36**, 1627-1639 (1964).

Acknowledgements. We thank Johnson-Matthey (Dr I. McGill and Dr M. Doyle) for assistance and for the loan of special samples of palladium. IMI Titanium (Mr J. R. B. Gilbert) provided titanium and information. We thank the following for assistance: P. Fozard, M. Newan, J. Monahan, R. Morrison, H. Bishop, V. Moore and colleagues, J. Asher, P. W. Swinden, A. M. Leatham, R. A. P. Wiltshire, D. A. Webb, J. O. W. Norris, R. Roberts, R. Crispin, C. Westcott, R. Neat, D. Robinson, H. Watson and G. McCracken. We also thank Dr D. Schriffrin, Dr P. T. Greenland and Dr D. Morrison for discussions and Dr R. Bullough for support. This work was financed by the Underlying Science programme of the UKAEA, and UK department of Energy and the Commission of the European Communities.

Natural Variability of the Climate System and Detection of the Greenhouse Effect

T. M. L. Wigley and S. C. B. Raper

Editor's Note

The observation that global temperatures had increased on average over the twentieth century had, by the late 1980s, led to fears that the predicted global warming due to the emission of greenhouse gases in human activities was already underway. But it was possible that the rising (but fluctuating) temperatures were instead caused by natural processes, such as long-term cyclical variations in the climate system. Here Tom Wigley and Sarah Raper of the University of East Anglia in England study that possibility. Their calculations of the planet's energy balance, taking cyclic patterns of ocean circulation into account, shows that these patterns can cause appreciable century-scale variations in temperature—but not enough to account for all the observed warming.

Global mean temperatures show considerable variability on all timescales. The causes of this variability are usually classified as external or internal[1], and the variations themselves may be usefully subdivided into low-frequency variability (timescale ≥ 10 years) and high-frequency variability (≤ 10 years). Virtually nothing is known about the nature or magnitude of internally generated, low-frequency variability. There is some evidence from models, however, that this variability may be quite large[1,2], possibly causing fluctuations in global mean temperature of up to 0.4 °C over periods of thirty years or more (see ref. 2, Fig. 1). Here we show how the ocean may produce low-frequency climate variability by passive modulation of natural forcing, to produce substantial trends in global mean temperature on the century timescale. Simulations with a simple climate model are used to determine the main controls on internally generated low-frequency variability, and show that natural trends of up to 0.3 °C may occur over intervals of up to 100 years. Although the magnitude of such trends is unexpectedly large, it is insufficient to explain the observed global warming during the twentieth century.

OBSERVED global mean temperatures show considerable interannual variability. If the data of Jones et al.[3] are filtered using a 10-year gaussian filter, overall, the high-frequency and the low-frequency standard deviations over 1867–1982 are 0.175 °C, 0.078 °C and 0.148 °C, respectively. Thirty-three percent of the high-frequency variance can be identified with the El Niño/Southern Oscillation phenomenon (ENSO). If this is factored out by simple linear regression against the Darwin–Tahiti pressure index of the Southern Oscillation[4], the remaining high-frequency standard deviation is 0.063 °C, a value that is

气候系统的自然变率与温室效应的检测

威格利，雷珀

编者按

全球气温观测值在 20 世纪普遍上升，这导致 20 世纪 80 年代末期人类对因自身活动排放温室气体而引起的全球变暖的恐惧。但这种气温上升（波动上升）也可能是由自然过程引起的，如气候系统的长周期变化。英国东安格利亚大学的汤姆·威格利和萨拉·雷珀就对此可能性做了研究。他们计算全球能量平衡时考虑了大洋环流的周期性模态，结果表明这些模态可以引起气温百年尺度的显著变化，但还不足以解释所有观测到的变暖幅度。

全球平均温度的变化体现在多种时间尺度上。变化的原因通常可以分为外部原因和内部原因两种 [1]，而变化本身则可以分为低频变化（时间尺度 ≥10 年）和高频变化（时间尺度 ≤10 年）。事实上，对于内部原因所导致的低频变率，无论是其机理还是幅度，我们都一无所知。然而，从模式研究获得的证据表明，这种变率可能相当大 [1,2]，在 30 年或更长的时间范围中引起全球平均气温波动达 0.4℃（见参考文献 2，图 1）。本文我们将展示海洋如何在自然强迫下被动调制并产生低频气候变率，从而产生世纪时间尺度的增温趋势的。我们还利用简单气候模式模拟来确定内成因低频变率的主要控制因素，模拟结果还显示在 100 年的时间段内可能会有 0.3℃ 的自然增温趋势。虽然这种变暖趋势已经非常大，但仍不足以解释观测到的 20 世纪全球变暖。

观测中的全球平均气温体现了明显的年际变率。倘若利用一个 10 年周期的高斯滤波器对琼斯等 [3] 的数据进行滤波，那么 1867~1982 年之间的高频信号和低频信号的标准差分别为 0.175℃、0.078℃ 和 0.148℃。其中 33% 的高频变率是由厄尔尼诺和南方涛动（ENSO）造成的。倘若对达尔文—塔希提南方涛动指数 [4] 作一元线性回归将该变率剔除出去，剩下的高频变率的标准差则变为 0.063℃，该值非常稳定，随

remarkably stable in time: 1867–88, 0.069 °C; 1889–1910, 0.062 °C; 1911–32, 0.061 °C; 1933–54, 0.064 °C; 1955–76, 0.065 °C. A very small fraction of this residual variability is due to the effects of major volcanic eruptions which have an identifiable cooling signal lasting for a few years[5-7]. The remainder is probably due largely to the internal variability of the atmosphere, manifest at least partly as global-scale changes in the cloud radiation budget[8]. If these variations are the high-frequency component of random, white-noise forcing, they must, because of the thermal inertia of the oceans, produce global mean temperature changes that have enhanced low-frequency variability. We aim to determine the magnitude of this low-frequency variability.

Global mean temperature changes $(\Delta T(t))$ in response to forcing $\Delta Q(t)$ can be modelled using an energy-balance model of the form[9,10]

$$\phi \rho ch \frac{\mathrm{d}\Delta T}{\mathrm{d}t} + \lambda \Delta T = \Delta Q - \Delta F \tag{1}$$

$$\Delta F = -\phi \rho c \left(K \frac{\partial \Delta \theta}{\partial z} + W \Delta \theta \right)_{z=0} \tag{2}$$

$$\frac{\partial \Delta \theta}{\partial t} - W \frac{\partial \Delta \theta}{\partial z} = K \frac{\partial^2 \Delta \theta}{\partial z^2} \tag{3}$$

In equation (1), ϕ (≈ 0.7) is a factor accounting for land/sea differences in heat capacity[10], ρ is the density and c the specific heat capacity of ocean water, h is the mean depth of the ocean mixed layer, λ is a feedback parameter[11] and ΔF is the flux of heat out of the mixed layer into the deeper ocean. ΔF (equation (2)) is estimated using an upwelling diffusive parameterization of vertical mixing. $\Delta \theta(z, t)$ is the temperature change at depth z below the mixed layer, W is the upwelling velocity and K is the vertical diffusivity.

If ΔQ is white-noise forcing with a uniform spectrum, then the thermal inertia of the ocean will produce a redder spectrum with a preponderance of variance at low frequencies, as pointed out by Hasselmann[12]. Although the longer-term climate consequences have been explored in the frequency domain[13], they have never been properly quantified in the context of climate change on a 10–100-yr timescale.

Equations (1)–(3) can be solved exactly in the frequency domain, using the boundary conditions $\Delta \theta_{z=0} = \Delta T$ and $\partial \theta / \partial z$ tending to zero for large z, to give

$$S_T = S_Q \lambda^{-1} \left\{ \left(1 - \frac{\tau W}{2h} + \frac{\tau}{2h} \sqrt{\frac{v^2 + W^2}{2}} \right)^2 + \left(2\pi f \tau + \frac{\tau}{2h} \sqrt{\frac{v^2 - W^2}{2}} \right)^2 \right\}^{-1} \tag{4}$$

where $S_Q(f)$ is the power spectrum of the forcing at frequency f (yr^{-1}), $S_T(f)$ is the power spectrum of the mixed layer temperature, τ is a mixed-layer timescale

$$\tau = \phi \rho ch / \lambda \tag{5}$$

($\tau \approx$ 2–8 yr) and v is a characteristic velocity defined by

时间没有太大变化：1867~1888 年为 0.069℃；1889~1910 年为 0.062℃；1911~1932 年为 0.061℃；1933~1954 年为 0.064℃；1955~1976 年为 0.065℃。在剩余的这部分高频变率中，有很小一部分是由火山喷发引起的，这一点可以通过持续数年的降温信号识别出来 [5-7]。其余的变率则很可能是由大气的内部变化所致，云和辐射平衡在全球尺度上的变化至少可以部分证明这点 [8]。倘若这些变率是随机白噪音强迫的高频组分，那么由于海洋的热惯性，这些变率将导致全球平均气温发生变化，并由此增强低频变率。我们的目的就是要确定这种低频变率的幅度。

全球平均温度变化（$\Delta T(t)$）对外部强迫（$\Delta Q(t)$）的响应可用能量平衡模式 [9, 10] 表示如下：

$$\phi \rho c h \frac{\mathrm{d}\Delta T}{\mathrm{d}t} + \lambda \Delta T = \Delta Q - \Delta F \tag{1}$$

$$\Delta F = -\phi \rho c \left(K \frac{\partial \Delta \theta}{\partial z} + W \Delta \theta \right)_{z=0} \tag{2}$$

$$\frac{\partial \Delta \theta}{\partial t} - W \frac{\partial \Delta \theta}{\partial z} = K \frac{\partial^2 \Delta \theta}{\partial z^2} \tag{3}$$

方程（1）中，ϕ（≈ 0.7）为陆海热容差异系数 [10]，ρ 为海水密度，c 为海水的比热容，h 表示海洋混合层的平均深度，λ 为反馈参数 [11]，ΔF 为由混合层进入深层海洋的热通量。ΔF（方程（2））是对垂直混合流进行"涌升－扩散"参数化估算出的。$\Delta \theta(z, t)$ 表示混合层以下深度 z 处的温度变化，W 为涌升速度，K 为垂直扩散系数。

假设 ΔQ 为具有均匀频谱的白噪声强迫，那么，正如哈塞尔曼 [12] 所指出的那样，海洋的热惯性将会形成一个低频变率占优势的红噪声谱。虽然前人对长期气候变化的频谱问题已有所研究 [13]，但对于 10~100 年的时间尺度上的气候变化还没有给出恰当的量化。

利用边界条件 $\Delta \theta_{z=0} = \Delta T$，以及当 z 较大时 $\partial \theta / \partial z$ 趋向于 0，方程（1）~（3）在频域内可解：

$$S_T = S_Q \lambda^{-1} \left\{ \left(1 - \frac{\tau W}{2h} + \frac{\tau}{2h} \sqrt{\frac{v^2 + W^2}{2}} \right)^2 + \left(2\pi f \tau + \frac{\tau}{2h} \sqrt{\frac{v^2 - W^2}{2}} \right)^2 \right\}^{-1} \tag{4}$$

其中 $S_Q(f)$ 是当外部强迫频率为 $f(\mathrm{yr}^{-1})$ 时的功率谱，$S_T(f)$ 为混合层温度的功率谱，τ 表示混合层的时间尺度：

$$\tau = \phi \rho c h / \lambda \tag{5}$$

（$\tau \approx 2 \sim 8 \ \mathrm{yr}$），$v$ 为特征速度，可由以下方程表示：

$$v^4 = W^4 + 64\pi^2 f^2 K^2 \tag{6}$$

The ratio $\sqrt{S_T}/\sqrt{S_Q}$ may be considered as a frequency-dependent climate sensitivity. Climate sensitivity is normally defined as the inverse of the feedback parameter, to which $\sqrt{S_T}/\sqrt{S_Q}$ tends at low frequencies.

At high frequencies $(f \gtrsim 10^{-1}\,\mathrm{yr}^{-1})$,

$$S_T = S_Q/(2\pi\,\phi\rho chf)^2 \tag{7}$$

The high-frequency response is therefore independent of the feedback parameter (and hence the climate sensitivity). This means that the response of the climate system to high-frequency forcings such as volcanic eruptions and the seasonal insolation cycle must be virtually independent of the sensitivity. High-frequency information is therefore of little value in trying to estimate, empirically, the climate sensitivity. This is an obvious, but little appreciated result.

At low frequencies $(f \lesssim 10^{-3}\,\mathrm{yr}^{-1})$, S_T is approximately constant:

$$S_T = S_Q/\lambda^2 \tag{8}$$

This follows from the fact that surface temperature fluctuations track equilibrium values when the forcing period is much greater than the ocean response time. As $S_Q \approx (1\,\mathrm{W\,m}^{-2})^2$ (see below), $S_T(f=0)$ varies between $(0.3\,°\mathrm{C})^2$ at $\lambda = 3$ and $(1.0\,°\mathrm{C})^2$ at $\lambda = 1$. Thus, passive internal variability can account for only a small fraction of climate variability on the ice-age timescale, in agreement with current thinking about the importance of orbital forcing. Qualitatively similar results to those above have been given by Lemke[13], but the variability derived here is much lower because we have used more realistic feedback parameter values.

In the time domain, important results can be obtained analytically[10,14-16], but in the context of stochastic forcing it is more informative to proceed through numerical integration of the equations. We have used a generalization of this type of model in which the Earth is divided into land and ocean "boxes" in each hemisphere (see ref. 17). To facilitate comparison with greenhouse studies, we specify climate sensitivity in terms of the equilibrium warming for a doubling of atmosphere CO_2, $\Delta T_{2x} = 1.5-4.5\,°\mathrm{C}$, related to λ by

$$\lambda^{-1} = \Delta T_{2x}/\Delta Q_{2x} \tag{9}$$

where ΔQ_{2x} is taken as $4.39\,\mathrm{W\,m}^{-2}$ (refs 18, 19). Vertical heat transport in the ocean is assumed to be an upwelling diffusive process.

$$v^4 = W^4 + 64\pi^2 f^2 K^2 \tag{6}$$

比值 $\sqrt{S_T}/\sqrt{S_Q}$ 可视为以频率为变量的气候敏感度指数。气候敏感度指数通常定义为反馈参数的倒数，低频时 $\sqrt{S_T}/\sqrt{S_Q}$ 即趋向于该值。

在高频强迫下（$f \geqslant 10^{-1}\,\mathrm{yr}^{-1}$），

$$S_T = S_Q / (2\pi\phi\rho chf)^2 \tag{7}$$

高频响应因此与反馈参数无关（从而也与气候敏感度指数无关）。这就意味着气候系统对高频强迫，如火山喷发及辐射的季节循环等的响应，与气候敏感度基本无关。因此，单从经验上来说高频信息对估算气候敏感度没什么价值。这是很显然、却很少有人了解的结果。

在低频强迫下（$f \leqslant 10^{-3}\,\mathrm{yr}^{-1}$），$S_T$ 大致为一个常数：

$$S_T = S_Q/\lambda^2 \tag{8}$$

这恰好是与事实相符的，即当强迫周期远大于海洋响应时间时，表层海水温度会围绕平衡值上下波动。由于 $S_Q \approx (1\,\mathrm{W \cdot m^{-2}})^2$（见下文），因此，当 λ 分别为 3 和 1 时，$S_T(f=0)$ 在 $(0.3℃)^2$ 和 $(1.0℃)^2$ 之间波动。那么，从冰期时间尺度上来说，被动内成因变率在气候变率中仅占很小的一部分，这与当前人们理解的轨道强迫的重要性一致。从定性的角度上，上述结果与莱姆基[13]给出的结果相似，但本文得到的变率要低得多，因为我们采用了更实际的反馈参数。

在时域内，许多重要结果可以通过解析获得[10,14-16]，但对于随机强迫因子，利用数值积分法可以从方程中获得更多的信息。本文我们采用了一种抽象的地球气候模式，将地球分为南、北半球上的陆地和海洋"箱体"（见参见文献17）。为了便于与温室研究相比较，我们规定气候敏感度为大气 CO_2 浓度加倍时大气的平衡温度，即 ΔT_{2x} 为 1.5~4.5℃，它与 λ 有关：

$$\lambda^{-1} = \Delta T_{2x}/\Delta Q_{2x} \tag{9}$$

其中，ΔQ_{2x} 取 4.39 $\mathrm{W \cdot m^{-2}}$（见参考文献 18、19）。同时假定海洋中的垂直热传输为典型的涌升—扩散过程。

Our aim is to determine the magnitude of the decadal to century timescale variations in global mean temperature under the constraint that they are compatible with the observed high-frequency variations. The model is therefore forced with random interannual variations in ΔQ; specifically, global mean gaussian white-noise forcing.

The total variance of the forcing required to match observed high-frequency temperature variations (σ_Q^2) can be estimated from the spectral solution, knowing the high-frequency variance of the global mean temperature data. The implied value of σ_Q is ~ 1 W m^{-2}. This value is consistent with the observed month-to-month variations in the Earth's radiation budget due to cloudiness variations[8], which have a standard deviation of 3.3 W m^{-2}. If month-to-month variations are uncorrelated, then the interannual standard deviation should be ~ 1 W m^{-2}. This may be interpreted as a forcing term provided that the radiation budget changes are not themselves dependent on temperature changes (M. I. Hoffert, personal communication). Although such variations may, in general, be affected by ENSO events, the data in ref. 8 come from months with relatively small values of the Southern Oscillation Index (SOI) and show no correlation with SOI.

After forcing the model with gaussian white noise with $\sigma_Q = 1$ W m^{-2}, we then adjusted the forcing (by a factor of 0.72 to 1.04 depending on model parameters) so as to match precisely the observed high-frequency variations in ΔT ($\sigma_T = 0.063°C$), and then examined the low-frequency characteristics of the output. The σ_T value used here corresponds to the global mean temperature record with ENSO factored out. This is appropriate, primarily because the spectrum of the ENSO part of the signal (as determined by the Darwin-Tahiti pressure index used here[20]) has negligible low-frequency variance and so cannot lead to any noticeable low-frequency response. Simulations of 100,000 years length were performed for a wide range of values of the parameters that control model output.

The low-frequency character of the simulated global mean temperature variations that is of particular interest here is that around the century timescale, as this is particularly pertinent to the issue of greenhouse-gas forcing. This is in the frequency region in which the results begin to show appreciable λ dependence (see equation (4)). To compare the simulations with observations most readily, we examined the distribution of trends (dT_L) of durations (L) from 10 to 1,000 years.

Typical simulated variations in global mean temperature are shown in Fig. 1. These variations are qualitatively similar to observed changes over the past 100 years or more[3]. The 10–100-yr timescale fluctuations can be seen to be substantial. These are the result of the thermal inertia of the oceans acting in a purely passive mode, independent of any external forcing changes and independent of active oceanic effects which might be associated with circulation changes.

我们的目的是要确定出，在与观测到的高频变率幅度相符的约束条件下，十年到百年尺度上的全球平均温度的变率大小。因此，本模式中给了一个随机的年际变率 ΔQ，具体地说就是全球平均的高斯白噪音强迫。

输入模式的强迫信号的总方差，需要与观测到的温度的高频方差（σ_Q^2）相一致，已知全球平均温度的高频分量，可以做功率谱来估计观测到的高频信息。由此得出的 σ_Q 约为 1 W·m^{-2}。该值与所观测到的因云量变化[8]而导致地球辐射平衡的逐月变化一致，其中云量变化的标准差为 3.3 W·m^{-2}。如果逐月变化之间互不相关，那么其年际标准差应约为 1 W·m^{-2}。这可以解释为由于某种强迫因子的存在，辐射平衡变化本身与温度变化无关（霍费尔特，个人交流）。虽然从总体上来说这种变化可能会受 ENSO 事件的影响，但参考文献 8 中的数据是在南方涛动指数（SOI）相对较小的月份中得到的，且与 SOI 之间没有表现出相关性。

对模式输入高斯白噪音强迫 σ_Q= 1 W·m^{-2}，然后再对强迫信号加以调整（根据模式参数的不同，乘以一个大小为 0.72~1.04 的系数），从而使之与观测到的 ΔT 的高频部分（σ_Q= 0.063℃）精确匹配，最后对所输出的低频特征进行仔细研究。这里采用的 σ_T 值与剔除了 ENSO 事件后的全球平均温度纪录相一致。这样做的合理性主要在于，ENSO 谱低频变化的信号（由达尔文 - 塔希提气压指数决定[20]）可以忽略不计，因此也就不会产生任何明显的低频响应。模拟的总积分长度为 10 万年，其中赋予了控制模式输出结果的参数值较宽的变化范围。

在模拟出的全球平均温度变化的众多低频特征中，本文感兴趣的是百年尺度上的低频变化特征，因为它与温室气体强迫的相关性最大。在该频率范围内，模拟结果对 λ 有较好的依赖性（见方程 (4)）。为了使模拟结果与观测值之间更容易比较，我们还仔细研究了持续时间（L）从 10 年到 1000 年之间变化趋势的分布情况（$\mathrm{d}T_L$）。

模拟的全球平均气温的典型变化见图 1。从定性的角度上说，这些变化与过去 100 年乃至更长时间的观测结果相似[3]。可以看出 10~100 年时间尺度上的波动十分显著。这是海洋热惯性效应以完全被动的形式作用的结果，与外部强迫的变化无关，与可能和环流变化有关的主动海洋作用亦无关。

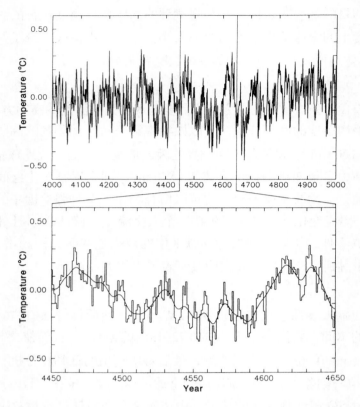

Fig. 1. Simulation of internally generated natural variability of global mean temperature ($\Delta T_{2x} = 4.0$ °C, $K = 1.0$ cm^2 s^{-1}). The upper panel is the fifth 1,000 years of a 100,000-yr run, with 200 years enlarged in the lower panel. The smooth curve in the lower panel shows filtered values to highlight the lower frequency variations.

The magnitude of this passive internal variability depends on the model parameters, as shown in Table 1. (The results shown in Table 1 are for globally coherent forcing, but they are insensitive to the degree of aggregation of the forcing.) Low-frequency variability, as judged by any of the parameters shown, increases with increasing ΔT_{2x} and decreasing K as predicted by the analytical results. Simulated lag-1 autocorrelations (r_1; that is, the correlation between successive annual mean values) are similar to those observed in the data of Jones et al.[3]. The data, however, behave quite differently from what would be expected if a first-order autoregressive process described the temperature variations (as assumed, for example, in ref. 21), pointing to the importance of higher-order effects (see ref. 22). The 100-year trend confidence limits, although substantial, are much less than the observed trend of 0.5 °C over the past 100 years. In the sense that passive internal variability represents the most basic underlying natural variability of the climate system, this result indicates that the observed warming trend is highly statistically significant. Based on the results presented here, the 90% confidence limits for a trend of 0.5 °C range from 0.34–0.66 °C to 0.24–0.76 °C depending on climate sensitivity. (Confidence limits of 90% are given here because the significance test for a warming trend is only one-tailed.)

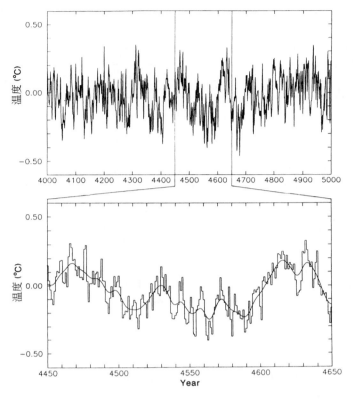

图 1. 全球平均气温内自然变率（$\Delta T_{2x} = 4.0℃$，$K = 1.0 \text{ cm}^2 \cdot \text{s}^{-1}$）。上图为 10 万年的模拟结果中第五个千年的结果，下图是对其中 200 年结果的放大。下图中的平滑曲线突出显示了滤波后的低频变率。

 这种被动内变率的振幅取决于模式参数，见表1。（表1所列数值是对于典型的全球一致的强迫因素而言，它们对于强迫因子不同程度的组合并不敏感。）根据表中所列参数判断，低频变率随 ΔT_{2x} 的升高和 K 的降低而增加，这与解析解的预测一致。模拟出的滞后 1 年自相关系数（r_1，即某年与后面一年平均值的相关系数）与琼斯等[3] 获得的观测结果相似。然而，倘若一阶自回归过程描述了温度的变化（如参考文献 21 中所假定的那样），那么数据的表现则与预期大为不同，说明高阶效应也起着重要作用（见参考文献 22）。虽然百年趋势达到了显著性水平，但相对于过去 100 年实际观测结果中 0.5℃ 的变化则要小得多了。鉴于被动内变率代表着气候系统最基本的潜在的自然变率，该结果意味着观测到的变暖趋势在统计学意义上具有超乎寻常的显著性。基于这里给出的结果，当温度变化 0.5℃ 时（根据气候敏感性的不同，温度变化范围在 0.34~0.66℃ 和 0.24~0.76℃ 之间），取置信水平 90%。（这里所取的置信水平为 90%，因为对变暖趋势仅作了单侧显著性检验。）

Table 1. Statistical characteristics of model-generated natural variability for different model parameters

Sensitivity, ΔT_{2x}	1.5				3.0				4.5			
Diffusivity, $K=$	0.0*	0.5	1.0	2.0	0.0*	0.5	1.0	2.0	0.0*	0.5	1.0	2.0
Autocorrelation (r_1)	0.73	0.64	0.61	0.59	0.83	0.72	0.69	0.65	0.87	0.75	0.72	0.68
Standard deviations†												
σ_1	0.14	0.12	0.12	0.12	0.19	0.15	0.14	0.14	0.23	0.16	0.16	0.15
σ_{10}	0.09	0.08	0.08	0.08	0.14	0.11	0.11	0.10	0.19	0.13	0.12	0.12
Trends (90% band)‡												
10 yr	±0.39	±0.31	±0.29	±0.28	±0.49	±0.35	±0.33	±0.31	±0.55	±0.37	±0.34	±0.31
30 yr	±0.30	±0.24	±0.24	±0.24	±0.46	±0.32	±0.30	±0.29	±0.59	±0.36	±0.33	±0.31
100 yr	±0.18	±0.17	±0.17	±0.18	±0.31	±0.25	±0.25	±0.25	±0.43	±0.30	±0.29	±0.29

Mixed-layer depth was taken as 70 m and upwelling rate chosen to ensure that W/K remained constant, with $W = 4$ m yr^{-1} for $K = 1$ cm^2 s^{-1}. Low-frequency variability is larger for larger mixed-layer depth. The other model parameter that influences results is the temperature of the sinking water, which we have taken to be constant here (that is, $\Pi = \Delta T_\phi / \Delta T = 0$; see ref. 24 for support of this assumption). Taking $\Pi > 0$ reduces the low-frequency variability slightly. Lag-1 autocorrelations are the means of values for 100-year samples. Model runs were 100,000 years. Temperatures in °C.
* W set to zero too (corresponding to a mixed-layer ocean model).
† σ_1 is the standard deviation of the full time series of annual values. σ_{10} is the standard deviation of non-overlapping 10-year means.
‡ 90% of all values lay within the limits shown.

Table 1 also shows that the variability for a mixed-layer-only ocean ($K = 0$, $W = 0$) is appreciably greater than for non-zero K (as can also be seen from equation (4)). Simulations by Robock[1] and Hansen et al.[2], which are based on mixed-layer ocean formulations, have therefore probably overestimated the degree of low-frequency variability that might arise through this internal mechanism.

These results have direct bearing on the value of the climate sensitivity parameter (that is, on ΔT_{2x} or λ), and hence on the issue of detecting the greenhouse effect on climate. Gilliland and Schneider[23] and Wigley and Raper[17] have noted that the observed warming, if interpreted solely as a greenhouse signal, implies a rather low value for the climate sensitivity, $\Delta T_{2x} = 1.3–2.0$ °C (the range of values arises from uncertainties in other model parameters). If one allows for passive internal variability, the range of possible ΔT_{2x} values increases substantially, to 1.0–2.8 °C. Higher values can be admitted only if the present model substantially underestimates the lag effect of oceanic thermal inertia, or if other external forcing factors or internal effects (such as ocean circulation changes) are invoked. Because of a dearth of suitable data, however, these possibilities cannot be ruled out, so neither can one rule out high values of climate sensitivity. Thus, although we still cannot claim to have unequivocally detected the greenhouse effect, our consideration of passive internal variability virtually eliminates this internal mechanism as a possible sole explanation of the recent global warming. Although our analysis has increased the range of uncertainty in the empirical value of ΔT_{2x}, this has served mainly to bring the empirical result more in line with the range of ΔT_{2x} values estimated from general circulation models

表 1. 不同模式参数下模拟出的自然变率统计特征

气候敏感度 ΔT_{2x}	1.5				3.0				4.5			
扩散系数 $K=$	0.0*	0.5	1.0	2.0	0.0*	0.5	1.0	2.0	0.0*	0.5	1.0	2.0
自相关系数(r_1)	0.73	0.64	0.61	0.59	0.83	0.72	0.69	0.65	0.87	0.75	0.72	0.68
标准差†												
σ_1	0.14	0.12	0.12	0.12	0.19	0.15	0.14	0.14	0.23	0.16	0.16	0.15
σ_{10}	0.09	0.08	0.08	0.08	0.14	0.11	0.11	0.10	0.19	0.13	0.12	0.12
趋势(置信水平90%)‡												
10年	±0.39	±0.31	±0.29	±0.28	±0.49	±0.35	±0.33	±0.31	±0.55	±0.37	±0.34	±0.31
30年	±0.30	±0.24	±0.24	±0.24	±0.46	±0.32	±0.30	±0.29	±0.59	±0.36	±0.33	±0.31
100年	±0.18	±0.17	±0.17	±0.18	±0.31	±0.25	±0.25	±0.25	±0.43	±0.30	±0.29	±0.29

混合层深度取 70 m,选择合适的涌升速率以保证 W/K 为常数,其中当 $K=1\,cm^2 \cdot s^{-1}$ 时,$W=4\,m \cdot yr^{-1}$。混合层的深度越大,低频变率也越大。影响结果的另一个模型参数是下沉水的温度,这里我们假定为常数(即 $\Pi=\Delta T_\phi/\Delta T=0$,支持这一假定的相关信息参见文献 24)。当取 $\Pi>0$ 时低频变率会略微降低。滞后 1 年的自相关系数是 100 年样本的平均值。模拟时长为 10 万年。温度单位为 ℃。

* W 设为 0(意味着该模式是混合层海洋模式)。

† σ_1 为年均值完整时间序列的标准差。σ_{10} 为非重叠 10 年平均值的标准差。

‡ 90% 的概率位于此界限内。

从表 1 还可看出,在仅有混合层的海洋中($K=0$,$W=0$),其温度的变化比 K 不为零时的值要大得多(从方程(4)中亦可看出)。因此,罗伯克[1] 和汉森等[2] 根据混合层海洋模式得到的模拟结果很可能高估了低频变化的程度,因为这种内部机制也会引起低频变化。

上述结果与气候敏感度参数(即 ΔT_{2x} 或 λ)的值有直接关系,因此,也与检测温室效应对气候的影响问题有关。吉利兰和施奈德[23] 以及威格利和雷珀[17] 早就指出,倘若把观测到的气温变暖仅仅解释为温室效应的信号,将意味着气候的敏感性非常低,$\Delta T_{2x}=1.3\sim 2.0\,℃$(该范围是由模式其他参数的不确定性造成的)。倘若将被动内变率考虑进来,则 ΔT_{2x} 的范围将大大增加,变为 1.0~2.8 ℃。若当前模式大大低估了海洋热惯性的滞后效应,或进一步考虑其他外强迫因子以及内部反馈(比如,大洋环流的变化),则可以得到更高的气候敏感度。由于缺乏适当的数据,上述的各种可能性都无法排除,因此也无法剔除气候敏感度的高值。综上所述,虽然还不能断言我们已明确地探测出了温室效应的影响,但我们对被动内成因变率的考虑实际上已经排除了这种内部机制作为近百年全球变暖单一解释的可能。尽管我们的分析结果使得 ΔT_{2x} 经验值的不确定性增大,但这与大气环流模式估计的 ΔT_{2x} 变化范围

(namely, 1.5–4.5 °C), strengthening the degree of consistency between model predictions and observations.

(**344**, 324-327; 1990)

T. M. L. Wigley and S. C. B. Raper
Climatic Research Unit, University of East Anglia, Norwich NR4 7TJ, UK

Received 4 January; accepted 9 February 1990.

References:

1. Robock, A. *J. Atmos. Sci.* **35**, 1111-1122 (1978).

2. Hansen, J. *et al. J. Geophys. Res.* **93**, 9341-9364 (1988).

3. Jones, P. D., Wigley, T. M. L. & Wright, P. B. *Nature* **322**, 430-434 (1986).

4. Jones, P. D. *Clim. Mon.* **17**, 80-89 (1989).

5. Kelly, P. M. & Sear, C. B. *Nature* **311**, 740-743 (1984).

6. Sear, C. B., Kelly, P. M., Jones, P. D. & Goodess, C. N. *Nature* **330**, 365-367 (1987).

7. Bradley, R. S. *Clim. Change* **12**, 221-243 (1988).

8. Ramanathan, V. *et al. Science* **243**, 57-63 (1989).

9. Hoffert, M. I. & Flannery, B. P. in *Projecting the Climatic Effects of Increasing Carbon Dioxide* (eds MacCracken, M. C. & Luther, F. M.) 149-190 (US Department of Energy, Washington, DC, 1985).

10. Wigley, T. M. L. & Schlesinger, M. E. *Nature* **315**, 649-652 (1985).

11. Schlesinger, M. E. *Clim. Dynam.* **1**, 35-51 (1986).

12. Hasselmann, K. *Tellus* **28**, 473-485 (1976).

13. Lemke, P. *Tellus* **29**, 385-392 (1977).

14. Watts, R. G. *J. Geophys. Res.* **90**, 8067-8070 (1985).

15. Lebedeff, S. A. *J. Geophys. Res.* **93**, 14243-14255 (1988).

16. Morantine, M. & Watts, R. G. *J. Geophys. Res.* (in the press).

17. Wigley. T. M. L. & Raper, S. C. B. *Nature* **330**, 127-131 (1987).

18. Kiehl, J. T. & Dickinson, R. E. *J. Geophys. Res.* **92**, 2991-2998 (1987).

19. Wigley, T. M. L. *Geophys. Res. Lett.* **14**, 1135-1138 (1987).

20. Ropelewski, C. F. & Jones, P. D. *Mon. Weath. Rev.* **115**, 2161-2165 (1987).

21. Wigley, T. M. L. & Jones, P. D. *Nature* **292**, 205-208 (1981).

22. Tsonis, A. A. & Elsner, J. B. *Geophys. Res. Lett.* **16**, 795-797 (1989).

23. Gilliland, R. L. & Schneider, S. H. *Nature* **310**, 38-41 (1984).

24. Harvey, L. D. D. & Schneider, S. H. *J. Geophys. Res.* **90**, 2191-2205 (1985).

Acknowledgements. This work was supported by a grant from the US Department of Energy, Carbon Dioxide Research Division.

（即 1.5~4.5℃）更加一致，增强了模式预测结果与观测值之间的一致性。

（齐红艳 翻译；闻新宇 审稿）

Limits on the Emission of Neutrons, γ-Rays, Electrons and Protons from Pons/Fleischmann Electrolytic Cells

M. H. Salamon *et al.*

Editor's Note

Of the many experiments conducted worldwide to investigate the claim of Martin Fleischmann and Stanley Pons to have carried out nuclear fusion by benchtop electrolysis in 1989, those reported here provided some of the most compelling contrary results. Michael Salamon was a physicist at the same university (Utah) as Pons, and he obtained Pons' agreement to re-run the experiments using the same apparatus. After exhaustive trials, Salamon's team found no evidence of "cold fusion". Pons' claim that excess heat had been generated in one event after a power failure had prevented the computer from collecting data only added to the growing scepticism and suspicion about the original claim. At one point, these experiments provoked threats of legal action against Salamon.

Emissions of γ-rays from the cold-fusion cells used by Pons and Fleischmann were monitored in Pons' laboratory at the University of Utah by NaI detectors nearly continuously over a five-week period. No evidence of fusion activity was observed above power limits varying between 10^{-12} and 10^{-6} W for the known fusion reactions. In addition, neutron-track detectors indicated an integrated upper limit of approximately 1 emitted neutron per second from any of the cold-fusion cells over a period of 67 hours.

PONS and Fleischmann[1] claim to have achieved "cold fusion" of deuterium nuclei in electrolytic cells containing palladium cathodes and D_2O (with 0.1 M LiOD) electrolyte, which produced excess heat of the order of a few watts. Their claim was based on the lack of a known electrochemical mechanism for the observed heat excess and the emission of γ-rays and neutrons at levels slightly above background. These latter data have been criticized[2-4], but reports of tritium production in similar cells[5] and the discrepancy between cell power inputs and outputs in several laboratories[6] have sustained the controversy despite a large number of negative results[4].

The known d + d and d + p reactions and their energy yields (Q) are[7]: d(d, p)t ($Q = 4.03$ MeV); d(d, n)^{3}He ($Q = 3.27$ MeV); d(d, γ)^{4}He ($Q = 23.85$ MeV); d(d, e)^{4}He (internal conversion) ($Q = 23.85$ MeV); d(p, γ)^{3}He ($Q = 5.49$ MeV).

庞斯/弗莱施曼电解池的中子、γ射线、电子和质子发射的上限

萨拉蒙等

编者按

全世界进行了许多实验来研究马丁·弗莱施曼和斯坦利·庞斯所声称的已在 1989 年利用台式电解实现了核聚变的断言，这篇文章中所报道的内容则提供了一些最具说服力的反面结果。迈克尔·萨拉蒙是与庞斯同一所学校（犹他大学）的物理学家，他得到了庞斯的允许，使用同一装置重复了那些实验。在彻底的尝试之后，萨拉蒙的团队没有找到"冷核聚变"的证据。庞斯声称在断电妨碍了计算机收集数据之后，确实有过剩热量产生。这一说法只会增加大家对最初断言的怀疑。这些实验曾一度为萨拉蒙招致诉讼威胁。

犹他大学庞斯的实验室通过 NaI 探测器对庞斯和弗莱施曼使用的冷核聚变电解池放射出的 γ 射线进行了五个星期近乎连续的记录。已知的聚变反应的功率上限是 $10^{-12} \sim 10^{-6}$ W，在这个功率限制之上没有观察到任何聚变活动的证据。此外，中子径迹探测器表明，在 67 小时内，从其中任何一个冷核聚变电解池中发射出来的中子总数上限约为每秒一个中子。

庞斯和弗莱施曼[1] 宣称在含有钯阴极和 D_2O 电解质（含 0.1 M LiOD）的电解池中实现了氘核的"冷核聚变"，该反应产生了数量级为几瓦的过剩热量。他们的结论是基于以下理由得出的：缺乏已知的电化学机制来解释热量过剩以及略微高于本底的 γ 射线和中子的放射。上述数据的后者已经遭到批判[2-4]，尽管存在大量的负面结果[4]，但是在类似的电解池中产生氚的报告[5] 和一些实验室[6] 中电解池输入功率和输出功率之间的差异仍然使得这场论战得以持续。

已知的 d+d 和 d+p 反应和它们的能量产率（Q）为[7]：d(d, p)t（$Q = 4.03$ MeV）；d(d, n)^{3}He（$Q = 3.27$ MeV）；d(d, γ)^{4}He（$Q = 23.85$ MeV）；d(d, e$^-$)^{4}He（内转换）（$Q = 23.85$ MeV）；d(p, γ)^{3}He（$Q = 5.49$ MeV）。

Several weeks after his initial press announcement, Pons allowed us into his laboratory to make independent measurements of any radiation emanating from his operating electrolytic cells. Using equipment that was immediately available, a lead-shielded sodium iodide (NaI) detector (8 × 4 in.) was installed below his cells (Fig. 1) and collected data nearly continuously for over five weeks in a γ-ray energy range of 0.1–25.5 MeV. In addition, several neutron detectors, which integrated the neutron flux over a period of approximately three days, were placed within the water tank adjacent to the cells; these were made of ^{235}U foils sandwiched between nuclear-track-detecting plastic film.

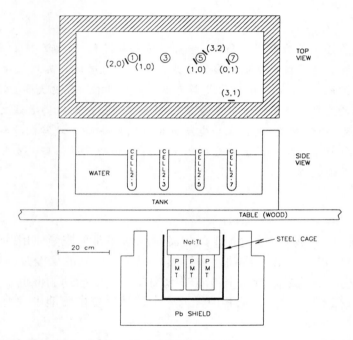

Fig. 1. Side view of the geometry of the electrolytic cells and NaI detector, and top view of the cells with neutron-detecting sandwiches in place (thickline segments). Cells 2-1, 2-5 and 2-7 have palladium cathodes with diameters/lengths (in cm) respectively of 0.4/1.25, 0.4/10.0 and 0.1/10.0; cell 2-3 has a platinum cathode of dimensions 0.1/10.0. The two numbers (n, m) shown for each sandwich in the top view are the number of fission fragments counted in the plastic film adjacent to the uranium foil (without, with) Cd covers. Only one plastic film per foil was analysed.

NaI Detection of γ-Rays

Four open cells (no gas collection) underwent electrolysis nearly continuously while the NaI detector was collecting data (9 May to 16 June). These cells consisted of D_2O (0.1 M LiOD) electrolyte with platinum anodes; the cathodes were as described in Fig. 1. The cells were run in constant-current mode, and current settings were varied over the five-week interval.

The NaI detector system was placed under the table supporting the water tank and cells, so as not to interfere with other research activities in Pons' laboratory. Any γ-rays produced in the cells would thus pass through water, water tank and table before being detected by the

在最初的声明发表之后数周，庞斯允许我们进入他的实验室，对从他运行的电解池中放射的所有辐射进行独立的测量。我们使用的是即时可用装置，将一个铅屏蔽的碘化钠（NaI）探测器（8 in×4 in）安装在他的电解池下方（图 1），并在五周内几乎连续地对能量范围在 0.1~25.5 MeV 之内的 γ 射线进行了数据收集。此外，还将几个中子探测器放置在水槽中，与电解池相邻，它们对大约 3 天的时间段内的中子流进行了累计；这些中子探测器由夹在核径迹探测塑料薄膜之间的 ^{235}U 箔组成。

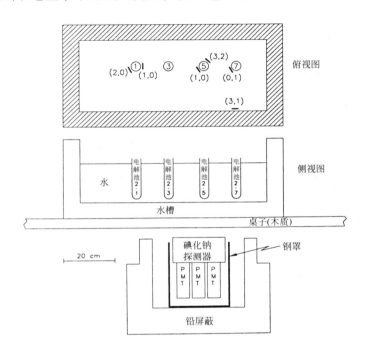

图 1. 电解池和 NaI 探测器布局的侧视图，以及相应位置（粗线部分）的可探测中子的三明治结构的电解池俯视图。电解池 2-1、2-5 和 2-7 的钯阴极直径 / 长度（以厘米为单位）分别为 0.4/1.25、0.4/10.0 和 0.1/10.0；电解池 2-3 有尺寸为 0.1/10.0 的铂阴极。俯视图中每一个三明治结构显示的两个数字 (n, m) 分别是没有镉覆盖层和有镉覆盖层的铀箔塑料薄膜中记录的裂变碎片数目。只分析每个箔中的一个塑料薄膜。

γ 射线的 NaI 探测

让四个开放的电解池（不进行气体收集）近乎连续地进行电解，同时 NaI 探测器在收集数据（5 月 9 日至 6 月 16 日）。这些电解池由 D_2O（0.1 M LiOD）电解质和铂阳极构成；阴极如图 1 所示。电解池在恒电流模式下运行，电流设定值在五周内是变动的。

NaI 探测器系统被放置于支撑水槽和电解池的桌子下方，这样就不会对庞斯实验室里的其他研究活动形成干扰。电解池中产生的任何 γ 射线在被 8 in×4 in 的 NaI

8 × 4 in. NaI detector. The energy-dependent, absolute efficiency for γ-ray detection in the photo-peak (corresponding to complete γ-ray energy conversion within the scintillator) was determined with standard γ-ray sources in a separate laboratory, where an identical configuration of water, tank, table and detector could be installed or removed at will. Radiation limits given below are based on the absolute efficiency for a source at the location of cell 2-1.

Spectral data accumulated by a pulse-height analyser were downloaded to a microcomputer every 0.5 or 1 h (live time) continuously over the five-week observation period, thereby minimizing the effect of integrated background on transient signals. The system's gain was set so that γ-rays in the energy interval 0.1–25.5 MeV were recorded. An aggregate spectrum corresponding to 785 h of operation is shown in Fig. 2a, b.

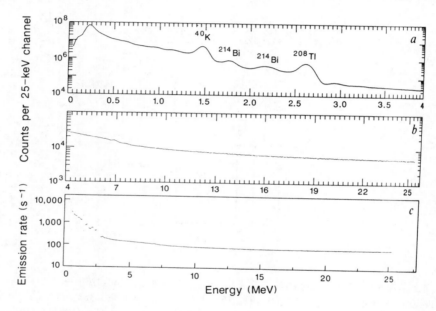

Fig. 2. *a, b*, Aggregate γ-ray spectrum for 785 h of live collection time. The dominant background lines are [40]K (1.4608 MeV), [214]Bi (1.7645 Mev), [208]Tl (2.6146 MeV), a backscatter peak at ~0.23 MeV, and a broad peak at ~2.17 MeV due to two lines, [214]Bi (2.1186, 2.2042 MeV). The detector energy resolution is given by $R = 0.07E^{-1/2}(1+1.3/E)^{1/2}$, with E in MeV, where the leading factor is the detector's optimal resolution and the additional factor is caused by the presence of noise at the charge-integrating input of the pulse-height analyser's analog-to-digital converter. The integral nonlinearity of the system electronics was found to be <0.1% over the interval 0.1–3.5 MeV, and 0.2% over the full interval 0.1–25.5 MeV. System gain variations (owing to phototube drift, for example) were monitored and found to be <3.5% over the full five-week interval and <0.5% over any 24-h interval; *c*, γ-ray source emission-rate limit against energy for the general γ-ray search over the range 0.1–25.5 MeV (see text). The probability of falsely rejecting a signal at these limits is <10⁻³.

Individual spectra (1,116), each of 0.5 or 1.0 h live integration time (for a total of 831.0 h of live time), were searched for transient γ-ray signals above background. Background for each individual spectrum was obtained by averaging several (10–50) successive spectra to

探测器探测到以前，都会先通过水、水槽和桌子。在光电峰中对 γ 射线进行探测的与能量有关的绝对效率（与在闪烁体中 γ 射线完全的能量转换相对应）可在一个独立实验室中用标准 γ 射线源进行确认，该独立实验室中可对水、水槽、桌子和探测器进行同样的配置和任意的去除。下面给出的辐射限是基于放置在电解池 2-1 处的源的绝对效率得到的。

将通过脉冲高度分析仪累积的 γ 谱数据在五周的观察时间内每隔半小时或者 1 小时（活时间）连续地下载到一台微机上，从而将瞬态信号的本底累积效应降至最低。设定了系统的增益以使 0.1~25.5 MeV 能量区间内的 γ 射线可以被记录下来。仪器运行 785 小时所得到的累积 γ 谱如图 2a 和 2b 所示。

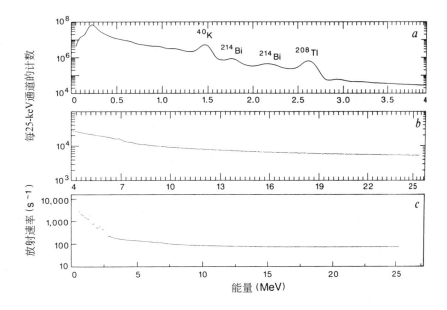

图 2. a 和 b, 785 小时的活时间收集的累积 γ 射线谱。主要的本底峰为 ^{40}K（1.4608 MeV）、^{214}Bi（1.7645 MeV）和 ^{208}Tl（2.6146 MeV），而一个约 0.23 MeV 处的背散射峰和一个约 2.17 MeV 处的宽峰源自 ^{214}Bi 的两个峰（2.1186 MeV 和 2.2042 MeV）。探测器能量分辨率由 $R = 0.07E^{-1/2}(1+1.3/E)^{1/2}$ 给出，E 的单位为 MeV，式中的主导因素是探测器的最优分辨率，附加的因素是由于脉冲高度分析仪的模数转换器的电荷积分输入存在噪音而导致的。系统电子部件的积分非线性在 0.1~3.5 MeV 的区间内小于 0.1%，在整个 0.1~25.5 MeV 区间为 0.2%。对系统增益变化（比如由于光电流漂移）的监测表明，在整个五周的时间内，变化小于 3.5%，而在任何 24 小时区间内，变化小于 0.5%；c，在 0.1~25.5 MeV 的范围内，对全体 γ 射线进行搜寻得到的 γ 射线源的放射速率限值与能量的关系（见正文部分）。在这些限值以内的信号被漏记的概率小于 10^{-3}。

逐条 γ 谱（1,116 条）、逐段时间（每一段活时间积分的时长为 0.5 或 1 小时，活时间共计 831.0 小时）地寻找瞬时高于本底的 γ 射线信号。每条 γ 谱的本底要用若干（10~50）条连续的本底 γ 谱取平均而得到一个合成 γ 谱来求得，然后，从原始的

form an aggregate spectrum, which was then subtracted from the original spectrum to form a "residual spectrum". This was performed for each individual spectrum, yielding 1,116 residual spectra. Any transient anomalous signals of duration <10–50 h would then appear in the residual spectra as positive excesses amidst Poisson fluctuations about zero. Signals of longer duration were searched for with even greater sensitivity by performing a similar operation on the collection of aggregate spectra.

To correct for temporal variations in the detector system's gain and pedestal (the pulse-height-analyser channel corresponding to zero energy), the gain and pedestal were determined for each individual spectrum by fitting to the background γ-ray lines. All spectra were then rescaled to a common gain with zero offset before background subtraction, thus minimizing artefacts in the residual spectra arising from gain or zero shifts, or both.

Neutron flux limits: $d(d, n)^3He$. Neutrons from the $d(d, n)^3He$ fusion channel have an initial kinetic energy of 2.45 MeV and a mean free path in water of 4.9 cm, which decreases to ~0.4 cm as the neutron thermalizes. Because each cell is surrounded by several inches of water, most neutrons emitted would thermalize in the surrounding water bath and generate a 2.22-MeV γ-ray from the $n(p, d)\gamma$ reaction; Monte Carlo calculations show for a point source of 2.45-MeV neutrons located at cell 2-1 that 62% of the emitted neutrons would be captured by hydrogen in the water bath. The absolute photopeak detection efficiency (for cell 2-1), measured with a Am-Be neutron source, was found to be 3.0×10^{-3}.

The presence of a γ-ray signal above background at 2.2 MeV was sought in each residual spectrum by fitting a gaussian (of central energy 2.2 MeV and variance determined by detector resolution) to the residual spectrum in the energy interval 2.0–2.4 MeV. The frequency distribution of the fitted amplitudes, in units of pW of fusion power, is shown in Fig. 3a. Of these 1,114 spectra, the maximum fitted amplitude is 10 pW. In this distribution (and others following) we have excluded two spectra that contained photopeaks due to ^{22}Na and ^{137}Cs sources brought into the laboratory by other personnel.

γ 谱中扣去此本底而得到"剩余谱"。对于每条 γ 谱进行这一扣除后就得到 1,116 条剩余谱。于是，在小于 10～50 小时内任何瞬时的异常信号都会在剩余谱中以零点附近一片泊松涨落之上的正剩余的形式显示出来。持续时间更长的信号还可以通过对合成 γ 谱的集合进行相似的操作来寻找，而且其灵敏度还更高些。

为了能够对探测器系统的增益和消隐脉冲电平（对应于能量为零的脉冲高度分析仪的通道）的短暂变化进行校正，通过把每一个单独的 γ 谱对 γ 射线本底进行拟合的方法来对增益和消隐脉冲电平进行确定。然后在扣除本底之前，所有的 γ 谱被重新调节到通常具有零偏置的增益水平，这样可以减小剩余 γ 谱中由增益或零点漂移或者两者兼而有之所带来的伪差。

中子流的限值：d(d, n)³He　来自核聚变通道 d(d, n)³He 的中子具有 2.45 MeV 的初始动能和在水中 4.9 cm 的平均自由程，由于中子热化，它的自由程会缩减为 0.4 cm。由于每一个电解池都被数英寸的水浴包围，大多数放射出的中子会在周围的水浴中热化并通过 n(p, d)γ 反应产生 2.22 MeV 的 γ 射线；蒙特卡洛计算表明，对位于 2-1 电解池处的 2.45 MeV 的点中子源而言，62% 放射出的中子会被水浴中的氢捕获。通过一个 Am-Be 中子源测得，绝对的光电峰探测效率（对 2-1 电解池）为 3.0×10^{-3}。

通过对 2.0～2.4 MeV 能量区间的剩余 γ 谱进行高斯拟合（以 2.2 MeV 为中心能量，方差由探测器分辨率确定），每一个剩余 γ 谱中都可以观察到一个位于 2.2 MeV 处的高于本底的 γ 射线信号。拟合幅值的频数分布以 pW 为核聚变功率的单位，如图 3a 所示。在这 1,114 个 γ 谱中，拟合出的最大幅值为 10 pW。在这个分布（以及后面其他的分布）中我们排除了两个图谱，因为它们含有来自 ²²Na 和 ¹³⁷Cs 源的光电峰，这是由于其他人将这两种放射源带入实验室造成的。

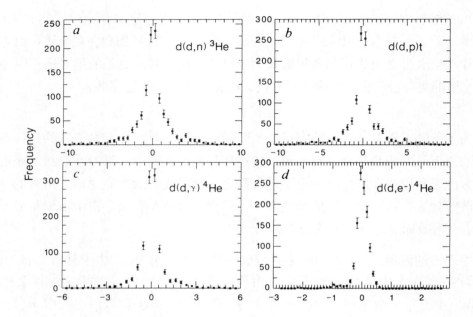

Fig. 3. Estimated rates for the four d + d fusion reactions. For each of the 1,114 γ-ray spectra obtained from data-collection episodes lasting 0.5–1 h, a residual spectrum was obtained by subtracting an averaged background spectrum from the signal. A fit was then made to each residual by scaling the expected form of the γ-ray spectrum for each reaction; the fit yields a magnitude that can be positive or negative. The figures here are histograms of those 1,114 magnitudes. In *a* and *b*, the rate is expressed in units of fusion power (*a*: pW; *b*: mW); for *c* and *d*, reaction rates are used (*c*: s^{-1}; *d*: 10^3 s^{-1}). In each case the histogram is approximately a gaussian distribution of amplitudes centred around zero, indicating no measurable rates for any of the fusion reactions.

Proton flux limits: d(d, p)t. The fusion channel d(d, p)t ($Q = 4.03$ MeV) has been a leading candidate for the cold-fusion process, both because of reports of excess tritium production[5] and because its reaction products come to rest within the palladium electrode (the range of a 3-MeV proton in palladium is ~ 30 μm; ref. 8), thereby presumably avoiding the paradox of watts of fusion power being generated without observed particle emissions. In fact, a strong and distinct γ-ray signature exists for this reaction: the 3.02-MeV protons cause Coulomb excitation of the even–even isotopes of Pd, whose radiative de-excitations, between 0.37 and 0.56 MeV, are detectable by the NaI detector with efficiencies η given in Table 1. This table, adapted from ref. 9, lists for each Pd isotope its E2 (electric quadrupole) γ-ray energy and thick-target radiation yield (excitations per microcoulomb of protons) for 100% isotopically enriched samples, along with photopeak detection efficiency assuming cell 2-1 as the source, plus a factor accounting for absorption of the E2 γ-ray within the Pd cathode. Figure 4 shows a NaI γ-ray spectrum from a 3-mm target of natural Pd exposed to a beam of 3.02-MeV protons from a Van de Graaf accelerator (W. Schier, personal communication). Peaks at 0.37, 0.43 and 0.51 MeV are observed with their expected strengths.

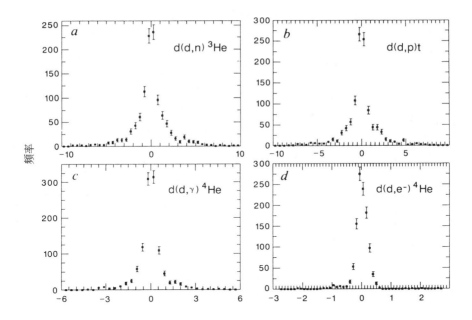

图 3. 对四个 d + d 核聚变反应估算的速率。对于数据采集区间持续 0.5~1 小时的 1,114 条 γ 射线谱中的每一条，从信号中减去平均化的本底 γ 谱可以得到一条剩余 γ 谱。通过调节每一个反应的已知形式的 γ 射线谱的比例，对每一个剩余光谱进行拟合；拟合得到的数量级可以为正也可以为负。这里的图是所有 1,114 条 γ 谱的柱状图。在 a 和 b 中，速率以聚变的功率为单位（a: pW; b: mW）; c 和 d 中，反应速率为通常使用的单位（c: s^{-1}; d: $10^3\,s^{-1}$）。每一个图中，柱状图大致呈现为零点附近的高斯分布，表明对于任何一个核聚变反应没有可测量的速率。

质子流的限值：d(d, p)t 核聚变通道 d(d, p)t（Q = 4.03 MeV）是冷核聚变过程的一个最有可能的反应，这既是因为有过量氚产生的报告 [5]，也是因为它的反应产物被固定在了钯电极中（3 MeV 的质子在钯中的范围约为 30 μm；参考文献 8），因此有可能避免"产生了瓦特量级的聚变功率却没有观察到粒子发射"的佯谬。事实上，一个强而明显的 γ 射线特征存在于这一反应中：3.02 MeV 的质子导致钯同位素偶-偶核的库仑激发，退激发时它辐射出的 0.37 MeV 到 0.56 MeV 之间的辐射可以被 NaI 探测器以表 1 中给出的效率 η 探测到。这个表由参考文献 9 改编而来，列出了每一种钯同位素的 E2（电四极）γ 射线的能量和 100% 同位素富集的样品的厚靶辐射产额（每微库仑质子的激发量），同时还假设了电解池 2-1 为源的光电峰探测效率，并考虑到在钯阴极内部 E2 γ 射线吸收的修正因子。图 4 显示了一个从暴露在源自范德格拉夫加速器的 3.02 MeV 质子束中的 3 mm 的天然钯靶所放射出的 NaI γ 射线谱（希尔，个人交流）。在 0.37 MeV、0.43 MeV 和 0.51 MeV 处观察到了峰值，并且与预期的强度一致。

Table 1. Radiation yields of 3-MeV protons in palladium electrodes

Isotope (E2 energy) (MeV)	Isotopic fraction	Proton energy (MeV)	Excitation/μC	NaI detector efficiency η	Pd escape probability
^{104}Pd(0.555)	11.0	3.30	$5.08(0.16)\times10^5$	2.3×10^{-3}	0.81
		2.40	$4.35(0.17)\times10^4$		
^{106}Pd(0.513)	27.3	3.30	$7.47(0.18)\times10^5$	2.3×10^{-3}	0.80
		3.00	$4.00(0.12)\times10^5$		
		2.70	$1.98(0.06)\times10^5$		
^{108}Pd(0.433)	26.7	3.30	$1.19(0.03)\times10^6$	2.2×10^{-3}	0.77
		3.00	$7.02(0.19)\times10^5$		
		2.70	$3.76(0.08)\times10^5$		
^{110}Pd(0.374)	11.8	3.30	$1.82(0.04)\times10^6$	2.1×10^{-3}	0.73
		3.00	$1.11(0.02)\times10^6$		
		2.70	$6.15(0.13)\times10^5$		

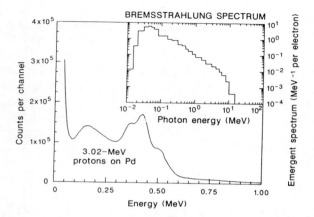

Fig. 4. Electric-quadrupole (E2) γ-ray lines from the isotopes of Pd, excited by 3.02-MeV protons, as measured by a 3 × 3 in. NaI detector. Three lines at 0.37, 0.43 and 0.51 MeV constitute a clear γ-ray signature for the reaction d(d, p)t (a fourth line at 0.56 MeV from ^{104}Pd is too weak to be seen here). Their collective backscatter peak is at ~0.16 MeV. Inset: The emergent bremsstrahlung spectrum for an electron emitted at 20 MeV at the centre of a cylinder of H_2O, of height 36 cm and diameter 36 cm. The normalization is for a single electron, with the γ-ray flux integrated over the cylinder surface; the area under the spectrum corresponds to 1.1 photons per electron, including a small δ-function contribution of 0.511-MeV annihilation quanta not shown in the figure. This spectrum was obtained using the Monte Carlo code ETRAN[15], which treats the coupled electron–photon transport using a recently developed set of bremsstrahlung cross-sections[16].

Convolving these line strengths with the resolution of the NaI detector, and using the efficiency factors from Table 1, a theoretically generated spectrum was scaled to optimally fit the 0.362–0.613-MeV region of each residual spectrum. The frequency distribution of the 1,114 fitted scaling factors (in units of mW of fusion power) is shown in Fig. 3b. None of the scaling factors exceeds 10 mW. This limit is comparable to the sensitivity of the calorimetric measurements made on these cells.

表 1. 3 MeV 的质子在钯电极中的辐射产额

同位素（E2 能量）(MeV)	同位素丰度	质子能量（MeV）	激发/μC	NaI 探测器效率 η	钯的逃逸概率
^{104}Pd(0.555)	11.0	3.30	$5.08(0.16) \times 10^5$	2.3×10^{-3}	0.81
		2.40	$4.35(0.17) \times 10^4$		
^{106}Pd(0.513)	27.3	3.30	$7.47(0.18) \times 10^5$	2.3×10^{-3}	0.80
		3.00	$4.00(0.12) \times 10^5$		
		2.70	$1.98(0.06) \times 10^5$		
^{108}Pd(0.433)	26.7	3.30	$1.19(0.03) \times 10^6$	2.2×10^{-3}	0.77
		3.00	$7.02(0.19) \times 10^5$		
		2.70	$3.76(0.08) \times 10^5$		
^{110}Pd(0.374)	11.8	3.30	$1.82(0.04) \times 10^6$	2.1×10^{-3}	0.73
		3.00	$1.11(0.02) \times 10^6$		
		2.70	$6.15(0.13) \times 10^5$		

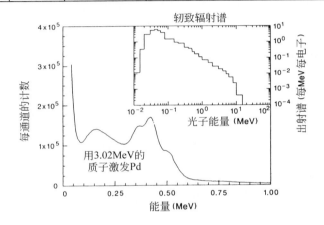

图 4. 来自钯同位素的电四极（E2）γ射线峰，通过 3.02 MeV 的质子激发，用 3 in×3 in 的 NaI 探测器测量。0.37 MeV、0.43 MeV 和 0.51 MeV 处的三个峰构成了 d(d, p)t 反应清晰的 γ射线特征（0.56 MeV处 ^{104}Pd 的第四峰很弱，在这里难以看清）。它们共有的背散射峰在约 0.16 MeV 处。插图：从一个高 36 cm、直径 36 cm 的水柱中心出射的在 20 MeV 处的电子的出射轫致辐射谱。对单个电子进行归一化，将 γ射线流沿柱状体的表面积分；光谱下的面积对应于每电子 1.1 个光子，包括 0.511 MeV 的湮灭光子的 δ 函数导致的一小部分（没有在图中显示）。这个 γ谱使用蒙特卡洛代码 ETRAN[15] 得到，该代码使用最近发展的轫致辐射截面方法[16] 对耦合的电子－光子输运进行了处理。

以 NaI 探测器的分辨率对这些峰强度进行卷积，并使用表 1 中的有效因子，对理论产生的 γ谱按比例进行缩放以使其与每个剩余 γ谱的 0.362~0.613 MeV 区域拟合最佳。1,114 个拟合比例因子(以聚变功率的 mW 为单位)的频数分布示于图 3b 中。没有一个比例因子超过 10 mW。这个限值与在这些电解池上进行的量热测量的灵敏度相似。

More stringent limits can be placed on this channel by recognizing that the tritium, emitted with kinetic energy of 1.0 MeV, can initiate the t(d, n)^{4}He reaction. By integrating the energy-dependent reaction cross-section[10] over the range of the tritium within the Pd, we obtain a d + t fusion probability of 4×10^{-5} per emitted tritium, assuming a 1:1 d:Pd ratio in the lattice. (We note that the probability p that a 1.0-MeV triton will produce a neutron within a deuterated palladium lattice via the reaction t(d, n)^{4}He can be expressed as a function of r, the deuterium-to-palladium ratio (by number): $p = a_0 + a_1 r + a_2 r^2$, where $a_0 = 9.63 \times 10^{-8}$, $a_1 = 4.48 \times 10^{-5}$ and $a_2 = -5.40 \times 10^{-6}$. This expression, based on nuclear cross-sections from ref. 10 and hydrogen stopping power from ref. 17, is accurate to $\leqslant 10\%$ and is valid for $0.4 \leqslant r \leqslant 1.5$.) Monte Carlo calculations show that 39% of the resulting $\sim$14-MeV (centre-of-mass) neutrons will thermalize and be captured by protons within the water tank, yielding a 2.2-MeV γ-ray signal. From the absence of this signal, we obtain an upper limit of the fusion power amplitude of 0.4 μW.

γ-ray flux limits: d(d, γ)^{4}He, d(p, γ)^{3}He, monoenergetic γ. A search was performed for 23.85-MeV γ-ray from d(d, γ)^{4}He by fitting the expected line profile of a 23.85-MeV γ-ray to the residual spectra over the energy interval 23.6–24.1 MeV. Figure 3c shows the resulting distribution of fitted source emission rates; the maximum fitted rate is 5 s^{-1}, corresponding to a fusion power of 20 pW. A similar search was performed for 5.49-MeV γ-rays from d(p, γ)^{3}He; the maximum fitted source emission rate of 10 s^{-1} corresponds to a fusion power of $\sim$10 pW.

A general search was also performed throughout the entire 0.1–25.5-MeV energy interval for possible γ-ray lines above background in each residual spectrum. Candidates were required to have at least one channel with counts in excess of 3σ (σ being the propagated Poisson error for that channel's count) and a summed excess of 9σ in the adjacent channels spanning the full width at half maximum of a γ-ray peak at the sampled energy. The only candidates found were due to imperfect rescaling of the spectrum's gain and zero relative to averaged background; these were identified by the presence of adjacent positive and negative excursions of equal magnitude, with a zero-crossing at a known background peak position. No other candidate γ-ray lines were found. Allowing for detector efficiency, this yields the relationship between γ-ray emission-rate limit and energy (for cell 2-1) shown in Fig. 2c.

Internal-conversion electron flux limits: d(d, e$^-$)^{4}He. Even though nuclear de-excitation by internal conversion is greatly suppressed relative to radiative de-excitation for low-atomic-mass nuclei and for photon energies much greater than the electron mass, it has been suggested that cold fusion may in fact be occurring via internal conversion[11], which would produce an electron that carries off 23.8 MeV in kinetic energy.

Figure 4 shows the calculated bremsstrahlung spectrum emerging from a point-isotropic source of 20-MeV electrons located at the centre of a cylinder of water 36 cm in diameter ($\sim$4 MeV are assumed to have been lost within the Pd cathode[12]). The spectrum, normalized to one source electron, has an integrated area of 1.1 photons per electron.

通过认定以动能 1.0 MeV 放射出来的氚能够引发 t(d, n)⁴He 反应，可以确定这个通道更为严谨的限值。通过对钯中氚的能量范围内能量依赖反应的截面[10]进行积分，假设晶格中 d∶Pd 的比例为 1∶1，每发射一个氚引发 d + t 聚变的概率为 4×10^{-5}。（我们注意到 1.0 MeV 的氚核在氘化钯的晶格中通过反应 t(d, n)⁴He 产生一个中子的概率 p 可以表达为氚与钯之比（原子数之比）r 的函数：$p = a_0 + a_1 r + a_2 r^2$，其中 $a_0 = 9.63 \times 10^{-8}$，$a_1 = 4.48 \times 10^{-5}$，$a_2 = -5.40 \times 10^{-6}$。这个表达式是基于参考文献 10 中的核反应截面和文献 17 中的氢的遏止率得到的，其精度 ≤10%，在 $0.4 \leqslant r \leqslant 1.5$ 范围内有效。）蒙特卡罗计算显示，得到的约 14 MeV（质心）的中子中，39% 会热化并被水槽中的质子捕获，得到一个 2.2 MeV 的 γ 射线信号。从这一信号的缺失情况来看，我们得到核聚变功率幅值的上限为 0.4 μW。

γ 射线流的限值：d(d, γ)⁴He，d(p, γ)³He，单能 γ 射线 通过将预期的 23.85 MeV 的 γ 射线谱线轮廓对剩余 γ 谱在 23.6~24.1 MeV 能量区间内进行拟合，来搜索来自反应 d(d, γ)⁴He 的 23.85 MeV γ 射线。图 3c 显示了源发射速率分布的拟合结果；最大拟合速率为 $5\ \mathrm{s}^{-1}$，对应的核聚变功率为 20 pW。对 d(p, γ)³He 反应放出的 5.49 MeV 的 γ 射线也进行了类似的搜索；最大的源放射拟合速率 $10\ \mathrm{s}^{-1}$ 对应于约 10 pW 的核聚变功率。

在每个剩余 γ 谱中对整个 0.1~25.5 MeV 能量区间内高于本底的可能 γ 射线峰进行了总体搜寻。符合条件的可能情况需要有至少一个通道计数高于 3σ（σ 为那个通道计数的传递泊松误差），并且延展到取样能量处 γ 射线峰的半高宽的临近通道计数和要大于 9σ。找到的唯一可能的 γ 射线峰是由于 γ 谱增益不完善的缩放和平均本底零点不准而造成的；这些可以通过其邻近的正漂移和负漂移的数量级相同，以及在一个已知的本底峰的位置过零点，来进行识别。没有发现其他的可能的 γ 射线峰。结合探测器效率，得到了 γ 射线放射速率限值和能量的相互关系（对电解池 2-1 而言），如图 2c 所示。

内转换电子流的限值：d(d, e⁻)⁴He 即使对于低原子量的核以及光子能量远高于电子质量的情形，内转换引起的核退激相对于辐射退激是被大大地抑制了的，仍有人认为冷核聚变实际上可以通过内转换发生[11]，这一过程会产生携带有 23.8 MeV 动能的电子。

图 4 显示了计算出的一个位于 36 cm 直径的水圆柱体中心各向同性的 20 MeV 电子点源所产生的轫致辐射光谱（假定在钯阴极内有约 4 MeV 的损失[12]）。归一化到一个源电子，光谱拥有的积分面积为每电子 1.1 个光子。这个轫致辐射光谱，经

This bremsstrahlung spectrum, modified by detector efficiency, was scaled to obtain an optimal fit to each residual spectrum, giving a best-fit number of bremsstrahlung photons for each spectrum. Figure 3d shows the frequency distribution of the electron emission rate corresponding to the fitted bremsstrahlung photon number. The maximum fitted election emission rate, 2.6×10^3 electrons per second, corresponds to a fusion power level of 10 nW.

Neutron Detection with Nuclear Track Detectors

A significantly lower limit than the 10 pW discussed above on the mean neutron production rate during a 67-h interval (16–19 May) was obtained with neutron-detecting sandwiches made of ^{235}U-enriched (80%) uranium foils and nuclear-track-detecting plastic, Lexan polycarbonate. Six sandwiches were installed in the water tank containing the cells (Fig. 1); each consisted of two uranium foils, each with an area of 1.4 cm^2 and mass ~0.078 g, held between two pieces of 0.01-in.-thick Lexan polycarbonate. One of the two foils was shielded against slow neutrons (<0.5 eV) by two cadmium covers.

The fission capture cross-section for ^{235}U is 1.4 barn at 2.5 MeV, increasing to 580 barn at thermal energies. Some of the neutrons emitted at 2.45 MeV from the cells will be captured by ^{235}U nuclei during their diffusion within the water bath. The fission fragments have a typical range of a few micrometres in U; those that escape the foil enter the plastic film and rupture polymer bonds, thereby creating a nuclear track that can be viewed microscopically after chemical etching with NaOH (ref. 13). (The track registration threshold of Lexan is such that the numerous α particles produced by the ^{238}U component of the U foils do not produce visible tracks.)

The absolute neutron detection efficiency was measured with a ^{252}Cf source in a large water tank, with foil sandwiches placed relative to the source identically to those in Pons' laboratory, and was found to be 1.3×10^{-5} fission tracks per emitted neutron for a foil with no Cd cover; for those foils with Cd covers, the efficiency was a factor of about three lower.

Fission track counts for each sandwich's pair of foils are shown in Fig. 1, the first number being the count for the foil without a Cd cover and the second being that with. There was no indication of an excess neutron signal from any of the cells; in fact, the control sandwich, adjacent to the water-tank wall, registered one of the highest fission-track counts, these being a measure of the dominant background source, cosmic-ray neutrons[14]. If we assume zero background, however, the fission track counts at cell 2-5 correspond to a mean neutron emission rate of 0.8 s^{-1} over the 67-h integration period, with a 99% confidence-level upper limit on neutron emission rate from cell 2-5 (based on counts in foils without Cd covers) of 1.8 s^{-1}, corresponding to a fusion power level of 0.9 pW.

Pons has informed us that "no neutron detectors were ever placed in a tank when a cell in that tank was generating excess enthalpy".

过探测器效率修正后，调整其比例以得到对每一剩余光谱的最佳拟合，从而给出每一个光谱最佳拟合的轫致辐射光子的数目。图 3d 显示对应于拟合的轫致辐射光子数目的电子发射速率频数分布。电子发射速率的最大拟合值为每秒 2.6×10^3 个电子，对应于核聚变功率水平为 10 nW。

使用核径迹探测器的中子探测

通过由富集 ^{235}U（80%）铀箔和核径迹探测塑料（即莱克森聚碳酸酯）组成的中子探测三明治结构，得到了一个明显小于 10 pW 的上限，这个值是根据前面讨论的基于 67 小时区间（5 月 16 日至 19 日）的平均中子产率得到的。六个三明治结构被安装在了含有电解池的水槽中（图 1）；每一个含有两层铀箔，每一层铀箔面积约为 1.4 cm^2，质量约为 0.078 g，夹在两层 0.01 in 厚的莱克森聚碳酸酯之间。两片铀箔之一用两层镉屏蔽掉慢中子（<0.5 eV）。

^{235}U 的裂变捕获截面在 2.5 MeV 处为 1.4 靶恩，在热能下增大到 580 靶恩。一些从电解池中放射的 2.45 MeV 的中子在水浴里扩散期间会被 ^{235}U 捕获。裂变碎片在铀中有一个数微米的长度范围；那些逃离铀箔的裂变碎片会进入塑料薄膜并破坏高分子化学键，从而产生一个核径迹，该径迹经 NaOH 腐蚀后可以通过显微镜观察到（参考文献 13）。（莱克森聚碳酸酯的径迹记录阈值使得铀箔中的 ^{238}U 组分产生的为数众多的 α 粒子不会产生可见的径迹。）

通过一个位于大水槽中的 ^{252}Cf 源对绝对的中子探测效率进行了测量，箔的三明治结构相对于源的放置位置与庞斯实验室的装置位置相同，结果在没有镉覆盖层的箔，每个放射的中子有 1.3×10^{-5} 个裂变径迹；对那些有镉覆盖层的箔，效率变为原来的 $\frac{1}{3}$。

每一对由薄膜组成的三明治结构的裂变径迹计数如图 1 所示，第一个数字是没有镉覆盖层的箔，第二个对应有镉覆盖层的箔。没有迹象表明从任何一个电解池中曾放射出电中子本底高出 1 个中子的信号；实际上在临近水槽壁、用于对照的三明治结构中，记录到一个最高的裂变径迹计数，这些是对主要的本底源——宇宙射线中子[14] 的测量。然而，如果我们假定本底为零，电解池 2-5 的裂变径迹计数在 67 小时积分区间内对应的平均中子发射速率就为 0.8 s^{-1}，来自电解池 2-5 的中子放射速率的上限置信水平为 99%，（基于没有镉覆盖层的箔所得的计数）为 1.8 s^{-1}，对应的核聚变功率水平为 0.9 pW。

庞斯已经告知我们"当水槽中的电解池产生过剩焓时，水槽中并没有放置过中子探测器"。

Fusion Limits and Excess Heat Production

During the 831 h (live time) of monitoring γ-ray emissions from electrolytic cells in Pons' laboratory, no evidence was seen of radiation from any known d + d (or p + d) fusion reaction. The upper limits placed on power from these reactions range between 10^{-12} and 10^{-6} W, which are many orders of magnitude lower than the sensitivity of the calorimetric measurements made by Pons' group; therefore, if a heat excess were to have occurred during our period of observation, one could conclude that no known fusion process contributed significantly to that excess.

At one point, the D_2O in cell 2-1 was observed to boil for ~2 h. Figure 5*a* shows an aggregate γ-ray spectrum for the 2.5 h that included this boiling episode, and Fig. 5*b* is the residual spectrum after subtraction of the previous 2.5 h of data. No spectral features of fusion are present in this residual spectrum. After completing our analysis, we were informed that we should not "reference these events as being due to release of excess thermal energy" (S. Pons, personal communication), because this boiling event may very well have a conventional explanation. Unfortunately we have not received any numerical data on excess heat production during the 831 h of our monitoring, so we are not able to correlate the absence of nuclear signatures with the presence of anomalous heat.

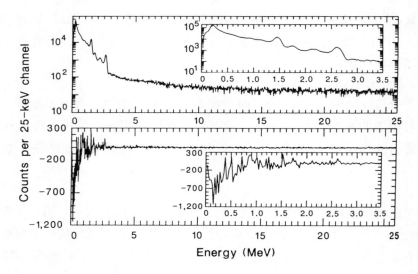

Fig. 5. *a*, γ-ray spectrum accumulated over a 2.5-h interval that included a ~2-h period during which cell 2-1 was observed to boil the D_2O electrolyte. The inset is an expansion of the low-energy end of the spectrum. *b*, Residual spectrum after subtraction of the spectrum accumulated for the preceding 2.5 h. The negative excess at low energy is due to a slight (0.1%) gain shift that occurred during this 5-h period (these spectra were not rescaled).

We were told, however, that "there was a two-hour segment in which there was excessive thermal release from cell 2-1... Unfortunately, your computer and detector were not under power at that time since they had not been reset from a power failure which had occurred in the lab" (S. Pons, personal communication). Although 48 h of data were

核聚变限值和过剩热量的产生

在庞斯实验室中监测电解池 γ 射线放射的 831 小时（活时间）期间，没有发现任何已知的 d + d（或 p + d）核聚变反应辐射的证据。这些反应的功率上限在 10^{-12} W 到 10^{-6} W 之间，这比庞斯研究组进行的量热测量的灵敏度低很多个数量级；因此，如果在我们的观察期间发生热量过剩，我们能够得出的结论是，没有已知的核聚变过程对这一过剩有明显贡献。

我们曾一度观察到电解池 2-1 中的 D_2O 沸腾了约 2 小时。图 5a 显示了包括这个沸腾过程的 2.5 小时的累积 γ 射线谱，图 b 是减去沸腾开始之前 2.5 小时的数据后的剩余 γ 谱，剩余 γ 谱没有出现核聚变的 γ 谱特征。在完成我们的分析之后，我们被告知我们不应该"把这些事件归因于有过量热能释放"（庞斯，个人交流），因为对这个沸腾的事件可以有一个很好的传统解释。不幸的是，在我们监测的 831 小时期间，我们并没有获得任何关于过剩热量产生的计算数据，所以我们不能够将核信号的缺失与异常热量的存在关联起来。

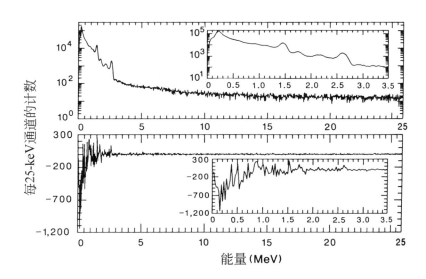

图 5. *a*，累积 2.5 小时的 γ 射线谱。其中包括一个约 2 小时的区间，在此期间在电解池 2-1 中观察到了 D_2O 电解质沸腾。插图是对 γ 谱低能端的放大。*b*，扣除沸腾开始之前 2.5 小时累积的 γ 谱之后的剩余 γ 谱。低能量处的负盈余是源于发生在整个 5 小时期间的一个微小的（0.1%）增益漂移（这些 γ 谱没有经过再标定）。

然而，我们被告知"曾经有两个小时的时间段内电解池 2-1 有过剩的热量释放……不幸的是，当时你们的计算机和探测器并没有在工作，因为在实验室发生断电之后，它们没有得到重启"（庞斯，个人交流）。尽管因为雷击，48 小时的数据确实丢失了，然而我们能估算出在这 2 小时的时段内，核聚变能量的平均上限对于

indeed lost because of a lightning strike, we can nevertheless estimate mean upper limits for fusion power of $\sim 10^{-2}$ W for d(d, p)t and 10^{-6} W for d(d, n)^{3}He during this 2-h episode, because a fraction of the neutrons produced from these reactions would activate the ^{23}Na in the NaI detector, producing ^{24}Na. As ^{24}Na decays with a 15.0-h half-life, a spectral signature of a neutron burst would be present even several days after the burst. None was observed, leading to the conclusion that neither the d(d, p)t nor the d(d, n)^{3}He reaction was responsible for this anomalous heat burst.

In addition, we later learned that a low-level, d.c. heat excess was observed during our monitoring period (S. Pons, EPRI Conference, University of Utah, 16 August 1989); if this is the case, this excess did not originate from known nuclear processes.

(**344**, 401-405; 1990)

M. H. Salamon*, M. E. Wrenn†, H. E. Bergeson*, K. C. Crawford‡, W. H. Delaney*†, C. L. Henderson†‡, Y. Q. Li*, J. A. Rusho*, G. M. Sandquist‡ & S. M. Seltzer§
* Department of Physics, † Environmental Radiation and Toxicology Laboratory and ‡ Nuclear Engineering Department, University of Utah, Salt Lake City, Utah 84112, USA
§ National Institute of Standards and Technology, Gaithersburg, Maryland 20899, USA

Received 26 September 1989; accepted 30 January 1990.

References:

1. Fleischmann, M., Pons, S. & Hawkins, M. *J. electroanalyt. Chem.* **261**, 301-308(1989); and erratum, **263**, 187-188 (1989).

2. Petrasso, R. D. *et al. Nature* **339**, 183-185(1989); and erratum, **339**, 264 (1989).

3. Fleischmann, M., Pons, S. & Hoffman, R. J. *Nature* **339**, 667 (1989).

4. Petrasso, R. D. *et al. Nature* **339**, 667-669 (1989).

5. Wolf, K. *et al. Proc. Workshop on Cold Fusion* Santa Fe, May 23-25, (1989).

6. *Proc. Workshop on Cold Fusion* Santa Fe, May 23-25, (1989).

7. Zel'dovich, Ya. B. & Gershtein, S. S. *Sov. Phys. Usp.* **3**, 593-623 (1961).

8. Barkas, W. H. & Berger, M. J. in *Studies in Penetration of Charged Particles in Matter* 103-172 (Natn. Acad. Sci. Natn. Res. Council Publn 1133, Washington, DC, 1964).

9. Stelson, P. H. & McGowan, F. K. *Phys. Rev.* **110**, 489-506 (1958).

10. Fowler, J. L. & Brolley, J. E. Jr *Rev. mod. Phys.* **28**, 103-134 (1956).

11. Walling, C. & Simons, J. *J. Phys. Chem.* **93**, 4693-4696 (1989).

12. Berger, M. J. & Seltzer, S. M. in *Studies in Penetration of Charged Particles in Matter* 69-98 (Natn. Acad. Sci. Natn. Res. Council Publn 1133, Washington, DC, 1964).

13. Fleischer, R. L., Price, P. B. & Walker, R. M. *Nuclear Tracks in Solids* (University of California Press, Berkeley, 1975).

14. Hess, W. N., Canfield, E. H. & Lingenfelter, R. E. *J. Geophys. Res.* **66**, 665-677 (1961).

15. Seltzer, S. M. in *Monte Carlo Transport of Electrons and Photons* (eds Jenkins, T. M., Nelson, W. R. & Rindi, A.) (Plenum, New York, 1988).

16. Seltzer, S. M. & Berger, M. J. *Nucl. Instrum. Meth.* **B12**, 95-134 (1985).

17. Andersen, H. H. & Ziegler, J. F. *Hydrogen Stopping Powers and Ranges in all Elements* (Pergamon, New York, 1977).

Acknowledgements. We thank S. Pons, M. Anderson and M. Hawkins for their hospitality during our work in their laboratory. We thank K. Wolf for alerting us to the t(d, n)^{4}He reaction that follows d(d, p)t, and K. Drexler for suggesting neutron detection via activation of ^{23}Na within our detector. We also thank R. Lloyd, W. Schier, D. Leavitt, F. Steinhausler and P. Bergstrom for valuable assistance, R. Petrasso for a careful review of an earlier manuscript, P. B. Price, M. Solarz, S. Barwick, R. Huber, R. Price and C. DeTar for helpful conversations, and R. Cooper for technical assistance. This work was supported by the State of Utah. S.M.S. was supported by the Office of Health and Environmental Research, US Department of Energy.

d(d, p)t 反应约为 10^{-2} W，对于 d(d, n)^{3}He 反应为 10^{-6} W，因为这些反应产生的中子的一部分会活化 NaI 探测器中的 ^{23}Na，从而产生 ^{24}Na。由于 ^{24}Na 以 15 小时的半衰期进行衰变，一个猝发中子的光谱信号在猝发之后的数天还可以观察到。由于什么也没有观察到，我们得出了以下结论，即不论是 d(d, p)t 还是 d(d, n)^{3}He 反应都不是这一异常的猝发热量的原因。

另外，我们后来知道，在我们的监测期间观察到了一个低水平的热量过剩（庞斯，美国电力科学研究院（EPRI）会议，犹他大学，1989 年 8 月 16 日）；如果这是事实，这一过剩并非源自已知的核过程。

（李琦 翻译；李兴中 审稿）

Positioning Single Atoms with a Scanning Tunnelling Microscope

D. M. Eigler and E. K. Schweizer

Editor's Note

The scanning tunnelling microscope was invented in the early 1980s as a tool for imaging the surfaces of materials at atomic resolution. As its needle-like metal tip moves just above the surface, electrons can jump the gap to produce an electrical current that changes as the gap size varies, offering a topographic map. In the late 1980s it became clear that electrical pulses applied to the tip could remove or alter the surface material. Here Don Eigler and Eric Schweizer at IBM's research laboratories in California show that the tip can be used to drag individual xenon atoms over a surface and position them at will. Their spelling of the company name in 35 atoms became an icon of nanotechnology.

Since its invention in the early 1980s by Binnig and Rohrer[1,2], the scanning tunnelling microscope (STM) has provided images of surfaces and adsorbed atoms and molecules with unprecedented resolution. The STM has also been used to modify surfaces, for example by locally pinning molecules to a surface[3] and by transfer of an atom from the STM tip to the surface[4]. Here we report the use of the STM at low temperatures (4 K) to position individual xenon atoms on a single-crystal nickel surface with atomic precision. This capacity has allowed us to fabricate rudimentary structures of our own design, atom by atom. The processes we describe are in principle applicable to molecules also. In view of the device-like characteristics reported for single atoms on surfaces[5,6], the possibilities for perhaps the ultimate in device miniaturization are evident.

THE tip of an STM always exerts a finite force on an adsorbate atom. This force contains both Van der Waals and electrostatic contributions. By adjusting the position and the voltage of the tip we may tune both the magnitude and direction of this force. This, taken together with the fact that it generally requires less force to move an atom along a surface than to pull it away from the surface, makes it possible to set these parameters such that the STM tip can pull an atom across a surface while the atom remains bound to the surface. Our decision to study xenon on nickel (110) was dictated by the requirement that the corrugations in the surface potential be sufficiently large for the xenon atoms to be imaged without inadvertently moving them, yet sufficiently small that, when desired, enough lateral force could be exerted to move xenon atoms across the surface.

用扫描隧道显微镜定位单个原子

艾格勒，施魏策尔

编者按

扫描隧道显微镜发明于20世纪80年代初，是在原子级分辨率上对材料表面成像的一种工具。随着它的针状金属尖端在材料表面上移动，电子通过隧道效应穿过针尖与样品表面的间隙从而产生电流，电流强度随间隙大小不同而发生改变，从而描绘出材料表面的形貌。20世纪80年代后期，通过在探针尖端应用电脉冲可以移动或改变材料表面。本文中加利福尼亚IBM研究实验室的唐·艾格勒和埃里克·施魏策尔描述了利用针尖在材料表面拖动单个氙原子并进行任意定位。他们用35个原子拼写出的公司名称成为纳米技术的一个标志。

自从宾尼希和罗雷尔在20世纪80年代初发明扫描隧道显微镜（STM）[1,2]以来，它就以空前的分辨率为我们提供了关于材料表面和被吸附原子及分子的图像。STM还被用来修饰表面，例如将分子局部地固定在表面上[3]，以及将一个原子从STM的探针尖端转移到材料表面[4]。本文中我们报道了在低温下（温度为4 K）利用STM以原子级精度把单个氙原子定位在单晶镍表面上。这种能力使我们可以逐个原子地制作我们设计的基本结构。我们所描述的这个过程原则上同样适用于分子。从已报道的表面上单个原子的独特性质[5,6]来看，最终实现功能器件最小化的可能性是显而易见的。

STM的探针尖端总是对被吸附原子施加一个有限的力。这个力中同时包含着范德华力和静电力的贡献。通过调整针尖的位置和电压，我们可以调节此力的大小和方向。此外，考虑到沿着表面移动原子比将其拖离表面更省力这一事实，我们可以通过设置这些参数，使STM针尖拉动一个原子穿过表面的同时，仍保持该原子结合在表面上。出于以下原因我们决定研究镍（110）面上的氙：表面电势起伏可以足够大，使得我们可以对氙原子成像，而又不会不经意地移动它们；另外在需要时，表面电势的起伏还可以足够小，使得我们可以施加足够的侧向力在表面上移动氙原子。

The experiments were performed using an STM contained in an ultra-high-vacuum system and cooled to 4 K. The entire chamber housing the microscope was cooled to 4 K, which so reduced the contamination rate of the sample surface through adsorption of residual gases that no measurable contamination occurred over weeks. The stability of the sample and of the microscope due to the low temperature are such that one may perform experiments on a single atom for days at a time. This stability proved to be an operational necessity for performing these experiments. This notwithstanding, it is important to realize that the process that we describe for sliding atoms on a surface is fundamentally temperature independent.

The nickel sample was processed by cycles of argon-ion sputtering, annealing in a partial pressure of oxygen to remove surface carbon, and flash annealing. After cooling to 4 K the sample was imaged with the STM and found to be of acceptable quality. Figure 1a is an image of the surface taken under constant-current scanning conditions after dosing with xenon to the desired coverage. This image was obtained with a tip bias voltage of 0.010 V relative to the sample, and a tunnel current of 10^{-9} A. Each xenon atom appears as a 1.6-Å-high bump on the surface, apparently at random locations. At this gap impedance the interaction of the xenon with the tip is sufficiently weak to leave the xenon essentially unperturbed during the imaging process.

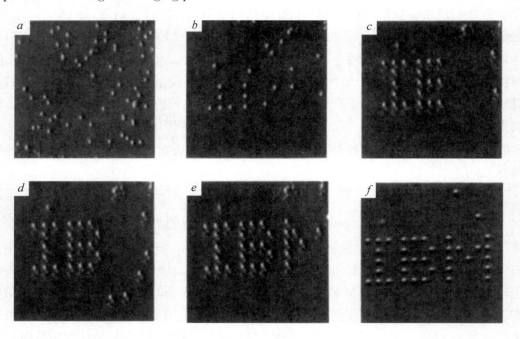

Fig. 1. A sequence of STM images taken during the construction of a patterned array of xenon atoms on a nickel (110) surface. Grey scale is assigned according to the slope of the surface. The atomic structure of the nickel surface is not resolved. The $\langle 1\bar{1}0 \rangle$ direction runs vertically. a, The surface after xenon dosing. b–f, Various stages during the construction. Each letter is 50 Å from top to bottom.

实验在一台含有超高真空系统的 STM 上进行，同时系统被冷却至 4 K。将容纳显微镜的整个样品室冷却至 4 K，通过吸收残余气体可以降低样品表面的污染速率，使其在几星期内没有可测量到的污染发生。低温保证了样品和显微镜的稳定性，这使得人们可以对单个原子进行一次长达数天的实验。我们已证明这一稳定性是进行实验的必要操作条件。尽管如此，还要注意到，我们所描述的在表面上移动原子的过程本质上是不依赖于温度的。

我们利用氙离子对镍样品进行反复喷溅，在氧分压中退火以除去镍表面的碳，且经快速退火完成样品处理。在冷却至 4 K 后，用 STM 对样品成像，确定其表面足够清洁。图 1a 是将氙添加到预期覆盖度后在恒定电流扫描条件下获得的表面图像。该图像是在相对于样品 0.010 V 的针尖偏压和 10^{-9} A 的隧道电流条件下获得的。每个氙原子看起来就像表面上一个 1.6 Å 高的团块，并且明显地处于随机位置。在隧道结阻抗的条件下，氙原子与针尖的相互作用非常弱，因此在成像过程中，氙原子基本不受到扰动。

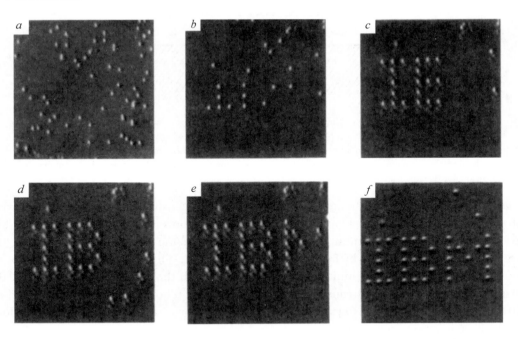

图 1. 在镍（110）表面上构建排列成图案的氙原子阵列过程中拍摄的一系列 STM 图像。根据表面的斜率确定灰度。对镍表面的原子结构未进行分辨。〈1$\bar{1}$0〉方向为垂直指向。a，加入氙之后的表面。b~f，构建过程中的各个阶段。每个字母从顶部到底部是 50 Å。

To move an atom we follow the sequence of steps depicted in Fig. 2. We begin by operating the microscope in the nonperturbative imaging mode described above to locate the atom to be moved and to target its destination. We stop scanning and place the tip directly above the atom to be moved (a). We then increase the tip–atom interaction by lowering the tip toward the atom (b); this is achieved by changing the required tunnel current to a higher value, typically in the range $1-6\times10^{-8}$ A, which causes the tip to move towards the atom until the new tunnel current is reached. We then move the tip under closed-loop conditions across the surface, (c), at a speed of 4 Å per second to the desired destination (d), dragging the xenon atom with it. The tip is then withdrawn (e) by reducing the tunnel current to the value used for imaging. This effectively terminates the attraction between the xenon and the tip, leaving the xenon bound to the surface at the desired location.

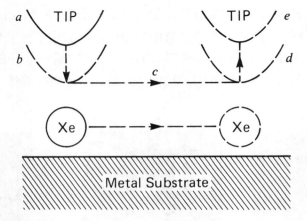

Fig. 2. A schematic illustration of the process for sliding an atom across a surface. The atom is located and the tip is placed directly over it (a). The tip is lowered to position (b), where the atom–tip attractive force is sufficient to keep the atom located beneath the tip when the tip is subsequently moved across the surface (c) to the desired destination (d). Finally, the tip is withdrawn to a position (e) where the atom–tip interaction is negligible, leaving the atom bound to the surface at a new location.

Figure 1 is a sequence of images taken during our first construction of a patterned array of atoms, and demonstrates our ability to position atoms with atomic precision. The exact periodicity of the xenon spacing is derived from the crystalline structure of the underlying nickel surface (which is not resolved in Fig. 1). The nickel (110) surface has an unreconstructed rectangular unit cell and is oriented such that the short dimension of the rectangular surface unit cell runs vertically in the image. The xenon atoms are spaced on a rectangular grid which is four nickel unit cells long horizontally and five unit cells long vertically, corresponding to 14×12.5 Å.

Although the STM tip is made from tungsten wire, the true chemical identity and the structure of the outermost atoms of the tip are not known to us. We find that for any given tip and bias voltage, there is a threshold height below which the tip must be located to be able to move xenon atoms parallel to the rows of nickel atoms, and a lower threshold

按照图 2 所示的一系列步骤来移动单个原子。用上文所描述的无干扰成像模式操作显微镜，找到待移动原子，瞄准其目的地。然后停止扫描，将针尖置于待移动原子的正上方 (a)。接着，我们通过将针尖向着原子下降 (b) 来增加针尖–原子之间的相互作用；通过增大所需隧道电流值，一般是达到 1×10^{-8} A 至 6×10^{-8} A 的范围时，即可实现这一点，这一电流范围使得针尖移向原子，直至达到新的隧道电流值。接着，我们在闭合回路的条件下移动针尖穿过表面 (c)，以 4 Å/s 的速度移向目的地 (d)，同时始终拖带着氙原子。然后，通过将隧道电流减少到成像所需的值使针尖后撤 (e)。这就有效地终止了氙与针尖之间的吸引力，将氙留在了表面上所预期的位置。

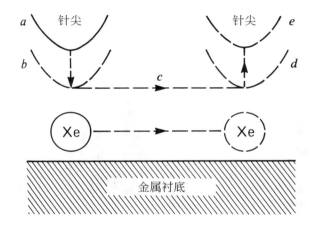

图2. 在表面移动原子过程的示意图。定位原子，针尖位于其正上方 (a)。将针尖降低到一定位置 (b)，在针尖随后移过表面 (c) 到达目的地 (d) 期间，原子–针尖之间的吸引力足以维持原子固定在针尖下方。最后，将针尖后撤到一个位置 (e)，此时原子–针尖相互作用小到可忽略，把原子留在表面上的一个新位置。

图 1 是在我们首次构建排列成图案的氙原子阵列过程中所拍摄的一系列图像，证明了我们能够以原子级精度放置原子。氙原子间距的精确周期可以利用背景镍表面的晶体结构（在图 1 中没有进行分辨）得到。镍（110）表面有一个未重现出来的矩形单胞，其方向为矩形表面单胞的短边处于图像中的垂直方向。这些氙原子间隔排列在一个矩形网格中，水平方向上为四个镍单胞长，垂直方向上为五个晶胞长，面积相当于 14 Å × 12.5 Å。

尽管 STM 针尖是用钨丝制成的，但是我们并不知道针尖最外围原子的真实化学特性与结构。我们发现对于任何给定的针尖和偏压，都存在着一个临界高度，针尖必须位于这个高度以下才能沿着平行于镍原子阵列的方向移动氙原子，还存在着一

height for movement perpendicular to the rows of nickel atoms. This is consistent with a simple model wherein the xenon interaction with the metal surface is approximated by pairwise interactions with the individual nickel atoms. Simple investigations showed that the magnitude or sign of the applied voltage had no significant effect on the threshold tip height. This suggests that the dominant force between the tip and the xenon atom is due to the Van der Waals interaction, but this tentative conclusion requires further investigation.

In Fig. 3 we show a sequence of images demonstrating how a simple structure, the linear multimer, may be fabricated using this process. First we slide xenon atoms into a chosen row of nickel atoms. We next slide a xenon atom along the row to a position where it will bind with a neighbouring xenon to form a dimer. We repeat the process, forming a linear trimer, then a linear tetramer, and so on. From these images we find that the linear xenon chain along the $\langle 1\bar{1}0 \rangle$ direction of the nickel (110) surface is stable, the xenon atoms occupying every other surface unit cell along a row of nickel atoms. Attempts to pack the xenon atoms closer were unsuccessful. We find the xenon–xenon spacing along the row to be uniform (excluding end effects) to within 0.2 Å.

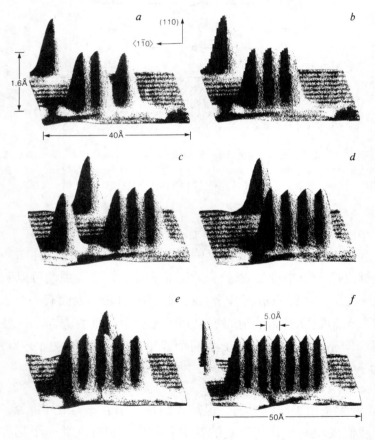

Fig. 3. Various stages in the construction of a linear chain of xenon atoms on the nickel (110) surface. The individual xenon atoms appear as 1.6-Å-high protrusions in these images. The rows of nickel atoms

个垂直于镍原子阵列移动时的更低临界高度。这与如下的简单模型是相一致的，其中氙与金属表面的相互作用近似于单个镍原子的成对相互作用。简单的研究表明外加电压的大小和方向对于临界针尖高度没有显著影响。这意味着针尖与氙原子之间的主要作用力应归结为范德华相互作用，但是这个初步结论还需要进一步的研究。

在图 3 中，我们给出了一系列图像来说明怎样利用这个过程来搭建一个简单结构，即线型多聚体。首先，将氙原子滑入一个选定的镍原子行中。接下来，沿着该行滑动一个氙原子使其到达一个能与邻近氙原子连接形成二聚体的位置。我们重复这一过程，形成一个线型三聚体，接着是线型四聚体，依此类推。从这些图像中，我们发现沿着镍原子（110）表面上 $\langle 1\bar{1}0 \rangle$ 方向的线型氙原子链是稳定的，氙原子沿着一行镍原子间隔占据表面单胞。使氙原子堆积得更近的尝试是不成功的。我们发现沿着行方向的氙–氙间距是相同的（除了末端效应以外），误差在 0.2 Å 以内。

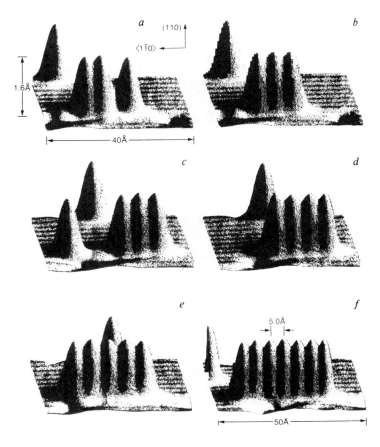

图 3. 在镍（110）表面上构建线型氙原子链的各个阶段。在这些图像中单个氙原子显示为 1.6 Å 高的突出物。镍原子行看起来犹如明暗交替的条纹。可以看到镍表面有若干处点缺陷。*a*，已装配好的氙原子

are visible as alternating light and dark stripes. Several point defects are visible in the nickel surface. *a*, The assembled xenon dimer. To the right of the dimer, a xenon atom has been moved into position for forming a xenon trimer. *b*, Formation of the xenon linear trimer. *c–f*, Various stages in construction of the linear heptamer, a process that can be completed in an hour. The xenon atoms are 5 Å apart, occupying every other unit cell of the nickel surface.

We anticipate that there will be a limiting class of adsorbed atoms and molecules that may be positioned by this method. Many new avenues of investigation are open to us. It should be possible to assemble or modify certain molecules in this way. We can build novel structures that would otherwise be unobtainable. This will allow a new class of surface studies that use the STM both to fabricate overlayer structures and to probe their properties. The prospect of atomic-scale logic circuits and other devices is a little less remote.

(**344**, 524-526; 1990)

D. M. Eigler & E. K. Schweizer[*]
IBM Research Division, Almaden Research Center, 650 Harry Rd, San Jose, California 95120, USA
[*]Permanent address: Fritz-Haber-Institut, Faradayweg 4-6, D-7000 Berlin 33, FRG.

Received 17 January; accepted 9 March 1990.

References:
1. Binnig, G., Rohrer, H., Gerber, Ch. & Weibel, E. *Appl. Phys. Lett.* **40**, 178-180 (1982).
2. Binnig, G., Rohrer, H., Gerber, Ch. & Weibel, E. *Phys. Rev. Lett.* **49**, 57-61 (1982).
3. Foster, J. S., Frommer, J. E. & Arnett, P. C. *Nature* **331**, 324-326 (1988).
4. Becker, R. S., Golovchenko, J. A. & Swartzentruber, B. S. *Nature* **325**, 419-421 (1987).
5. Lyo, I.-W. & Avouris, P. *Science* **245**, 1369-1371 (1989).
6. Bedrossion, P., Chen, D. M., Mortensen, K. & Golovchenko, J. A. *Nature* **342**, 258-260 (1989).

Acknowledgements. This work would not have occurred were it not for the patient and visionary management of the IBM Research Division.

二聚体。在二聚体的右侧，一个氙原子已进入恰当的位置，准备形成一个三聚体。b，氙原子线型三聚体的形成。c~f，构建线形七聚体的各个阶段，这个过程能够在一小时内完成。氙原子间距为 5 Å，各自占据相邻的镍表面单胞。

我们预期将会有一类特定的被吸附的原子和分子可以用这种方法来定位。很多新的研究途径展现在我们面前。应该有可能以这种方式来组装或修饰某些分子。我们能够构建出用其他办法无法得到的新型结构。这将引出一系列新的表面研究工作，即利用 STM 构建吸附层结构并探查其性质。这样，离实现原子尺度的逻辑电路和其他器件的梦想又近了一步。

（王耀杨 翻译；王琛 审稿）

Ozone Loss in the Arctic Polar Vortex Inferred from High-Altitude Aircraft Measurements

M. H. Proffitt *et al.*

Editor's Note

Although researchers had found previously that stratospheric ozone is depleted over the Arctic as well as over the Antarctic (where a "hole" was first observed in 1985), there had been no direct evidence that the Arctic hole is caused by the same chemical process—reaction with chlorine-containing compounds produced by break-up of anthropogenic chlorofluorocarbons—as that in the Antarctic. Here Michael Proffitt of the US National Oceanic and Atmospheric Administration in Colorado and co-workers supply that evidence. Measurements made by a high-altitude aircraft in 1989 showed that the losses of ozone were correlated with high concentrations of chlorine monoxide, the key chemical species involved in the ozone-destroying reactions.

The Arctic polar vortex in winter is known to be chemically primed for ozone depletion, yet it does not exhibit the large seasonal ozone decrease that characterizes its southern counterpart. This difference may be due in part to a net flux of ozone-rich air through the Arctic vortex, which can mask ozone loss. But by using a chemically conserved tracer as a reference, significant ozone loss can be identified. This loss is found to be correlated with high levels of chlorine monoxide, suggesting that much of the decrease in ozone is caused by anthropogenic emissions of chlorofluorocarbons.

IN 1985 Farman *et al.*[1] reported that spring values of total column ozone over Halley Bay, Antarctica, had decreased considerably during the previous decade, and they suggested that certain chlorine-containing compounds could be causing the observed ozone depletion. Further studies have supported these findings[2-5] and refined understanding of high-latitude ozone loss.

During the 1987 Airborne Antarctic Ozone Experiment (AAOE)[5] *in situ* measurements of many chemical species and meteorological parameters were made from a NASA high-altitude aircraft (ER-2) on twelve flights out of Punta Arenas, Chile (53° S), at cruise altitudes of ~17–19 km. *In situ* measurements of ozone (O_3)[6], nitrous oxide $(N_2O$—a chemically conserved tracer)[7], chlorine monoxide (ClO)[8], temperature, pressure and wind speed[9] were made.

Potential temperature (Θ) is a measure of entropy and is calculated from measured pressure and temperature. In the absence of diabatic processes, parcels tend to move

北极极涡臭氧的亏损——来自高海拔航空测量的结果

普罗菲特 等

编者按

尽管学者之前已经发现北极平流层存在像南极那样的臭氧损耗（南极的臭氧洞首次发现于1985年），但是还没有直接证据证明北极的臭氧洞是由与南极同样的化学过程——O_3 与含氯的化合物（人类活动释放出的氯氟烃分解形成的）反应造成的。本文中，来自科罗拉多州的美国国家海洋与大气管理局的迈克尔·普罗菲特和他的同事们提供了这一证据。1989年进行的高空航测的结果显示臭氧的亏损与高浓度的一氧化氯相关，一氧化氯是臭氧破坏反应中的关键化学物质。

我们都知道，冬季北极极涡的臭氧损耗主要是由化学原因造成的，但其季节性臭氧亏损量没有南极极涡的那样大。造成这种差异的原因可能部分是由于北极极涡存在富含臭氧的空气净通量，从而掩盖臭氧的亏损。然而以化学保守示踪气体作为参照，即可识别出显著的臭氧亏损。研究发现，该亏损量与一氧化氯的含量较高有关，这表明，臭氧层的亏损主要是由人类释放的氯氟烃引起的。

1985年，法曼等[1]研究发现，过去10年中，南极哈雷湾观测站上空春季臭氧柱总量的下降非常明显，并且他们认为，所观测到的臭氧损耗可能是由某些含氯化合物引起的。进一步的研究结果也都支持上述结论[2-5]，并且完善了对高纬度地区臭氧亏损的认识。

在1987年南极臭氧空中实验（AAOE）[5]期间，美国宇航局的高空飞机（ER-2）对许多化学物质和各气象参数进行了现场测定，该飞机飞行了12次，起飞于智利蓬塔阿雷纳斯（53°S），飞行高度约为17~19千米。调查期间，现场测定了臭氧（O_3）[6]、一氧化二氮（N_2O——一种化学保守示踪气体）[7]、一氧化氯（ClO）[8]、温度、压力以及风速[9]等。

位温（Θ）是熵的一个量度标准，根据所测定的压力和温度计算而来。在绝热条件下，气团将沿等熵面运动，并与该面上其他气团相混合。由于 Θ 会随高度的增

on constant Θ surfaces and mix with other parcels on that surface. Because Θ increases with altitude, and air movement is stratified somewhat by Θ, we use it here in place of altitude as a vertical coordinate. Using Θ, diabatic processes (net heating or cooling) can be more easily identified. The aircraft flights were usually to 72° S on surfaces of constant Θ (isentropic). AAOE lasted from 17 August to 22 September, covering late winter and early spring in the Southern Hemisphere. It was found that the O_3 mixing ratio at 72° S decreased by 61% at $\Theta = 425$ K (17 km) over a 30-day period[6] and was precisely collocated with very high ClO mixing ratios[10]. Calculations indicated that the observed concentration of ClO was high enough to link the O_3 decrease to catalytic destruction by chlorine[11-13]. These calculations, however, included two important assumptions: that diabatic cooling was negligible and that the vortex air was not being replenished by O_3-rich air from outside the polar jet. This view of the polar jet as a "containment vessel" is supported in the analyses of some authors[1,14-16] but not by others[17-22].

Possible Arctic ozone loss has also been reported recently. Balloon data taken during 1989 suggest that ozone depletion occurred late in January at an altitude of 22–26 km over Kiruna, Sweden (68° N)[23], and that there was a depleted ozone layer from 18 to 24 km from 24 January to 22 February over Alert, Canada (82° N)[24]. Another indication of possible ozone loss in the Arctic winter was found by the Ozone Trends Panel[25], where a comparison of total column ozone data from 1979–80 with 1986–87 shows a decrease of 4–10% between 65° and 80° N during the period from November to February.

An aircraft campaign, similar to AAOE, the Airborne Arctic Stratospheric Expedition (AASE) was based at Stavanger, Norway (59° N) from 3 January to 10 February 1989, to study ozone destruction mechanisms during the Arctic mid-winter[26]. The instrumentation used on the 14 ER-2 flights was virtually identical to that used in the Antarctic, but the aircraft flew nearer the pole in the Arctic, usually to 79° N. Although the Antarctic vortex persists well into spring, the less stable Arctic vortex usually dissipates in late winter and so the Arctic measurement campaign had to be conducted earlier in the season. Large photochemical ozone loss was not expected during this period of minimum solar radiation and, as anticipated, no large isentropic temporal decrease in ozone was found in the Arctic.

The analysis we present is based on a moving coordinate system defined vertically by Θ and horizontally by latitude referenced to the vortex boundary, which was defined as the latitude of peak wind speed as measured from the aircraft. The average latitude of the boundary is 68° N with a standard deviation of 3°. For the analysis that follows, the data will be considered in three regions: the vortex exterior (from aircraft take-off at 59° N to the boundary), the outer vortex (the first 8° of latitude inside the vortex boundary, comprising about 60% of the vortex volume) and the inner vortex (the remainder of the vortex, usually including the pole). The outer vortex receives more solar radiation than the inner vortex, and so photochemical ozone loss is more likely to occur there.

加而增大，而且空气的运动会由于 Θ 而在一定程度上被分层，因此在这里我们用 Θ 来替代高度作为垂直坐标。那么利用 Θ 就可以较容易地将非绝热过程（净加热或冷却）识别出来。飞机一般沿 Θ 为常数的平面（等熵面）运动至 72°S。南极臭氧空中实验从 8 月 17 日持续到 9 月 22 日，覆盖了南半球的冬末和春初时节。研究发现，$\Theta = 425\,K$（17 千米）时，72°S 处 O_3 的混合比在 30 天内下降了 61%[6]，与 ClO 的高混合比精确地相对应[10]。计算结果表明，所观测到的 ClO 浓度很高，足以把 O_3 的减少与氯引起的催化分解作用联系起来[11-13]。不过这些计算包含两个非常重要的前提：非绝热冷却可以忽略不计；并且极涡内的空气没有得到极地急流外部富含臭氧的空气的补充。将极地急流看作是"安全壳"，这一点已经得到一些学者[1,14-16]分析结论的支持，但也有另一些学者的研究不支持该观点[17-22]。

近来有研究发现北极臭氧层也可能存在亏损。1989 年获得的热气球资料显示：1 月末在瑞典的基律纳（68°N）上空 22~26 千米处发生臭氧损耗[23]，且在 1 月 24 日至 2 月 22 日期间，加拿大的阿勒特（82°N）上空 18~24 千米处的臭氧层也存在损耗[24]。此外，国际臭氧预测专家小组[25]也发现冬季北极存在臭氧亏损迹象，他们将 1979~1980 年与 1986~1987 年的臭氧柱总量资料进行对比，发现从 11 月到 2 月期间 65°N~80°N 之间臭氧的减少量约为 4%~10%。

1989 年 1 月 3 日到 2 月 10 日期间，我们在挪威斯塔万格（59°N）地区组织了一项类似于 AAOE 的高空调查活动，即北极平流层飞机探测（AASE），目的是研究冬季中期北极地区臭氧的破坏机制[26]。14 次 ER-2 航次中采用的仪器与南极臭氧空中实验中的几乎相同，只是飞行位置距北极点更近一些，一般可达 79°N 处。尽管南极极涡可一直持续到春季，但北极极涡相对不稳定，一般在冬末就消失了。因此，北极地区的测量活动必须在更早的时间进行。当太阳辐射量最低时，我们预期不会出现因光化作用而引起臭氧大量亏损的情况，而正如所预料的一样，在北极并未发现臭氧含量沿等熵面有明显下降的现象。

本文的分析基于以 Θ 为垂直坐标、以相对于极涡边界的纬度为水平坐标的动态坐标系，其中极涡边界是由飞机上测定的峰值风速所在纬度决定的。边界的平均纬度为 68°N，标准偏差为 3°。在接下来的分析中，我们将数据分为三个不同的区域：极涡外部（从飞机起飞的位置 59°N 到极涡边界处）、外极涡（从极涡边界向内 8 个纬度，约构成整个极涡体积的 60%）以及内极涡（剩下的极涡部分，一般包括极点）。外极涡接收到的太阳辐射多于内极涡，因此，外极涡发生臭氧光化亏损的可能性更大。

An analysis similar to that used to show that there is ozone loss outside the Antarctic ozone hole[27] will be used to show that there is also significant ozone loss in the Arctic vortex. Fundamental to the arguments presented is that standard gas-phase photochemistry identifies the primary source region for O_3 and the loss region for N_2O as the tropical middle stratosphere and also predicts long photochemical lifetimes for N_2O and O_3 (more than a year) for high-latitude winter[28-31]. From this, we deduce that air parcels at high latitudes with the same N_2O mixing ratios should have very similar O_3 mixing ratios. Deviations from this behaviour thus indicate chemical ozone loss occurring by processes not included in standard gas-phase photochemistry models[32].

In the following section, O_3 and N_2O data are presented and their relative behaviour during the mission characterized. In the section that follows, we argue that the vortex behaves as a "flowing processor" and these data are evaluated in this context, and an apparent O_3 loss is identified within the vortex. The origin of the loss is shown to be chemical rather than dynamical, to be enhanced in the outer vortex, and to have occurred both during and before the mission. The O_3 and N_2O data taken outside the vortex where O_3 loss is expected to be small are compared with values found within the vortex where an O_3 loss is identified. The loss in the outer vortex is linked with high concentrations of ClO.

O_3 and N_2O at High Latitudes

There are insufficient simultaneous measurements of lower stratospheric O_3 and N_2O available to determine an accurate climatology for these trace species, and so our analysis relies solely on the measurements made during AASE. An example of mid-latitude N_2O and O_3 data is given in Fig. 1a. These data are from an AASE transit flight on 21 February 1989 at 37–39° N latitude. A nearly linear relationship between O_3 and N_2O can be seen. Although the data only include N_2O values down to 165 parts per 10^9 by volume (p.p.b.v.), the fit to the data agrees well with the linear fit to observations taken by the ATMOS (Atmospheric Trace Molecule Spectroscopy) instrument[33] during May 1985 at 28° N and 48° S from Spacelab 3. The linear fit to ATMOS data shown in Fig. 1a includes all data with $N_2O > 50$ p.p.b.v., and extends the range of the linear relation, seen in the AASE data. The potential temperature, Θ, of each data point is indicated by colour and symbol type. As is typical of the lower stratosphere (altitude <25 km), O_3 increases with altitude (increasing Θ) whereas N_2O decreases. At mid-latitudes, O_3 peaks typically above 30 km and then decreases, but N_2O continues to decrease with increasing altitude. Maximum O_3 mixing ratios at high latitudes are between 25 and 30 km, about 5–10 km above ER-2 altitudes[23,24].

采用与分析南极臭氧洞外存在臭氧亏损相类似的方法 [27] 进行分析，结果显示，北极极涡内也存在明显的臭氧亏损。该结论的前提是，标准气相光化学反应识别出 O_3 的主要来源区和 N_2O 的主要亏损区均为热带中平流层，并且预测冬季高纬地区 N_2O 和 O_3 的光化学寿命较长（大于一年）[28-31]。在此基础上，我们推导出，在高纬地区具有相同 N_2O 混合比的气团，其 O_3 的混合比应该非常接近。倘若与上述特征不一致，那么就意味着引起化学性臭氧亏损的部分过程并未包含在标准气相光化学模型内 [32]。

以下将给出在这次任务期间获得的 O_3 和 N_2O 的有关资料及二者之间的相关特征。之后，我们将讨论极涡作为"气流处理器"的相关情况，并对这些资料加以评估，进而发现在极涡内存在明显的 O_3 亏损。臭氧亏损表现出是由化学因素引起的，而非动力因素，而且臭氧亏损在外极涡更强，在本调查进行前后均有发生。将从臭氧亏损较小的极涡外部得到的 O_3 和 N_2O 数据与发现臭氧亏损的极涡内的数据进行了对比。外极涡 O_3 的亏损与 ClO 的浓度较高有关。

高纬地区的 O_3 和 N_2O

由于对平流层低层 O_3 和 N_2O 浓度的同步测定不足，无法精确确定出这些痕量气体的气候学特征，所以我们的分析只能依赖于 AASE 期间的测定结果。图 1a 所示为中纬度地区 N_2O 和 O_3 数据的一个实例。这些数据均来自 AASE 1989 年 2 月 21 日在 37°N ~ 39°N 间的一次过境飞行。从图中可以看出，O_3 和 N_2O 之间近于线性相关。虽然图中仅包含了浓度为 165 ppbv（译者注：ppbv，体积混合比，10⁻⁹。）以上的数据值，但其拟合结果与 1985 年 5 月利用大气痕量分子光谱仪（ATMOS）[33] 在 28°N 和 48°S 从空间实验室 3 得到的观测数据的线性拟合结果非常一致。对 ATMOS 数据的线性拟合结果见图 1a，其包含了 $N_2O > 50$ ppbv 的所有数据，并且扩展了 AASE 数据中见到的线性相关关系的范围。各数据点的位温 Θ 以不同颜色和符号类型表示。平流层低层（高度 < 25 千米）的典型特征是 O_3 随高度增加（Θ 增加）而增加，而 N_2O 则减少。在中纬度地区，O_3 一般在 30 千米以上达到峰值，之后就开始降低，而 N_2O 则随高度的增高继续降低。高纬地区 O_3 的最大混合比出现在 25 ~ 30 千米之间，约位于 ER-2 的飞行高度之上 5 ~ 10 千米处 [23,24]。

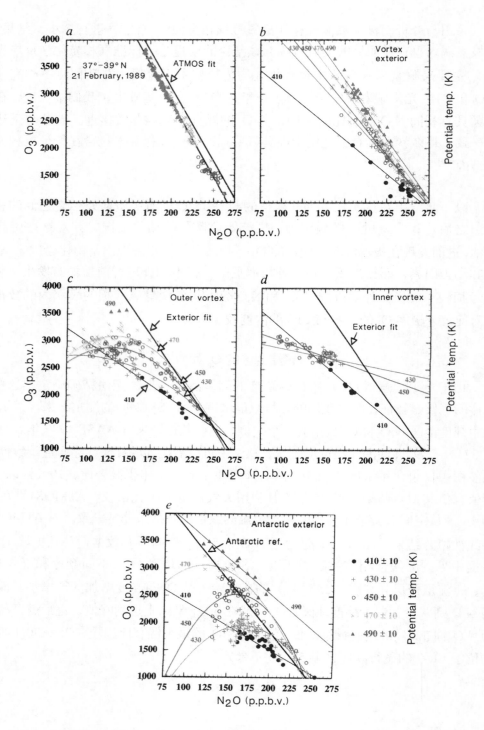

Fig. 1. O_3 is plotted against N_2O and colour coded for Θ. *a*, Data from 21 February 1989 at 37–39° N latitude averaged for 100 s (about 10′ of latitude) and a linear fit to that data. Also shown is linear fit to ATMOS data taken from Spacelab 3 at 28° S and 40° N latitude in May 1985. *b*, All AASE data taken in vortex exterior (59° N to vortex boundary) with $\Theta > 400$ K, and averaged for each flight leg over 1° of

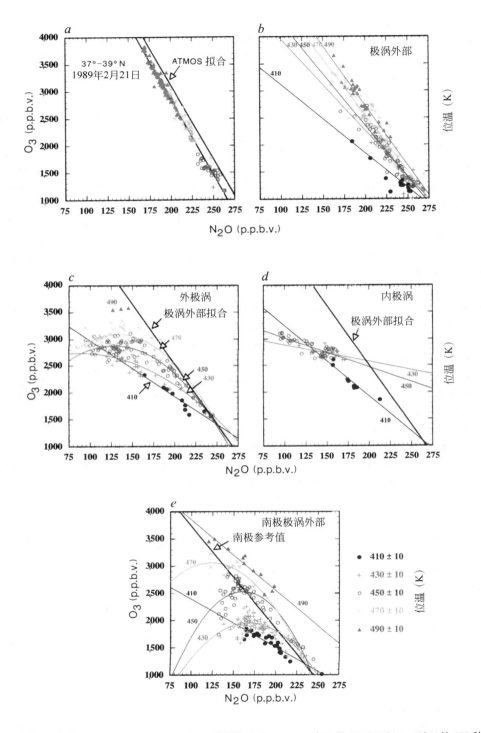

图1. O_3 与 N_2O 之间的关系，不同的 Θ 用不同的颜色表示。a，1989 年 2 月 21 日 37° N ~ 39° N 处 100 秒（约 10′纬度）的平均值，并对数据作了线性拟合。另外还给出了空间实验室 3 于 1985 年 5 月在 28° S 和 40° N 处获得的 ATMOS 数据的线性拟合结果。b，极涡外部（59° N 到极涡边界）$\Theta > 400$ K 时的所有 AASE 数据，所取值为各航次由边界起每增加 1° 的平均值，并对各个 Θ 段的数据作了拟合，详细讨论

latitude relative to the boundary of the vortex. Fits to data are provided for Θ bins and are discussed in the text. *c*, Same as (*b*) except that the data are from the outer vortex (the first 8° of latitude inside vortex boundary). *d*, Same as (*b*) except that the data are from the inner vortex (all of vortex interior more than 8° of latitude inside the vortex boundary). *e*, Same as (*b*) except the data are from the exterior of the Antarctic vortex during AAOE (1987).

Figure 1*b* represents all data with $\Theta > 400$ K taken in the vortex exterior. Also shown are linear fits to each of the Θ bins. Except at the lowest Θ, these data are very similar to those found in Fig. 1*a*, but with greater variability, and with lower values of O_3 relative to N_2O. The plot in Fig. 1*c* shows all the AASE data with $\Theta > 400$ K that are in the outer vortex. A linear fit is shown for the 410 K bin with quadratic fits for the three middle bins. The highest bin (490 K) has too few data to justify a fit. Figure 1*d* shows data from the inner vortex. Comparing Fig. 1*b–d*, the fits for the 410 K bin are all very similar, but there is little similarity in the fits to the other Θ bins. The uniformity below 420 K indicates that air is free to move from inside to outside the vortex at this level, suggesting that the "bottom of the vortex" is where $\Theta = 410\pm10$ K.

Another important criterion for comparing Fig. 1*b–d*, and indicative of chemical loss of O_3, is the deviation of O_3 mixing ratios relative to N_2O from the mid-latitude values shown in Fig. 1*a*. It is clear that for a constant value of N_2O, O_3 progressively decreases from the mid-latitudes, to the vortex exterior, to the outer vortex. In Fig. 1*b*, *c*, O_3 also decreases with decreasing Θ. The characteristic of decreasing O_3 with decreasing Θ for a constant value of N_2O will be referred to as "O_3–Θ dependence". There is a small O_3–Θ dependence in the vortex exterior and a larger one in the outer vortex, but none is evident in the mid-latitude data, nor in the inner vortex. The O_3–Θ dependence in Fig. 1*b*, *c* is not a result of downward mixing of air from above the O_3 maximum because O_3 and Θ are negatively correlated above the maximum, whereas the O_3–Θ dependence in Fig. 1*b*, *c* is positive. This implies that the O_3–Θ dependence is not a result of dynamics, but of chemistry.

This O_3–Θ dependence was also clearly seen in the Antarctic exterior (Fig. 1*e*) and seems much like the Arctic outer vortex (Fig. 1*c*). Also given in Fig. 1*e* is the Antarctic reference that was used for assessing O_3 loss[27]. That reference was based on a more restricted data set than is available for the Arctic, and may underestimate O_3 loss because it was chosen very conservatively.

Isopleths for N_2O (lines of constant N_2O) within our Θ–latitude coordinate system are shown in Fig. 2*a*. Each point is an average over 1° of latitude and over all flights of the mission. Polynomial fits are provided for each of the N_2O bins and are good approximations to the N_2O isopleths. The poleward decrease in Θ along the isopleths indicates diabatic cooling within the vortex. Diabatic cooling rates during the mission have been approximated theoretically[34] and from AASE N_2O data[35]. Although these analyses do not necessarily represent average vortex conditions, they do imply that cooling of at least 0.9 K per day in Θ (0.4 K per day in temperature) occurred during the mission both inside and outside the vortex.

见正文。c，同 b，只是数据为外极涡（极涡边界以内最外部的 8 个纬度）数据。d，同 b，为内极涡（除了最外层 8 个纬度以外的所有极涡内部分）数据。e，同 b，数据为 AAOE 期间（1987）获得的南极极涡外部数据。

图 1b 所示为极涡外部获得的 $\Theta > 400$ K 时的所有数据。同时还给出了各个 Θ 段的线性拟合结果。这些数据，除 Θ 为最低值时以外，均与图 1a 相似，只是其变率要大得多，而且 O_3 相对于 N_2O 的比值较小。图 1c 为 $\Theta > 400$ K 时外极涡的所有 AASE 数据。对 Θ 为 410 K 段的数据作了线性拟合，对中间三段则采用了二次拟合。最高的一段（Θ 为 490 K）数据较少，无法进行拟合。图 1d 为内极涡的相关数据。比较图 1b~d 可以发现，Θ 为 410 K 段的拟合结果均非常接近，但其他 Θ 值下的拟合结果则差别很大。Θ 为 420 K 以下的一致特性表明，在这一高度上空气可在极涡内外自由流动，也就意味着极涡的底界位于 $\Theta = 410 \pm 10$ K 附近。

比较图 1b~d 和揭示 O_3 的化学亏损的另一个重要标准就是 O_3 与 N_2O 的混合比相对于图 1a 中纬度地区的偏移量。显然，当 N_2O 含量不变时，从中纬度地区向极涡外部，一直到外极涡，O_3 含量是逐渐降低的。在图 1b 和 c 中 O_3 含量亦随 Θ 值的降低而降低。N_2O 值恒定时，O_3 含量随 Θ 值的降低而减少的特征，可称为"O_3-Θ 的依赖关系"。极涡外部 O_3-Θ 的相关性较小，在外极涡两者的相关性较大，不过，在中纬度地区以及内极涡中，两者则没有明显的相关性。图 1b、c 所示的 O_3-Θ 的依赖关系并非空气从臭氧含量的最大值之上向下混合的结果，因为从 O_3 含量的最大值往上，O_3 和 Θ 应呈负相关关系，而在图 1b、c 中两者之间为正相关。这说明，O_3-Θ 的依赖关系并非动力作用的结果，而是化学过程所致。

从南极极涡外部的相关数据中（图 1e）也可清楚地看到 O_3 与 Θ 的这种依赖关系，而且与北极外极涡（图 1c）颇为相似。图 1e 中还给出了用于评估南极 O_3 亏损的参考系 [27]。该参考系是基于比北极更严格的数据库得到的结果，而且，由于数据选择非常保守，所以有可能会低估 O_3 的亏损量。

图 2a 为我们的位温－纬度坐标系中 N_2O 的等值线图（N_2O 为常数的线）。各数据点都是所有航次 1 个纬度上测定结果的平均值。对每组 N_2O 浓度值的每个段都作了多项式拟合，结果与 N_2O 的等值线吻合良好。Θ 沿等值线向极点逐渐降低，说明极涡内部存在非绝热冷却。本调查期间的非绝热冷却速率是根据 AASE 的 N_2O 数据 [35] 估计的，与理论值 [34] 接近。尽管上述分析并不足以代表极涡内部的平均状况，但从中确实可以看出，该调查期间，极涡内外的 Θ 每天都至少降低 0.9 K（即温度每天降低 0.4 K）。

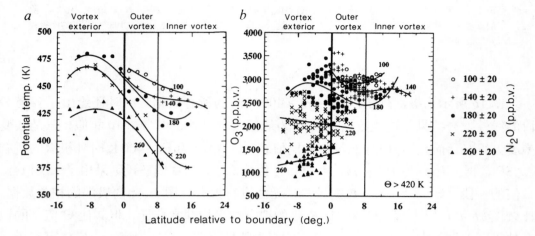

Fig. 2. a, N₂O isopleths on a coordinate system of Θ plotted against latitude relative to the boundary of the vortex. Data from the entire mission are averaged over 1° of latitude relative to the vortex boundary and plotted along with polynomial fits for each of the N₂O bins. b, All O₃ data with Θ > 420 K are plotted against latitude relative to the boundary and binned by N₂O. Data are averages over 100-s intervals (about 10′ of latitude). A fit is provided for each bin.

Figure 2b confirms the O_3 loss seen in Fig. 1a–d but in a spatial context, by plotting O_3 against latitude relative to the vortex boundary for the same five N_2O bins of Fig. 2a. Only data above 420 K are plotted, to exclude data that may be affected by the relatively unrestricted horizontal exchange of air at the bottom of the vortex. Again polynomial fits are included for each of the N_2O bins and terminated where the data end. In the outer vortex, O_3 decreases towards the pole, and where there are data within the inner vortex, the fits there either increase or flatten out indicating less ozone loss. The outer vortex receives more solar radiation, and so the observed spatially enhanced decrease is consistent with O_3 being photochemically destroyed.

O₃ Loss in a Flowing Processor

Early research indicated that tropospheric air enters the lower stratosphere in the tropics and exits at higher latitudes[36,37] and this is still generally accepted[30]. That is, the dominant atmospheric circulation is upward at low latitudes where heating lifts air into the region of the stratosphere where ozone is produced, then poleward and at high latitudes downward, due to diabatic cooling. As previously mentioned, some authors believe that the Antarctic jet effectively terminates the poleward component, but only the question of Arctic containment will be discussed here.

It has been shown that total column O_3 substantially increases at polar latitudes in the Northern Hemisphere throughout the winter months[38-40]. Because O_3 is not created at high latitudes during the winter, any increase in column O_3 must be a result of poleward flux. A recent comprehensive analysis[41] shows that the meridionally averaged O_3 column at polar latitudes increases by 40 to 70 Dobson Units (DU) per month from December to February, corresponding to column changes of about 12–20% per month. With regard to 1989,

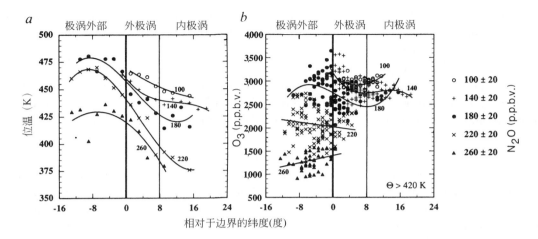

图2. a，N_2O 等值线坐标图，其中横坐标为到极涡边界的纬度值，纵坐标为 Θ。整个调查期间的数据均已处理为相对于极涡边界 1 个纬度上的平均值，同时还给出了每组 N_2O 浓度值的多项式拟合结果。b，所有 $\Theta > 420$ K 的 O_3 含量与到边界距离之间的关系，根据 N_2O 浓度范围将数据分组。图中数据均为 100 秒间隔（约 10' 纬度）上的平均值。对不同 N_2O 浓度范围下的结果分别作了拟合曲线。

图 $2b$ 为 O_3 与到极涡边界的纬度距离之间的关系，它在空间上证实了图 $1a\sim d$ 所显示的 O_3 亏损量，图 $2b$ 与图 $2a$ 中 N_2O 的浓度值均分为 5 个分档。由于极涡底部空气的水平交换相对比较自由，为避免受其影响，图中仅画出了 420 K 以上的值。图中同样给出了各组 N_2O 浓度值的多项式拟合结果，拟合在数据结束的地方终止。在外极涡中，O_3 向极点逐渐减少，而内极涡中出现的各数据点的拟合结果则表现为逐渐增加或变平，说明那里存在较少的臭氧亏损。外极涡接收的太阳辐射较多，因此所观测到的在空间中含量越来越低与 O_3 受到了光化分解是一致的。

气流处理器中 O_3 的亏损

早期研究显示，在热带地区，对流层空气会进入平流层低层，然后在高纬度地区流出[36,37]，该观点至今仍被广为认同[30]。也就是说，低纬地区的大气循环以上升运动为主，在这里空气受热上升进入形成 O_3 的平流层，之后向两极运动；到了高纬地区，又由于非绝热冷却作用而做向下运动。如前所述，有些学者认为，南极急流有效地终止了向极地运动分量，不过在此我们仅讨论北极地区的相关遏制机制问题。

已有研究证明，整个冬季北半球极地纬度地区的 O_3 柱总量增加明显[38-40]。由于冬季在高纬地区不会有 O_3 产生，所以，O_3 柱总量任何一点的增加必定是由向极地通量所致。近期的综合分析[41]表明，从 12 月到 2 月，极地地区 O_3 柱总量的经向平均值，每月增加 40~70 多布森单位（DU），对应每月的柱量变化为 12%~20%。在

satellite total column data show an increase of about 15% in the outer vortex during the mission, and an increase of more than 15% is evident from 11 column measurements and 19 balloon soundings taken from 10 January to 8 February at 82°N (ref. 42). The column increase can only be explained by a poleward flux of mid-latitude air that carries more O_3 into the polar vortex than is removed by dynamical or chemical processes. We deduce therefore, both from the Arctic long-term record and analysis of 1989 data, that the vortex is not isolated, although the Arctic polar jet may restrict poleward flux.

A more difficult question to answer that is somewhat controversial is "At what altitudes does significant mass enter the Arctic vortex?". Leovy et al.[43] argue that diabatic descent within the vortex, along with major and minor stratospheric warming events in the middle stratosphere, account for the polar column increase, and Kent et al.[44] use aerosol extinction measurements to indicate that mass flow into the vortex is somewhat restricted at its boundary. These analyses may seem to imply, but they do not conclusively show, that the polar jet completely isolates the vortex in the lower stratosphere. For consider the following: (1) The analysis of Leovy et al. indicates that only one-third of the total column O_3 increase occurred above 30 mbar (~23 km). (2) Kent et al. infer from vertical mass-flux rates near the pole that the flux into the vortex between 14 and 24 km is approximately equal to the downward flux within the vortex from above 24 km. (3) Only 20–25% of the Arctic winter O_3 column is above 25 km and 12–20% column increases occur each winter month. This implies that a mass of O_3 equivalent to its column above 25 km must be added to the column within the vortex every 1–2 months, plus an additional amount to balance any flow out of the bottom of the vortex. Furthermore, if (2) is accurate, then the column increase below 23 km from (1) could result primarily from O_3 flux into the vortex in the lower stratosphere rather than from vertical descent. This flux could occur during warming events[43] (isentropic) or from diabatic circulation into the vortex. The qualitative arguments that follow do not generally rely on either of these positions, but the arguments involved in quantifying O_3 loss do.

Searching for a possible explanation for the O_3–Θ dependence that is consistent with Fig. 1a–d and does not require a large winter O_3 loss, we consider that the loss may have occurred before winter. Theoretical and experimental evidence for a net O_3 loss over Antarctica during the continuous daylight of the summer has been presented by Farman et al.[45]. The authors report that the loss is not primarily due to chlorine but to low concentrations of N_2O_5 and an associated enhancement of the NO_x catalytic cycle in the middle stratosphere. These loss mechanisms apply as well to the Arctic. For the summertime loss to affect our wintertime analysis requires that a substantial part of the depleted lower-stratospheric air remains at high latitudes until the polar vortex has formed in November, and is then contained at polar latitudes until the end of the mission in February. Diabatic cooling during the winter without concurrent O_3 loss implies an isentropic O_3 increase (because O_3 increases with Θ), but this was not observed. Therefore the O_3–Θ dependence is not simply a residual of summertime loss, but must reflect wintertime loss. Furthermore, the O_3 climatology discussed earlier[41] shows a column increase of 12–20% per month from December to February, but also shows that the

1989 年，卫星测得该任务期间外极涡的 O_3 柱总量增加约 15%，而从 1 月 10 日到 2 月 8 日在 82°N 得到的 11 个 O_3 柱测量结果和 19 个热气球探测结果，则显示了该增量高于 15%（参考文献 42）。O_3 柱总量的增加只能解释为：由中纬地区流入极涡的空气中含有的 O_3 量大于动力或化学过程对 O_3 的去除量。因此，我们根据北极长期记录以及对 1989 年数据的分析认为，虽然北极急流会限制空气的向极流动，但极涡并非是孤立的。

还有一个更为困难和具有争议的问题，即 "气团在什么高度大规模进入北极极涡？"。利奥维等 [43] 认为，极涡内非绝热下降及发生于平流层中层的大小变暖事件是极地地区 O_3 柱总量增加的原因所在，而肯特等 [44] 则利用气溶胶的消光测量法证明，气团在进入极涡时在一定程度上被限制在了极涡的边界。上述分析似乎意味着，但却并不能确凿证明，极地急流使平流层低层的极涡完全孤立开来。我们可以考虑以下几个方面：（1）利奥维等的分析说明，仅有三分之一的 O_3 柱增加量发生在 30 毫巴（约 23 千米）以上的条件下。（2）肯特等根据极地附近的垂直质量通量速率推出，14～24 千米之间进入极涡的通量与 24 千米以上极涡内的向下通量大体相等。（3）北极冬季的 O_3 柱总量仅有 20%～25% 位于 25 千米以上，而 O_3 柱总量在冬季的月增加量为 12%～20%。这就意味着，每一到两个月，就需要相当于 25 千米以上 O_3 柱总量这样的量加入极涡的 O_3 柱，再加上一份额外的量来平衡极涡底部流出的量。此外，倘若（2）是准确的，那么根据（1）推出的 23 千米以下 O_3 柱总量的增加应该主要来源于平流层低层进入极涡的 O_3 通量，而非垂直递减所致。该通量可能在变暖事件（等熵条件下）期间发生 [43]，也可通过非绝热循环作用进入极涡。虽然后来的许多定量论证都不是根据以上任何一个条件得出的，但相关的 O_3 亏损的定性论证却是由此而来。

既要解释 O_3 与 Θ 之间的相关关系使之与图 1a~d 所示一致，冬季 O_3 亏损量又不能过大，基于这两点考虑我们认为，臭氧的亏损可能是在冬季之前发生的。法曼等 [45] 提出了关于夏季极昼期间南极上空出现 O_3 净亏损的大量理论和实验证据。他们研究发现，O_3 亏损的主要原因不是氯的作用，而应归因于较低的 N_2O_5 浓度以及由此引发的平流层中层 NO_x 催化循环的加强。上述亏损机制同样适用于北极。要让夏季 O_3 的亏损影响我们对冬季的分析，则大部分贫 O_3 的平流层低层空气必须一直停留在高纬地区，直到 11 月份极涡形成，而且直到 2 月份任务结束时一直被控制在极地地区，冬季非绝热冷却过程并未伴随着 O_3 的亏损，这说明存在 O_3 的等熵增加（因为 O_3 含量随 Θ 的增大而增大），但我们并没有观测到这一点。因此，O_3 与 Θ 之间的依赖关系并不是一种简单的夏季亏损的残余问题，而一定是反映了冬季的亏损。此外，早前关于 O_3 的气候学讨论 [41] 表明，从 12 月到 2 月 O_3 柱总量每月增加

column decrease reaches a maximum in May at 12% per month, decreasing almost linearly to no change in October. Assuming the column loss in summer is representative of chemical O_3 loss, we conclude that a summer loss of O_3, terminating months before AASE, is not likely to contribute substantially to the loss reported here. But to quantify its possible effect requires very accurate O_3 and N_2O data measured simultaneously throughout the polar lower stratosphere in autumn and winter, and no such data are available.

Returning to the O_3–Θ dependence, a plausible explanation for the low O_3 and its dependence on Θ can be constructed in the context of a "flowing processor". First, recall that air is diabatically cooling both inside and outside the vortex, that N_2O is chemically inert in the high latitude winter, and that mixing ratios do not change due to expansion and contraction. Therefore, if mixing of air parcels of differing N_2O content is ignored, the movement of a parcel that is diabatically cooling must be restricted to a surface described by the N_2O isopleth on which that parcel resides. This can be visualized with or without containment of the lower vortex. Consider an air parcel initially a few degrees of latitude outside the vortex that is diabatically cooling. The parcel remains on a surface of constant N_2O, so as Θ decreases, the parcel moves poleward and downward into the vortex (see Fig. 2a) thus describing a "flow" into the vortex in the lower stratosphere. Alternatively, if the lower vortex is assumed to be contained by the polar jet, the cooling would be characterized as a change in N_2O on a surface of constant potential temperature, Θ (ref. 35). In this case the flow is vertical and downward as the isopleths sink. But in both cases, there is flow through the surfaces of constant Θ within the vortex in the lower stratosphere.

Let us hypothesize that by some chemical "process", as an air parcel diabatically cools, O_3 is lost, and see if the resulting "flowing processor" would produce the observed data. Figure 2b shows O_3 decreasing poleward along the N_2O isopleths, in the outer vortex, but not in the inner vortex. That is, the O_3 loss seems to be less in the inner vortex. Therefore our cooling/O_3-loss hypothesis, together with an enhanced loss in the outer vortex (where there is greater solar radiation), is consistent with Fig. 2, with or without mass flux into the lower vortex.

Similar reasoning can also be applied to Fig. 1b–d to again test our expanded hypothesis, this time assuming that there is mass flux into the lower vortex. Consider an air parcel with, for example, N_2O = 175 p.p.b.v. originally outside the boundary at Θ= 470 K and O_3 = 3,050 p.p.b.v. (Fig. 1b). Later that parcel contains only 2,400 p.p.b.v. of O_3 when Θ = 430 K inside the boundary (Fig. 1c), representing a 20% O_3 loss. But the inner vortex O_3 at 430 K is 2,700 p.p.b.v. and, as previously noted, shows no O_3–Θ dependence (Fig. 1d). Again, these data indicate that increased exposure to solar radiation in the outer vortex enhances the O_3 loss. The lack of O_3–Θ dependence in the inner vortex could be a result of enhanced isentropic mixing in that region and the low O_3 may be due to transport from the outer vortex where the loss is primarily occurring. The summertime O_3 loss discussed earlier could also explain part of the inner vortex loss.

$12\% \sim 20\%$，但同样也表明，之后 O_3 柱总量的速率几乎直线降低，直到 10 月份才保持不变，5 月份的下降量最大，达到 12%。假设夏季 O_3 柱的亏损代表 O_3 的化学亏损，那么我们就可以得出，在 AASE 实验之前的夏季 O_3 亏损对本文所说的 O_3 亏损量的贡献可能没有那么大。然而，为了量化其潜在的影响，就要求对秋冬季整个极地平流层低层 O_3 和 N_2O 的含量有非常准确的同步测定值，然而目前并没有这样的资料。

我们再回到 O_3 与 Θ 的依赖关系上，可以通过"气流处理器"的情形对低 O_3 含量及 O_3 对 Θ 的依赖关系构建一种可能的解释。首先，我们知道，极涡内外的空气都是非绝热冷却的；N_2O 在高纬地区的冬季表现为化学上的惰性；并且空气的混合比并不因膨胀或压缩而改变。因此，倘若忽略不同 N_2O 含量的气团之间的混合，非绝热冷却气团的运动将被限制在气团所在的 N_2O 等值线所确定的面上。不管有无极涡低层的阻碍都可以设想到这种情况。考虑一下，有一个气团最初位于极涡外几个纬度远处，正处于非绝热冷却状态。该气团一直逗留在 N_2O 的等值面上，因此，随着 Θ 的降低，该气团将向极地且向下运动，进入极涡（见图 2a），进而如同一股"流"进入了平流层低层的极涡中。或者这样考虑，倘若极涡低层包含于极地急流内，这种冷却将以等位温面上 N_2O 的变化为特征（参考文献 35）。在这种情况下，气流是垂直向下的，表现为等熵递减。但在两种情况下，平流层低层极涡内的等位温面都有气流穿过。

下面我们假设，随着一个气团的非绝热冷却，某些化学"过程"可导致 O_3 的亏损，来看一下由此形成的"气流处理器"是否可以产生我们所观测到的数据。图 2b 显示，O_3 在外极涡沿 N_2O 的等值面呈向极降低，而在内极涡则没有。也就是说，内极涡中 O_3 的亏损似乎要少些。因此，我们的冷却 / O_3 亏损假说，以及外极涡（太阳辐射更强的地方）O_3 亏损增加，均与图 2 一致，与有无气流进入极涡低层无关。

对于图 1b ~ d 也可运用同样的推理，从而再次验证我们的扩展假说，而这一次我们假设有气流进入极涡低层。假设某气团 N_2O 的浓度为，比如 175 ppbv，最初位于气团边界外，$\Theta = 470 \ K$，O_3 浓度为 3,050 ppbv（图 1b）。随后，当边界内 $\Theta = 430 \ K$ 时（图 1c），该气团中 O_3 的浓度变为 2,400 ppbv，说明 O_3 亏损了 20%。而在内极涡中，当 $\Theta = 430 \ K$ 时，O_3 的浓度则为 2,700 ppbv，而且，如前所述，O_3 与 Θ 没有表现出依赖关系（图 1d）。那么上述数据再次表明，外极涡中太阳辐射的增加加重了其 O_3 的亏损。内极涡中 O_3 与 Θ 不存在依赖关系可能是该区等熵混合作用加强的结果，而其 O_3 含量较低可能是由外极涡的向内传输造成的，因为外极涡是最早发生 O_3 亏损的。前面讨论的夏季 O_3 的亏损也可部分地解释内极涡 O_3 的亏损。

As discussed above, air parcels at high latitudes with the same N_2O mixing ratios would be expected to have very similar wintertime O_3 mixing ratios. This was deduced without requiring the somewhat controversial assumption of significant mass flux into the vortex in the lower stratosphere. How accurately we can quantify O_3 loss from N_2O depends on how well the O_3 and N_2O reference relationship is known, and this is related to the altitude of mass flux. That is, a significant flux across the boundary at or near flight altitudes implies that air sampled inside the boundary recently entered the vortex, carrying with it the measured characteristics of the exterior. A path higher in the stratosphere requires the assumption that the O_3–N_2O reference relationship is preserved at altitudes above the region sampled by the aircraft, and therefore implies greater uncertainty in the amount of O_3 loss. Figure 1a supports this assumption.

To quantify O_3 loss within the vortex, a linear least-squares fit to all the exterior data (Fig. 1b) is calculated, excluding those points at the bottom of the vortex where $\Theta < 420$ K. This fit is shown in Fig. 1c, d and is given by

$$O_3^*(\text{p.p.b.v.}) = 7{,}019 - 22.42 \times N_2O \ (\text{p.p.b.v.})$$

where O_3^* approximates the O_3 mixing ratio in the vortex exterior from the mixing ratio of N_2O. For any sampled parcel inside the vortex, O_3^* can be calculated from its N_2O content with a negative value for $O_3 - O_3^*$ representing loss relative to the vortex exterior. The mid-latitude O_3–N_2O fit (Fig. 1a) is not used as a reference, instead we use the data in the vortex exterior for the comparison. For the reasons discussed in this section, $O_3 - O_3^*$ may overestimate O_3 loss within the vortex.

Figure 3 shows $O_3 - O_3^*$ plotted against latitude relative to the vortex boundary for $\Theta = 430 \pm 10$ K and 450 ± 10 K. Loss in excess of 1,500 p.p.b.v. is found in the outer vortex with about two-thirds of that loss in the inner vortex. The data are also binned into early (before 30 January) and late data (the remainder). There are small temporal changes seen in the outer vortex, although Fig. 3a includes virtually no data from the first half of January because early flight legs were above $\Theta = 440$ K. Temporal changes are better represented in Fig. 3b, showing a decrease of ~500 p.p.b.v. This isentropic decrease in O_3 is a result of the temporal changes in N_2O, not absolute O_3 changes. Therefore, isentropic temporal analysis of O_3 alone will not reveal the true temporal decrease.

通过上述讨论我们知道，高纬地区具有相同 N_2O 混合比的气团，其冬季 O_3 混合比应该非常相近。该结论的得出并不要求以有争议的假定——"平流层低层有大量的气流通量进入极涡"为基础。利用 N_2O 对 O_3 亏损进行量化可达到怎样的精度，取决于我们对 O_3 和 N_2O 之间的参照关系的了解程度，而这又与气流通量的高度有关。也就是说，大量气流在飞机飞行高度上或附近穿过极涡边界就意味着边界内采到的空气样品是刚刚进入极涡的，仍带有外部气体的特征。平流层中存在更高的气流路径需要的前提是，O_3 与 N_2O 之间的参照关系在飞机采样区域之上仍然保持不变，那么也就意味着 O_3 的亏损量更不确定。图 1a 就支持了这一假定。

为了量化极涡内 O_3 的亏损，我们计算出了极涡外所有数据的线性最小二乘法拟合结果（图 1b），剔除了极涡底部 $\Theta < 420$ K 时的那些点。该拟合结果见图 1c、d，其表达式为：

$$O_3^* \, (\text{ppbv}) = 7,019 - 22.42 \times N_2O \, (\text{ppbv})$$

其中，O_3^* 是根据 N_2O 的混合比得到的极涡外 O_3 混合比的近似值。对于在极涡内采到的所有样本，其 O_3^* 值都可通过 N_2O 的含量计算出来，当 $O_3^* - O_3$ 为负时，表示 O_3 相对于极涡外部发生了亏损。我们并未使用中纬地区 O_3–N_2O 的拟合结果（图 1a）作为参照系，而是采用极涡外的数据来进行比较。鉴于本部分已论述过的原因，O_3–O_3^* 可能会高估极涡内 O_3 的亏损。

图 3 所示为 $\Theta = 430 \pm 10$ K 和 $\Theta = 450 \pm 10$ K 时，O_3–O_3^* 与到极涡边界的纬度之间的关系。在外极涡中发现 O_3 的亏损超过 1,500 ppbv，内极涡中的亏损量约为该值的三分之二。我们还将数据分成了早期数据（1 月 30 日以前的）和晚期数据（剩余数据）。我们可以看到，外极涡中 O_3 随时间有少量变化，尽管图 3a 中并未包含 1 月份前半个月的任何数据，因为早期的飞行航段均在 $\Theta = 440$ K 以上。图 3b 中 O_3 随时间的变化表现得更明显，约下降了 500 ppbv。O_3 含量的这种等熵下降是 N_2O 随时间变化的结果，而不是 O_3 的绝对变化。因此，仅仅分析 O_3 随时间发生的等熵变化，并不能揭示其随时间发生的真实变化。

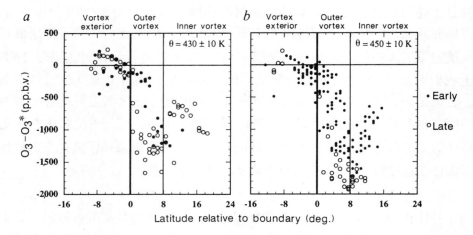

Fig. 3. $O_3 - O_3^*$ plotted against latitude relative to the vortex boundary for the early data (before 30 January) and the late data (the remainder of the mission), each point representing, from a flight leg, the average over 1° of latitude relative to the boundary. Negative values indicate loss of O_3 relative to the vortex exterior. *a*, Includes only those points with $\Theta = 430 \pm 10$ K. *b*, Includes only those points with $\Theta = 450 \pm 10$ K.

An O_3 decrease of 13 ± 8 p.p.b.v. per day has been reported by others[35] also using AASE data. The analysis was restricted to a few vertical profiles within the vortex and required a diabatic cooling rate estimated from N_2O and an assumption of strictly vertical descent. If the same cooling rates (0.9 K per day in Θ) are applied to the fits in Fig. 1*c* and no account is made for O_3 flux into the vortex, loss rates of from 9 p.p.b.v. per day where $N_2O = 210$ p.p.b.v. to 24 p.p.b.v. per day where $N_2O = 130$ p.p.b.v. are obtained.

As O_3 is low within the vortex early in the mission, a result of O_3 flux from above or from the exterior of the vortex without concurrent O_3 loss would be increased O_3 relative to N_2O; that is, the interior O_3–N_2O relationship would appear increasingly similar to the exterior relationship. This was not observed, again implying, as found in the discussion on summertime loss, that O_3 was chemically destroyed during the mission. From Fig. 3, O_3 loss had occurred by January. Further analysis of individual flights reveals that, on the first flight, 3 January, ~1,000 p.p.b.v. of O_3 had been lost at 465 K; that is, substantial O_3 loss had occurred before the mission.

Our analysis of the flowing processor still leaves an important question unanswered: "What is the cause of the O_3 loss?". As previously mentioned, the cause of the Antarctic O_3 loss has been attributed to catalytic destruction by chlorine, and, to a lesser degree, bromine. Model calculations for the Arctic based on measured ClO and BrO suggest that O_3 loss approached 12% (about 12 p.p.b.v. per day) during the Arctic campaign[46]. Coupled photochemical–microphysical lagrangian model calculations indicate that an O_3 loss of more than 20 p.p.b.v. per day could have been sustained throughout much of February[47]. Solar radiation and measured ClO increased substantially during the mission[48], so losses should be much less in early January. Therefore, the loss indicated in our analysis for early January is too large to match these model studies. But meteorological data show

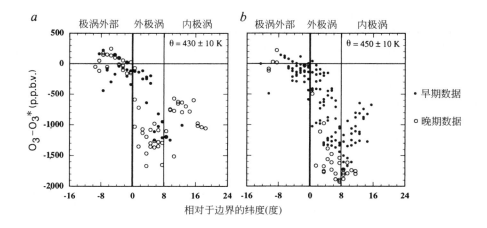

图 3. $O_3 - O_3^*$ 与到极涡边界的纬度之间的关系。其中包含早期数据（1 月 30 日以前）和晚期数据（任务执行期间的剩余数据），每个点代表一个航次中相对于边界 1 个纬度上的平均值。负值表示相对于极涡外 O_3 的亏损。a，仅包括 $\Theta = 430 \pm 10$ K 时的各点。b，仅包括 $\Theta = 450 \pm 10$ K 时的各点。

其他学者[35]根据 AASE 的有关数据得到 O_3 每天降低 13 ± 8 ppbv。该分析仅限于在一些极涡内的垂向剖面上进行，并且需要通过 N_2O 估算出非绝热冷却速率，同时还需假定气团严格垂直下降。倘若将相同的冷却速率（Θ 每天降低 0.9 K）应用到图 1c 的拟合结果中，并且没有其他因素造成 O_3 进入极涡，就能得到 O_3 的亏损率为从每天 9 ppbv（$N_2O = 210$ ppbv 时）到每天 24 ppbv（$N_2O = 130$ ppbv 时）。

在任务早期，极涡内 O_3 的含量较低，由于有一个来自极涡上部或外部的 O_3 通量，同时又没有 O_3 亏损发生，所以 O_3 相对于 N_2O 的含量将增加；也就是说，极涡内 O_3 与 N_2O 之间的关系与极涡外越来越相似。但我们并未观测到这种现象，这再次说明，如同关于夏季亏损的讨论一样，任务期间 O_3 的亏损是由化学因素造成的。从图 3 可以看出，到 1 月份时，O_3 亏损已经发生了。对各航次的进一步分析显示，1 月 3 日第一个航次时，465 K 处 O_3 降低了约 1,000 ppbv；也就是说，在任务开始之前 O_3 就已发生大量亏损了。

在我们关于气流处理器的分析中，还有一个问题始终未得到解决，即"O_3 亏损的原因是什么？"。前面提到，南极 O_3 的亏损被归因于氯的催化分解作用，溴也在较小程度上造成了这一亏损。根据所测定的 ClO 和 BrO 得到的北极地区的模拟计算结果显示，调查期间北极 O_3 的亏损量接近 12%（约为每天 12 ppbv）[46]。耦合的光化学—微物理学拉格朗日模式计算结果表明，2 月份的大部分时间里，O_3 每天的亏损量保持在 20 ppbv 以上[47]。任务期间太阳辐射和 ClO 的测定结果显著增大[48]，因此，1 月初 O_3 的亏损应该小得多。所以，我们所分析出的 1 月初的 O_3 亏损值远大于模式计算的结果。但气象数据显示，11 月末气压为 30 毫巴时，气温已足够低，可以

that temperatures were low enough to form polar stratospheric clouds at 30 mbar by late November (A. F. Tuck, personal communication), and the eccentricity of the Arctic vortex is sufficient to frequently carry outer vortex air into sunlit regions. These episodic conditions may be sufficient to produce a significant O_3 loss at 30 mbar during late November and December. Diabatic cooling could bring this somewhat depleted air to ER-2 flight altitudes by early January. Summertime O_3 loss might also have some residual effect.

One of the striking results in the Antarctic campaign was the observed rapid decrease in O_3 and simultaneous increase in ClO as the aircraft crossed into the ozone hole along an isentropic flight leg[10]. On 9 February 1989, a similar but less dramatic isentropic O_3 decrease was observed poleward of the Arctic boundary[49] that was coincident with very high ClO and is shown in Fig. 4a, b. Figure 4a shows decreasing O_3 poleward of the vortex boundary that is collocated with decreasing N_2O. This positive correlation between O_3 and N_2O inside is contrasted by the usual negative correlation seen outside the boundary, implying O_3 loss within the vortex. Figure 4b shows no O_3 loss outside the boundary, substantial loss inside (implied by negative values for $O_3 - O_3^*$), and that the loss occurs precisely where ClO increases dramatically. Figure 4c demonstrates that this correlation between O_3 loss and ClO in the outer vortex persists throughout the mission and is evident even with constant N_2O. In this plot of all outer vortex data, ClO is the abscissa and $O_3 - O_3^*$ the ordinate with Θ restricted to 435 ± 15 K. The data are tightly binned by N_2O value and each bin is provided with a linear fit. It is evident that O_3 loss and ClO are positively correlated over a wide range of N_2O, and the linear fits are surprisingly similar, although their slopes increase at the higher N_2O values.

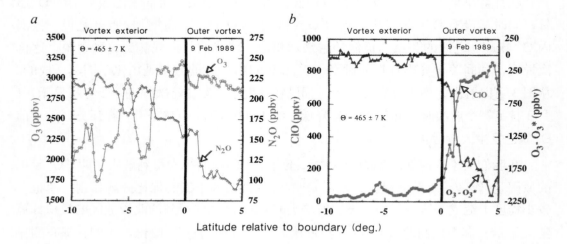

Latitude relative to boundary (deg.)

形成极地平流层云（塔克，个人交流），并且北极极涡的离心率足以使其经常携带外极涡空气进入到阳光照射的区域。11 月末和 12 月期间，这些不定期发生的情况可能足以在 30 毫巴的气压下使 O_3 发生明显的亏损。到 1 月初，非绝热冷却过程可能会将这种有些贫 O_3 的空气带到 ER-2 飞机的飞行高度上。夏季的 O_3 亏损也可能有一定的残留效应。

南极调查活动中的一个重大发现就是，当飞机沿一条等熵航线越过边界进入臭氧洞时，观测到了 O_3 的快速减少，同时伴随着 ClO 的增加[10]。1989 年 2 月 9 日，在北极极涡边界向极方向也观测到了类似的 O_3 浓度沿等熵面降低，只是程度稍弱[49]，这一点与极高的 ClO 浓度是一致的，如图 4a、b 所示。图 4a 所示为极涡边界向极方向 O_3 的减少，对应着 N_2O 的减少。极涡内 O_3 与 N_2O 之间的这种正相关关系与通常在边界外见到的负相关性恰恰相反，说明极涡内有 O_3 亏损。图 4b 显示，边界外没有 O_3 亏损，边界内则亏损严重（从 $O_3 - O_3^*$ 为负值可以看出），而 O_3 的亏损恰好就在发生 ClO 显著增加的地方。图 4c 展示了外极涡中 O_3 与 ClO 之间的这种关系在整个调查期间一直存在，而且即使在 N_2O 含量不变时，这种关系也非常明显。该图所示为外极涡的全部数据，其中横坐标为 ClO，纵坐标为 $O_3 - O_3^*$，Θ 限制在 435 ± 15 K。所有数据均根据 N_2O 的值作了严格的划分，并对每部分数据都作了线性拟合。很显然，在很广的 N_2O 值范围内，O_3 亏损与 ClO 之间存在正相关关系，而且各部分的线性拟合结果都惊人地相似，尽管它们的斜率在 N_2O 值较大时会增大。

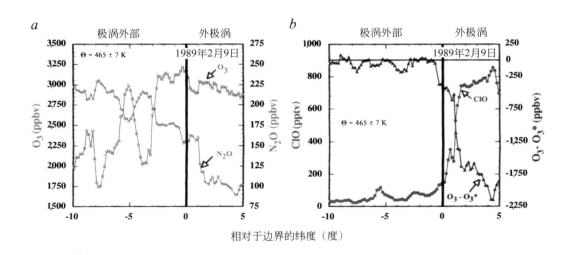

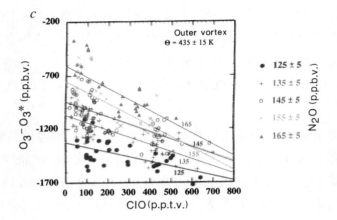

Fig. 4. *a*, O$_3$ and N$_2$O data from 9 February 1989 are plotted against latitude relative to the boundary along a flight leg with $\Theta = 465\pm7$ K. *b*, Same flight as in (*a*) except O$_3$ – O$_3^*$ and ClO are plotted against latitude relative to the boundary. Negative values for O$_3$ – O$_3^*$ indicate O$_3$ loss relative to the vortex exterior. *c*, O$_3$ – O$_3^*$ is plotted against ClO, including all mission data in the outer vortex with $\Theta = 435\pm15$ K. Data are 100-s averages that are binned by N$_2$O and a linear fit is provided for each bin.

Summary

Evaluating O$_3$ loss in the Arctic winter is complex because of our limited understanding of the effects of polar dynamics. Although there seems to be a consensus on significant diabatic cooling at high latitudes, and poleward flux into the Arctic vortex, there are uncertainties in the cooling rates and differing opinions on the altitude at which air is supplied to the vortex. Descent and poleward flux into the vortex (regardless of the altitude of the flux), along with concurrent O$_3$ loss together form a "flowing processor", accepting air rich in O$_3$ from lower latitudes, and liberating air somewhat depleted in O$_3$ through the bottom of the vortex. The relative rates of O$_3$ loss and its resupply determine whether a signature of that loss will be evident in isentropic and column analyses. To avoid these problems we have used a chemically conserved tracer, N$_2$O, to infer Arctic O$_3$ loss, a method similar to that used to infer loss in the exterior of the Antarctic ozone hole[27].

The analysis reveals an *in situ* O$_3$ loss of 500–1,500 p.p.b.v. (12–35%) throughout the vortex relative to its exterior. This corresponds to a decrease in column O$_3$ of about 6% over the 4 km depth covered in this analysis. If this loss is of anthropogenic origin emerging during the past decade, the decrease we report is consistent with the 4–10% long-term seasonal column change found by the Ozone Trends Panel[25]. The rate of O$_3$ loss has been approximated by assuming vertical descent and a conservative cooling rate. Losses of 9–24 p.p.b.v. per day are obtained for parcels with N$_2$O from 210 p.p.b.v. to 130 p.p.b.v., respectively. These rates are comparable to but slightly higher than model calculations. Larger cooling rates and deviations from vertical descent will both increase this difference.

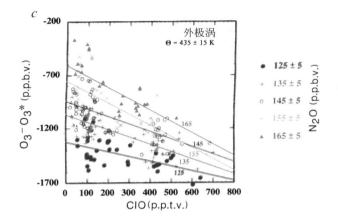

图 4. *a*，1989 年 2 月 9 日，飞机沿 $\Theta = 465 \pm 7$ K 飞行时，O_3 和 N_2O 的数据与到边界的纬度之间的关系。*b*，与 *a* 同一航次的 $O_3 - O_3^*$ 和 ClO 与到边界的纬度之间的关系。$O_3 - O_3^*$ 为负值时，表示 O_3 相对于极涡外部是亏损的。*c*，$O_3 - O_3^*$ 与 ClO 的关系图，其中包含了 $\Theta = 435 \pm 15$ K 时外极涡的全部调查数据。所有数据均为 100 秒的平均值，且根据 N_2O 的浓度将其分为 5 组，同时给出了各组数据的线性拟合结果。

总　结

由于我们对极地地区动力作用的了解有限，所以对北极地区冬季 O_3 亏损的评估变得非常复杂。虽然在关于高纬地区非绝热冷却过程以及存在向极气流通量进入北极极涡方面似乎已达成一致认识，但冷却速率仍不确定，对于空气进入极涡的高度问题也存在不同意见。进入极涡的递减和极向通量（无论通量的高度如何），以及同时发生的 O_3 亏损，共同形成一个"气流处理器"，接收来自低纬地区的富含 O_3 的空气，并由极涡底部释放出 O_3 含量相对较少的空气。O_3 的相对亏损速率及其再补偿机制决定了在等熵分析和 O_3 柱分析中 O_3 亏损的特征是否明显。为了避免上述这些问题的发生，我们采用了具有化学守恒性质的痕量气体 N_2O，来推断北极地区 O_3 的亏损情况，这与评估南极臭氧洞外 O_3 的亏损时所采用的方法 [27] 类似。

分析表明，相对于极涡外部来说，整个极涡内现场测定到的 O_3 亏损量约为 500 ~ 1,500 ppbv（12% ~ 35%）。这对应于本文所分析的 4 千米高的 O_3 柱总量约 6% 的减少量。倘若该亏损量是由过去十年中人类活动的影响造成的，那么，我们所得到的 O_3 减少量与国际臭氧预测专家小组 [25] 发现的 O_3 柱长期季节性变化量为 4% ~ 10% 这一结果是一致的。通过假定气流垂直下降和较保守的冷却率大体估计出 O_3 的亏损速率。当气团中 N_2O 浓度为从 210 ppbv 到 130 ppbv 时，对应的 O_3 的亏损率大致为每天 9 ~ 24 ppbv。该速率值略高于模式计算结果。冷却速率以及与垂直递减率的偏差增大时，都会增大这种差异。

An O_3 loss was observed in early January that is too large to match model studies. The Arctic vortex polar asymmetry contrasts with the more symmetric Antarctic vortex, and the asymmetry could enhance early O_3 loss in the Arctic relative to the seasonally comparable period in the Antarctic. This would be due to episodic exposure to sunlight during the low-latitude excursions of the polar jet. The low values of O_3 found on 3 January indicate substantial O_3 loss before the mission and may result from this intermittent exposure.

We have found that the O_3 loss is correlated with elevated ClO in the outer vortex, along with enhancement of O_3 loss where there is maximum exposure of the vortex to sunlight. This suggests, but does not prove, that chlorine is an important factor in the ozone decrease. The agreement between this analysis and model studies is not perfect, particularly in early January. Perhaps alternative explanations of the data will emerge that do not require such large wintertime O_3 loss. In any case, it is clear that accurate evaluation of Arctic O_3 loss must account for the effects of polar dynamics.

(**347**, 31-36; 1990)

M. H. Proffitt[*]**, J. J. Margitan**[†]**, K. K. Kelly**[‡]**, M. Loewenstein**[§]**, J. R. Podolske**[§] **& K. R. Chan**[§]

[*] NOAA Aeronomy Lab, 325 Broadway, Boulder, Colorado 80303 and CIRES, University of Colorado, Boulder, Colorado 80309, USA

[†] Jet Propulsion Laboratory, California Institute of Technology, Pasadena, California 91109, USA

[‡] NOAA Aeronomy Lab, 325 Broadway, Boulder, Colorado 80303, USA

[§] NASA Ames Research Center, Moffett Field, California 94035, USA

Received 21 December 1989; accepted 19 July 1990.

References:

1. Farman, J. C., Gardiner, B. G. & Shanklin, J. D. *Nature* **315**, 207-210 (1985).

2. Hofmann, D. J., Harder, J. W., Rolf, S. R. & Rosen, J. R. *Nature* **326**, 59-62 (1987).

3. de Zafra, R. L. *et al. Nature* **328**, 408-411 (1987).

4. Solomon, S., Mount, G. H., Sanders, R. W. & Schmeltekopf, A. L. *J. Geophys. Res.* **92**, 8329- 8338 (1987).

5. *J. Geophys. Res.* **94**, Nos. D9 and D14 (1989).

6. Proffitt, M. H. *et al. J. Geophys. Res.* **94**, 16547-16555 (1989).

7. Loewenstein, M., Podolske, J. R., Chan, K. R. & Strahan, S. E. *J. Geophys. Res.* **94**, 11589- 11598 (1989).

8. Brune, W. H., Anderson, J. G. & Chan, K. R. *J. Geophys. Res.* **94**, 16649-16663 (1989).

9. Chan, K. R., Scott, S. G., Bui, T. P., Bowen, S. W. & Day, J. *J. Geophys. Res.* **94**, 11573-11587 (1989).

10. Proffitt *et al. J. Geophys. Res.* **94**, 11437-11448 (1989).

11. Anderson, J. G. *et al. J. Geophys. Res.* **94**, 11480-11520 (1989).

12. Jones, R. L. *et al. J. Geophys. Res.* **94**, 11529-11558 (1989).

13. Rodriguez, J. M. *et al. J. Geophys. Res.* **94**, 16683-16703 (1989).

14. Farman, J. C. *Phil Trans. R. Soc.* B **279**, 261-271 (1977).

15. Juckes, M. N. & McIntyre, M. E. *Nature* **328**, 590-596 (1987).

16. Hartmann, D. L. *et al. J. Geophys. Res.* **94**, 16779-16795 (1989).

17. Danielsen, E. F. & Houben, H. *Anthropogene Beeinflussung der Ozonschicht,* 191-242 (DECHEMA-Frankfurt am Main, 1988).

18. Tuck, A. F. *J. Geophys. Res.* **94**, 11687-11737 (1989).

19. Proffitt, M. H. *et al. J. Geophys. Res.* **94**, 16797-16813 (1989).

20. Murphy, D. M. *et al. J. Geophys. Res.* **94**, 11669-11685 (1989).

21. Watterson, I. G. & Tuck, A. F. *J. Geophys. Res.* **94**, 16511-16525 (1989).

22. Cariolle, D., Lasserre-Bigorry, A. & Royer, J.-F. *J. Geophys. Res.* **95**, 1883-1898 (1990).

我们观测到的 1 月初 O_3 亏损量比模式研究结果要大得多。北极极涡的不对称性与更为对称的南极极涡形成对比，而这种不对称性又会使得早期北极的 O_3 亏损相对于同时期的南极有所加剧。这可能是由于极地急流向较低纬度偏移时间歇性地暴露于阳光下造成的。1 月 3 日出现的 O_3 低值表明，该调查之前已存在明显的 O_3 亏损了，而且可能就是由这种间歇性暴露于阳光下引起的。

我们已发现，外极涡中 O_3 的亏损与 ClO 浓度的升高有关，同时，在极涡照射太阳光最大的位置，O_3 亏损也会加剧。这说明，但并不能证明，氯是引起臭氧层亏损的重要因素。本文分析结果与模式研究之间的一致性不能堪称完美，尤其是在 1 月初时。当然，或许还存在其他关于上述数据的解释，从而不需要如此大的 O_3 亏损量。不管怎样，显然，要准确估算北极 O_3 的亏损量就必须考虑极地动力作用的影响。

（齐红艳 翻译；安俊岭 审稿）

23. Hofmann, D. J. *et al. Nature* **340**, 117-121 (1989).

24. Evans, W. F. J. *Geophys. Res. Lett.* **17**, 167-170 (1990).

25. Ozone Trends Panel *Present State of Knowledge of the Upper Atmosphere, 1998, NASA Ref. Publn 1208* (Natn. Tech. Inf. Serv., Springfield, Virginia, 1989).

26. *Geophys. Res. Lett.* **17**, No. 4 (1990).

27. Proffitt, M. H., Fahey, D. W., Kelly K. K. & Tuck, A. F. *Nature* **342**, 233-237 (1989).

28. Solomon, S., Garcia, R. R. & Stordal, F. *J. Geophys. Res.* **90**, 12981-12989 (1985).

29. Garcia, R. R. & Solomon, S. *J. Geophys. Res.* **90**, 3850-3868 (1985).

30. Brasseur, G. J. & Solomon, S. *Aeronomy of the Middle Atmosphere* 2nd Edn (Reidel, Dordrecht, 1986).

31. Perliski, L. M., Solomon, S. & London, J. *Planet Space Sci.* **37**, 1527-1538 (1989).

32. Strahan, S. E. *et al. J. Geophys. Res.* **94**, 16749-16756 (1989).

33. Gunson, M. R. *et al. J. Geophys. Res.* (in the press).

34. Rosenfield, J. E., Schoeberl, M. R., Lait, L. R. & Newman, P. A. *Geophys. Res Lett.* **17**, 345-348 (1990).

35. Schoeberl, M. R. *et al. Geophys. Res. Lett.* **17**, 469-472 (1990).

36. Brewer, A. W. *Q. Jl R. Met. Soc.* **75**, 351-363 (1949).

37. Dobson, G. M. G. *Proc. R. Soc.* A**236**, 187-193 (1956).

38. Brewer, A. W. & Wilson, A. W. *Q. Jl R. Met. Soc.* **94**, 249-265 (1968).

39. Dütsch, H. U. *Can. J. Chem.* **52**, 1491-1504 (1974).

40. London, J. F., Bojkov, S., Oltmans, S. & Kelley, J. I. *Atlas of the Global Distribution of Total Ozone July 1957-June 1967* NCAR tech. Note 113 (NCAR, Boulder, 1976).

41. Bojkov, R. D. & Rumen, D. *Met. Atmos. Phys.* **38**, 117-130 (1988).

42. *Ozone Data for the World, Atmospheric Environment Service* Vol. 30, No. 3, 312-318 (Can. Atmos. Envir. Serv. & World Met. Org., Toronto, 1989).

43. Leovy, C. B. *et al. J. Atmos. Sci.* **42**, 230-244 (1985).

44. Kent, G. S., Trepte, C. R., Farrukh, U. H & McCormick, M. P. *J. Atmos. Sci.* **42**, 1536-1551 (1985).

45. Farman, J. C., Murgatroyd, R. J., Silnickas, A. M. & Thrush, B. A. *Q. Jl R. met Soc.* **111**, 1013-1028 (1985).

46. Salawitch, R. J. *et al. Geophys. Res. Lett.* **17**, 561-564 (1990).

47. McKenna, D. S. *et al. Geophys. Res. Lett.* **17**, 553-556 (1990).

48. Brune, W. H., Toohey, D. W., Anderson, J. G. & Chan, K. R. *Geophys. Res. Lett.* **17**, 505-508 (1990).

49. Browell, E. V. *et al. Geophys. Res. Lett.* **17**, 325-328 (1990).

Acknowledgements. We thank Ed Danielsen, Stuart McKeen, George Mount, Susan Solomon, Michael Trainer and Adrian Tuck for their helpful comments, William Brune and Darin Toohey for the use of the ClO data, Melanie Steinkamp and Cynthia Proffitt for their help in Stavanger, Ken Aikin for producing the figures, and the ER-2 pilots and ground crew.

Solid C$_{60}$: a New Form of Carbon

W. Krätschmer *et al.*

Editor's Note

Since the discovery of C$_{60}$ in 1985, this exotic molecule had languished in limbo, since there was no proof of its alleged soccer-ball cage structure. That changed with the publication of this paper from the groups of Wolfgang Krätschmer in Heidelberg and Donald Huffman in Arizona, which described a way to make C$_{60}$ in large quantities. Whereas the original discovery had relied on tiny amounts generated by laser beams, the new method involved simply passing an electrical current through rods of graphite. The researchers were able to make enough of the material to adduce strong experimental evidence for its geometric cage structure. This breakthrough led to the award of the 1996 Nobel Prize in Chemistry to C$_{60}$'s original discoverers.

A new form of pure, solid carbon has been synthesized consisting of a somewhat disordered hexagonal close packing of soccer-ball-shaped C$_{60}$ molecules. Infrared spectra and X-ray diffraction studies of the molecular packing confirm that the molecules have the anticipated "fullerene" structure. Mass spectroscopy shows that the C$_{70}$ molecule is present at levels of a few percent. The solid-state and molecular properties of C$_{60}$ and its possible role in interstellar space can now be studied in detail.

FOLLOWING the observation that even-numbered clusters of carbon atoms in the range C$_{30}$–C$_{100}$ are present in carbon vapour[1], conditions were found[2-4] for which the C$_{60}$ molecule could be made dominant in the large-mass fraction of vapourized graphite. To explain the stability of the molecule, a model was proposed of an elegant structure in which the carbon atoms are arranged at the 60 vertices of a truncated icosahedron, typified by a soccer ball. The structure, dubbed buckminsterfullerene[2] because of its geodesic nature, has been the subject of several theoretical stability tests[5,6] and has been discussed widely in the literature. Calculations of many physical properties have been made, including electron energies[7-9], the optical spectrum[9], vibrational modes[10-15], and the electric and magnetic properties[16,17]. There has been speculation on the possible chemical and industrial uses of C$_{60}$ (ref. 2), and on its importance in astrophysical environments[18-20]. Until now, it has not been possible to produce sufficient quantities of the material to permit measurement of the physical properties, to test the theoretical calculations, or to evaluate the possible applications.

Some of us have recently reported evidence[21,22] for the presence of the C$_{60}$ molecule in soot condensed from evaporated graphite. The identification was based primarily on the observed isotope shifts of the infrared absorptions when ^{12}C was replaced by ^{13}C,

固态C$_{60}$：碳的一种新形式

克雷奇默等

编者按

自1985年发现C$_{60}$以来，因为没有证据证明其所谓的足球笼状结构，这个奇特的分子被冷落在边缘。这一现象随着海德堡大学的沃尔夫冈·克雷奇默和亚利桑那大学的唐纳德·赫夫曼发表的论文而改变，该论文描述了一种大量制备C$_{60}$的方法。C$_{60}$最初的发现建立在激光束产生的微量物质上，而这个新方法只是简单地使电流经过石墨棒。研究人员能够做出大量的原料，为几何笼状结构提供强有力的实验证据。这一突破使C$_{60}$的最初发现者们获得1996年诺贝尔化学奖。

一种新形式的纯净、固态的碳已经被合成出来，它由足球形状的C$_{60}$分子以略显杂乱的六方密堆积形式构成。对分子堆积形式的红外光谱和X射线衍射研究确认分子具有预期的"富勒烯"结构。质谱显示其中还有百分之几的C$_{70}$分子存在。于是现在就可以详细地研究C$_{60}$分子的固态与分子性质，以及它在星际空间中可能发挥的作用了。

在碳蒸气中观察到了处于C$_{30}$~C$_{100}$范围内的偶数个碳原子簇[1]之后，已经找到了能使C$_{60}$分子成为气化石墨产物主要成分的反应条件[2-4]。为了解释这种分子的稳定性，一种具有精巧结构的模型被提出来：其中碳原子排布于一个截角二十面体的60个顶点处，就像一个足球那样。这一结构——由于其测地学性质而被称为巴克敏斯特富勒烯[2]——曾是几种理论性稳定试验的对象[5,6]，也曾在文献中进行过广泛的探讨。人们已经对其很多种物理性质进行了计算，其中包括电子能量[7-9]、光谱[9]、振动模式[10-15]以及电磁学性质[16,17]。曾有过关于C$_{60}$可能的化学与工业应用（参考文献2），以及它在天体物理环境中的重要性[18-20]的推测。到目前为止，仍然没能制备出足够量的原料来保证其物理性质的测定，以及检验理论计算结果，或是评估其可能的应用。

我们中的一些人最近报道了关于从气化石墨中凝华得到的炭黑中存在C$_{60}$分子的证据[21,22]。鉴定的主要依据是当 ^{12}C 被 ^{13}C 所取代时，在红外吸收中观测到的同

and on comparison of the observed features with theoretical predictions. The measured infrared and ultraviolet absorption bands were superimposed on a rather large continuum background absorption from the graphitic carbon which comprised $\geqslant 95\%$ of the sample. Here we report how to extract the carrier of the features from the soot, how to purify it, and evidence that the material obtained is in fact primarily C$_{60}$.

Method of Production

The starting material for our process is pure graphitic carbon soot (referred to below as simply soot) with a few percent by weight of C$_{60}$ molecules, as described in refs 21, 22. It is produced by evaporating graphite electrodes in an atmosphere of ~100 torr of helium. The resulting black soot is gently scraped from the collecting surfaces inside the evaporation chamber and dispersed in benzene. The material giving rise to the spectral features attributed to C$_{60}$ dissolves to produce a wine-red to brown liquid, depending on the concentration. The liquid is then separated from the soot and dried using gentle heat, leaving a residue of dark brown to black crystalline material. Other non-polar solvents, such as carbon disulphide and carbon tetrachloride, can also dissolve the material. An alternative concentration procedure is to heat the soot to 400 °C in a vacuum or in an inert atmosphere, thus subliming the C$_{60}$ out of the soot (W. Schmidt, personal communication). The sublimed coatings are brown to grey, depending on the thickness. The refractive index in the near-infrared and visible is about two. To purify the material, we recommend removing the ubiquitous hydrocarbons before the concentration procedure is applied (for example, by washing the initial soot with ether). Thin films and powder samples of the new material can be handled without special precautions and seem to be stable in air for at least several weeks, although there does seem to be some deterioration with time for reasons that are as yet unclear. The material can be sublimed repeatedly without decomposition. Using the apparatus described, one person can produce of the order of 100 mg of the purified material in a day.

Studies by optical microscopy of the material left after evaporating the benzene show a variety of what appear to be crystals—mainly rods, platelets and star-like flakes. Figure 1 shows a micrograph of such an assemblage. All crystals tend to exhibit six-fold symmetry. In transmitted light they appear red to brown in colour; in reflected light the larger crystals have a metallic appearance whereas the platelets show interference colours. The platelets can be rather thin and are thus ideally suited for electron-diffraction studies in an electron microscope (see the inset in Fig. 3).

位素位移，以及所观测的特征峰与理论预测之间的比较。所测得的红外和紫外吸收谱是叠加在较大的连续本底吸收上的，这种本底吸收来自于占样品总量95%以上的石墨碳。本文中我们将报道如何从炭黑中提取具有这些特征峰的物质，如何将其提纯，以及证明所得物质实际上主要是C$_{60}$。

制备方法

我们的原材料是纯的石墨炭黑（相当于下面所说的纯炭黑），其中含有几个重量百分比的C$_{60}$分子，如参考文献21和22中所述。通过在约100 torr氦气气氛中气化石墨电极来制备。将所得的黑色炭黑从气化室的凝结面上轻轻地刮下，并将其分散在苯中。该物质能够产生C$_{60}$特征峰，并且溶解后生成的液体根据浓度不同可以呈现酒红色到棕褐色。接着将该液体与炭黑分离，并通过温和加热蒸干，残留一种从深褐色到黑色的晶体物质。其他非极性溶剂，例如二硫化碳和四氯化碳，也能溶解该物质。另一种富集过程，是将炭黑在真空或者惰性气氛中加热到400 ℃，使C$_{60}$从炭黑中升华（施密特，个人交流）。升华得到的薄层依其厚度不同而呈现为棕色到灰色。在近红外和可见光区的折射率约为2。为提纯该物质，我们建议在实施富集过程之前先除掉普遍存在的烃类（例如通过用乙醚清洗最初的炭黑）。新物质的薄膜或粉末样品无需特别小心地加以处理，因为它似乎能在空气中至少稳定存在几个星期，尽管由于目前尚不清楚的原因，确实存在着一些随时间而出现的变质。这种物质可以反复进行升华而不会分解。利用我们所描述的装置，一个人一天能够制备出百毫克量级的提纯后的该物质。

对苯蒸发后残留物质的光学显微研究显示出各种看起来像晶体的物质——主要是杆状、片状和星状薄片。图1显示了这样一组集合物的显微图。所有晶体都倾向于呈现六重对称性。在透射光中，它们的颜色呈现为从红色到棕色；在反射光中，较大的晶体具有金属般的外观，而片状薄片则显示出干扰色。片状体可以非常薄，因此十分适合于在电子显微镜中进行电子衍射研究（参见图3中的插入图）。

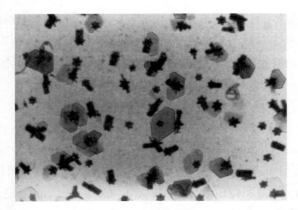

Fig. 1. Transmission micrograph of typical crystals of the C$_{60}$ showing thin platelets, rods and stars of hexagonal symmetry.

Mass Spectroscopy

The material has been analysed by mass spectrometry at several facilities. All mass spectra have a strong peak at mass 720 a.m.u., the mass of C$_{60}$. Significant differences in the spectra occur only at masses lower than 300 a.m.u. Most of these differences seem to originate from the different ionization techniques and in the different methods of desorbing molecules from the sample. Mass spectra recorded at low and high resolution are shown in Fig. 2. The spectra were obtained using a time-of-flight secondary-ion mass spectrometer[23] and a C$_{60}$-coated stainless-steel plate. In the mass range above 300 a.m.u., the spectrum is dominated by C$_{60}$ ions and its fragments (even-numbered clusters of atomic carbon), and C$_{70}$ ions. In this sample, the ratio of C$_{70}$ to C$_{60}$ is ~0.1. The high-resolution mass spectrum shows approximately the expected isotope pattern for C$_{60}$. The increasing background in the low-resolution mass spectrum is not produced by the sample—such backgrounds also occur in blank measurements on uncoated stainless-steel substrates.

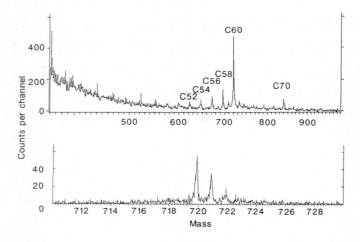

Fig. 2. Low-resolution (top) and high-resolution time-of-flight mass spectra of positive ions obtained from coatings of solid C$_{60}$. A 5-keV Ar$^+$ ion beam was used to sputter and ionize the sample. The isotope pattern (bottom) is approximately that expected for C$_{60}$ molecules composed of ^{12}C and ^{13}C isotopes of natural abundance.

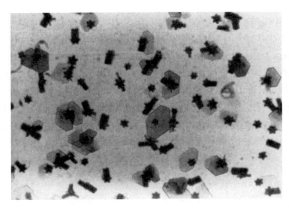

图 1. C$_{60}$ 典型晶体的透射显微镜图，呈现为薄片状、杆状和具有六边形对称性的星状。

质谱分析法

已经在几个实验室用质谱对该物质进行了分析。所有的谱图都在 720 amu，即 C$_{60}$ 的质量处有一个强峰。不同质谱之间的显著差异只出现在小于 300 amu 的质量部分。这些差异中的大部分可能源于不同的电离技术和从样品中脱附分子的不同方法。图 2 显示了以低的和高的分辨率记录的质谱。谱图是利用飞行时间二次离子质谱仪[23]和 C$_{60}$ 覆盖的不锈钢平板获得的。在超过 300 amu 的质量范围中，主要是 C$_{60}$ 离子及其碎片（偶数个碳原子的原子簇），还有 C$_{70}$ 离子。在这份样品中，C$_{70}$ 与 C$_{60}$ 的比例约为 0.1。高分辨率质谱图显示出与预期的 C$_{60}$ 近似的同位素分布。在低分辨质谱图中，不断升高的本底并不是由样品产生——对无覆盖层不锈钢基底进行的空白检测中也会出现这样的本底。

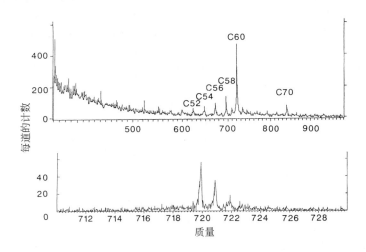

图 2. 固体 C$_{60}$ 覆盖层的低分辨率（上部）和高分辨率的飞行时间正离子质谱图。用一条 5 keV 的 Ar$^+$ 离子束来轰击电离样品。同位素分布（下部）与预期的按自然界中 ^{12}C 和 ^{13}C 同位素丰度构成的 C$_{60}$ 分子大致相同。

So far, the cleanest mass spectra have been obtained when the material was evaporated and ionized in the vapour phase by electrons. In such spectra the low-mass background is substantially reduced and the entire mass spectrum is dominated by C$_{60}$ ions and its fragments. The ratio of C$_{70}$ to C$_{60}$ in these mass spectra is ~0.02 and seems to be smaller than that shown in Fig. 2. Both ratios are of the order of those reported from laser-evaporation experiments[2,3]. We assume, as previously suggested[24], that the C$_{70}$ molecule also has a closed-cage structure, either elongated[24] or nearly spherical[25]. Further details of the mass spectroscopy of the new material will be published elsewhere.

Structure

To determine if the C$_{60}$ molecules form a regular lattice, we performed electron and X-ray diffraction studies on the individual crystals and on the powder. A typical X-ray diffraction pattern of the C$_{60}$ powder is shown in Fig. 3. To aid in comparing the electron diffraction results with the X-ray results we have inset the electron diffraction pattern in Fig. 3. From the hexagonal array of diffraction spots indexed as shown in the figure, a d spacing of 8.7 Å was deduced corresponding to the (100) reciprocal lattice vector of a hexagonal lattice. The most obvious correspondence between the two types of diffraction is between the peak at 5.01 Å of the X-ray pattern and the (110) spot of the electron diffraction pattern, which gives a spacing of ~5.0 Å. Assuming that the C$_{60}$ molecules are behaving approximately as spheres stacked in a hexagonal close-packed lattice with a c/a ratio of 1.633, d spacings can be calculated. The results are shown in Table 1. The values derived from this interpretation are $a=10.02$ Å and $c=16.36$ Å. The nearest-neighbour distance is thus 10.02 Å. For such a crystal structure the density is calculated to be 1.678 g cm^{-3}, which is consistent with the value of 1.65±0.05 g cm^{-3} determined by suspending crystal samples in aqueous GaCl$_3$ solutions of known densities. Although the agreement shown in Table 1 is good, the absence of the characteristically strong (101) diffraction of the hexagonal close-packed structure, and the broad continuum in certain regions suggest that the order is less than perfect. Further, X-ray diffraction patterns from carefully grown crystals up to 500 μm in size with well developed faces yielded no clear spot pattern (in contrast to the electron diffraction pattern on micrometre-sized crystals). It therefore appears that these larger crystals do not exhibit long-range periodicity in all directions.

Table 1. X-ray diffraction results

Measured 2θ (deg)	Measured d spacing (Å)	Calculated d spacing (Å)	Assignment (hkl)
10.2 shoulder	8.7	8.68	(100)
10.81	8.18	8.18	(002)
		7.68	(101)
17.69	5.01	5.01	(110)
20.73	4.28	4.28	(112)
21.63	4.11	4.09	(004)
28.1	3.18	3.17	(114)

目前为止，最干净的质谱图是通过使该物质气化并用电子使其在气相中电离而获得的。在这些谱图中，低质量本底明显减弱，整张谱图主要就是 C$_{60}$ 离子及其碎片。在这些质谱中 C$_{70}$ 与 C$_{60}$ 的比例约为 0.02，比图 2 中似乎还要小些。这两个比值和激光气化实验[2,3]中所报道的数值具有相同的数量级。如同此前曾提出的[24]，我们认为 C$_{70}$ 分子也具有闭合的笼状结构，或者是伸长的[24]或者是近似球形的[25]。更多关于这种新物质的质谱详细情况将另外发表。

结　　构

为了确定 C$_{60}$ 分子是否形成规则晶格，我们对单个晶体和粉末进行了电子和 X 射线衍射研究。图 3 显示的是一张典型的 C$_{60}$ 粉末 X 射线衍射图。为了便于比较电子衍射结果与X射线衍射结果，我们在图 3 中插入了电子衍射图。在如图中所示确定指标的衍射点的六方排列中，推测 8.7 Å 的 d 间距对应于六方晶系中的（100）倒易晶格矢量。两类衍射之间最明显的对应关系存在于 X 射线图中位于 5.01 Å 处的峰与电子衍射图中的（110）点——它给出了约 5.0 Å 的间距。假定 C$_{60}$ 分子类似于叠放在六方密堆积晶格中的球体，其中 c/a 比例为 1.633，可以计算出 d 间距。结果列在表 1 中。从这一注释中可以导出的数值是 $a=10.02$ Å 和 $c=16.36$ Å。于是最近相邻间距就是 10.02 Å。对这样一种晶体结构计算出的密度应该是 1.678 g·cm^{-3}，它与通过将样品悬浮于已知密度的 GaCl$_3$ 水溶液中而测定的数值 1.65 ± 0.05 g·cm^{-3} 是一致的。尽管表 1 中显示出很好的一致性，但六角密堆积结构所特有的（101）强衍射的缺失，以及某些区域中宽的连续性，表明晶体的有序性不够完美。此外，利用精心生长出来的尺寸达到 500 μm 且具有良好晶面的晶体得到的X射线衍射图却无法得到清晰的光斑花样（这与对微米尺寸的晶体所进行的电子衍射图是不同的）。由此可见，这些较大的晶体并不是在所有方向上都显示出长程周期性。

表1. X射线衍射结果

测得的2θ（deg）	测得的 d 间距（Å）	计算的 d 间距（Å）	指数(hkl)
10.2 肩峰	8.7	8.68	(100)
10.81	8.18	8.18	(002)
		7.68	(101)
17.69	5.01	5.01	(110)
20.73	4.28	4.28	(112)
21.63	4.11	4.09	(004)
28.1	3.18	3.17	(114)

Continued

Measured 2θ (deg)	Measured d spacing (Å)	Calculated d spacing (Å)	Assignment (hkl)
30.8	2.90	2.90	(300)
32.7	2.74	2.73	(006)

Assignments for a hexagonal lattice using $a=10.02$ Å, $c=16.36$ Å. $(1/d^2) = \dfrac{4}{3}[(h^2+hk+k^2)/a^2]+l^2/c^2$.

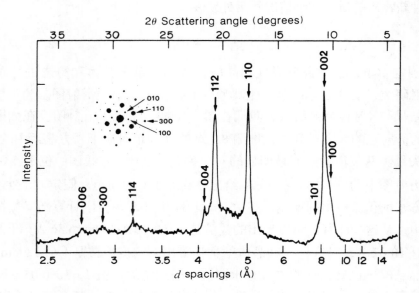

Fig. 3. X-ray diffraction pattern of a microcrystalline powder of C$_{60}$. Inset (upper left) is a single-crystal electron diffraction pattern indexed with Miller indices compatible with the X-ray pattern. The pattern is from a thin platelet such as those in Fig. 1 with the electron beam perpendicular to the flat face.

A likely explanation for these facts lies in the disordered stacking of the molecules in planes normal to the c axis. It is well known that the positions taken by spheres in the third layer of stacking determines which of the close-packed structures occurs, the stacking arrangement in a face-centred cubic structure being ABCABC... whereas that in a hexagonal close-packed structure is ABABAB... If the stacking sequence varies, the X-ray lines owing to certain planes will be broadened by the disorder whereas other lines will remain sharp. Such disordered crystalline behaviour was observed long ago in the hexagonal close-packed structure of cobalt[26-28] where X-ray diffraction lines such as (101), (102) and (202) were found to be substantially broadened by the stacking disorder. Reflections from planes such as (002) remain sharp because these planes have identical spacings in the face-centred cubic and hexagonal close-packed structures. For the planes producing broadened diffraction peaks because of this kind of disorder, the following condition for the Miller indices (hkl) has been shown to apply[27,29]: $h-k=3t\pm1$ (where t is an integer) and $l\neq0$. None of these broadened reflections are apparent in the X-ray pattern of Fig. 3. This may explain the weakness of the characteristically strong (101) peak. Whether or not this stacking disorder is related to the presence of the possibly elongated C$_{70}$ molecule has yet to be determined.

测得的2θ（deg）	测得的 d 间距（Å）	计算的 d 间距（Å）	指数(hkl)
30.8	2.90	2.90	(300)
32.7	2.74	2.73	(006)

六方晶系的指数使用a=10.02 Å，c=16.36 Å。$(1/d^2) = \frac{4}{3}[(h^2+hk+k^2)/a^2]+l^2/c^2$。

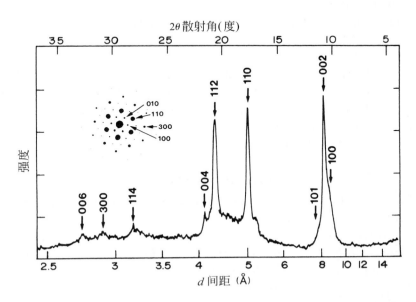

图 3. C₆₀ 微晶粉末的 X 射线衍射图。插入图（左上方）是使用密勒指数表示的单晶电子衍射图，与 X射线图相一致。该图是以垂直于平面方向的电子束作用于图 1 中那样的薄片而得到的。

对于这些事实的一个可能的解释，就是垂直于 c 轴的平面内的分子的无序堆积。众所周知，球体在第三个堆积层中所占据的位置决定了密堆积结构出现的方式，面心立方结构中的堆积方式为 ABCABC… 而在六方密堆积结构中堆积方式是 ABABAB…，如果堆积方式变化了，那么对应于某些平面的X射线谱线将会由于无序性而变宽，而其他谱线则保持尖锐。人们很久以前就已在钴的六方密堆积结构中观测到这种无序的晶体行为[26-28]，其中，诸如（101）、（102）和（202）等 X 射线衍射谱线都由于堆积无序性而明显变宽。来自诸如（002）等平面的反射峰保持尖锐，因为这些平面在面心立方和六方密堆积结构中有相同的面间距。对于那些由于这类无序性导致衍射峰变宽的平面，就可以应用下列以密勒指数（hkl）表示的条件[27,29]：$h-k=3t\pm l$（其中 t 是一个整数）并且 $l\neq0$。在图 3 的 X 射线衍射图中，这些变宽的衍射峰全都不明显。这也许可以解释特征性的强（101）峰为什么会变弱。目前还不能确定这种堆积的无序性是否与可能存在的拉长 C₇₀ 分子有关系。

715

In small crystals at least, the C_{60} molecules seem to assemble themselves into a somewhat ordered array as if they are effectively spherical, which is entirely consistent with the hypothesis that they are shaped like soccer balls. The excess between the nearest-neighbour distance (10.02 Å) and the diameter calculated for the carbon cage itself (7.1 Å) must represent the effective van der Waals diameter set by the repulsion of the π electron clouds extending outward from each carbon atom. Because the van der Waals diameter of carbon is usually considered to be 3.3–3.4 Å the packing seems a little tighter than one might expect for soccer-ball-shaped C_{60} molecules. The reason for this has not yet been determined.

In summary, our diffraction data imply that the substance isolated is at least partially crystalline. The inferred lattice constants, when interpreted in terms of close-packed icosahedral C_{60}, yield a density consistent with the measured value. Further evidence that the molecules are indeed buckminsterfullerene and that the solid primarily consists of these molecules comes from the spectroscopic results.

Spectroscopy

The absorption spectra of the graphitic soot[21,22] showed evidence for the presence of C_{60} in macroscopic quantities. Following the purification steps described above the material can be studied spectroscopically with the assurance that the spectra are dominated by C_{60}, with some possible effects from C_{70}. Samples were prepared for spectroscopy by subliming pure material onto transparent substrates for transmission measurements. Depending on the pressure of helium in the sublimation chamber, the nature of the coatings can range from uniform films (at high vacuum) to coatings of C_{60} smoke (sub-micrometre microcrystalline particles of solid C_{60}) with the particle size depending to some extent on the pressure.

Figure 4 shows the transmission spectrum of an ~2-μm-thick C_{60} coating on a silicon substrate. The infrared bands are at the same positions as previously reported[21,22], with the four most intense lines at 1,429, 1,183, 577 and 528 cm⁻¹; here, however, there is no underlying continuum remaining from the soot. In many of our early attempts to obtain pure C_{60}, there was a strong band in the vicinity of 3.0 μm, which is characteristic of a CH-stretching mode. After much effort this contaminant was successfully removed by washing the soot with ether and using distilled benzene in the extraction. The spectrum in Fig. 4 was obtained when the material cleaned in such a manner was sublimed under vacuum onto the substrate. The spectrum shows very little indication of CH impurities. Vibrational modes to compare with the measured positions of the four strong bands have been calculated by several workers[10-15]. As noted previously, the presence of only four strong bands is expected for the free, truncated icosahedral molecule with its unusually high symmetry. Also present are a number of other weak infrared lines which may be due to other causes, among which may be absorption by the C_{70} molecule or symmetry-breaking produced (for example) by isotopes other than ^{12}C in the C_{60} molecule or by mutual interaction of the C_{60} molecules in the solid. Weaker features at ~2,330 and 2,190 cm⁻¹, located in the vicinity of the free CO_2 and CO stretching modes, may imply some

至少在小晶体中，C$_{60}$ 分子似乎会组合成一种相当有序的排列形式，就像它们真的是球体那样——这与它们的形状像足球的假说完全吻合。最小相邻距离（10.02 Å）和对碳笼本身进行计算而得到的直径（7.1 Å）的差值代表了从每个碳原子向外伸展的 π 电子云的斥力所决定的有效范德华直径。因为通常认为碳原子的范德华直径为 3.3~3.4 Å，所以这种堆积看来比足球形 C$_{60}$ 分子所预期的要紧凑一点。至今尚不能确定其中缘由。

总的来说，我们的衍射数据表明，分离出的物质至少部分是晶体。前面谈到的晶格常数，在用密堆积二十面体型 C$_{60}$ 来解释时，能导出一个与测量值相一致的密度。关于该分子实际上就是巴克敏斯特富勒烯，以及固体主要由这种分子组成的更多证据，则是来自于光谱结果。

光 谱 学

石墨炭黑的吸收光谱[21,22]给出了 C$_{60}$ 以宏观量存在的证据。经过上面所描述的提纯步骤之后，可以对该物质进行光谱学研究，通过谱图确认物质的主要成分为 C$_{60}$，某些可能的效应则来自于 C$_{70}$。通过将纯物质升华到供透射观测用的透明基底表面，可以制备出光谱用样品。随着升华室内的氩气压力的变化，覆盖层的状态可以从均匀薄膜（高真空下）到粒子尺寸在某种程度上取决于压力的 C$_{60}$ 烟尘（固体 C$_{60}$ 的亚微米级微晶颗粒）覆盖层。

图 4 显示出覆盖在硅基底上的一个约 2 μm 厚的 C$_{60}$ 覆盖层的透射光谱。红外谱带位于与此前报道的[21,22]相同的位置，四个最强的谱线位于 1,429 cm^{-1}、1,183 cm^{-1}、577 cm^{-1} 和 528 cm^{-1} 处；但是在这里，不存在残存于炭黑中的基底连续谱。在很多我们试图获得纯 C$_{60}$ 的早期努力中，都有一个位于 3.0 μm 附近的强谱带，那是 CH 伸缩模式所特有的。经过多次努力，终于成功地除掉了这一污染，方法是用乙醚清洗炭黑再用蒸馏苯提取。图 4 中的光谱就是将以这种方式清洗过的原料在真空条件下升华到基底表面而获得的。光谱几乎没有显示出 CH 杂质的迹象。参照四个强谱带的测定位置，已经有若干位研究者[10-15]对振动模式进行了计算。如同之前已经谈到的，只有四个强谱带存在，这对于这种具有很高对称性的截角二十面体自由分子来说是意料之中的。还有很多其他的弱红外谱线出现，它们可能是来自其他原因，其中可能包括 C$_{70}$ 分子的吸收，或者是由 C$_{60}$ 分子中 ^{12}C 以外的同位素所产生的对称性分裂，或者是由于固体中 C$_{60}$ 分子的相互作用。处于约 2,330 cm^{-1} 和

attachment of the CO_2 or CO to a small fraction of the total number of C$_{60}$ molecules. Another notable feature is the peak at 675 cm^{-1}, which is weak in the thin-film substrates but almost as strong as the four main features in the crystals. We suspect that this vibrational mode may be of solid state rather than molecular origin.

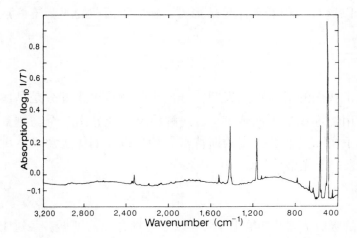

Fig. 4. Infrared absorption spectrum of a coating, ~2 μm thick, of solid C$_{60}$ on a silicon substrate, referenced to a clean silicon substrate. Apparent negative absorptions are due to the coating acting in part as a non-reflecting layer.

Figure 5 shows an absorption spectrum taken on a uniform film coated on a quartz glass substrate. The ultraviolet features are no longer obscured by the graphitic carbon background as in our previous spectra[22]. Broad peaks at 216, 264 and 339 nm dominate the spectra. Weaker structures show up in the visible, including a plateau between ~460 and 500 nm and a small peak near 625 nm. At the bottom of Fig. 5 we have shown positions and relative oscillator strengths taken from Larsson, Volosov and Rosén[9] calculated for the C$_{60}$ molecule. They also reported a variety of forbidden bands with the lowest energy ones in the vicinity of 500 nm. There seems to be a rough correspondence between our measurements on solid films and the allowed transitions predicted for the molecule. The possibility exists, however, that one or more of the absorption features shown in Fig. 5 are due to C$_{70}$. We still do not observe a band at 386 nm in our films, as observed[30] using a laser depletion spectroscopy method and attributed to the C$_{60}$ molecule. Quite similar spectra to that in Fig. 5 have been recorded for microcrystalline coatings deposited at helium pressures of 100 torr, for example. The peaks occur at the slightly shifted positions of 219, 268 and 345 nm.

2,190 cm⁻¹ 的较弱特征峰，位于自由 CO_2 和 CO 伸缩模式的附近，可能意味着占总数一小部分的 C_{60} 分子上附着一些 CO_2 或 CO。另一个显著特征是位于 675 cm⁻¹ 的峰，它在薄膜基底上是微弱的，但是在晶体中却与四个主要特征峰几乎一样强。我们怀疑这种振动模式可能是源于固体状态而不是分子本身。

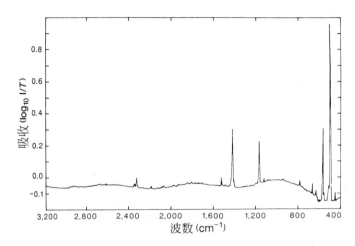

图 4. 覆盖在硅基底上的约 2 µm 厚 C_{60} 固体的红外吸收光谱，参比于干净的硅基底。负吸收来源于部分作为非反射层的覆盖层。

图 5 所示的是覆盖在石英玻璃基底上的均匀薄膜所测得的吸收光谱。紫外特征峰不再像在我们以前的光谱[22]中那样为石墨碳本底所掩盖。位于 216 nm、264 nm 和339 nm 处的宽峰是谱图中的主要峰。较弱的峰在可见光区显现出来，包括约 460 nm 到 500 nm 之间的一个高台和 625 nm 附近的一个小峰。在图 5 的底部，我们给出了拉松、沃洛索夫和罗森对于 C_{60} 分子计算的位置和相对振子强度[9]。他们还报道了500 nm 附近的多个具有最低能量的禁带。在我们对固体薄膜的测量结果与对分子所预期的允许跃迁之间似乎存在着一种大致的一致性。但是存在着这样的可能性，图 5 中所显示的一个或多个吸收特征峰是来自于 C_{70} 的。我们还没有在薄膜中观测到 386 nm 处的一个谱带——它来自于 C_{60} 分子，利用激光亏蚀光谱法[30]可以观测到。目前已报道了与图 5 中所示颇为相似的光谱图，例如在 100 torr 氦气压力下沉积得到的微晶覆盖物。其谱峰的位置略微移动，分别出现在 219 nm、268 nm 和 345 nm 处。

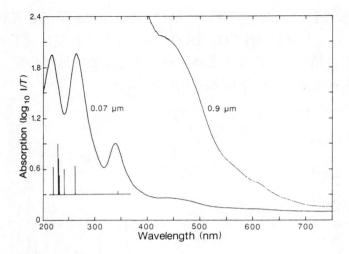

Fig. 5. Visible–ultraviolet absorption spectra of two thicknesses of solid C$_{60}$ on quartz. The calculated[9] positions and relative oscillator strengths for allowed transitions of C$_{60}$ are shown on the bottom.

Possible Interstellar Dust

The original stimulus for the work[2] that led to the hypothesis of the soccer-ball-shaped C$_{60}$ molecule, buckminsterfullerene, was an interest in certain unexplained features in the absorption and emission spectra of interstellar matter. These include an intense absorption band at 217 nm which has long been attributed to small particles of graphite[31], a group of unidentified interstellar absorption bands in the visible that have defied explanation for more than 70 years[31,32], and several strong emission bands attributed to polycyclic aromatic hydrocarbons[33,34]. Based on the visible and infrared absorption spectra of Figs 4 and 5, we do not see any obvious matches with the interstellar features. The ultraviolet band at 216–219 nm has a similar peak wavelength to an interstellar feature, although the other strong bands of the spectrum have no interstellar counterparts. As the influence of C$_{70}$ absorptions on the spectrum is not yet known, a conclusive comparison with the 217-nm interstellar band is difficult. We note that the visible–ultraviolet spectrum presented here is characteristic of a solid, rather than of free molecules. In addition, these new results do not relate directly to absorption in the free C$_{60}^+$ molecular ion, which has been envisaged[19] to explain the diffuse interstellar bands. Nevertheless, these data should now provide guidance for possible infrared detection of the C$_{60}$ molecule, if it is indeed as ubiquitous in the cosmos as some have supposed.

Summary

To our method for producing macroscopic quantities of C$_{60}$, we have added a method for concentrating it in pure solid form. Analyses including mass spectroscopy, infrared spectroscopy, electron diffraction and X-ray diffraction leave little doubt that we have produced a solid material that apparently has not been reported previously. We call the solid fullerite as a simple extension of the shortened term fullerene, which has been applied to the large cage-shaped molecules typified by buckminsterfullerene (C$_{60}$). The

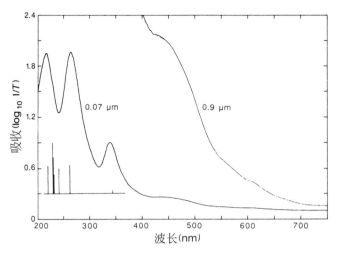

图 5. 石英上两个厚度的固体 C₆₀ 的可见 − 紫外吸收光谱。计算得到的 C₆₀ 跃迁所允许的位置[9]和相对振子强度显示于底部。

可能的星际尘埃

引出足球形 C₆₀ 分子（巴克敏斯特富勒烯）假说这一研究[2]的最初动力，是对于星际物质的吸收和发射光谱中某些无法解释的特征峰的兴趣。其中包括位于 217 nm 处的一个强吸收带（一直以来都被归结为小的石墨颗粒[31]），可见区中一组无法识别的星际吸收带（得不到解释已经超过 70 年了[31,32]），以及归结为多环芳烃的若干个强发射带[33,34]。根据图 4 和图 5 中的可见与红外吸收光谱，我们没有看到任何与星际特征峰的明显匹配。处于 216~219 nm 的紫外区谱带具有与一个星际特征峰相似的峰值波长，尽管其他强的光谱带没有星际对应物。由于还不知道 C₇₀ 吸收对于谱图的影响，与 217 nm 星际带进行结论性的比较是困难的。我们注意到，这里所呈现的可见−紫外光谱是一种固体而非游离分子所特有的。而且，这些新的结果与游离 C₆₀⁺ 分子离子的吸收并没有直接关系，这一吸收曾被设想用来解释扩散星际谱带[19]。尽管如此，现在这些数据应该还是能为 C₆₀ 分子可能的红外检测提供指导，如果它确实像某些人所设想的那样普遍存在于宇宙之中。

总　　结

针对我们用来制备宏观量 C₆₀ 的方法，我们补充了一个以纯的固态形式富集它的方法。包括质谱、红外光谱、电子衍射和X射线衍射在内的各种分析使得下面的事实几无异议：我们已经制备出一种此前明显没有报道过的固体物质。我们称该固体为富勒烯固体，它是富勒烯这个缩写词的简单衍生；富勒烯则用来表示以巴克敏斯特富勒烯（C₆₀）为代表的大型笼状分子。现在可以对 C₆₀ 的各种物理和化学性质

various physical and chemical properties of C$_{60}$ can now be measured and speculations concerning its potential uses can be tested.

(**347**, 354-358; 1990)

W. Krätschmer[*], **Lowell D. Lamb**[†], **K. Fostiropoulos**[*] **& Donald R. Huffman**[†]

[*] Max-Planck-Institut für Kernphysik, 6900 Heidelberg, PO Box 103980, Germany
[†] Department of Physics, University of Arizona, Tucson, Arizona 85721, USA

Received 7 August; accepted 7 September 1990.

References:

1. Rohlfing, E. A., Cox, D. M. & Kaldor, A. *J. Chem. Phys.* **81**, 3322-3330 (1984).
2. Kroto, H. W., Heath, J. R., O'Brien, S. C., Curl, R. F. & Smalley, R. E. *Nature* **318**, 162-163 (1985).
3. Zhang, Q. L. *et al. J. Phys. Chem.* **90**, 525-528 (1986).
4. Liu, Y. *et al. Chem. Phys. Lett.* **126**, 215-217 (1986).
5. Newton, M. D. & Stanton, R. E. *J. Am. Chem. Soc.* **108**, 2469-2470 (1986).
6. Lüthi, H. P. & Almlöf, J. *Chem. Phys. Lett.* **135**, 357-360 (1987).
7. Satpathy, S. *Chem. Phys. Lett.* **130**, 545-550 (1986).
8. Haddon, R. C., Brus, L. E. & Raghavachari, K. *Chem. Phys. Lett.* **125**, 459-464 (1986).
9. Larsson, S., Volosov, A. & Rosén, A. *Chem. Phys. Lett.* **137**, 501-504 (1987).
10. Wu, Z. C., Jelski, D. A. & George, T. F. *Chem. Phys. Lett.* **137**, 291-294 (1987).
11. Stanton, R. E. & Newton, M. D. *J. Phys. Chem.* **92**, 2141-2145 (1988).
12. Weeks, D. E. & Harter, W. G. *Chem. Phys. Lett.* **144**, 366-372 (1988).
13. Weeks, D. E. & Harter, W. G. *J. Chem. Phys.* **90**, 4744-4771 (1989).
14. Elset, V. & Haddon, R. C. *Nature* **325**, 792-794 (1987).
15. Slanina, Z. *et al. J. molec. Struct.* **202**, 169-176 (1989).
16. Fowler, P. W., Lazzeretti, P. & Zanasi, R. *Chem. Phys. Lett.* **165**, 79-86 (1990).
17. Haddon, R. C. & Elser, V. *Chem. Phys. Lett.* **169**, 362-364 (1990).
18. Kroto, H. *Science* **242**, 1139-1145 (1988).
19. Kroto, H. W. in *Polycyclic Aromatic Hydrocarbons and Astrophysics* (eds Léger, A. *et al.*) 197-206 (Reidel, Dordrecht, 1987).
20. Léger, A., d'Hendecourt, L., Verstraete, L. & Schmidt, W. *Astr. Astrophys.* **203**, 145-148 (1988).
21. Krätschmer, W., Fostiropoulos, K. & Huffman, D. R. in *Dusty Objects in the Universe* (eds Bussoletti, E. & Cittone, A. A.) (Kluwer, Dordrecht, in the press).
22. Krätschmer, W., Fostiropoulos, K. & Huffman, D. R. *Chem. Phys. Lett.* **170**, 167-170 (1990).
23. Steffens, P., Niehuis, E., Friese, T. & Benninghoven, A. *Ion Formation from Organic Solids* (ed. Benninghoven, A.) Ser. chem. Phys. Vol. 25, 111-117 (Springer-Verlag, New York, 1983).
24. Kroto, H. W. *Nature* **329**, 529-531 (1987).
25. Schmalz, T. G., Seitz, W. A., Klein, D. J. & Hite, G. E. *J. Am. Chem. Soc.* **110**, 1113-1127 (1988).
26. Hendricks, S. B., Jefferson, M. E. & Schultz, J. F. *Z. Kristallogr.* **73**, 376-380 (1930).
27. Edwards, O. S., Lipson, H. & Wilson, A. J. C. *Nature* **148**, 165 (1941).
28. Edwards, O. L. & Lipson, H. *Proc. R. Soc.* **A180**, 268-277 (1942).
29. Houska, C. R., Averbach, B. L. & Cohen, M. *Acta Metal.* **8**, 81-87 (1960).
30. Heath, J. R., Curl, R. F. & Smalley, R. E. *J. Chem. Phys.* **87**, 4236-4238 (1987).
31. Huffman, D. R. *Adv. Phys.* **26**, 129-230 (1977).
32. Herbig, E. *Astrophys. J.* **196**, 129-160 (1975).
33. Léger, A. & Puget, J. L. *Astr. Astrophys. Lett.* **137**, L5-L8 (1984).
34. Allamandola, L. J., Tielens, A. G. & Barker, J. R. *Astrophys. J.* **290**, L25-L28 (1985).

Acknowledgements. W. K. and K. F. thank our colleagues F. Arnold, J. Kissel, O. Möhler, G. Natour, P. Sölter, H. Zscheeg, H. H. Eysel, B. Nuber, W. Kühlbrandt, M. Rentzea and J. Sawatzki. L. D. L. and D. R. H. thank our colleagues J. T. Emmert, D. L. Bentley, W. Bilodeau, K. H. Schramm and D. R. Luffer. D. R. H. thanks the Alexander von Humboldt Stiftung for a senior US Scientist award. We also thank H. W. Kroto and R. F. Curl for discussions.

进行检测，也可以检验关于它的潜在应用方面的推测了。

（王耀杨 翻译；周江 审稿）

Light-Emitting Diodes Based on Conjugated Polymers

J. H. Burroughes *et al.*

Editor's Note

After the discovery of electrically conducting polymers in the 1970s, subsequent work identified several organic polymers with semiconducting electrical behaviour. One of them—poly (*p*-phenylene vinylene) or PPV—was prepared by Richard Friend and his co-workers at Cambridge. Here they show that PPV can be used in polymer light-emitting diodes (LEDs), which emit a yellowish light when an electrical current is passed through them. In conventional inorganic LEDs, new colours demand new materials. But the wavelength of light from polymer LEDs can be tuned by chemically modifying the polymer backbone. Such devices, spanning the entire visible spectrum, are now used in prototype commercial light-emitting displays. Being all-plastic, they can be rolled up like paper and fabricated using cheap printing technologies.

Conjugated polymers are organic semiconductors, the semiconducting behaviour being associated with the π molecular orbitals delocalized along the polymer chain. Their main advantage over non-polymeric organic semiconductors is the possibility of processing the polymer to form useful and robust structures. The response of the system to electronic excitation is nonlinear—the injection of an electron and a hole on the conjugated chain can lead to a self-localized excited state which can then decay radiatively, suggesting the possibility of using these materials in electroluminescent devices. We demonstrate here that poly(*p*-phenylene vinylene), prepared by way of a solution-processable precursor, can be used as the active element in a large-area light-emitting diode. The combination of good structural properties of this polymer, its ease of fabrication, and light emission in the green–yellow part of the spectrum with reasonably high efficiency, suggests that the polymer can be used for the development of large-area light-emitting displays.

THERE has been long-standing interest in the development of solid-state light-emitting devices. Efficient light generation is achieved in inorganic semiconductors with direct band gaps, such as GaAs, but these are not easily or economically used in large-area displays. For this, systems based on polycrystalline ZnS have been developed, although low efficiencies and poor reliability have prevented large-scale production. Because of the high photoluminescence quantum yields common in organic molecular semiconductors, there has long been interest in the possibility of light emission by these organic semiconductors through charge injection under a high applied field (electroluminescence)[1-7]. Light-emitting devices are fabricated by vacuum sublimation of the organic layers, and although the

基于共轭聚合物的发光二极管

伯勒斯等

编者按

20 世纪 70 年代发现了导电聚合物，几种具有半导体电性能的有机聚合物被随后的研究所证实。其中之一的聚对苯撑乙烯（PPV）是由剑桥大学的理查德·弗兰德及其同事们制备的，它可被用在聚合物发光二极管（LED）中，当有电流通过时该器件发出淡黄色的光。对于传统的无机 LED 来说，若想得到新的发光颜色需要新的材料。但是，聚合物 LED 的发光波长可以通过对聚合物骨架进行化学修饰来调节，器件的发射光谱覆盖整个可见光谱区，现在它们被用作商业发光显示器的原型器件。可以采用低成本的印刷工艺制作全塑料的聚合物 LED，它能像纸一样卷起。

共轭聚合物是有机半导体，其半导体性能与沿聚合链离域的 π 分子轨道有关。与非聚合物的有机半导体相比，共轭聚合物的主要优点是它的可加工性，能形成有用而又耐用的结构。聚合物对电激发的响应是非线性的，在共轭链上注入一个电子和一个空穴能够形成一个自局域激发态，随后它能够以辐射方式衰减，这就表明可以在电致发光器件中应用这些材料。这里我们要论述的聚对苯撑乙烯，是通过它的前驱体溶液进行加工而获得的，它被用作大面积发光二极管中的活性成分。该聚合物具有良好的结构性质，制备简单，在光谱中的绿-黄光波段有相当高的发光效率，这些优点使该聚合物能够用于发展大面积发光显示器。

人们对于固态发光器件的发展保持着长久的兴趣。诸如砷化镓等直接带隙无机半导体能实现有效发光，但是将它们用于大面积显示器既不容易也不经济。基于此，已发展出基于多晶硫化锌的体系，但效率低和可靠性较差等缺点使其不宜进行大规模生产。由于有机分子半导体普遍具有高的光致发光量子效率，长期以来，人们一直在关注利用这些有机半导体在外加强场条件下通过电荷注入而发光（电致发光）的可能性 [1-7]。发光器件是通过有机层的真空升华而制成的，尽管它的发光效率很高且发光颜色选择范围很大，但是通常存在着这样的问题：升华而得到的有机薄

efficiencies and selection of colour of the emission are very good, there are in general problems associated with the long-term stability of the sublimed organic film against recrystallization and other structural changes.

One way to improve the structural stability of these organic layers is to move from molecular to macromolecular materials, and conjugated polymers are a good choice in that they can, in principle, provide both good charge transport and also high quantum efficiency for the luminescence. Much of the interest in conjugated polymers has been in their properties as conducting materials, usually achieved at high levels of chemical doping[8], and there has been comparatively little interest in their luminescence. One reason for this is that polyacetylene, the most widely studied of these materials, shows only very weak photoluminescence. But conjugated polymers that have larger semiconductor gaps, and that can be prepared in a sufficiently pure form to control non-radiative decay of excited states at defect sites, can show high quantum yields for photoluminescence. Among these, poly(*p*-phenylene vinylene) or PPV can be conveniently made into high-quality films and shows strong photoluminescence in a band centred near 2.2 eV, just below the threshold for π to π^* interband transitions[9,10].

We synthesized PPV (I) using a solution-processable precursor polymer (II), as shown in Fig. 1. This precursor polymer is conveniently prepared from α,α'-dichloro-*p*-xylene (III), through polymerization of the sulphonium salt intermediate (IV)[11-13]. We carried out the polymerization in a water/methanol mixture in the presence of base and, after termination, dialysed the reaction mixture against distilled water. The solvent was removed and the precursor polymer redissolved in methanol. We find that this is a good solvent for spin-coating thin films of the precursor polymer on suitable substrates. After thermal conversion (typically $\geqslant 250\,°C$, *in vacuo*, for 10 h), the films of PPV (typical thickness 100 nm) are homogeneous, dense and uniform. Furthermore, they are robust and intractable, stable in air at room temperature, and at temperatures $>300\,°C$ in a vacuum[11].

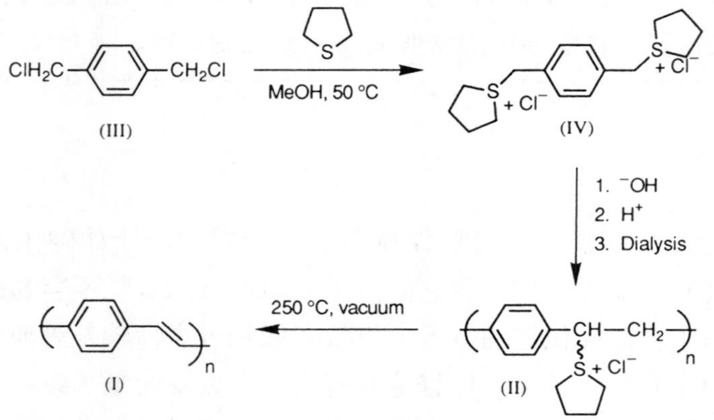

Fig. 1. Synthetic route to PPV.

Structures for electroluminescence studies were fabricated with the PPV film formed on a bottom electrode deposited on a suitable substrate (such as glass), and with the top electrode

膜的长期稳定性不够强，导致其易于发生重结晶和其他结构性变化。

改善这些有机层的结构稳定性的一种方法是从分子材料转向大分子材料，而共轭聚合物就是一个好的选择，因为从原理上讲，它们不仅能提供良好的电荷传输并能为发光提供高的量子效率。对于共轭聚合物的极大兴趣一直集中于它们作为导体材料的性质上，这些性质通常是通过大量的化学掺杂来实现的[8]，而它们的发光现象极少引起人们的注意。出现这种情况的一个原因是它们中被广泛研究的聚乙炔只呈现出很弱的光致发光。但是，那些具有较宽半导体能隙并且可以制备成十分纯的形式来控制其在缺陷位处的激发态非辐射衰减的共轭聚合物，能够表现出高光致发光的量子效率。其中，聚对苯撑乙烯（PPV）能很方便地制成高质量的薄膜，并且在一个以 2.2 eV 为中心的带显示出很强的光致发光，刚好低于从 π 到 π^* 的带间跃迁的阈值[9,10]。

我们利用一种可溶液加工的前驱体聚合物（II）合成了 PPV（I），如图 1 所示。该前驱体聚合物制备起来很方便，是由 α,α'-二氯对二甲苯（III）通过锍盐中间产物（IV）的聚合[11-13]得到的。在碱性条件下的水/甲醇混合物中进行聚合。反应终止后，对反应混合物进行蒸馏水透析。除去溶剂，将前驱体聚合物重新溶于甲醇中。我们发现对于在适当基质上旋涂制备前驱体聚合物薄膜来说，甲醇是一种好的溶剂。经过热转化之后（典型条件是 ≥250 ℃，真空中持续 10 小时），形成的 PPV 薄膜（典型厚度为100 nm）是同质、致密而均匀的。此外，该薄膜坚固而无延展性，在室温下时空气中以及温度＞300 ℃时在真空中都是稳定的[11]。

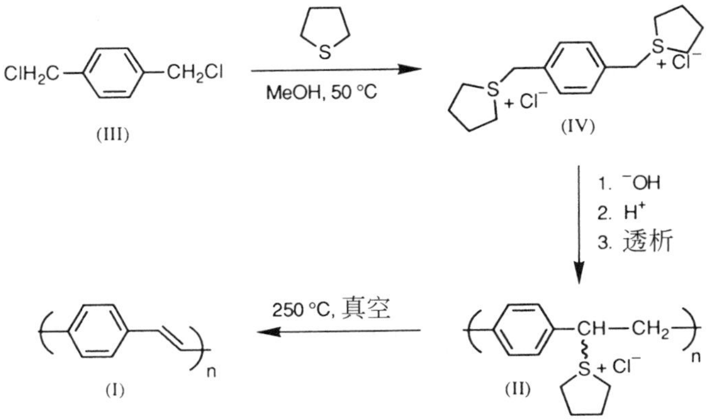

图 1. PPV 的合成路线。

用于进行电致发光研究的器件的制备过程如下：先在适当基底（例如玻璃）上沉积一个底部电极，之后在该电极上形成 PPV 薄膜，最后在全部转换的 PPV 薄膜

formed onto the fully converted PPV film. For the negative, electron-injecting contact we use materials with a low work function, and for the positive, hole-injecting contact, we use materials with a high work function. At least one of these layers must be semi-transparent for light emission normal to the plane of the device, and for this we have used both indium oxide, deposited by ion-beam sputtering[14] and thin aluminium (typically 7–15 nm). We found that aluminium exposed to air to allow formation of a thin oxide coating, gold and indium oxide can all be used as the positive electrode material, and that aluminium, magnesium silver alloy and amorphous silicon hydrogen alloys prepared by radiofrequency sputtering are suitable as the negative electrode materials. The high stability of the PPV film allows easy deposition of the top contact layer, and we were able to form this contact using thermal evaporation for metals and ion-beam sputtering for indium oxide.

Figures 2 and 3 show typical characteristics for devices having indium oxide as the bottom contact and aluminium as the top contact. The threshold for substantial charge injection is just below 14 V, at a field of 2×10^6 V cm^{-1}, and the integrated light output is approximately linear with current. Figure 4 shows the spectrally resolved output for a device at various temperatures. The spectrum is very similar to that measured in photoluminescence, with a peak near 2.2 eV and well resolved phonon structure[9,10]. These devices therefore emit in the green–yellow part of the spectrum, and can be easily seen under normal laboratory lighting. The quantum efficiency (photons emitted per electron injected) is moderate, but not as high as reported for some of the structures made with molecular materials[2-7]. The quantum efficiencies for our PPV devices were up to 0.05%. We found that the failure mode of these devices is usually associated with failure at the polymer/thin metal interface and is probably due to local Joule heating there.

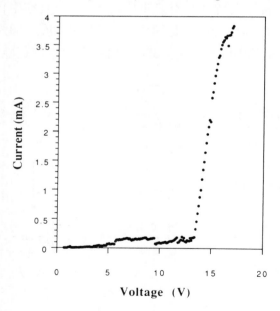

Fig. 2. Current–voltage characteristic for an electroluminescent device having a PPV film 70 nm thick and active area of 2 mm², a bottom contact of indium oxide, and a top contact of aluminium. The forward-bias regime is shown (indium oxide positive with respect to the aluminium electrode).

上形成顶部电极。对于负的电子注入接触，我们使用低功函材料；而对于正的空穴注入接触，我们使用高功函材料，其中至少有一层对于与器件平面正交的发光必须是半透明的。为此，我们同时使用了通过离子束溅射法沉积的氧化铟[14]和薄层的铝（典型厚度为 7~15 nm）。我们发现暴露在空气中的铝能够形成薄的氧化物覆盖层，金和氧化铟都能被用作正电极材料，而铝、镁银合金和通过射频溅射所制得的非晶硅氢合金都适合作负电极材料。PPV 薄膜的高度稳定性使顶部接触层的沉积很容易实现，因而我们可以利用金属的热蒸镀法和氧化铟的离子束溅射法形成这种接触。

图 2 和图 3 体现出以氧化铟作为底部接触且以铝作为顶部接触的器件的典型特性。大量电荷注入的阈值正好低于 14 V，对应的电场强度为 2×10^6 V·cm^{-1}，积分光输出随电流的变化近似为线性的。图 4 给出了电致发光器件在不同温度下的光谱分辨输出，其光谱与光致发光谱非常类似，在 2.2 eV 附近存在峰值，且清晰的声子结构[9,10]。这些器件发出光谱中的绿 – 黄光波段的光，而且在正常的实验室光照条件下很容易被看到。量子效率（每注入一个电子所发出的光子类）适中，但是没有某些利用分子材料制成的结构所报道得那样高[2-7]。我们的 PPV 器件的量子效率达到 0.05%。我们发现这些器件中的失效模式通常都与聚合物/薄金属界面处的失效有关，这可能是因为那里的局部焦耳热引起的。

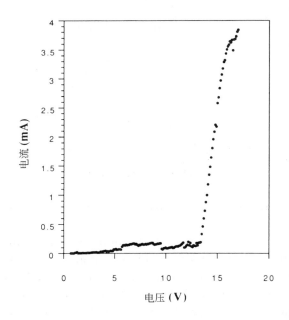

图 2. PPV 薄膜电致发光器件的电流 – 电压特性图。PPV 薄膜厚度为 70 nm，发光面积为 2 mm²，底部接触为氧化铟，顶部接触为铝。图中显示的是正向偏置状态的曲线（氧化铟相对于铝电极为正）。

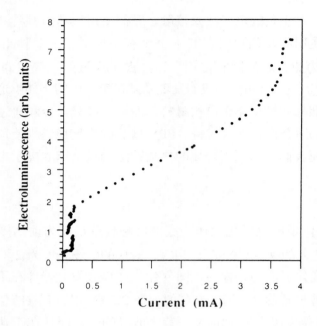

Fig. 3. Integrated light output plotted against current for the electroluminescent device giving the current–voltage characteristic in Fig. 2.

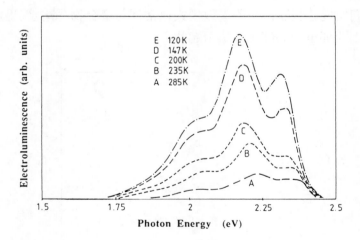

Fig. 4. Spectrally resolved output for an electroluminescent device at various temperatures.

The observation and characterization of electroluminescence in this conjugated polymer is of interest in the study of the fundamental excitations of this class of semiconductor. Here, the concept of self-localized charged or neutral excited states in the nonlinear response of the electronic system has been a useful one. For polymers with the symmetry of PPV , these excitations are polarons, either uncharged (as the polaron exciton) or charged (singly charged as the polaron, and doubly charged as the bipolaron)[15,16]. We have previously assigned the photoluminescence in this polymer to radiative recombination

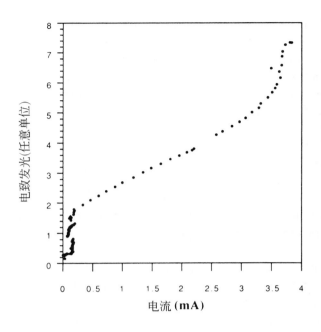

图 3. 电致发光器件的积分光输出与电流的关系图（该器件的电流－电压特性曲线如图 2 所示）。

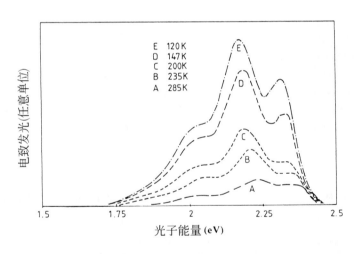

图 4. 电致发光器件在不同温度时的光谱分辨输出。

观测和描述该共轭聚合物中电致发光现象是对这类半导体基本的激发过程进行研究的兴趣所在。这里，电子体系中非线性响应的自局域带电或中性激发态概念已成为一个有用的概念。对于具有像 PPV 一样对称性的聚合物，这些激发是极化子，或者是不带电荷的（如极化激子）或者是带电荷的（带单个电荷的极化子，以及带两个电荷的双极化子）[15,16]。之前我们将这种聚合物中的光致发光归因于由链间激发

of the singlet polaron exciton formed by intrachain excitation[9,10] and, in view of the identical spectral emission here, we assign the electroluminescence to the radiative decay of the same excited state. The electroluminescence is generated by recombination of the electrons and holes injected from opposite sides of the structure, however, and we must consider what the charge carriers are. We have previously noted that bipolarons, the more stable of the charged excitations in photoexcitation and chemical doping studies, are very strongly self-localized, with movement of the associated pair of energy levels deep into the semiconductor gap, to within 1 eV of each other[9]. In contrast, the movement of these levels into the gap for the neutral polaron exciton, which one-electron models predict to be the same as for the bipolaron[15], is measured directly from the photoluminescence emission to be much smaller, with the levels remaining more than 2.2 eV apart. For electroluminescence then, bipolarons are very unlikely to be the charge carriers responsible for formation of polaron excitons, because their creation requires coalescence of two charge carriers, their mobilities are low and the strong self-localization of the bipolaron evident in the positions of the gap states probably does not leave sufficient energy for radiative decay at the photon energies measured here. Therefore, the charge carriers involved are probably polarons. The evidence that they can combine to form polaron excitons requires that the polaron gap states move no further into the gap than those of the polaron exciton and may account for the failure to observe the optical transitions associated with the polaron.

The photoluminescence quantum yield of PPV has been estimated to be ~8%. It has been shown[10,17] that the non-radiative processes that limit the efficiency of radiative decay as measured in photoluminescence are due to migration of the excited states to defect sites which act as non-radiative recombination centres, and also, at high intensities, to collisions between pairs of excited states. These are processes that can, in principle, be controlled through design of the polymer, and therefore there are excellent possibilities for the development of this class of materials in a range of electroluminescence applications.

(**347**, 539-541; 1990)

J. H. Burroughes[*‡], D. D. C. Bradley[*], A. R. Brown[*], R. N. Marks[*], K. Mackay[*], R. H. Friend[*], P. L. Burns[†] & A. B. Holmes[†]

[*] Cavendish Laboratory, Madingley Road, Cambridge CB3 OHE, UK

[†] University Chemistry Laboratory, Lensfield Road, Cambridge CB2 1EW, UK

[‡] Present address: IBM Thomas J. Watson Research Centre, Yorktown Heights, New York 10598, USA

Received 21 August; accepted 18 September 1990.

References:

1. Vincent, P. S., Barlow, W. A., Hann, R. A. & Roberts, G. G. *Thin Solid Films* **94**, 476-488 (1982).

2. Tang, C. W. & VanSlyke, S. A. *Appl. Phys. Lett.* **51**, 913-915 (1987).

3. Tang, C. W., VanSlyke, S. A. & Chen, C. H. *J. appl. Phys.* **65**, 3610-3616 (1989).

4. Adachi, C., Tokito, S., Tsutsui, T. & Saito, S. *Jap. J. appl. Phys.* **27**, 59-61 (1988).

5. Adachi, C., Tsutsui, T. & Saito, S. *Appl. Phys. Lett.* **55**, 1489-1491 (1989).

形成的单重态极化激子的辐射复合[9,10]，而考虑到这里有同样的辐射光谱，我们将电致发光归结为相同激发态的辐射衰减。但是电致发光是由器件的相反两边注入的电子和空穴复合而产生，我们必须考虑电荷载流子是什么。之前我们已经注意到双极化子是指在光致激发与化学掺杂研究中更为稳定的带电激发，它们是极强的自局域的，伴随着双极化子能级向半导体带隙深入运动，彼此间在 1 eV 之内[9]。相反，对于中性极化子激子来说，根据单电子模型这些能级向能隙的移动程度与双极化子的相同[15]，由光致发光直接测得的能级移动是很小的，并且保持着超过 2.2 eV 的间隔。那么对于电致发光来说，双极化子不可能是使极化激子得以形成的电荷载流子，因为它们的产生需要两个电荷载流子的结合，它们的迁移率很低，而且明显出现在能隙状态所处位置的双极化子的强自局域，可能没有给在这里测得的光子能量留下足够的能量进行辐射衰减。因此，参与其中的载流子可能是极化子。关于它们能够结合而形成极化激子的这一证据，要求极化子能隙状态向能隙的运动不超过极化激子的，从而可以解释为什么无法观测到与极化子有关的光跃迁。

PPV 的光致发光量子效率估算约为 8%。研究表明[10,17]：无辐射跃迁过程限制光致发光中测得的辐射衰减效率，该无辐射过程是来自于激发态向作为无辐射复合中心的缺陷位点的迁移；而在高强度时，该无辐射过程还可归结为激发态对之间的碰撞。这些过程原则上是能够通过聚合物的设计来控制的，因此在一系列电致发光应用中发展这类材料具有极大的可能性。

(王耀杨 翻译；于贵 朱道本 审稿)

6. Adachi, C., Tsutsui, T. & Saito, S. *Appl. Phys. Lett.* **56**, 799-801 (1989).

7. Nohara, M., Hasegawa, M., Hosohawa, C., Tokailin, H. & Kusomoto, T. *Chem. Lett.* 189-190 (1990).

8. Basescu, N. *et al. Nature* **327**, 403-405 (1987).

9. Friend, R. H., Bradley, D. D. C. & Townsend, P. D. *J. Phys.* D**20**, 1367-1384 (1987).

10. Bradley, D. D. C. & Friend, R. H. *J. Phys.: Condensed Matter* **1**, 3671-3678 (1989).

11. Bradley, D. D. C. *J. Phys.* D**20**, 1389-1410 (1987).

12. Murase, I., Ohnishi, T., Noguchi, T. & Hirooka, M. *Synthetic Metals* **17**, 639-644 (1987).

13. Stenger-Smith, J. D., Lenz, R. W. & Wegner, G. *Polymer* **30**, 1048-1053 (1989).

14. Bellingham, J. R., Phillips, W. A. & Adkins, C. J. *J. Phys.: Condensed Matter* **2**, 6207-6221 (1990).

15. Fesser, K., Bishop, A. R. & Campbell, D. K. *Phys. Rev.* B**27**, 4804-4825 (1983).

16. Brazovskii, S. A. & Kirova, N. N. *JEPT Lett.* **33**, 4-8 (1981).

17. Bradley, D. D. C. *et al. Springer Ser. Solid St. Sci.* **76**, 107-112 (1987).

Acknowledgements. We thank J. R. Gellingham, C. J. Adkins and W. A. Phillips for their help in preparing the indium oxide films. We thank SERC and Cambridge Research and Innovation Ltd for support.

Evidence for a Common Central-Engine Mechanism in all Extragalactic Radio Sources

S. Rawlings and R. Saunders

Editor's Note

Quasars are the most extreme example of "active galactic nuclei" (AGN). All such objects generate a lot of energy within a small space, but their observed characteristics vary widely. While it was generally believed that the intense energy output is caused by massive black holes at the centres of these galaxies, direct evidence was lacking. Steve Rawlings and Richard Saunders of Cambridge University here describe a relationship between the total energy of AGN and the luminosity carried by narrow emission lines. They concluded that all AGN have the same origin, with a black hole "central engine". This rapidly became known as the "standard model" and is the currently accepted picture.

Extragalactic radio sources produce radio waves and narrow emission lines by very different physical processes: synchrotron radio emission arises from lobes filled with magnetized plasma extending over scales of kiloparsecs to megaparsecs, fed by the total kinetic power, Q, of jets driven by a central engine, whereas narrow-line luminosity L_{NLR} arises from gas, typically concentrated in the inner few kiloparsecs, that has been photoionized by a nuclear source. We report here the discovery of a close relationship between Q and L_{NLR}—an approximate proportionality which extends over four orders of magnitude from low-Q radio sources with relaxed structures to high-Q, radio-luminous classical double-lobe radio galaxies. Objects with broad Balmer lines follow the same trend as those without, showing that quasar-like photoionizing sources are ubiquitous but not always obvious. Moreover, all radio-source central engines channel at least as much power into the jets as is radiated by accretion: this high efficiency implies that the engine is a massive spinning black hole which both powers the jets and controls the accretion rate.

WE have recently found a positive correlation between the narrow-line luminosities and the radio luminosities of an unbiased sample of low-redshift ($z < 0.5$) Fanaroff and Riley[1] (hereafter FR) class II radio galaxies[2], providing quantitative evidence that the production of nuclear optical line emission and the production of large-scale radio emission are somehow intrinsically linked. The radio luminosity, L_{rad}, of an extended extragalactic radio source is much smaller than the bulk kinetic power Q that goes into increasing the energy (stored in fields and particles) of the growing lobes and pushing back the external medium[3]. Because Q is a much more direct measure than L_{rad} of what powers the radio source, and as some scatter in the relationship between L_{rad} and L_{NLR} may be induced simply by the effects of the lobe environment, we investigate here the observational relation between Q and L_{NLR}.

所有河外星系射电源有共同中央引擎机制的证据

罗林斯，桑德斯

编者按

类星体是"活动星系核"中最极端的例子，它们在狭小的空间内产生巨大的能量，但是观测特性变化很大。人们普遍认为其剧烈的能量产出是这些星系中心的大质量黑洞造成的，但却缺乏直接的证据。本文中，剑桥大学的史蒂夫·罗林斯和理查德·桑德斯描述了活动星系核的总能量与窄发射线光度之间的关系。他们的结论是：所有的活动星系核有相同的起源，那就是拥有一个黑洞"中央引擎"。很快该理论即作为"标准模型"为人所知，并且也是现在人们接受的图景。

河外射电源通过很不相同的物理过程产生射电波和窄发射线：同步射电辐射产生于延伸数千秒差距到数百万秒差距的充满磁化等离子体的瓣状结构，由中央引擎驱动的喷流的总动能功率（Q）提供能量；而窄线光度 L_{NLR} 则来自被核心源光致电离的气体，这些气体一般聚集在靠内的几千秒差距范围内。在此我们报告一个新发现，即喷流功率 Q 与窄发射谱线的光度 L_{NLR} 近似成正比关系；对从疏松结构的低喷流功率射电源到高喷流功率的经典双瓣强射电星系，此关系在超过 4 个量级的范围内均成立。有、无宽巴耳末线的天体具有相同的趋势，表明类似类星体的光致电离源是普遍存在的，但并非总是明显的。此外，所有射电源中央引擎为喷射提供了至少和吸积盘辐射一样多的功率；这么高的效率意味着该中央引擎是质量巨大的旋转黑洞，该黑洞既为喷流提供功率又控制着吸积率。

我们最近发现，低红移（$z<0.5$）FRII（FR，法纳罗夫与赖利的缩写[1]）射电星系[2]的一个无偏样本的射电光度与窄线的光度存在正相关，这提供了定量证据表明星系核光学谱线辐射的产生与大尺度射电辐射的产生有着某种内在联系。一个延展的河外射电源的射电光度为 L_{rad}，总动能功率 Q 注入到射电瓣里（存储在场和粒子中）使瓣的能量增加，不断膨胀，并推回外部介质，而 L_{rad} 比 Q 要小得多[3]。因为对向射电源提供能量而言，与 L_{rad} 相比，Q 是一种更加直接的测量量；在 L_{rad} 与 L_{NLR} 的关系中的一些弥散可能只是瓣的环境效应引起的，因此我们在此只研究观测到的 Q 与 L_{NLR} 的关系。

For a total lobe energy E, an efficiency η that allows for work done on the external medium, and a lobe age T, the power $Q = E/T\eta$. We first take E as the equipartition energy[4]. (The main assumption here is that the electrons and the magnetic field make an equal contribution to the total energy density, which corresponds closely to the minimum value required to produce the observed synchrotron emission; this energy density is integrated over the volume of the radio source to produce the equipartition energy.) We take η to be 0.5, a value suggested by identifying compact hotspots as the working surfaces of relativistic jets[5]. We can thus evaluate Q for a source if T is known. Spectral ages are available for a number of radio galaxies; these are derived using standard formulae that relate the curvature of radio spectra to the energy losses incurred by relativistic electrons because of their own synchrotron radiation and because they scatter microwave-background photons by the inverse Compton process[6]. Where spectral ages are unavailable, we can estimate the age as follows. For a lobe of length $D/2$, width W and growth speed $V = D/2T$, we can relate the equipartition pressure p_{eq} in the lobe to the confining density ρ by $\rho V^2 = kD^2W^{-2}p_{eq}$; k reflects how the lobes are confined. D, W and p_{eq} are all straightforward to measure. For $k = 25$ there is good agreement between the estimated and spectral ages of the 16 FRII radio galaxies for which both have been reliably measured[7], and we therefore adopt this value. Sufficiently accurate estimates of ρ can be made from X-ray and optical data[5].

We have evaluated Q for the 39 FRII radio galaxies in our unbiased sample of ref. 2; details of the assumptions made and the data used are given in Table 1. In Fig. 1 we plot Q against L_{NLR}; the method used to calculate L_{NLR} from spectrophotometric data is described in the caption. There is a strong positive correlation extending over roughly two orders of magnitude in each variable, which is significantly better than the correlation between L_{rad} and L_{NLR} (ref. 2). Our unbiased sample was drawn from the complete 3CR sample[8], but our selection criteria excluded three classes of radio source: (1) those of FR class I; (2) those associated with quasars rather than galaxies; (3) all objects at $z > 0.5$. To include these in our investigation, we also plot those 3CR objects in each class for which there are suitable data to calculate Q and L_{NLR}. For the FRIs, values of E and spectral ages were used as above; for the quasars and high-z radio galaxies, growth speeds of $0.1c$ were assumed based on existing values of T for similar objects (for example, ref. 6). With the addition of these objects, Q and L_{NLR} are correlated over approximately four orders of magnitude in each variable with scatter of only one order of magnitude; the best-fit line $Q \propto L_{NLR}^{0.9\pm0.2}$ implies that the relationship is close to a proportionality.

当瓣总能量为 E，对外部介质做功效率为 η，瓣的年龄为 T 时，功率 $Q = E/T\eta$。我们首先把 E 看作均分能量[4]。(这里主要的假设是，电子和磁场对于总能量密度的贡献相等，该能量密度值接近产生观测到的同步辐射所需的最小值；该能量密度通过对整个射电源体积进行积分从而得到均分能量) 我们令 $\eta = 0.5$，该值是把致密热斑确认为相对论喷流的工作面得到的[5]。因此，如果 T 是已知的，那么我们就可以估计出一个射电源的功率 Q。若干射电星系的光谱年龄是已知的，这是通过标准方程得到的，这些方程给出了射电光谱的曲率与相对论电子的能量损失的关系，而这些电子的能量损失是由于它们自身的同步辐射以及对微波背景辐射光子的逆康普顿散射[6]。对于光谱年龄未知的情况，我们可以按照如下方式估计年龄：对于长度为 $D/2$，宽度为 W，膨胀速度为 $V = D/2T$ 的瓣，我们可以通过公式 $\rho V^2 = kD^2 W^{-2} p_{eq}$ 将瓣中的均分压强 p_{eq} 与约束密度 ρ 联系起来，其中 k 反映瓣的约束程度，D、W 和 p_{eq} 都可以直接测量得到。对于 $k = 25$ 的情况，对 16 个 FRII 型射电星系，根据上式估计的年龄与光谱年龄有很好的一致性[7]，这些年龄都是经过可靠测量的，因此我们将 k 取值为 25。从 X 射线和光学数据中可以足够精确地估计 ρ 值[5]。

在参考文献 2 我们的无偏样本中，我们已经估算出 39 个 FRII 型射电星系的 Q 值；其中所作假设和采用数据详见表 1。图 1 给出了 Q 与 L_{NLR} 的关系图，并且在图注中描述了利用分光光度数据计算 L_{NLR} 的方法。在每个变量的大致跨越两个量级的范围内，Q 与 L_{NLR} 存在强的正相关，明显高于 L_{rad} 与 L_{NLR} 之间的相关性(文献 2)。我们的无偏样本取自完整的 3CR 样本[8]，但是我们的挑选标准排除了三类射电源：(1) FRI 型射电源；(2) 与类星体相伴而不是与星系相伴的射电源；(3) 所有 $z > 0.5$ 的天体。为了在我们的研究中包含这些射电源，我们也绘出了具有适合计算 Q 与 L_{NLR} 的数据的以上三类 3CR 天体。对于 FRI 型射电源，均分能量 E 与光谱年龄的取值将如上使用；对于类星体和高红移的射电星系，根据类似天体已有的 T 值可以假定其增长速度为 $0.1c$ (参考文献 6)。加入以上天体之后，在每个变量跨越大约四个量级的范围内，Q 与 L_{NLR} 相关，而且弥散仅为一个量级。最佳拟合曲线 $Q \propto L_{NLR}^{0.9 \pm 0.2}$ 表明二者的关系接近正比。

Table 1. Data for calculation of jet power

Name	T (yr)	n_e (m^{-3})	Q (W)	Name	T (yr)	n_e (m^{-3})	Q (W)
a, Unbiased sample: 39 FRII radio galaxies with $z < 0.5$							
3C33		5×10^{1}	9×10^{37}	3C284	3×10^{7}		1×10^{38}
3C35	1×10^{8}		1×10^{37}	3C285	4×10^{7}		1×10^{37}
3C42		5×10^{2}	3×10^{38}	3C295		1×10^{4}	7×10^{38}
3C46		1×10^{2}	4×10^{38}	3C300	3×10^{7}		1×10^{38}
3C67		1×10^{4}	2×10^{38}	3C303		5×10^{2}	5×10^{37}
3C79	6×10^{6}		6×10^{38}	3C319	3×10^{7}		4×10^{37}
3C98		5×10^{1}	3×10^{37}	3C321		1×10^{1}	1×10^{38}
3C109		5×10^{1}	6×10^{38}	3C326		1×10^{0}	1×10^{38}
4C14.11		1×10^{3}	5×10^{37}	3C341		1×10^{1}	2×10^{39}
3C123		1×10^{3}	5×10^{38}	3C349		5×10^{1}	2×10^{38}
3C173.1		1×10^{2}	5×10^{38}	3C381		1×10^{2}	2×10^{38}
3C184.1	3×10^{7}		4×10^{37}	3C382		5×10^{1}	3×10^{37}
DA240		5×10^{0}	1×10^{37}	3C388		1×10^{3}	3×10^{37}
3C192		5×10^{1}	5×10^{37}	3C390.3		1×10^{2}	5×10^{37}
3C219	6×10^{7}		1×10^{38}	3C401		1×10^{3}	1×10^{38}
3C223		1×10^{1}	2×10^{38}	3C436	2×10^{7}		9×10^{37}
4C73.08	3×10^{7}		6×10^{37}	3C438		5×10^{3}	3×10^{38}
3C234	5×10^{6}		3×10^{38}	3C452	3×10^{7}		6×10^{37}
3C236	8×10^{7}		1×10^{38}	3C457		1×10^{1}	1×10^{39}
3C244.1	7×10^{6}		3×10^{38}				
b, 3CR FRIs with 178-MHz radio luminosity $< 2\times10^{25}$ W Hz^{-1}sr^{-1}							
3C31	4×10^{8}		8×10^{35}	3C338	3×10^{7}		1×10^{36}
3C66B	3×10^{7}		2×10^{36}	NGC6251	1×10^{8}		5×10^{36}
3C76.1	8×10^{7}		1×10^{36}	3C465	2×10^{8}		5×10^{36}
3C264	1×10^{7}		3×10^{36}				

Equipartition energy was calculated assuming no energy in protons, minimum and maximum frequencies of 10 MHz and 10 GHz, and a volume-filling factor of one. Spectral ages T, where available, were taken from the literature (refs 6, 7, 14 for the FRIIs and refs 15–21 for the FRIs); confining electron number densities n_e were estimated, where required, using the available X-ray and optical data[5,7] and were related to gas density ρ by $\rho = 1.4 n_e m_p$ (m_p is the proton rest mass). High-z FRII radio sources studied were 9 3CR quasars with $z < 1$ (3C47, 3C175, 3C196, 3C215, 3C249.1, 3C263, 3C275.1, 3C334, 3C351) and 24 3CR radio galaxies (3C6.1, 3C22, 3C34, 3C55, 3C172, 3C175.1, 3C184, 3C217, 3C226, 3C228, 3C247, 3C263.1, 3C265, 3C268.1, 3C277.2, 3C280, 3C289, 3C330, 3C337, 3C340, 3C343.1, 3C352, 3C427.1, 3C441). The references for the radio data for all objects are given in ref. 8. We take the Hubble constant H_0 to be 50 km s^{-1} Mpc^{-1}, and the cosmological density parameter Ω_0 and the cosmological constant Λ to be zero.

表 1. 喷流功率的计算数据

a, 无偏样本：39 个 FRII 射电星系 (z<0.5)							
名称	T (yr)	n_e(m^{-3})	Q (W)	名称	T (yr)	n_e(m^{-3})	Q (W)
3C33		5×10^1	9×10^{37}	3C284	3×10^7		1×10^{38}
3C35	1×10^8		1×10^{37}	3C285	4×10^7		1×10^{37}
3C42		5×10^2	3×10^{38}	3C295		1×10^4	7×10^{38}
3C46		1×10^2	4×10^{38}	3C300	3×10^7		1×10^{38}
3C67		1×10^4	2×10^{38}	3C303		5×10^2	5×10^{37}
3C79	6×10^6		6×10^{38}	3C319	3×10^7		4×10^{37}
3C98		5×10^1	3×10^{37}	3C321		1×10^1	1×10^{38}
3C109		5×10^1	6×10^{38}	3C326		1×10^0	1×10^{38}
4C14.11		1×10^3	5×10^{37}	3C341		1×10^1	2×10^{39}
3C123		1×10^3	5×10^{38}	3C349		5×10^1	2×10^{38}
3C173.1		1×10^2	5×10^{38}	3C381		1×10^2	2×10^{38}
3C184.1	3×10^7		4×10^{37}	3C382		5×10^1	3×10^{37}
DA240		5×10^0	1×10^{37}	3C388		1×10^3	3×10^{37}
3C192		5×10^1	5×10^{37}	3C390.3		1×10^2	5×10^{37}
3C219	6×10^7		1×10^{38}	3C401		1×10^3	1×10^{38}
3C223		1×10^1	2×10^{38}	3C436	2×10^7		9×10^{37}
4C73.08	3×10^7		6×10^{37}	3C438		5×10^3	3×10^{38}
3C234	5×10^6		3×10^{38}	3C452	3×10^7		6×10^{37}
3C236	8×10^7		1×10^{38}	3C457		1×10^1	1×10^{39}
3C244.1	7×10^6		3×10^{38}				
b, 3CR FRI 类射电星系，其 178 MHz 的射电光度 < 2×10^{25} W·Hz^{-1}·sr^{-1}							
3C31	4×10^8		8×10^{35}	3C338	3×10^7		1×10^{36}
3C66B	3×10^7		2×10^{36}	NGC6251	1×10^8		5×10^{36}
3C76.1	8×10^7		1×10^{36}	3C465	2×10^8		5×10^{36}
3C264	1×10^7		3×10^{36}				

在均分能量的计算中，假定质子没有能量，最小和最大频率分别为 10 MHz、10 GHz，体积填充因子为 1。表中光谱年龄 T（如果有的话）皆取自参考文献（关于 FRII 型的文献参见 6、7、14，关于 FRI 型的文献参见 15~21）；在需要的地方，束缚电子数密度 n_e 可以通过可用的 X 射线和光学数据进行估算[5,7]，并且通过公式 $\rho = 1.4 n_e m_p$ 与气体密度 ρ 联系起来（m_p 是质子的静止质量）。这里研究的高红移 FRII 型射电源是 9 个 $z<1$ 的 3CR 类星体（分别为：3C47、3C175、3C196、3C215、3C249.1、3C263、3C275.1、3C334、3C351）和 24 个 3CR 射电星系（3C6.1、3C22、3C34、3C55、3C172、3C175.1、3C184、3C217、3C226、3C228、3C247、3C263.1、3C265、3C268.1、3C277.2、3C280、3C289、3C330、3C337、3C340、3C343.1、3C352、3C427.1、3C441）。以上所有天体的射电数据的参考文献均在参考文献 8 中给出。我们采用的哈勃常数 H_0 为 50 km·s^{-1}·Mpc^{-1}，宇宙学密度参数 Ω_0 和宇宙学常量 Λ 均为 0。

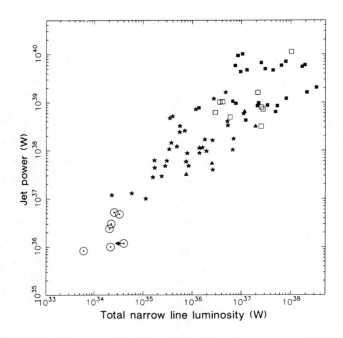

Fig. 1. Bulk kinetic power of jet Q plotted against total narrow-line luminosity L_{NLR} for the radio sources in Table 1. $\odot$, FRI sources; $\star$, FRII radio galaxies in our unbiased sample of objects with $z < 0.5$; $\blacktriangle$, broad-line radio galaxies; $\blacksquare$, radio galaxies with $0.5 < z < 1$; $\square$, quasars with $z < 1$. L_{NLR} has been measured for all objects in our unbiased sample; there are no missing points or upper limits. For the FRIs, we have used the 7 with 178-MHz radio luminosity $< 2 \times 10^{25}$ W Hz^{-1} sr^{-1} for which suitable data are available; there are 7 other FRIs for which there are no data but these have similar structures, sizes and radio luminosities to those used here and bias is unlikely. For the high-z FRII radio sources, there are suitable data for 24 of the 28 possible radio galaxies and 9 of the 12 possible quasars. The spectrophotometric data for most of the objects were taken from refs 2, 11, 22, with additional data for 3C76.1 (ref. 23; an upper limit), 3C196 (ref. 24), 3C275.1 (ref. 25), the new identification for 3C326 (ref. 26), 3C334 (ref. 27), 3C338 (refs 8, 28). We measured a flux of Hα + [N II] of 7.5×10^{-18} W m^{-2} for NGC6251 during the observing run described in ref. 29. For 3C31, 3C66B and 3C465, we used the data in ref. 30, calibrated against the stellar light of our NGC6251 spectrum (using an aperture correction), and obtained Hα + [N II] fluxes of 5.5, 11.0 and 7.5×10^{-18} W m^{-2}, respectively. As these spectra imply a low ionization parameter we have assumed for these objects that $L_{H\alpha + [N\ II]} \approx L_{[O\ II]}$. L_{NLR} represents the total luminosity of all optical narrow lines and Lyα, and is calculated[7] as $3 \times (3 \times L_{[O\ II]} + 1.5 \times L_{[O\ III]})$, where we have made use of the close relationships between the fluxes of low- and high-ionization lines with [O II] (3,727 Å) and [O III] (5,007 Å), respectively, and have adopted a median value for the ratio of total recombination-line radiation to total forbidden-line radiation. If only one oxygen line was measured we estimated the other, where possible, using measurements of other lines of similar ionization, otherwise we used the relation in ref. 29 at $z < 0.5$ and $L_{[O\ III]} = 4 \times L_{[O\ II]}$ at $z > 0.5$ (ref. 22); $L_{[N\ II]}$ ([N II] at 6,548 and 6,583 Å) was sometimes substituted for $L_{[O\ II]}$.

A striking feature of Fig. 1 is that quasars and broad-line radio galaxies follow the general trend defined by the narrow-line radio galaxies (NLRGs), despite the vast differences in their continua. This is important evidence supporting models in which NLRGs have central quasars hidden from us by obscuration but not hidden from their associated narrow-line regions[9,10]. We note that quasars may appear to have higher L_{NLR} than NLRGs with similar L_{rad} (ref. 11) because objects likely to be classified as quasars will be biased

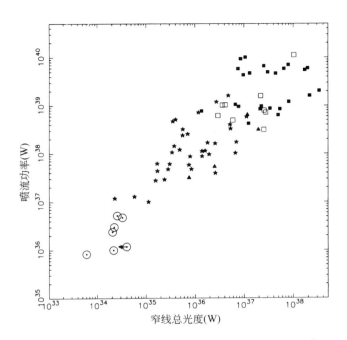

图 1. 给出了表 1 中射电源的喷流总动能功率 Q 与窄线总光度 L_{NLR} 的关系。⊙ 代表 FRI 型射电源；★ 代表我们的 $z<0.5$ 的天体的无偏样本中的 FRII 型射电星系；▲ 代表宽线射电星系；■ 代表 $0.5<z<1$ 的射电星系；□ 代表 $z<1$ 的类星体。在我们的无偏样本中，已测量了所有天体的 L_{NLR} 值，不存在丢失的点或上限。对于 FRI 型射电源，我们采用了 178 MHz 波段射电光度小于 2×10^{25} W·Hz^{-1}·sr^{-1} 的 7 个射电源，它们有合适的数据；有另外 7 个 FRI 型射电源没有数据，但它们与以上采用的 7 个具有类似的结构、尺寸和射电光度，因此不太可能有偏差。对于高红移的 FRII 型射电源，28 个可能的射电星系中有 24 个有合适的数据，12 个可能的类星体中有 9 个。大多数研究对象的分光光度数据来源于参考文献 2、11 和 22，还有一些数据来自 3C76.1（参考文献 23，上限值）、3C196（参考文献 24）、3C275.1（参考文献 25）、新证认的 3C326（参考文献 26）、3C334（参考文献 27）和 3C338（参考文献 8 和 28）。在参考文献 29 描述的观测过程中，我们测量了 NGC6251 的 Hα+[N II] 流量，为 7.5×10^{-18} W·m^{-2}。对于 3C31、3C66B 和 3C465，我们采用了参考文献 30 中的数据，根据我们测量的 NGC6251 恒星光谱（使用了孔径校正）进行了校准，获得的 Hα+[N II] 流量分别为 5.5×10^{-18} W·m^{-2}、11.0×10^{-18} W·m^{-2}、7.5×10^{-18} W·m^{-2}。由于这些光谱意味着较低的电离参数，我们假定 $L_{H\alpha+[N\,II]}\approx L_{[O\,II]}$。$L_{NLR}$ 代表了所有光学窄线和 Lyα 弧的总光度，可以通过 $3\times(3\times L_{[O\,II]}+1.5\times L_{[O\,III]})$ 计算得到[7]，上式利用了 [O III]（5,007 Å）和 [O II]（3,727 Å）的高低电离谱线流量的紧密关系，并且使用了总复合线辐射和总禁线辐射比率的中值。如果只测量了一条氧的谱线，那么我们就在可能的情况下通过测量类似电离态的其他谱线估计另一条谱线；否则，我们将在 $z<0.5$ 时采用参考文献 29 中的关系式，在 $z>0.5$ 时参考文献 22 中的公式 $L_{[O\,III]}=4\times L_{[O\,II]}$，在有些情况下 $L_{[O\,II]}$ 可以被 $L_{[N\,II]}$（[N II] 位于 6,548 Å 和 6,583 Å 的谱线）代替。

　　图 1 中值得注意的是，类星体和宽线射电星系遵循由窄线射电星系（NLRGs）确定的大致趋势，尽管它们的连续谱差异巨大。这一点是支持如下模型的重要证据：NLRGs 存在中心类星体，被遮挡而不为我们所见，但是可从与它们相伴的窄线区发现[9,10]。我们注意到，与具有相似的 L_{rad} 的 NLRGs 相比，类星体看起来可能具有更高的 L_{NLR}（参考文献 11），因为可能被归为类星体的天体倾向于具有较高的光致电离

to higher photoionizing luminosity L_{phot} and thus higher L_{NLR}, and the combination of Q–L_{NLR} proportionality and its scatter will contrive to give quasars apparently higher L_{NLR} at constant Q and thus similar L_{rad}.

We now consider accretion rates, first in the low-Q ($Q \leqslant 10^{38}$ W) objects of Fig. 1. These often contain huge stored energies E ($\sim 10^{53}$ J, equivalent to 5×10^5 $M_\odot$) and must therefore contain central masses $\geqslant 10^7$ $M_\odot$, with corresponding Eddington luminosities $L_{Edd} \geqslant 10^{38}$ W. For L_{phot} to exceed such values given the observed $L_{NLR} \leqslant 10^{36}$ W, covering factors $\kappa \leqslant 0.01$ are required, smaller than those observed in quasars (we assume equal power in photon flux per frequency decade); further, their low ionization parameters would require extreme gas densities in the narrow-line region (electron density $n_e \gg 10^8$ m^{-3}). Thus the accretion rate must be below the Eddington limit in low-Q objects.

In high-Q objects, where the energy stored in lobes is similar but L_{phot} much higher than in low-Q objects, super-Eddington accretion cannot be similarly ruled out. Any change from sub- to super-Eddington accretion as a function of Q is achieved without a discontinuity in Fig. 1, however, as may be possible with the recent model of Bell[12]. Alternatively, in all objects with radio jets, the accretion may be sub-Eddington and the central masses correspondingly large. The fraction of the power from the nucleus that is channelled into jets supports this hypothesis. Figure 1 shows that this fraction is roughly the same for all objects and indeed even for $\kappa \approx 0.01$, the radiated and bulk kinetic power are roughly equal. Thus any process whereby accretion drives the jets directly would be implausibly efficient. (Both equipartition energy E and spectral age T have the same dependence on the volume-filling factor, which is the only factor that allows E to be an overestimate of the true lobe energy. Thus, as a decrease in η also increases Q, the values of Q we use are truly minimum ones, making an even better case for high efficiency.) We are led to a model in which the radiation arises from accretion, but the jet power is produced by a machine, which, to satisfy Fig. 1, must also *control* the accretion rate. A possible model involves jets that are driven by the extraction of rotational energy from a spinning black hole, ringed by an ion-supported torus[13]. Whatever the model, it must explain the two key features of the ratio of the outputs in radiated and bulk kinetic form seen in Fig. 1: (1) why it is at most of the order of unity; (2) why it is independent of the total power over four orders of magnitude. Both features may prove particularly challenging to models that exclude central massive black holes.

Finally, we emphasize that the objects we studied were known *a priori* to contain large-scale radio jets. Many objects have high narrow-line luminosities but negligible large-scale radio emission, such as the radio-quiet quasars. These do not obey the relation of Fig. 1. This implies that the formation of radio jets requires specific physical attributes independent of the accretion rate (such as that the central black hole be large and spinning), or that the bulk outflow is formed but then disrupted within the host galaxy. Either way, the radio-quiet and radio-loud objects are physically distinct.

(**349**, 138-140; 1991)

光度 L_{phot}，因而有较高的 L_{NLR}，而 Q 与 L_{NLR} 的正比性以及它的弥散将使得类星体在 Q 值恒定以及相似 L_{rad} 的条件下具有明显较高的 L_{NLR}。

现在我们来考虑图 1 中低喷流功率 Q（$Q \leqslant 10^{38}$ W）天体的吸积率。这其中经常包含巨大的储能 E（约 10^{53} J，等价质量为 5×10^5 $M_\odot$），因此必须包含有中心质量 $\geqslant 10^7$ $M_\odot$，相应的爱丁顿光度 $L_{Edd} \geqslant 10^{38}$ W。对于超过该值的光致电离光度 L_{phot}，考虑到观测到的 $L_{NLR} \leqslant 10^{36}$ W，覆盖因子需要满足 $\kappa \leqslant 0.01$，该值比类星体中观测到的要小（我们假定每 10 倍频程的光子流量具有相同的功率）；而且，它们的低电离参数在窄线区将要求极端的气体密度（电子密度 $n_e \gg 10^8$ m^{-3}）的存在。因此，吸积率必须小于低 Q 值天体的爱丁顿极限。

在高喷流功率的天体中，存贮在瓣中的能量相似，但是其 L_{phot} 比低 Q 值天体高得多，"超爱丁顿吸积"不能类似地被排除。如图 1 所示，吸积率从亚爱丁顿到超爱丁顿吸积范围内是 Q 的连续函数，然而，这一点在最近的贝尔（Bell）模型中也是可能的 [12]。或者存在另一种可能，在所有的有射电喷流的天体中，吸积也许都是"亚爱丁顿吸积"，中心质量也相应地很大。核心区功率传送给喷流的比例支持这个假说。从图 1 可以看出，对于所有的天体而言，这个比例大体是相同的（即使对于 $\kappa \approx 0.01$ 也是如此）；辐射功率与总动能功率是大体相等的。因此，任何借助吸积直接驱动喷流的过程都异常有效。（均分能量 E 和光谱年龄 T 对体积填充因子有相同的依赖关系，该填充因子是允许 E 的估计值高于实际的瓣能量的唯一因子。因此，因为 η 的减小会增加 Q，我们使用的 Q 值实际上是最小值，使得较高效率的情况更好）。因此我们有以下的模型：辐射来自吸积，但是喷流功率由某种机制产生，该机制为了满足图 1 必须也能够**控制**吸积率。一个可能的模型涉及喷流被由旋转黑洞抽出的旋转能量所驱动，黑洞外环绕了一个离子支撑的环 [13]。但无论模型是什么，它必须能够解释图 1 中辐射能与总动能比值的两个关键特征：（1）为什么比值正好是 1 的量级；（2）为什么比值大小与总功率大小（在超过四个量级范围上）无关。这两个特征对于那些排除中心大质量黑洞的模型都构成了相当大的挑战。

最后，我们强调，我们研究的天体事先已知包含大尺度的射电喷流。许多天体具有高窄线光度却有可以忽略的大尺度射电辐射，例如射电宁静类星体。这些天体不遵循图 1 中的关系。这意味着，射电喷流的形成需要独立于吸积率的特殊物理属性（比如中心黑洞大且在旋转），或者尽管形成大规模外流但是很快在宿主星系中分散开。不过，无论是哪种情况，射电宁静天体和射电噪天体在物理上是有区别的。

（金世超 翻译；蒋世仰 审稿）

Steve Rawlings and Richard Saunders

Mullard Radio Astronomy Observatory, Cavendish Laboratory, Madingley Road, Cambridge CB3 OHE, UK

Received 5 September; accepted 8 November 1990.

References:

1. Fanaroff, B. L. & Riley, J. M. *Mon. Not. R. astr. Soc.* **167**, 31P-35P (1974).

2. Rawlings, S., Saunders, R., Eales, S. A. & Mackay, C. D. *Mon. Not. R. astr. Soc.* **240**, 701-722 (1989).

3. Longair, M. S., Ryle, M. & Scheuer, P. A. G. *Mon. Not. R. astr. Soc.* **164**, 243-270 (1973).

4. Miley, G. K. *A. Rev. Astr. Astrophys.* **18**, 165-218 (1980).

5. Rawlings, S. in *The Interstellar Medium In External Galaxies* (eds Hollenbach, D. J. & Thronson, H. A.) 188-190 (NASA Conf. Publ. 3084, 1990).

6. Leahy, J. P., Muxlow, T. W. B. & Stephens, P. M. *Mon. Not. R. astr. Soc.* **239**, 401-440 (1989).

7. Rawlings, S. thesis, Univ. of Cambridge (1988).

8. Laing, R. A., Riley, J. M. & Longair, M. S. *Mon. Not. R. astr. Soc.* **204**, 151-187 (1983).

9. Scheuer, P. A. G. in *Superluminal Radio Sources* (eds Zensus J. A. & Pearson T. J.) 104-113 (Cambridge University Press, 1987).

10. Barthel, P. D. *Astrophys. J.* **336**, 606-611 (1989).

11. Jackson, N. & Browne, I. W. A. *Nature* **343**, 43-45 (1990).

12. Bell, A. R. *Nature* **345**, 136-138 (1990).

13. Rees, M. J., Begelman, M. C., Blandford, R. D. & Phinney, E. S. *Nature* **295**, 17-21 (1982).

14. Alexander, P. & Leahy, J. P. *Mon. Not. R. astr. Soc.* **225**, 1-26 (1987).

15. Laycock, S. C. thesis, Univ. of Cambridge (1987).

16. Northover, K. J. E. *Mon. Not. R. astr. Soc.* **165**, 369-379 (1973).

17. Macklin, J. T. *Mon. Not. R. astr. Soc.* **203**, 147-155 (1983).

18. Bridle, A. H. & Vallée, J. P. **86**, 1165-1174 (1981).

19. Burns, J. O., Schwendeman, E. & White, R. A. *Astrophys. J.* **271**, 575-585 (1983).

20. Saunders, R., Baldwin, J. E., Pooley, G. G. & Warner, P. J. *Mon. Not. R. astr. Soc.* **197**, 287-300 (1981).

21. Leahy, J. P. *Mon. Not. R. astr. Soc.* **208**, 323-345 (1984).

22. McCarthy, P. J. thesis, Univ. of California at Berkeley (1989).

23. Yee, H. K. C. & Oke, J. B. *Astrophys. J.* **226**, 753-769 (1978).

24. Fabian, A. C., Crawford, C. S., Johnstone, R. M., Allington-Smith, J. R. & Hewett, P. C. *Mon. Not. R. astr. Soc.* **235**, 13P-18P (1988).

25. Hintzen, P. & Stocke, J. *Astrophys. J.* **308**, 540-545 (1986).

26. Rawlings, S., Saunders, R., Miller, P., Jones, M. E. & Eales, S. A. *Mon. Not. R. astr. Soc.* **246**, 21P-23P (1990).

27. Steiner, J. E. *Astrophys. J.* **250**, 469-477 (1981).

28. Gunn, J. E., Stryker, L. L. & Tinsley, B. M. *Astrophys. J.* **249**, 48-67 (1981).

29. Saunders, R., Baldwin, J. E., Rawlings, S., Warner, P. J. & Miller, L. *Mon. Not. R. astr. Soc.* **238**, 777-790 (1989).

30. Yee, H. K. C. & De Robertis, M. M. in *Active Galactic Nuclei* (eds Osterbrock, D. E. & Miller, J. S.) 457-459 (Kluwer, Dordrecht, 1989).

Acknowledgements. We thank P. Miller for help with compiling data on 3CR objects and P. Hughes for comments. SR is supported by a Research Fellowship at St John's College Cambridge.

Estimates of the Effect of Southern Ocean Iron Fertilization on Atmospheric CO$_2$ Concentrations

F. Joos *et al.*

Editor's Note

In the 1980s, oceanographer John Martin proposed that phytoplankton growth in the oceans might be fertilized by adding iron to seawater, drawing down the greenhouse gas carbon dioxide from the atmosphere and thereby engineering climate. Here Ulrich Siegenthaler and co-workers investigate the feasibility of this idea. They calculate how big an effect on atmospheric CO$_2$ such iron-stimulated growth might have over 100 years, and conclude that it could be significant—but not enough by itself to offset the main climate effects of unchecked CO$_2$ emissions. Moreover, their simple ocean model neglects various complicating factors. So they caution against seeing this as a "quick fix" for climate change. It now seems that iron-fertilization effects might actually be rather small.

It has been suggested[1-3] that fertilizing the ocean with iron might offset the continuing increase in atmospheric CO$_2$ by enhancing the biological uptake of carbon, thereby decreasing the surface-ocean partial pressure of CO$_2$ and drawing down CO$_2$ from the atmosphere. Using a box model, we present estimates of the maximum possible effect of iron fertilization, assuming that iron is continuously added to the phosphate-rich waters of the Southern Ocean, which corresponds to 16% of the world ocean surface. We find that after 100 years of fertilization, the atmospheric CO$_2$ concentration would be 59 p.p.m. below what it would have been with no fertilization, assuming no anthropogenic CO$_2$ emissions, and 90–107 p.p.m. less when anthropogenic emissions are included in the calculation. Such a large uptake of CO$_2$ is unlikely to be achieved in practice, owing to a variety of constraints that require further study; the effect of iron fertilization on the ecology of the Southern Ocean also remains to be evaluated. Thus, the most effective and reliable strategy for reducing future increase in atmospheric CO$_2$ continues to be control of anthropogenic emissions.

A flux of dead biogenic organic matter from the ocean surface continuously transports carbon (and nutrients) to depth and thus influences the surface concentration of total dissolved inorganic carbon (Σ CO$_2$). Model studies have shown that variations in the efficiency of biological uptake and export of organic carbon in the Southern Ocean, where concentrations of the nutrients P and N are high, can lead to alterations of atmospheric CO$_2$ in excess of 100 p.p.m.[4-7]. Recently, it has been suggested that biological production in these regions may be limited by a restricted supply of iron[8-11]. Although the hypothesis that iron is the ultimate limiting factor there is controversial[12-14], we adopt

南大洋铁施肥对大气CO_2浓度的影响评估

约斯等

编者按

20 世纪 80 年代，海洋学家约翰·马丁提出假设，即向海水中施加铁元素可能促进浮游植物的生长，从而降低大气中温室气体 CO_2 的含量，进而影响气候变化。在本文中，乌尔里克·西根塔勒及其合作者研究了这个设想的可行性。他们计算了铁促进生长作用在超过 100 年的时间内对大气中 CO_2 含量可能产生多大的影响，得出的结论是：该作用可能具有重要意义——但单凭这一作用并不足以抵消未加遏制的 CO_2 排放对气候产生的影响，而且，计算所应用的简单海洋模型忽略了各种复杂因素。因此，他们告诫不要把这种方法视为影响气候变化的"权宜之计"。现在看来，铁施肥的效果似乎微乎其微。

有学者提出[1-3]，向海洋中投放铁可以增强生物对碳的吸收，从而降低海洋表面的 CO_2 分压，使 CO_2 得以从大气进入海洋并沉降下来，进而抵消大气 CO_2 含量的持续增加。南大洋占世界大洋面积的 16%，其水体中富含磷酸盐，在不断增加该水体中铁的假设下，我们利用箱式模型研究了铁施肥可能带来的最大效应，结果发现：假设无人类活动产生 CO_2 排放，经过 100 年的铁施肥，大气中 CO_2 的浓度将比未进行铁施肥时的值低 59 ppm，而当计算中包含人类活动排放的 CO_2 时，则会低 90~107 ppm。然而在实际操作过程中，由于各种条件的限制，海洋不太可能吸收如此多的 CO_2，这些限制还需要进一步研究。铁施肥效应对南大洋生态的影响也有待于评估。因此，减少未来大气中 CO_2 增加最有效和最可靠的措施仍然是持续控制人类活动产生的 CO_2 排放。

来自大洋表层水体的死亡生物源有机物，源源不断地将碳（及营养盐）输送至大洋深处，进而影响表层水体中总溶解无机碳的浓度（ΣCO_2）。模型研究表明，在南大洋，由于 P 和 N 的浓度均较高，生物对有机碳吸收和输出效率的差异可导致大气中 CO_2 浓度相差 100 ppm 以上[4-7]。近来，有学者提出上述海域的生物生产量可能受到有限铁供给量的限制[8-11]。虽然对于铁是否为最终限制因子的假设还存有争议[12-14]，

it here to obtain upper-limit estimates of the possible reduction in atmospheric CO_2. Because the ratio of iron to carbon incorporated in plants is rather low, between 1:10,000 and 1:100,000[15,16], the amount of iron required to carry out this fertilization is relatively modest: ~10^6 tons of iron per year assuming that all the iron goes into organic matter. Our model study differs from that of Peng and Broecker[17] in the area fertilized (16% of the world ocean rather than 10%), and in that we include scenarios with anthropogenic CO_2 emissions for which we find that fertilization has a greater effect than when we assume no man-made emissions.

We consider there to be three factors that exert the most important control on the response of atmospheric CO_2 to an enhanced carbon uptake resulting from iron fertilization. First is the reduction in average ΣCO_2 per unit area that occurs when fertilization is started. We take the supply of phosphate from depth as a reasonable guide to the maximum potential biological uptake of carbon, although we recognize that light supply, our ability to spread iron efficiently over the large ocean areas involved, the behaviour of the ocean ecosystem, and other processes may interfere long before the phosphate is depleted. (Carbon cycling is linked to that of phosphate through the Redfield ratio of C:P = 130 in organic matter.[18]) Second is the area over which the fertilization occurs. We use a recent analysis of National Oceanic Data Center phosphate data (S. Levitus and R. G. Najjar, personal communication) to estimate that the Southern Ocean's (>30° S) water volume in the depth range 0–75 m with phosphate $\geq$ 1.0 mmol m^{-3} amounts to 15.8% of the world ocean volume in the same depth range. The average phosphate content of this volume is 1.63 mmol m^{-3}. We therefore take the high-latitude box of our "standard" model to consist of 16% of the world ocean area (with 9.7% as an alternative case corresponding to the area used by Peng and Broecker[17]), and we determine the enhancement to the biological production by forcing a reduction of phosphate by 1.5 mmol m^{-3} in the surface box of this area. Third is the reduction in CO_2 partial pressure resulting from a given carbon removal. We have found that this is considerably larger at high rather than at low CO_2 levels because of the nonlinear relation between P_{CO_2} and ΣCO_2. We use three different anthropogenic CO_2 emission scenarios to examine the contribution of this nonlinearity, one in which the ocean and atmosphere are initialized at the pre-industrial value of 278 p.p.m with no anthropogenic sources, a "constant-emission" scenario, and a "business-as-usual" scenario (see Table 1 legend for descriptions of the scenarios).

但据此模型我们可以估算出大气中 CO₂ 可能减少的上限值。由于植物体内铁/碳比值非常低，约为1:10,000 至 1:100,000 [15,16]，所需的施铁量也相对较少：假定所有的铁都进入到有机质中，则每年仅需约 10^6 t 铁。我们的模型研究与彭和布勒克模型[17]的不同之处在于施铁海域的面积不同（分别占世界大洋的 16% 和 10%），此外，我们还考虑了人为 CO₂ 排放的各种情景，从中发现，考虑人为 CO₂ 排放比不考虑时的，铁施肥效应更显著。

我们认为大气 CO₂ 浓度对由铁施肥导致海洋 CO₂ 吸收增强的响应受三个最重要因素的控制。首先是当铁施肥开始时，单位面积上 ΣCO₂ 平均值降低。我们认为大洋深层磷酸盐供给是生物最大潜在碳吸收的一个合理指标，尽管我们认识到，远在磷酸盐耗尽之前，该吸收值可能已受到光照、研究者在所研究的广大海域有效施铁的能力、海洋生态系统行为以及其他一些作用的干扰。（碳循环与磷酸盐循环之间的关系可用雷德菲尔德比值表示，有机质中 C : P = 130。[18]）第二个因素是施铁的大洋面积。我们利用近期国家海洋数据中心的磷酸盐资料分析结果（莱维图斯和纳贾尔，个人交流）估算出南大洋（>30°S）0~75 m 深度范围内，磷酸盐含量 ≥ 1.0 mmol · m⁻³ 的水量占相同深度上世界大洋总水量的比重达 15.8%。该水体中磷酸盐的平均含量为 1.63 mmol · m⁻³。因此我们设定，我们的"标准"模型中高纬度箱体占世界大洋面积的 16%（另外，为了与彭和布勒克[17]采用的模型面积相比较，我们还设定了 9.7% 的情况作为备选方案）。同时，通过使该海域表层箱体中磷酸盐浓度降低 1.5 mmol · m⁻³ 我们确定了生物生产的增量。第三个因素是碳移除量一定时 CO₂ 分压的降低。我们发现 CO₂ 浓度较高时，分压的降低程度远远大于 CO₂ 浓度较低时，这是因为 P_{CO_2} 与 ΣCO₂ 之间呈非线性关系。我们利用三种不同人为 CO₂ 排放情景来分析这种非线性的影响。第一种情景是假定海洋和大气中 CO₂ 含量均恢复到工业化以前的 278 ppm，不存在任何人为来源；第二和第三种情景分别为"恒量排放"和"照常排放"（关于各情景的详细描述见表 1 注）。

Table 1. Projected changes in atmospheric CO_2 partial pressures resulting from various scenarios beginning in 1990

Scenario*	After 50 years			After 100 years		
	A Unfertilized	B Fertilized	Effect of fertilization (B–A)	C Unfertilized	D Fertilized	Effect of fertilization (D–C)
High-latitude area fraction=9.7%†						
Initialized at pre-industrial levels						
Our model	0	−26	−26	0	−39	−39
Peng and Broecker‡	–	–	–	0	−34	−34
Constant-emission	80	46	−34	156	98	−58
Business-as-usual	150	114	−36	430	362	−68
High-latitude area fraction=16.0%						
Initialized at pre-industrial levels	0	−41	−41	0	−59	−59
Constant-emission	79	24	−55	151	61	−90
Business-as-usual	146	88	−58	417	310	−107

* The scenario which is initialized at pre-industrial levels of atmospheric CO_2 has no anthropogenic source of CO_2 to the atmosphere, thus the CO_2 drawdown by the ocean results in a reduction below the initial pre-industrial value of 278.3 p.p.m. In the "constant-emission" scenario, atmospheric CO_2 content is prescribed using observations until 1990[23], after which the CO_2 emission to the atmosphere is fixed at the model-determined value of 6.15 Gt C yr^{-1} in 1990. In the "business-as-usual" scenario, the atmospheric CO_2 content is prescribed until 1989, after which the annual emission increases according to the IPCC business-as-usual scenario[22], in which the man-made emissions increase linearly with time from 6.0 Gt C yr^{-1} in 1990 to 22.4 Gt C yr^{-1} in 2100. The 1990 atmospheric CO_2 partial pressure is 355 p.p.m.

† The area fraction of 9.7% in our model corresponds to the same area in m^2 as chosen by Peng and Broecker[17].

‡ The Peng and Broecker[17] model is initialized at 280 p.p.m. and has a phosphate reduction of 1.6 mmol m^{-3}. The result given here is for their scenario with 17.5×10^6 m $^{-3}$ s^{-2} of water upwelling in the high latitudes and being placed directly into the deep ocean.

The rate at which atmospheric CO_2 is taken up by the oceans also depends on the rate at which the ocean circulation and mixing transport to the abyss the excess CO_2 that invades the fertilized region from the atmosphere. As discussed below, we find that this factor is less critical than those mentioned above. Figure 1 shows the model we use to simulate the ocean circulation and mixing. Parameter values are obtained by fitting the model to pre-bomb ^{14}C observations as well as the GEOSECS bomb inventory estimates of Broecker et al.[19] (U. S. and F. J., to be published elsewhere). However, the bomb inventory estimates in the Southern Ocean were not considered adequate for use in the fitting exercise because the bomb signal is not easy to discern from the natural ^{14}C background; the data in the Southern Ocean are scanty, especially from pre-bomb time; and the bomb inventories south of 46° S show considerable variation. Instead, we checked our model with high-latitude CFC-11 observations, obtaining a standing crop of 1,976 nmol m^{-2} for 1984, comparable to an estimate of 1,950±550 nmol m^{-2} obtained for the same period from measurements south of 46° S by Weiss et al.[20] in the South Atlantic, by the Pacific Marine Environmental Laboratory of the National Oceanic and Atmospheric Administration in the South Pacific (R. H. Gammon and D. Weisgarver, personal communication), and by R. Weiss (personal communication), also in the South Pacific.

表 1. 不同情景下大气 CO₂ 分压的变化预测（自 1990 年开始）

情景 *	50 年后			100 年后		
	A 未施铁	B 施铁	施铁的效果（B－A）	C 未施铁	D 施铁	施铁的效果（D－C）
高纬海域所占面积为 9.7%†						
初始化至工业化以前的水平	0	–26	–26	0	–39	–39
我们的模型	—	—	—	0	–34	–34
彭和布勒克‡	80	46	–34	156	98	–58
恒量排放	150	114	–36	430	362	–68
照常排放						
高纬海域所占面积为 16.0%						
初始化至工业化以前的水平	0	–41	–41	0	–59	–59
恒量排放	79	24	–55	151	61	–90
照常排放	146	88	–58	417	310	–107

* 在将大气中的 CO₂ 含量恢复至工业化以前的水平这一情景中，没有人类活动产生的 CO₂ 进入大气，因此海洋的吸收作用造成大气中 CO₂ 的含量低于工业化以前的 278.3 ppm。在"恒量排放"的情景中，1990 年以前大气 CO₂ 的含量是根据观测结果指定的 [23]，1990 年后进入大气的 CO₂ 含量规定为模型确定的 $6.15\ Gt \cdot C \cdot yr^{-1}$。根据 IPCC，"照常排放"情景中，1989 年以前大气中 CO₂ 的浓度是指定的，1989 年以后的 CO₂ 年排放量 [22] 一直增大，其中人类活动引起的排放量随时间线性增加，由 1990 年的 $6.0\ Gt \cdot C \cdot yr^{-1}$ 增长到了 2100 年的 $22.4\ Gt \cdot C \cdot yr^{-1}$。1990 年大气 CO₂ 分压为 355 ppm。

† 本模型中 9.7% 的部分与彭和布勒克 [17] 所选的海域面积相等，面积单位为 m²。

‡ 彭和布勒克 [17] 的模型初始化到了 280 ppm，且磷酸盐的减少量为 $1.6\ mmol \cdot m^{-3}$。表中所列结果是用于以下情景，并且设定高纬度海域的上升流水体为 $17.5 \times 10^{6}\ m^{-3} \cdot s^{-2}$，且直接进入深海。

　　海洋对大气 CO₂ 的吸收速率也取决于大洋环流与混合流将进入铁施肥海域的过量 CO₂ 从大气传送到深海的速率。研究发现，该因素的影响比前面提到的其他因素要小一些，具体讨论如下。图 1 所示为我们采用的模拟大洋环流与混合流的模型。通过将模型与 pre-bomb ¹⁴C（原子弹爆炸前放射性碳 14 同位素）测定结果以及布勒克等 [19] 在"地球化学海洋断面研究"（GEOSECS）计划中估计的原子弹爆炸总量进行拟合得到模型的各参数值（西根塔勒和约斯，发表于别处）。不过，在拟合过程中我们并未充分考虑南大洋的原子弹爆炸总量，因为很难从天然的 ¹⁴C 背景下分辨出原子弹爆炸的信号；南大洋的数据也较少，尤其是来自原子弹爆炸前的数据；再者，46°S 以南的原子弹爆炸总量差别也很大。因此我们采用高纬 CFC-11 的观测结果代为检验我们的模型，从中得出 1984 年的现存量为 $1,976\ nmol \cdot m^{-2}$，这与同一时间内韦斯等 [20] 在 46°S 以南的南大西洋测定的值、美国国家海洋与大气管理局的太平洋海洋环境实验室在南太平洋测得的结果（甘蒙和韦斯加弗，个人交流）以及韦斯（个人交流）在南太平洋得到的值 $1,950 \pm 550\ nmol \cdot m^{-2}$ 是一致的。

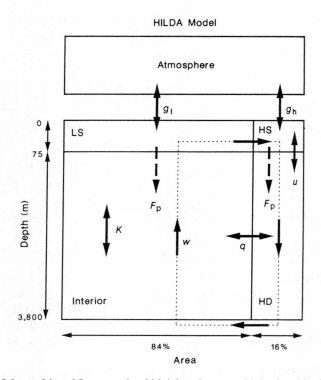

Fig. 1. Structure of the model used for our study, which is based on a model developed by G. Shaffer (personal communication) and one of us (J.L.S.). The ocean interior is resolved by a vertical stack of boxes connected by advection (w) and diffusion (K). The high-latitude regions are simulated by two well-mixed boxes which are connected to each other by mixing (u). The parameter q is a rudimentary representation of the ventilation of the interior oceans by high-latitude waters. The model parameters obtained by fitting bomb and natural ^{14}C are: $K = 465 + 7{,}096 \times \exp(-(z-75\ \mathrm{m})/253\ \mathrm{m})\ \mathrm{m^2\ yr^{-1}}$; $w = 0.44\ \mathrm{m\ yr^{-1}}$ (equivalent to 4.24×10^6 $\mathrm{m^3\ s^{-1}}$); $u = 38\ \mathrm{m\ yr^{-1}}$ ($69.8 \times 10^6\ \mathrm{m^3\ s^{-1}}$); $q = 0.00186\ \mathrm{yr^{-1}}(79.5 \times 10^6\ \mathrm{m^3\ s^{-1}})$; gas-exchange rate ($g_l$, g_h) at 280 p.p.m. $= 15.1\ \mathrm{mol\ m^{-2}\ yr^{-1}}$; ocean surface area $= 3.62 \times 10^{14}\ \mathrm{m^2}$; depth of mixed layer $= 75\ \mathrm{m}$; average depth of ocean $= 3{,}800\ \mathrm{m}$. We solve conservation equations for the perturbation of phosphate and $CO_2(c_{\mathrm{pert.}} = c_{\mathrm{actual}} - c_{\mathrm{unpert.}})$ with an initial condition for $c_{\mathrm{pert.}}$ of 0 everywhere. The relation between changes of $\Sigma\ CO_2$ and P_{CO_2} is calculated using the equations of Peng $et\ al.$[24]. The phosphate and carbon removed from the surface high-latitude box are regenerated to the dissolved form in the deep box below (dashed arrows, F_p = perturbation flux of particulate carbon and phosphorus). A small amount of this excess phosphate makes its way through the deep sea to low-latitude surface waters, where it is removed and regenerated below with an exponential scale depth of 1,160 m obtained from a fit to oceanic nutrient data by G. Shaffer and J.L.S. Multiplying the resulting phosphate fluxes by the C:P Redfield ratio (130) gives the corresponding carbon fluxes. LS, low-latitude surface; HS, high-latitude surface; and HD, high-latitude deep boxes.

Figure 2 summarizes results from the iron fertilization assuming the business-as-usual and constant-emission CO_2 scenarios. Without fertilization, the increase in atmospheric CO_2 from its 1990 value of 355 p.p.m. is 146 p.p.m. after 50 years, and 417 p.p.m. after 100 years in the business-as-usual scenario (Fig. 2a). When iron fertilization is initiated, an additional flux of organic carbon out of the high-latitude surface box is stimulated. Its size is approximately constant at 5.5 Gt C yr^{-1} after an initial peak in the first year. This increased carbon flux leads to a massive decrease in the high-latitude surface P_{CO_2} (see Fig.

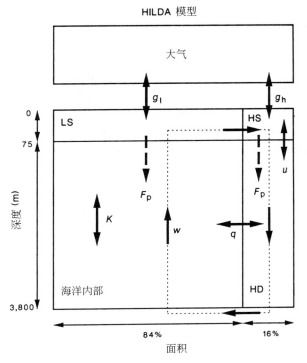

图 1. 本研究采用模型的结构，是基于谢弗（个人交流）和本文作者之一（萨缅托）设计的模型。该模型将海洋内部分解为垂直堆叠的箱体，箱与箱之间以对流（w）和扩散（k）作用相联结。高纬度地区可分为两个充分混合的箱体，两者通过混合作用（u）相联系。用参数 q 大致代表高纬度水体形成的海洋内部流通作用。模型参数是输入原子弹爆炸 ^{14}C 和天然 ^{14}C 得到的，分别为：$K = 465 + 7,096 \times \exp(-(z-75m)/253m)$ $m^2 \cdot yr^{-1}$；$w = 0.44$ m · yr^{-1}（相当于 $4.24 \times 10^6 m^3 \cdot s^{-1}$）；$u = 38$ m · yr^{-1}（$69.8 \times 10^6 m^3 \cdot s^{-1}$）；$q = 0.00186$ yr^{-1}（79.5×10^6 $m^3 \cdot s^{-1}$）；气体浓度为 280 ppm 时，气体交换速率（g_1, g_h）= 15.1 mol · $m^{-2} \cdot yr^{-1}$；大洋表面积 = $3.62 \times 10^{14} m^2$；混合层深度 = 75 m；大洋平均水深 = 3,800 m。当我们解磷酸盐和 CO_2 扰动作用的守恒方程（$c_{pert.} = c_{actual} - c_{unpert.}$）时，$c_{pert.}$ 的初始值全部为 0。利用彭等 [24] 的方程计算得到 ΣCO_2 与 P_{CO_2} 之间的变化关系。磷酸盐和碳从高纬度海洋表层箱体移除后以溶解态进入下部的深水箱体（虚线箭头，F_p = 碳、磷颗粒态的扰动通量）。少量过剩的磷酸盐从深海进入到低纬度地区的海洋表层水体，并在那里再次从表层移除进入下部水体，根据谢弗和萨缅托的大洋营养盐数据拟合结果，其指数标度深度为 1,160 m。将所得的磷通量乘以雷德菲尔德比值 C ：P（130）即得到相应的碳通量。LS 代表低纬度地区海水表层；HS 为高纬度地区海水表层；HD 表示高纬度海区的深水箱体。

图 2 所示为"照常排放"和"恒量排放"情景下，铁施肥结果的概况。在"照常排放"情景下，不施铁肥时，大气 CO_2 浓度由 1990 年 350 ppm，经过 50 年和 100 年，分别增加了 146 ppm 和 417 ppm（图 2a）。铁施肥开始后，促使额外的有机碳从高纬度海洋表层箱体中排出。所增加的量在第 1 年出现一个峰值后，其余年份基本保持不变，均为 5.5 Gt · C · yr^{-1} 左右。由此导致的 CO_2 通量的持续增加使得高纬度海洋

2b), and a resulting enhancement of atmospheric CO$_2$ uptake so that the atmospheric CO$_2$ now increases by only 88 p.p.m. after 50 years (60% of the increase in the unfertilized scenario) and by 310 p.p.m. after 100 years (74% of the increase in the unfertilized scenario). The decrease in atmospheric P_{CO_2} resulting from iron fertilization reduces the low-latitude air–sea difference so that the response of the low latitude regions is opposite in sign to that of the high latitudes (Fig. 2b). After 100 years, the additional CO$_2$ flux from the atmosphere to the high-latitude box in the iron fertilization scenario is 2.65 Gt C yr^{-1}. This is partly balanced by a reduction of 0.51 Gt C yr^{-1} in the low-latitude uptake of anthropogenic CO$_2$, for a net annual oceanic uptake of 2.13 Gt C yr^{-1} due to iron fertilization.

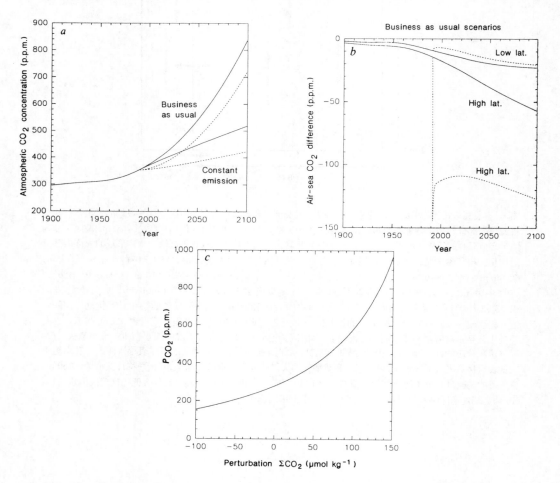

Fig. 2. a, Future atmospheric CO$_2$ concentration in the business-as-usual and constant-emission scenarios. The solid line is our prediction without iron fertilization, the dashed line shows what might occur with iron fertilization. b, The air–sea CO$_2$ difference of the iron-fertilized business-as-usual scenario (dashed lines) and the non-fertilized business-as-usual scenario (solid lines). c, Dependence of the partial pressure of CO$_2$ on Σ CO$_2$ in high-latitude surface water ($T = -0.22$ °C). With increasing CO$_2$ concentrations, the slope of the curve increases, and so does the change in P_{CO_2} for a given change in ΣCO$_2$.

表层海水中 P_{CO_2} 大大降低（见图 $2b$），进而造成表层海水对大气 CO_2 的吸收作用加强。这样，经过 50 年和 100 年后，大气中 CO_2 的浓度分别仅增加了 88 ppm（是不施铁时增加量的 60%）和 310 ppm（是不施铁时增加量的 74%）。铁施肥使大气中 P_{CO_2} 降低，进而减小了低纬度地区的气－海差异，因此低纬度地区的响应方式恰与高纬度地区相反（图 $2b$）。进行铁施肥 100 年后，由大气进入高纬度海域增加的 CO_2 通量为 $2.65 \ Gt \cdot C \cdot yr^{-1}$。这些增量部分被低纬度海域吸收人为 CO_2 的减少量 $0.51 \ Gt \cdot C \cdot yr^{-1}$ 所平衡，因为由铁施肥带动的海洋对 CO_2 的年净吸收量为 $2.13 \ Gt \cdot C \cdot yr^{-1}$。

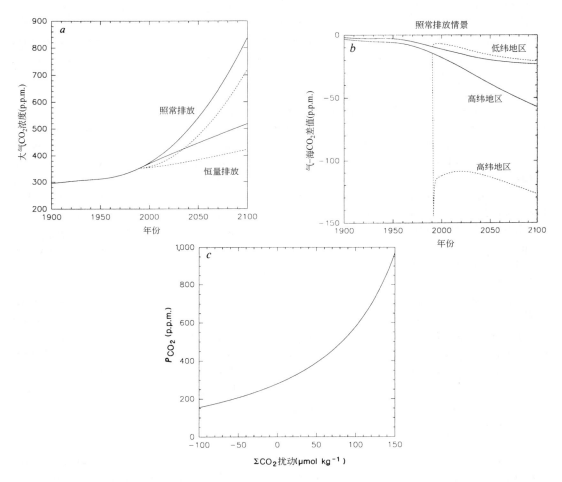

图 2. a，"照常排放"和"恒量排放"情景下，未来大气中的 CO_2 浓度。实线表示不施铁时的预测结果，虚线为铁施肥时可能的结果。b，"照常排放"情景下，铁施肥（虚线）和未经铁施肥（实线）时 CO_2 浓度的气－海差异。c，CO_2 分压对高纬度地区表层海水中 ΣCO_2 的依赖性（$T=-0.22℃$）。随着 CO_2 浓度的增大，曲线的斜率不断增大，而当 ΣCO_2 的变化量一定时，P_{CO_2} 的变化也随之增大。

The effect of the nonlinearity of the carbon chemistry equations can be discerned by comparing the three scenarios shown in Table 1. The constant-emission scenario with fertilization of 16% of the world ocean shows a reduction of 90 p.p.m. in the increase of atmospheric CO_2 resulting from 100 years of iron fertilization, compared with 59 p.p.m. for the scenario initialized at 278 p.p.m. The further increase in atmospheric CO_2 in the business-as-usual scenario has a still larger effect: 107 p.p.m. The dependence on the prevailing atmospheric CO_2 concentrations can be understood when considering that P_{CO_2}, depends in a nonlinear way on ΣCO_2. The higher the atmospheric concentration of CO_2, the larger the change in oceanic P_{CO_2} for a given reduction of ΣCO_2 due to iron fertilization (see Fig. 2c). We find that the percentage reduction in atmospheric CO_2 concentration which would occur after 100 years of iron fertilization decreases with higher CO_2 levels (21% for pre-industrial initialization, 14% for the business-as-usual scenario). This is in contrast to the assertion of Peng and Broecker[17] that the relative reduction is constant.

Peng and Broecker[17] emphasize that the key to evaluating the impact of iron fertilization is the rate of vertical exchange in the Southern Ocean. We find that the uncertainty in the calibration of the high-latitude transport parameters u and w gives error limits of $^{+14\%}_{-24\%}$ for the absolute value of the iron-induced reduction in atmospheric CO_2 for the pre-industrial scenario. Therefore, the precise magnitude of the vertical exchange seems not to be as critical as uncertainties in other processes. This is also supported by the fact that Peng and Broecker's result agrees well with ours for the same pre-industrial scenario (Table 1), although their high-latitude vertical exchange, which is calibrated with bomb-produced radiocarbon, is considerably weaker than our vertical exchange calibrated by oceanic distribution of CFC-11.

The effect of ocean area is readily apparent from the results summarized in Table 1. An increase in the fertilized area from 9.7% to 16% leads to an almost linear increase in the effect of iron fertilization of ~60%. Broecker[21] argues that their choice of the smaller area was intended to compensate for the fact that much of the Antarctic is in darkness during part of the year. We attempted to compensate for this effect by fertilizing the ocean for only six months of the year. The CO_2 uptake in the business-as-usual case went down from 107 p.p.m. to 88 p.p.m. far less than the drop to 68 p.p.m. which occurs when using the smaller area.

To be effective, iron fertilization has to be applied continuously so that the atmosphere-ocean system does not revert to its unfertilized state. This is shown in Fig. 3, which shows what happens if iron fertilization is terminated after 50 years. At 50 years the ocean in the business-as-usual iron fertilization simulation has taken up 57.9 p.p.m. more CO_2 than the non-fertilized ocean. If fertilization is stopped at this point, the difference between the fertilized and non-fertilized scenarios reduces to 35.5 p.p.m. after 100 years.

通过比较表 1 列出的三种不同情景，可以清楚看出碳化学方程的非线性效应。在"恒量排放"情景下，对世界大洋面积的 16% 进行铁施肥显示：100 年导致大气中增加的 CO₂ 减少量为 90 ppm。而还原至 278 ppm 的情景下则为 59 ppm。"照常排放"情景下，由于大气中 CO₂ 浓度的进一步升高，该效应更明显：为 107 ppm。当认识到 P_{CO_2} 与 ΣCO_2 之间是一种非线性关系后，就很容易理解施铁作用与当前大气 CO₂ 浓度的依赖关系了。铁施肥带动的 ΣCO_2 的减少量一定时，大气 CO₂ 浓度越高，海洋中 P_{CO_2} 的变化量越大（见图 2c）。我们发现，经过 100 年的铁施肥后，大气 CO₂ 浓度降低的百分比会随着 CO₂ 浓度的升高而降低（在工业化以前的初始值情景下为 21%，照常排放情景下为 14%）。这点与彭和布勒克 [17] 的结论恰恰相反，他们认为相对降低量是恒定的。

彭和布勒克 [17] 强调，南大洋的垂直交换速率是评估铁施肥影响的关键所在。而我们研究发现，"工业化以前"情景下，由于对高纬度地区传输参数 u 和 w 的校准存在不确定性，据此得出的由铁引起的大气 CO₂ 浓度减少量的绝对值误差范围为 −24%~+14%。因此，垂直交换量的大小精确与否似乎并没有其他过程中的不确定性来得关键。这一点还可通过另一事实得到证明，即虽彭和布勒克得出的高纬度海区的垂直交换量（经过原子弹爆炸产生的放射性碳校准）比我们采用 CFC-11 海洋分布校准得到的值小得多，但其"工业化以前"的情景得到的结果却与我们对同一时期得到的结果是一致的（表 1）。

据表 1 所列结果来看，海洋面积大小的影响是显而易见的。铁施肥海域面积由 9.7% 增加到 16%，导致铁施肥的效果几近直线地提高了约 60%。布勒克 [21] 曾指出：南极许多海域在一年中的一段时间内会处于黑暗之中，因此为了弥补这一点，他们选用了较小的海域面积。而我们则采用每年只施铁 6 个月的方式来弥补这种影响。"照常排放"情景下，CO₂ 的吸收仅由 107 ppm 降到了 88 ppm，远小于采用较小面积时降至 68 ppm 的减少量。

铁施肥必须持续进行，才能有效防止大气–海洋系统回复到未铁施肥的状态。如图 3，展示的是 50 年后终止铁施肥将出现的情况。"照常排放"情景下，经过 50 年的铁施肥可促使海洋多吸收 CO₂ 57.9 ppm。倘若此时终止铁施肥，100 年后铁施肥与不铁施肥情景下的差异将减小为 35.5 ppm。

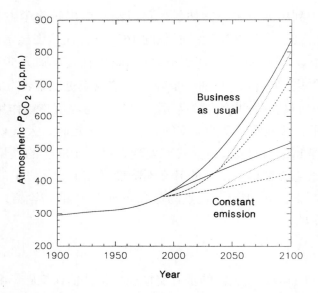

Fig. 3. The effect of stopping iron fertilization after 50 years (dotted line) is depicted for the business-as-usual and constant-emission scenarios. The solid line is the unfertilized scenario, the dashed line is the scenario for continuous fertilization.

Changes in the Earth's equilibrium temperature are logarithmically related to the atmospheric CO_2 content, with a doubling of CO_2 leading to an equilibrium warming of between 1.5 °C and 4.5°C, with a preferred value of 2.5 °C (ref. 22). A useful index of the significance of a given CO_2 increase is the factor $\ln(P_{CO_2}/278)/\ln(2)$ which, multiplied by 2.5 °C, will give the equilibrium warming resulting from a given CO_2 increase. Thus, the atmospheric CO_2 concentration of 771 p.p.m. reached by 2090 in the business-as-usual scenario will give an equilibrium warming of 3.7 °C. The 107-p.p.m. additional oceanic uptake resulting from iron fertilization gives an equilibrium warming of 3.1 °C instead. On the other hand, the unfertilized constant-emission scenario, which reaches 505 p.p.m. in 2090, gives a significantly smaller equilibrium warming of 2.2 °C, which is reduced to 1.4°C with the 90 p.p.m. additional oceanic uptake resulting from iron fertilization. These numbers can be compared with the 0.9 °C equilibrium warming that can be expected from the present atmospheric CO_2 content of 355 p.p.m. It should be kept in mind that the transient warming is smaller than, and not necessarily proportional to, the equilibrium warming, due primarily to the uptake of heat by the ocean.

The most important conclusion we draw from our calculations is that, although the effect of iron fertilization is large enough to justify further study, the effect of a significant change in the emissions of CO_2 is even larger. We emphasize the preliminary nature of our calculations and the fact that all the assumptions we have made have been biased so as to yield an upper limit.

(**349**, 772-775; 1991)

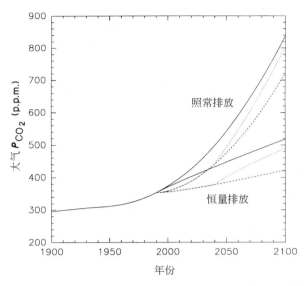

图 3. "照常排放"和"恒量排放"情景下，倘若 50 年后停止铁施肥将产生的影响（虚线）。实线表示不施铁的情景，虚线表示持续施铁的情景。

地球平衡温度的变化与大气的 CO_2 含量呈对数相关，当 CO_2 浓度提高至原来的两倍时，地球温度将变暖 1.5~4.5℃ 来维持平衡，首选值为 2.5℃（参考文献 22）。对于给定的 CO_2 浓度增加量的意义可用指标 $\ln(P_{CO_2}/278)$ / $\ln(2)$ 来衡量，将指标乘以 2.5℃ 即可得到该 CO_2 增量下维持地球平衡的增温值。那么，照常排放情景下，到 2090 年大气 CO_2 浓度达 771 ppm 时，相应的增温将为 3.7℃。而在铁施肥作用下，由于海洋额外吸收了 107 ppm 的 CO_2，相应的增温将为 3.1℃。另一方面，在不施铁的恒量排放情景下，2090 年的大气 CO_2 浓度将达到 505 ppm，相应的增温仅为 2.2℃，而铁施肥带动海洋额外吸收的 90 ppm 可使该平衡增温值降至 1.4℃。这个数值与目前 355 ppm 的大气 CO_2 含量条件下 0.9℃ 的平衡增温值差不多。需要注意的是，由于海洋对热量的吸收，瞬时增温小于平衡增温，并且不一定与平衡增温呈正比。

通过本文的研究，我们得到的最重要的结论就是：虽然铁施肥的影响很大，有必要对其进行进一步的研究，但 CO_2 排放量的巨大变化造成的影响更大。还要强调的是，本文只是初步的计算结果，而且，本文采用的所有假设都是有偏向性的，目的是为了得到上限值。

（齐红艳 翻译；李道季 审稿）

F. Joos[*], J. L. Sarmiento[†] & U. Siegenthaler[*]

[*] Physics Institute, University of Bern, CH-3012 Bern, Switzerland

[†] Atmospheric and Oceanic Sciences Program, Princeton University, Princeton, New Jersey 08544, USA

Received 5 November 1990; accepted 5 February 1991.

References:

1. Booth, W. *Washington Post*. A1 (20 May 1990).

2. Baum, R. *Chem. Engng News* **68**, 21-24 (1990).

3. Martin, J. H., Fitzwater, S. E. & Gordon, R. M. *Global Biogeochem. Cycles* **4**, 5-12 (1990).

4. Knox, F. & McElroy, M. B. *J. Geophys. Res.* **84**, 2503-2518 (1984).

5. Siegenthaler, U. & Wenk, T. *Nature* **308**, 624-626 (1984).

6. Sarmiento, J. L. & Toggweiler, J. R. *Nature* **308**, 621-624 (1984).

7. Sarmiento, J. L., Toggweiler, J. R. & Najjar, R. *Phil. Trans. R. Soc.* **A325**, 3-21 (1988).

8. Martin, J. H. & Fitzwater, S. E. *Nature* **331**, 341-343 (1988).

9. Martin, J. H. & Gordon, R. M. *Deep-Sea Res.* **35**, 177-196 (1988).

10. Martin, J. H., Gordon, R. M., Fitzwater, S. & Broenkow, W. W. *Deep-Sea Res.* **36**, 649-680 (1989).

11. Martin, J. H. *Paleoceanography* **5**, 1-13 (1990).

12. de Baar, H. J. W. *et al. Mar. Ecol. Prog. Ser.* **65**, 105-122 (1990).

13. Banse, K. *Limnol. Oceanogr.* **35**, 772-775 (1990).

14. Dugdale, R. C. & Wilkerson, F. P. *Global Biogeochem. Cycles* **4**, 13-20 (1990).

15. Anderson, G. C. & Morel, F. M. M. *Limnol. Oceanogr.* **27**, 789-813 (1982).

16. Morel, F. M. & Hudson, R. J. in *Chemical Processes in Lakes* (ed. Stumm, W.) 251-270 (Wiley, New York, 1985).

17. Peng, T.-H. & Broecker, W. S. *Nature* **349**, 227-229 (1991).

18. Toggweiler, J. R. & Sarmiento, J. L. in *The Carbon Cycle and Atmospheric CO2: Natural variations Archean to Present* Vol. 32, Geophysical Monograph Series (eds. Sundquist, E. T. & Broecker, W. S.) 163-184 (American Geophysical Union, Washington, DC, 1985).

19. Broecker, W. S. Peng, T.-H., Östlund, G. & Stuiver, M. *J. Geophys Res.* **90**, 6953-6970 (1985).

20. Weiss, R. F., Bullister, J. L., Warner, M. J., Van Woy, F. A. & Salameh, P. K. *Ajax Expedition Chlorofluorocarbon Measurements* (Scripps Institution of Oceanography Reference 90-6, La Jolla, 1990).

21. Broecker, W. S. *Global Biogeochem. Cycles* **4**, 1-2 (1990).

22. Houghton, J. T., Jenkins, G. J. & Ephraums, J. J. (eds) *Climate Change,* The IPCC Scientific Assessment (Cambridge, University Press, 1990).

23. Siegenthaler, U. & Oeschger, H. *Tellus* **39B**, 140-154 (1987).

24. Peng, T.-H., Takashi, T. & Broecker, W. S. *Tellus* **39B**, 439-458 (1987).

Acknowledgements. We appreciate the great help given to F. J. by M. Warner in setting up our CFC runs, and his generosity and that of R. Gammon in helping us to obtain the CFC data needed to estimate the CFC inventories. R. Fink developed our carbonate system algorithm and R. Slater helped with the phosphate data analysis. J. R. Toggweiler and J. Orr provided helpful comments on the manuscript. F. J. and U. S. acknowledge the hospitality of the Atmospheric and Oceanic Sciences Program during their extended visit to Princeton. This work was funded by subcontracts with Martin Marietta Systems, Inc., under contract with the Carbon Dioxide Research Division, US Department of Energy; by a follow-up contract directly from the Carbon Dioxide Research Division of the Department of Energy; and by the National Science Foundation.

Superconductivity at 18 K in Potassium-Doped C$_{60}$

A. F. Hebard *et al.*

Editor's Note

The discovery in 1990 of a method for making large quantities of the cage-like carbon molecule C$_{60}$ led to intensive research into its physical and chemical behaviour. Here Art Hebard and colleagues at AT&T Bell Laboratories in New Jersey report one of the most striking outcomes of that work: when doped with alkali metals, C$_{60}$ becomes superconducting at low temperatures, conducting electricity without resistance. The discovery followed soon after the Bell Labs team found that the doped solid had metallic conductivity. The onset temperature of superconductivity is relatively high compared to normal metals, and inspired hopes that it might be made higher still—as indeed it soon was. The finding never spawned practical applications, but was of immense theoretical interest.

The synthesis of macroscopic amounts of C$_{60}$ and C$_{70}$ (fullerenes)[1] has stimulated a variety of studies on their chemical and physical properties[2,3]. We recently demonstrated that C$_{60}$ and C$_{70}$ become conductive when doped with alkali metals[4]. Here we describe low-temperature studies of potassium-doped C$_{60}$ both as films and bulk samples, and demonstrate that this material becomes superconducting. Superconductivity is demonstrated by microwave, resistivity and Meissner-effect measurements. Both polycrystalline powders and thin-film samples were studied. A thin film showed a resistance transition with an onset temperature of 16 K and essentially zero resistance near 5 K. Bulk samples showed a well-defined Meissner effect and magnetic-field-dependent microwave absorption beginning at 18 K. The onset of superconductivity at 18 K is the highest yet observed for a molecular superconductor.

THE sensitivity to air of alkali-metal-doped fullerenes (A$_x$C$_n$) limits the choice of sample preparation and characterization techniques. To avoid sample degradation, we carried out reactions with the alkali metal vapour and C$_{60}$ in sealed tubes either in high vacuum or under a partial pressure of helium. The C$_{60}$ was purified by chromatography[1] of fullerite[2] and was heated at 160 °C under vacuum to remove solvents.

Small amounts of the individual fullerenes (~0.5 mg) were placed in quartz tubes with alkali metals and sealed under vacuum. These samples were subjected to a series of heat treatments and tests for superconductivity by 9-GHz microwave-loss experiments[5]. Preliminary tests indicated that only the K-doped C$_{60}$ showed a response consistent with a superconducting transition (Fig. 1). For this reason, together with the fact that K$_x$C$_{60}$ showed the highest film conductivity[1], we focused our studies on the K-doped compound.

掺钾的 C_{60} 在 18 K 时的超导性

赫巴德等

编者按

1990 年制备大量笼状碳 C_{60} 分子方法的发现引起了人们对其物理和化学性质的集中研究。本文中，新泽西州的美国电话电报公司贝尔实验室的阿特·赫巴德和同事们报道了这项工作中的一个最显著的成果：当掺入碱金属时，C_{60} 在低温下变成超导体，能够无阻导电。这是贝尔实验室继发现掺杂入金属的 C_{60} 具有金属导电性后的又一个发现。与一般的金属相比，它的超导起始温度相对较高，从而激发了人们使之更高的期望，不久，这就成为了事实。尽管此发现还未推广至实际应用中，但其引起了巨大的理论研究兴趣。

宏观量的 C_{60} 和 C_{70}（富勒烯）的合成[1]已经激发了很多关于其化学和物理性质的研究[2,3]。最近我们的实验表明：掺碱金属后的 C_{60} 和 C_{70} 具有导电性[4]。本文中我们论述了针对掺钾 C_{60} 的薄膜样品和块状样品的低温研究，并且说明了这种材料能变得具有超导性。超导性是通过微波、电阻率和迈斯纳效应的测试来说明的。我们对多晶粉末和薄膜样品分别进行了研究。结果表明，薄膜呈现出以 16 K 为起始温度的电阻转变，而且在温度接近 5 K 时就具有实质上的零电阻。块状样品呈现出明显的迈斯纳效应，且温度达到 18 K 时出现了随磁场变化的微波吸收现象。到目前为止，18 K 是人们所观测到的分子超导体最高的超导性起始温度值。

掺碱金属的富勒烯（A_xC_n）对于空气的敏感性限制了样品的制备和表征技术的选择。为了避免样品变质，我们让碱金属蒸气和 C_{60} 在高真空或者是具有氦分压的密封管中进行反应。C_{60} 是利用色谱法[1]对富勒烯固体[2]进行提纯且于 160 ℃ 在真空中加热除去溶剂而得到的。

将少量的单体富勒烯（约为 0.5 mg）与碱金属同置于石英管中，并在真空条件下密封。将这些样品进行一系列热处理后，通过 9 GHz 微波损失实验进行超导性检测[5]。初步的检测表明，只有掺钾的 C_{60} 表现出与超导转变相一致的反应（如图 1 所示）。由于这个原因，再加上 K_xC_{60} 显示出最高的薄膜导电性的事实[1]，我们集中研究了掺钾的化合物。

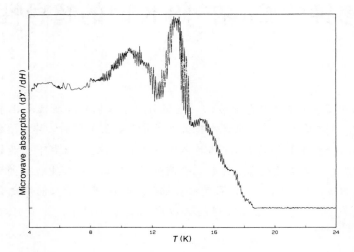

Fig. 1. Microwave loss as a function of temperature for K$_x$C$_{60}$ in a static field of 20 Oe.

The conductivity measurements were performed on potassium-doped films of C$_{60}$ that were prepared in a one-piece all-glass version of the apparatus described previously[4]. This reaction vessel was sealed under a partial pressure of helium before reaction. This configuration allowed both *in situ* doping and low-temperature studies of thin films. All measurements were made in a four-terminal Van der Pauw configuration using a 3-μA a.c. current at 17 Hz. Figure 2 shows the temperature dependence of the resistivity of a 960-Å-thick K$_x$C$_{60}$ film. The film was doped with potassium until the resistivity had fallen to 5×10^{-3} Ω cm. The resistivity increases by a factor of two on cooling the sample to near 20 K. Below 16 K, the resistivity starts to decrease; zero resistivity ($<10^{-4}$ of the normal state) is obtained below 5 K. The 10–90% width of the transition is 4.6 K. At 4 K we measured the lower bound to the critical current to be 40 A cm^{-2}.

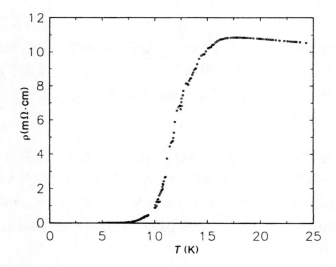

Fig. 2. Temperature dependence of the electrical resistivity of a 960-Å-thick film of K$_x$C$_{60}$.

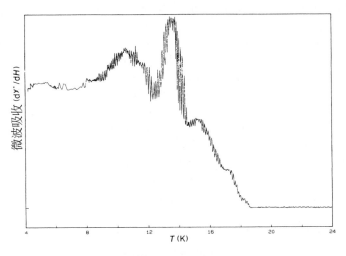

图 1. K_xC_{60} 在 20 Oe 的静场中的微波损失关于温度的函数。

对掺钾的 C_{60} 薄膜进行导电性测试，薄膜于先前曾描述过的[4]整体型全玻璃装置中制备。这种反应容器是在反应前具有氦分压的条件下密封的。这种构造可以同时允许原位掺杂和薄膜的低温研究。所有的测量均在四端范德堡配置中进行，条件为 17 Hz 频率的 3 μA 交流电。图 2 显示出厚度为 960 Å 的 K_xC_{60} 薄膜的电阻率随温度的变化关系。用钾掺杂薄膜，直到电阻率下降至 5×10^{-3} Ω·cm 为止。在将样品冷却至 20 K 左右时，电阻率增大了 2 倍。在温度低于 16 K 时，电阻率开始减小；在温度为 5 K 以下时得到零阻抗（＜正常态时的 10^{-4}）。电阻变化 10%~90% 所对应的温度间隔为 4.6 K。温度为 4 K 时我们测得临界电流的下限值为 40 A·cm⁻²。

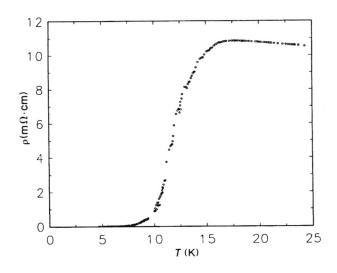

图 2. 厚度为 960 Å 的 K_xC_{60} 薄膜电阻率随温度的变化关系。

A bulk polycrystalline sample of nominal composition K_3C_{60} was prepared by reaction of 29.5 mg of C_{60} with 4.8 mg potassium. The amount of potassium was controlled volumetrically by using potassium-filled pyrex capillary tubing cut to size in a dry box. The reaction was run with the C_{60} in a 5-mm fused silica tube joined to a larger tube in which the potassium-containing capillary was placed. The tube was sealed after being evacuated and refilled with 10^{-2} torr of helium to serve later as a thermal-exchange gas for low-temperature measurements. With the C_{60}-containing end of the tube at room temperature, the potassium was distilled from the capillary in a furnace at 200 °C. Some reaction of the potassium with the quartz tube, visible as a dark brown discoloration, was observed at this temperature. Unreacted potassium was observed after this period. Following distillation of the potassium to the C_{60} end, the tube was shortened by sealing to about 8 cm and heated to 200 °C for 36 h. Finally, the tube was resealed to a length of about 4 cm for magnetic measurements.

The temperature dependence of the d.c. magnetization of the sample with nominal composition K_3C_{60} was measured in a SQUID magnetometer (Fig. 3). On zero-field cooling the sample to 2 K, a magnetic field of 50 Oe was applied. On warming, this field is excluded by the sample to 18 K; this verifies the presence of a superconducting phase. The bulk nature of superconductivity in the sample is demonstrated unambiguously by cooling in a field of 50 Oe. A well defined Meissner effect (flux expulsion) develops below 18 K. The shape of the magnetization curve, in particular the temperature-independent signal at low temperature, indicates good superconducting properties for this sample. Also noteworthy is the relatively narrow transition width. The magnitude of the flux exclusion for the zero-field-cooled curve corresponds to 1% volume fraction. This small fraction is possibly due to non-optimal doping or the granular nature of the sample. The large value of the Meissner effect for the field-cooled curve relative to the total exclusion, however, indicates bulk superconductivity in the electrically connected regions.

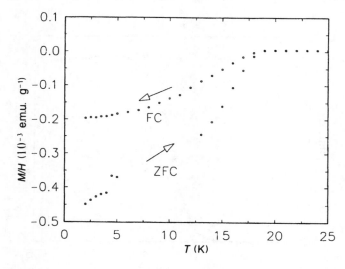

Fig. 3. Temperature dependence of the magnetization of a K_xC_{60} crystalline sample. The direction of temperature sweep in the field-cooled (FC) and the zero-field-cooled (ZFC) curves is indicated by the arrows.

标称成分为 K$_3$C$_{60}$ 的块状多晶样品是通过将 29.5 mg C$_{60}$ 与 4.8 mg 钾反应来制备的。通过控制体积调节钾的含量，即在干燥器中把充满钾的耐热玻璃毛细管裁割至适当体积。将一个装有 C$_{60}$ 的 5 mm 熔封石英管与一个放有含钾的毛细管的较大管子联结在一起，使反应得以进行。在抽真空并重新填入 10^{-2} torr 的氦作为随后的低温测量中的热交换气体后，将管密封。保持含 C$_{60}$ 的管末端处于室温状态，在温度为 200 ℃ 的炉子中将钾从毛细管中蒸馏出来。在这个温度下观察到钾与石英管的某些反应，可以看到有深褐色的褪色斑点。之后能够观察到未反应的钾。接着将钾蒸馏到 C$_{60}$ 末端，用密封方法将管子截短至约 8 cm，并将其加热到温度为 200 ℃，保持 36 小时。最后，将管子再次密封至约 4 cm 的长度以备磁学检测。

用超导量子干涉磁强计测试了标称成分为 K$_3$C$_{60}$ 的样品的直流磁化随温度变化的关系（如图 3 所示）。在零场中，冷却样品到 2 K，再对样品加 50 Oe 的磁场。加热温度直到 18 K 时，样品都可将该场排出；这就证明了一个超导相的存在。通过在 50 Oe 的场冷却，已明确地说明了样品中超导性的体特征。温度低于 18 K 时出现了明显的迈斯纳效应（磁通排出）。磁化曲线的形状，特别是低温下与温度无关的现象，表明该样品具有良好的超导性。同样值得我们注意的是相当狭窄的转变温度范围。零场冷却曲线对应的磁通排出的大小表明超导体积比为 1%。如此小的超导体积比可能是由于非理想掺杂或者是样品的粒状性质。但是，场冷却曲线的迈斯纳效应相对于总排出量的大的数值表明样品电连通区域中显著的体超导性。

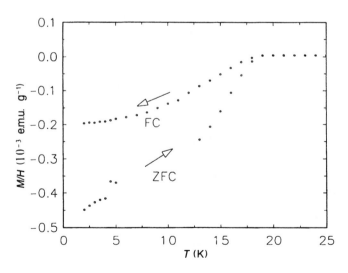

图 3. K$_x$C$_{60}$ 晶体样品的磁化随温度的变化关系。箭头指出了场冷却（FC）与零场冷却（ZFC）曲线中的温度扫描方向。

The universally accepted tests for superconductivity, namely a transition to zero resistance and a Meissner effect showing the expulsion of magnetic field, demonstrate unequivocally the existence of superconductivity in K$_x$C$_{60}$. The 18-K transition temperature is the highest yet reported for a molecular superconductor. This may be compared with the previously reported occurrence of superconductivity at 0.55 K in potassium-intercalated graphite[6]. We expect that optimization of composition and crystallinity will lead to further improvement in the superconducting properties.

(**350**, 600-601; 1991)

A. F. Hebard, M. J. Rosseinsky, R. C. Haddon, D. W. Murphy, S. H. Glarum, T. T. M. Palstra, A. P. Ramirez & A. R. Kortan

AT&T Bell Laboratories, Murray Hill, New Jersey 07974-2070, USA

Received 26 March; accepted 4 April 1991.

References:

1. Kroto, H. W., Heath, J. R., O'Brien, S. C., Curl, R. F. & Smalley, R. E. *Nature* **318**, 162-164 (1985).

2. Kratschmer, W., Lamb, L. D., Fostiropoulos, K. & Huffman, D. R. *Nature* **347**, 354-358 (1990).

3. Meijer, G. & Bethune, D. S. *J. Chem. Phys.* **93**, 7800-7802 (1990).

4. Haddon, R. C. *et al. Nature* **350**, 320-322 (1991).

5. Haddon, R. C., Glarum, S. H., Chichester, S. V., Ramirez, A. P. & Zimmerman, N. M. *Phys. Rev.* B **43**, 2642- 2647 (1991).

6. Hannay, N. B. *et al. Phys. Rev. Lett.* **14**, 225-226 (1965).

Acknowledgements. We thank G. Dabbagh, S. J. Duclos, R. H. Eick, A. T. Fiory, R. M. Fleming, M. L. Kaplan, K. B. Lyons, A. V. Makhija, B. Miller, A. J. Muller, K. Raghavachari, J. M. Rosamilia, L. F. Schneemeyer, F. A. Thiel, J. C. Tully, R. Tycko, R. B. Van Dover, J. V. Waszczak, W. L. Wilson and S. M. Zahurak for valuable contributions to this work.

得到普遍认可的超导性检测，即零电阻的转变与表现为磁场排出的迈斯纳效应，明确地证明了 K$_x$C$_{60}$ 中超导性的存在。18 K 的转变温度是到目前为止关于分子超导体报道中最高的温度值。这可以与以前报道的插钾层的石墨在 0.55 K 时超导性的出现[6]相比较。我们期望对成分与结晶度的优化能够进一步改善超导性质。

（王耀杨 翻译；韩汝珊 郭建栋 审稿）

Synthesis from DNA of a Molecule with the Connectivity of a Cube

J. Chen and N. C. Seeman

Editor's Note

When this paper by Junghuei Chen and Nadrian Seeman at New York University was published, it looked like a clever but peculiar curiosity. It describes the use of standard biotechnological methods to link short DNA strands into a framework with the topology of a cube. But this synthesis was in fact a harbinger of the field of DNA nanotechnology, in which DNA is used as a programmable molecular building block that will self-assemble into a wide variety of precisely specified structures with nanometre-scale dimensions. The result also set new standards for the production of topological supermolecules in which the components are united by physical interlinking, like the links of a chain. Such assemblies permit the controlled, switchable movement of molecules.

A principal goal of biotechnology is the assembly of novel biomaterials for analytical, industrial and therapeutic purposes. The advent of stable immobile nucleic acid branched junctions[1-4] makes DNA a good candidate for building frameworks to which proteins or other functional molecules can be attached and thereby juxtaposed[5-7]. The addition of single-stranded "sticky" ends[8] to branched DNA molecules converts them into macromolecular valence clusters that can be ligated together[1]. The edges of these frameworks are double-helical DNA, and the vertices correspond to the branch points of junctions. Here, we report the construction from DNA of a covalently closed cube-like molecular complex containing twelve equal-length double-helical edges arranged about eight vertices. Each of the six "faces" of the object is a single-stranded cyclic molecule, doubly catenated to four neighbouring strands, and each vertex is connected by an edge to three others. Each edge contains a unique restriction site for analytical purposes. This is the first construction of a closed polyhedral object from DNA.

THE synthetic scheme, shown in Fig. 1, is to synthesize ten strands, corresponding to two squares, and then to ligate them together. This scheme permits phosphorylation at three stages, so that intermediate products of a well-defined nature can be analysed: (1) the 80-mer circles, strands 1 and 6 are phosphorylated, cyclized by ligation, and then associated with the other strands that make up their squares; (2) the two squares are annealed with only those phosphates on the end-labelled C, C', D and D'; (3) the last phosphorylation before reconstitution puts a 5' phosphate on all unphosphorylated strands, and is followed by the final ligation. The sequences of the individual strands (see legend to Fig. 1) have been assigned using the program SEQUIN (ref. 9). Each square contains no repeated contiguous stretch of 6 nucleotides[1,9]. Only 28 of 480 such sequences are duplicated in the entire cube. In principle, only two of the steps used are necessary for the synthesis of the cube: (1) ligation of C and D, simultaneously with the covalent cyclization of strands 1 and 6, followed by (2) the ligation of A and B. The five steps shown in Fig. 1 are a response to the failure of that approach.

用 DNA 合成具有立方连接形式的分子

陈荣辉，西曼

编者按

当组约大学的陈荣辉和纳德里安·西曼发表这篇文章时，它看起来像一个精巧而奇特的游戏之作。它对使用标准的生物技术方法来连接短 DNA 链形成立方拓扑结构进行了描述。这个合成实际上是 DNA 纳米技术领域的一个先驱，其中 DNA 作为一个可编程的分子构建模块，将自组装成各种各样严格特异的、纳米尺度的结构。这一结果也为制备拓扑超分子树立了新的标准，在这些超分子中组件像链条一样通过物理作用连接起来。这种组装允许分子的可控及可逆运动。

生物技术的一个主要目标，就是装配各种新型生物材料以供分析、工业和医疗用。结构稳固的核酸分叉连接的出现[1-4]，使 DNA 成为构建蛋白质或其他功能分子得以附着进而并列其上的骨架结构[5-7]的良好选择。添加单链"黏性"末端至分叉的 DNA 分子[8]上，可以使 DNA 转化为能够连接在一起的大分子共价簇[1]。这种骨架的边框是双螺旋 DNA，顶点则对应于交叉连接的分支点。本文中，我们要报道的是用 DNA 构造的一种共价闭合的立方体分子复合物，其中包含围绕着 8 个顶点排布的 12 个等长的双螺旋棱。它的 6 个"面"中的每一个都是单链的环状分子，与 4 个相邻链形成双链连接，而每个顶点则通过一条棱与三个其他的顶点连接。每条棱中有一个独特的分析用的限制酶切位点。这是利用 DNA 构造的第一个闭合型多面体。

图 1 中显示了合成路线，先合成 10 条链，对应于 2 个正方形，再将其连接在一起。这一路线分三阶段完成磷酸化作用，从而能够对性质明确的中间产物进行分析：（1）链 1 和链 6 通过磷酸化后连接形成 80 个核苷酸单元的环，接着与其他链连接各自构成正方形；（2）只对在 C、C′、D 和 D′ 末端标记磷酸基的正方形进行退火连接；（3）重组前的最后一步磷酸化，对所有未磷酸化的链的 5′ 端进行磷酸化，接着进行最终的连接。利用 SEQUIN 程序（参考文献 9）确定每条链的序列（见图 1 图注）。每个正方形中不含重复的连续六核苷酸片段[1,9]。在整个立方体中的 480 个这样的序列中，只有 28 个是重复序列。原则上讲，在所用到的合成步骤中只有两步是合成立方体所必需的：（1）C 和 D 的连接，同时伴随着链 1 和链 6 的共价方式成环，接着是（2）A 和 B 的连接。图 1 中所显示的五步是针对上述方法的失败而采取的对策。

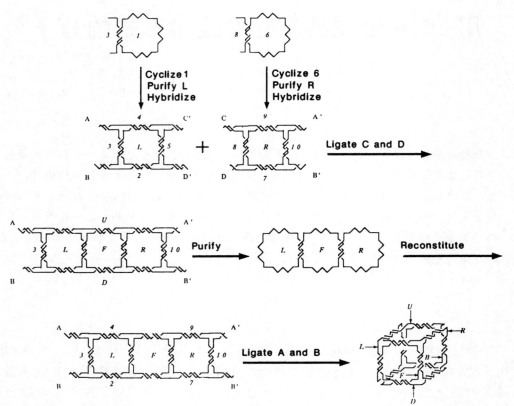

Fig. 1. The synthetic scheme used to synthesize the cube-like object. This diagram illustrates the strand identification used in the text. Numbers refer to strand numbers. We have used the convention that as a new strand is formed by ligation, its identification changes from one or more numbers to a letter corresponding to its position in the final object. For example, strand 1 is synthesized as a linear molecule, but is referred to as L once it is cyclized. The six final strands in the object are referred to as L (left), R (right), U (up), D (down), F (front) and B (back). Depiction of twisting between strands is confined to the central portion of each edge for clarity, following a previous convention[7]. This scheme depicts 5 steps (separating 6 stages) in the synthesis of the three-dimensional, 3-connected DNA object, after individual strands have been purified. The first step has two parts, the cyclization of the full-length strands 1 and 6 to form L and R, respectively. These two cycles are then hybridized with strands 2–5 and 7–10, respectively, to form the constituent squares shown in the second step. These squares are ligated together at the complementary sticky ends C' and C (5 base 5' overlap) and D and D' (4 base 3' overlap). This reaction forms strands U, F and D. U and D are discarded in a purification on a denaturing gel that isolates the L–F–R triple complex. The L–F–R–2–3–4–7–9–10 complex is then reconstituted and the final ligations are performed to close sites A and A' (4 base 5' overlap) and B and B' (5 base 3' overlap), as well as to seal the nicks in U (4–9) and D (2–7). This series of reactions forms the entire 3-D, 3-connected[14] object. Note that each edge is doubly linked to each of its four neighbouring strands. Denoting an edge by the two strands that comprise it, the restriction sites are: LF, *Dde*I; FU, *Bst*EII; RU, *Sau*96I; BU, *Bst*NI; LF, *Rsa*I; FR, *Bst*UI; RB, *Hha*I; BL, *Alu*I; FD, *Hinf*I; RD, *Taq*I; BD, *Sty*I; LD, *Hae*III. The sequences of the individual strands are: strand 1: CTTGCTCATACTGCATTCGGCCAGCCTGACATCA-CCGTGTACGCCCAAACCTTTCAACTTAGATGGTAGAAGGAGGGCAG; strand 2: CGCTGTGGGTCA-GGCTGGCCGAATGCAGAGCCAATCCTTGG; strand 3: GATTGGCTTATGAGCAAGCTGCCCTCCTC-GTTAGTT; strand 4: CTGGAACTAACGTCTACCATCTAAGTTGAAAGTCTCTTG; strand 5: GTGACCA-AGAGAGTTTGGGCGTACACGGTGATCCACAGCGACTC; strand 6: CGTGCTAACAGGTAGAGTTCG-ACGAATTACACAAATCGGCGGCAATACTATCCCGACTTGGACCAGCCTTTCGCCATCTCG; strand 7: GTGATTGG TAATTCGTCGAACTCTACCCTGAATGCGAGT; strand 8: GCATTCAGTGTTAGCACGCG-AGATGGCGTTCTGACG; strand 9: GTCACCGTCAGAAAAAGGCTGGTCCAAGTCGGGGCAGCGT-C; strand 10: CCAGGACGCTGCATAGTATTGCGCCGATTTGTCAATCACCCAAG.

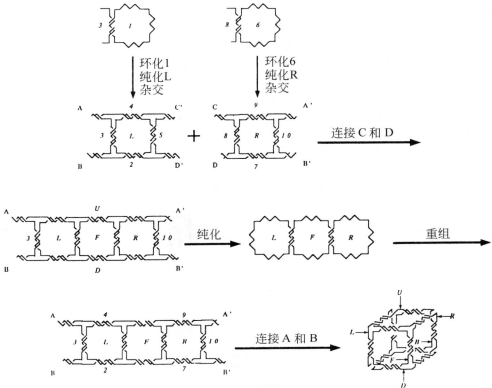

图 1. 立方体状物体的合成路线。此流程图对正文中提及的各条链进行了标注。数字代表各链的编号。我们遵循如下惯例：当一个新的链由于连接而形成时，对它的标注从一个或多个数字变成它在最终对象中所在位置对应的字母。例如，链 1 在刚合成时是一个线形分子，但是在成环后则记为 L。最终立方体中 6 个链记为 L(左)、R（右）、U（上）、D（下）、F（前）和 B（后）。为清晰见，对链与链之间螺旋的描述仅限于每条棱的中心部分，这遵循此前的惯例[7]。本路线图描述了单独各链在经过提纯后合成三维的三联通 DNA 物体的 5 个步骤（分为 6 个阶段）。第一步包括两个部分，完整长度的链 1 和链 6 环化分别形成 L 和 R。接着，这两个环分别与链 2~5 和链 7~10 杂交，形成第二步中所显示的正方形组件。这些正方形通过互补的黏性末端 C′ 与 C（5 碱基 5′ 重叠）和 D 与 D′（4 碱基 3′ 重叠）连接在一起。该反应形成 U 链、F 链和 D 链。利用变性凝胶进行提纯，分离出 L–F–R 三元复合物，丢弃成分 U 和 D。接着重组复合物 L–F–R–2–3–4–7–9–10，完成最终连接过程，连接位置 A 与 A′（4 碱基 5′重叠）和 B 与 B′（5 碱基 3′ 重叠），并且封住 U（4~9）和 D（2~7）的缺口。这一系列反应形成了一个整体的三维、三联通[14]物体。注意每条棱与其 4 条邻近链都是双重连接的。每条棱是用构成它的 2 条链来表示的，限制性酶切位点为：LF，*Dde*I；FU，*Bst*EII；RU，*Sau*96I；BU，*Bst*NI，LF，*Rsa*I；FR，*Bst*UI；RB，*Hha*I；BL，*Alu*I；FD，*Hinf*I；RD，*Taq*I；BD，*Sty*I；LD，*Hae*III。各个链的序列为：链 1，CTTGCTCATACTGCATTCGGCCAG CCTGACATCACCGTGTACGCCCAAACCTTTCAACTTAG-ATGGTAGAAGGAGGGCAG；链 2，CGCTGTGGGTCAGGCTGGCCGAATGCAGAGCCAATCCTTGG；链 3，GATTGGCTTATGAGCAA GCTGCCCTCCTCGTTAGTT；链 4，CTGGAACTAACGTCTACCATC-TAAGTTGAAAGTCTCTTG；链 5，GTGACCAAGAGAGTTTGGGCGTACACGGTGATCCACAGCGAC-TC；链 6，CG TGCTAACAGGTAGAGTTCGACGAATTACACAAATCGGCGCAATACTATCCCGACTTG-GACCAGCCTTTCGCCATCTCG；链 7，GTGATTGGTAATTCGTCGAACTCTACCCTGAATGCGAGT；链 8，GCATTCAGTGTTAGCACGCGAGATGGCGTTCTGACG；链 9，GTCACCGTCAGAAAAAGGC-TGGTCCAAGTCGGGGCAGCGTC；链 10，CCAGGACGCTGCATAGTATTGCGCCGATTTGTCAATC-ACCCAAG。

Figure 1 shows the strand numbering and nomenclature used. The association of L with strands 2–5 is shown in Fig. 2; similar results are obtained with R and strands 7–10. We show that these fifth-order reactions go largely to completion, but this does not guarantee that all strands are double-helical. For example, strand 2 might be paired with strands 3 and 5, but not with L. Both here and in the reconstitution steps below, we use susceptibility to restriction endonucleases as an assay for perfect pairing, as most of our sites are recognized by enzymes with exclusively double-helical activity. In each case, complete digestion indicates that the relevant strands have completely hybridized.

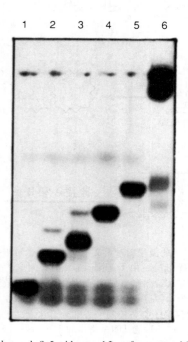

Fig. 2. The association of individual strands 2–5 with strand L to form a quadrilateral. Autoradiogram of a native gel in which strand L has been labelled and cyclized previous to the reactions shown. The first five lanes shown indicate the sequential addition of strands 2–5 to stand L. Lane 1: strand L; lane 2: L+2; lane 3: L+2+3; lane 4: L+2+3+4; lane 5: L+2+3+4+5. Lane 6 shows the ligation of two quadrilaterals to form the belt-like structure shown in Fig. 1, following ligation of ends C and D. The dark band near the top of the well in lane 6 contains the belt-like intermediate and many failure products as well, indicating that one cannot separate the desired product by native gel electrophoresis. The topmost band (top of the well) contains a complex of smaller species that cannot penetrate the gel. The DNA molecules used are synthesized on an Applied Biosystems 380B automatic DNA synthesizer, removed from the support and deprotected using routine phosphoramidite procedures[15]. DNA molecules are purified from denaturing gels. Hybridized complexes are formed by mixing a stoichiometric quantity of each strand, as estimated by absorbance at 260 nm; this mixture is the heated to 90 °C for 5 min and slowly cooled. Errors in stoichiometry are corrected by electrophoresing the complex on a non-denaturing gel, and extracting the appropriate band from the gel. Except where noted in the text, all gels contain 6% polyacrylamide (19:1, acrylamide:bisacrylamide).

Ligation of square L to square R forms the tricyclic belt, shown at the third stage of Fig. 1. The desired product of the ligation is not separable from other products on non-denaturing gels (Fig. 2), but successful double ligation of cohesive ends C and D is identified by a 3-circle catenated intermediate (L–F–R) after treatment with exonuclease III. Figure 3 shows a denaturing

图 1 中显示了各链的编号和所用的命名法。图 2 中显示了 L 与第 2~5 链的结合；R 与第 7~10 链结合得到类似的结果。我们要指出，尽管这五步反应基本上是完整的，但这并不能保证所有链都是双螺旋的。例如，第 2 链可能会与第 3 链和第 5 链配对，而不是与 L。在这里及以下的重组步骤中，我们用对限制性内切核酸酶的敏感性作为完美配对的一种检验，因为大多数位点可被专一双螺旋活性的酶所识别。在每种情况下，完全降解表明相应的各链已经完全杂交。

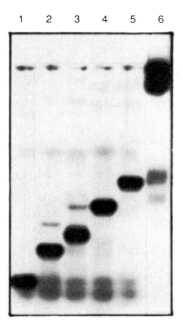

图 2. 第 2~5 各链与 L 链结合以形成一个四边形。此图为非变性凝胶的放射自显影图，其中 L 链在反应前就已被标记且成环。图示的前 5 个泳道依次是第 2~5 链对于 L 链的相继叠加。泳道 1：L 链；泳道 2：L+2；泳道 3：L+2+3；泳道 4：L+2+3+4；泳道 5：L+2+3+4+5。泳道 6 显示出 2 个四边形的连接，在末端 C 和 D 的连接之后形成如图 1 所示的带状结构。泳道 6 中靠近胶孔的黑色谱带中包含带状中间产物和很多种副产物，这意味着我们不可能使用非变性凝胶电泳方法分离出所需产物。最顶端的谱带（胶孔顶端）中包含一种少量无法渗入凝胶的复合物。所用的 DNA 分子是在应用生物系统 380B 自动型 DNA 合成仪中合成的，从支持物上洗脱后再用常规的亚磷酰胺过程去保护 [15]。DNA 分子通过变性凝胶电泳纯化。每条链的浓度通过 260 nm 处的紫外吸光度进行估算，按照化学计量比混合杂交；将混合物在 90 ℃加热 5 分钟后缓慢冷却。通过将复合物在非变性凝胶上电泳纯化来校正化学计量比的偏差。除非文中特别指明，所有的凝胶中都包含 6% 的聚丙烯酰胺（丙烯酰胺：双丙烯酰胺为 19：1）。

图 1 中的第三阶段显示，将正方形 L 连接到正方形 R 上形成了 3 个环的带状分子。连接过程的目标产物与其他产物在非变性凝胶上是不可分离的（图 2），但经过核酸外切酶 III 处理后，可以鉴别出三索烃的中间产物（L–F–R），表明黏性末端

gel with numerous exonuclease III-resistant product bands following ligation of C and D. Figure 3 also shows the products obtained when 21 nucleotide pairs per edge are used, rather than 20; the L–F–R band is virtually absent. We purify the catenated L–F–R core of the belt on denaturing gels, and then reconstitute it by the adding the missing six strands, now phosphorylated. Once closed, the cube consists of six linked circles, corresponding to the six faces of the object, and labelled left (L), right (R), up (U), down (D), front (F) and back (B). Figure 4 shows a denaturing gel containing the results of the final ligation. The cube comigrates with a 5-strand standard, but can be purified on 13% denaturing gels containing 1.25% bisacrylamide. The yields from square ligation and from final closure are each about 10%.

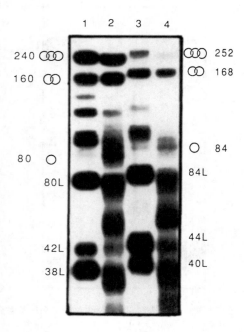

Fig. 3. The products of the first ligation (ends C and D). Autoradiogram of a denaturing gel illustrating the products of ligating two quadrilaterals together at ends C and D. Kinase labelling and ligations were as described[7]. The quadrilaterals are radioactively labelled on the F strand. The first two lanes illustrate the ligation of quadrilaterals containing 20 nucleotide pairs per edge, whereas the quadrilaterals used for the second two lanes contain 21 nucleotide pairs per edge. Lanes 1 and 3 show all the products, and lanes 2 and 4 show the products following digestion with exonuclease III. Small products seen in these lanes result from incomplete digestion. The symbols on the left and right indicate the total number of nucleotides in the species in the band with the indicated mobility. L means linear species that degrade upon treatment with exonuclease III. The other symbols indicate circular or catenated species, with two linked circles indicating the L–F or F–R catenane (Fig. 1), and three linked circles denoting that L–F–R catenane (Fig. 1). Note the virtual absence of this material in the lane 4, indicating that 21 nucleotide pairs per edge are inappropriate for closing the central cycle.

C 和 D 成功地进行了双重连接。图 3 的变性胶表明在 C 和 D 连接后形成了大量耐核酸外切酶 III 的产物。图 3 还表明，在每个棱上有 21 对而不是 20 对核苷酸时得到的产物中完全没有 L–F–R 带。我们将变性凝胶中的索烃 L–F–R 带纯化，接着添加缺失的 6 个链将其重组，使其磷酸化。闭合后，立方体包含 6 个连接的环，相当于它的 6 个面，并记为左(L)、右 (R)、上 (U)、下 (D)、前 (F) 和后 (B)。图 4 显示了含有最终连接产物的变性凝胶。立方体与由 5 链组成的基准物一同迁移，但是可以在含 1.25% 双丙烯酰胺的 13% 变性凝胶上提纯。正方形连接和最终闭合过程的产率都约为 10%。

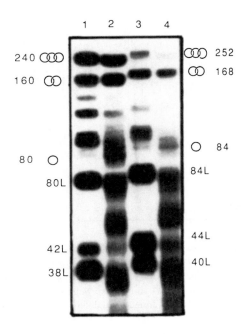

图 3. 第一次连接（末端 C 和 D）的产物。变性凝胶的放射自显影图显示了 2 个四边形在末端 C 和 D 连接所得产物的情况。激酶标记和连接如前所述[7]。在四边形中的 F 链上进行了放射性标记。前 2 个泳道中显示了每条棱中含 20 对核苷酸的四边形的连接，之后的 2 个泳道中所用的四边形则是每条棱中含 21 对核苷酸。泳道 1 和 3 中显示出全部产物，而泳道 2 和 4 中则显示了经核酸外切酶III降解后的产物。上述泳道中看到的小分子产物来自于不完全降解。左侧和右侧的标记则表明具有图示移动性的谱带中产物里的核苷酸总数。L 表示经核酸外切酶III处理后分解产生的线形产物。其他符号则表示环形或索烃产物，2 个相连圆环的符号指 L–F 索烃或 F–R 索烃（图 1），而 3 个相连圆环则表示 L–F–R 索烃（图 1）。注意该物质在泳道 4 中完全没有出现，表明每条包含 21 对核苷酸的棱不容易形成闭合的中心环。

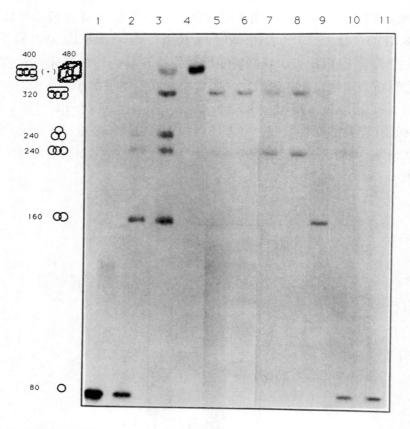

Fig. 4. Products of the final ligation step. Autoradigram of denaturing gels showing the formation and analysis of the products of the final ligation step. The same labelling conventions apply as in Fig. 3. In addition symbols have been added to indicate other structures: Three cyclic rings correspond to a corner (for example, L–F–U (Fig. 1)); the 4-cycle symbol corresponds to a molecule with the connectivity of L–F–R–U (Fig. 1); the 5-cycle symbol corresponds to the cube lacking a single strand, for example, L–F–R–U–D (Fig. 1); the 6-cycle structure is drawn as the cube representation of Fig. 1. All material has been treated with exonuclease III. Lane 1 contains a cyclic 80-mer marker. Lane 2 contains markers (individually synthesized and then combined) corresponding to the intermediate products (up to four cycles) shown on the left. Lane 3 illustrates the products of the final ligation. The portion of the gel containing the 80-mer circle in this lane was lost during manipulation. The top most band in this lane contains a mixture of the 6-cycle final product and the 5-cycle failure product, as indicated by the (+) symbol. These materials have been separated, and lane 4 contains the purified 6-cycle final product (see text). The digestions in lanes 5–11 were all performed on this purified material, which has been labelled in strand U. Lane 5 illustrates the digestion of the product with *Bst*UI(FR) and lane 6 illustrates the digestion of the product with *Rsa*I(LF) to yield 4-cycle products. Lane 7 illustrates the double digestion of the product with *Alu*I(BL) and *Hha*I(RB) to yield a 3-cycle belt. Lane 8 illustrates the double digestion of the final product with *Bst*UI(FR) and *Rsa*I(LF) to yield another belt. Note that the presence of this belt implies the successful ligation of each bond indicated in the final step. Lane 9 shows digestion with *Alu*I(BL) and *Taq*I(RD) to yield a 2-circle catenane. Note the absence of a doublet, suggesting the absence of mixed (single and double) catenation species. Lanes 10 and 11 are a duplicate experiment in which the product has been digested with *Alu*I(BL), *Hha*I(RB), *Bst*UI(FR) and *Rsa*I(LF). The product is a single 80-mer circle; absence of 160-mer circles indicates that no detectable doubling of the belt has occurred.

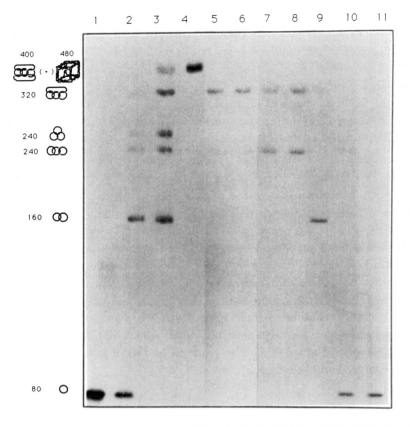

图 4. 最终连接步骤的产物。变性凝胶的放射自显影图显示出最终连接步骤产物的形成和对这些产物的分析。所用标记方式与图 3 中的相同。额外添加一些符号以表示其他结构：3 个圆环成环形排列对应于一个转角（例如图 1 中的 L–F–U）；四环符号对应于具有 L–F–R–U（图 1）连接形式的分子；五环符号对应于缺一条单链的立方体，例如 L–F–R–U–D（图 1）；六环结构则代表图 1 中的立方体形式。所有物质都已用核酸外切酶 III 处理过。泳道 1 中包含具有 80 个核苷酸的环状标记物。泳道 2 中包含对应于左侧所示中间产物（直到 4 个环的为止）的标记物（独立合成后再结合而成）。泳道 3 显示出最终连接产物。在处理过程中，该泳道中含 80 个核苷酸的环对应的带丢失了。该泳道中最顶端的谱带包含纯化的六环最终产物与五环副产物的混合物，用符号（+）表示。已经对这些物质进行了分离，泳道 4 中包含纯化的六环最终产物（见正文）。泳道 5~11 是纯化后的物质经过降解后的产物，将这些产物在 U 链上进行了标记。泳道 5 中显示了经过 BstUI（FR）降解后的产物，而泳道 6 中则显示经过 RsaI（LF）降解后得到的四环产物。泳道 7 中显示了经过 AluI（BL）和 HhaI（RB）双重降解后产生的三环带状分子。泳道 8 中显示了最终产物经过 BstUI（FR）和 RsaI（LF）双重降解后产生的另外一条带状分子。注意这种带状分子的出现意味着最终步骤中所涉各键的成功连接。泳道 9 显示了经过 AluI（BL）和 TaqI（RD）降解后产生的二环索烃分子。注意双谱线没有出现，表明没有混合的（单的和双的）索烃产物。泳道 10 和 11 是重复实验，其中产物已用 AluI（BL）、HhaI（RB）、BstUI（FR）和 RsaI（LF）进行了降解。产物是单个的 80 个核苷酸的环；没有出现 160 个核苷酸的环意味着没有可见的带状分子耦合过程发生。

Restriction of each edge individually results in the production of a 4-circle molecule (see for example Fig. 4, lanes 5 and 6; also data not shown). The final ligation forms the U, B and D circles. Restriction of the L–F and F–R edges results in the U–B–D triple catenane (Fig. 4, lane 8). This is the most robust proof of formation of the cube, as the belt present at the start of the last step is destroyed by restriction. Whether the final product corresponds to a single or multiple cycles of the belt (octagonal prism, dodecagonal prism, and so on) may be determined by the size of the U or D strand: at the concentrations used (10 nM in belt), the cube is the main product (Fig. 4, lanes 10 and 11).

The side of the belt facing the reader at the branch points (Fig. 1) corresponds to the major groove of DNA, whereas the minor groove is away from the reader. We do not know on which side we have closed the belt, nor whether we have a mixture. Model building[10] suggests that closure behind the page (minor groove) results in a large and more open structure. We have noted that the belt containing 20 nucleotide pairs per edge is much more readily formed than the one containing 21 nucleotide pairs per edge. This finding suggests that the twist around the F square, when attached to the L and R squares, is less than the eight cycles one would expect[11,12]. Presumably this decreased twist occurs at the site of the junctions. Whether it is shaped like a cube or another parallelopiped, the very tight angles between the object's negatively charged edges are probably more difficult to realize than the angles that characterize better approximations to the sphere[13]. The synthesis of this object establishes that it may be feasible to make larger and more complex objects[13,14].

(350, 631-633; 1991)

Junghuei Chen & Nadrian C. Seeman
Department of Chemistry, New York University, New York, NY 10003, USA

Received 7 November 1990; accepted 11 February 1991.

References:
1. Seeman, N. C. *J. theor. Biol.* **99**, 237-247 (1982).
2. Seeman, N. C. & Kallenbach, N. R. *Biophys J.* **44**, 201-209 (1983).
3. Kallenbach, N. R., Ma, R.-I. & Seeman, N. C. *Nature* **305**, 829-831 (1983).
4. Seeman, N. C. *J. Biomol. Str. Dyns* **3**, 11-34 (1985).
5. Robinson, B. H. & Seeman, N. C. *Prot. Engn.* **1**, 295-300 (1987).
6. Hopfield, J. J., Onuchic, J. N. & Beratan, D. N. *Science* **241**, 817-820 (1988).
7. Chen, J.-H., Kallenbach, N. R. & Seeman, N. C. *J. Am. Chem. Soc.* **111**, 6402-6407 (1989).
8. Cohen, S. N., Chang, A. C. Y., Boyer, H. W. & Helling, R. B. *Proc. Natl. Acad. Sci. U.S.A.* **70**, 3240-3244 (1973).
9. Seeman, N. C. *J. Biomol. Str. Dyns* **8**, 573-581 (1990).
10. Seeman, N. C. *J. Biomol. Str. Dyns* **5**, 997-1004 (1988).
11. Wang, J. C. *Proc. Natl. Acad. Sci. U.S.A.* **76**, 200-203 (1979).
12. Rhodes, D. & Klug, A. *Nature* **286**, 573-578 (1980).
13. Williams, R. *The Geometrical Foundation of Natural Structure* (Dover, New York, 1979).
14. Wells, A. F. *Three-dimensional Nets and Polyhedra* (Wiley, New York, 1977).
15. Caruthers, M. H. in *Chemical and Enzymatic Synthesis of Gene Fragments* (eds Gassen, H. G. & Lang, A.) 71-79 (Verlag Chemie, Weinheim, 1981).

Acknowledgements. We thank R. Sheardy, S. Fischer, D. Schwartz and N. Kallenbach for discussions and encouragement, and for the use of equipment in their laboratories. This research has been supported by grants from the Office of Naval Research and the NIH to N.C.S., and by a Margaret and Herman Sokol Fellowship to J.C.

每条棱的限制性酶切分别导致一种四环分子的生成（例如见图4，泳道5和6；其他数据并未显示）。最后一步的连接过程形成了U环、B环和D环。对于L–F和F–R棱的限制性酶切产生U–B–D三索烃（图4，泳道8）。这是立方体形成的最有力的证明，因为经过限制性酶切后显示的这条带正是最后一步的反应物。最终产物究竟是对应于单个还是多重的带状分子的环（八棱柱、十二棱柱等等），也许可以通过U链或D链的尺寸来确定：在所使用的浓度条件（条带的浓度为10 nM）下，立方体为主要产物（图4，泳道10和11）。

带状分子在分支点部位面向读者的一侧（图1）对应于DNA的大沟，而小沟则位于远离读者的一侧。我们不知道带状分子是在哪一侧闭合的，也不知道我们得到的是否是混合物。建模研究[10]表明，页面背面（小沟）的闭合导致大的并且更为开放的结构。我们已经注意到，每条棱中包含20对核苷酸的带状分子比每条棱中包含21对核苷酸的带状分子更容易形成。这个发现意味着，在附着于L和R正方形上时，F正方形附近的螺旋数比人们预期的8周[11,12]要少。据推测，这一减少的螺旋数出现在分支点部位。无论其形状是像立方体还是别的某种平行六面体，该物体带负电荷的棱之间极为紧凑的角度很可能使得它更接近于球形的角度[13]。这一立方体的合成使我们相信，合成更大、更复杂的物体[13,14]或许是可行的。

（王耀杨 翻译；刘冬生 审稿）

Recent Variations in Arctic and Antarctic Sea-Ice Covers

P. Gloersen and W. J. Campbell

Editor's Note

One of the major concerns about the threat of global warming was that the melting of ice sheets would raise sea levels. Melting sea ice has no such effect, however, because the floating ice displaces its own volume of water. Yet melting of sea ice could offer a gauge of temperature change, and would have drastic consequences for polar ecology, particularly at the north pole (where the ice cap is all sea ice). Here Per Gloersen and William J. Campbell use satellite measurements to deduce that sea ice coverage in the Arctic has indeed been decreasing over the past decade. Although they see no such trend in the Antarctic, it subsequently became clear that sea ice is declining at both poles.

Variations in the extents of sea-ice cover at the poles and the areas of open water enclosed within them were observed every other day during the interval 1978–1987 by a satellite-borne scanning multispectral microwave radiometer. A band-limited regression technique shows that the trends in coverage of the Arctic and Antarctic sea-ice packs are not the same. During these nine years, there are significant decreases in ice extent and open-water areas within the ice cover in the Arctic, whereas in the Antarctic, there are no significant trends.

THE scanning multichannel microwave radiometer (SMMR) which operated on board the Nimbus-7 satellite from October 1978 to August 1987, the longest interval of observation yet accomplished by a satellite-borne passive microwave instrument, allowed observations to be made of the entire Arctic and Antarctic sea-ice covers every two days through the clouds during night and day. It has thus provided a unique almost decade-long record of the large-scale behaviour of sea ice on Earth.

Sea ice is an important part of the global climate system. The two key aspects of the complex and dynamic sea-ice covers are ice extents (the total area enclosed by the ice–ocean edges) and the area of open water within them, consisting of cracks called leads and large amorphous openings called polynyas, from the Russian word for lake. The sea-ice extent affects the amount of solar radiation absorbed in its hemisphere and alters the atmosphere–ocean exchanges of heat, moisture and momentum. The area of open water within the ice pack, even when small compared with the ice extent, is critically important

南北极海冰覆盖面积的近期变化

格勒埃尔森，坎贝尔

编者按

全球变暖最主要的威胁之一是冰盖消融导致的海平面上升，但海冰融化不会产生这样的效应，因为海冰已经在海洋中。海冰融化可以用于估计气温变化，也可以显著影响极地尤其是北极（其冰帽全部属于海冰）的生态环境。佩尔·格勒埃尔森和威廉·坎贝尔使用卫星观测资料推断出过去十年，北极海冰覆盖面积确实在减小。虽然他们在南极没有发现这样的趋势，但随后的研究清楚地认识到两极海冰的覆盖面积都在减少。

利用星载扫描多波段微波辐射计，对 1978 年到1987 年的南北两极海冰覆盖范围以及被其包围的无冰水面面积的变化进行了隔日观测。采用带限回归技术分析，结果显示南北两极海冰覆盖面积的变化趋势存在差异。在这九年间，北极海冰的范围及其所包围的无冰水面面积明显减少，而南极地区则无明显变化趋势。

扫描多通道微波辐射计（SMMR）装载于雨云 7 号卫星上，从 1978 年 10 月运行至 1987 年 8 月，这是星载无源微波仪所完成的时间间隔最长的一次观测。不管昼夜，它都可穿过云层对整个南北两极的海冰覆盖范围进行监测，每两天记录一次观测结果。因此，它提供了一份将近十年之久的独一无二的关于地球海冰大范围状况的观测记录。

海冰是全球气候系统的重要组成部分。对于复杂而多变的海冰覆盖面积而言，冰的范围（被冰－洋边缘包围的总面积）及其所包围的无冰水面面积是两个关键方面。其中，无冰水面又由裂缝和大片无定形的敞水组成，分别被称为冰间水道和冰间湖（polynya，冰间湖，该词源于俄语，是湖的意思）。海冰范围影响着该半球吸收的太阳辐射量并且改变大气与海洋之间热量、水汽以及动量的交换情况。虽然与海冰覆盖范围相比，浮冰所包围的无冰水面面积很小，但却至关重要，因为相同面

because the fluxes of heat and moisture through a given area of open water are 2–3 orders of magnitude greater than through the same area of sea ice[1]. The multispectral and dual-polarized observations with the SMMR allow determinations of ice extent and open water with greater accuracies than those obtainable with earlier satellite sensors. The accuracy of the ice edge positions determined by SMMR is about half the diameter of the SMMR field of view, or about 25 km (ref. 2). The precision of the open-water estimates is estimated to be within 5% in the Arctic Ocean and 9% for other seas where large amounts of thin ice are present[3].

The SMMR observations made over nearly nine years, uncorrected for instrument drift, were used in a recent paper[4] to derive variations of the extents of Arctic and Antarctic sea ice and the open-water areas within the ice–ocean edge. The ordinary linear regression analysis of these uncorrected data indicated that trends of −4% and −5% in the maxima and minima, respectively, of the annual ice extents occurred in the Arctic over the 8.8-year span. The goodness-of-fit parameters (R^2) were 0.4 and 0.1, respectively. In the Antarctic, the trend in the ice-extent maxima was −3% ($R^2=0.1$). But a statistically more significant negative trend of 5% ($R^2=0.8$) was found for the peaks in the sum of the two polar ice packs, which is termed the annual global ice extent. These trends were obtained from a very small sample of the total SMMR data set: that is, only the data at the time of the peaks of the winter extents and the troughs of the summer extents.

The key question posed by this earlier paper, and left unanswered, was the following: if the maxima of the global ice extents show a significant negative 8.8-year trend, what occurred within the separate Arctic and Antarctic sea-ice extent curves, the sources of this trend, other than at their annual extrema? We surmised that the trends of the individual annual ice extents could only be discerned by analysing all the data on the ice extents. Perhaps the answer lay in the shape of the individual annual ice-extent oscillations.

Here we present the entire set of these SMMR observations of Arctic and Antarctic sea-ice extent and enclosed open water, which have been corrected for instrumental drift and variations with ecliptic angle. We also give the results of an analysis of the full data set based on band-limited regression[5] (BLR) which succeeds in accurately determining their trends allowing for the serial correlation present in the raw data.

Instrument Stability

Since the earlier publication[4], there has been additional analysis of the SMMR instrument drift (P.G. *et al.*, manuscript in preparation). First, the annual and semi-annual cycles were removed from the measurements of average radiance from the oceans from $50°\,N$ and $50°\,S$ to the edges of the Arctic and Antarctic ice packs, respectively. Second, the orbital data for the ascending and descending nodes were averaged separately in each hemisphere to observe the seasonal variations of solar effects on the instrument[6]. This procedure for removing the annual and semi-annual cycles also removes the nine-year means, and when the four results for the ascending and descending, north and south polar averages were compared, they were found to be nearly identical.

积下，通过无冰水面的热通量和水汽通量比通过海冰的要大 2~3 个数量级[1]。相比早期采用卫星传感器获得的结果来说，在利用 SMMR 得到的多波段和双极化观测结果中，海冰范围和无冰水面测定的准确度大大提高。由 SMMR 确定的冰缘位置准确度约为 SMMR 视场直径的一半，即 25 km 左右[2]。在北冰洋中对无冰水面的估计值的精度约在 5% 以内，其他海域由于薄冰较多，精度可达 9%[3]。

最近有篇文章[4]利用近九年来 SMMR 的监测结果（未经仪器漂移校正），对南北极海冰范围和冰－洋边缘内的无冰水面面积的变化做了研究。对上述未校正数据的普通线性回归分析结果表明，在这 8.8 年中，北极历年海冰范围改变的极大、极小值分别为 –4% 和 –5%。拟合优度参数（R^2）分别为 0.4 和 0.1。南极冰范围变化趋势的极大值则为 –3%（$R^2=0.1$）。但当把两极浮冰范围的峰值相加，就可发现一个在统计学上更为显著的减少趋势，达 5%（$R^2=0.8$），其中两极浮冰之和称为年全球冰范围。上述变化趋势仅由整个 SMMR 数据库中的很小一部分样本得出，即仅采用了冬季冰范围达到峰值和夏季冰范围最小时的数据。

早前的文章提出了一些关键问题但未给出答案：倘若全球海冰范围的最大值在 8.8 年中呈现为显著的减小趋势，那么除了年极值以外，南北两极的海冰范围曲线分别发生了怎样的变化呢？这种趋势的原因又是什么？我们认为，只有对所有海冰范围数据加以分析才能找出海冰范围各年的变化趋势，也许答案就在于各年海冰范围振荡曲线的形状中。

在此我们给出 SMMR 监测到的关于南北两极海冰范围及其所包围无冰水面的全部数据，并且对所有数据作了仪器漂移校正和黄道角变化校正。考虑到原始数据的序列相关性，我们还给出了整个数据库的带限回归[5]（BLR）分析结果，从中成功准确地确定出它们的变化趋势。

仪器的稳定性

自从早前的文章发表以来[4]，就有了对 SMMR 的仪器漂移的追加分析（佩尔·格勒埃尔森等，手稿准备中）。首先，将年周期和半年周期分别从由 50°N 和 50°S 到南北极浮冰群边缘的海洋的平均辐射值中去除。其次，分别对南北半球上处于上升和下降结点处的轨道数据求平均值，以获得太阳辐射对仪器的季节性影响[6]。在去除年周期和半年周期的过程中还去除了九年的平均值，而比较所得四个结果（南、北极上升与下降的平均值）发现，它们几乎完全相同。

An average of the polar ocean radiances between the 50° parallels and the ice edges was the radiation reference used for the detection and subsequent correction of SMMR instrument drift (P.G. *et al.*, manuscript in preparation) in the four channels used in the calculations of sea-ice concentration[3]: the horizontally and vertically polarized components at wavelengths of 0.8 and 1.7 cm were used. Briefly, the instrument drift was determined on the premise that the averaged polar ocean radiances are invariant with time, and so the observed drift in these ocean radiances constitutes instrument drift. The relative changes observed in each of the channels support this premise. The premise does not preclude observing changes in the ice pack because the increases in sea surface temperature needed to melt the pack ice are so small that they may not be observable in the SMMR record. As the radiometers are of the Dicke type, no drifts are expected when observing targets radiometrically equivalent to the internal warm references, and none were found. The actual correction for drift was then scaled according to where the observed radiance fell between the values for the ocean and warm reference.

Sea-Ice Extents and Open-Water Areas

The SMMR radiances used in this analysis have been corrected for the aforementioned drifts and for variations with ecliptic angle[6]. In addition, we have modified the earlier ice-extent calculations by using the 15% ice concentration isopleth as the ice edge and employed a weather filter[7] to reduce false ice signatures over the oceans due to storms. We decided to use the 15% isopleth for the ice edge to be consistent with similar analyses of the Nimbus-5 microwave data[8,9]. In the earlier SMMR study[4], only the weather filter was used, which places the ice edge between the 8% and 12% ice concentration isopleths, depending on ice type. Finally, we improved on the land masks used earlier[4] for the SMMR data, and we also improved the ice extent calculations by using both the equatorial and polar Earth radii rather than just the equatorial radius as was done in the Nimbus-5 studies. The net result of these improvements is that the SMMR ice-extent variations shown in Fig. 1 are ~7% greater in the Arctic than those reported earlier[4], and about the same in the Antarctic. With proper use of the Earth's radii, the Nimbus-5 data for the Arctic ice extent would have been ~1% greater.

The ice-extent and open-water variations in the Arctic and Antarctic were determined with all of the corrected SMMR data obtained over the polar ice covers. On average, data were taken every other calender day, but there were brief intervals of everyday operation or no operation, occurring in less than 1% of the data set. An uneven data set is not suitable for the analysis used here, and so the earlier data set was edited to produce an evenly spaced time series of alternate days by removal of extra days (1% of the original data) and interpolation to fill the few gaps, adding 1% to the original data.

计算海冰密集度[3]时需采用 SMMR 仪器的四个波段：波长为 0.8 cm 和 1.7 cm 的水平和垂直极化分量。南北纬 50°纬度圈到冰缘线之间的极地海洋的辐射平均值是用于探测并随后校正该四个波段上 SMMR 仪器漂移的辐射基准（佩尔·格勒埃尔森等，手稿准备中）。简单地说，确定仪器漂移的前提是，平均极地海洋辐射不随时间变化，因此在这些海洋辐射条件下观察到的漂移就构成了仪器漂移。在各波段上观测到的相对变化支持这一前提。该前提并不排除浮冰中所观测到的变化，因为融化浮冰群只需要海表温度上升很小的幅度，以至于在 SMMR 的记录中可能看不出来。由于所采用的辐射计为迪克型，因此当所观测的目标辐射量与内部热标准的相等时应该不会发生漂移，而实际上也确实未发现漂移。这样，我们就可以根据观测到的辐射值落在海洋与热标准值之间的位置来确定漂移校正值了。

海冰范围和无冰水面面积

本文分析采用的 SMMR 辐射已经经过上述的漂移校正和黄道角变化校正[6]。此外，我们对之前的冰范围计算值也作了修正，即使用冰密集度为 15% 的等密集度线作为冰缘线，同时，我们还引入了一个天气滤波器[7]，以降低由于风暴而在海洋上产生的错误冰信号。我们决定采用 15% 的等密集度线作为冰缘线，以便与前人对雨云 5 号卫星上的微波数据作的类似分析[8,9]相一致。早期对 SMMR 的研究中[4]仅使用天气滤波器，并且根据冰型的不同，将冰缘线选在 8%~12% 的等密度线之间。最后，我们改进了之前采用的 SMMR 数据的陆地模板[4]，并通过同时采用赤道半径和极半径以改进冰范围的计算，而不是如雨云 5 号的相关研究那样仅采用赤道半径。上述改进的净结果是，如图 1 所示的北极 SMMR 冰范围变化比之前报道的结果要大 7% 左右，而在南极则基本相同。恰当应用地球的半径，雨云 5 号卫星数据得到的北极冰范围就会增加大约 1%。

根据获自极地冰覆盖的所有校正过的 SMMR 数据，我们确定出南北两极冰范围和无冰水面面积的变化。平均来说，每两天采集（一次）数据，但也有每天采集和两天均未采集的情况，不过这些数据只占整个数据库不到 1%。不均匀的数据库不适用于本文的分析方法，因此，我们对原始数据作了加工，即去掉多采集的数据（原始数据的 1%）并插入一些空缺的数据（向原始数据增加了 1%），以产生均匀分布的隔日时间序列。

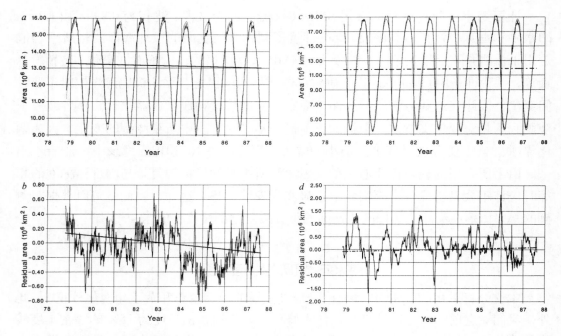

Fig. 1. Sea-ice extents (the areas enclosed by the margin of the sea-ice covers) and residuals for a and b, the Arctic and, c and d, the Antarctic from 25 October 1978 to 20 August 1987, and their trends. The Arctic trend (solid line) is a 2.1% decline over the 8.8-year interval under discussion, and is significant to the 96% confidence level. The Antarctic trend (dashed line) is statistically insignificant. The extents are determined from the horizontally and vertically polarized radiances at wavelengths of 0.8 and 1.7 cm obtained by the SMMR on board the Nimbus-7 satellite. Also shown in a and c are the modelled seasonal oscillations composed of ten sinusoids comprising the first five harmonics of the annual cycle, whose amplitudes were obtained by an ordinary least-squares fit to the data. The residuals shown in b and d result from subtracting these modelled oscillations from the data, and emphasize the superimposed BLR trend lines. The radiances are corrected for long-term instrument drift and variations with ecliptic angle.

Trends in the Ice Covers

A band-limited regression (BLR) technique[5] has been used previously to establish coherence between atmospheric carbon dioxide and global temperature[10]. We will use this technique to obtain an offset and a trend in the SMMR data, which are serially correlated and therefore cannot be analysed properly by standard linear regression. Briefly, the method entails smoothing the data with a multiband filter, and then determining the trend in the filtered data, from which the high-frequency fluctuations and seasonal cycle have been removed. The basis for this technique is the matrix, U.

$$U_{ij} = [\sin 2\pi W(i{-}j)/\pi(i{-}j)]; \; i, j = 0, 1, 2, \ldots, N{-}1 \tag{1}$$

where $0 < W \leqslant 1/2$ is a bandwidth parameter, and $N = 1,612$ is the number of observations. W was chosen so that $W = 4/N$. The bandpass filter used in this approach consists of the first eight eigenvectors and the corresponding eigenvalues of the matrix, U, obtained from its singular value decomposition[11], designated as an $8 \times 1,612$ matrix, V, and an 8×8 diagonal matrix, S, respectively. Because of the rapid falloff of the magnitudes of the

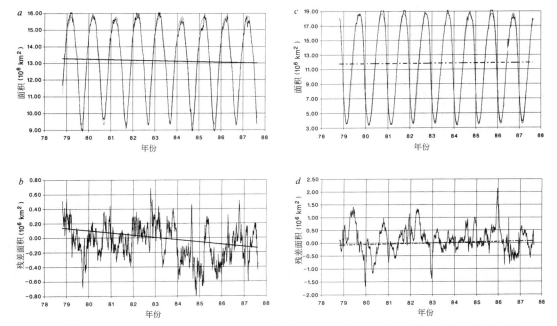

图 1. 1978 年 10 月 25 日至 1987 年 8 月 20 日，北极（a 和 b）和南极（c 和 d）的海冰范围（海冰覆盖边缘所包围的区域）、残差及其变化趋势。在所讨论的 8.8 年时间里，北极的变化趋势（实线）为 2.1% 的下降，达到了 96% 的显著置信水平。南极的变化趋势（虚线）在统计上并不显著。上述冰范围是从装载于雨云 7 号卫星上的 SMMR 在 0.8 cm 和 1.7 cm 的波段上的水平和垂直极化辐射率得出的。图 a 和图 c 还给出了季节性振荡的模拟结果，由 10 个正弦曲线组成，构成了年际波动的前 5 个谐波，其振幅是对数据作普通最小二乘法拟合得到的。图 b 和图 d 所示的残差是从数据中减掉上述模拟波动的结果，并突出了叠加的带限回归趋势线。图中所示辐射率均已经过长期仪器漂移校正和黄道角变化校正。

海冰覆盖面积的变化趋势

带限回归（BLR）分析技术[5] 先前已被用来确定大气二氧化碳含量与全球温度之间的相关性[10]。在此我们将利用该技术来获取 SMMR 数据的偏移和变化趋势，因为这些数据均呈序列相关，利用标准线性回归无法作出恰当分析。简单地说，该方法需要一个多频带滤波器对数据进行平滑处理，然后再从已过滤数据中确定变化趋势，这些数据中的高频波动和季节性波动也已经被扣除。该方法的基础是矩阵 U。

$$U_{ij} = [\sin 2\pi W (i-j)/\pi (i-j)]; \; i, j = 0, 1, 2\cdots, N-1 \qquad (1)$$

其中 $0 < W \leqslant 1/2$ 为带宽参数；$N=1,612$ 代表观测结果的数量。设 $W=4/N$。该方法中采用的带通滤波器由矩阵 U 的前 8 个特征向量及其对应的特征值组成，通过奇异值分解[11] 可分别得到一个 $8 \times 1,612$ 的矩阵 V 和一个 8×8 的对角矩阵 S。由于特征

eigenvalues, a very close approximation (called elsewhere truncated series regression[5]) to the original matrix, U, is obtained as follows:

$$U = VSV' \qquad (2)$$

where the prime indicates a matrix transpose. The method continues by formulating the offset and trend in a 1,612×2 design matrix, D, and obtaining the offset and trend in a coefficient vector, $\mathbf{a}$, as follows:

$$\mathbf{a} = (D'UD)^{-1}(D'U\mathbf{y}) \qquad (3)$$

where $\mathbf{y}$ is the data vector. The standard deviations of $\mathbf{a}$ are also obtained from D, V, and $\mathbf{y}$, in a manner[5] too lengthy to be outlined here.

When this method is applied to the data on the extent of Arctic sea ice obtained from SMMR, a trend of -0.0315×10^6 km^2 per year is found, with a standard deviation of 0.0143×10^6 km^2 per year. Over the SMMR operational period of 8.8 years, this represents a 2.1±0.9% decline in the Arctic sea-ice extent. As the basis function of eight eigenvalues was used to determine an offset and trend, the net number of degrees of freedom to be used in the statistical, single-sided t-test[5] is six, and the confidence level of the determination is 96.5%, based on the ratio of the trend to the standard deviation, which is 2.20. The trend so determined is smaller than the -4% and -5% trends reported earlier[4] for the maximum and minima, respectively, of the Arctic sea-ice extent, but as mentioned above, these earlier calculations were based on a standard linear regression analysis of uncorrected SMMR data of annual extrema and a lower (8–12%) ice concentration for the ice edge than the 15% used here. The Arctic decline reported here is greater than the -1.4% reported recently[12] for an eight-year interval of annually averaged uncorrected SMMR data. On the other hand, we have found that annually averaging the corrected data over an interval of eight years (so as to average over complete seasonal cycles) before running a linear regression, as done with the uncorrected data earlier[12], gives a trend of -2.2% for the Arctic extent, but the statistical significance of the trend so determined is not valid.

Application of the BLR technique to Arctic open-water area within the ice cover yields a trend of $-3.5 \pm 2.0\%$, at a confidence level of 93.5%. Thus the trends for both the Arctic ice extent and the open water are negative. These trends indicate that for the Arctic the area covered by sea ice decreased less than its ice extent. Application of the technique to the Antarctic sea-ice extent and open-water area leads to statistically insignificant results, as the standard deviations of the trends are greater than the trends themselves. The results are summarized in Table 1 and illustrated in Figs 1 and 2.

值的量级迅速下降，根据公式：

$$U = VSV'$$ (2)

可得到原始矩阵 U 的一个近似矩阵（在别的地方被称为截断序列回归[5]）。V' 代表转置矩阵。然后在 $1,612 \times 2$ 的设计矩阵 D 中用公式表示偏移和变化趋势，利用系数向量 **a** 来求出偏移和变化趋势，如下：

$$\mathbf{a} = (D'UD)^{-1}(D'U\mathbf{y})$$ (3)

公式中 **y** 为数据矢量。根据 D、V 和 **y** 还可求出 **a** 的标准差，不过因其表达式[5] 过于冗长，在此不予列出。

当把该方法应用到由 SMMR 得到的北极海冰范围数据时，发现海冰范围的变化量为 -0.0315×10^6 km² · yr⁻¹，标准偏差为 0.0143×10^6 km² · yr⁻¹，这意味着在 SMMR 运行的 8.8 年间，北极海冰范围下降了 $2.1\% \pm 0.9\%$。由于计算偏移和变化趋势时采用了 8 个特征值的基函数，所以在统计上的单侧 t 检验[5] 中使用的自由度为 6，所得结果的置信度为 96.5%，这是基于变化趋势与标准偏差的比值 2.20 确定的。据此得出的北极海冰范围的最大、最小值分别小于之前报道的 -4% 和 -5%[4]，但如上所述，之前那些计算结果是根据未经校正的 SMMR 数据中年度极值的标准线性回归分析得到的，而且当时所用冰缘线的冰密集度（8%~12%）低于这里的 15%。我们所得出的北极海冰减少比新近利用八年未校正的 SMMR 数据的年均值得到的 -1.4%[12] 更高。另一方面，我们还发现，倘若和前人对未校正数据的处理一样[12]，在做线性回归分析之前将八年的校正数据求平均（以便对完整的季节性波动求平均），得到北极冰范围的变化为 -2.2%，但这一趋势未能通过显著性检验。

对北极海冰包围的无冰水面面积应用带限回归分析方法，得到的变化趋势为 $-3.5\% \pm 2.0\%$，置信水平为 93.5%，因此，北极冰覆盖范围和无冰水面面积的变化均为负值。这些趋势表明北极地区海冰覆盖面积的减少量低于冰范围的减少量。利用该方法对南极海冰范围和无冰水面面积进行分析则未得到统计上显著的结果，因为变化趋势的标准偏差比这些趋势本身要大得多。所有结果总结于表 1，如图 1、图 2 所示。

Table 1. Band-limited regression analysis of polar sea-ice covers

	Slope (10^6 km^2 yr^{-1})	Standard deviation (10^6 km^2 yr^{-1})	8.8-yr trend	Confidence level
Arctic sea-ice extent	−0.0315	0.0143	−2.1±0.9%	96.5%
Antarctic sea-ice extent	+0.0177	0.0188	*	*
Arctic leads and polynyas	−0.0102	0.0058	−3.5±2.0%	93.5%
Antarctic leads and polynyas	+0.0020	0.0044	*	*

*Statistically insignificant.

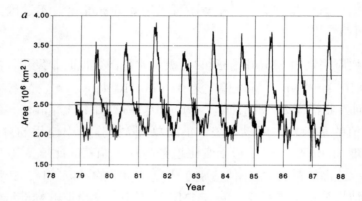

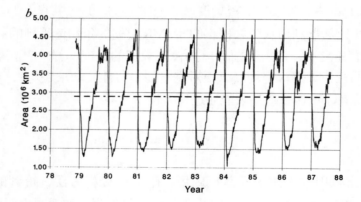

Fig. 2. Open water within the ocean–ice boundary (leads and polynyas) for *a*, the Arctic and *b*, the Antarctic from 25 October 1978 to 20 August 1987, and their trends. The Arctic trend (solid line) is a 3.5% decline over the 8.8-year interval under discussion, and is significant to the 93% confidence level. The Antarctic trend (dashed line) is statistically insignficant.

We are confident that the BLR analysis reported here more accurately represents the actual trends than results based on ordinary linear regression analysis of uncorrected SMMR data, whether on the annual averages or annual extrema.

表 1. 极地海冰覆面积的带限回归分析

	斜率 （10^6 km^2 · yr^{-1}）	标准差 （10^6 km^2 · yr^{-1}）	8.8 年的变化趋势	置信水平
北极海冰范围	−0.0315	0.0143	−2.1% ± 0.9%	96.5%
南极海冰范围	+0.0177	0.0188	*	*
北极冰间水道和冰间湖	−0.0102	0.0058	−3.5% ± 2.0%	93.5%
南极冰间水道和冰间湖	+0.0020	0.0044	*	*

* 统计上不显著

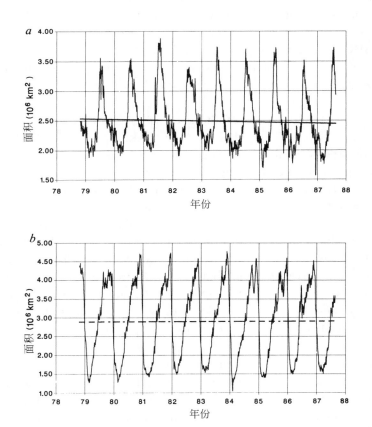

图 2. 1978 年 10 月 25 日至 1987 年 8 月 20 日，海−冰边界所包围的无冰水面面积（冰间水道与冰间湖）
及其变化趋势，*a* 为北极，*b* 为南极。在所讨论的 8.8 年中北极地区的变化趋势（实线）减小了 3.5%，
置信水平为 93%，而南极地区的变化趋势（虚线）在统计上不显著。

我们确信，与前人利用未校正 SMMR 数据得到的普通线性回归分析结果相比，
本文采用的带限回归分析方法不管是在年度平均值或年度极值上都更能准确地代表
实际的变化趋势。

Discussion

A number of studies have indicated that changes in the global average air temperature might be detectable by observing changes in the extents of the polar sea-ice covers[8,9,13-17,23]. The Nimbus-7 SMMR observations give us a unique look at the variations of these extents every two days for almost a decade, and thus provide the most accurate and comprehensive such record yet obtained. The trend obtained by BLR analysis of the Arctic sea-ice extent (Table 1) may be a signal of climate change. It should be said that the near-decade of SMMR observations is not sufficiently long to establish a climate trend clearly. What sea-ice data are available to extend the record? The interval 1973–76 was covered by an earlier passive microwave radiometer flown in space, the electrically scanned microwave radiometer (ESMR) on board the Nimbus-5 satellite. We have not attempted to treat the ESMR data in the same manner as the SMMR data, because they are not as accurate. The sea-ice record for the time before ESMR is made up largely of data from visible-light sensors flown on the early meteorological satellites; the combination of polar clouds and poor lighting conditions has resulted in a fragmented data set of limited quality for the sea-ice extent.

Whether or not the SMMR record of the decrease in the extents of the Arctic sea-ice cap signals a climate change is therefore an open question. These findings are, however, consistent with records of significant changes in other large-scale phenomena which have occurred over longer periods, including the SMMR decade. A marked increase in the global atmospheric air temperature[18,19] commenced in 1974 and persisted until the 1980s, which became distinctly the warmest interval in the record lasting for more than 100 years, albeit in the lower latitudes. A warming of the Alaskan Arctic permafrost, typically 2–4 °C, commenced during the past 100 years, and during the SMMR lifetime the average increase[20] was 0.5 °C. A decrease in the extent of the Arctic sea-ice cover has been cited as a possible cause for this warming[20], but any permafrost warming corresponding to a change in sea-ice extent would have occurred over much longer times than addressed here. On the other hand, there has been no evidence of warming in ocean surface temperatures in the northern hemisphere during this interval[21].

We do not know the causes of this asymmetry between the hemispheres, with a significant decrease in Arctic sea-ice extent, but no corresponding decrease in the Antarctic. It is interesting to note that a recent simulation with a coupled ocean–atmosphere model[22] of the atmospheric response to a doubling of the global CO_2 level over a century shows an interhemispheric asymmetry in the warming of surface air temperatures, with the Antarctic increasing very slowly and the Arctic faster.

We do know that sea ice exists in those parts of the Earth where global warming is expected to be the greatest. We also know that the sea-ice covers, with their high albedos and insulating effect between the polar atmospheres and oceans, are a key part of the climate machine. That the variations of the Arctic and Antarctic sea-ice extents and enclosed open water have behaved asymmetrically over nearly a decade is a new finding which must be considered in predictions of global change.

(**352**, 33-36; 1991)

讨　论

许多研究显示，通过监测极地海冰覆盖范围的变化可探测全球平均气温的变化[8,9,13-17,23]。雨云 7 号卫星的 SMMR 观测结果为我们提供了一份独一无二的资料，它涵盖了近十年来所有隔日观测的冰范围变化，是目前获得的最准确最全面的记录。对北极海冰范围数据（表 1）用带限回归分析得出的变化趋势可能是气候变化的一个信号。应该说，近十年的 SMMR 观测时间跨度不够长，并不足以清楚地确定出气候的变化趋势，那么什么样的海冰数据可以延长该记录呢？之前，装载于雨云 5 号卫星上的无源微波辐射计，即电子扫描微波辐射计（ESMR）曾得到了 1973 年到 1976 年间的数据。我们并不打算用处理 SMMR 数据的方法来处理 ESMR 数据，因为后者并不是很准确。ESMR 之前的海冰数据记录主要是来自早期气象卫星上携带的可见光传感器，极地地区的云层加上较差的光照条件，使得关于海冰范围的数据非常不完整，而且数据质量不高。

因此，SMMR 记录的北极海冰冰帽范围的减小是否意味着气候的变化还有待研究。然而，这些发现与其他一些在更长时期内发生的大尺度现象的显著变化记录（涵盖 10 年的 SMMR 数据）是一致的。1974 年全球气温有一次明显升高[18,19]，并且一直持续到了 20 世纪 80 年代。这是 100 多年来记录到的发生在低纬地区最温暖的一段时期。过去的 100 年来，阿拉斯加的永久冻土温度升高了，一般为 2~4℃，其中 SMMR 运行期间平均升高了 0.5℃[20]。北极海冰覆盖范围的减小已被认为是造成该变暖的可能原因之一[20]，然而，与海冰范围变化相对应的冻土温度的升高所发生的时间要比这里所提到的时间长得多。另一方面，在这期间，并未发现有北半球海洋表面温度升高的证据[21]。

北极地区海冰范围明显减少，而在南极却没有相应变化，我们还不清楚这种不对称现象的原因。有趣的是，最近有人利用耦合海－气模型[22]模拟大气对全球 CO_2 含量在 100 年内增加一倍的响应情况，结果显示，南北半球之间地表气温的上升也是不对称的，其中南极升温非常缓慢，而北极则快些。

我们已经知道，海冰存在于地球上增暖最显著的地方。我们还知道，海冰具有很高的反射率，且在极地大气与海洋之间起着很强的保温作用，因此是气候系统的关键组成部分。然而，我们观察到南北极海冰范围及其包围的无冰水面面积在近 10 年的记录中的变化是不对称的，这是一项新发现，在预测全球变化时必须考虑到这一点。

（齐红艳 翻译；聂军胜 审稿）

Per Gloersen and William J. Campbell[*]

Laboratory for Hydrospheric Processes, NASA Goddard Space Flight Center, Code 971, Greenbelt, Maryland 20771, USA

[*] Ice and Climate Project, US Geological Survey, University of Puget Sound, Tacoma, Washington 98416, USA

Received 8 April; accepted 31 May 1991.

References:

1. Badgley, F. I. in *Proc. Symp. Arctic Heat Budget and Atmospheric Circulation* (ed. Fletcher, J. O.) 267-277 (1966).

2. Campbell, W. J. *et al. J. Geophys. Res.* **92**, 6805-6824 (1987).

3. Cavalieri, D. J., Gloersen, P. & Campbell, W. J. *J. Geophys. Res.* **89**, 5355-5369 (1984).

4. Gloersen, P. & Campbell, W. J. *J. Geophys. Res.* **93**, 10666-10674 (1988).

5. Lindberg, C. R. *J. R. stat. Soc.* B (submitted).

6. Francis, E. A., thesis, Univ. of Oregon State (1987).

7. Gloersen, P. & Cavalieri, D. J. *J. Geophys. Res.* **91**, 3913-3919 (1986).

8. Zwally, H. J. *et al. NASA SP*-459 (U.S. GPO, Washington DC, 1983).

9. Parkinson, C. L. *et al. NASA SP*-489 (U.S. GPO, Washington DC, 1987).

10. Kuo, C., Lindberg, C. & Thomson, D. J. *Nature* **343**, 709-714. (1990).

11. Press, W. H., Flannery, B. P., Teukolsky, S. A. & Vetterling, W. T. *Numerical Recipes in C* (Cambridge University Press, 1989).

12. Parkinson, C. L. & Cavalieri, D. J. *J. Geophys. Res.* **94**, 14499-14523 (1989).

13. Sissla, J. F., Sabatini, R. R. & Ackerman, H. J. *Polar Res.* **16**, 367-373 (1972).

14. Streten, N. A. *Arch. Meteorol. geophys. Bioklimatol. Ser.* A22, 129-134 (1973).

15. Budd, W. F. *J. Glaciol.* **15**, 417-426 (1975).

16. Kukla, G. & Gavin, J. *Science* **215**, 497-503 (1981).

17. Carsey, F. D. *J. Geophys. Res.* **87**, 5809-5835 (1982).

18. Jones, P. D. *et al. Nature* **322**, 790 (1988).

19. Hansen, J. & Lebedeff, S. *Geophys. Res. Lett.* **15**, 323-326 (1988).

20. Lachenbruck, A. H., Cladouhos, T. T. & Saltus, R. W. *Permafrost* **3**, 9-17 (ed. Senneset, K.) (Tapir, Trondheim, Norway, 1988).

21. Reynolds, W. R., Folland, C. K. & Parker, D. E. *Nature* **341**, 728-731 (1989).

22. Stouffer, R. J., Manabe, S. & Bryan, K. *Nature* **342**, 660-662 (1989).

23. Zwally, H. J., Parkinson, C. L. & Comiso, J. C. *Science* **220**, 1005-1012 (1983).

Acknowledgements. We thank C. R. Lindberg of AT&T Bell Laboratories, H. F. Lins of the US Geological Survey Water Resources Division and A. J. Busalacchi of the NASA Goddard Laboratory for Hydrospheric Processes for critical readings of this paper and helpful suggestions.

Predominance of Long-Wavelength Heterogeneity in the Mantle

Wei-jia Su and A. M. Dziewonski

Editor's Note

Convective flow in the Earth's mantle drives plate tectonics at the surface, but the structure of the convection cells has been much debated. The nature of the mantle is hard to study, as it is too deep for direct access. But seismic waves travelling through the Earth's interior offer a natural probe somewhat akin to ultrasound imaging: the waves travel at different speeds in material of different structure or composition. Here Wei-jia Su and Adam Dziewonski at Harvard University use seismic-wave travel times to "image" the lateral non-uniformities in the mantle, which are thought to reflect the patterns of convection. They find that the most prominent heterogeneities are large: around 6,000 km across when projected onto the Earth's surface.

Analysis of travel-time anomalies of long-period shear waves recorded by the Global Digital Seismographic Network indicates that mantle heterogeneities, which probably reflect patterns of mantle convection, occur most prominently on length scales greater than about 6,000 km, when projected onto a two-dimensional map at the Earth's surface. Models of mantle convection will need to be able to produce a similar power spectrum.

SEISMIC wave speeds change with temperature and composition; so does the Earth's density. It was expected, therefore, from the beginning of global seismic tomography (imaging in three dimensions of small deviations of wave speeds from a spherically symmetric reference model) that the method could provide the critical evidence needed for an improved understanding of the Earth's global dynamics. In 1977, Dziewonski *et al.*[1] wrote: "Lateral variation of the physical properties of the matter within the earth must be the cause as well as the result of the dynamic processes occuring in its interior. There is, as yet, no consistent explanation of the driving mechanism of the plate motions... Knowledge of the three-dimensional perturbations of the physical parameters could provide clues to the nature of the mechanism as well as constraints for its quantitative solution." Recently, Olson *et al.*[2] have described the remarkable convergence of results in seismic tomography, mantle geochemistry and numerical modelling of mantle convection. They present a picture of whole-mantle convection dominated by large-scale flow which is consistent with most of the currently available results.

地幔中长波长非均匀性的主导作用

苏魏佳，杰翁斯基

编者按

地幔中的热对流驱动着地表的板块构造，但是关于对流单元的结构却存在很大的争议。对地幔本质的研究非常困难，因为地幔非常深，难以直接进行观测。但地震波可以穿过地球内部，从而提供了一个天然探头，这有点类似于超声成像：地震波在穿过不同结构或成分的物质时，速度也不同。本文中，哈佛大学的苏魏佳和亚当·杰翁斯基利用地震波走时，来"描绘"地幔的横向非均匀性，而一般认为这种非均匀性反映了对流模式。他们发现，最显著的非均匀处非常大：如果投影到地表，其跨度约为 6,000 km。

对全球数字地震台网记录的长周期剪切波走时异常的分析表明，地幔存在非均匀性，投影到地表二维图后主要出现在大于约 6,000 km 的尺度上，这种非均匀性可能反映了地幔对流模式。由此地幔对流模型需要产生一个相似的功率谱。

地震波速度和地球密度都随温度与物质组成的变化而变化。因此，从全球地震层析成像（采用球对称参考模型，利用速度残差来进行三维成像）提出之时，人们就期望它能为进一步认识地球动力过程提供重要证据。1977 年，杰翁斯基等 [1] 在文章中写道："地球内部物质物理性质的横向变化既是地球内部动力学过程的原因又是其结果。迄今为止，关于板块运动的驱动机制并没有一致的解释。对物理参数三维扰动的认识可能为这种机制的本质及其定量解的约束提供线索。"最近，奥尔森等 [2] 发现地震层析成像、地幔地球化学和地幔对流的数值模拟等方面的成果明显趋于一致。他们提供了由大尺度流支配的全地幔对流图像，与大部分现有的成果一致。

But the distribution of power in the spectrum of mantle heterogeneity obtained by seismic methods has not yet been satisfactorily investigated. In some models, the spherical harmonic expansion is truncated *a priori* at a low degree; for example, degree two[3], four[4], six[5-7] or eight[8]. Alternatively there is a class of models represented by tens of thousands of unknown parameters[9,10]. The nominal horizontal resolution of these models reaches degrees as high as $l = 36$ in the spherical harmonic expansion, and they can have a nearly white spectrum[11]. There are also uncertainties in modelling of mantle convection; to make computation feasible, it is carried out for Rayleigh numbers two orders of magnitude lower than thought to be appropriate[2]. Consequently, one could expect features at higher wavenumbers in the actual convection pattern than those predicted by calculations (for example in ref. 12). To make proper use of the information provided by seismic tomography and modelling of convection, we must know the spectral distribution of lateral heterogeneity in the mantle.

Worse still, the low-order models may be biased, as well as being incomplete, because of the uneven distribution of sources and receivers, if there is significant power in the rejected part of the spectrum. Two recent papers suggest that this may be the case. Gudmundsson *et al.*[13] presented results of a statistical analysis of the P-wave travel-time residuals and concluded that in the upper mantle the spectrum of lateral heterogeneity is white, down to wavelengths as short as 100–200 km. Snieder *et al.*[14] suggested that what seem to be large-scale features in both upper- and lower-mantle tomographic models may be an artefact of low-pass filtration of relatively narrow structures such as mid-ocean ridges or subduction zones. In reality, they say, the highly anomalous properties are limited to narrow zones, whose width is an order of magnitude less than indicated by the tomographic models. If either the above statements is correct, then much of the tomographic work may be wrong or, at best, misleading. In turn, this could invalidate conclusions such as those of Olson *et al.*[2], which convey the impression that the basic question of geodynamics (the driving mechanism of plate tectonics) has been conceptually answered.

Seismic tomography involves a quantitative and qualitative leap from consideration of one-dimensional Earth structure. For example, Dziewonski and Anderson[15] used four unknowns to obtain the lower mantle P-velocity in a spherically symmetric PREM model, whereas the low-order model of Dziewonski[5] used 245 parameters to describe the same region in three dimensions, an increase by a factor of sixty. Even greater increases are typical of the "block" models: the lower-mantle part of a model of Clayton and Comer[9] contains a three-dimensional array of 57,000 cells, more than 14,000 times the number of parameters in PREM. But this is a "mathematical trickery"; the available data do not carry this much independent information. For instance, in their waveform inversion of over 2,000 seismograms, each of several hours duration, Woodhouse and Dziewonski[8] found that only 192 significant eigenvalues (independent parameters), out of 324 required by their low-order model of the upper mantle, led to a discernible decrease in variance. It seems, therefore, that the data base is insufficient to provide a three-dimensional image with enough lateral and radial resolution to verify the conclusions of Gudmundsson *et al.*[13] or Snieder *et al.*[14], or to confirm or disprove the validity of the assumptions made in the

然而由地震学方法得到的地幔非均匀性功率谱的功率分布至今尚未得到令人满意的研究结果。在一些模型中，球谐展开式为低阶次（例如，2 阶 [3]、4 阶 [4]、6 阶 [5-7] 或 8 阶 [8]）时已被先验截断。另一类模型则由成千上万个未知参数 [9,10] 表示，这些模型的标称水平分辨率在球谐展开式中阶次高达 $l = 36$，并且得到的几乎是白谱 [11]。由于在地幔对流模拟中存在不确定性因素，为了使计算可行，使用了比原本认为合适的量级低两阶的瑞利数 [2]。结果，相比通过计算预测的波数（例如参考文献 12），人们在实际对流模式中能在更高阶波数上找到特征。为了合理利用地震层析成像和对流模拟提供的信息，我们必须要知道地幔横向非均匀性的功率谱分布情况。

更糟糕的是，由于震源和接收器不是均匀分布的，如果显著的功率处于功率谱中被排除的部分，低阶模型可能会出现偏差并且不完善。两篇最近的文章表明情况确实如此。古德蒙松等 [13] 展示了 P 波走时残差的统计分析结果，并得出上地幔的横向非均匀性谱是白噪声谱，波长下限达 100~200 km。斯奈德等 [14] 提出：表面上看，上地幔和下地幔层析模型得到的似乎是大尺度特征，实际则可能是相对窄的构造，比如大洋中脊或是俯冲带低通滤波的人为假象。实际上他们认为这些高度异常的特征仅限于狭窄的区域，这些区域的宽度比层析模型得到的宽度量级要低一级。如果上述的其中一个说法是正确的，那么大部分的层析成像工作可能是错的，至少是误导人的。反过来说，这使得奥尔森等 [2] 的结论失效，这些结论让人误以为关于地球动力学的基本问题（板块构造的驱动机制）已经得到了概念性的解答。

从考虑一维地球结构开始，地震层析成像经历了量和质的飞跃。比如，杰翁斯基和安德森 [15] 使用 4 个未知数得到球形对称 PREM 模型中的下地幔 P 波速度，而杰翁斯基 [5] 的低阶模型则使用 245 个参数描述同一区域的三维空间，参数增加了 60 倍。更大的改进则是典型的"块体"模型：克莱顿和科默 [9] 模型的下地幔部分包含了一个拥有 57,000 个单元块的三维阵列，比 PREM 模型中参数数量的 14,000 倍还多。然而这仅仅是个"数学假象"，实际获得的数据不会携带如此多的独立信息。比如，伍德豪斯和杰翁斯基 [8] 对超过 2,000 个地震剖面进行了波形反演，他们发现在每一段数小时的时间内，他们的上地幔低阶模型所需的 324 个参数中只有 192 个有效特征值（独立参数），这一现象导致参数的方差明显降低。因此，这些基础的数据似乎不足以为三维成像提供足够的横向和径向分辨率，这样就无法证实古德蒙松等 [13] 和斯奈德等 [14] 的结论，也无法证实或反驳在低阶扩展模型中提出的假设。即便目前

low-order expansion models. This, we believe, would be true even if the data used so far were supplemented by those recorded by the expanding global network of high-quality seismographic stations and by measurements from projects such as the International Seismic Observing Period[16].

Here we step back to complete the missing stage in the progression of seismology from one to three dimensions by investigating a two-dimensional surface projection of three-dimensional lateral heterogeneity. Seismic tomography may be compared to inferring the three-dimensional shapes of objects from the shadows they cast on a screen (measurements on the Earth's surface). This can be tricky but, with only elementary precautions, a simple inspection of the "shadows" should allow us to decide whether there are relatively few large objects or many small ones. If the former is true, then the low-order expansion is justified, and a global three-dimensional inversion can be attempted with a good chance of success. If the shadows indicate predominance of small-scale objects or a uniform mixture of sizes (white spectrum), the problem is much more difficult.

An ideal data set for a two-dimensional study might consist of measurements of vertical ScS travel-time anomalies on a uniformly distributed, dense grid of points. In our "shadow" analogy, the rays are in this case at normal incidence to the screen and the problems resulting from oblique illumination are avoided. One could perform spherical harmonic analysis of such a data set and obtain information on the spectral distribution of lateral heterogeneity without solving a two- or three-dimensional inverse problem. In this way, a much higher horizontal resolution could be reached even when the smoothing effect of integration along the ray path and the lack of depth resolution are taken into account. This particular experiment is not feasible, because the distribution of earthquakes and stations is far from that needed. But, with minor complications, other seismic phases can be used instead.

The Data Set

We choose the phase that seismologists call SS. It is a downward-radiated shear wave reflected once at the Earth's surface, roughly at the mid-point of its path between the source and receiver. We use SS waves recorded in the epicentral distance range from 50° to 150°. The ray paths for these two distances are shown in Fig. 1a, in which we also show the S phase at 50°. The depths at which these S-wave rays bottom are between 750 and 2,000 km. This helps to avoid complications caused by the steep gradients and discontinuities in the upper mantle as well as the high level of heterogeneity in the lowermost mantle[5,17]. Also, we use only the transverse (SH) component of the ground motion. The displacements recorded on the vertical or longitudinal components (P–SV) are much more complex because of the P to S and S to P conversions.

使用的数据加上由高质量地震台组成的全球网络记录的数据和像国际地震观测期[16]这类项目的观测数据，我们认为情况也是如此。

这里我们后退一步，通过研究三维横向非均匀的二维平面投影，来完善刚才介绍地震学从一维到三维的发展过程中漏掉的阶段。可以将地震层析成像比拟为通过投射在屏幕上的阴影（在地表的测量），来推断目标物体的三维形状。这项工作虽然棘手，但是只要我们稍加注意，通过对"阴影区"的简单检查就可以判断存在相对较大的目标物体还是许多小的物体。如果是前者，那么低阶扩展模型就是正确的，我们可以尝试做全球的三维反演，而且成功的概率很大。如果阴影显示大部分是小尺寸目标物体或者是各种尺寸物体的均匀混合（白谱），那问题就会麻烦很多。

对于二维研究而言，理想的数据集应该是由在均匀分布、密集的网格点上垂直的 ScS 走时异常测量数据组成。在我们的"影子"类比法中，射线以正常入射角进入屏幕，从而避免倾斜照明引起的问题。人们可以对这样的数据集进行球谐分析，从而不需要解决二维或三维反演问题就能得到横向非均匀性的谱分布信息。这样即使考虑到沿射线路径的积分平滑效应以及深度分辨率的缺乏，也能得到一个更高的水平分辨率。然而这一特殊实验是不可行的，因为地震和地震台站的分布远远不是要求的那样。然而，也可以用其他的震相代替，只是稍微复杂一些。

数 据 集

我们选择了地震学家们称为 SS 的震相。这是一种向下传播的剪切波，在地球表面反射一次，大约位于震源和接收器之间的中点处。我们在震中距 50°~150° 的范围内利用 SS 波进行记录。这两个距离的射线路径如图 1a 所示，并且给出了 50° 处的 S 震相。S 波到达的深度可达 750~2,000 km，这有助于避免由上地幔较陡的梯度和间断性以及地幔底层的高度非均匀性引起的复杂情况[5,17]。此外，我们仅利用了地震动的横向（SH）组分。由于 P 波向 S 波以及 S 波向 P 波的转换，垂向或纵向组分（P–SV）上记录到的位移要复杂得多。

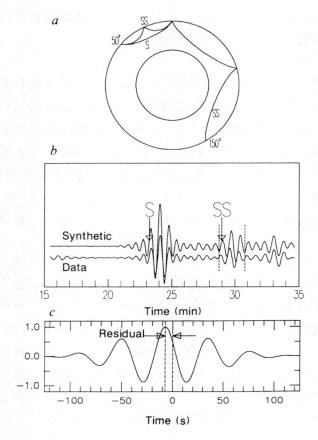

Fig. 1. *a*, S and SS ray paths for the distance 50° (left), and SS ray path for the distance 150° (right). *b*, A comparison of an observed seismogram (24 March 1984) with the corresponding synthetic seismogram calculated for the spherical Earth model PREM[15]. Within the dashed lines is the isolated SS phase. *c*, The correlogram for the SS phase in the observed and synthetic seismograms. The offset between the maximum of the correlogram function and time $t = 0$ indicates a -7.4-s residual between the observed and predicted travel times, meaning that the observed SS arrives earlier than predicted by PREM.

Our data come from the recordings of long-period channels of the Global Digital Seismographic Network. Their response is poor for periods shorter than 15 s and reading of arrival times of individual phases is very inaccurate. Instead, we determine the differences between the recording and the synthetic seismogram computed for the spherically symmetric reference model PREM[15]. Figure 1*b* compares an observed seismogram (bottom) with the corresponding synthetic seismogram (top) calculated by superposition of ~11,000 normal modes[18]. Both the observed and synthetic seismograms are low-pass filtered with a cut-off period of 32 s. We obtain the source mechanism required for calculating the synthetic seismogram from the Harvard catalogue, which contains over 8,000 centroid-moment tensor solutions for all events between 1977 and 1989[19] likely to be used for the present purpose. Figure 1*c* shows the cross-correlation between the sections of the observed and synthetic seismograms delineated by the vertical dashed lines. The time at which the cross-correlation function reaches maximum is the measurement sought[20].

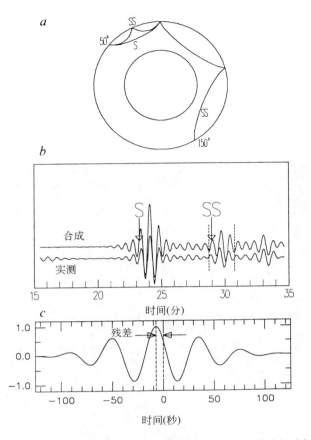

图 1. *a*, S 与 SS 波在 50° 距离时的路径（左），以及 SS 波在 150° 距离时的路径（右）。*b*, 实测地震图（1984 年 3 月 24 日）与通过球对称地球模型 PREM[15] 计算的合成地震图的对比。虚线以内部分为单独的 SS 震相。*c*, 实测与合成 SS 震相的相关图。相关函数的最大值与 *t* = 0 时的值之间的偏离代表了实测与预计走时之间 –7.4 秒的残差，说明实测的 SS 震相比通过 PREM 预测的到达时间更早。

　　我们的数据来自全球数字地震台网的长周期通道记录。它对于小于 15 秒的周期响应较弱，并且单一震相波至的读数很不精确。我们采用实测记录和由球对称地球模型 PREM[15] 计算得到的合成地震图之间的差作为替代指标。图 1*b* 将实测地震图（底部）和相应的由大约 11,000 个简正振型[18] 叠加计算得到的合成地震图（顶部）进行了对比。实测和合成的地震图都经过了带有 32 秒截止周期的低通滤波。从哈佛大学矩心矩张量目录 1977 年到 1989 年间[19] 所有同相轴的超过 8,000 个矩心矩张量解中，我们获得了计算合成地震图所需要的震源机制，它们可以用来实现我们的研究目的。图 1*c* 中由垂直虚线描出的部分显示了实测的和合成的地震图之间的互相关。互相关函数达到最大值的时间就是我们寻求的观测值[20]。

We selected 429 earthquakes of appropriate size and distribution from the period 1977–89; these yielded 3,313 satisfactory measurements of the SS residuals in the appropriate distance range whose mid-path surface reflections are shown in Fig. 2a. The coverage is better in the Northern Hemisphere, but it is adequate for our purpose south of the equator. Figure 2b shows the SS residuals projected on a roughly equally spaced grid corresponding to 5°×5° at the Equator. Following Woodward and Masters[21], the displayed values are averages of all available data within 5° of a given grid point. The values shown are corrected for the topography, bathymetry and crust thickness[22].

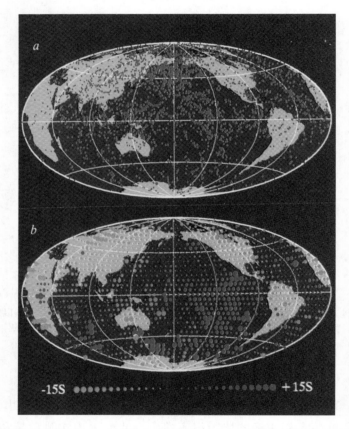

Fig. 2. a, Distribution of SS-phase mid-path bounce points at the Earth's surface; each circle represents one of the 3,313 data points in this study. b, Travel-time residuals for the SS phase projected on an equally spaced grid (5°×5° at the equator). The residuals are smoothed by a moving cap of radius 5°. The values shown are corrected for topography, bathymetry and crystal thickness.

There are SS residual values for 1,452 caps, or more than 90% of all the grid points. Even visual examination of Fig. 2b shows the anomalies tend to change slowly with position, even though the smoothing introduced by averaging involves only the adjacent grid points. The other conclusion is that there is a clear correlation between the sign of the anomaly and the tectonic nature of the mid-path reflection point. This means that the upper-mantle structure underneath that point is the most obvious contributor to the anomaly.

我们选择了发生于 1977~1989 年间 429 个大小与分布适当的地震，得到了 3,313 个在适当距离内的 SS 震相残差的满意测量值，它们中途地表反射点如图 2a 所示。北半球的覆盖率较好，但赤道以南的覆盖率对我们的目的而言也已足够。图 2b 展示了 SS 震相残差投影到与赤道上 5°×5° 相当面积的大致等距网格的情况。接着在伍德沃德和马斯特斯 [21] 的研究中，显示的数值是给定网格点 5° 范围内所有可用数据的平均值，并经过了地形、水深测量与地壳厚度的校正 [22]。

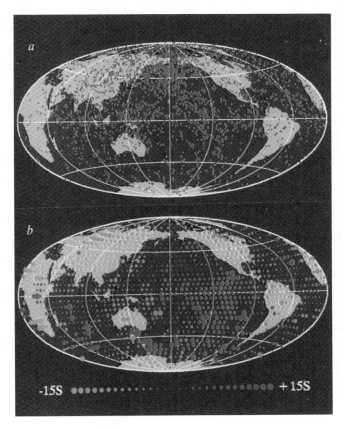

图 2. a, SS 震相中途反射点在地球表面的分布，每个圆点代表本研究 3,313 个数据点中的一个。b, 投影到等距网格（赤道处 5°×5°）的 SS 震相走时残差。残差使用半径 5° 的移动球冠进行了平滑处理。图中数据经过了地形、水深测量和晶体厚度的校正。

1,452 个球冠或者说 90% 以上的网格点都有 SS 震相残差数值。虽然只是通过对相邻点做平均来进行平滑处理，但仅对图 2b 做目测就能发现异常随位置缓慢变化。另一个结论是异常信号与中途反射点的构造性质有明显联系，这说明该点下面的上地幔构造是造成异常的最明显因素。但是，下地幔的影响也很重要 [21]。尽管下地幔

Nevertheless, contributions from the lower mantle are also important[21]; although the r.m.s. heterogeneity is less than in the upper mantle, the path segments are significantly longer (see Fig. 1a).

Our choice of the SS phase was influenced by the results of Woodward[22] and Woodward and Masters[17,21] who measured travel-time differences between SS and S as well as between ScS and S. The differential travel-time approach has the advantage of being relatively insensitive to the source parameters and to the structure near the source and the receiver. The "absolute" travel-time approach has the principal advantage of a wider range of epicentral distances in which measurements can be made (50–150°, as compared with 50–100° for SS–S). This is the main reason for our relatively good coverage of the Southern Hemisphere. Also, the interference of other phases such as ScS may be less critical when cross-correlation is made with respect to a synthetic seismogram, as the interfering phase is present in both seismograms.

SS Spectra and Synthetic Tests

We fit spherical harmonics of degrees 0–36 to the data from 1,452 grid points shown in Fig. 2b. The associated Legendre functions are normalized

$$p_l^m = (2-\delta_{m,0})^{1/2}(2l+1)^{1/2}\left[\frac{(l-m)!}{(l+m)!}\right]^{1/2} P_{lm} \qquad (1)$$

so that the r.m.s. value over the surface of the sphere is equal to one for each sine or cosine harmonic. We use spherical splines[23], although with coverage as complete as that shown in Fig. 2b, a direct least-squares fit would be stable. In choosing the accuracy of the fit to the data, we consider two cases. First, the data should be fitted as accurately as possible: this is the "exact" solution. Second, the data should be fitted to give a r.m.s. error of 1 s, which seems conservative considering the potential sources of error: this is the "damped" solution. The coefficients for the latter solution are listed in Table 1 for the first eight orders. Figure 3a shows the sums

$$D_l = \sum_{m=0}^{l} A_{lm}^2 + B_{lm}^2 \qquad (2)$$

for both solutions. There is very little power in "damped" solution beyond about degree 10. The power decreases less rapidly for the "exact" fit, but even in this case it approaches zero for degrees greater than 20.

均方根不均一性要比上地幔小，但传播距离明显更长（见图 1a）。

在伍德沃德 [22] 以及他和马斯特斯 [17,21] 的研究中测量了 SS 震相与 S 震相之间以及 ScS 震相与 S 震相之间的走时差，我们对 SS 震相的选择受他们成果的影响。走时差值法的优点在于它对震源参数与震源和检波器附近的构造不敏感。绝对走时法的主要优点则在于它具有更广的可测量震中距范围（与 SS–S 法的 50°～100°范围相比可达到 50°～150°）。这是我们在南半球得到较好覆盖率的主要原因。另外，由于两类地震图中都有干扰震相存在，因此，像 ScS 等其他干扰震相在经过合成地震图的互相关后就变得不那么严重。

SS 相位谱与合成试验

我们对图 2b 中 1,452 个网格点的数据进行了 0 到 36 阶的球谐分析，相关的勒让德函数已被归一化：

$$p_l^m = (2-\delta_{m,0})^{1/2}(2l+1)^{1/2}\left[\frac{(l-m)!}{(l+m)!}\right]^{1/2} P_{lm} \tag{1}$$

由此，球体整个表面的均方根值对于每一个球谐正弦或余弦都为 1。虽然对于图 2b 那样完整的覆盖率而言，最小二乘拟合较为稳定，但我们还是使用球形样条函数 [23]。在选择拟合精度时，我们考虑了两种情况。第一，数据拟合要尽可能的精确：这是"精确"解。第二，数据拟合产生的均方根误差应为 1 秒，考虑到潜在的误差来源，这应该是保守的：这是"阻尼"解。表 1 列出了前 8 阶的阻尼解系数。图 3a 表示的是两组解之和：

$$D_l = \sum_{m=0}^{l} A_{lm}^2 + B_{lm}^2 \tag{2}$$

阻尼解的功率在大约 10 阶之后变得很小，而精确解的功率降低相对缓慢，但在 20 阶之后也趋于 0。

Table 1. Coefficients of spherical harmonics

			Upper mantle								Lower mantle									
	SS residuals		k=0		k=1		k=2		k=3		k=0		k=1		k=2		k=3		k=4	
l m	A	B	A	B	A	B	A	B	A	B	A	B	A	B	A	B	A	B	A	B
0 0	−1.15		−0.29		1.30		−0.23		−0.10		−0.64		−0.57		0.41		0.02		1.72	
1 0	−1.70		3.30		2.60		0.53		0.93		0.73		−0.44		−0.26		−0.13		−0.14	
1	−1.00	−1.23	4.78	2.03	1.42	1.30	−0.23	1.30	−0.21	0.53	−0.50	0.18	0.17	−0.15	0.03	0.39	−0.26	0.26	−0.12	0.15
2 0	−0.68		1.02		2.28		−0.48		−0.82		0.64		−1.62		0.02		0.49		−0.42	
1	−0.16	0.11	−0.84	0.32	0.77	−1.56	0.66	−2.47	−0.66	−2.37	−0.32	0.30	0.26	−0.27	−0.04	−0.30	0.24	−0.26	0.05	−0.31
2	0.12	1.19	1.61	−4.06	1.04	0.63	1.72	0.64	0.83	0.52	−2.03	−1.16	0.99	−0.44	0.05	−0.34	0.17	0.30	0.06	−0.18
3 0	0.17		0.43		0.12		−0.20		0.13		−0.86		0.37		0.24		0.24		−0.05	
1	−0.04	−0.14	1.07	0.73	0.44	0.22	0.70	−0.35	0.20	−0.13	−1.03	−0.42	0.46	0.21	0.03	−0.27	0.27	−0.09	0.15	0.00
2	0.45	−0.71	−0.67	1.73	−1.44	2.02	−0.17	0.50	−0.34	0.24	−0.23	1.07	0.09	0.30	0.25	−0.02	0.30	−0.50	0.29	−0.32
3	−0.17	−0.66	0.50	1.26	−1.66	−0.18	−1.55	−0.96	−0.44	0.10	−0.69	0.07	−0.17	−0.06	0.09	0.20	0.00	0.25	0.18	−0.19
4 0	−0.33		1.36		1.70		0.80		−0.15		−0.22		0.26		−0.21		−0.17		−0.05	
1	0.13	0.29	−0.45	0.03	0.52	0.72	1.19	0.55	0.24	0.05	−0.14	−0.14	−0.18	−0.67	−0.06	0.05	0.08	0.32	−0.16	0.33
2	0.52	−0.49	−2.09	0.68	−1.24	1.15	0.23	0.00	0.66	−1.13	0.38	−0.29	−0.24	−0.06	0.04	−0.31	−0.17	−0.24	−0.10	0.05
3	−0.03	−0.18	0.03	0.04	−1.28	0.24	−0.49	−0.01	−0.06	0.60	−0.23	0.62	0.30	0.22	0.39	0.00	−0.01	0.14	0.13	0.16
4	−0.28	−0.55	−0.06	3.41	0.98	1.95	0.39	1.39	0.60	−0.25	0.24	0.59	0.38	−0.21	0.18	0.12	−0.15	−0.42	−0.50	0.03
5 0	0.50		−2.41		−1.87		0.11		0.33		0.35		−0.18		0.19		0.08		0.22	
1	−0.22	−0.28	2.03	0.19	1.32	0.16	0.00	0.65	−0.80	−0.35	−0.01	−0.38	−0.20	0.15	0.17	0.59	0.22	0.48	0.15	0.27
2	0.04	0.15	−1.97	0.44	−2.44	−0.45	−0.68	−0.66	0.18	−0.13	0.42	−0.46	0.08	−0.25	0.21	0.19	0.12	0.48	−0.12	−0.10
3	−0.23	−0.05	−0.82	1.55	−0.20	1.76	−0.22	−0.15	0.42	−0.22	−0.18	0.12	0.10	0.28	−0.28	0.22	−0.33	0.19	−0.25	0.20
4	−0.46	0.40	3.06	−2.38	2.89	−2.81	0.48	−0.76	−0.37	0.03	0.09	0.40	−0.27	0.45	0.02	0.23	0.13	−0.17	0.13	0.17
5	−0.69	0.18	1.11	0.90	0.55	0.54	0.19	0.01	0.63	−0.35	−0.22	0.04	0.17	0.20	0.10	0.11	0.19	0.25	−0.13	0.19
6 0	−0.42		0.40		0.91		0.58		0.48		−0.09		−0.17		−0.16		−0.19		0.17	
1	0.20	0.19	−0.61	−0.91	−0.35	−0.57	0.08	−0.14	−0.26	0.24	−0.04	−0.24	−0.04	−0.02	0.19	0.03	0.09	0.00	−0.02	0.09
2	0.59	0.10	−1.08	0.39	−1.00	1.34	−1.02	1.36	0.19	0.09	−0.13	0.01	−0.05	−0.52	−0.10	−0.10	−0.01	0.08	0.14	0.00
3	0.17	−0.69	−0.08	2.22	0.24	0.78	−0.22	−0.37	0.53	−0.26	0.21	−0.10	0.12	0.36	0.01	−0.40	0.07	−0.19	0.36	0.43
4	−0.16	−0.05	0.22	0.98	0.91	0.05	0.99	0.02	0.50	0.35	0.57	−0.16	0.03	−0.45	−0.06	−0.10	−0.25	0.15	−0.06	0.32
5	−0.50	0.31	1.15	0.50	1.28	0.59	0.46	0.16	−0.55	−0.56	−0.49	−0.34	0.19	−0.19	−0.13	−0.30	0.10	−0.17	0.34	0.16
6	−0.34	−0.02	0.25	0.88	−0.54	0.61	−1.01	−0.03	−0.44	0.11	0.22	−0.09	0.17	0.10	0.24	−0.12	−0.21	−0.09	−0.24	0.03
7 0	0.14		−1.00		−0.64		0.15		0.31		−0.40		0.17		0.08		0.08		0.17	
1	−0.05	−0.30	−0.30	1.54	−0.22	1.12	−0.16	0.34	−0.42	−0.38	−0.55	0.34	−0.08	0.05	−0.05	−0.08	0.04	−0.24	0.13	0.15
2	0.12	−0.14	−0.10	1.52	0.41	1.30	0.40	0.77	−0.03	0.26	−0.06	−0.18	0.65	−0.09	0.22	−0.02	0.19	0.17	0.36	0.24
3	0.12	0.13	−0.22	1.34	−1.06	0.68	−0.98	−0.71	0.13	0.40	0.25	−0.62	−0.04	−0.38	0.22	0.13	−0.23	0.41	−0.55	0.11
4	0.33	−0.04	0.31	−0.63	−0.69	0.78	−0.83	0.17	0.25	0.36	−0.24	0.28	−0.08	−0.29	−0.06	−0.09	0.25	−0.34	0.48	−0.37
5	0.18	0.35	0.55	−0.72	0.23	−0.45	0.09	−0.85	−0.32	0.21	−0.42	−0.16	−0.11	−0.12	−0.02	−0.16	−0.15	−0.34	0.01	−0.06
6	0.00	0.12	0.08	−1.15	0.06	−1.40	−0.27	−0.30	−0.56	−0.07	−0.70	0.31	−0.08	−0.26	−0.21	0.05	−0.24	−0.12	0.17	0.59
7	−0.21	−0.06	−0.93	0.06	−0.68	−0.55	−0.35	0.28	0.38	0.11	−0.37	−0.19	−0.10	−0.10	−0.14	0.14	0.17	0.40	0.14	−0.06
8 0	0.50		−1.04		−1.11		−0.37		−0.12		0.00		0.37		−0.02		−0.07		−0.11	
1	0.06	0.17	−0.72	−0.40	−0.26	−0.02	−0.32	−0.11	−0.52	−0.32	0.25	0.31	0.19	0.36	0.07	−0.04	0.06	−0.02	0.04	−0.05
2	−0.19	−0.18	−0.78	0.35	−1.01	0.00	−1.04	0.05	−0.50	0.00	−0.12	0.21	0.12	−0.16	−0.18	0.13	−0.32	0.08	0.01	0.11
3	0.36	−0.32	0.25	0.36	0.84	0.06	0.93	−0.43	0.88	0.02	−0.24	0.28	0.24	0.42	0.18	0.18	0.23	0.21	−0.17	0.21
4	−0.01	0.23	−0.31	1.21	0.58	0.23	0.53	−0.07	0.33	0.02	0.49	−0.09	−0.23	−0.06	−0.23	0.17	−0.38	0.23	−0.08	0.00
5	0.16	0.03	−0.73	−0.06	−0.63	0.25	0.19	0.31	−0.23	0.44	0.08	0.00	−0.09	−0.40	0.03	0.14	−0.20	0.23	−0.01	0.08
6	0.14	−0.08	−0.38	0.68	−0.28	−0.31	0.55	−0.16	−0.28	−0.45	0.34	0.05	−0.01	0.24	−0.28	0.05	0.11	0.10	0.27	0.06
7	−0.26	−0.07	0.85	−0.07	0.07	0.27	−1.31	0.10	−0.85	0.18	−0.20	−0.33	0.08	−0.48	0.08	0.03	0.12	0.37	−0.34	−0.06
8	−0.04	0.04	0.14	0.27	−0.39	0.26	0.04	−0.51	−0.24	−0.11	0.09	0.33	0.01	0.04	−0.01	−0.14	−0.08	0.03	0.21	0.22

The first column gives the coefficients of spherical harmonics up to degree $L = 8$ of the full ($L = 36$) expansion of travel-time residuals which fitted the data with a r.m.s. error 1 s. The travel-time residual for these coefficients is $\delta t = \sum_{l=0}^{L} \sum_{m=0}^{l} (A_l^m \cos m\phi + B_l^m \sin m\phi) \, p_l^m(\theta)$, with p_l^m defined in equation 1. Columns 2–10 are spherical harmonic coefficients of the whole-mantle S velocity model SH425.2. The velocity perturbation is $\delta v_s / v_s = 10^{-3} \sum_{k=0}^{K} \sum_{l=0}^{L} \sum_{m=0}^{l} f_k(x) \, (_kA_l^m \cos m\phi + {_kB_l^m} \sin m\phi) \, p_l^m(\theta)$. For definitions of $f_k(x)$, see ref. 5 for the lower mantle and ref. 8 for the upper mantle.

表1. 球谐系数

l m	SS残差	上地幔				下地幔				
		k=0	k=1	k=2	k=3	k=0	k=1	k=2	k=3	k=4
	A B	A B	A B	A B	A B	A B	A B	A B	A B	A B
0 0	−1.15	−0.29	1.30	−0.23	−0.10	−0.64	−0.57	0.41	0.02	1.72
1 0	−1.70	3.30	2.60	0.53	0.93	0.73	−0.44	−0.26	−0.13	−0.14
1 1	−1.00 −1.23	4.78 2.03	1.42 1.30	−0.23 1.30	−0.21 0.53	−0.50 0.18	0.17 −0.15	0.03 0.39	−0.26 0.26	−0.12 0.15
2 0	−0.68	1.02	2.28	−0.48	−0.82	0.64	−1.62	0.02	0.49	−0.42
2 1	−0.16 0.11	−0.84 0.32	0.77 −1.56	0.66 −2.47	−0.66 −2.37	−0.32 0.30	0.26 −0.27	−0.04 −0.30	0.24 −0.26	0.05 −0.31
2 2	0.12 1.19	1.61 −4.06	1.04 0.63	1.72 0.64	0.83 0.52	−2.03 −1.16	0.99 −0.44	0.05 −0.34	0.17 0.30	0.06 −0.18
3 0	0.17	0.43	0.12	−0.20	0.13	−0.86	0.37	0.24	0.24	−0.05
3 1	−0.04 −0.14	1.07 0.73	0.44 0.22	0.70 −0.35	0.20 −0.13	−1.03 −0.24	0.46 0.21	0.03 −0.27	0.27 −0.09	0.15 0.00
3 2	0.45 −0.71	−0.67 1.73	−1.44 2.02	−0.17 0.50	−0.34 0.24	−0.23 1.07	0.09 0.30	0.25 −0.02	0.30 −0.50	0.29 −0.32
3 3	−0.17 −0.66	0.50 1.26	−1.66 −0.18	−1.55 −0.96	−0.44 0.10	−0.69 0.07	−0.17 −0.06	0.09 0.20	0.00 0.25	0.18 −0.19
4 0	−0.33	1.36	1.70	0.80	−0.15	−0.22	0.26	−0.21	−0.17	−0.05
4 1	0.13 0.29	−0.45 0.03	0.52 0.72	1.19 0.55	0.24 0.05	−0.14 −0.14	−0.18 −0.67	−0.06 0.05	0.08 0.32	−0.16 0.33
4 2	0.52 −0.49	−2.09 0.68	−1.24 1.15	0.23 0.00	0.66 −1.13	0.38 −0.29	−0.24 −0.06	0.04 −0.31	−0.17 −0.24	−0.10 0.05
4 3	−0.03 −0.18	0.03 0.04	−1.28 0.24	−0.49 −0.01	−0.06 0.60	−0.23 0.62	0.30 0.22	0.39 0.00	−0.01 0.14	0.13 0.16
4 4	−0.28 −0.55	−0.06 3.41	0.98 1.95	0.39 1.39	0.60 −0.25	0.24 0.59	0.38 −0.21	0.18 0.12	−0.15 −0.42	−0.50 0.03
5 0	0.50	−2.41	−1.87	0.11	0.33	0.35	−0.18	0.19	0.08	0.22
5 1	−0.22 −0.28	2.03 0.19	1.32 0.16	0.00 0.65	−0.80 −0.35	−0.01 −0.38	−0.20 0.15	0.11 0.59	0.22 0.48	0.15 0.27
5 2	0.04 0.15	−1.97 0.44	−2.44 −0.45	−0.68 −0.66	0.18 −0.13	0.42 −0.46	0.08 −0.25	0.21 0.19	0.12 0.48	−0.12 −0.10
5 3	−0.23 −0.05	−0.82 1.55	−0.20 1.76	−0.22 −0.15	0.42 −0.22	−0.18 0.12	−0.28 0.22	−0.33 0.19	−0.25 0.20	0.13 0.17
5 4	−0.46 0.40	3.06 −2.38	2.89 −2.81	−0.49 −0.76	−0.37 0.03	0.09 0.40	−0.27 0.45	0.02 0.23	0.13 −0.17	0.13 0.17
5 5	−0.69 0.18	1.11 0.90	0.55 0.54	0.19 0.01	0.63 −0.35	0.09 0.00	0.17 0.20	0.10 0.11	0.00 0.25	−0.13 0.19
6 0	−0.42	0.40	0.91	0.58	0.48	−0.09	−0.17	−0.16	−0.19	0.17
6 1	0.20 0.19	−0.61 −0.91	−0.35 −0.57	0.08 −0.14	−0.26 0.24	−0.04 −0.24	−0.04 −0.02	0.19 0.03	0.09 0.00	−0.02 0.09
6 2	0.59 0.10	−1.08 0.39	−1.00 1.34	−1.02 1.36	0.19 0.09	−0.13 0.01	−0.05 −0.52	−0.10 −0.10	−0.01 0.08	0.14 0.00
6 3	0.17 −0.69	−0.08 2.22	0.24 0.78	−0.22 −0.37	0.53 −0.26	0.21 −0.10	0.12 0.36	0.01 −0.40	0.07 −0.19	0.36 0.43
6 4	−0.16 −0.05	0.22 0.98	0.91 0.05	0.99 0.02	0.50 0.35	0.57 −0.16	0.03 −0.45	−0.06 −0.10	−0.25 0.15	−0.06 0.32
6 5	−0.50 0.31	1.15 0.50	1.28 0.59	0.46 0.16	−0.55 −0.56	−0.49 −0.34	0.19 −0.19	−0.13 −0.30	0.10 −0.17	0.34 0.16
6 6	−0.34 −0.02	0.25 0.88	−0.54 0.61	−1.01 −0.03	−0.44 0.11	0.22 −0.09	0.17 0.10	0.24 −0.12	−0.21 −0.09	−0.24 0.03
7 0	0.14	−1.00	−0.64	0.15	0.31	−0.40	0.17	0.08	0.08	0.17
7 1	−0.05 −0.30	−0.30 1.54	−0.22 1.12	−0.16 0.34	−0.42 −0.38	−0.55 0.34	−0.08 0.05	−0.05 −0.08	0.04 −0.24	0.13 0.15
7 2	0.12 −0.14	−0.10 1.52	0.41 1.30	0.40 0.77	−0.03 0.26	−0.06 −0.18	0.65 −0.09	0.22 0.02	0.19 0.17	0.36 0.24
7 3	0.12 0.13	−0.22 1.34	−1.06 0.68	−0.98 −0.71	0.13 0.40	0.25 −0.62	−0.04 −0.08	0.22 0.13	0.23 0.41	0.53 0.11
7 4	0.33 −0.04	0.31 −0.63	−0.69 0.78	−0.83 0.17	0.25 0.36	−0.24 0.28	−0.08 −0.12	−0.06 −0.09	0.25 −0.34	0.48 −0.37
7 5	0.18 0.35	0.55 −0.72	0.23 −0.45	0.09 −0.85	−0.32 0.21	−0.42 −0.16	−0.11 −0.29	−0.02 −0.14	−0.15 −0.31	0.01 −0.06
7 6	0.00 0.12	0.08 −1.15	0.06 −1.40	−0.27 −0.30	−0.56 −0.07	−0.70 0.31	−0.08 −0.04	−0.21 0.05	−0.24 −0.12	0.17 0.59
7 7	−0.21 −0.06	−0.93 0.06	−0.68 −0.55	−0.35 0.28	0.38 0.11	−0.37 −0.19	−0.10 −0.10	−0.14 0.14	0.17 0.40	0.14 −0.06
8 0	0.50	−1.04	−1.11	−0.37	−0.12	0.00	0.37	−0.02	−0.07	−0.11
8 1	0.06 0.17	−0.72 −0.40	−0.26 −0.02	−0.32 −0.11	−0.52 −0.32	0.25 0.31	0.19 0.36	0.07 −0.04	0.06 −0.02	0.04 −0.05
8 2	−0.19 −0.18	−0.78 0.35	−1.01 0.00	−1.04 0.05	−0.50 0.00	−0.12 0.21	0.12 −0.16	−0.18 0.13	−0.32 0.08	0.01 0.11
8 3	0.36 −0.32	0.25 0.36	0.84 0.06	0.93 −0.43	0.88 0.02	−0.24 0.28	0.24 0.42	0.18 0.18	0.23 0.21	−0.17 0.21
8 4	−0.01 0.23	−0.31 1.21	0.58 0.23	0.53 −0.07	0.33 0.07	0.49 −0.09	−0.23 −0.06	−0.23 0.17	−0.38 0.23	−0.08 0.00
8 5	0.16 0.03	−0.73 −0.06	−0.63 0.25	0.19 0.31	−0.23 0.44	0.08 0.00	−0.09 −0.40	0.03 0.14	−0.20 0.23	−0.01 0.08
8 6	0.14 −0.08	−0.38 0.68	−0.28 −0.31	0.55 −0.16	−0.28 −0.45	0.34 0.05	−0.01 0.24	−0.28 0.05	0.11 0.10	0.27 0.06
8 7	−0.26 −0.07	0.85 −0.07	0.07 0.27	−1.31 0.10	−0.85 0.18	−0.20 −0.33	0.08 −0.04	0.08 0.14	0.12 0.37	−0.34 −0.06
8 8	−0.04 0.04	0.14 0.27	−0.39 0.26	0.04 −0.51	−0.24 −0.11	0.09 0.33	0.01 0.04	−0.01 −0.14	−0.08 0.03	0.21 0.22

第一列给出了走时残差所有阶（L = 36）球谐展开式中的前8阶球谐系数，与数据有1秒的拟合均方根误差。这些系数的走时残差为 $\delta t = \sum_{l=0}^{L} \sum_{m=0}^{l} (A_l^m \cos m\phi + B_l^m \sin m\phi)\, p_l^m(\theta)$, p_l^m 由方程1定义。第二至第十列是全地幔S波速度模型SH425.2的球谐系数。速度扰动为 $\delta v_s/v_s = 10^{-3} \sum_{k=0}^{K} \sum_{l=0}^{L} \sum_{m=0}^{l} f_k(x)({}_kA_l^m \cos m\phi + {}_kB_l^m \sin m\phi)\, p_l^m(\theta)$, 关于 $f_k(x)$ 的定义，下地幔的见参考文献5，上地幔的见参考文献8。

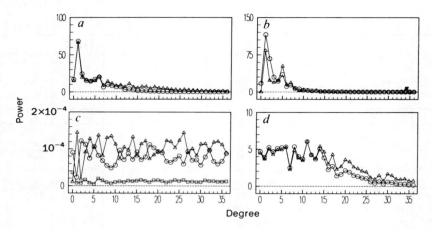

Fig. 3. Power in each harmonic degree, as defined by equation (2), for the spherical harmonic expansions of *a*, different fits to the observed SS travel-time residuals (△ , exact; ○ , damped); *b*, the damped fit to SS travel-time residuals predicted by the upper-mantle model M84C (△) and the whole-mantle S-wave model SH425.2 (○); *c*, the velocity anomalies ($\delta v/v$) at 100 (△); 500 (○) and 1,500 km (□) in the "random" model, and *d*, SS travel-time residuals predicted by the random structure up to degree 36 (△ , exact; ○ , damped). The power is expressed in units of s^2, except for (*c*), where the units are dimensionless.

It is instructive to calculate the SS residuals for existing models of the Earth and compare their spectra with those in Fig. 3*a*. We use two Earth models: the first is the upper-mantle model M84C[8]; the other is a new whole-mantle shear-velocity model SH425.2. It is based on the same data set as model U84L85/SH[24-26], but subsets of data have been weighted differently and the model is less damped. The number of eigenvalues used is 425, out of 729, and three iterations of the nonlinear inverse problem were completed. The crustal correction is that used in ref. 8. The radial variations are described, as in model U84L85/SH, by the Legendre polynomials up to degree 3 in the upper mantle and degree 4 in the lower mantle; the spherical harmonic expansion is truncated at degree eight in both regions. The coefficients of model SH425.2 are listed in Table 1. The SS residuals are calculated using the ray-tracing algorithm of Julian and Gubbins[27] for exactly the same source–receiver pairs for which we have observations, and the residuals have been averaged at the same grid points as shown in Fig. 2*b*. The power spectra for both models are shown in Fig. 3*b*. It is clear that the overall distribution of power in the "damped" model is very similar to that predicted by the three-dimensional models of the mantle; significant differences exist only for degree 1 for model SH425.2 and degree 5 for M84C.

Integration of anomalies along a ray path is a smoothing process, however, and one could still suppose that the actual structure has a substantial power at high orders. To answer this question, we have created a velocity model in which the anomalies are random at each depth and the r.m.s. perturbation changes with depth in the same way as the power in model SH425.2. The random variations have been scaled such that at each depth the expected total power for each degree should remain constant. This is shown in Fig. 3*c* for three different depths.

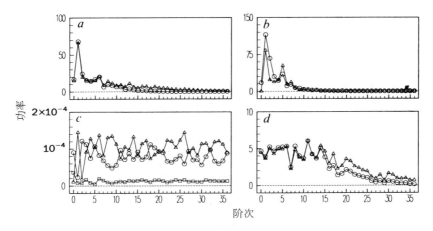

图 3. 球谐展开式每一阶次的功率由方程（2）定义。*a*, 不同的实测 SS 走时残差的拟合（△，精确解；○，阻尼解）；*b*, 由上地幔模型 M84C（△）和全地幔 S 波速模型 SH425.2（○）预测 SS 震相走时残差的阻尼解拟合；*c*, "随机"模型中 100 km（△）、500 km（○）和 1,500 km（□）处的速度异常（$\delta v/v$）；*d*, 36 阶内随机结构预测的 SS 震相走时残差（△，精确解；○，阻尼解）。除了图 *c*，图中功率以 s^2 为单位，图 *c* 无量纲。

计算已存在的地球模型的 SS 震相残差并将其功率谱与图 3*a* 进行对比是有意义的。我们选择了两个地球模型：一个是上地幔模型 M84C[8]；另一个是新型全地幔剪切波速度模型 SH425.2。它与 U84L85/SH 模型 [24-26] 一样建立在同一数据集上，但数据子集的权重不同，并且模型的阻尼系数较小。从 729 个特征值中选取了 425 个，关于非线性反演问题的三次迭代也已完成。地壳校正使用的是参考文献 8 中的方法。如同 U84L85/SH 模型中那样，径向变化由勒让德多项式表示，前 3 阶为上地幔而 4 阶为下地幔，两个区域的球谐展开式都取到了 8 阶。表 1 列出了模型 SH425.2 的系数。利用朱利安和格宾斯 [27] 的射线追踪式对我们观察的震源－接收器组的 SS 震相残差进行计算，并把残差按图 2*b* 所示的网格点进行了平均。图 3*b* 所示的是两个模型的功率谱。很显然，"阻尼"模型的总体功率分布与地幔三维模型预测的十分接近，仅在 SH425.2 模型的 1 阶区与 M84C 模型的 5 阶区存在较大差异。

尽管沿射线进行异常积分是一个平滑过程，但我们仍然可以假设实际构造在较高阶还有高功率。为了解答这一问题，我们建立了这样的速度模型：在这模型中不同深度的异常是随机的，而均方根干扰随深度的变化与 SH425.2 模型中功率变化的方式一致。随机变化经过一定程度的放大，以便使各个深度上各阶次的总功率期望是恒定值。图 3*c* 展示了三个深度的情况。

Using this hypothetical model, we calculated the SS residuals in exactly the same way as described above, and Fig. 3*d* shows the spectral power for the "damped" and "exact" spherical harmonic fits. Calculating the SS residuals for the random structure is equivalent to evaluating the response of a complex filter. If the filter were "all-pass", the spectra in Fig. 3*d* would be roughly flat for all orders from 0 to 36. Instead, the response is "all-pass" up to $l \approx 15$, and then it begins to decrease gradually. This decrease reflects the smoothing effect of integration along the ray path and averaging of data over the spherical caps. These spectra are distinctly different from the observed spectra in Fig. 3*a*, where the abrupt decrease in power occurs at $l = 6$. The synthetic spectra have much more energy at high angular order numbers, so that the smoothing through integration is not sufficient to mask the presence of high-wavenumber structure.

Discussion

Figure 4*a* is a map derived by the synthesis of the spherical harmonic coefficients for degrees 1–36 obtained in a "damped" fit to the observed SS residuals. Figure 4*b* is the same as 4*a* but for the residuals predicted by model SH425.2. Figure 4*c* is also the same as 4*a*, but for the "random" model. This figure reflects, roughly, the pattern of the SS residuals appropriate for an upper mantle with a spectrum of lateral heterogeneity such as proposed by Gudmundsson *et al.*[13]. The spectral content of this prediction is very different from that of the observations in Fig. 4*a*.

The similarity between Fig. 4*a* and *b* is striking: the correlation coefficient for degrees 1–36 is 0.74, but it is as high as 0.86 for degrees 1–6. The correlation coefficient is above 0.79 for each degree from 1 to 6; it drops suddenly to 0.29 for degree 7 and to 0.20 for degree 8, indicating that the power beyond degree 6 might be too low to be resolved on the global scale. It should be pointed out that the SS data were not explicitly used in deriving model SH425.2. Even though ~60% of events used were the same, the method of Woodhouse and Dziewonski[24] uses entire waveforms, which consist of mantle waves and many other body wave phases in addition to SS (see Figs 3 and 5 in Dziewonski and Woodhouse[25]). With the principal difference between the observed and predicted residuals limited to a region of the East Pacific Rise and South America, the agreement indicates that the "average path approximation"[8] works rather well not only for surface waves but also for body waves.

利用此假设模型，我们严格按照上文所述的方法计算 SS 震相残差，图 3d 展示了"阻尼"与"精确"球谐拟合的谱功率。计算随机结构的 SS 残差等同于评价复合滤波器的响应。如果滤波器是"全通"的，那么图 3d 中从 0 到 36 阶的所有谱型应该大致是平的。实际情况是，只有约 15 阶以前是"全通"响应，之后就逐渐下降。这一衰减反映了沿射线积分与对球冠上数据进行平均的平滑作用。这些谱与图 3a 中功率在 $l=6$ 处突然下降的观测谱明显不同。合成谱在高的角阶数处有更多能量，因此通过积分平滑不足以掩盖高波数构造的存在。

讨　论

将实测 SS 残差进行"阻尼"拟合，获得 1 到 36 阶球谐系数，综合得到图 4a。图 4b 的做法与图 4a 相同，但残差是通过 SH425.2 模型预测的。图 4c 的做法也与图 4a 相同，只是残差来自于"随机"模型。这幅图大致反映了适用于有横向非均匀性功率谱的上地幔的 SS 残差模式，正如古德蒙松 [13] 提出的那样。这一预测内容与图 4a 中的观测结果有很大不同。

图 4a 与图 4b 有惊人的相似性：1 到 36 阶的相关系数是 0.74，而 1 到 6 阶的相关系数则高达 0.86。1 到 6 阶每一阶的相关系数均高于 0.79，但 7 阶突然降到 0.29，8 阶突然降到 0.20，这意味着 6 阶以上的功率太弱，在全球尺度上无法分辨出来。应当指出的是，衍生模型 SH425.2 并没有直接使用 SS 震相数据。尽管使用的同相轴中有约 60% 是相同的，但是伍德豪斯和杰翁斯基 [24] 的方法使用的是整套波形，包括 SS 波、地幔波以及很多其他的体波相位(见伍德豪斯和杰翁斯基 [25] 的图 3 与图 5)。实测残差与预测残差的主要差异性限于东太平洋海隆与南美洲两个区域，而其一致性则表明"平均路径拟合" [18] 对体波和面波都是同样有效的。

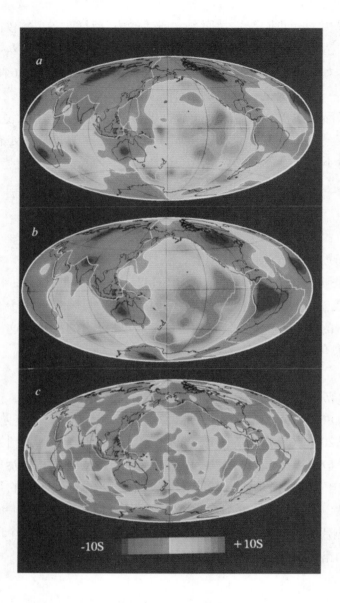

Fig. 4. a, Map of the observed SS travel-time residuals synthesized from spherical harmonic coefficients up to l=36. b, As for a, but for residuals predicted by the whole-mantle S-wave model SH425.2. c, As for b, but for the random velocity model. The travel-time residual scale range is ±10 s.

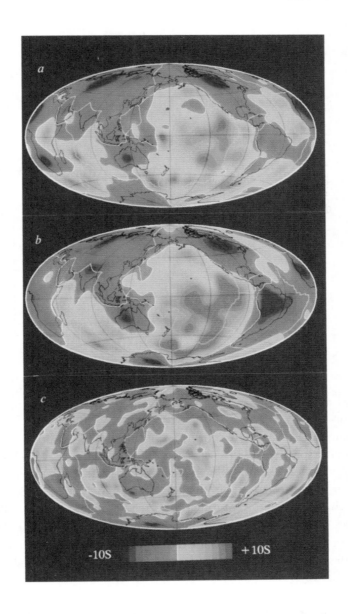

图 4. *a*, 根据 36 阶以内的球谐系数综合出的 SS 观测走时残差图。*b*, 与 *a* 同, 但残差是通过全地幔 S 波速模型 SH425.2 预测的。*c*, 与 *b* 同, 但残差来自随机速度模型。走时残差标度范围为 ±10 秒。

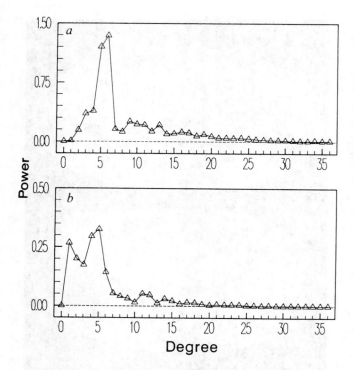

Fig. 5. Power in each harmonic degree for the spherical harmonic expansions of $\delta v_p / v_p$ given by the whole-mantle P-velocity model of Inoue *et al.*[10]. *a*, Layer 4 (148–238 km), *b*, layer 16 (2,566–2,900 km).

The principal conclusion to be drawn from Figs 3 and 4 is that most of the power in the lateral heterogeneity spectrum with wavelengths greater than ~1,000 km is contained in angular order numbers 6 and below, which correspond to wavelengths greater than 6,000–7,000 km at the surface. Only in this way could a low-order model such as SH425.2 predict so well the observations at much shorter resolving lengths. This means that important features of the early tomographic models such as the degree 2 anomaly in the transition zone[3] or the ring of high velocities circumscribing the Pacific basin[1,5] are not artefacts of low-pass filtration of much narrower structures[14], but a reflection of the actual properties of the Earth.

This conclusion is supported by four other studies, the first two of which mainly bear on the properties of the upper mantle. Woodward and Masters[21] investigated SS–S residuals, and although their geographical coverage of the mid-path surface reflection points is sparser than ours, particularly in the Southern Hemisphere, the dominating influence of the large-scale heterogeneities is clear both in the raw and in the smoothed data. Zhang and Tanimoto[28] conducted a high-resolution study of a global distribution of the Love-wave phase velocities for waves of period 80–200 s. They found that the spectrum of the "local" phase velocities[29] is dominated by low-order spherical harmonics. Their conclusions are fully compatible with those presented here, even though the data used were different.

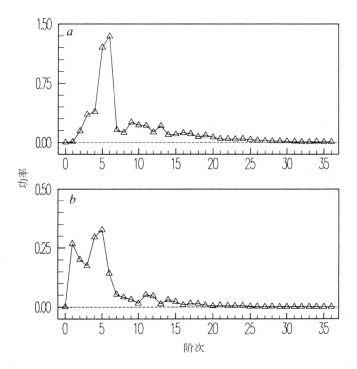

图 5. 球谐展开式各阶次的功率，$\delta v_p/v_p$ 由井上等人 [10] 的全地幔 P 波速度模型所决定。a, 第四层（149~238 km）；b, 第十六层 (2,566~2,900 km)

　　从图 3 和图 4 可以得到的主要结论是：波长大于约 1,000 km 的横向非均匀性谱的主要能量包含于角阶数 6 或更低处，这与地球表面大于 6,000~7,000 km 的波长相对应。只有这样，低阶模型（如 SH425.2）在短得多的波长分辨上才能较好地预测观测值。这就意味着早期层析模型的重要特征（如转换带 [3] 的 2 阶异常，或是限制在太平洋洋盆 [1,5] 的高速环带）不是对较窄构造 [14] 进行低通滤波造成的人为假象，而是地球真实属性的反映。

　　这个结论可以由其他四项研究支持，前两个主要和上地幔的性质有关，伍德沃德和马斯特斯 [21] 研究了 SS–S 残差，尽管他们的地表中途反射点的地理覆盖范围比我们的稀疏，特别是在南半球，但是大尺度非均匀性支配性的影响在原始数据和平滑后的数据中都是清晰可见的。张和谷本 [28] 对周期 80~200 秒的波进行了勒夫波相速度全球分布的高分辨率研究。他们发现"局部"相速度谱 [29] 主要由低阶球谐函数所控制。尽管使用的数据不同，他们的结论和本文提出的十分相符。

821

The third study is also by Woodward and Masters[17]. Their pattern of ScS−S residuals indicates the paramount influence of large-scale heterogeneity. Because the paths of ScS and S in the upper mantle are similar, the residuals must originate in the lower mantle. Through an ingenious test[30], they demonstrate that the principal contribution comes from depths greater than 2,000 km, as predicted by model L02.56 (ref. 5). The fourth study is different in nature, because it involves a very-large-scale inversion. Inoue et al.[10] use the P-wave travel-time anomalies taken from the bulletins of the International Seismological Centre to obtain velocity perturbations in 16 spherical shells spanning the whole mantle, each divided into 32×64, or 2,048, blocks (5.6°×5.6°) for a total of 32,768 unknown parameters. The problem obviously has too many parameters but a stable, converging solution is obtained by using smoothing criteria. The authors kindly made their model available to us, and we have found the spherical harmonic coefficients up to degree 36 for each shell. Figure 5 shows power spectra for two shells: one in the upper mantle, the other in the lower mantle. In both cases there is very little power for degrees greater than 6; thus 2,048 parameters in each of the two shells are well represented by only 48 spherical harmonic coefficients. We found similar results for the other shells.

Of course, smaller-scale features do exist. This is certainly true near the Earth's surface, where for example, sharp boundaries between the continental and oceanic structures cannot be effectively described by the low-order expansion. Correlations between the distribution of hot spots and large-scale low-velocity anomalies near the core-mantle boundary (see plate 2g in ref. 26) indicate that there might be a relationship, perhaps nonlinear, between the large- and small-scale features.

The expansion of the plate velocity field in terms of spherical harmonic coefficients, with the spheroidal and toroidal components, may serve as a useful analogy, as the random measurement errors are not involved. Hager and O'Connell[31] found that the power spectrum of these coefficients decreases rapidly, roughly as l^{-2}, not unlike the SS spectrum: The explanation is that the velocity field is dominated by very few large plates with nearly constant velocities, thus giving rise to low-degree energy. The discontinuities are represented by a spectrum that decreases as l^{-2} in the two-dimensional case. Although the individual coefficients at high l are small, their effect can be large on summation because they are in phase.

We think that our result can be interpreted as follows. The field of velocity anomalies is dominated by entities whose horizontal dimensions are several thousand kilometres. Velocity anomalies change smoothly within these entities. The velocities may change abruptly at the boundaries. Also, there may be a finite number of smaller-scale anomalies that are planar in shape (subduction zones) or linear (plumes), but the total power associated with these features is insufficient to bias the results of a properly carried our "low-order" inversion.

These results impose constraints on modelling of mantle convection. The experiments of Hager et al.[32] and Forte and Peltier[33] demonstrate that seismic velocity anomalies are

第三个研究也是伍德沃德和马斯特斯 [17] 做的。他们的 ScS–S 残差模式指出了大尺度非均匀性的最大影响。因为 ScS 和 S 的路径在上地幔是相似的，所以残差肯定是来源于下地幔的。通过一个巧妙的试验 [30]，他们证明了其主要来源于大于 2,000 km 的深度，正如模型 L02.56（参考文献 5）所预测的那样。第四个研究在本质上与其他三个不同，因为它包含了一个很大尺度的反演。井上等 [10] 使用来自国际地震中心公报的 P 波走时异常来获得跨越整个地幔的 16 个球壳的速度扰动，每个球壳被分成 32×64 或 2,048 块（5.6°×5.6°），总共有 32,768 个未知参数。问题显然在于有太多参数，但是使用平滑准则可以得到一个稳定的收敛解。这些作者很乐意将他们的模型对我们公开，从中我们发现了每个球壳高达 36 阶的球谐系数。图 5 显示了两个球壳的功率谱：一个在上地幔，另一个在下地幔。在两种情形中，6 阶以上的功率很低，仅仅 48 个球谐系数就可以很好地表示两个球壳中每一个的 2,048 个参数。我们发现其他球壳也有相似的结果。

当然，较小尺度特征确实存在。例如，在地球表面，确实无法用低阶展开式来有效地表述陆地结构和海洋结构之间的陡峭边界。核幔边界附近热点的分布和大尺度低速异常（见参考文献 26 的插图 2g）之间的相关性表明，在大尺度和小尺度特征之间可能存在某种关系，也许是非线性关系。

由于不考虑随机测量误差，带有球形和环形分量且由球谐系数表示的板块速度场的展开式可以作为一种有效的类比。黑格和奥康奈尔 [31] 发现这些系数的功率谱以 l^{-2} 的速度迅速衰减，正如 SS 谱，解释如下：速度场受少数几块具有恒定速度的大板块支配，导致了低能量。在二维情况下，以 l^{-2} 的速度衰减的功率谱代表间断面。尽管单个的系数在较高的 l 值处很小，然而由于是同相位，所以它们的叠加效应会很大。

我们认为我们的结果可以进行如下解释。速度异常场受水平维度为几千公里的实体所支配。在这些实体内，速度异常的变化平缓，速度在边界处可能会突然变化。而且，可能存在有限数量的小尺度异常，其形状是平面的（俯冲带）或线性的（地幔柱），但是和这些特征相关联的总功率不足以对合理进行的"低阶"反演结果造成偏差。

这些结果给地幔对流建模增加了约束条件。黑格等 [32] 及福特和佩尔蒂埃 [33] 的实验证明地震速度异常主要由温差引起。（不能排除化学不均一性的存在，但是在大

principally caused by differences in temperature. (The presence of chemical heterogeneity cannot be ruled out, but its effect on lateral variations in velocity seems to be minor throughout most of the mantle, with the possible exception of the D'' layer.) Assuming that perturbations in velocities are proportional to those in temperature, the temperature field of a successful mantle convection model integrated along the SS ray paths, for example, should be characterized by a spectrum similar to that in Fig. 3a.

Some final remarks with regard to seismological practice. The main reason why our experiment and those of Woodward and Masters[17,21] or Zhang and Tanimoto[28] have succeeded is that they were performed at relatively long periods. With a cut-off period of 32 s, each of our SS ray paths samples an average volume at least 1,000 times as large as 1 Hz frequency, which is characteristic of the P-waves reported in the bulletins of the International Seismological Centre. This automatically eliminates most of the noise associated with small-scale structures. Explanation of a spectrum from a single source–station pair may, for a low-order normal mode, require integration over the entire volume of the Earth[34]. Long-period, large-wavelength data are very effective volume integrators, and their availability is essential for studying the Earth on a global scale. Our experiment defines this scale to be confined to degrees less than 10. A global network of about 100 well distributed seismographic stations equipped to provide high-quality long- and very-long-period data should be sufficient for this purpose. It is encouraging that the deployment of such a network is under way, and that there is even some prospect of permanent stations emplaced in boreholes in the deep ocean bottom[35].

(**352**, 121-126;1991)

Wei-jia Su and Adam M. Dziewonski
Department of Earth and Planetary Sciences, Harvard University, Cambridge, Massachusetts 02138, USA

Received 2 April; accepted 18 June 1991.

References:

1. Dziewonski, A. M., Hager, B. H. & O'Connell, R. J. *J. Geophys. Res.* **82**, 239-255 (1977).
2. Olson, P., Silver, P. G. & Carlson, R. W. *Nature* **344**, 209-215 (1990).
3. Masters, G., Jordan, T. H., Silver, P. G. & Gilbert, F. *Nature* **298**, 609-613 (1982).
4. Morelli, A. & Dziewonski, A. M. *Nature* **325**, 678-683 (1987).
5. Dziewonski, A. M. *J. Geophys. Res.* **89**, 5929-5952 (1984).
6. Nataf, H.-C., Nakanishi, I. & Anderson, D. L. *J. Geophys. Res.* **91**, 7261-7307 (1986).
7. Tanimoto, T. *Geophys. J. Int.* **100**, 327-336 (1990).
8. Woodhouse, J. H. & Dziewonski, A. M. *J. Geophys. Res.* **89**, 5953-5986 (1984).
9. Clayton, R. W. & Comer, R. P. *EOS Trans. Am. geophys. Un (Abstr.)* **64**, 776 (1983).
10. Inoue, H., Fukao, Y., Tanabe, K. & Ogata, Y. *Phys. Earth Planet. Inter.* **59**, 294-328 (1990).
11. Clayton, R. W. & Comer, R. P. *Terra Cognita* **4**, 282 (Abstr.) (1984).
12. Bercovici, D., Schubert, G. & Glatzmaier, G. A. *Science* **244**, 950-955 (1989).
13. Gudmundsson, O., Davies, J. H. & Clayton, R. W. *Geophys. J. Int.* **102** 25-43 (1990).
14. Snieder, R., Beckers, J. & Neele, F. *J. Geophys. Res.* **96**, 501-515 (1991).
15. Dziewonski, A. M. & Anderson, D. L. *Phys. Earth Planet. Inter.* **25**, 297-356 (1981).
16. Engdahl, E. R. *EOS Trans. Am. geophys. Un.* **70**, 1501 (1989).
17. Woodward, R. L. & Masters, G. *Nature* (in the press).

824

部分地幔中，它对速度横向变化的影响似乎较小，D'' 层可能是个例外。）假定速度扰动与温度扰动成比例，比如，一个沿着 SS 射线路径积分的成功的地幔对流模型的温度场，就应该以与图 3a 相似的功率谱为特征。

　　最后的一些讨论是关于地震学实践的。伍德沃德和马斯特斯 [17,21] 或张和谷本 [28] 的试验以及我们的试验取得成功的主要原因是，这些实验是在相对长的周期上做的。我们的每条 SS 射线路径的截止周期是 32 秒，采样的平均范围至少是 1 Hz 频率的 1,000 倍，这是国际地震中心公报报道的 P 波特征。这自动消除了大部分跟小尺度构造相关联的噪声。对低阶简正振型，以单个震源－台站数据对来解释功率谱可能需要对地球的整个体积进行积分 [34]。长周期、长波长数据是有效的体积积分器，并且对于在全球尺度研究地球是必不可少的。我们的实验将这一尺度限制为小于 10 阶。一个由大约 100 个分布均匀、可提供高质量长周期或甚长周期数据的地震台站组成的全球台网应该足以实现这一目的。令人鼓舞的是，这样一个地震台网正在部署之中，并且甚至有可能在深海底部的钻井中建立永久测站 [35]。

（陈林 张新彦 翻译；张忠杰 审稿）

18. Dziewonski, A. M., Chou, T.-A. & Woodhouse, J. H. *J. Geophys. Res.* **86**, 2825-2852 (1981).

19. Dziewonski, A. M., Ekström, G., Woodhouse, J. H. & Zwart, G. *Phys. Earth Planet. Inter.* **62**, 194-207 (1990).

20. Su, W.-J., Dziewonski, A. M. & Woodhouse, J. H. *EOS Trans. Am. geophys. Un. (Abstr.)* **71**, 556 (1990).

21. Woodward, R. L. & Masters, G. *J. Geophys. Res.* **96**, 6351-6377 (1991).

22. Woodward, R. L. thesis, Univ. of California (1989).

23. Shure, L., Parker, R. L. & Backus, G. E. *Phys. Earth planet. Inter.* **28**, 215-229 (1982).

24. Woodhouse, J. H. & Dziewonski, A. M. *EOS Trans. Am. geophys. Un.* **67**, 307 (1986).

25. Dziewonski, A. M. & Woodhouse, J. H. *Science* **236**, 37-48 (1987).

26. Woodhouse, J. H. & Dziewonski, A. M. *Phil. Trans. R. Soc. Lond.* A**328**, 291-308 (1989).

27. Julian, B. R. & Gubbins, D. *Geophys. J. R. astr. Soc.* **43**, 95-113 (1977).

28. Zhang, Y.-S. & Tanimoto, T. *Phys. Earth planet Int.* **66**, 160-202 (1991).

29. Jordan, T. H. & Lynn, W. S. *J. Geophys. Res.* **79**, 2679-2685 (1974).

30. Jordan, T. H. *Geophys. J. R. astr. Soc.* **52**, 441-455 (1978).

31. Hager, B. H. & O'Connell, R. J. *Tectonophysics* **50**, 111-133 (1978).

32. Hager, B. H., Clayton, R. W., Richards, M. A., Comer, R. P. & Dziewonski, A. M. *Nature* **313**, 541-545 (1985).

33. Forte, A. M. & Peltier, W. R. *J. Geophys. Res.* **92**, 3645-3679 (1987).

34. Giardini, D., Li, X. & Woodhouse, J. H. *Nature* **325**, 405-411 (1987).

35. Purdy, G. M., Dziewonski, A. M., Orcutt, J. A., Kanamori, H. & Duennebier, F. K. *EOS Trans. Am. geophys. Un. (Abstr.)* **70**, 1230 (1989).

Acknowledgements. Much of our data set and the analytical tools were developed in collaboration with J. Woodhouse. We thank R. Woodward for his computer programs and critical reading of the manuscript, and H. Inoue for numerical details of his model. We thank the staff of the Albuquerque Seismological Laboratory of the US Geological Survey for providing data from the Global Digital Seismographic Network. This work was supported by the NSF.

Helical Microtubules of Graphitic Carbon

S. Iijima

Editor's Note

Techniques for mass-producing cage-like carbon molecules called fullerenes, reported in 1990, led to a surge of interest in the complex molecular topologies that graphite-like carbon could adopt. Here Sumio Iijima, a microscopist at the NEC Corporation in Japan, reports the most significant of these: the sheets of carbon, he says, can roll up into tubular forms that nest inside one another. These so-called carbon nanotubes are very stiff and strong, and have become the main focus of research into carbon nanotechnology, for example offering ultrasmall needles, containers and electrical conductors. They are in a sense the ultimate carbon fibre—a material with which Iijima already had a great deal of experience.

The synthesis of molecular carbon structures in the form of C_{60} and other fullerenes[1] has stimulated intense interest in the structures accessible to graphitic carbon sheets. Here I report the preparation of a new type of finite carbon structure consisting of needle-like tubes. Produced using an arc-discharge evaporation method similar to that used for fullerene synthesis, the needles grow at the negative end of the electrode used for the arc discharge. Electron microscopy reveals that each needle comprises coaxial tubes of graphitic sheets, ranging in number from 2 up to about 50. On each tube the carbon-atom hexagons are arranged in a helical fashion about the needle axis. The helical pitch varies from needle to needle and from tube to tube within a single needle. It appears that this helical structure may aid the growth process. The formation of these needles, ranging from a few to a few tens of nanometres in diameter, suggests that engineering of carbon structures should be possible on scales considerably greater than those relevant to the fullerenes.

SOLIDS of elemental carbon in the sp^2 bonding state can form a variety of graphitic structures. Graphite filaments can be produced, for instance, when amorphous carbon filaments formed by thermal decomposition of hydrocarbon species are subsequently graphitized by heat treatment[2,3]. Graphite filaments can also grow directly from the vapour-phase deposition of carbon[4,5], which also produces soot and other novel structures such as the C_{60} molecule[6-8].

Graphitic carbon needles, ranging from 4 to 30 nm in diameter and up to 1 μm in length, were grown on the negative end of the carbon electrode used in the d.c. arc-discharge evaporation of carbon in an argon-filled vessel (100 torr). The gas pressure was much lower than that reported for the production of thicker graphite filaments[5]. The apparatus is very similar to that used for mass production of C_{60} (ref. 9). The needles seem to grow

石墨碳的螺旋状微管

饭岛澄男

编者按

1990 年报道的宏量生产笼状碳分子富勒烯的技术，激发了人们对类石墨碳复杂分子拓扑学的浓烈兴趣。在本文中，日本电气股份有限公司的显微镜专家饭岛澄男报道了其中最重要的发现：碳层可以卷成嵌套的管状形式。这些所谓的碳纳米管非常坚硬、坚固，已成为碳纳米技术研究的主要焦点，例如，该材料可作为超小的针尖、容器及导体。它们在某种意义上是完美的碳纤维 —— 一种饭岛已经做过大量研究的材料。

C_{60} 和其他富勒烯等分子碳结构的合成 [1] 激起了人们对于由石墨碳层演变成的结构的强烈兴趣。这里我要报道一种由针状管组成的新型碳结构。该管状物是利用一种与富勒烯合成中所用方法相似的电弧放电气化的方法制备的，它在电弧放电所用的负电极端生长。电子显微镜研究表明，每根管状物都是由共轴的石墨碳层管组成，层数从 2 到 50 左右。管上由碳原子组成的六边形沿管轴呈螺旋状排列。管与管之间以及同一根管内的层与层之间的螺距均不相同。这种螺旋结构可能有助于生长过程。这些直径从几到几十纳米针形的管状物的形成表明，构筑尺度显著大于富勒烯的碳结构是有可能的。

处于 sp^2 成键状态的碳的单质固体可以形成多种石墨结构。例如，将由烃类物质热分解所形成的无定形碳丝利用热处理手段进行后继石墨化时，可以生成石墨细丝 [2,3]。通过碳的气相沉积也可以直接生成石墨丝 [4,5]，这种方法还用于生成炭黑和其他诸如 C_{60} 分子的新结构 [6-8]。

将碳电极置于充氩（100 torr）容器中进行直流电弧放电将碳气化就可在负电极端生长出直径从 4 nm 至 30 nm、长度可达 1 μm 的石墨碳针形管状物。容器内气体的压力远远低于已报道的制备较粗的石墨丝所需的压力 [5]。这种装置与批量生产 C_{60} 所用的装置（参考文献 9）很像。针形管状物似乎只在电极上的某些区域

plentifully on only certain regions of the electrode. The electrode on which carbon was deposited also contained polyhedral particles with spherical shell structures, which were 5–20 nm in diameter. The needle structures were examined by transmission electron microscopy (electron energies of 200 keV).

High-resolution electron micrographs of typical needles show (002) lattice images of the graphite structure along the needle axes (Fig. 1). The appearance of the same number of lattice fringes from both sides of a needle suggests that it has a seamless and tubular structure. The thinnest needle, consisting of only two carbon-hexagon sheets (Fig. 1b), has an outer and inner tube, separated by a distance of 0.34 nm, which are 5.5 nm and 4.8 nm in diameter. The separation matches that in bulk graphite. Wall thicknesses of the tubules range from 2 to 50 sheets, but thicker tubules tend to be polygonized. This low dimensionality and cylindrical structure are extremely uncommon features in inorganic crystals, although cylindrical crystals such as serpentine[10] do exist naturally.

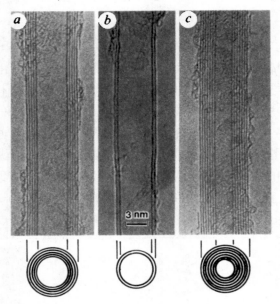

Fig. 1. Electron micrographs of microtubules of graphitic carbon. Parallel dark lines correspond to the (002) lattice images of graphite. A cross-section of each tubule is illustrated. a, Tube consisting of five graphitic sheets, diameter 6.7 nm. b, Two-sheet tube, diameter 5.5 nm. c, Seven-sheet tube, diameter 6.5 nm, which has the smallest hollow diameter (2.2 nm).

The smallest tube observed was 2.2 nm in diameter and was the innermost tube in one of the needles (Fig. 1c). The diameter corresponds roughly to a ring of 30 carbon hexagons; this small diameter imposes strain on the planar bonds of the hexagons and this causes two neighbouring hexagons on the ring to meet at an angle of $\sim 6°$. For the C_{60} molecule, the bending angle is 42°, which is much larger than for these tubes. The C–C bond energy calculated for the C_{60} molecule is smaller than that of graphite[11], suggesting that bending the hexagons in C_{60} lowers the bond energy. A similar effect of the bending on bonding energies might apply here. One of the key questions about the tubular structure is how

中才能充分地生长。在碳沉积的电极上也含有具球壳结构的多面体颗粒，其直径为5~20 nm。用透射电子显微镜（200 keV 电子能量）对针形管状物的结构进行了观测。

典型针形管状物的高分辨电子显微镜照片显示出石墨结构中沿着管轴方向的（002）晶格图像（图 1）。管状物两侧相同数目的晶格条纹表明它具有无缝的管状结构。最薄的一根管（图 1b）仅由两个六边形碳层组成，外管和内管间距 0.34 nm，直径分别为 5.5 nm 和 4.8 nm。这个间隔与大块石墨中的间隔相吻合。微管壁的厚度从 2~50 层不等，但是较厚的微管容易多边形化。这种低维的圆柱形结构在无机晶体中是极为罕见的特性，尽管诸如蛇纹石等圆柱形晶体[10] 在自然界中也确实存在。

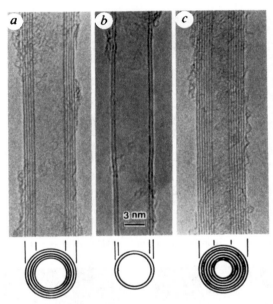

图 1. 石墨碳微管的电子显微图像。平行暗线对应于石墨的（002）晶格图像。对每根管描绘出一个横截面。a，由五个石墨层组成的管，直径 6.7 nm。b，双层管，直径 5.5 nm。c，七层管，直径 6.5 nm，具有最小的空心直径（2.2 nm）。

已观测到的最小管的直径为 2.2 nm，是某一管状物的最内层管（图 1c）。该直径大致相当于由 30 个碳六边形构成的环；这么小的直径给六边形的平面键施加了张力，因而导致环上两个相邻六边形出现约 6° 的夹角。对于 C_{60} 分子，弯曲角为 42°，比上述管结构中的要大很多。由 C_{60} 分子计算出的 C–C 键能比石墨的小[11]，这意味着 C_{60} 中六边形的弯折降低了键能。弯折效应对于键能的类似影响在这里也适用。关于微管结构的一个关键问题是如何打破在石墨中存在的 ABAB 六方堆积序列，因

the ABAB hexagonal stacking sequence found in graphite is relaxed, as it is impossible to retain this ideal graphite structure for coaxial tubes. There should be a shortage of 8–9 hexagons in going from one circumference of a tube to that inside it. Disordered graphitic stacking is known as turbostratic stacking, but no detailed accounts of stacking patterns in such structures have been reported. The argument here is also applicable to the spherical graphitic particles mentioned earlier[6].

All the electron diffraction patterns (Fig. 3) taken from individual carbon needles are indexed by the $\{h0l\}$ and $\{hk0\}$ spots for hexagonal symmetry. The patterns always show strong $(00l)$ spots when the needle axes are perpendicular to the [001] axis, supporting the idea of a coaxial arrangement of graphitic tubes. As shown in Fig. 2, two side portions of each tube (indicated by shading and labelled "V") will be oriented so that the (002) planes satisfy the Bragg diffraction condition for the incident electron beam, and thus give $(00l)$-type spots. Individual (002) planes in these portions are directly imaged in Fig. 1.

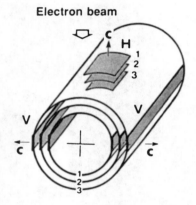

Fig. 2. Clinographic view of a possible structural model for a graphitic tubule. Each cylinder represents a coaxial closed layer of carbon hexagons. The meaning of the labels V and H is explained in the text.

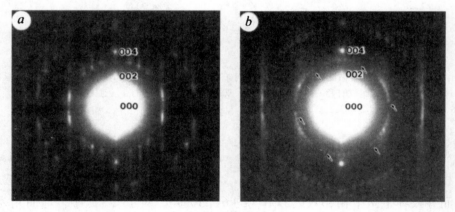

Fig. 3. Electron diffraction patterns from individual microtubules of graphitic carbon. The patterns show $mm2$ symmetry, and are indexed by multiple superpositions of $\{h0l\}$-type reflections and $\{hk0\}$ reflections of graphite crystal. The needle axes are horizontal. a, Superposition of three sets of $\{hk0\}$ spots taken from a seven-sheet tubule. b, Superposition of four sets of $\{hk0\}$ spots from a nine-sheet tubule.

为对于共轴管来说，要保留这一理想石墨结构是不可能的。一个管的周长比套在里面的管的周长多 8~9 个六元环的长度。无序的石墨堆积方式称为乱层堆积，但是还没有关于这种结构中堆积模式的详细报道。这里的论述也适用于早先谈到过的球状石墨颗粒[6]。

对于由单个碳管状物获得的所有电子衍射图（图 3），都已经根据六方对称性用 {h0l} 和 {hk0} 对衍射点进行了指标化。当管轴垂直于 [001] 轴时，图案中总是呈现出强的（00l）晶面衍射点，这验证了石墨管共轴排布的观点。如图 2 所示，每根管的两个边缘部分（用阴影表示，标记为"V"）将会选取使（002）面对于入射电子束满足布拉格衍射条件的取向，从而给出 (00l) 型的衍射点。这部分的每个（002）面直接描绘于图 1 中。

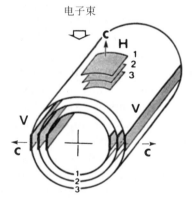

图 2. 石墨微管的一种可能结构模型的斜影视图。每个圆柱代表一个碳六边形的共轴闭合层。正文中解释了标记 V 和 H 的含义。

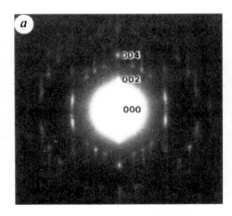
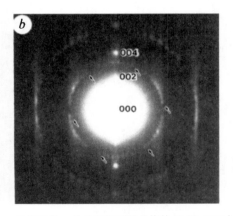

图 3. 单个石墨碳微管的电子衍射图。图案呈现出 mm2 对称性，并且根据石墨晶体的 {h0l} 型反射与 {hk0} 型反射的多重叠加指标化。管轴是水平的。a，一个七层微管的三组 {hk0} 点的重叠。b，一个九层微管的四组 {hk0} 点的重叠。

The $\{hk0\}$ patterns as a whole show $mm2$ mirror symmetry about the needle axis, and consist of multiple sets of $\{hk0\}$ spots. For example, three sets of $(hk0)$ spots seem to form ring patterns, only (100)- and (220)-type spots being seen (Fig. 3a). The diffraction pattern was obtained from a single tube consisting of seven sheets, confirmed by examining the electron microscope image. Referring again to Fig. 2, the top portion of the outermost tube, labelled "H", and its counterpart on the bottom of the tube, give independently one set each of $\{hk0\}$ patterns. If these two portions of the cylinder have the same orientation, they produce an identical $\{hk0\}$ pattern. If three hexagon sheets on the tubes 1, 2 and 3 were oriented differently, they would give six different $\{hk0\}$ spot patterns. Such a top–bottom effect is one of the requirements for the mirror symmetry. Another requirement is a helical arrangement of carbon hexagons on individual tubes, described further below.

Consider rotation of individual graphite sheets with respect to the needle axes. To explain the graphitic tube structure, the tube is cut at one side along the needle axis and unrolled. This is illustrated schematically in Fig. 4a. Fewer hexagons are drawn, than would form a real tube, but the essential needle geometry correctly represents one of our experimental diffraction patterns. A cylindrical tube can be formed by rolling up the hexagonal sheet about the filament axis (drawn by the heavy line) so as to superimpose hexagons labelled A and B at the top on A′ and B′ at the bottom. It will be found that the hatched hexagons are aligned perfectly to make a helix around the needle axis (see Fig. 4b). The helical arrangement of the hexagons is responsible for the mirror symmetry as observed in the experimental diffraction patterns. One complete spiral rotation leaves a pitch three hexagons in height at the tip of the needle. There are many possible pitches in the helix, depending on the orientation of the sheet with respect to the needle axis. In other words, the orientation of a hexagon sheet can be determined uniquely by referring to the needle axis. If hexagons A and B coincide with those labelled C and D, the needle axis will be along [010] and thus there will be no spiral rows of hexagons. This has, however, rarely been observed.

作为整体的 {hk0} 花样呈现为关于管轴的 mm2 镜面对称，花样由多组 {hk0} 点组成。例如三组 (hk0) 点似乎可形成环状花样，但只能看到 (100) 和 (220) 类型的点 (图 3a)。通过电子显微图像加以确认可知，这个衍射图来自于一个七层管。在图 2 中，对标记为 "H" 的最外层管的顶部，以及它在管底部的对应部分，各自独立地给出一组 {hk0} 花样。如果圆柱的这两个部分有相同的取向，就会给出同一个 {hk0} 花样。如果管 1、2 和 3 上的三个六边形层取向各不相同，它们就会给出 6 组不同的 {hk0} 点花样。这种顶-底效应是镜面对称的必要条件之一。另一个必要条件是碳六边形在单个管上的螺旋形排布，下面将会进一步描述。

考虑单个石墨层相对于管轴的旋转。为解释石墨管结构，将管沿着管轴方向裁开并展开。图 4a 中概略地显示出这一过程。画出的六边形比能形成一个真正管的六边形数目要少，但是基本的管状结构已正确地呈现出我们得到的实验衍射花样之一。通过将六边形层围绕管轴 (用粗线画出) 卷起，使得标记为 A 和 B 的顶部六边形叠合在底部的 A′ 和 B′ 上，可以形成一个圆柱形管。可以发现，标记为阴影的六边形完美地排成一条环绕管轴的螺旋 (参见图 4b)。六边形的螺旋排布是实验衍射花样中所观测到的镜面对称性的原因。一个完整的旋周在管端口处带来三个六边形高的螺距。螺旋中还存在着很多可能的螺距，这取决于层相对于管轴的取向。换言之，六边形层的取向可以参照管轴而唯一地确定。如果六边形 A 和 B 与标记为 C 和 D 的六边形重合，那么管轴就会沿 [010] 方向，因而也就不会存在六边形的螺旋形排列。但是，很少观测到这种情况。

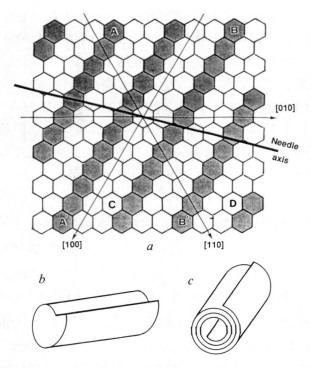

Fig. 4. *a*, Schematic diagram showing a helical arrangement of a graphitic carbon tubule, which is unrolled for the purposes of explanation. The tube axis is indicated by the heavy line and the hexagons labelled A and B, and A′ and B′, are superimposed to form the tube (for the significance of C and D, see text). *b*, The row of hatched hexagons forms a helix on the tube. The number of hexagons does not represent a real tube size, but the orientation is correct. *c*, A model of a scroll-type filament.

Because of the helical structure, the {*hk*0} spot patterns should always contain sets of even numbers of spots. Occasionally, sets of odd numbers of spots occur, such as the groups of three shown in Fig. 3*a*. These can be explained by frequent coincidence of the top and bottom sheet orientations. Such an accidental coincidence will be increased for hexagonal symmetry of individual hexagon sheet when it is rolled. Consider the sets of four of {*hk*0} in Fig. 3*b*. Each of the sets of spots, which have equal intensity distributions, is rotated by ~6° about the (000) origin, or the needle axis. We take one set of (*hk*0) spots (indicated by arrows), corresponding to one of the hexagon sheets, as a reference whose [100] axis is rotated by 3° about the needle axis. The other three sets of spots are then rotated by 6°, 12° and 24° from the reference sheet. Considering the fact that the needle consists of only nine sheets and each set of {*hk*0} spots is generated from only three or four sheets, it is reasonable that every three or four sheets are rotated stepwise by 6° about the *c* axis. Any translational shift of the sheets cannot be detected in the electron diffraction patterns. A systematic change in sheet orientations was confirmed by (*h*0*l*)-type lattice image observations. The question of whether the systematic variation in the rotation angles in successive tubules acts to stabilize the structure remains to be answered.

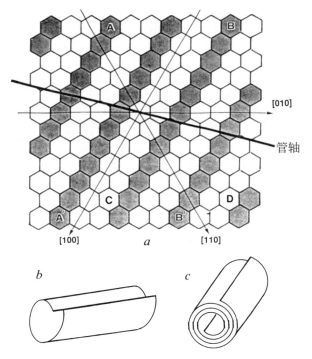

图 4. *a*，石墨碳微管螺旋形排布的示意图，为便于解释而将其铺开。管轴用粗线表示，标记为 A 和 B 的六边形与 A′ 和 B′ 的六边形重叠而形成该管（C 和 D 的意义参见正文）。*b*，标为阴影的六边形队列形成管上的一条螺旋。六边形的数目并不代表真正的管尺寸，不过取向是准确的。*c*，一条卷轴形细丝的模型。

由于具有螺旋形结构，$\{hk0\}$ 衍射点花样应该总是包含偶数组点。奇数组点偶尔会出现，例如图 3*a* 中的三组的情况。这可以用时常发生的顶部与底部层取向的一致来解释。当单独六边形层卷起呈六方对称性时，这种偶然的一致将会有所增加。请见图 3*b* 中的四组 $\{hk0\}$ 点。具有同等强度分布的每一组点都相对于 (000) 原点或管轴旋转了约 6°。我们选取对应于一个六边形层的一组 $(hk0)$ 点（用箭头表示）作为参考，它的 [100] 轴相对于管轴旋转了 3°。于是，另外三组点对于参考面就旋转了 6°、12° 和 24°。考虑到管状物只由九层组成而且每一组 $\{hk0\}$ 点都只由三或四个层所产生，那么下列说法就是合理的：每三或四个层相对于 *c* 轴依次旋转 6°。在电子衍射花样中不能检测出层的任何平移变换。对 $(h0l)$ 型晶格图像的观测证实了层取向中的逐步变化。系列微管中旋转角的逐渐变化是否有助于稳定结构的问题仍然有待回答。

The tips of the needles are usually closed by caps that are curved, polygonal or cone-shaped. The last of these have specific opening angles of about 19° or 40°, which can be rationalized in terms of the way that a perfect, continuous hexagonal network can close on itself.

According to Bacon's scroll model for tubular needle growth, needles could be formed by rolling up single carbon-hexagon sheets to form tubular filaments as illustrated in Fig. 4c. Such filaments should have edge overlaps on their surfaces. But I have observed no overlapping edges for the needles described here. Instead, I have observed concentric atomic steps around the needles (I have not confirmed that these are helical). On the basis of these new experimental findings on needle morphologies, I propose a new growth model for the tubular needles. That is, individual tubes themselves can have spiral growth steps at the tube ends (Fig. 4b). It is worth mentioning that the spiral growth steps, which are determined by individual hexagon sheets, will have a handedness. The growth mechanism seems to follow a screw dislocation model analogous to that developed for conventional crystals, but the helical structure is entirely different from the screw dislocation in the sense that the present crystals have a cylindrical lattice.

(**354**, 56-58; 1991)

Sumio Iijima
NEC Corporation, Fundamental Research Laboratories, 34 Miyukigaoka, Tsukuba, Ibaraki 305, Japan

Received 27 August; accepted 21 October 1991.

References:

1. Kroto, H. W., Heath, J. R., O'Brien, S. C., Curl, R. F. & Smalley, R. E. *Nature* **318**, 162-163 (1985).
2. Oberlin, A. & Endo, M. *J. Cryst. Growth* **32**, 335-349 (1976).
3. Speck, J. S., Endo, M. & Dresselhaus, M. S. *J. Cryst. Growth* **94**, 834-848 (1989).
4. Tibbetts, G. G. *J. Cryst. Growth* **66**, 632-638 (1984).
5. Bacon, R. *J. appl. Phys.* **31**, 283-290 (1960).
6. Iijima, S. *J. Cryst. Growth* **50**, 675-683 (1980).
7. Iijima, S. *J. Phys. Chem.* **91**, 3466-3467 (1987).
8. Kroto, H. W. *Science* **242**, 1139-1145 (1988).
9. Krätschmer, W., Lamb, L. D., Fostiropoulos, K. & Huffman, D. R. *Nature* **347**, 354-358 (1990).
10. Whittaker, E. J. W. *Acta Cryst.* **21**, 461-466 (1966).
11. Saito, S. & Oshiyama, A. *Phys. Rev. Lett.* **66**, 2637-2640 (1991).

Acknowledgements. I thank Y. Ando for the carbon specimens.

通常用曲线形、多边形或者锥形的帽将针形管的尖端封闭。最后一种形状具有约为 19°或 40°的张角，它可以用如下方式推导出来：一个完美、连续的六方网络可以自身闭合。

根据培根提出的微管形管状物生长的卷轴模型，管状物可以通过卷起六边形碳原子单层而变成如图 4c 所示的微管形细丝的方式来形成。这种细丝应该在其表面上存在边缘重叠。但是我从未在这里所描述的管状物中看到过重叠的边缘。我倒是曾经见过围绕管的同心原子台阶（我不能确定它们是螺旋状的）。基于对管状物形态的上述新实验发现，我为微管形管状物提出一种新的生长模型。即单根管本身即可在管末端发生螺旋形台阶生长（图 4b）。值得一提的是，螺旋形生长台阶具有手性——这由六边形单层所决定。生长机制似乎遵循一种螺旋位错模型，它与为常规晶体所建立的模型类似，但是就当前晶体具有圆柱形晶格的意义而言，螺旋结构完全不同于螺旋位错。

（王耀杨 翻译；李彦 审稿）

A Planetary System around the Millisecond Pulsar PSR1257+12

A. Wolszczan and D. A. Frail

Editor's Note

Millisecond pulsars spin so rapidly that it is possible to make extremely precise measurements of their rotation rate—they are very good clocks. Here Alex Wolszczan and Dale Frail analyse the timing and pulse characteristics of the pulsar PSR 1257+12, and find that these suggest it is orbited by two planets, of masses 2.8 and 3.4 times the mass of the Earth. These were the first "extrasolar" planets (those around stars other than the Sun) to be discovered. But their environment does not seem conducive to life, and so there was still much excitement when the first planet around a Sun-like star was discovered only a few years later.

Millisecond radio pulsars, which are old ($\sim 10^9$ yr), rapidly rotating neutron stars believed to be spun up by accretion of matter from their stellar companions, are usually found in binary systems with other degenerate stars[1]. Using the 305-m Arecibo radiotelescope to make precise timing measurements of pulses from the recently discovered 6.2-ms pulsar PSR1257+12 (ref. 2), we demonstrate that, rather than being associated with a stellar object, the pulsar is orbited by two or more planet-sized bodies. The planets detected so far have masses of at least 2.8 $M_\oplus$ and 3.4 $M_\oplus$, where $M_\oplus$ is the mass of the Earth. Their respective distances from the pulsar are 0.47 AU and 0.36 AU, and they move in almost circular orbits with periods of 98.2 and 66.6 days. Observations indicate that at least one more planet may be present in this system. The detection of a planetary system around a nearby (~ 500 pc), old neutron star, together with the recent report on a planetary companion to the pulsar PSR1829−10 (ref. 3) raises the tantalizing possibility that a non-negligible fraction of neutron stars observable as radio pulsars may be orbited by planet-like bodies.

THE 6.2-ms pulsar PSR1257+12 (Fig. 1) was discovered during the search at high galactic latitudes for millisecond pulsars conducted in February 1990 with the 305-m Arecibo radiotelescope at a frequency of 430 MHz (ref. 2). The characteristics of this survey and the details of data analysis are described elsewhere[4]. The confirming observations made on 5 July 1990 have been followed by routine pulse timing measurements of the new pulsar. A total of 4,040 pulse time-of-arrival (TOA) observations have been accumulated so far, with the Arecibo radiotelescope, the 40-MHz, three-level correlation spectrometer and the Princeton Mark III pulsar processor at 430 MHz and 1,400 MHz. A typical uncertainty in the TOAs derived from 1-min pulse integrations is ~ 15 µs.

毫秒脉冲星PSR1257+12的行星系统

沃尔兹森，弗雷尔

编者按

毫秒脉冲星自转速度非常快，我们可以极其精确地测定它们的自转速率——它们是非常准的时钟。本文亚历山大·沃尔兹森和戴尔·弗雷尔分析了脉冲星 PSR1257+12 的测时和脉冲特征，发现这些特征表明有分别为 2.8 倍地球质量和 3.4 倍地球质量的两个行星环绕其转动。这是最早发现的"系外"行星（围绕除太阳外的其他恒星的行星），但是它们的环境似乎不利于生命存在，所以仅仅几年后当人们发现第一颗围绕类太阳恒星公转的行星时仍感到十分兴奋。

射电毫秒脉冲星是年老的（约 10^9 年），通过吸积伴星物质而自转加速的快速旋转中子星，通常发现于与另外的简并星组成的双星系统中[1]。我们使用直径 305 米的阿雷西博射电望远镜精确测量最近发现的 6.2 毫秒脉冲星 PSR1257＋12（参考文献 2）的脉冲到达时间，表明这颗脉冲星为两颗甚至更多颗行星大小的天体所环绕运动，而不是跟一颗恒星相伴。目前探测到的这两颗行星质量至少为 2.8 $M_\oplus$ 和 3.4 $M_\oplus$，这里 $M_\oplus$ 为地球质量。它们各自距离脉冲星 0.47 AU 和 0.36 AU，在周期为 98.2 天和 66.6 天的近圆轨道上运行。观测显示这个系统可能至少还存在一颗行星。在附近的（约 500 秒差距）年老中子星周围探测到的一个行星系统，以及最近报道的脉冲星 PSR1829–10 的行星伴星（参考文献 3），促使人们思考这样一种可能：相当一部分表现为射电脉冲星的中子星周围可能被类行星天体环绕。

6.2 毫秒脉冲星 PSR1257＋12（图 1）是于 1990 年 2 月用 305 米阿雷西博射电望远镜在 430 MHz 频段上对高银纬区域搜寻毫秒脉冲星时发现的（参考文献 2）。这次巡天的特点和数据分析细节另文介绍[4]。1990 年 7 月 5 日确认这颗新脉冲星后，我们对它做了一系列常规脉冲到达时间测量。目前我们使用阿雷西博射电望远镜、40 MHz 的三级相关频谱仪以及在 430 MHz 和 1,400 MHz 频段的普林斯顿标记 III 脉冲星处理器，总共积累了 4,040 次脉冲到达时间（TOA）观测。1 分钟的脉冲积分得到的典型 TOA 误差约为 15μs。

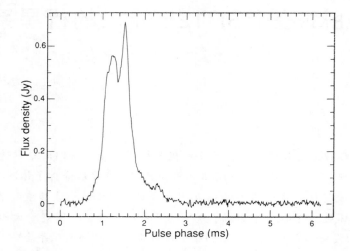

Fig. 1. The average pulse profile of PSR1257+12 at 430 MHz. The effective time resolution is ~12 μs.

The standard analysis of the timing data has been carried out using the model fitting program TEMPO[5] and the Center for Astrophysics Solar System ephemeris PEP740R. With a growing time span of the TOA measurements, it had gradually become clear that the TOAs showed an unusual variability superimposed on an annual sinusoidal pattern caused by a small (~1′) error in the assumed pulsar position. To separate these effects unambiguously, a timing-independent, interferometric position of PSR1257+12 was measured with the Very Large Array (VLA) in its A-array configuration on 19 July and again on 18 September 1991. The ~0.1″ accuracy of the resulting pulsar position was achieved by referencing the fringe phase to a point-source calibrator 1.7° away.

A least-squares fit of a simple model, which involved the pulsar's rotational period, P, and its derivative, $\dot{P}$, as free parameters and the fixed VLA position (Table 1), to the timing data spanning the period of 486 days resulted in post-fit residuals shown in Fig. 2a. The residuals, which measure the difference between the predicted and the actual TOAs, show a quasiperiodic "wandering" over the entire pulsar period. A closer examination of this effect has revealed that it was caused by two strict periodicities of 66.6 and 98.2 days in the pulse arrival times. This is further demonstrated in Fig. 2b and c, which shows post-fit residuals after fitting each of the two periods separately to the above data, assuming simple keplerian binary models involving a low-mass binary companion to the pulsar. Evidently, fitting for one of the assumed binary periods leaves the other one as a post-fit residual, implying that the pulse arrival times of PSR1257+12 are indeed affected by two independent periodicities. Further detailed analysis has shown that the periodicities are independent of radio frequency and that other millisecond pulsars routinely observed at Arecibo with the same data acquisition equipment show no such effect in their timing residuals.

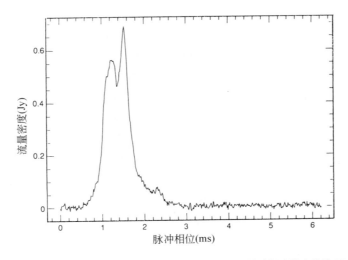

图 1. PSR1257 + 12 在 430 MHz 上的平均脉冲轮廓。有效时间分辨率约为 12μs。

我们使用模型拟合程序 TEMPO[5] 和天体物理太阳系中心历表 PEP740R 对测时数据进行标准分析。随着 TOA 测量时间跨度的增大，我们逐渐清楚，TOAs 显示了由于脉冲星假设位置的小误差（约 1′）导致的周年正弦形态上叠加了一个不寻常的变化。为了明确地区分这些效应，1991 年 7 月 19 日和 9 月 18 日，我们利用甚大阵（VLA）以 A 阵形测量了 PSR1257 + 12 的干涉仪位置，这与测时无关。以 1.7° 外的点源校准源的条纹相位为参考，我们得到的脉冲星位置坐标精度达到了约 0.1″。

用一个包括脉冲星自转周期 P，及其导数 $\dot P$ 作为自由参数的简单模型，加上确定的 VLA 位置（表 1），对跨度 486 天的测时数据做最小二乘法拟合，得到图 2a 中显示的拟合残差。残差是用来测量模型预测值和实际 TOAs 之间的差，这个源的残差表明在整个脉冲星周期内存在一个准周期"游荡"。对这个效应的进一步研究显示，这是脉冲到达时间中两个严格的 66.6 天和 98.2 天的周期性导致的。假设一个简单开普勒双星模型，其中脉冲星有一个小质量伴星，对以上两个周期的每个周期的数据分别进行拟合，拟合后残差分别如图 2b 和图 2c 所示，进一步证明了这两个周期性的存在。很明显，对假设的两个双星周期性中的一个进行拟合，得到的拟合后残差正好显示出另一个周期性。这表明 PSR1257 + 12 的脉冲到达时间实际上受到两个相互独立的周期性影响。进一步的仔细分析显示周期性和射电频率无关，在阿雷西博利用同样数据接收仪器对其他毫秒脉冲星进行常规观测，它们的测时残差没有显示这种效应。

843

Table 1. Parameters of the PSR1257 + 12 system

Pulsar parameters		
Rotational period, P	0.00621853193177 ± 0.00000000000001 s	
Period derivative, $\dot{P}$	$1.21 \times 10^{-19} \pm 2 \times 10^{-21}$ s s^{-1}	
Right ascension (B1950.0, VLA)	12 h 57 min 33.131 s ± 0.015	
Right ascension (B1950.0, timing)	12 h 57 min 33.126 s ± 0.003	
Declination (B1950.0, VLA)	12° 57′ 05.9″± 0.1	
Declination (B1950.0, timing)	12° 57′ 06.60″± 0.02	
Epoch	JD 2448088.9	
Dispersion measure	10.18 ± 0.01 pc cm^{-3}	
Flux density (430 MHz)	20 ± 5 mJy	
Flux density (1,400 MHz)	1.0 ± 0.2 mJy	
Surface magnetic field, B	8.8×10^8 G	
Characteristic age, τ_c	0.8×10^9 yr	
Keplerian orbital parameters		
Projected semimajor axis, $a_1 \sin i$	1.31 ± 0.01 light ms	1.41 ± 0.01 light ms
Eccentricity, e	0.022 ± 0.007	0.020 ± 0.006
Epoch of periastron, T_o	JD 2448105.3 ± 1.0	JD 2447998.6 ± 1.0
Orbital period, P_b	5751011.0 ± 800.0 s	8487388.0 ± 1800.0 s
Longitude of periastron, ω	252°±20°	107°±20°
Parameters of the planetary system		
Planet mass, $m_{2,3}$ ($M_\oplus$)	3.4/sin i	2.8/sin i
Distance from the pulsar, d (AU)	0.36	0.47
Orbital period, P_b (days)	66.6	98.2

Millisecond pulsars are extremely stable rotators. Systematic timing observations of objects like the 1.5-ms pulsar 1937+21 (ref. 6) have not revealed any timing noise, quasiperiodic TOA variations or "glitches" at the level often found in the population of younger pulsars and believed to be related to neutron star seismology[7]. The frequency independence of the amplitude of TOA variations in PSR1257+12 rules out propagation phenomena, such as those detected in eclipsing binary pulsars[8,9], as a possible source of the observed periodicities. The integrated pulse profiles of PSR1257+12 do not show any morphological changes that might indicate the presence of a free precession of the pulsar spin axis[10,11] or any magnetospheric phenomena at the level that could lead to periodic TOA variations of the measured magnitude. Consequently, the most plausible remaining alternative is that PSR1257+12 has two low-mass companions and that their orbital motion is responsible for the observed TOA variations.

表 1. PSR1257+12 系统的参数

脉冲星参数		
自转周期，P	$0.00621853193177 \pm 0.00000000000001$ s	
周期导数，$\dot{P}$	$1.21 \times 10^{-19} \pm 2 \times 10^{-21}$ s $\cdot$ s^{-1}	
赤经（B1950.0，VLA）	12 h 57 min 33.131 s ± 0.015	
赤经（B1950.0，测时）	12 h 57 min 33.126 s ± 0.003	
赤纬（B1950.0，VLA）	$12°57'05.9'' \pm 0.1$	
赤纬（B1950.0，测时）	$12°57'06.60'' \pm 0.02$	
历元	JD 2448088.9	
色散量	10.18 ± 0.01 pc $\cdot$ cm^{-3}	
流量密度（430 MHz）	20 ± 5 mJy	
流量密度（1,400 MHz）	1.0 ± 0.2 mJy	
表面磁场强度，B	8.8×10^{8} G	
特征年龄，τ_c	0.8×10^{9} 年	
开普勒轨道参数		
投影半长轴，$a_1 \sin i$	1.31 ± 0.01 light ms	1.41 ± 0.01 light ms
偏心率，e	0.022 ± 0.007	0.020 ± 0.006
近星点历元，$T_\circ$	JD 2448105.3 ± 1.0	JD 2447998.6 ± 1.0
轨道周期，P_b	5751011.0 ± 800.0 s	8487388.0 ± 1800.0 s
近星点经度，ω	$252° \pm 20°$	$107° \pm 20°$
行星系统参数		
行星质量，$m_{2,3}$（$M_\oplus$）	$3.4 / \sin i$	$2.8 / \sin i$
与脉冲星的距离，d（AU）	0.36	0.47
轨道周期，P_b（天数）	66.6	98.2

  毫秒脉冲星是极为稳定的转子。对1.5毫秒脉冲星1937+21（参考文献6）这样的天体进行系统的测时观测，并没有发现任何测时噪声、准周期 TOA 变化和经常在年轻脉冲星族中发现的自转突变（自转突变被认为同中子星星震学相关[7]）。PSR1257＋12的TOA变化幅度和频率无关，这点排除了传播效应作为观测到周期性原因的可能性，例如那些在掩食脉冲双星中探测到的传播效应[8,9]。PSR1257＋12的积分脉冲轮廓没有显示任何一种形态变化能够表明脉冲星自转轴存在一个自由进动[10,11]，或者一些磁层现象大到能够产生所测量到的幅度的 TOA 周期变化。因此，最有可能的情况是，PSR1257＋12具有两个小质量伙伴星，它们的轨道运动导致了观测到的TOA变化。

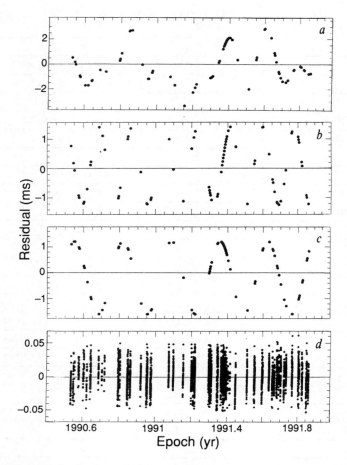

Fig. 2. The post-fit residuals of pulse arrival times from PSR1257+12. *a*, Fit for rotational parameters only (VLA position of the pulsar fixed); *b*, fit for a 98.2-day keplerian orbit (leaves a 66.6-day periodicity as residual); *c*, fit for a 66.6-day keplerian orbit (leaves a 98.2-day periodicity as residual); *d*, fit for all parameters of *a–c*.

To analyse this exciting possibility further, we have modified the code of the TEMPO program to accommodate a timing model including multiple, noninteracting keplerian orbits. The result of a fit of the model including the rotational and positional parameters of the pulsar as well as the two, five-parameter keplerian orbits to the entire data set is shown in Fig. 2*d*. The post-fit r.m.s. residual of the resultant timing model is ~18 μs (comparable to the individual TOA uncertainties) and the remaining residuals contain very little systematic variation. The model parameters of the pulsar and its assumed two companions are listed in Table 1. The derived parameters have been obtained from standard considerations involving very low-mass objects in keplerian orbits around a $1.4M_\odot$ neutron star. The pulsar period variations predicted by this model are displayed in Fig. 3 together with the observed period values derived from timing data. Note that the presence of the planet-sized bodies orbiting the pulsar results in apparent period variations of only ± 15 ps. This is caused by the pulsar's spatial motions which are characterized by the projected maximum velocity and displacement amplitudes of ±0.7 m s^{-1} and ±900 km, respectively.

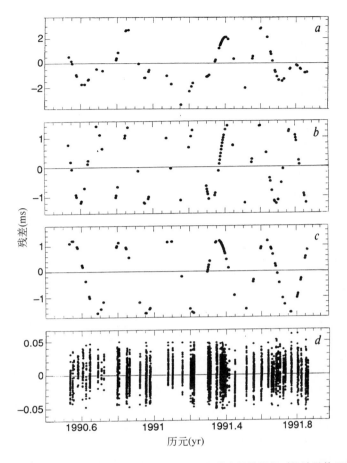

图 2. PSR1257+12 脉冲到达时间的拟合后残差。a，仅对自转参数的拟合（脉冲星的 VLA 坐标确定）；b，对 98.2 天开普勒轨道的拟合（残差的周期为 66.6 天）；c，对 66.6 天开普勒轨道的拟合（残差的周期为 98.2 天）；d，用 $a\sim c$ 所有参数拟合。

　　为了进一步分析这种令人兴奋的可能性，我们修改了 TEMPO 程序的代码来适应包含多个非相互作用的开普勒轨道的测时模型。用包含脉冲星的旋转和位置参数以及其他两个伴星的 5 个开普勒轨道参数的模型拟合整个数据集，结果见图 2d。合成测时模型的拟合后均方根残差约为 18 μs（相当于单个 TOA 误差），剩下的残差几乎不存在系统变化。脉冲星和假设的两个伴星的模型参数见表 1。导出参数是通过有非常小质量天体绕 $1.4M_{\odot}$ 的中子星做开普勒轨道运动的标准考量得到的。这个模型预言的脉冲星周期变化和由测时数据推出的观测周期值都示于图 3。注意，脉冲星周围环绕的行星尺度天体的存在仅产生 ±15 ps 的可见的周期变化。这是脉冲星的空间运动导致的，空间运动的特征为最大投影速度和位移幅度分别为 ±0.7 m · s^{-1} 和 ±900 km。

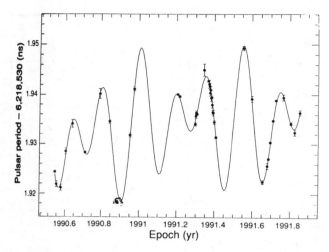

Fig. 3. Period variations of PSR1257+12. Each period measurement is based on observations made on at least two consecutive days. The solid line denotes changes in period predicted by a two-planet model of the 1257+12 system.

The high quality of the two-companion model fit to the pulsar timing data covering several orbital cycles provides compelling evidence that PSR1257+12 possesses a planetary system consisting of at least two planet-sized bodies. The possibility of more planets around PSR1257+12 is indicated by a 0.7″ discrepancy between the VLA and the timing positions, which is considerably greater than the conservative error estimates (Table 1). This discrepancy may arise from a bias in the timing position caused by a presence of a third planet with orbital period close to one year. Because the currently measured value of the second period derivative, $\ddot{P}$, of the pulsar is not significant, the effect of any outer planets that could be present in the 1257+12 system would be entirely absorbed in $\dot{P}$.

The characteristics of the 1257+12 planets are not unlike those of the inner Solar System. Both planets circle the pulsar at distances similar to that of Mercury in its orbit around the Sun. Assuming a random distribution of the inclinations, i, of orbital planes, there is a 50% probability that $i \geqslant 60°$, so that the median values of the permissible masses are $3.2 M_\oplus$ and $3.9 M_\oplus$, respectively (see Table 1). Interestingly, the ratio of orbital periods, 1.476 ±0.001, is close to a 3/2 orbital resonance of the type often encountered in the Solar System, either between planetary satellites, between Jupiter and some asteroids, or even Neptune and Pluto[12]. Also, the similarity of the measured eccentricities combined with the ~180° separation of the pericentres of the orbits can be easily understood in terms of secular perturbations of the orbital elements of the two planets (see, for example ref. 13). Finally, a hypothetical energy flux at the planets' distance from the pulsar (~0.4 AU) due to the neutron star's rotational energy loss ($\dot{E} = I\omega\dot{\omega}$, where I is the moment of inertia and $\omega = 2\pi/P$) is ~4 × 10⁷ erg cm⁻² s⁻¹ . This is ~30 times the solar constant and corresponds to a black-body temperature of ~670 K, which is similar to the measured dayside surface temperature of Mercury (see, for example, ref. 14).

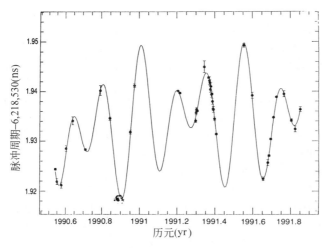

图 3. PSR1257+12 周期的变化。每一周期测量值都基于至少连续两天的观测。实线表示 1257+12 的 2 个行星系统的模型所预期的周期变化。

两个伴星模型对覆盖几个轨道周期的脉冲星测时数据的高质量拟合强有力地证明了 PSR1257+12 是由至少两颗行星尺度天体组成的行星系统。更多天体环绕 PSR1257 +12 的可能性蕴含在 VLA 和测时位置 0.7″ 的差异中，这比保守的误差估计要大很多（表1）。这个差异可能是由于轨道周期接近一年的第三颗行星的存在导致的测时位置偏差。因为目前该脉冲星的周期二阶导数 $\ddot{P}$ 的测量值不是很显著，1257＋12 系统中存在外行星的效应可整个被 $\ddot{P}$ 吸收。

PSR1257＋12 的行星特征与太阳系内行星相似。两个行星都以类似水星绕太阳的轨道距离环绕着脉冲星运动。假定轨道平面倾角 i 随机分布，$i \geqslant 60°$ 的概率为 50%，所以两行星可能的质量中值分别为 3.2 $M_{\oplus}$ 和 3.9 $M_{\oplus}$（见表1）。有趣的是，两个轨道周期的比率为 1.476 ± 0.001，接近于太阳系中常遇到的 3/2 轨道共振类型，或者是行星的卫星之间，或者是木星和一些小行星之间，甚至是海王星和冥王星之间[12]。并且，对于测量到的两个轨道相似偏心率和约 180° 的近心点间隔，考虑到两个行星轨道成分的长期扰动，这都是可以很容易理解的（参见文献 13）。最后，假设的由于中子星自转动能损失（$\dot{E} = I\omega\dot{\omega}$，这里 I 是转动惯量，$\omega = 2\pi/P$）导致的行星距离脉冲星（约 0.4 AU）处的能流约为 4×10^7 erg·cm^{-2}·s^{-1}，这约为太阳常数的 30 倍，对应的黑体温度约为 670 K，与测量到的水星光面的表面温度相似（参见文献 14）。

The possibility of the existence of planet-sized bodies orbiting neutron stars has been contemplated in the past[15,16]. The most recent evidence has been presented by Bailes *et al*[3], who have detected a ~6-month periodicity in the timing residuals of a relatively young pulsar, PSR1829–10, which is interpreted in terms of the orbital motion of a ~$10M_\oplus$ companion. A number of mechanisms have been proposed to explain a planet around PSR1829–10 (refs 17–21). In the case of PSR1257+12, its old age and a low surface magnetic field (Table 1) are typical of neutron stars which are believed to evolve in low-mass binary systems and are spun up to the observed millisecond periods by accretion of matter from their stellar companions[1]. As it is not very likely that any primordial planets would survive this kind of evolution[22], the observed 1257+12 system probably consists of "second generation" planets created at or after the end of the pulsar's binary history. Because a second supernova explosion is not expected to occur in a low-mass binary, such planets could form a stable system of bodies orbiting an old neutron star. Another important evolutionary constraint is provided by the observed very low eccentricities ($e \approx 0.02$) of the planetary orbits and the near-resonance ratio of the orbital periods. These characteristics suggest that the planets were created from some form of accretion disk that would naturally provide means to circularize the orbits and to bring them close to a 3/2 resonance[12]. Consequently, it seems that any plausible mechanism for the creation of a planetary system around a millisecond pulsar must provide a way to remove its stellar companion in a manner different from the disruption of a binary system caused by a supernova explosion and to retain enough circumpulsar matter to form planet-sized objects.

Within the constraints provided by the observational evidence, it is tempting to postulate that the 1257+12 system simply represents one of the possible outcomes of a neutron star evolution in a low-mass binary system[1]. As two examples of companion-star evaporation by millisecond pulsars have already been detected[7,8], this mechanism seems to account naturally for the absence of such a companion to PSR1257+12. In this case, one way to supply the material for planet creation could be a disk formed out of the ablated stellar matter ejected from the binary system[23,34]. The existence of such an "outer disk" around the eclipsing binary pulsar PSR1957+20 could explain the observed orbital decay of this system[25].

The results described here strongly suggest that one of the nearby galactic millisecond pulsars, PSR1257+12, is accompanied by a system of two or more planet-sized bodies. The pulse timing method (similar to the analysis of single-line spectroscopic binaries) was used to detect a ±0.7 m s^{-1} pulsar "wobble" caused by orbital motions of the planets. In fact, planetary masses smaller than that of the Moon could easily be detected with this technique. At present, this kind of accuracy is entirely inaccessible to the optical methods of planetary system detection[26]. The existence of both the 1257+12 planetary system and the object orbiting the pulsar PSR1829–10 seems to suggest that planets can form under a variety of conditions. This notion and the possibility of a non-negligible frequency of occurrence of planets around neutron stars, if confirmed, will have far-reaching consequences for our understanding of the formation and evolution of planetary systems

　　过去研究人员一直设想中子星周围具有行星尺度的天体环绕的可能性[15,16]。最近的证据来自拜莱斯等人的研究[3]，他们在一颗相对年轻的脉冲星 PSR1829–10 的测时残差中探测到一个约 6 个月的周期性，这可以用一颗质量约为 10 $M_{\oplus}$ 的伴星的轨道运动来解释。研究者提出了一系列尝试解释一颗行星环绕 PSR1829–10 的机制（参考文献 17~21）。对于 PSR1257+12，它较老的年龄和较低的表面磁场强度（表 1）是一类中子星的典型特征，这类中子星被认为是在小质量双星系统中演化，并通过吸积伴星的物质而自转加速到现在我们观测到的毫秒周期[1]。由于原初行星不大可能在这样的演化中存活下来[22]，观测到的 1257+12 系统可能是由在脉冲星的双星历史末期或之后产生的"二代"行星组成。因为在小质量双星中不大可能发生第二次超新星爆发，这样的行星才可能形成环绕一颗年老中子星运动的稳定天体系统。另外一个重要的演化限制是观测到的行星轨道的极小的偏心率（e 约等于 0.02）和轨道周期的近共振比率。这些特征表明行星是从某种吸积盘产生的，这种吸积盘能够自然提供圆化轨道的途径，从而让它们接近于 3/2 共振[12]。因此，任何生成环绕毫秒脉冲星的行星系统的可能机制都必须提供一种移除恒星伴星的途径，这种途径不同于超新星爆发所引起的双星系统的瓦解，并且能够留住足够多的环绕脉冲星的物质来形成行星尺度的天体。

　　在所提供的观测证据的限制之内，我们倾向于推测 1257+12 系统仅代表中子星在小质量双星系统中演化的一个可能结果[1]。随着研究人员探测到两颗毫秒脉冲星蒸发伴星的事例[7,8]，这个机制似乎自然地解释了为什么 PSR1257+12 缺少这样一颗伴星。在这种情形下，生成行星物质的一个来源可能是双星系统喷出的融化恒星物质所形成的一个物质盘[23,24]。如果在食脉冲双星 PSR1957+20 周围存在这种"外盘"，就能够解释这个系统观测到的轨道衰减[25]。

　　上述结果强有力地表明，PSR1257+12———一颗邻近的河内毫秒脉冲星，由两个或更多行星尺度的天体系统环绕。用脉冲测时方法（类似于单谱线分光双星分析）已经探测到一个由行星轨道运动引起的 $\pm 0.7 \ \mathrm{m \cdot s^{-1}}$ 的脉冲星"摇晃"。事实上，这种技术可以轻易探测到质量小于月球的行星。目前，这种精度在探测行星系统的光学方法中尚未达到[26]。1257+12 行星系统和环绕脉冲星 PSR1829–10 的天体似乎表明行星能在多种环境下形成。这个想法以及以不可忽略的频率出现围绕中子星的行星这样的可能性一旦被证实，将对我们理解行星系统的形成和演化以及未来搜寻太

and for future strategies of searches for planets outside the Solar System.

(**355**, 145-147; 1992)

A. Wolszczan[*] and D. A. Frail[†]
[*] National Astronomy and Ionosphere Center, Arecibo Observatory, Arecibo, Puerto Rico 00613, USA
[†] National Radio Astronomy Observatory, Socorro, New Mexico 87801, USA

Received 21 November; accepted 9 December 1991.

References:

1. Bhattacharya, D. & van den Heuvel, E. P. J. *Phys. Rep.* **203**, 1-124 (1991).

2. Wolszczan, A. *IAU Circ.* No. 5073 (1990).

3. Bailes, M., Lyne, A. G. & Shemar, S. L. *Nature* **352**, 311-313 (1991).

4. Wolszczan, A. *Nature* **350**, 688-690 (1991).

5. Taylor, J. H. & Weisberg, J. M. *Astrophys. J.* **345**, 434-450 (1989).

6. Davis, M. M., Taylor, J. H., Weisberg, J. M. & Backer, D. C. *Nature* **315**, 547-550 (1985).

7. Alpar, M. A., Nandkumar, R. & Pines, D. *Astrophys. J.* **311**, 197-213 (1986).

8. Fruchter, A. S., Stinebring, D. R. & Taylor, J. H. *Nature* **333**, 237-239 (1988).

9. Lyne, A. G. *et al. Nature* **347**, 650-652 (1990).

10. Shaham, J. *Astrophys. J.* **214**, 251-260 (1977).

11. Nelson, R. W., Finn, L. S. & Wasserman, I. *Astrophys. J.* **348**, 226-231 (1990).

12. Peale, S. J. *Ann. Rev. Astr. Astrophys.* **14**, 215-246 (1976).

13. Dermott, S. F. & Nicholson, P. D. *Nature* **319**, 115-120 (1986).

14. Vilas, F. in *Mercury* (eds Vilas, F., Chapman, C. R. & Matthews, M. S.) 59-76 (University of Arizona Press, Tucson, 1988).

15. Richards, D. W., Pettengill, G. H., Counselman, C. C. III & Rankin, J. M. *Astrophys. J.* **160**, L1-6 (1970).

16. Demiański, M. & Prószyński, M. *Nature* **282**, 383-385 (1979).

17. Podsiadlowski, Ph., Pringle, J. E. & Rees, M. J. *Nature* **352**, 783-784 (1991).

18. Fabian, A. C. & Podsiadlowski, Ph. *Nature* **353**, 801-801 (1991).

19. Lin, D. N. C., Woosley, S. E. & Bodenheimer, P. H. *Nature* **353**, 827-829 (1991).

20. Krolik, J. H. *Nature* **353**, 829-831 (1991).

21. Wasserman, I., Cordes, J. M., Finn, L. S. & Nelson, R. W. *Cornell Univ. preprint* (1991).

22. Nakano, T. *Mon. Not. R. astr. Soc.* **224**, 107-130 (1987).

23. Shu, F. H., Lubow, S. H. & Anderson, L. *Astrophys. J.* **29**, 223-241 (1979).

24. Rudak, B. & Paczyński, B. *Acta Astr.* **31**, 13-24 (1981).

25. Ryba, M. F. & Taylor, J. H. *Astrophys. J.* **380**, 557-563 (1991).

26. Black, D. C. *Space Sci. Rev.* **25**, 35-81 (1980).

Acknowledgements. We thank D. Backer, P. Nicholson, B. Paczyński, F. Rasio, S. Shapiro, J. Taylor and S. Teukolsky for discussions. We also thank J. Taylor for making available the Princeton Mark III processor. Arecibo Observatory is part of the National Astronomy and Ionosphere Center, which is operated by Cornell University under contract with the NSF. The VLA is operated by the NRAO under cooperative agreement with the NSF. D.A.F. is supported by an NSERC postdoctoral fellowship and an NRAO Jansky fellowship.

阳系外行星的策略产生深远的影响。

（肖莉 翻译；徐仁新 审稿）

Photochromism Induced in an Electrolytically Pretreated MoO₃ Thin Film by Visible Light

Yao *et al.*

Editor's Note

Research on smart materials, which change their properties in response to some external stimulus, gathered pace in the 1990s, helping to change the image of materials science from a rather staid branch of engineering to a dynamic, multi-disciplinary science. "Smart windows"—transparent materials that can be switched to a more opaque state—have been long known; in particular, photochromic glass, which darkens on exposure to light, was developed in the 1960s and has been used for sunglasses. This paper by researchers at the University of Tokyo described a new kind of stable photochromic material made from thin films of molybdenum oxide that becomes more opaque when irradiated with visible light, unlike previous transition-metal-based photochromic substances that worked only at ultraviolet wavelengths. The paper, now highly cited, set the foundation for several later advances in photochromic films and stimulated interest in applications ranging from indoor light control to display screens and light-activated memory devices.

Photochromic materials, whose optical absorption properties change in response to light, are important for a number of technological applications. A stable, reusable photochromic thin-film could be used, for example, in optical displays and high-density memories. Thin films of some transition-metal oxides can be coloured blue by band-gap excitation using ultraviolet light[1-6]. For use with common semiconductor laser sources, however, photochromic materials are required that respond to visible light. Here we report on the preparation of visible-light-sensitive, reversibly photochromic films of MoO₃. Pretreated, vacuum-evaporated MoO₃ thin films were slightly blued by cathodic polarization in a non-aqueous electrolyte; subsequent irradiation with visible light in air produced a strong colour enhancement. The photochromism could be erased by anodic polarization, and the coloration-decoloration process was repeatable over at least five cycles. The behaviour of these films contrasts with those blued by band-gap irradiation, which were not responsive to visible light.

THE MoO₃ amorphous film was prepared by vacuum evaporation of high-purity MoO₃ powders (99.9%) onto a 1-mm-thick NESA glass substrate (5×2.5 cm), with a typical film thickness of ~1,000 nm being obtained. Photochromic experiments were done in air, and a 500-W high-pressure mercury lamp was used as a light source. For band-gap excitation, the light fell directly on the sample, whereas for the visible-light experiments a sharp cut-off filter was used to obtain light of wavelength ⩾500 nm. The

电解预处理 MoO₃ 薄膜的可见光变色

姚建年等

编者按

智能材料是对外界刺激响应而改变自身性能的材料。20 世纪 90 年代，对智能材料的研究得到了快速发展，这使材料科学从工程学一个相当保守的分支转变为一个充满活力的多学科交叉科学。"灵巧窗"——能够转变为不透明状态的透明材料——早已为人们所熟知，尤其是光照后颜色加深的光致变色玻璃，这种材料于 20 世纪 60 年代得到发展并已经应用于太阳镜中。由东京大学科研人员所发表的这篇文章描述了一种由氧化钼薄膜构成的新型稳定的光致变色材料，该材料在可见光照射下能够变得更不透明，而在此之前基于过渡金属的光致变色材料只对紫外光响应。这篇现今被广泛引用的论文为光致变色薄膜的发展奠定了基础，激发了人们对室内光线调控、显示屏幕和光存储器件的研究兴趣。

光致变色材料是光照后光吸收性能发生变化的材料，在许多重要的技术领域有潜在的应用前景。例如稳定的、可重复使用的光致变色薄膜可以应用于光学显示器和高密度存储领域。一些过渡金属氧化物薄膜可以通过紫外光的带隙激发而变成蓝色[1-6]。然而如果使用普通的半导体激光光源，就要求光致变色材料必须对可见光响应。本文报道了具有可逆可见光变色性能的 MoO₃ 薄膜的制备。在非水电解质中对预处理过的真空蒸镀 MoO₃ 薄膜进行阴极极化使其呈浅蓝色，然后在空气中用可见光照射会产生显著的颜色增强。这种光致变色可以通过阳极极化进行擦除，并且着色—消色过程可以重复至少 5 个循环。相比之下，那些利用带隙激发变蓝的薄膜则对可见光没有响应。

将高纯 MoO₃ 粉末（99.9%）利用真空蒸镀方法蒸镀到 1 mm 厚的 NESA 玻璃基底上（5×2.5 cm）制备 MoO₃ 非晶态薄膜，得到的薄膜厚度大约为 1,000 nm。利用 500 W 高压汞灯作为光源在空气中进行光致变色实验。对于带隙激发，光直接照射到样品上。而对于可见光实验，利用截止型滤光片得到波长 ⩾ 500 nm 的光，光照

size of the illuminated area was varied from ∼1 mm^2 to 1.8 cm^2, but this did not affect the characteristics of the photochromic response. In the electrochromic experiments, the sample was dipped into 0.1 M LiClO$_4$/propylene carbonate solution. Platinum and Ag/AgCl electrodes were used as counter and reference electrodes, respectively. The surface area of the MoO$_3$ film in contact with the electrolyte was 1.8 cm^2. Because we did not add any redox couple into the electrolyte, the reactions occurring at the counter-electrode were probably the reduction and oxidation of water present as an impurity in the electrolyte.

Because freshly prepared MoO$_3$ is colourless and transparent, it does not show photochromism on irradiation by visible light. After being slightly blued by electrochromism, however, it becomes sensitive to visible light. Figure 1a shows the changes in the absorption spectrum of the MoO$_3$ thin film, with spectra for both the prepared amorphous film and the electrolytically pretreated film being shown. This result was obtained as follows. First, the absorption spectrum of the prepared MoO$_3$ colourless film was recorded (curve A). Next, the film was polarized at −0.1 V versus Ag/AgCl for 3 min in the electrolyte. The film was slightly coloured, as indicated by curve B. The change in absorbance from curve A to curve B was ∼0.05 at 800 nm. This electrolytically pretreated film was then irradiated with visible light for 10 min in air. The irradiated part was blued deeply (curve C): the change in absorbance was ∼0.3 at 800 nm. Similar colour enhancement was also observed on near-infrared irradiation (λ ⩾ 700 nm). This result indicates that even when excited by a broad absorption band (500–1,000 nm), the photochromic reaction is induced in this pretreated MoO$_3$ film. The possibility that this colour enhancement was caused by a thermal process could be excluded because the colour enhancement induced by visible light was affected neither by putting a thermal cut-off filter between the cell and the light source nor by doing the irradiation at 80 °C.

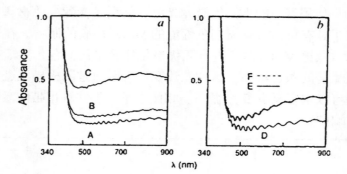

Fig. 1 Absorption spectra of a MoO$_3$ thin film. a, MoO$_3$ thin film as prepared by vacuum evaporation (curve A); spectrum taken after polarization at −0.1 V versus Ag/AgCl for 3 min in 0.1 M LiClO$_4$/propylene carbonate solution (curve B); and taken after the film in curve B was irradiated with visible light (λ ⩾ 500 nm) for 10 min in air (curve C). b, MoO$_3$ thin film as prepared by vacuum evaporation (curve D); taken after D was irradiated with ultraviolet light for 8 min in air (curve E); and taken after E was irradiated with visible light (λ ⩾ 500 nm) for 10 min in air (curve F).

面积在大约 1 mm² 到 1.8 cm² 之间可调变化，这种光照面积的改变不影响薄膜的光致变色响应。在电致变色实验中，样品浸入到 0.1 M LiClO₄/碳酸丙烯酯溶液中，分别以 Pt 和 Ag/AgCl 电极作为对电极和参比电极。MoO₃ 薄膜与电解质的接触面积是 1.8 cm²。由于我们在电解质中没有添加任何氧化还原电对，在对电极上发生的反应很可能是作为杂质存在的水的还原和氧化反应。

新制备的 MoO₃ 薄膜是无色透明的，因而用可见光照射不发生光致变色。但是利用电致变色使其变为淡蓝色以后，薄膜可以对可见光响应。图 1a 为新制备的非晶态薄膜和电解预处理 MoO₃ 薄膜的吸收光谱变化。吸收光谱的测量是按如下方式进行的：首先检测新制备的无色 MoO₃ 薄膜的吸收光谱（曲线 A），然后将薄膜置于电解液中在相对 Ag/AgCl 电极 –0.1 V 的条件下极化 3 min，薄膜变为淡蓝色，并得到曲线 B。在 800 nm 处曲线 A 到 B 的吸光度变化为 0.05 左右。随后将电解预处理的薄膜在空气中用可见光照射 10 min。照射部分变成深蓝色（曲线 C）：在 800 nm 处的吸光度变化约为 0.3。利用近红外光（波长 ≥ 700 nm）照射也得到了相似的颜色增强效果。这表明即使采用宽吸收带（500~1,000 nm）激发也可以诱导电解预处理 MoO₃ 薄膜的光致变色反应。因为在电解池和光源之间加入可阻断热量的滤光片或者在 80℃ 的条件下进行可见光照射都没有影响颜色增强的程度，因此可以排除由于热效应导致的颜色增强。

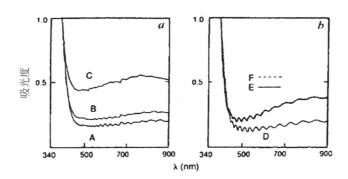

图 1. MoO₃ 薄膜的吸收光谱。a, 新制备的真空蒸镀 MoO₃ 薄膜（曲线 A）；在 0.1 M LiClO₄/碳酸丙烯酯电解液中，将 A 样品在相对 Ag/AgCl 电极 − 0.1 V 条件下极化 3 min（曲线 B）；将 B 样品在空气中用可见光（波长 ≥500 nm）照射 10 min（曲线 C）。b, 新制备的真空蒸镀 MoO₃ 薄膜（曲线 D）；将 D 样品在空气中用紫外光照射 8 min（曲线 E）；将 E 样品在空气中用可见光（波长 ≥500 nm）照射 10 min（曲线 F）。

Figure 1*b* shows, in contrast, that a MoO_3 film blued by band-gap irradiation pretreatment was not sensitive to visible light irradiation in air, even though the absorption spectrum of a film blued in this way (curve E) is very similar in shape to that of a film blued by the electrochromic reaction.

Photochromism induced in MoO_3 thin films by visible light has not, to the best of our knowledge, been reported previously. After coloration by visible light irradiation, the MoO_3 thin film was exposed in air for a prolonged period. No absorbance change was detected from films continuously exposed in air for seven months after the initial coloration, indicating that the coloured film was very stable in air.

The MoO_3 film coloured by visible light irradiation also showed good reversibility in its coloration-decoloration process. This was confirmed by the following experiments, done at constant current. First, the film was slightly blued by electrochromism with a current density of -5.5 μA cm^{-2} for 17 min, then irradiated by visible light for 15 min. For decoloration, this deeply coloured film was polarized anodically with a current density of $+5.5$ μA cm^{-2} for 34 min. The resulting bleached sample was still slightly coloured. Therefore it was deeply coloured again by visible light irradiation and decoloured repeatedly by the same procedure. The results are summarized in Fig. 2. If the film was completely decoloured, it was no longer sensitive to visible light. But if the colourless film was slightly blued again, it became sensitive to visible light.

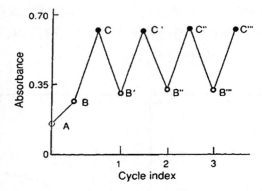

Fig. 2 The absorbance change (Δ_{abs}) of MoO_3 thin film at 800 nm during coloration and decoloration. The electrochemical polarization was done at constant current. A, Taken after a freshly prepared MoO_3 thin film was repeatedly polarized four times cathodically (-5.6 μA cm^{-2}) and anodically ($+0.6$ μA cm^{-2}) for 17 min. B, Taken after film A was polarized cathodically (-5.6 μA cm^{-2}) for 17 min, or film C anodically ($+5.6$ μA cm^{-2}) for 35 min. C, Taken after B was irradiated with visible light for 15 min in air.

The conventional photochromic processes is explained as follows[3]. When a thin film of MoO_3 is irradiated by ultraviolet light, electrons and holes are formed, thereby allowing the photogenerated holes to react with surface-adsorbed species, causing the film to be negatively charged. The positive ions on the surface, protons in the present case, are then injected into the film by Coulomb attraction, forming the hydrogen molybdenum bronze. The observed visible-light-induced photochromic reaction might, however, originate from

如图 1*b* 所示，虽然利用带隙激发预处理而变蓝的 MoO$_3$ 薄膜在吸收光谱形状上（曲线 E）与电致变色反应使其变蓝的薄膜非常相似，但对空气中可见光的照射没有响应。

据我们所知，MoO$_3$ 薄膜的这种可见光变色性能尚未被报道。将由可见光照射导致变色的 MoO$_3$ 薄膜长时间暴露在空气中，连续放置七个月后着色膜的吸光度没有发生变化，表明着色膜在空气中非常稳定。

经可见光照射着色的 MoO$_3$ 薄膜在着色—消色过程中还表现出了优良的可逆性。这可以通过在恒定电流下的实验证实：首先，将薄膜在 –5.5 µA·cm^{-2} 的电流密度下电致变色 17 min 使之呈淡蓝色，然后用可见光照射 15 min。将这个深色薄膜在 +5.5 µA·cm^{-2} 的电流密度下阳极极化 34 min 使薄膜褪色。得到的漂白样品仍然呈现淡淡的颜色，因此可以通过可见光照射使其颜色再次得到增强，然后重复同样的步骤进行消色，结果见图 2。如果薄膜被完全褪色，就不会再对可见光响应。但是如果将无色薄膜再次变为淡蓝色，又可以恢复对可见光的响应。

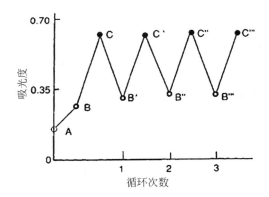

图 2. MoO$_3$ 薄膜在恒定电流电化学极化条件下进行着色—消色循环时，在 800 nm 波段处的吸光度变化（Δ_{abs}）。A，将新制备的 MoO$_3$ 薄膜分别经阴极极化（–5.6 µA·cm^{-2}）和阳极极化（+0.6 µA·cm^{-2}）17 min，并重复这个过程 4 次以后测得。B，将 A 阴极极化（–5.6 µA·cm^{-2}）17 min 后或 C 阳极极化（+5.6 µA·cm^{-2}）35 min 后测得。C，将 B 在空气中用可见光照射 15 min 后测得。

传统的光致变色过程如下 [3]：当 MoO$_3$ 薄膜被紫外光照射时，会产生电子和空穴，光生空穴可以与表面吸附物质发生反应，使薄膜带负电荷。然后表面上的正离子，也就是质子通过库仑引力注入薄膜中，形成氢钼青铜结构。我们这里所观测到的可见光光致变色则反应机理完全不同。在可见光区的宽吸收带来源于 Mo^{5+} 到 O

859

a different reaction mechanism. The broad absorption band in the visible region is due to the charge-transfer transition from Mo^{5+} to the oxide ligands, producing Mo^{6+} (refs 7,8). Therefore, it is apparent that the excitation of this broad band does not produce electron-hole pairs in the film. We suggest that the MoO$_3$ film changes to an intermediate metastable state during the electrolytic reaction and is then converted by visible light into stable molybdenum bronze.

At present the origin of the intermediate metastable state is not known, although the key to the problem is probably that the visible-light-sensitive photochromism is observed only with films slightly blued by the electrochromic reaction and not by the conventional band-gap photochromic reaction. One possible explanation is based on the difference between the sizes of the positive ions in the bronze. The injected positive ions for the electrochromic and photochromic reactions are Li$^+$ and H$^+$, respectively. Because Li$^+$ is much larger than H$^+$, the structural changes are much larger in films coloured by the electrochromic reaction than in those coloured by the photochromic reaction. Therefore when Li$^+$ is injected into the film, its structural distortion may result in a unique intermediate metastable state which can be converted to the stable bronze structure by visible irradiation. Another explanation is based on the energy difference between optical excitation and electrolytic polarization. The optical band-gap excitation energy is enough to produce stable molybdenum bronze directly, whereas that of the electrolytic reduction is not. Experiments to elucidate the mechanism are now being done.

Figure 3 shows a scheme using a combination of the "electrochemical mode" and the "photon mode" in a MoO$_3$ thin film to achieve a display device, for example. Starting with a colourless MoO$_3$ film (stage A), it is slightly blued by cathodic polarization (electrochemical mode) to generate a visible-light-sensitive material (stage B). Then the desired pattern is written on it by visible light irradiation (photon mode, stage C). This pattern is easily erased at will either to the pretreated stage (stage B) or to the initial stage (stage A) by controlling the time for anodic polarization, and the film can be used repeatably.

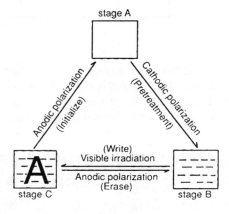

Fig. 3 Proposed application of the visible-light-enhanced photochromic reaction in display device.

(**355**, 624-626; 1992)

配体的电荷转移，产生 Mo^{6+}（参考文献 7、8），因此这个宽吸收带的激发显然无法使薄膜产生电子—空穴对。我们认为，可能的机理是在电解反应过程中 MoO_3 薄膜先转变为过渡亚稳态，然后经可见光照射转变为稳定的钼青铜。

目前还不清楚这种过渡亚稳态的产生机制，只有解决了为什么只有经电致变色反应变为淡蓝色的薄膜才具有可见光响应的光致变色性能，而传统带隙激发变色后的薄膜却无此性能，才可能了解其形成原因。一个可能的原因是基于青铜结构中阳离子尺寸的差别。电致变色和光致变色反应中注入的阳离子分别是 Li^+ 和 H^+，因为 Li^+ 要远远大于 H^+，所以通过电致变色反应着色的薄膜结构变化要远大于经过光致变色着色的薄膜。因此当 Li^+ 注入薄膜时，结构畸变可能产生一种特殊的过渡亚稳态，而可见光照射会使这种亚稳态转变为稳定的青铜结构。另外一个解释是，由光激发和电解极化的能量差异造成。光学带隙的激发能量足以直接生成稳定的钼青铜，而电解还原则无法实现。目前阐述这一机理的工作还在进行中。

图 3 给出了利用"电化学模式"和"光子模式"相结合的方式将 MoO_3 薄膜用于显示器件的示意图。从无色 MoO_3 薄膜出发（状态 A），通过阴极极化变得微蓝（电化学模式），得到可见光响应的材料（状态 B）。然后通过可见光照写入想要的图案（光学模式，状态 C）。通过控制阳极极化的时间，既可以将写入图案擦除到预处理状态（状态 B），也可以擦除到最初状态（状态 A），薄膜可以重复使用。

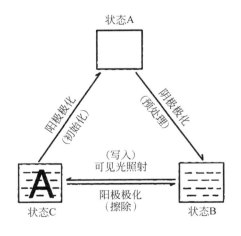

图 3. 可见光增强的光致变色反应在显示器件中的可能应用。

（马颖 翻译；姚建年 审稿）

J. N. Yao, K. Hashimoto & A. Fujishima
Department of Synthetic Chemistry, Faculty of Engineering, The University of Tokyo, 7-3-1, Hongo, Bunkyo-ku, Tokyo 113, Japan

Received 21 August; accepted 3 December 1991.

References:
1. Deb, S. K. *Phil. Mag.* **27**, 801-822 (1973).
2. Deb, S. K. *J. appl. Phys.* **37**, 4818-4825 (1966).
3. Yao, J. N., Loo, B. H. & Fujishima, A. *Ber. Bunseng. Phys. Chem.* **94**, 13-17 (1990).
4. Colton, R. J., Guzman, A. M. & Rabalais, J. W. *Acct. Chem. Res.* **11**, 170-176 (1978).
5. Fleisch, T. H. & Mains, G. J. *J. Chem. Phys.* **76**, 780-786 (1982).
6. Shigesato, Y. *Jap. J. appl. Phys.* **30**, 1457-1462 (1991).
7. Faughnan, B. & Crandall, R. S. *Appl. Phys. Lett.* **31**, 834-836 (1977).
8. Kitao, M., Yamada, S., Hiruta, Y., Suzuki, N. & Urade, K. *Appl. Surf. Sci.* **33/34**, 812-817 (1988).

The C. *elegans* Genome Sequencing Project: a Beginning

J. Sulston *et al.*

Editor's Note

Here British biologist John Sulston and colleagues describe developments during the first year of the collaborative *Caenorhabditis elegans* genome sequencing project. Sulston believed the small genome would prove a useful pilot for sequencing the human genome. And given the worm's popularity as a lab model for studying gene function and development, the researchers hoped its DNA sequence would also shed light on human biology. In this first phase, the team developed methods amenable to large-scale sequencing and report the sequence of three gene-rich DNA sections. The finished sequence was published six years later, making *C. elegans* the first multicellular organism to have its genome completely sequenced. The complete human genome, which benefited from the techniques developed here, was published in 2003.

The long-term goal of this project is the elucidation of the complete sequence of the *Caenorhabditis elegans* genome. During the first year, methods have been developed and a strategy implemented that is amenable to large-scale sequencing. The three cosmids sequenced in this initial phase are surprisingly rich in genes, many of which have mammalian homologues.

THE realization that the human genome can be sequenced in its entirety has stimulated great interest in genome analysis[1,2] and efforts have already begun to construct genetic and physical maps[3] and to improve DNA sequencing methods[4]. In pursuit of this great enterprise, it will be necessary to sequence and analyse the smaller genomes of experimentally tractable organisms which will serve as pilot systems for evaluating technology and also provide information essential for interpreting the human sequence. The genomes of single-celled organisms such as *Escherichia coli* and *Saccharomyces cerevesiae* will reveal features peculiar to the basic functions shared by all living things. Analysis of simple animal genomes intermediate in size and complexity between those of yeast and man will help us to understand the more complex features of mammals.

The genome of the small nematode *C. elegans* is a good candidate for complete sequence analysis[5]. This organism has been used to investigate animal development and behaviour[6,7]. Its small size and short generation time facilitate genetic analysis, and more than 900 loci have now been identified through mutations[8]. Each animal develops with essentially

秀丽隐杆线虫基因组测序计划：一个开端

萨尔斯顿等

编者按

在本文中，英国生物学家约翰·萨尔斯顿和他的同事们描述了秀丽隐杆线虫基因组计划第一年的进展。萨尔斯顿相信这个小基因组将被证明是人类基因组计划的有效先导。线虫作为实验室模式生物，在研究基因功能与发育方面有很高的普及性，研究人员希望它的 DNA 序列也能为人类生物学提供线索。在第一阶段，研究团队建立了适用于大规模测序的实验方法，并报道了 3 个基因密集区的序列。全部基因组序列于 6 年后发表，使得秀丽隐杆线虫成为第一个完成全基因组测序的多细胞生物。在 2003 年发表的人类全基因组序列从本项目建立的技术中获益良多。

本项目的长期目标是阐明秀丽隐杆线虫全基因组序列。第一年，研究者们建立了测序方法，并制定了一个适用于大规模测序的策略。在初始阶段所测序的三个黏粒（cosmid）中，基因之丰富令人惊讶，其中许多都有哺乳类的同源基因。

由于认识到人类基因组可以被完全测序，激发出人们对基因组分析的巨大兴趣 [1,2]，人们已经开始努力构建遗传和物理图谱 [3] 以及改进 DNA 测序的方法 [4]。为追求这一伟大目标，有必要对基因组较小且易于实验操作的模式生物进行测序和分析。这些模式生物将作为前期实验系统用于技术评估，并为解析人类基因序列提供基础信息。大肠杆菌和酿酒酵母等单细胞生物的基因组，尤其能够揭示所有生命体共同拥有的基本功能特征。通过对大小和复杂性介于酵母和人类之间的简单动物基因组进行分析，将帮助我们理解哺乳类更复杂的特征。

一种小型线虫——秀丽隐杆线虫是开展全基因组序列分析得很好选择 [5]。这种生物已被广泛用于研究动物的发育和行为 [6,7]。其个体小、世代短，便于进行遗传分析，目前已经通过分析突变体鉴定了 900 多个基因位点 [8]。每个个体发育时的细胞分化模式基本相同，而这整个模式是已知的 [9-11]。这种线虫的解剖结构简单，只有

the same pattern of cell divisions, and this entire pattern is known[9-11]. The anatomy is simple, with only 959 somatic cells, and the ultrastructure established — for example, the complete connectivity of its 302 neurons has been determined[12].

Many genes required for normal development and behaviour are being studied. With the aid of an active transposon system[13-15] and a physical map of the genome[16-18], they can be readily cloned. Methods for transformation have been developed which allow reintroduction of engineered genes[19-21]. The similarity of many of these genes to those in mammals is often extensive, supporting the contention that information obtained in the nematode will be relevant to understanding the biology of man.

The *C. elegans* genome contains an estimated 100 megabases (10^8 bases), less than the size of an average human chromosome. Generally genes in *C. elegans* have smaller and fewer introns than their mammalian counterparts[22] and the gene density is high (see below). A clonal physical map of the nematode genome is nearly complete[18]. A combination of cosmid and yeast artificial chromosomal (YAC) clones has been used to reconstruct more than 95 megabases (Mb) of the genome. More than 90 Mb have been positioned along the chromosomes using genetically mapped sequences and through *in situ* hybridization of cloned sequences. Fewer than 40 gaps now remain in the map and progress towards closure is proceeding steadily (A.C. *et al.*, unpublished results).

We have embarked on a project to determine the entire sequence of the nematode genome. The region where we began is the centre of chromosome III (Fig. 1). There is good cosmid coverage over most of several megabases, and the few areas lacking cosmid coverage are spanned by YACs. The region lies in the central gene-rich cluster of chromosome III, where several genes of interest have been mapped.

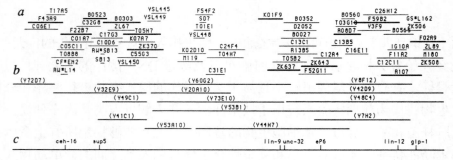

Fig. 1. Physical map of the region where the sequencing project has begun. *a*, Selected overlapping cosmid and lambda clones are represented by the horizontal lines. The cosmids which have been sequenced and reported here are underlined in bold, as well as the additional cosmids underway at present. *b*, The overlapping YAC clones from the region bridge the segments not represented in cosmid clones above. Methods must still be developed to capture sequence efficiently from the spans presently cloned in YACs only. *c*, Six genes and markers known to lie in the regions from genetic and other studies[50]. The genes *unc-32* and *sup-5* are less than 0.1 centimorgans apart on the genetic map of chromosome III. Because of the way the physical map was constructed[16,17], the physical distance separating these two genes can only be estimated to be more than 150 kb, yielding a ratio of more than 1.5 Mb per centimorgan. This metric is typical of the central chromosomal clusters in *C. elegans*.

959 个体细胞，并已建立超微结构——例如，其 302 个神经元全部连通的情况 [12] 已经被确定。

我们正在对正常发育和行为所需的许多基因进行研究。成功克隆这些基因需要一个活跃的转座子系统 [13-15] 和一张基因组物理图谱 [16-18] 的辅助。我们还建立了允许再引入工程基因 [19-21] 的转化方法。这些基因与哺乳动物的基因十分相似，支持了关于从该线虫研究中获得的信息将有助于理解人类生物学的观点。

秀丽隐杆线虫的基因组包含大约 100 兆碱基对（10^8 碱基），小于一条人类染色体的平均大小。通常来说，秀丽隐杆线虫基因的内含子比哺乳动物的内含子 [22] 更小更少，而基因的密度较高（如下）。该线虫基因组的物理图谱克隆已基本完成 [18]。使用黏粒和酵母人工染色体（YAC）克隆相结合的方法重构了该基因组中超过 95 Mb 基（Mb）的区域；采用遗传定位序列和克隆序列原位杂交法，已经沿染色体定位了超过 90 Mb。目前该图谱上仅剩不到 40 个空缺，填补缺口工作正在稳步进行中（库尔松等，未发表结果）。

我们已经着手开展一个项目，以确定该线虫基因组的全序列。我们从第Ⅲ染色体的中部开始（图 1）。几个兆碱基的序列大多与黏粒重叠较好，而少数缺少黏粒覆盖的区域则采用酵母人工染色体进行扩充。该区域位于第Ⅲ染色体中部基因丰富的簇中，在这里我们已经定位了一些人们感兴趣的基因。

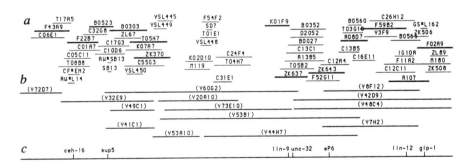

图 1. 测序项目起始区域的物理图谱。*a*，水平线代表选定的重叠黏粒和 λ 克隆。这里已经测序并报道的黏粒下面用粗线标记，其余正在测序的黏粒也是如此。*b*，该区域重叠的酵母人工染色体克隆连接了上述黏粒克隆没有体现的片段。仍需建立仅从克隆在酵母人工染色体中的扩展区有效捕获序列的方法。*c*，从遗传学和其他研究 [50] 中获知位于该区域的六个基因和遗传标记。在第Ⅲ染色体的遗传学图谱上，基因 *unc-32* 和 *sup-5* 的遗传距离小于 0.1 厘摩。由于构建该物理图谱所采用的方法 [16,17]，只能估计分隔这两个基因的物理距离超过 150 kb，达到了每厘摩大于 1.5 Mb 的比例。这一尺度在秀丽隐杆线虫的中央染色体簇上很典型。

Strategy and Methods

The physical map of *C. elegans* was constructed using cosmid and YAC clones, but directed sequencing of even cosmid clones proved impractical because of the presence of repeat sequences and problems with obtaining sufficient quantities of template DNA. Thus we began by generating random subclones from sheared, sized DNA[23,24]. Libraries of small inserts (1–3 kilobases (kb)) were convenient and larger insert libraries (6–9 kb) were useful for establishing continuity in gap closure.

To collect the sequence data, we relied largely on two fluorescent-based sequence-gel readers, the Applied Biosystems ABI 373A and the Pharmacia ALF, which provide data directly in machine-readable form. All data were transferred to Unix-based Sun workstations. A display editor was developed to allow rapid clipping of the vector from the 5′ end and unreliable sequence from the 3′ end[25].

In the first phase of data generation, single reads of about 400 base pairs (bp) were taken from one end of the random clones using the ABI 373 instrument and *Taq* polymerase with a cycle sequencing protocol that reduced the amount of template necessary[26,27]. After 100–350 reads were obtained (the optimal number will ultimately depend on relative costs and has not been established; Table 1) and assembled into contigs using Staden's assembly program[28], the project switched to a directed phase for closure and finishing. As a preliminary directed step, a reverse read was sometimes obtained from the opposite end of selected inserts to help establish linkage, double stranding and gap closure. Further directed sequencing required custom oligonucleotide primers, whose selection was aided by OSP (for oligonucleotide selection program)[29]. For technical reasons, the Pharmacia ALF was more convenient for reads from custom primers[30]. After gap closure and double stranding, in some cases further reads had to be taken, often with different chemistries[31,32], to resolve ambiguities. Final editing, and indeed editing throughout the project, was assisted by the ability to recall the original trace data for any region of concern from the editor program. Further details of our sequencing strategy will be published elsewhere[33,34].

Table 1. Sequencing strategies and statistics

Cosmid clone	B0303	ZK637	ZK643
Insert DNA size (bp)	41,071	40,699	39,528
Random subclone libraries size range:	5–6 kb	9–14 kb	1–2 kb, 6–9 kb, 9–14 kb
cloning vector:	pUC118[47]	pBS[48]	M13mp18[49], pEMBL9, pBS
Random sequencing method	ds, ABI	ds, ABI; ss, [32]p	ss, ABI
Number of random subclones	197	102	360
Number of reverse primer readings	119	70	0
Closure method	ss/ds, ALF	ds, [32]p	ss, ALF

策略和方法

采用黏粒和酵母人工染色体克隆来构建秀丽隐杆线虫的物理图谱时，由于存在重复序列，以及无法获得足够数量的模板 DNA，对黏粒克隆进行直接测序还是不现实的。因而我们首先使用剪切成一定大小的 DNA 生成随机亚克隆[23,24]。小的插入片段（1~3 kb）文库使用十分方便，而较大的插入片段（6~9 kb）文库可用于在弥合空缺时建立连续性。

我们主要依靠美国应用生物系统公司的 ABI 373A 和法玛西亚公司的 ALF 两部荧光测序凝胶阅读仪来收集测序数据，这些设备可以直接以机器可读格式提供数据。所有数据都转入基于 Unix 的 Sun 工作站。我们还开发了一个演示编辑器，以便迅速从 5′ 端去掉载体序列，从 3′ 端删除[25]不可靠序列。

在生成数据的第一阶段，采用可降低模板需求量的环形测序法[26,27]，使用 ABI 373 设备和 *Taq* 聚合酶，从随机克隆的一端得到了大约 400 个碱基对（bp）的单个测序片段。在获得 100~350 个测序片段（理想数据量最终取决于相关测序费用，该统计结果尚未建立；表 1），并采用施塔登氏（Staden's）拼接程序[28]拼接成重叠群（contigs）之后，该项目转入了定向的消除缺口与完成阶段。作为一个初步定向步骤，有时会从选定插入片段的另一端获取一个反向测序片段，以帮助建立关联、形成双链和消除缺口。进一步的定向测序需要定制的寡聚核苷酸引物，用 OSP（寡聚核苷酸选择程序）[29]帮助选择引物。由于技术原因，法玛西亚公司 ALF 对来自定制引物的测序结果更为方便[30]。在消除缺口和形成双链之后，有时必须获取更多的测序片段来解决不确定的序列，通常采用不同的化学方法[31,32]。就任何所关注区域，通过编辑程序回溯原始序列峰图数据的能力，将会有助于最后的编辑，乃至贯穿整个项目的编辑工作。关于我们测序策略的更多细节将发表在其他地方[33,34]。

表 1. 测序策略和统计结果

黏粒克隆	B0303	ZK637	ZK643
插入的 DNA 大小（bp）	41,071	40,699	39,528
随机亚克隆文库的大小范围	5~6 kb	9~14 kb	1~2 kb, 6~9 kb, 9~14 kb
克隆载体	pUC118[47]	pBS[48]	M13mp18[49], pEMBL9, pBS
随机测序方法	ds, ABI	ds, ABI; ss, 32P	ss, ABI
随机亚克隆的数量	197	102	360
反向引物测序的数量	119	70	0
消除缺口的方法	ss/ds, ALF	ds, 32P	ss, ALF

Continued

Cosmid clone	B0303	ZK637	ZK643
Oligonucleotide primers required	102	417	100
Total number of readings	440	589	496
Average bp per read (vector sequence removed)	415	339	390
Total bp read (for assembly)	171,375	184,000	186,437
Final sequence redundancy	3.6	3.4	4.3

Abbreviations: ss, single-stranded template; ds, double-stranded template; AB1, Applied Biosystems Inc. 373A sequence-gel reader; ALF, Pharmacia ALF sequence-gel reader.

Once the final sequence was obtained, the databases were searched for similarities using the algorithm BLAST[35]. In addition, we have started to interpret the sequence directly. The program GENEFINDER (P.G. and L.H., unpublished) uses a statistically rigorous treatment of likelihoods to find possible genes. Other features, such as repeated sequences, are also being examined. The annotated sequences have been submitted to Genbank and EMBL databases. To present the sequences in the context of our knowledge about the worm, we developed a *C. elegans* database, ACEDB, which holds not only the available sequences for the nematode, but also physical and genetic map information, along with reference lists and strain information (R.D. and J.T.-M., unpublished).

Sequences

Three cosmids have so far been completed (sequences submitted to the EMBL and Genbank databases) during the development of our strategy, each with method variations to improve efficiency (Table 1). The first cosmid, ZK637, was sequenced using a minimum of random clones and radioactively labelled primers for walking. The number of primers required proved costly, and the use of films to collect data made editing difficult. ZK643 was partly sequenced using restriction enzyme partial digestion for the random clone production: although subclone recovery was high, these clones were biased in their representation. B0303 DNA was sheared to produce the subclones and, as for ZK637, reverse primer sequencing was used to establish linkage before beginning directed sequencing. Closure for both ZK643 and B0303 was done using directly labelled primers on the Pharmacia ALF.

The overlap of the manual, radiolabelled sequence with the fluorescent shotgun reads in ZK637 amply confirms the fidelity of the fluorescent method. The accuracy of the base calling was tested by comparing a sampling of individual sequence reads with the final edited sequence (Fig. 2). Generally the only errors found in the first 300 bases of a read could be attributed to compressions or stops due to gel or enzyme limitations. Above 300, software limitations predominate, with increasing numbers of sites at which either no base call can be made or errors in the base calling occur. The failure to call a base is not a serious problem as no false information enters the database. By far the most common error is overcalling the number of bases in a run, but undercalls and miscalls also occur; these errors are easily corrected, once attention has been drawn to them, by reference to the traces.

黏粒克隆	B0303	ZK637	ZK643
所需寡聚核苷酸引物数量	102	417	100
总测序片段的数量	440	589	496
每个测序片段的平均碱基对数（去除载体序列）	415	339	390
测序碱基对总数（用于拼接）	171,375	184,000	186,437
最终序列冗余	3.6	3.4	4.3

缩写：ss，单链模板；ds，双链模板；ABI，应用生物系统公司 373A 测序凝胶测序仪；ALF，法玛西亚公司 ALF 测序凝胶测序仪。

在获得最终序列之后，采用 BLAST 算法[35] 在数据库中查找相似序列。此外，我们还开始直接解释序列。GENEFINDER 程序（格林和伊利耶，未发表）用统计上严格的似然性处理寻找可能的基因。对重复序列等其他特征序列，也进行了分析。解释过的序列已经提交到 Genbank 和 EMBL 数据库。为结合我们关于该线虫的知识来介绍这些序列，我们建立了一个秀丽隐杆线虫数据库 ACEDB，该数据库不仅包含这种线虫已有的序列，而且包括其物理和遗传图谱资料，以及相关文献列表和品系信息（德宾和蒂里－米格，未发表）。

序　　列

在我们制定策略的过程中，已经完成了三个黏粒的测序（序列已提交到 EMBL 和 Genbank 数据库），每个都有提高效率的改进方案（表 1）。第一个黏粒，ZK637，是采用最小随机克隆和放射性标记引物进行步移来完成测序。所需引物数量很大，且采用胶片收集数据使得编辑非常困难。ZK643 的部分测序是采用限制性酶部分消化随机克隆产物来完成的：尽管亚克隆的回收率很高，但是这些克隆在代表性上有偏好。B0303 DNA 被剪切以生成亚克隆，并按照对 ZK637 使用的方法，在开始定向测序之前用反向引物测序建立片段连锁。ZK643 和 B0303 消除缺口都是在法玛西亚公司 ALF 上使用直接标记引物完成的。

人工放射性标记序列与 ZK637 中的荧光鸟枪法测序片段的重叠，充分证实了荧光法的可靠性。通过比较单个序列测序片段样本和最终的编辑后序列，检验了碱基读取的精确性（图 2）。一般来说，在某一测序片段的前 300 个碱基中发现的错误，可能是由于凝胶或酶的限制而导致密集或停顿。超过 300 个碱基，则主要是软件的限制，导致碱基无法读取或出现读取错误的位点数量上升。无法读取碱基不是一个严重问题，因为并没有错误信息进入数据库。目前最常见的错误是在跑胶时重复读取碱基，然而少读或误读也会发生；一旦注意到这些错误，则很容易通过查找原始数据来纠正。

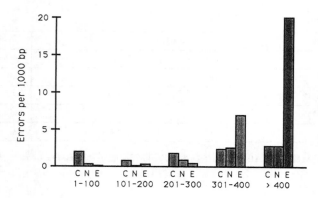

Fig. 2. The types of errors found when comparing the initial machine reads with the final edited sequence. The errors are broken down into the following categories: errors due to either the enzyme or the gel, resulting in compressions or stops (C) and errors due to the software, where there was either no call made (N, nocall) or an error made in base calling (E). In the last case the software has either inserted an extra base (an overcall), failed to recognize a base (an undercall) or simply called the wrong base (a miscall). Nocalls are less troublesome than an error in base calling, and nocalls accounted for most of the software failures in the first 300 bases of the reads. Software errors, particularly base calling errors, predominated above 300 bases. The majority of these errors were overcalls (87), as opposed to undercalls (20) or miscalls (16). The data are taken from 89 reads of single-stranded templates, with average length of 427 bases (Fig.1), done on cosmid F59B2, for which changes in our data-handling software made the analysis easier. The data quality, however, should be similar in the cosmid sequences presented here.

The accuracy of the final sequence is difficult to estimate without extensive independent tests, but several factors give us confidence that the fidelity to the true genomic sequence is high. All sequences were determined at least once on both strands, with the exception of certain long tandem repeat sequences. Regions with compressions or other unresolved conflicts were resequenced. Possible errors indicated by the similarity searches and GENEFINDER analysis were checked. To detect major cloning artefacts, we compared the polymerase chain reaction products derived from the cosmids with both the predicted lengths and the products from genomic DNA across the sequenced regions . The walking primers often proved useful for this purpose. For one cosmid, part of the vector sequence was analysed which was derived from the random phase alone so that not every region had been sequenced on both strands; here only one base in 2,000 was at variance with the available sequence.

Using similarity searches and GENEFINDER to analyse these sequences, a high density of likely genes was revealed (Fig.3). One of the most striking similarities was found between the 22–26-kb region of ZK637 and the 116K subunit (relative molecular mass 116,000) of the rat vacuolar proton pump (Fig.4). The similarity falls into several blocks which GENEFINDER suggests are probably exons, and spans from residues 14 to 824 of the 838-amino-acid protein. The amino-terminal half is most highly conserved between the two sequences; in one stretch 99 of 139 residues (71%) are identical and in a second, 223 of 314 (71%) are identical, with no gaps introduced into the alignment. The carboxy-terminal half has less similarity but contains sequences similar to all eight

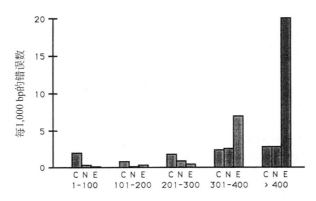

图 2. 与最终编辑后的序列比较，从最初机器所读取序列中发现的错误类型。这些错误被分为以下几类：由于酶或凝胶导致的密集或停顿而产生的错误（C），和因软件导致的错误，无信号（N）或是碱基读取错误（E）。在最后一种情况下，该软件或是插入了一个额外碱基（多读），未能读取一个碱基（少读）或是错误读取一个碱基（误读）。无信号比错误读取碱基带来的麻烦要少，而且在测序片段的前 300 个碱基，无信号占软件错误的大部分。超过 300 个碱基，软件错误，特别是碱基读取错误变成了主要问题。与少读（20）或误读（16）相比，这些错误中主要是多读（87 个）。这些数据是用黏粒 F59B2 进行实验获得的，涉及其单链模板的 89 个测序片段，平均长度为 427 个碱基（图 1），数据处理软件做了些改变，以易于分析。黏粒 F59B2 的数据质量应当与本文显示的黏粒序列相似。

没有广泛的独立检验，最终测序的精确性很难估计，但若干因素使我们确信，反映真实基因组序列的准确性是很高的。除一些较长的串联重复序列之外，所有序列至少在 DNA 的两条链上各确认了一次。那些密集区域或有其他不确定的区域被再次测序。对在相似性查找和 GENEFINDER 分析中产生的可能的错误进行了检验。为检测主要的人工克隆假象，我们比较了黏粒的聚合酶链式反应产物与基因组 DNA 相应区域的长度和产物。事实证明引物步移对实现这一目标非常有用。就其中一个黏粒来说，我们对载体序列的一部分进行了分析，因其仅来自随机阶段，因而并非两条 DNA 链的每个区域都进行了测序；在 2,000 个碱基中，只有一个与已有的序列不同。

采用相似性搜索和 GENEFINDER 来分析这些序列，发现了高密度的疑似基因（图 3）。最令人惊讶的是，ZK637 的 22~26 kb 区域和大鼠细胞液泡质子泵的 116K 亚基（相对分子量为 116,000）具有高度相似性（图 4）。两者的相似处分布于若干区段，GENEFINDER 将其读取为外显子，从这种有 838 个氨基酸的蛋白质的第 14 残基延伸至第 824 残基处。这两段序列的氨基端的一半高度保守；在其中一段，139 个残基中有 99 个是相同的（71%），而在第二段，314 个残基中有 223 个是相同的（71%），且在序列比对中没有出现空缺。而羧基端的一半相似性较低，但含有与我们推测的 8 个跨膜结构域相似的序列。其他具有广泛相似性的基因包括乙酰辅酶 A 乙酰基转

postulated transmembrane domains. Other extensive similarities were found to acetyl-CoA acetyltransferase, glutathione reductase, the arsenical pumpdriving ATPase, the hypothetical transposase TcA of the nematode transposon Tcl, and the host protective factor of the parasitic nematode *Trichostrongylus colubriformis*. Less extensive but still highly significant similarities (BLAST scores of >100 over one or two exons) were found with the 50S ribosomal protein L11 and the neutrophil oxidase factor. This last similarity includes a motif shared between the oxidase factor, yeast actinbinding protein ABP-1, acanthamoeba myosin IC and *src*-related kinase[36]. The hypothetical nematode protein has three copies of this motif. Finally, other more limited but still significant similarities of likely *C. elegans* coding regions were found with phenylethanolamine-*N*-methyltransferase, adenylyl cyclase, giant secretory protein, the yeast *CDC25* cell-cycle gene (and the *Drosophila string* homologue), glucose transporter and immediate early protein IE110 of herpes simplex virus. For adenylyl cyclase, several adjacent segments of B0303 showed similarity with a repeated motif of the cyclase sequence.

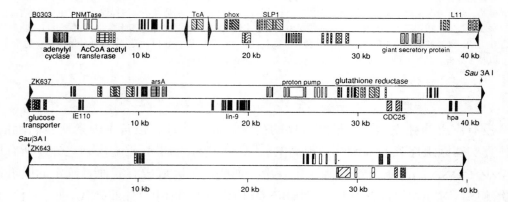

Fig. 3. The genes in the cosmids sequenced, as determined through homology searches, GENEFINDER analysis, and available cDNA sequences. The exons of predicted genes are indicated by shaded blocks, with different shading patterns indicating distinct genes. Those shown above centre for each cosmid are encoded by the top strand and those below by the bottom strand. The genes with significant similarities to genes in the databases are indicated by the name of the most similar sequence (see Fig. 4 for details). Also shown is the position of the *lin-9* gene, as determined from cDNA sequence (G. Beitel and R. Horvitz, personal communication). ZK637 and ZK643 overlap by the single *Sau*3a site indicated. The inverted repeats flanking the TcA homologue are indicated by shaded triangles. The region at 25.1 to 28.1 kb of ZK643 contains two predicted genes that overlap by 52 bases but use distinct reading frames in the overlapped segment. This is indicated in the diagram by different shading within the same block, but has not been confirmed by experiment. PNMTase, phenylethanolamine-*N*-methyltransferase; phox: neutrophil oxidase factor.

移酶、谷胱甘肽还原酶、砷驱动泵的三磷酸腺苷酶、线虫转座子 Tc1 的假想转座酶 TcA 以及寄生性线虫蛇形毛圆线虫的宿主保护因子。50S 的核糖体蛋白 L11 和嗜中性粒氧化酶因子，虽然序列跨度较短但仍在其中发现了高度相似性（一或两个外显子的 BLAST 值 >100），最后一个相似性包括了一个氧化酶因子、酵母肌动蛋白结合蛋白 ABP-1、棘阿米巴肌球蛋白 IC 和 *src* 相关激酶所共有的功能域 [36]。预测的线虫蛋白中有三个该功能域的拷贝。最后，其他长度更短但仍然与秀丽隐杆线虫预测编码区很相似的，包括苯基乙醇胺 –N– 甲基转移酶、腺苷酸环化酶、巨分泌蛋白、酵母 *CDC25* 细胞周期基因（以及果蝇 *string* 基因的同源基因）、葡萄糖转运蛋白和单纯疱疹病毒的即时早期蛋白 IE110。关于腺苷酸环化酶，B0303 的若干相邻片段与该环化酶序列的一个重复功能域显示出相似性。

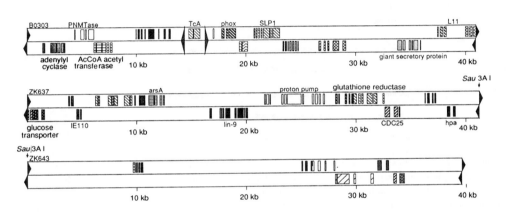

图 3. 在所测的黏粒中，采用同源搜索、GENEFINDER 分析和已知的 cDNA 序列确认的基因。阴影块表示所预测基因中的外显子，不同的阴影涂布方式表示不同的基因。标注在每个黏粒上部的是用上链编码的，而标注在下部的是用底链编码的。那些与数据库中基因显著相似的基因，用与其最相似的序列的名称标注（细节见图 4）。同时显示的还有用 cDNA 序列（比特尔 (Beitel) 和霍维茨，个人通信）确定的 *lin-9* 基因的位置。ZK637 和 ZK643 在单一 *Sau*3a 位点的重叠如图所示。在 TcA 同源基因侧翼的反向重复序列用阴影三角形表示。ZK643 的 25.1 到 28.1 kb 区域包含两个预测到的基因，它们有 52 个碱基的重叠，但在重叠片段使用各自的阅读框架。这一点在图上用同一方块的不同阴影来表示，但尚未经实验证明。PNMTase：苯基乙醇胺 –N– 甲基转移酶；phox：嗜中性粒氧化酶因子。

Fig. 4. The similarities of the predicted genes to previously known genes are shown in detail. The gene with the highest similarity to the proposed nematode gene is given on the left. On the right the exons of the predicted gene are indicated as blocks; homologous regions are shaded. Intervening sequences are indicated by lines and have been truncated. Hatched shading indicates regions with BLAST scores of 70 to 100, and solid shading indicates BLAST scores of greater than 100. Once similarities were detected with BLAST, the amino acids predicted from the gene were aligned with the matched gene using the FASTA algorithm[51]. The extent of the shading reflects the region with significant similarity determined from the FASTA output. For adenylyl cyclase, the locus CYAA$YEAST was used[52]; for phenylethanolamine, -*N*-methyl transferase, PNMT$HUMAN[53,54]; for acetylCoA acetyltransferase, THIL$RAT[55]; for Tc1 hypothetical protein A, CELTCB2[56]; for neutrophil oxidase factor, NOF$HUMAN[57]; for SLP1, SLP1$YEAST[58]; for giant secretory protein, BARG$CHITH[59]; for 50S ribosomal protein L11, RL11$ECOLI[60-62]; for glucose transporter, ATHSTP1[63]; for IE110, IE11$HSV11[64,65]; for arsenic ATPase ARSA$ECOLI[66]; for rat proton pump, RATPRPU[67]; for glutathione reductase, GSHR$ECOLI[68]; for CDC25/string, CC25$SCHPO[69]; for globin-like host protective antigen, TCSHGPR[70].

Altogether, GENEFINDER predicts a total of 33,573 bases (27%) of coding sequence in the total of 121,298 bases sequenced. For the individual cosmids the percentage of coding sequences are 37% for B0303, 33% for ZK637, and 13% for ZK643. The number of different genes represented is difficult to estimate, as at present there are no clear rules by which to distinguish ends of genes from introns. Taking into account factors such as the distinct homologies and the spacing and strandedness of exons, we would estimate B0303 contains 14 genes, ZK637 12 genes and ZK643 6 genes. Transcript analysis will be required to test these predictions. Several studies have already centred on genes in the

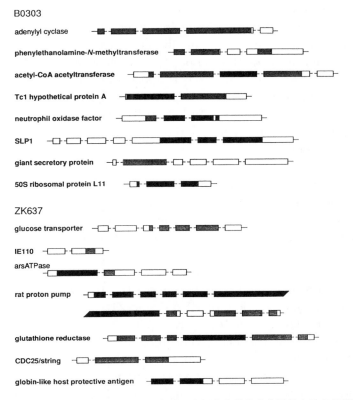

图 4. 详细展示了预测基因与此前已知基因的相似性。左侧是和该线虫基因具有最高相似性的基因。右侧用方块表示预测基因的外显子；同源区域用阴影表示。外显子之间的序列用虚线表示。浅色阴影表示 BLAST 值在 70 到 100 之间的区域，实阴影则表示 BLAST 值超过 100 的区域。一旦 BLAST 检测到了相似性，就采用 FASTA 算法，把从该基因中预测到的氨基酸与相应基因匹配 [51]。阴影的长度反映了根据 FASTA 结果认为有显著相似性区域。对于腺苷酸环化酶，采用了 CYAA$YEAST 基因位点 [52]；而对于苯基乙醇胺 –N– 甲基转移酶，采用 PNMT$HUMAN[53,54]；乙酰辅酶 A 乙酰基转移酶，THIL$RAT[55]；Tc1 假想蛋白 A，CELTCB2[56]；嗜中性粒氧化酶因子，NOF$HUMAN[57]；SLP1，SLP1$YEAST[58]；巨分泌蛋白，BARG$CHITH[59]；50S 的核糖体蛋白 L11，RL11$ECOLI[60-62]；葡萄糖转运蛋白，ATHSTP1[63]；IE110，IE11$HSV11[64,65]；砷三磷酸腺苷酶，ARSA$ECOLI[66]；大鼠质子泵，RATPRPU[67]；谷胱甘肽还原酶，GSHR$ECOLI[68]；CDC25/ 链，CC25$SCHPO[69]；类球蛋白宿主保护抗原，TCSHGPR[70]。

　　总之，在被测序的 121,298 个碱基序列中，GENEFINDER 总计预测了 33,573 个碱基（27%）的编码序列。就各黏粒来说，B0303 的编码序列占序列全长的 37%，ZK637 占 33%，而 ZK643 占 13%。关于所代表的不同基因数量则很难估计，因为目前没有明确的规则把基因的末尾从内含子中辨别出来。考虑到各计算因素如外显子的有区别的同源性、间隔和链型等，我们估计 B0303 包含 14 个基因，ZK637 含 12 个，而 ZK643 含 6 个。转录分析对检验上述预测是必需的。若干研究已经将该区域的基因作为重点。基因 *sup-5*（文献 37）已经被定位在 B0303 的末端附近。实

region. The gene *sup-5* (ref. 37) had been mapped close to the end of B0303; indeed, the B0303 sequence overlaps with the 4.2-kb region previously sequenced around the transfer RNA gene *sup-5* (K. Kondo and R.W., unpublished results). The genes *lin-9* (ref. 38) and *unc-32* (ref. 6) were known by transformation rescue to lie within ZK637 before sequencing began. The gene *lin-9* has been shown to correspond to the predicted gene on the bottom strand of ZK637 in the region 20.2–16.6, and the complementary DNA sequence used to refine the predictions of the GENEFINDER analysis (G. Beitel and R. Horvitz, personal communication). From its genetic position, *unc-32* is likely to be one of the genes immediately to the right of *lin-9*.

The sequences have also been scanned for repeats. Large, almost perfect inverted repeats (465/468) flank the region of B0303 near the 15-kb point (Fig. 3) that shares similarity with the TcA transposase; subsequent analysis revealed this region to represent a copy of the Tc1-related transposon Tc3 (D. Schneider, J. Collins and P. Anderson, personal communication). Examples of short tandemly repeated sequences include 21 copies of a 59-bp motif at 35 kb in ZK643 and two segments (11 and 13 copies) of an 11-bp motif inverted with respect to one another at 13.3 and 13.7 kb in ZK637. A larger duplicated segment is present spanning the join of ZK637 and ZK643, where blocks of 99,305 and 789 bp spread over 1.6 kb are almost exactly duplicated 4 kb away. A 500-bp region near 7 kb in ZK643 shares several fragments with strong homology (>90%) to an 800-bp region near 32 kb in B0303, the order and orientation of the fragments being different in the two cases. A 1-kb region near 38-kb in ZK643 contains large stretches of the nucleotide motif NGG tandemly repeated; the same motif is found at the fragile X site[39-41]. Some 20 copies of a 94-bp consensus sequence were found dispersed throughout the three cosmids, many in inverted pairs separated by up to 130 bp. Some copies showed a good match to the consensus (80–90% identity), whereas others diverged strongly or were incomplete. A search of Genbank showed the sequence to be specific to *C. elegans* and present in four copies in other entries. Although they are relatively few compared with those in mammalian DNA and are confined to local regions, these repeats would make impossible a walking strategy that relied primarily on cosmid templates.

Discussion

The first three cosmids of the nematode sequencing project are complete. They represent only 0.1% of the total genome, but the methods developed have the potential to be scaled up effectively to production level. We have used two commercially available sequencing machines, but because we are proceeding on a cosmid-by-cosmid basis we have the flexibility to change as new methods and machines are developed.

The essence of our approach is to follow a conventional "shotgun" phase, in which an initial read is taken from each subclone using a universal primer, with a "walking" phase, in which additional reads are taken from selected subclones by the use of selected custom primers. Each subclone is large enough to allow several walking steps to be taken. Thus the shotgun phase serves not only to provide much of the final sequence but also to map the subclones for the walking phase, and the traditional problem of closure is solved

际上，B0303 序列与先前测序的，在转运 RNA 基因 *sup-5* 附近约 4.2 kb 的区域重叠（孔多和威尔逊，未发表结果）。在测序开始前，通过转化恢复试验（transformation rescue），已知基因 *lin-9*（文献 38）和 *unc-32*（文献 6）位于 ZK637 中。已经表明，基因 *lin-9* 与 ZK637 的 20.2–16.6 区域底链的预测基因相对应，并使用互补 DNA 序列来优化 GNENFINDER 分析得到的预测（比特尔和霍维茨，个人通信）。从遗传学位置得知，*unc-32* 可能是紧临 *lin-9* 基因右侧的基因之一。

我们也对序列中的重复序列进行了分析。大片段的几乎完美的反向重复序列（465/468）位于 B0303 的 15 kb 位点附近的侧翼（图 3），与 TcA 转座酶有相似性。随后的分析表明，这一区域代表了与 Tc1 相关的转座子 Tc3 的一个拷贝（施奈德、柯林斯、安德森，个人通信）。短串联重复序列的例子，包括在 ZK643 的 35 kb 位置的 59 bp 保守序列的 21 份拷贝；分别位于 ZK637 的 13.3 和 13.7 kb 区域，11 bp 保守序列的两个互为反向的片段（分别为 11 和 13 个拷贝）。在 ZK637 和 ZK643 连接的区域出现了一个较大的重复片段，覆盖了 1.6 kb 长度的 99,305 bp 和 789 bp 区段在间隔 4 kb 对处精确复制。在 ZK643 靠近 7 kb 处的 500 bp 的区域，与 B0303 靠近 32 kb 处的 800 bp 的区域相比，若干片段有很高的同源性（>90%），但二者的顺序和方向不同。在 ZK643 靠近 38 kb 处的一个 1 kb 区域，包含大片段核苷酸保守序列 NGG 的串联重复；在具有脆性的 X 位点 [39-41] 也发现了同样的保守序列。在这三个黏粒上，发现散布着一个 94 bp 保守序列的约 20 份拷贝，许多是被多达 130 bp 分隔的反向重复对。某些拷贝显示出与保守序列的良好匹配（80%~90% 相同），而其他则变异较大或是不完整。在 Genbank 中检索，发现该序列是秀丽隐杆线虫特有的，在其他线虫记录中有四个拷贝。尽管它们与哺乳类 DNA 相比较少，并限定在局部区域，这些重复序列将会使主要依赖于黏粒模板的步移策略变得不可能。

讨　论

该线虫测序计划前三个黏粒已经完成。它们仅代表整个基因组的 0.1%，但所建立的方法有可能被有效规模化至生产水平。我们使用了两种商业测序设备，但由于我们是以逐个黏粒测序为基础进行的，当新的方法和设备产生以后，我们可以灵活调整。

我们策略的本质是传统的"鸟枪法"，使用一个通用引物，可以从每个亚克隆获得一个初始测序片段；下一阶段采取了"步移"法，即使用筛选出的特异引物，从选定的亚克隆中获得更多的测序片段。每个亚克隆大到足以允许采取若干步移步骤。因而鸟枪阶段不但提供了许多最终序列，而且可以对步移阶段的亚克隆进行定位。

efficiently without the requirement for high redundancy. Exactly when the switch is made from random clones to walking will be dictated by the costs and convenience of the two approaches.

The number of predicted genes in these cosmids is higher than would have been expected on the basis of genetic estimates of essential gene number[42] and on a previous transcript analysis around the vitellogenin genes[43]. The high gene density (one every 3–4 kb) may arise in part because the sample comes from the gene-rich cluster on chromosome III. But each chromosome contains a central gene-rich cluster, and the physical map shows that about half the genome is contained in such clusters. Extrapolating then from our (admittedly small) sample, C. elegans will have about 15,000 genes in the clusters alone. The other half of the DNA is not devoid of genes, but we do not yet have an accurate estimate of the gene density there. The high gene density makes genomic DNA sequencing an efficient approach to discovering complete coding sequences in C. elegans.

The discrepancy between genetic estimates of essential genes and our estimates of total genes based on sequence is similar to that found in other organisms. In yeast, where studies are most advanced, it is estimated that no more than one in six genes yields scorable phenotypes when function is eliminated[44]. In Drosophila, in the region between rosy and Bithorax, more than three times as many transcripts have been found as there are mutationally defined genes, even though this is a region held to be saturated genetically[45,46].

More accurate prediction of genes will be aided by the accumulation of more data, providing a better basis for statistical analysis. The GENEFINDER predictions are of limited use in this regard as they necessarily reflect the biases on which they are based. Nonetheless, the success of GENEFINDER at this early stage encourages our confidence that genomic sequence is an efficient means for finding not only genes but also the other information stored in the genome. In turn, the fraction of genes that yield similarities, already about a third, will only increase and these provide immediate insights on which to design experiments to test function.

Each cosmid sequence is submitted, as it is completed, to the databases. In addition, the sequence is entered in the C. elegans database being developed as part of this project. Here the sequence will be available in conjunction with the physical map, the genetic map, references and strains. The ability to view the sequence in the context of much of the available knowledge about the worm should speed the assignment of function to each sequence.

The test of our strategy will come in the next two years as we scale up our efforts: we will sequence 800 kb in the first year and 2,000 kb in the second. We anticipate the cost, currently estimated at $1 per base with current methods applied on production, will come down as we move to a mock production mode. Operator time should decrease with experience, new methods and increased automation. For example, we are experimenting with ways of preparing templates more rapidly and cheaply. Improved throughput for the

同时，无需大量的冗余测序，就把消除缺口的传统问题有效地解决了。从随机克隆转换到步移的具体时机是由这两种方法的成本和方便性来决定的。

与基于遗传学估计所预测到的主要基因数量[42]以及以前对卵黄蛋白原基因转录分析所得基因数量[43]相比，在这些黏粒中预测到的基因数量要多一些。较高基因密度（每3~4 kb一个基因）部分是由于样品来自第III染色体基因富集簇。不过每个染色体都包含一个重要的基因富集簇，物理图谱表明大约一半的基因组包含在这种簇里。根据我们的样品（应承认样本较小）推测，秀丽隐杆线虫仅在这些簇就有大约15,000个基因。基因组DNA的另一半并非没有基因，只是我们对该处的基因密度还没有精确估计。较高的基因密度使得基因组DNA测序成为揭示秀丽隐杆线虫完整编码序列的有效途径。

对重要基因的遗传学估计和我们根据序列对总基因数的估计存在差异，在其他生物中也存在这种类似差异。酵母的研究最为成熟，据计算当某种功能缺失时，仅有不超过六分之一的基因会产生可观测的表型[44]。在果蝇中，在基因 *rosy* 和 *Bithorax* 之间的区域，尽管这是一个遗传饱和区[45,46]，但所发现的转录物数量是以突变手段鉴定的基因数量的三倍以上。

积累更多的数据，提供更好的统计分析基础，将有助于更精确的基因预测。在这方面 GENEFINDER 预测的作用有限，并必然反映出了所依赖的方法学上的偏好。无论如何，GENEFINDER 在这一初期阶段的成功，促使我们相信，基因组测序是找到基因和其他储存在基因组中的信息的有效手段。反过来，存在相似性的基因片段目前已经达到1/3，这个数目一定会增加，这为我们设计检验各种功能的实验提供了直接的线索。

每个黏粒的测序一旦完成，结果立即提交到数据库。此外，作为本项目的内容之一，该序列还会被录入秀丽隐杆线虫数据库。在这里可获得与物理图谱、遗传学图谱、文献及品系相关联的序列信息。根据线虫的大部分已知信息来考察序列的能力，将加速与序列对应的功能解释。

随着投入不断增加，今后两年我们将对该策略进行检验：我们将在第一年测序800 kb，在第二年测序2,000 kb。采用目前方法进行生产，估计成本为每碱基1美元，随着我们转向类似于生产的模式，预计成本将下降。随着经验增多、新方法出现和自动化程度提升，操作时间将缩短。例如，我们正在采用更迅速而便宜的模板

sequencing machines, either by increasing the number of samples per run or by reducing the run time, is also under development by the manufacturers. Oligonucleotide costs are steadily declining with both reduced reagent usage and reduced reagent costs. Local preparation may make savings possible for some reagents in a large-scale operation. With these improvements, a reduction in costs to $0.50 per base seems realistic.

(**356**, 37-41;1992)

J. Sulston*, Z. Du†, K. Thomas*, R. Wilson†, L. Hillier†, R. Staden*, N. Halloran†, P. Green†, J. Thierry-Mieg‡, L. Qiu†, S. Dear*, A. Coulson*, M. Craxton*, R. Durbin*, M. Berks*, M. Metzstein*, T. Hawkins*, R. Ainscough* & R. Waterston†

* MRC Laboratory of Molecular Biology, Hills Road, Cambridge CB2 2QH, UK

† Department of Genetics, Box 8232, Washington University School of Medicine, 4566 Scott Avenue, St Louis, Missouri 63110, USA

‡ CNRS-CRBM et Physique-Mathématique, PO Box 5051, Montpellier 34044, France

Received 3 September 1991; accepted 4 February 1992.

References:

1. Watson, J. D. *Science* **248**, 44-49 (1990).

2. Cantor, C. R. *Science* **248**, 49-51 (1990).

3. Roberts, L. *Science* **249**, 1497 (1990).

4. Hunkapiller, T., Kaiser, R. J., Koop, B. F. & Hood, L. *Science* **254**, 59-67 (1991).

5. Roberts, L. *Science* **248**, 1310-1313 (1990).

6. Brenner, S. *Genetics* **77**, 71-94 (1974).

7. Wood, W. B. *et al. The Nematode Caenorhabditis elegans* (Cold Spring Harbor Laboratory. New York, 1988).

8. Edgley, M. L. & Riddle, D. L. *Genetic Maps* **5**, 3 (1990).

9. Sulston, J. E. & Horvitz, H. R. *Devl. Biol.* **56**, 110-156 (1977).

10. Kimble, J. E. & Hirsh, D. I. *Devl. Biol.* **70**, 396-417 (1979).

11. Sulston, J. E., Schierenberg, E., White, J. G. & Thomson, J. N. *Devl. Biol.* **100**, 64-119 (1983).

12. White, J. G., Southgate, E., Thomson, J. N. & Brenner, S. *Phil. Trans. R. Soc.* **314**, 1-340 (1986).

13. Emmons, S. W., Yesner, L., Ruan, K. S. & Katzenberg, D. *Cell* **32**, 55-65 (1983).

14. Eide, D. J. & Anderson, P. *Proc. Natl. Acad. Sci. U.S.A.* **82**, 1756-1760 (1985).

15. Moerman, D. G., Benian, G. M. & Waterston, R. H. *Proc. natn. Acad. Sci. U.S.A.* **83**, 2579-2583 (1986).

16. Coulson, A. R., Sulston, J. E., Brenner, S. & Karn, J. *Proc. Natl. Acad. Sci. U.S.A.* **83**, 7821-7825 (1986).

17. Coulson, A. R., Waterston, R. H., Kiff, J. E., Sulston, J. E. & Kohara, Y. *Nature* **335**, 184-186 (1988).

18. Coulson, A. *et al. BioEssays* **13**, 413-417 (1991).

19. Stinchcomb, D. T., Shaw, J. E., Carr, S. H. & Hirsh, D. I. *Molec. Cell. Biol.* **5**, 3484-3496 (1985).

20. Fire, A. *EMBO J.* **5**, 2673-2680 (1986).

21. Fire, A. & Waterston, R. H. *EMBO J.* **8**, 3419-3428 (1989).

22. Blumenthal, T. & Thomas, J. H. *Trends Genet.* **4**, 305-308 (1988).

23. Schriefer, L. A., Gebauer, B. K., Qiu, L. Q. Q., Waterston, R. H. & Wilson, R. K. *Nucleic Acids Res.* **18**, 7455-7456 (1990).

24. Deininger, P. L. *Analyt. Biochem.* **129**, 216-223 (1983).

25. Gleeson, T. & Hillier, L. *Nucleic Acids Res.* **19**, 6481-6483 (1991).

26. Smith, L. M. *et al. Nature* **321**, 674-679 (1986).

27. Craxton, M. *Methods: A Companion to Methods in Enzymology* **3**, 20-26 (1991).

28. Dear, S. & Staden, R. *Nucleic Acids Res.* **19**, 3907-3911 (1991).

29. Hillier, L. & Green, P. *PCR Meth. Appls* **1**, 124-128 (1991).

30. Ansorge, W., Sproat, B. S., Stegemann, J. & Schwager, C. *J. biophys. Biphys. Meth.* **13**, 315-323 (1986).

31. Mizusawa, S., Nishimura, S. & Seela, F. *Nucleic Acids Res.* **14**, 1319-1324 (1986).

32. Hawkins, T. L. & Sulston, J. E. *Nucleic Acids Res.* **19**, 2784 (1991).

制备方法。制造商也正在开发更高通量的测序设备，通过增加每次运行的样品数量，或是缩短运行时间。通过减少试剂使用量和降低试剂成本，寡聚核苷酸的成本正在稳步下降。在规模化的运作模式下，某些试剂本地生产也将节约成本。伴随着这些改进，把测序成本降低到每碱基 0.50 美元看来是可现实的。

（周志华 翻译；吕雪梅 审稿）

33. Hawkins, T. L., Du, Z., Halloran, N. D. & Wilson, R. K. *Electrophoresis* (manuscript submitted).

34. Craxton, M. in *DNA Sequencing: Laboratory Protacols* (eds Griffin, H. G. & Griffin, A. M.) (Humana, NJ, 1992).

35. Altschul, S. F., Gish, W., Miller, W., Myers, E. W. & Lipman, D. J. *J. Molec. Biol.* **215**, 403-410 (1990).

36. Drubin, D. G., Mulholland, J., Zhu, Z. & Botstein, D. *Nature* **343**, 288-290 (1990).

37. Wills, N. *et al. Cell* **33**, 575-583 (1983).

38. Ferguson, E. L. & Horvitz, H. R. *Genetics* **110**, 17-72 (1985).

39. Oberle, I. *et al. Science* **252**, 1097-1102 (1991).

40. Yu, S. *et al. Science* **252**, 1179-1181 (1991).

41. Verkerk, A. J. M. H. *et al. Cell* **65**, 905-914 (1991).

42. Herman, R. K. in *The Nematode* Caenorhabditis elegans (eds Wood, W. B. *et al.*) 17-45 (Cold Spring Harbor Laboratory, New York, 1988).

43. Heine, U. & Blumenthal, T. *J. Molec. Biol.* **188**, 301-312 (1986).

44. Olson, M. in *Genome Dynamics, Protein Synthesis and Energetics* (eds Broach, J. R., Pringle, J. R. & Jones, E. W.) 1-41 (Cold Spring Harbor, NY. 1991).

45. Hall, L. M. C., Mason, P. J. & Spierer, P. *J. Molec. Biol.* **169**, 83-96 (1983).

46. Bossy, B., Hall, L. M. C. & Spierer, P. *EMBO J.* **3**, 2537-2541 (1984).

47. Vieira, J. & Messing, J. *Meth. Enzym.* **153**, 3-11 (1987).

48. Short, J. M., Fernandez, J. M., Sorge, J. A. & Huse, W. D. *Nucleic Acids Res.* **16**, 7583-7600 (1988).

49. Yanisch-Perron, C., Vieira, J. & Messing, J. *Gene* **33**, 103-119 (1985).

50. Burglin, T. R., Finney, M., Coulson, A. & Ruvkin, G. *Nature* **341**, 239-243 (1989).

51. Pearson, W. R. & Lipman, D. J. *Proc. Natl. Acad. Sci. U.S.A.* **85**, 2444-2448 (1988).

52. Kataoka, T., Broek, D. & Wigler, M. *Cell* **43**, 493-505 (1985).

53. Kaneda, N. *et al. J. boil. Chem.* **263**, 7672-7677 (1988).

54. Sasaoka, T., Kaneda, N., Kurosawa, Y.,Fujita, K. & Nagatsu, T. *Neurochem. Int.* **15**, 555-565 (1989).

55. Fukao, T. *et al. J. Biochem., Tokyo* **106**, 197-204 (1989).

56. Prasad, S. S., Harris, L. J., Baillie, D. L. & Rose, A. M. *Genome* **34**, 6-12 (1991).

57. Leto, T. L. *et al. Science* **248**, 727-730 (1990).

58. Wada, Y., Kitamoto, K., Kanbe, T., Tanaka, K. & Anraku, Y. *Molec. Cell. Biol.* **10**, 2214-2223 (1990).

59. Lendahl, U. & Wieslander, L. *Cell* **36**, 1027-1034 (1984).

60. Dognin, M. J. & Wittman-Liebold, B. *Eur. J. Biochem.* **112**, 131-151 (1980).

61. Post, L. E., Strycharz, G. D., Nomura, M., Lewis, H. & Dennis, P. P. *Proc. Natl. Acad. Sci. U.S.A.* **76**, 1697-1701 (1979).

62. Downing, W. L., Sullivan, S. L., Gottesman, M. E. & Dennis, P. P. *J. Bact.* **172**, 1621-1627 (1990).

63. Sauer, N., Friedl, K. & Wicke, U. Genbank Accession Number X55350 (1991).

64. McGeoch, D. J. *et al. J. gen. Virol.* **69**, 1531-1574 (1988).

65. Perry, L. J., Rixon, F. J., Everett, R. D., Frame, M. C. & McGeoch, D. J. *J. gen. Virol.* **67**, 2365-2380 (1986).

66. Chen, C.-M., Misra, T. K., Silver, S. & Rosen, B. P. *J. biol. Chem.* **261**, 15030-15038 (1986).

67. Perin, M. S., Fried, V. A., Stone, D. K., Xie, X.–S. & Sudhof, T. C. *J. biol. Chem.* **266**, 3877-3881 (1991).

68. Greer, S. & Perham, R. N. *Biochemistry* **25**, 2736-2742 (1986).

69. Russell, P. & Nurse, P. *Cell* **45**, 145-153 (1986).

70. Frenkel, M. J., Dopheide, T. A., Wagland, B. M. & Ward, C. W. Genbank Accession Number M63263 (1991).

Acknowledgements. We thank G. Beitel and R. Horvitz for information on *lin-9*; P. Anderson for sequence of Tc3; M. Jier and R. Shownkeen for synthesis of oligonucleotides; and P. Kassos for preparing the manuscript. The work was supported by grants from the NIH Human Genome Center and the MRC HGMP, as well as our respective institutions.

Tectonic Forcing of Late Cenozoic Climate

M. E. Raymo and W. F. Ruddiman

Editor's Note

Since the 1980s, earth scientists had come increasingly to regard the planet as a complex system of interacting processes involving the oceans, atmosphere, biosphere, cryosphere and geosphere. They began to see subtle and unexpected interdependences of these various components of the "earth system". One such is described here by geophysicists Maureen Raymo and William Ruddiman, who explain how the formation of the Himalayas and the Tibetan plateau around 45 million years ago could have altered atmospheric carbon dioxide concentrations and led to the global cooling known to have happened then, largely through enhanced chemical reactions between minerals and CO_2 (weathering). These ideas had been developed earlier in the specialist literature, but were collected together here in an influential manner.

Global cooling in the Cenozoic, which led to the growth of large continental ice sheets in both hemispheres, may have been caused by the uplift of the Tibetan plateau and the positive feedbacks initiated by this event. In particular, tectonically driven increases in chemical weathering may have resulted in a decrease of atmospheric CO_2 concentration over the past 40 Myr.

THE past few years have seen increasing interest in the role that tectonic movements may play in controlling global climate, partly stemming from suggestions that the uplift of the Tibetan plateau in the late Cenozoic had a profound effect on atmospheric circulation[1,2]. In addition, it has been proposed that tectonically driven increases in chemical weathering rates over the same interval caused a drawdown of atmospheric carbon dioxide, leading to global cooling[3,4]. These hypotheses have provoked controversy in a wide range of fields. Geophysicists Molnar and England[5] put forth the inverse proposal that climate changes were responsible for the inferred increases in elevation and erosion. Geochemists[6-10] argued whether the ocean strontium isotope record could be used as a proxy for chemical weathering rates in the past. Climate modellers[10-13] discussed whether chemical erosion could increase without a concomitant increase in mantle degassing of CO_2, for which there is no evidence.

All of these issues are interrelated, with the consequences of one interpretation affecting the others. Here we review the multidisciplinary aspects of the uplift–climate problem, in particular addressing those issues that have provoked the most discussion and controversy over the past few years. We start by presenting evidence for Cenozoic climate trends, and

构造运动对晚新生代气候的影响

雷莫，拉迪曼

编者按

20 世纪 80 年代以来，地球科学家已经逐渐把整个行星作为相互作用的复杂系统来研究，涉及海洋、大气圈、生物圈、冰冻圈和岩石圈等多个圈层。他们开始探究这些"地球系统"的组成要素之间微妙的、不可预知的、相互依赖的联系。在本文中，地球物理学家莫琳·雷莫和威廉·拉迪曼描述了这样的一种相互作用：大约 4,500 万年前喜马拉雅山和青藏高原的隆起可能改变了大气中二氧化碳的浓度，进而导致当时的全球变冷，主要是通过加强矿物和二氧化碳之间直接的化学作用（即风化作用）实现的。这些观点在早先的专题文献中已详尽阐述，但本文把这些观点集中起来以更加有影响的方式作了进一步的阐述。

新生代全球气候变冷导致南北半球大陆冰盖大规模增大，可能是由于青藏高原的隆升以及由此导致的正反馈作用所致。特别是，构造运动导致化学风化作用增强，由此可能导致了过去 4,000 万年中大气 CO_2 浓度的降低。

近年来构造运动在控制全球气候中所起的作用受到越来越多的关注，部分是由于晚新生代青藏高原的隆升对大气环流有着深刻影响[1,2]这一观点的提出。此外，学者还提出，构造活动使同一时间段内的化学风化速率加快，从而导致大气中 CO_2 减少，进而引起全球变冷[3,4]。上述假说激发了各个学科领域的广泛争论。地球物理学家莫尔纳和英格兰[5]则提出了相反的观点，认为是气候变化导致了海拔升高和侵蚀作用增强。地球化学家[6-10]论证了海洋中锶同位素的记录能否作为过去化学风化速率的代用指标。气候模拟学家[10-13]则讨论了在缺少地幔中 CO_2 脱气作用伴随加强的情况下，化学侵蚀能否增强的问题，因为目前还没有地幔中 CO_2 脱气作用伴随增强的证据。

以上所有的问题是相互关联的，一个问题的解释结果能影响另外的问题。在本文中，我们从多学科角度回顾了有关隆升 – 气候的问题，特别是在过去几年中已经引起广泛讨论和争议的问题。首先，我们列举了新生代气候变化趋势的证据，接着

then discuss our uplift–erosion hypotheses, which we believe to be consistent with available late Cenozoic geological data.

Evidence for Cenozoic Climate Change

Because sedimentation occurs continuously in the deep sea, the best records of global Cenozoic climate variations come from the ocean. The oxygen isotopic composition of calcite, sensitive to both ice volume and ocean temperature, has been a particularly valuable tool for reconstructing past climate variations. As evaporation–precipitation processes preferentially concentrate the light isotope of oxygen, ^{16}O, in continental ice sheets, a pronounced enrichment in the oceanic $^{18}O/^{16}O$ ratio occurs during periods of glaciation. A temperature-dependent $^{18}O/^{16}O$ fractionation between calcite and water also works in the same direction (colder temperatures cause $^{18}O/^{16}O$ enrichment); thus, the $CaCO_3$ shells of marine organisms recovered from deep-sea sediment cores isotopically record information about both ice volume and ocean temperature in the past.

Oxygen isotope data for the past 55 Myr (refs 14, 15) show a long-term increase in $\delta^{18}O$ values punctuated by times of relatively rapid change (Fig. 1). The sharp increase in isotopic values in the early Oligocene (~36 Myr BP) may reflect the first major ice-growth event on Antarctica[16], which followed roughly 20 million years of cooling. Further increases in $\delta^{18}O$ in the middle Miocene and late Pliocene represent subsequent increases in ice volume in Antarctica and in the Northern Hemisphere respectively, although the exact portion attributable to ice volume rather than deep ocean cooling remains uncertain. Assuming no ice before the early Oligocene, Miller *et al.*[14] infer deep-water temperatures up to 12 °C warmer than present in the early Eocene, and Shackleton and Kennett[15] report data from the southern Pacific Ocean indicating deep and surface water temperatures up to 15 °C warmer in the early Eocene than at present.

In addition to the long-term cooling inferred from oxygen isotopes, enhanced differentiation of the mid-latitude continents into areas of wetter and drier climates is also indicated by the terrestrial fossil record (see ref. 17 for a summary of this evidence). At higher latitudes, Palaeocene subtropical flora have been identified in Alaska. Middle Oligocene vegetation at this latitude, however, indicates a temperature climate, and by the Pliocene, an essentially modern flora became established[18]. Likewise, progressive cooling of the polar regions is suggested by faunal macrofossil evidence from Ellsmere Island[19]. At high southern latitudes, the presence of Oligocene fossil pollen assemblages in Antarctica and Australia[20] suggests climates much warmer than present.

讨论隆升－侵蚀作用假说，我们相信该假说与已有的晚新生代地质资料相符。

新生代气候变化的证据

由于深海中的沉积作用是连续发生的，因此大洋沉积是记录新生代全球气候变化的最佳载体。方解石的氧同位素组成对冰储量和海水温度均非常敏感，是古气候变化重建十分有力的工具。由于蒸发－降水过程会使大陆冰盖优先富集质量较轻的同位素 ^{16}O，因此，冰期时海水中 $^{18}O/^{16}O$ 的比值会明显增大。方解石与水中 $^{18}O/^{16}O$ 的分馏受温度的影响，也向同一方向变化（温度降低导致 $^{18}O/^{16}O$ 比值增大）。因此，深海沉积物岩芯中得到的海洋生物 $CaCO_3$ 壳体的同位素记录了过去冰储量与海洋温度的相关信息。

近 5,500 万年来的氧同位素数据（参考文献 14、15）显示，$\delta^{18}O$ 值整体表现为长期升高，中间被几次相对较快的变化打断（图 1）。渐新世早期（距今约 3,600 万年）同位素比值的急剧增大可能反映了南极洲第一次较大的冰增长事件 [16]，随之而来的是持续约 2,000 万年的气候变冷。中新世中期和上新世晚期 $\delta^{18}O$ 值进一步增大，分别反映随后南极地区和北半球冰量的增长，不过氧同位素的增加值中可归因于冰量增加而非深海变冷的确切比例尚不确定。假设渐新世早期之前不存在冰川，米勒等 [14] 推论，始新世早期深层水温度约比现今高 12℃，而沙克尔顿和肯尼特 [15] 对南太平洋数据的研究则表明，始新世早期深层水及表层水的温度均比现今高 15℃。

除了根据氧同位素推断的长期降温以外，陆相化石记录还显示，中纬度大陆地区干湿气候分化日益加剧（关于该证据的概括见参考文献17）。在纬度较高的地区，如阿拉斯加，发现了古新世的亚热带植物群落。不过，渐新世中期相同纬度的植被指示的却是温带气候，而到了上新世，现代植物为主的群落已经确立[18]。同样地，来自埃尔斯米尔岛的动物大化石显示极地地区在日益变冷[19]。在南半球高纬度地区，南极及澳大利亚[20]地区渐新世化石孢粉组合意味着当时的气候比现在温暖。

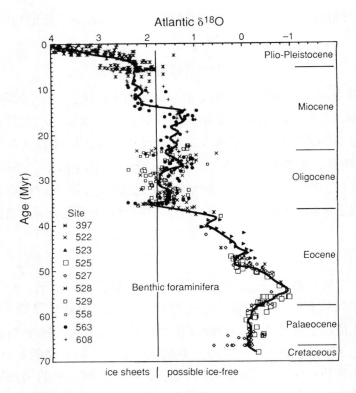

Fig. 1. Compilation of benthic $\delta^{18}O$ measurements from Deep Sea Drilling Program sites spanning the past 70 Myr. The long-term increase in $\delta^{18}O$ values reflects cooling of the deep ocean and growth of ice sheets at high latitudes (after ref. 14). $\delta^{18}O = [(^{18}O/^{16}O)_{sample} / (^{18}O/^{16}O)_{standard} - 1]$, where standard is PDB.

Overall, a preponderance of oceanic and terrestrial evidence points to a marked, progressive cooling of global climate beginning in the early Eocene. The most striking and convincing evidence of this climatic "deterioration" is the abundant glacial detritus (tills, moraines, ice-rafted sediments and so on) which now blankets the mid-to-high latitudes of both hemispheres, both in the ocean and on land. Superimposed on this long-term cooling trend are shorter climate oscillations and steps, such as the rapid shifts in $\delta^{18}O$ at ~35 Myr and 15 Myr (Fig. 1). These inferred ice-growth events may be in response to abrupt changes in "forcing", or they may reflect nonlinear (threshold) responses to more gradual changes in climate boundary conditions. In addition to the "steps", short intervals of climate amelioration are observed in the $\delta^{18}O$ record in the early Oligocene, late Oligocene and Miocene. Wolfe[18] inferred similar transient warming phases from floral macrofossil evidence from Alaska and the American northwest.

Climate Forcing Mechanisms

Since early last century, scientists have been searching for explanations for the climate cooling of the late Cenozoic[21-23]. The drift of continents over the poles is a popular idea, particularly for the Palaeozoic (for example refs 24–26); but such drift towards the poles has been minimal over the past 100 Myr and cannot explain the observed magnitude

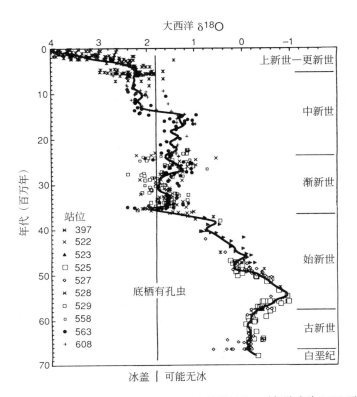

图 1. 由深海钻探计划站位获得的底栖有孔虫 $\delta^{18}O$ 测定结果汇总，时间跨度为 7,000 万年。$\delta^{18}O$ 值的长期升高趋势反映了深海大洋的变冷和高纬度地区冰盖的增长（据参考文献 14）$\delta^{18}O = [(^{18}O/^{16}O)_{样品}/(^{18}O/^{16}O)_{标准} - 1]$，PDB 标准。

　　总的来说，绝大多数海陆证据都表明，始新世早期全球气候显然开始逐渐变冷。大量的冰川碎屑（冰碛物、冰碛、冰筏沉积物等）正是这种气候"恶化"现象最显著也是最有力的证据，如今在南北半球中高纬度地区，无论是海洋还是陆地，冰川碎屑到处可见。叠加于这种长期变冷趋势之上的是短暂的气候振荡和阶梯，比如，$\delta^{18}O$ 在 3,500 万年和 1,500 万年处出现了快速波动（图 1）。上述推断而来的冰增长事件可能是对"驱动因子"突然变化的响应，也可能反映了对气候边界条件渐变的非线性（阈值）响应。除了"阶梯"式降温之外，从渐新世早期、渐新世晚期以及中新世的 $\delta^{18}O$ 记录还可以看到短暂的气候回暖。沃尔夫 [18] 根据阿拉斯加和美洲西北部地区的植物大化石证据也推断了类似的短暂升温阶段。

气候强迫机制

　　自上世纪初以来，科学家一直在寻找关于晚新生代气候变冷的解释 [21-23]。大陆漂移过极地是一种流行的观点，特别是在古生代（例如参考文献 24~26），但过去 1 亿年中这种向极漂移很小，无法解释所观测到的新生代全球变冷的程度 [27]。另一派

of Cenozoic global cooling[27]. Another family of climate-change mechanisms calls on tectonic movements that form sills or ocean gateways in climatically "critical" locations. For instance, thermal isolation caused by the development of the circum-Antarctic current when Antarctica separated from South America and Australia has often been invoked to explain the rapid cooling and glaciation of Antarctica in the Cenozoic[28,29]. These investigators suggest that greater meridional heat transport before the initiation of circum-Antarctic ocean circulation resulted in higher sea surface temperatures around Antarctica, effectively preventing continental ice sheets from developing. Experiments with general circulation models (GCMs)[30] suggest, however, that rather than decreasing the likelihood of glaciation, greater meridional heat transport would promote glaciation by increasing snowfall in an already cold polar region.

Likewise, the relationship between the emergence of the Isthmus of Panama and the initiation of Northern Hemisphere glaciation is unclear. The formation of the isthmus seems to pre-date widespread Northern Hemisphere glaciation by 0.5 to 2 Myr (ref. 31), and GCM simulations suggest that the deflection of warm Atlantic waters through the Panamanian passage would actually result in cooling in the high-latitude North Atlantic[32]. Thus, although local tectonic changes undoubtedly influence ocean circulation and heat transport, it is unclear how important these changes are in explaining either the stepwise coolings inferred from the Cenozoic $\delta^{18}O$ record or the long-term cooling trend observed for the Tertiary.

Many early "ice age" theories focused on possible effects that uplift and erosion of mountain ranges and plateaux could have on climate. Here we review new variations on these old themes; in particular, we propose that uplift of the Tibetan plateau has been the main driving force behind Cenozoic climate change. Although uplift during the Cenozoic has been inferred for many regions, including the Alps, East Africa, and parts of the Cordillera of North and South America (see ref. 17 for a summary), we focus on the Tibetan plateau because there is unequivocal evidence that it has been created during the Cenozoic, and because its unique size and location make it central to our hypotheses.

With a mean elevation of almost five kilometres and an area half the size of the United States, the Tibetan plateau is the most imposing topographic feature on the Earth's surface. It formed as a result of the collision of the Indo-Australian plate with the Asian plate; hard collision of these continents probably began in earnest in the middle Eocene (44–52 Myr ago; refs 33–35) and continues today. Little information is available on the elevation history of the plateau. In fact, we have only two firm data points: the modern elevation, and the presence of Cretaceous to lower Eocene marine limestones which show that much of the plateau was below sea level around 70–100 Myr ago with some areas still under water until ~52 Myr (refs 33–35). Although we know that the plateau got from point "a" to point "b", so to speak, a more detailed knowledge of its elevation history will clearly be essential both for understanding plate tectonic and geophysical processes[33-35] and for evaluating hypotheses that propose a link between climate change and plateau elevation.

气候变化机制则归因于构造运动，这些运动在气候带上的"关键"位置形成了海底山脊或海洋通道。例如，当南极洲从南美洲和大洋洲分离出去以后，环南极洋流的形成导致南极大陆被热隔离，这经常被用来解释新生代南极大陆的快速变冷和冰川作用[28,29]。这些研究者认为，环南极洋流开始之前较大的经向热量输送导致了南极大陆周围较高的海面温度，有效地阻止了大陆冰盖的发展。然而，大气环流模式[30]模拟结果显示，较大的经向热量输送促进冰川作用的进行，而不是降低冰川作用形成的可能性，因为它会使已经非常寒冷的极地地区降雪增加。

同样地，巴拿马地峡的出现与北半球冰川作用的开始之间的关系尚不清楚。地峡的形成似乎比广泛分布的北半球冰川作用早 50 万年至 200 万年（参考文献 31），而大气环流模式模拟结果显示，流经巴拿马水道的温暖大西洋水体的偏转实际上会导致北大西洋高纬度地区变冷[32]。因此，尽管局部的构造变化无疑会影响大洋环流和热量传输，但这些变化在解释根据新生代 $\delta^{18}O$ 记录推断出的阶段性变冷或观测到的第三纪长期变冷趋势等方面的重要性尚不明确。

许多早期的"冰期"理论关注的焦点是山脉和高原的隆升与侵蚀可能对气候产生的影响。本文我们将回顾一下关于上述老主题的一些新变化。特别是，我们提出，青藏高原的隆升是导致新生代气候变化的主要因素。虽然学者们推断出新生代许多地区都有隆起发生，包括阿尔卑斯山脉、东非以及南北美洲科迪勒拉山脉的部分区域（概述见参考文献 17），在这里我们主要关注的是青藏高原，因为有明确的证据显示它是在新生代形成的，还因为其独一无二的面积和位置，所以我们把它作为我们阐释隆升－侵蚀假说的重点。

青藏高原平均海拔近 5 千米，面积为美国的一半，是地球表面最为壮观的地形地貌。它由印度－大洋洲板块与亚洲板块相撞形成。上述板块之间的刚性碰撞很可能开始于始新世中期（4,400 万年至 5,200 万年前；参考文献 33~35）并一直持续到现在。对于青藏高原的海拔变化史我们知之甚少。事实上，我们仅有两个已经确定的数据点：现在的海拔，以及白垩系到下始新统之间海相灰岩的出现，后者说明 7 千万年至 1 亿年前青藏高原的大部分仍位于海平面以下，其中有些地区直到 5,200 万年前仍位于水下（参考文献 33~35）。虽然我们知道高原从"a"点上升到了"b"点，但可以这么说，要理解板块的构造运动和地球物理过程[33-35]，还必须要对其隆升史有更为详细的了解，这样才能对所提出的关于气候变化和高原海拔相互关联的假说进行评价。

One such hypothesis[1,2,36] notes that the modern Tibetan plateau is so high and so broad that it not only drives a regionally intense monsoon circulation, but also perturbs atmospheric circulation on a hemispheric scale. Ruddiman and colleagues[1,2,36] propose that the absence of this plateau before the Eocene would have resulted in significant climatological differences around the Northern Hemisphere. To test this idea, Ruddiman and Kutzbach[2] initiated a series of experiments using the National Center for Atmospheric Research (NCAR) GCM of the Earth's atmosphere in which they changed only the topography of the present landmasses. Their results (see also ref. 36) showed that many of the global changes in precipitation and temperature inferred by geologists and palaeobotanists to have occurred over the past 40 Myr were consistent with differences in the climates calculated by the model. For instance, relative to the zero-topography experiment, the GCM run with modern topography shows a decrease in summer precipitation around the Mediterranean caused by increased subsidence of dry air masses and stronger northeasterly winds. Similarly, the spread of summer-dry vegetation and increased dustiness in the Mediterranean region since the Miocene has been inferred from geobotanical and sedimentological evidence.

The palaeobotanical record reflects a trend from equable, moist temperate climates in the early and mid-Cenozoic to cold/warm and dry/wet regional patterns in the Northern Hemisphere today. The climate differences in the GCM experiments with and without topography are consistent with this trend toward increased seasonality and regional differentiation of climate. But as discussed by Ruddiman and Kutzbach[2], the GCM experiments do not show a pronounced drop in high-latitude summer temperatures as elevations are increased, suggesting that development of high topography alone is not sufficient to initiate the growth of large terrestrial ice sheets in both hemispheres. Experiments using GCM models incorporating important feedback processes (snow albedo, sea ice, mixed layer ocean temperatures) produce coolings that are larger by almost half than earlier versions (J. Kutzbach, personal communication). For the winter season, many regions cool by amounts that represent a considerable portion of the temperature changes inferred from geological records. For the crucial summer ablation season which controls ice volume, however, the amount of cooling remains far short of that required to explain long-term Cenozoic cooling. Additional factors, such as changes in atmospheric composition, seem to be required to explain global Cenozoic cooling.

The Cenozoic "Icehouse Effect"

It is widely accepted that changes in the concentration of radiatively important trace gases in the atmosphere (particularly CO_2) can alter the Earth's climate. A direct link between atmospheric temperature and CO_2 concentration is observed throughout the 140,000-year Vostok ice-core record of the last glacial–interglacial cycle[37], and many investigators have proposed a link between the evolution of global climate over the Cenozoic and changes in the composition of the Earth's atmosphere (for example refs 3, 23, 38–41). On timescales longer than a million years, atmospheric CO_2 levels are primarily controlled by the balance between the rate of volcanic input from the Earth's interior, and the rate of output through chemical weathering of rocks at the Earth's surface. These reactions can

其中一个这类假说[1,2,36]指出，现今的青藏高原非常高大宽广，它不仅驱动了强烈的区域性季风环流，并且还对半球尺度上的大气环流有影响。拉迪曼及其同事[1,2,36]提出，渐新世之前由于没有青藏高原，北半球周围的气候与现在大不相同。为了检验这一观点，拉迪曼和库茨巴赫[2]利用美国国家大气研究中心的大气环流模式进行了一系列实验，模式中仅改变的参数是现代陆地的地形。结果（见参考文献36）表明，地质学家和古植物学家们推测的近4,000万年来许多降雨和温度的全球变化都与模型计算出的气候变化一致。例如，相对于海拔为零的地貌的实验，现代地形下的大气环流模式模拟结果显示，地中海周围地区夏季降雨量减少，这是由下沉的干燥空气团的增加及东北风的增强所致。类似地，根据地植物学和沉积学证据，可以推断出：中新世以来，夏季干旱植被不断扩展，地中海地区粉尘增多。

古植物记录反映了由新生代早中期温和湿润的温带气候到现今北半球的区域性冷/暖和干/湿气候模式的变化。大气环流模式实验中有无高大地形的条件下模拟结果的差异与气候的季节性增强和区域性分化加强的趋势一致。但正如拉迪曼和库茨巴赫[2]所说，大气环流模式实验中，对于高纬地区，其夏季温度并没有随海拔的升高而显示出明显的降低，这说明仅有高大地形的发育并不足以使南北半球上大型陆地冰盖开始生长。添加了重要反馈过程（雪反射率、海冰、海洋混合层温度）的大气环流模式实验得到的降温程度几乎比之前的结果（库茨巴赫，私人交流）高出一半。对冬季而言，许多地区温度的降低幅度占根据地质记录推出的温度变化的相当大一部分。然而，对于控制着冰量的关键季节——夏季消融季来说，降温的幅度仍远远低于要解释的新生代长期变冷的值。要解释新生代的全球变冷，还需要考虑其他影响因素，如大气成分的变化等。

新生代"冰室效应"

人们普遍认为，大气中对于辐射非常重要的痕量气体（特别是CO_2）浓度的变化可以改变地球上的气候。通过对时间尺度长达14万年、记录了末次冰期–间冰期旋回的沃斯托克冰芯的研究[37]，发现大气温度和CO_2浓度之间存在直接关联，并且许多学者已经提出关于新生代全球气候演化和地球大气圈成分变化之间的关系（例如，参考文献3、23、38~41）。在百万年以上的时间尺度上，大气CO_2浓度主要受控于来自地球内部的火山输入速率和地表岩石化学风化产生的输出速率之间的平衡。

be simplified as

$$CaSiO_3 + CO_2 \underset{\text{metamorphism}}{\overset{\text{chemical weathering}}{\rightleftharpoons}} CaCO_3 + SiO_2$$

Two types of climate hypotheses have emerged: those in which variations in the atmospheric CO_2 levels are driven primarily by changes in volcanic outgassing, the main input term[38,40-42]; and those in which CO_2 variations are driven by changes in chemical erosion rates, the main output term[3,4,23]. The first class of models predicts an association between times of high CO_2 levels and high rates of chemical weathering; in contrast, the erosion models predict an association between low CO_2 levels and high chemical weathering rates. We evaluate these two predictions later.

Berner, Lasaga and Garrels[38] (hereafter referred to as BLAG) developed a numerical model of CO_2 inputs (through metamorphism and decarbonation reactions) and outputs (through chemical weathering) to the atmosphere over the past 100 Myr. They related the flux of CO_2 into the atmosphere linearly to the rate of seafloor production and hence subduction, and the output flux of CO_2 from the atmosphere to the area of continents available for chemical weathering, with atmospheric temperatures acting as a strong negative feedback (assuming that higher temperatures cause more chemical weathering). As formulated, their model produces higher CO_2 levels in the Cretaceous because of (1) more rapid seafloor spreading and volcanic outgassing of CO_2 at that time, and (2) a decrease in the land area available to chemical erosion, because of globally higher sea levels. The higher sea levels are in large part related to faster seafloor spreading rates and increased ridge volume.

Although the BLAG model and subsequent modifications[41,42] correctly yield higher global temperatures in the Cretaceous, the timing of the principal temperature change indicated by these models does not match the timing of the major climate cooling inferred from the geological record. In the BLAG models, the largest decline in atmospheric CO_2 and global temperatures occurs between 100 and 50 Myr ago (pre-Eocene), driven primarily by decreases in global seafloor spreading rates which control mantle outgassing and, indirectly, sea level. But geological evidence[43] suggests that the greater climate cooling occurred primarily between 50 Myr and the present (post-Eocene).

A possible explanation for this mismatch is suggested by erosion-driven CO_2 models[3,4,23]. On the basis of modern river studies[44,45], Raymo *et al.*[3] suggested that the long-term removal rate of CO_2 from the atmosphere by chemical erosion is a strong function of continental relief rather than area, and that atmospheric temperature exerts a relatively weak control on global chemical erosion rates. The logic is as follows: today, much of the Earth's land surface is characterized by low-lying, deeply weathered shield areas which contribute little to the global river flux of solutes. Even though chemical weathering is pervasive in these regions, the absolute rates are low. In contrast, mountainous regions are dominated by rapid mechanical erosion which, in turn, increases the surface area of fresh minerals available for chemical attack. Three further factors enhance chemical breakdown of detrital grains in mountainous regions: the abundance of easily weathered sedimentary

这些反应可以简单表示为：

$$CaSiO_3 + CO_2 \underset{\text{变质作用}}{\overset{\text{化学风化作用}}{\rightleftharpoons}} CaCO_3 + SiO_2$$

据此形成了两种气候假说：一种认为，大气中CO_2浓度的变化主要受火山排气作用这种主要输入形式变化的影响[38,40-42]；另一类认为，CO_2的变化受化学侵蚀速率这种主要输出形式的控制[3,4,23]。第一类模型预测高CO_2浓度与高速化学风化之间存在联系；与此相反，侵蚀模型则预测低CO_2浓度与高化学风化速率之间有关联。下文我们将对两种预测进行评估。

伯纳、拉萨加和加雷尔斯[38]（下文将以 BLAG 代替）设计了一个关于近 1 亿年来大气中CO_2的输入（通过变质作用和脱碳反应）与输出（通过化学风化作用）的数字模型。进入大气CO_2的通量与海底板块的形成和俯冲速率之间，以及大气CO_2的输出通量与可发生化学风化的大陆面积之间均呈线性相关，其中大气温度是一项很强的负反馈因素（假定温度越高化学风化越强）。按照所设计的运行，他们的模型得出白垩纪CO_2浓度较高，这是由于（1）当时的海底扩张速率很快，并且火山排气作用输出的CO_2也较多；（2）全球海平面升高，可发生化学侵蚀的陆地面积有所减少。较高的海平面很大程度上是由海底扩张速率的加快和洋中脊体积的增大造成的。

尽管 BLAG 提出的模型以及随后由此改进而来的模型[41,42]正确地得出白垩纪全球温度较高的结果，但这些模型所指示的主要温度变化的时间与根据地质记录推断出的气候变冷的时间并不匹配。在 BLAG 的模型中，大气中CO_2浓度与全球温度最明显的降低时间出现在 1 亿年至 5,000 万年前（始新世之前），主要是由全球海底扩张速率降低所致，海底扩张速率控制着地幔的排气作用，并间接影响海平面高度。但地质学证据显示，更大规模的气候变冷主要发生于 5,000 万年前至今的时期（始新世以后）。

侵蚀驱动的CO_2模型[3,4,23]提供了造成这种不匹配的一个可能的解释。雷莫等[3]根据现代河流的研究结果[44,45]提出，化学侵蚀引起的长期大气CO_2消耗速率是大陆地势高低而非面积的函数，而大气温度对全球化学侵蚀速率的影响则相对较弱。其原理如下：现今许多地表以极低的和深度风化的地盾为主要特征，这些特征对全球河流溶解物通量几乎没有贡献。即使这些地区的化学风化可以渗透下去，其绝对风化速率也很低。相反，多山地区以快速机械侵蚀为主，反过来还可以增加新鲜矿物的表面积，促使化学风化作用加强。在多山地区可加强碎屑颗粒的化学分解作用的

silicates derived from uplifted passive margin sequences (weathering of carbonates does not ultimately alter atmospheric CO_2), the orographic concentration of rainfall on mountain slopes, and steep slopes which flush away mechanical and chemical erosion products, constantly exposing fresh minerals.

These effects are most marked in the Himalaya. The collision of India with Asia resulted not only in the uplift, deformation and erosion of an antecedent passive margin, but also in the formation of the Tibetan plateau where incident solar heating in summer drives the strong atmospheric convection and rainfall associated with the Asian monsoon. (Numerical models suggest that the high topography of the Indian subcontinent is largely responsible for the intensity of the Asian monsoon[2,36,46-48].) Data from the eight largest rivers draining the Himalayan–Tibetan region (Table 1) show that almost 25% of the total dissolved load reaching the ocean today comes from a watershed area that represents only 5% of the Earth's land surface[49,50]. Thus, because of geologically unusual circumstances (the presence of a large plateau near a warm ocean), a disproportionate fraction of the Earth's chemical weathering occurs in this small region in Asia. The monsoon precipitation that we invoke is not the "normal" orographic rainfall found in areas where prevailing westerlies or easterlies impinge on meridional mountain ranges, but is caused by a thermally driven northward flux of moisture from the equatorial Indian Ocean. The Tibetan plateau lies in the latitude of the westerlies, but far from the main Atlantic moisture source, and "normal" orographic precipitation (on the western slopes) is small.

Table 1. Total river dissolved fluxes from Himalayan-Tibetan region

River	Dissolved solids (10^6 tons yr^{-1})	Drainage area (10^6 km^2)
Ganges/Brahamaputra	323.5	1.669
Yangtze (Chiang)	166	1.827
Si Kiang	132	0.464
Irrawaddy	91	0.414
Indus	62	0.916
Mekong	60	0.849
Huangho	33.5	0.814
Percentage of global total	25%	4.2%

Fluxes are from refs 49, 50.

On the basis of these and similar observations, we propose that late Cenozoic uplift of the Himalayan region and Tibetan plateau would have resulted in regionally, and hence globally, higher chemical erosion rates, causing a drawdown of atmospheric CO_2 and global cooling. The timing of this tectonically driven CO_2 decrease should be post-Eocene, coincident with the formation of the Tibetan plateau and in agreement with geological evidence for when global cooling was most rapid.

其他三个因素有：来自隆升被动大陆边缘层序的大量易风化沉积硅酸盐（碳酸盐的风化作用最终不会导致大气 CO_2 浓度发生改变）；山坡处地形引起的集中降雨；促使机械侵蚀或化学侵蚀的产物冲走的陡坡，这样可以持续暴露出新鲜的矿物。

在喜马拉雅地区上述作用最为显著。印度板块和亚洲板块的相撞不仅造成之前的被动大陆边缘隆升、变形和侵蚀，同时还形成了青藏高原，在这里夏季入射日照加热驱动强的大气对流并形成亚洲季风相关的降水。（数字模型研究表明，印度次大陆的较高地形是亚洲季风增强的主要原因 [2,36,46-48]。）发源于喜马拉雅 – 青藏高原地区的八条最大的河流（表 1）流域数据显示，如今到达海洋的溶解搬运载荷总量中有近 25% 来自仅占地球陆表面积 5% 的一个流域 [49,50]。因此，由于异常的地质环境（温暖大洋附近大型高原的出现），化学风化作用以与其面积不相称的比例发生于亚洲这块面积很小的地区。我们所说的季风降水并非指盛行西风或东风遇到南北向山脉时形成的地形雨，而是指由来自赤道印度洋的热驱动北向湿气流引起的降水。青藏高原与西风带属同一纬度，但距离西风带的主要湿气源——大西洋较远，其"正常的"地形降雨量（位于西坡）很小。

表 1. 喜马拉雅－青藏高原地区河流总溶解通量

河流	溶解质 (10^6 吨 / 年)	流域面积 (10^6 平方千米)
恒河 / 布拉马普特拉河 *	323.5	1.669
长江	166	1.827
西江	132	0.464
伊洛瓦底江	91	0.414
印度河	62	0.916
湄公河 †	60	0.849
黄河	33.5	0.814
在全球所占比例	25%	4.2%

通量值来自参考文献 49、50。
* 布拉马普特拉河发源于中国的西藏自治区，中国境内称雅鲁藏布江。
† 中国境内称澜沧江。

根据上述以及类似观测，我们提出晚新生代喜马拉雅地区和青藏高原的隆升能导致化学侵蚀速率区域性升高，进而加快全球化学侵蚀速率，导致大气中 CO_2 含量降低，全球变冷。该构造运动导致的大气 CO_2 降低的时间应发生在始新世以后，与青藏高原的形成时间一致，同时也与地质证据中全球温度降低最快的时间一致。

Proxies for Chemical Weathering Rates

One important difference between the two types of hypotheses described above is the prediction of when chemical weathering rates are greatest: in BLAG-type models, weathering rates increase as global temperatures rise, whereas in our model, weathering rate increases are correlated with falling global temperatures. To test these predictions, we need a proxy for global chemical erosion rates. Such a proxy may be the $^{87}Sr/^{86}Sr$ isotope record preserved in marine carbonates[3, 6-9, 51-55].

The seawater $^{87}Sr/^{86}Sr$ ratio recorded by marine carbonates (Fig. 2*a*) reflects a balance between input of radiogenic material, relatively high in $^{87}Sr/^{86}Sr$, weathered from continents (average value in present-day runoff is 0.7119; ref. 51) and nonradiogenic material of low $^{87}Sr/^{86}Sr$ introduced by hydrothermal activity (average value 0.7035). The isotopic composition of the river strontium flux is not invariant but depends on the lithology of the rocks being weathered[51-53]. Typically, carbonate weathering results in high river fluxes of strontium with low isotope ratios (<0.709), which would tend to buffer the oceanic value, whereas silicate weathering releases a low flux of relatively radiogenic strontium (>0.710; refs 8, 51, 53). An exception to this relationship has been proposed by Palmer and Edmond[8] who speculate that metamorphic repartitioning of elements in the orogenic zone of the Himalayas has resulted in the formation of extremely radiogenic (>0.720) easily weathered carbonates. Measurements of the isotopic composition of Himalayan limestones are needed to confirm this hypothesis. A third strontium input to the ocean, from redissolution of marine carbonates (average value 0.7084; ref. 51), buffers the isotope ratio of the oceanic strontium reservoir towards the integrated mean value of the preceding 10–15 Myr.

The pronounced post-Eocene rise in $^{87}Sr/^{86}Sr$ ratios (Fig. 2*a*) could be due to an increase in the delivery of radiogenic strontium from land, or to a decrease in seafloor hydrothermal activity. The widely held assumption that hydrothermal activity is a function of seafloor spreading rates, which are estimated from marine magnetic anomalies, can be used to estimate the hydrothermal flux of nonradiogenic strontium through time. Seafloor spreading rates seem to have changed little over the past 30–40 Myr (ref. 56), and it is widely agreed that the pronounced late Cenozoic increase in the oceanic $^{87}Sr/^{86}Sr$ ratio can therefore only be explained by a considerable increase in the delivery of radiogenic strontium from land. This could have been caused by increases in global chemical weathering rates[3,6,9,12] and/or the mean river isotopic composition of strontium[8-10].

化学风化速率的代用指标

上述两类假说之间的一个重要区别在于推测化学风化速率何时最大：在 BLAG 类的模型中，预测结果为风化速率随全球温度的升高而增加；而根据我们的模型得出的结果则显示，风化速率的升高与全球温度的降低有关。为了检验两种预测结果，我们需要找出一个全球化学侵蚀速率的代用指标。保存在海相碳酸盐中的 $^{87}Sr/^{86}Sr$ 同位素记录 [3,6-9,51-55] 可作为这样一个替代指标。

海相碳酸盐记录的海水 $^{87}Sr/^{86}Sr$ 比值（图 2a），反映了由陆地风化而来的 $^{87}Sr/^{86}Sr$ 比值相对较高的放射性成因物质的输入（现代径流的平均值为 0.7119；参考文献 51）与热液活动形成的 $^{87}Sr/^{86}Sr$ 比值相对较低的非放射性成因物质（平均值为 0.7035）之间的平衡关系。河流中锶通量的同位素组成并不是一成不变的，而是取决于被风化岩石的岩性 [51-53]。一般来说，碳酸盐风化会导致河流中锶通量较高，且其同位素比值较低（<0.709），这将可能使海洋中的同位素值被冲淡；而硅酸盐风化则会形成低通量的偏放射性成因的锶（>0.710；参考文献 8、51、53）。帕尔默和埃德蒙 [8] 则提出上述关系的一种例外情况，他们推测在喜马拉雅造山带中元素经变质作用重新分配，形成极偏放射性成因的（>0.720）易风化的碳酸盐。要证明该假说需要测定喜马拉雅石灰岩中的同位素组成。海洋的第三个锶输入来源是海相碳酸盐（平均值为 0.7084；参考文献 51）的再溶解，它会减小海洋锶存储汇中的同位素比值，使之趋于前 1,000 万年至 1,500 万年的总体平均值。

始新世以后 $^{87}Sr/^{86}Sr$ 比值的显著升高（图 2a）可归因于来自陆地的放射性锶的输送增加，或者海底热液活动的减弱。广泛接受的假设，即热液活动是海底扩张速率的函数，是根据海底磁异常得出的。这个假说可用来估算含非放射性锶的热液通量随时间的变化。近 3,000 万年至 4,000 万年来海底的扩张速率似乎变化不大（参考文献 56），因此人们普遍认可，只有陆源放射性锶输送量的明显增加才能解释晚新生代海洋中 $^{87}Sr/^{86}Sr$ 比值的显著升高。而陆源放射性锶的增加可能是由全球化学风化速率 [3,6,9,12] 增加和（或）河流中平均锶同位素组成 [8-10] 的升高造成的。

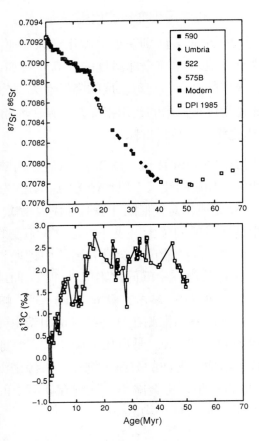

Fig. 2. *a*, Strontium isotopic composition of sea water for the past 70 Myr, based on analysis of marine carbonates (from ref. 9). *b*, $\delta^{13}C$ of bulk carbonate over the Cenozoic (from ref. 61). $\delta^{13}C = [(^{13}C/^{12}C)_{sample} / (^{13}C/^{12}C)_{standard}-1$], where standard is PDB.

Given the association between silicate weathering and high $^{87}Sr/^{86}Sr$ values, there are only two ways that rivers could become more radiogenic over the past 40 Myr without increasing silicate weathering rates. One is to decrease dramatically the delivery of low $^{87}Sr/^{86}Sr$ ratio strontium from carbonate weathering, requiring an unlikely reduction in the weathering rates of these types of rocks. The second, mentioned above, is to repartition radiogenic strontium by metamorphism, from resistant granites and gneisses into easily weathered carbonates[8]. Palmer and Edmond[8] attribute the unusually high strontium isotopic composition of the Ganges–Bramaputra river system to such "orogenic" repartitioning. But a related study[53] of the Ganges–Bramaputra headwaters proposes that the high $^{87}Sr/^{86}Sr$ ratios in these rivers are in fact due to intense chemical weathering of granites and gneisses (silicates).

Many studies of the Cenozoic strontium record[3,6,7,9,12,35] have concluded that the pronounced Cenozoic increase in oceanic $^{87}Sr/^{86}Sr$ ratios was due to increased rates of chemical weathering over this interval. Richter *et al.*[9] suggest that the strontium flux to the ocean has increased by ~40% over the past 40 Myr, an estimate which conservatively

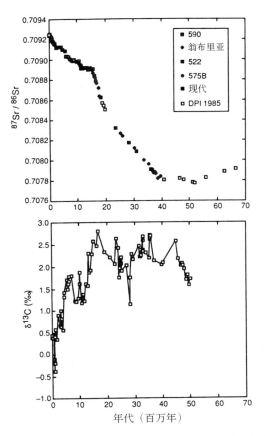

图 2. *a*, 基于海相碳酸盐分析得出的过去 7,000 万年中海水锶同位素组成（来自参考文献 9）。*b*，新生代全岩碳酸盐的 $\delta^{13}C$（来自参考文献 61）。$\delta^{13}C = [(^{13}C/^{12}C)_{样品} / (^{13}C/^{12}C)_{标准} - 1]$，PDB 标准。

　　鉴于硅酸盐风化作用与高 $^{87}Sr/^{86}Sr$ 比值之间存在关联，在硅酸盐风化速率不变的前提下，只有两种方式能使近 4,000 万年来河流中放射性锶增加。其一，由碳酸盐风化而来的低 $^{87}Sr/^{86}Sr$ 比值的锶输送显著降低，其中所要求的此类岩石的风化速率降低值几乎不可能达到。其二，如上所述，是通过变质作用对放射性锶进行再分配，将其从抗侵蚀的花岗岩和片麻岩转移到易侵蚀的碳酸盐岩中 [8]。帕尔默和埃德蒙 [8] 就将恒河 – 布拉马普特拉河河流体系统中异常高的锶同位素组成归因于这种"造山"再分配作用。但对恒河 – 布拉马普特拉河源头的相关研究 [53] 显示，这些河流中的高 $^{87}Sr/^{86}Sr$ 比值实际上是由于花岗岩和片麻岩（硅质）风化作用的增强所致。

　　许多关于新生代锶同位素记录的研究 [3,6,7,9,12,53] 一致认为，新生代时期海洋中 $^{87}Sr/^{86}Sr$ 比值的显著升高是由于该段时间内化学风化速率的提高所致。里克特等 [9] 提出，近 4,000 万年来，输入海洋的锶通量约增加了 40%，其中保守地估计了喜马拉

assumes that the strontium isotopic composition of Himalayan rivers increased from a "normal" global value of 0.7105 in the Oligocene to its present anomalously high value of 0.7127, and that hydrothermal exchange was proportional to the rate of seafloor generation. In addition, this study and others[6,53] concur with the suggestion[3] that erosion in the Himalaya has been responsible for a significant fraction of the observed increase in $^{87}Sr/^{86}Sr$. But the fraction attributable to erosion in low-latitude mountainous regions such as the Himalayas, as opposed to erosion by high-latitude continental ice sheets or alpine glaciers elsewhere, is poorly constrained. By assuming a link to more easily assessed rates of mechanical erosion, Hodell et al.[6] estimate that up to 50% of the increase in oceanic $^{87}Sr/^{86}Sr$ values over the past five million years may have been due to chemical erosion of the Canadian shield by the Laurentide ice sheet. Likewise, Miller et al.[57] proposed that glacial erosion in Antarctica was responsible for much of the increase in $^{87}Sr/^{86}Sr$ since the Eocene.

Although the evolution of the seawater strontium curve is consistent with a pronounced increase in chemical weathering since the Eocene, this interpretation is clearly not unique; a considerable fraction of the $^{87}Sr/^{86}Sr$ change could be due to variations in the isotope ratios in source rocks. The interpretation is further complicated by the fact that some strontium (albeit at generally low isotopic values) derives from the weathering of carbonates, a process which does not result in any net removal of CO_2 from the atmosphere. Ideally, we need a proxy for just the silicate component of weathering. Only with a number of weathering proxies, possibly including carbonate accumulation rates[3,58,59] or Ge/Si ratios[60], will we be able accurately to define global weathering rates in the geological past.

The Need for Negative Feedbacks

The erosion hypothesis described above predicts that chemical weathering rates can increase without a concomitant increase in mantle degassing rates. Increasing the erosional drawdown of CO_2 while holding the volcanic input constant would, however, deplete the atmosphere of all its CO_2 within a few million years[10]. By invoking tectonics as the main control on weathering intensity, we implicitly negate the importance of the temperature–weathering feedback which prevents a runaway "icehouse" (or "greenhouse") in BLAG-type carbon cycle models. Hence, a different negative feedback is needed, one that adds CO_2 back to the ocean–atmosphere reservoir without adding alkalinity (for instance, Ca^{2+}) which removes CO_2. Three processes that could provide such a feedback are discussed: imbalances in the organic carbon subcycle, precipitation of silicate minerals in the deep sea and seafloor weathering of basalt.

In addition to the carbonate–silicate cycle, the organic carbon subcycle, described schematically as

$$CO_2 + H_2O \underset{\text{oxidation}}{\overset{\text{organic C burial}}{\rightleftarrows}} CH_2O + O_2$$

雅地区河流中的锶同位素组成从渐新世"正常的"全球平均值 0.7105 增加到了现今异常高的 0.7127，并且热液交换与海底增生速率成一定的比例。另外，该研究与其他一些研究 [6,53] 均赞成一种观点 [3]，即喜马拉雅地区的侵蚀作用是造成所观测到的 $^{87}Sr/^{86}Sr$ 比值升高的主要因素。但在低纬度山区，如喜马拉雅地区，侵蚀作用因素所占的比例不受限制，这与其他高纬地区大陆冰盖或高山冰川的侵蚀作用有限相反。霍德尔等 [6] 通过设定一个较容易得到的机械侵蚀速率值估计，过去 500 万年中海洋 $^{87}Sr/^{86}Sr$ 比值升高达 50%，这可能是由劳伦泰德冰盖对加拿大地盾的化学侵蚀所致。同样地，米勒等 [57] 提出，南极大陆上的冰川侵蚀是造成始新世以来 $^{87}Sr/^{86}Sr$ 比值升高的主要原因。

虽然始新世以来海水锶同位素曲线的演化与化学风化作用的显著增强一致，但是化学风化作用增强显然并不是唯一的解释。原岩中锶同位素比值的变化是造成 $^{87}Sr/^{86}Sr$ 比值变化的主要原因。有些锶（尽管通常为低同位素值）来源于碳酸盐的风化，这一事实使上述解释工作更加复杂化，因为碳酸盐风化作用并不会使大气中的 CO_2 净含量减少。我们需要一个仅代表硅酸盐风化作用的理想代用指标。只有使用多个风化作用指标，我们才有可能准确地确定出地质历史时期全球风化作用的速率，这些风化作用指标或能包括：碳酸盐堆积速率 [3,58,59] 或者 Ge/Si 比值 [60] 等。

负反馈需求

上述侵蚀假说预测，在没有地幔脱气作用速率伴随增加的情况下，化学风化速率可以提高。然而，倘若在保持火山输入量不变的同时，增加侵蚀作用导致的 CO_2 的减少，几百万年内大气中的 CO_2 就会被完全消耗掉 [10]。我们将构造运动看作风化作用增强的主要影响因素，从而否定了温度 – 风化反馈的重要性，因为在 BLAG 类的碳循环模型中，这种反馈机制会阻碍快速"冰室效应"（或"温室效应"）的持续发展。因此，需要寻找一种不同的负反馈机制，以使 CO_2 回到海洋 – 大气存储汇中，同时不会引起碱度（如 Ca^{2+}）增加而导致 CO_2 被移除。下面我们将讨论能够提供此类反馈作用的三种作用：有机碳子循环的失衡、深海硅酸盐矿物的沉淀以及海底玄武岩的风化。

除碳酸盐 – 硅酸盐循环以外，有机碳子循环对大气 CO_2 循环的影响虽小但却非常重要，可简要表示如下：

$$CO_2 + H_2O \xrightleftharpoons[\text{氧化作用}]{\text{有机碳埋藏}} CH_2O + O_2$$

has a small but significant impact on the cycling of atmospheric CO_2. On average over the Phanerozoic, roughly 80% of the carbon removed from the ocean–atmosphere system was deposited as carbonates, whereas ~20% was buried as organic matter[61]. Because organic matter is extremely enriched in ^{12}C during photosynthesis, any change in the relative size of this reservoir through time would be reflected in a change in the $^{13}C/^{12}C$ ratio of the world's ocean and atmosphere (the surface carbon reservoir from which the organic matter is derived, or added to). If, for instance, organic carbon burial decreased over the past 40 Myr, the ocean–atmosphere reservoirs would become enriched in ^{12}C, the $^{13}C/^{12}C$ ratio of marine calcite would decrease, and a net addition of CO_2 to the atmosphere would occur. Such a change in the relative fraction of organic carbon buried would affect atmospheric CO_2 levels independently of global silicate weathering and mantle degassing rates.

The most complete compilation of bulk carbonate $\delta^{13}C$ values during the Cenozoic (Fig. 2b; ref. 61) shows just such a decrease. Using these data, Shackleton[61] estimated that the fraction of carbon buried as organic matter rather than carbonate dropped from 20% to 10% over the course of the Neogene, causing a net addition of CO_2 to the atmosphere (alternatively, the data are consistent with an increase in kerogen weathering relative to organic carbon burial, also leading to a net addition of CO_2 to the atmosphere). Such a change in the organic carbon subcycle is of the correct magnitude and direction to prevent a tectonically sustained increase in silicate weathering (of ~40%) from completely stripping the atmosphere of CO_2. Estimates depend on assumptions of how photosynthetic fractionation factors changed, when to define "steady state" (or the present long-term mean) and what carbon isotope data set is used. Similar studies using different assumptions and data bases have come to more conservative conclusions[12,41,42].

Why would the long-term burial rate of organic carbon have decreased over the past 40 Myr? Most organic carbon burial today takes place in shallow marine environments such as estuaries, continental shelves and deltas. In these well oxygenated environments, the burial rate of organic carbon is a positive function of the total sediment burial rate[62]. But because carbon isotope data suggest that less organic carbon was being buried in the late Cenozoic, while other evidence suggests that worldwide sedimentation rates have been increasing[63-65], it seems that this was not the main factor controlling organic carbon burial in recent geological history. On the other hand, increased erosion of continental shelves, estuaries and deltas as sea level dropped through the Cenozoic could have resulted in a decrease in organic carbon burial in the shallow marine realm[61] and an increase in the erosion of previously deposited organic-rich sediments.

A second possible control on organic carbon burial is nutrient supply: a decrease in organic carbon burial may have been caused by a decline in the amount of phosphorus and nitrogen available to form organic matter. This does not seem to be the case for the past 40 Myr, as the nutrient supply from rock weathering has, if anything, increased (as discussed above), and because much dissolved phosphorus currently entering the ocean is removed by inorganic precipitation[66].

整个显生宙中，从海洋－大气系统中移除的碳平均约有 80% 是以碳酸盐形式沉积下来的，而 20% 左右的碳则以有机碳形式埋藏下来[61]。由于在光合作用过程中有机质极富 ^{12}C，该碳汇的相对大小随时间发生的任何变化都会反映到世界大洋与大气（作为有机质来源的地表碳储集库）$^{13}C/^{12}C$ 比值的变化中。例如，倘若过去 4,000 万年中有机碳的埋藏量是减少的，那么，海洋－大气碳汇应该富含 ^{12}C，海洋方解石中 $^{13}C/^{12}C$ 的比值也应降低，由此大气中的 CO_2 浓度应该会净增加。埋藏有机碳相对分量的变化会影响大气 CO_2 水平，而该过程与全球的硅酸盐风化和地幔脱气作用速率均无关。

最全面的新生代全岩碳酸盐 $\delta^{13}C$ 值综合图（图 2b；参考文献 61）正显示了这一减少情况。沙克尔顿[61] 利用上述数据估算出，新近纪以来以有机质而非碳酸盐形式埋藏的那部分碳所占的比例从 20% 降到了 10%，导致大气中 CO_2 净增加（另外，这些数据与油母岩风化作用相对于有机碳埋藏作用的增强是相符的，这种增强也会导致大气 CO_2 净增加）。有机碳子循环这种变化的大小和方向恰好可以阻止构造运动引起的硅酸盐风化作用持续增强（约 40%），使大气中的 CO_2 不至于完全耗尽。估算结果取决于光合分馏系数如何变化、何时定义"稳态"（或现今的长期平均值）等假设，以及采用何种碳同位素数据集。采用不同假设和不同数据库的类似研究得到的结果相对更保守一些[12,41,42]。

过去 4,000 万年中有机碳的长期埋藏速率为什么会降低？现今多数有机碳埋藏发生于浅海环境，如河口、大陆架和三角洲等。在这些强氧化环境中，有机碳的埋藏速率是总沉积物埋藏速率的正函数[62]。但碳同位素数据显示，晚新生代埋藏的有机碳较少，而其他证据则表明世界范围内的沉积速率是增加的[63-65]，因此，这似乎并不是近代地质历史中影响有机碳埋藏的主要因素。另一方面，新生代以来，随着海平面下降，大陆架、河口和三角洲处的侵蚀不断加剧，也会导致浅海区域有机碳埋藏速率的降低[61]，并且早先沉积的富含有机质的沉积物侵蚀作用也增强。

营养盐的供给可能是影响有机质碳埋藏的另一个因素：有机碳埋藏的减少可能是由于可用于形成有机质的磷和氮减少所致。然而，过去 4,000 万年中情况并非如此，因为由岩石风化而来的营养盐是增加的（如果有变化的话）（正如前文所述），并且现在进入海洋的大部分溶解态磷是通过无机物的沉淀被移除的[66]。

A third possible control is the oxygen concentration in the deep ocean. Today many areas of the deep ocean are nearly anoxic[67]. Even lower dissolved oxygen concentrations could result in a considerable increase in marine organic carbon burial[68-70], although this point is controversial[71,72]. The oxygen content of the deep ocean is controlled by the temperature of the water as it leaves the surface, with O_2 concentrations increasing as sea surface temperatures decrease. Today deep waters form in polar regions with a dissolved O_2 concentration of ~ 350 µmol kg^{-1}. If high-latitude sea surface temperatures were $\sim 10\,°C$ warmer in the mid-Cenozoic, a level consistent with planktonic isotopes[14,73], then O_2 concentrations would have been only ~ 275 µmol kg^{-1}. The inferred increase through time in ocean oxygen concentrations could have resulted in decreased organic carbon burial.

Deep-ocean oxygen concentrations would decrease and sea level would fall as CO_2 concentrations in the atmosphere began to fall: as the climate gets colder, oxygen solubility in sea water increases and continental ice growth causes sea level to drop. Each of these changes, in turn, could lead to decreased organic carbon burial and addition of CO_2 to the atmosphere, providing a negative feedback to climate change. Increased continentality and aridity, associated with cooling global temperatures, could also have resulted in the shrinkage and drainage of freshwater marshes and swamps, again leading to a decrease in the burial of organic-rich sediments.

As originally pointed out by Shackleton[61], the bulk carbonate $\delta^{13}C$ data provide convincing evidence that there has been a net addition of light carbon (and CO_2) to the ocean and atmosphere since the Oligocene. We propose that this carbon flux would have partially counteracted a drawdown of atmospheric CO_2 by enhanced erosion of silicates. Before invoking organic carbon burial as an effective negative feedback to the global carbon cycle, however, one also has to consider the relative residence times of CO_2 (<1 Myr) and O_2 (~ 10 Myr) in the atmosphere. Any decrease in organic matter burial will result in net removal of O_2 from the atmosphere. Eventually the continued drawdown of O_2 will cause the partial pressure of oxygen in the atmosphere to fall, probably leading to organic carbon burial rates increasing again. Thus, the negative feedback to the carbonate–silicate cycle provided by the organic carbon subcycle would gradually become less effective five to ten million years after the "event" that initiated the change, a problem which may not be critical in the case discussed here; namely, gradually more intense forcing as the Tibetan plateau increases in elevation.

Two other processes have been proposed as negative feedbacks to atmospheric CO_2 decreases driven by enhanced silicate weathering. One is precipitation of silicate minerals on the sea floor (ref. 67, and W. Broecker, personal communication). Although this process is poorly understood (see summaries in refs 67, 74), much of the sodium and potassium entering the sea must be precipitated as silicate minerals. On the other hand, calcium derived from silicate weathering is mostly precipitated as carbonate, resulting in the net removal of CO_2 from the atmosphere. As atmospheric CO_2 falls, however, ocean pH rises (OH$^-$ rises), creating conditions more favourable to the precipitation of Ca as deep-sea silicates rather than carbonates. In this way, one could again decouple silicate weathering

第三个可能的影响因素是深海中氧的浓度。现今深海中许多地区都近于缺氧状态[67]。较低溶解氧浓度也可能导致海洋有机碳埋藏大量增加[68-70]，不过关于这一点还存在争议[71,72]。深海中的 O_2 含量是由海水表面温度控制的，随着海水表面温度的降低，O_2 浓度将会增加。现今的深海水体形成于极地海域，其溶解氧浓度约为 350 微摩尔 / 千克。如果新生代中期高纬度海域的海水表面温度比现在高约 10℃（该值与浮游生物同位素的测定结果一致[14,73]），那么当时 O_2 的浓度大概仅为 275 微摩尔 / 千克。由此推断的海洋中氧浓度随时间的升高可能导致了有机碳埋藏的减少。

当大气中 CO_2 的浓度开始降低时，深海中的氧浓度就会降低，海平面也会下降：随着气候逐渐变冷，海水中氧的溶解度增大，大陆冰川的增长导致海平面下降，任何这些变化反过来都会降低有机碳埋藏速率，增加大气中的 CO_2，对气候变化形成负反馈。随着全球温度的降低，气候大陆化和干旱程度不断加剧，也可能会导致淡水湖沼缩减与干涸，又进一步导致富含有机质沉积物的埋藏量降低。

正如沙克尔顿[61]最早指出的那样，全岩碳酸盐 $\delta^{13}C$ 数据充分证明，自渐新世以来，海洋与大气中 ^{12}C（和 CO_2）的净含量有所增加。我们认为，该碳通量部分抵消了由于硅酸盐侵蚀增强导致的大气 CO_2 的减少。然而，在将有机碳埋藏视为全球碳循环的有效负反馈之前，还必须考虑 CO_2（小于 100 万年）和 O_2（约 1,000 万年）在大气中的相对滞留时间。有机质埋藏量的任何一点降低都会导致大气中 O_2 的净减少。最终 O_2 的持续减少将使大气中的氧分压降低，很可能导致有机碳的埋藏速率再次升高。因此，在引发这一改变的"事件"以后 500 万年至 1,000 万年，有机碳子循环对碳酸盐 – 硅酸盐循环的负反馈作用会逐渐减弱。当然，这个问题并不是这里要讨论的关键问题。关键问题是驱动力作用随着青藏高原海拔的升高逐渐变强。

针对由硅酸盐风化作用增强导致的大气 CO_2 降低，还有学者提出了另外两种负反馈作用。其一是海底硅酸盐矿物的沉淀（参考文献 67 及与布勒克的私人交流）。虽然对该作用还了解甚少（见参考文献 67、74 的总论），大部分进入海洋的钠和钾一定都是以硅酸盐矿物的形式沉降下来的。另一方面，由硅酸盐风化而来的钙则大部分沉淀为碳酸盐，从而导致大气中 CO_2 含量的净减少。但随着大气中 CO_2 的减少，海洋 pH 值会升高（OH^- 浓度升高），所形成的环境条件将有利于 Ca 以深海硅酸盐形式而不是碳酸盐形式沉淀。通过这种方式我们也可以从大气 CO_2 水平中分离出硅

rates from atmospheric CO_2 levels. Seafloor weathering of basalt, described in the carbon-cycle model of François and Walker[12], provides a third mechanism to decouple silicate weathering, alkalinity and atmospheric CO_2 levels. In this process, hydrogen ions in ocean water react with seafloor basalts, releasing calcium ions which then combine with ocean carbon to form calcium carbonate. The net result is the removal of CO_2 from the ocean–atmosphere reservoir. But as atmospheric CO_2 falls, ocean pH and OH^- rise, creating conditions less favourable to the removal of CO_2 by this mechanism, again providing a negative feedback to a runaway "icehouse".

Given the suggestions above, it is certainly possible, if not probable, that increases in silicate weathering rates could be sustained for millions to tens of millions of years without an increase in mantle degassing rates. In particular, the assumption that rates of volcanism and silicate weathering need to be balanced on timescales longer than a million years[10] may not be necessary. One last possibility is that seafloor spreading rates are not a good proxy for mantle degassing rates. Caldeira[13] suggests that increased subduction of pelagic carbonates since the Jurassic has resulted in an increased metamorphic CO_2 flux from the mantle which is responsible for the higher rates of chemical erosion inferred for the late Cenozoic. This could provide the "extra" CO_2 needed to sustain high silicate weathering rates at a time when seafloor spreading are constant.

The Role of Positive Feedbacks

Molnar and England[5] proposed an interaction between climate and tectonics that on first reading seems the exact inverse of our uplift hypothesis, but in fact may provide a fully complementary source of positive feedback. They argue that late Cenozoic global cooling was responsible for increased mechanical erosion, which through isostasy would create mountain ranges with high peaks and deep valleys, rather than uplift causing climate changes and erosion. They suggested two mechanisms by which climate change intensified erosion: expansion of mountain glaciers around the world; and changes in atmospheric circulation, and thus in precipitation patterns. At the limit, this hypothesis might be interpreted as suggesting that high mountain ranges existed throughout the Cenozoic, and that the only change during the Cenozoic has been the effect of climate change on mountain relief. Such an interpretation would, however, leave the cause of Cenozoic cooling and circulation changes unresolved. In fact, Molnar and England[5] noted the need for a first cause of Cenozoic cooling, and acknowledged Tibetan uplift as a possible cause of climate change. Their basic disagreement is with the inference of accelerating late-Cenozoic uplift throughout the world.

It is consistent with both hypotheses to argue that uplift of Tibet (and possibly elsewhere) is a plausible first cause of Cenozoic climate changes (through circulation changes and weathering), but that climate change (in particular, glacier activity) then caused additional erosion, exhumation and isostatic uplift in other regions, including some mountain belts regarded as orogenically "dead" from the standpoint of horizontal plate tectonic motions. Thus, the arguments of Molnar and England can be viewed as a positive feedback

酸盐的风化速率。弗朗索瓦和沃克 [12] 提出的碳循环模型中所描述的海底玄武岩风化作用为分离硅酸盐风化速率、碱度及大气中 CO_2 水平提供了第三种机制。在该作用中，海水中的氢离子与海底玄武岩发生反应，释放出的钙离子与海洋中的碳相结合，形成碳酸钙。最终的结果是从海洋 – 大气碳汇中将 CO_2 移除。但是，随着大气中 CO_2 的减少，海洋 pH 值和 OH^- 浓度上升，形成不利于 CO_2 移除的条件，再次为快速"冰室效应"提供了负反馈机制。

鉴于上述论点，即使地幔脱气速率不升高，硅酸盐风化作用速率增加也完全有可能（如果不是很有可能的话）维持成百上千万年的时间。特别是，关于火山作用与硅酸盐风化作用速率达到平衡的时间要长于百万年 [10] 的假定可能没有必要。最后一种可能性是，海底扩张速率并非地幔脱气速率的良好替代指标。卡尔代拉 [13] 提出，自侏罗纪以来，远洋碳酸盐的俯冲量不断增加，已导致来自地幔的变质 CO_2 通量增加，而这正是推断出的晚新生代高速化学侵蚀的原因所在。当海底扩张速率恒定不变时，这可以提供维持高速硅酸盐风化作用所需的"额外"CO_2。

正反馈的作用

莫尔纳和英格兰 [5] 提出一种气候和构造运动之间的相互作用，乍看起来似乎正与我们所提出的隆升假说相反，但实际上，可作为正向反馈的全面补充。他们认为，晚新生代全球变冷导致机械侵蚀加剧，根据地壳均衡理论，这种机械侵蚀作用会形成具高峰深谷的山脉，而不是隆升导致了气候变化和侵蚀作用的发生。他们提出了气候变化加剧侵蚀作用的两种机制：世界范围内高山冰川的扩张；大气环流的改变以及由此带来的降水格局的变化。从某种程度上来说，该假说可以这样解释：整个新生代一直存在高大山脉，并且新生代中发生的仅有变化是气候变化对山脉地势的影响。然而这无法解释新生代变冷和环流变化的原因。事实上，莫尔纳和英格兰 [5] 也意识到其中缺少引起新生代降温的首要原因，并且认为青藏高原的隆升是气候变化的一个可能因素。他们的根本异议在于晚新生代全球加速隆升的推论。

两种理论一致认为，青藏高原（可能也包括其他地方）的隆升可能是引起晚新生代气候变化（通过环流变化和风化作用）的首要原因，但是这种气候变化（特别是冰川运动）又会导致其他地区，包括按照水平板块构造运动的观点已经被认为是"死亡"的造山带，形成额外的侵蚀、剥离以及均衡隆升作用。由此，莫尔纳和英格兰的观点可以看为一种正反馈机制，在这种机制下隆升带来的侵蚀会引起全球变冷，

mechanism, whereby uplift-induced erosion initiates global cooling, which then causes further glacial erosion and cooling worldwide.

An important implication of the plateau uplift hypothesis is that even steady-state plate motions can lead to non-steady-state effects on climate and, hence, possibly global relief. Continent–continent collisions which result in plateaux of the magnitude of Tibet are infrequent and episodic. Consequently, the accompanying effects of uplift (perturbations of atmospheric flow, large monsoons, and intense erosion and weathering), should be comparably infrequent. Over the past 700 Myr, only two other time periods were characterized by Tibetan-size plateaux, the late Precambrian and the late Palaeozoic[75]; these were also intervals of widespread continental glaciation[4]. In summary, despite the continuous presence throughout geological history of high mountain terrain along the convergent margins of the world, it may be the rarer occurrence of plateaux that can drive climate away from steady state and decouple rates of horizontal and vertical tectonic movement.

Evaluating the Effects on Climate

We propose that over the past 40 Myr, uplift of the Tibetan plateau has resulted in stronger deflections of the atmospheric jet stream, more intense monsoonal circulation, increased rainfall on the front slopes of Himalayas, greater rates of chemical weathering and, ultimately, lower atmospheric CO_2 concentrations. These changes in climate may initiate strong positive feedbacks to global cooling through glacier-driven erosion[5]. A negative feedback, acting either through the organic carbon subcycle or elsewhere, must also occur to prevent the atmosphere from being completely stripped of CO_2. This model implies that atmospheric CO_2 levels are not maintained at steady state by the temperature–weathering feedback during times of intense tectonism (which may last many millions of years).

To evaluate the linkages between uplift, weathering and climate proposed here, proxy data for global chemical weathering rates over the Cenozoic and a better understanding of the elevation history of the Tibetan plateau are needed. We also need a quantitative understanding of the long-term carbon cycle, in particular the magnitude and source of variations in the organic subcycle and seafloor weathering. Ultimately, direct determination of atmospheric CO_2 levels over the past 100 Myr will be essential if we are to evaluate the uplift–erosion model[3,4] and other carbon-cycle climate models[38,41]. The most promising technique for this is the inference of atmospheric CO_2 levels from measurements of $\delta^{13}C$ in marine organic matter[76-78].

(**359**, 117-122; 1992)

M. E. Raymo[*] and W. F. Ruddiman[†]

[*] Department of Earth, Atmospheric, and Planetary Sciences, Massachusetts Institute of Technology, Cambridge, Massachusetts 02139, USA

[†] Department of Environmental Sciences, University of Virginia, Charlottesville, Virginia 22903, USA

从而导致进一步的冰川侵蚀和世界范围的变冷。

高原隆升假说具有一个重要含意——即使稳定板块运动也能对气候产生非稳态的影响，进而影响到全球地形。能够形成像青藏高原这样巨大高原的陆陆碰撞只是罕见、偶然的事件。因此，与隆升作用相伴的其他效应（如气流扰动作用、大型季风的形成，以及侵蚀、风化作用的加剧）相较之下应该也比较罕见。近 7 亿年来，与青藏高原隆升规模相当的情况仅有两次，分别发生在前寒武纪晚期和晚古生代 [75]。而这两段时期也是陆地冰川作用广泛分布的时期 [4]。概括说来，尽管地质历史时期全球汇聚型大陆边缘不断有高山地形出现，然而要形成可以改变全球稳定气候状态并使构造运动水平和垂直速率降低的高原却更为罕见。

对气候影响的评估

我们认为，过去 4,000 万年中，青藏高原的隆升使得大气急流偏转增大、季风环流加强、喜马拉雅山前坡降雨增多、化学风化作用速率加快，最终导致大气 CO_2 浓度降低。上述气候变化可能会通过冰川侵蚀作用启动全球变冷的正反馈机制 [5]。与此同时，必定也会有通过有机碳子循环或其他作用运行的负反馈机制，来阻碍大气 CO_2 的完全移除。该模型说明，在强烈的构造运动期（可能会持续数百万年），温度 – 风化作用反馈作用并不能使大气 CO_2 水平维持在稳定状态。

为了评价本文提到的隆升、风化作用和气候之间的关系，还需要有新生代全球化学风化速率的代用指标数据，并对青藏高原的隆升史有进一步了解。另外，我们还需要对长期碳循环有定量的认识，特别是有机碳子循环和海底风化作用变化的大小和原因。最后，如果我们要评价隆升 – 侵蚀模型 [3,4] 和其他碳循环气候模型 [38,41]，那么对过去 1 亿年中大气 CO_2 水平的直接确定也是必不可少的，而能够实现这一点的最有前景的方法应该是根据海洋有机质中 $\delta^{13}C$ 的测定结果推断大气的 CO_2 水平 [76-78]。

（齐红艳 翻译；李吉均 审稿）

References:

1. Ruddiman, W. F. & Raymo, M. E. *The Past Three Million Years: Evolution of Climatic Variability in the North Atlantic Region* (eds Shackleton, N. J., West, R. G. & Bowen, D. Q.) 227-234 (Cambridge Univ. Press, Cambridge, 1988).

2. Ruddiman, W. F. & Kutzbach, J. E. *J. Geophys. Res.* **94**, 18409-18427 (1989).

3. Raymo, M. E., Ruddiman, W. F. & Froelich, P. N. *Geology* **16**, 649-653 (1988).

4. Raymo, M. E. *Geology* **19**, 344-347 (1991).

5. Molnar, P. & England, P. *Nature* **346**, 29-34 (1990).

6. Hodell, D. A., Mead, G. A. & Mueller, P. A. *Chem. Geol.* (*Isotop. Geosci. Sec.*) **80**, 291-307 (1990).

7. Capo, R. C. & DePaolo, D. J. *Science* **249**, 51-55 (1990).

8. Palmer, M. R. & Edmond, J. M. *Geochim. Cosmochim. Acta* **56**, 2099-2111 (1992).

9. Richter, F. M., Rowley, D. B. & DePaolo, D. J. *Earth Planet. Sci. Lett.* **109**, 11-23 (1992).

10. Berner, R. A. & Rye, D. M. *Am. J. Sci.* **292**, 136-148 (1992).

11. Sundquist, E. T. *Quat. Sci. Rev.* **10**, 283-296 (1991).

12. François, L. M. & Walker, J. C. G. *Am. J. Sci.* **292**, 81-135 (1992).

13. Caldeira, K. *Nature* **357**, 578-581 (1992).

14. Miller, K. G., Fairbanks, R. G. & Mountain, G. S. *Paleoceanography* **2**, 1-19 (1987).

15. Shackleton, N. J. & Kennett, J. P. *Init. Rep. Deep Sea Drilling Proj.* **29** (ed. Kennett, J. P.) 801-807 (U.S. Government Printing Office, Washington DC, 1975).

16. Barrett, P. J., Elston, D. P., Harwood, D. M., McKelvey, B. C. & Webb, P.-N. *Geology* **15**, 634-637 (1987).

17. Ruddiman, W. F., Prell, W. L. & Raymo, M. E. *J. Geophys. Res.* **94**, 18379-18391 (1989).

18. Wolfe, J. A. *Palaeogeogr. Palaeoclimatol Palaeoecol.* **9**, 25-57 (1971).

19. McKenna, M. C. *Palaeogeogr. Palaeoclimatol Palaeoecol.* **30**, 349-362 (1980).

20. Kemp, E. M. *Palaeogeogr. Palaeoclimatol. Palaeoecol.* **24**, 169-208 (1978).

21. Lyell, C. *Principles of geology* (Murray, London, 1875).

22. Dana, J. D. *Am. J. Sci.* **22**, 305-334 (1856).

23. Chamberlin, T. C. *J. Geol.* **7**, 545-584; 667-685; 751-787 (1899).

24. Crowell, J. C. & Frakes, L. A. *Am. J. Sci.* **268**, 193-224 (1970).

25. Caputo, M. V. & Crowell, J. C. *Geol. Soc. Am. Bull.* **96**, 1020-1036 (1985).

26. Crowley, T. J., Mengel, J. G. & Short, D. A. *Nature* **329**, 803-807 (1987).

27. Barron, E. J. *Palaeogeogr. Palaeoclimatol. Palaeoecol.* **50**, 45-61 (1985).

28. Kennett, J. P. *J. Geophys. Res.* **82**, 3843-3860 (1977); *Mesozoic and Cenozoic Oceans* (ed. Hsu, K. J.) 119-122 (Am. geophys. Un., Washington DC, 1986).

29. Barker, P. F. & Burrell, J. *Antarctic Geoscience* (ed. Craddock, C.) 377-385 (Univ. of Wisconsin, Madison, 1982).

30. Oglesby, R. J. *Clim. Dynam.* **3**, 135-156 (1989).

31. Keigwin, L. D. *Science* **217**, 350-353 (1982).

32. Maier-Reimer, E., Mikolajewicz, U. & Crowley, T. *Paleoceanography* **5**, 349-366 (1990).

33. Mercier, J.-L., Armijo, R., Tapponnier, P., Carey-Gailhardis, E. & Lin, H. T. *Tectonics* **6**, 275-304 (1987).

34. Molnar, P. *Phil. Trans. R. Soc. Lond.* **A326**, 33-88 (1988); *Am. Scient.* **77**, 350-360 (1989).

35. Harrison, T. M., Copeland, P., Kidd, W. S. F. & Yin, A. *Science* **255**, 1663-1670 (1992).

36. Kutzbach, J. E., Guetter, P. J., Ruddiman, W. F. & Prell, W. L. *J. Geophys. Res.* **94**, 18393-18407 (1989).

37. Barnola, J. M., Raynaud, D., Korotevich, Y. S. & Lorius, C. *Nature* **329**, 408-414 (1987).

38. Berner, R. A., Lasaga, A. C. & Garrels, R. M. *Am. J. Sci.* **283**, 641-683 (1983).

39. Barron, E. J. & Washington, W. M. *The Carbon Cycle and Atmospheric CO₂: Natural Variations Archean to Present* (eds Sundquist, E. T. & Broecker, W. S.) 546-553 (Am. geophys. Un., Washington DC, 1985).

40. Walker, J. C. G., Hays, P. B. & Kasting, J. F. *J. Geophys. Res.* **86**, 9976-9782 (1981).

41. Lasaga, A. C., Berner, R. A. & Garrels, R. M. *The Carbon Cycle and Atmospheric CO₂: Natural Variations Archean to Present* (eds Sundquist, E. T. & Broecker, W. S.) 397-410 (Am. geophys. Un., Washington, DC, 1985).

42. Berner, R. A. *Science* **249**, 1382-1386 (1990); *Am. J. Sci.* **291**, 339-376 (1991).

43. Crowley, T. J. & North, G. N. *Paleoclimatology*, 339 (Oxford Univ. Press, New York, 1991).

44. Gibbs, R. J. *Science* **156**, 1734-1737 (1967).

45. Stallard, R. F. & Edmond, J. M. *J. Geophys. Res.* **88**, 9671-9688 (1983); Stallard, R. F. *Physical and Chemical Weathering in Geochemical Cycles* (eds Lerman, A. & Meybeck, M.) 225-246 (Kluwer, Dordrecht, Holland, 1988).

46. Manabe, S. & Terpstra, T. B. *J. Atmos. Sci.* **31**, 3-42 (1974).

47. Hahn, D. G. & Manabe, S. *J. Atmos. Sci.* **32**, 1515-1541 (1975).

48. Druyan, L. M. *J. Clim.* **2**, 127-139; 347-355 (1982).

49. Meybeck, M. *Hydrol. Sci. Bull.* **21**, 265-284 (1976).

50. Pinet, P. & Souriau, M. *Tectonics* **7**, 563-582 (1988).

51. Palmer, M. R. & Edmond, J. M. *Earth Planet. Sci. Lett.* **92**, 11-26 (1989).

52. Palmer, M. R. & Edlerfield, H. *Nature* **314**, 526-528 (1985).

53. Krishnaswami, S., Trivedi, J. R., Sarin, M. M., Ramesh, R. & Sharma, K. K. *Earth Planet. Sci. Lett.* **109**, 243-253 (1992).

54. Brass, G. W. *Geochim. Cosmochim. Acta* **40**, 721-730 (1976).

55. Burke, W. H. *et al. Geology* **10**, 516-519 (1982).

56. Komintz, M. A. *Am. J. Petrol. Geol. Mem.* **46**, 109-127 (1984).

57. Miller, K. G., Feigenson, M. D., Wright, J. D. & Clement, B. M. *Paleoceanography* **6**, 33-52 (1991).

58. Davies, T. A., Hay, W. W., Southam, J. R. & Worsley, T. R. *Science* **197**, 53-55(1977).

59. Opdyke, B. N. & Wilkinson, B. H. *Paleoceanography* **3**, 685-703 (1988).

60. Shemesh, A., Mortlock, R. A. & Froelich, P. N. *Paleoceanography* **4**, 221-234 (1989).

61. Shackleton, N. J. *Marine Petroleum Source Rocks* (eds Brooks, J. & Fleet, A. J.) 423-434 (Geological Society of London, 1987).

62. Berner, R. A. & Canfield, D. E. *Am. J. Sci.* **289**, 333-361 (1989).

63. Donnelly, T. W. *Geology* **10**, 451-454 (1982).

64. Hay, W. W. *Proc. int. Geol. Congr. 27th* **6**, 15-38 (1984).

65. Hay, W. W., Shaw, C. A. & Wold, C. N. *Geol. Rundsch.* **78**, 207-242 (1989).

66. Froelich, P. N., Bender, M. L., Luedtke, N. A., Heath, G. R. & DeVries, T. *Am. J. Sci.* **282**, 474-511 (1982).

67. Broecker, W. S. & Peng, T.-H. *Tracers in the Sea* (Eldigio, Palisades, New York, 1982).

68. Demaison, G. J. & Moore, G. T. *Bull. Am. Assoc. Petrol. Geol.* **64**, 1179-1209 (1980).

69. Emerson, S., Fischer, K., Reimers, C. & Heggie, D. *Deep Sea Res.* **32**, 1-21 (1985).

70. Emerson, S. *The Carbon Cycle and Atmospheric CO₂: Natural Variations Archean to Present* (eds Sundquist, E. T. & Broecker, W. S.) 78-87 (Am. geophys. Un., Washington DC, 1985).

71. Pedersen, T. F. & Calvert, S. E. *Am. Assoc. Petrol. Geol. Bull.* **74**, 454-466 (1990).

72. Betts, J. N. & Holland, H. D. *Palaeogeogr. Palaeoclimatol. Palaeoecol.* **97**, 5-18 (1991).

73. Keigwin, L. D. & Corliss, B. H. *Geol. Soc. Am. Bull.* **97**, 335-345 (1986).

74. Drever, J. I. *The Geochemistry of Natural Waters* (Prentice-Hall, Englewood Cliffs, New Jersey,1988).

75. Dewey, J. F. & Burke, K. C. A. *J. Geol.* **81**, 683-692 (1973).

76. Arthur, M. A., Dean, W. E. & Claypool, G. E. *Nature* **315**, 216-218 (1985).

77. Jasper, J. P. & Hayes, J. M. *Nature* **347**, 462-464 (1990).

78. Rau, G. H., Froelich, P. N., Takahashi, T. & DesMarais, D. J. *Paleoceanography* **6**, 335-347(1991).

Acknowledgements. We thank W. Dietrich, R. Jeanloz, W. Broecker and P. Molnar for reviews. D. DePaolo and K. Miller provided copies of their figures. This work was supported by the NSF.

915

Curling and Closure of Graphitic Networks under Electron-Beam Irradiation

D. Ugarte

Editor's Note

After the discovery of cage-like carbon molecules called fullerenes and tubular structures called carbon nanotubes, it was suspected that sheets of graphite-like carbon might adopt a range of nanoscale structures in a kind of molecular origami. Here Daniel Ugarte at EPFL in Lausanne, Switzerland, reports another such variant: onion-like structures comprised of nested spherical shells of carbon. Some suggested that these were like giant fullerenes, although it transpired that the shells contain many crystal defects and breaks. Carbon "onions" with hollow centres have since been used to study encapsulated materials, and intense pressures at their centres may transform graphite-like carbon into diamond.

The discovery[1] of buckminsterfullerene (C_{60}) and its production in macroscopic quantities[2] has stimulated a great deal of research. More recently, attention has turned towards other curved graphitic networks, such as the giant fullerenes (C_n, $n>100$)[3,4] and carbon nanotubes[5-8]. A general mechanism has been proposed[9] in which the graphitic sheets bend in an attempt to eliminate the highly energetic dangling bonds present at the edge of the growing structure. Here, I report the response of carbon soot particles and tubular graphitic structures to intense electron-beam irradiation in a high-resolution electron microscope; such conditions resemble a high-temperature regime, permitting a degree of structural fluidity. With increased irradiation, there is a gradual reorganization of the initial material into quasi-spherical particles composed of concentric graphitic shells. This lends weight to the nucleation scheme proposed[9] for fullerenes, and moreover, suggests that planar graphite may not be the most stable allotrope of carbon in systems of limited size.

THE remarkable stability of the C_{60} molecule has been attributed to its highly symmetrical structure where the carbon atoms are arranged at the vertices of a truncated icosahedron[1]. The C_{60} molecule may be viewed as a hexagonal graphitic sheet which, by incorporating pentagons, has eliminated all dangling bonds, curling to form a hollow ball (7.1 Å in diameter). For all fullerenes, the strain due to the bending of the sp^2 orbitals tends to concentrate at the vertices of the pentagons. The outstanding stability of the C_{60} molecule is due both to the fact that this is the smallest carbon cage where there are no adjacent pentagons, and to its spherical form which allows the strain to be symmetrically distributed over all atoms[10].

石墨网络在电子束照射下的卷曲与闭合

丹尼尔·乌加特

编者按

在发现称为富勒烯的笼状碳分子和称为碳纳米管的微管结构分子后，有人估计层状石墨碳可能产生一系列折纸状纳米尺度分子。本文中，瑞士洛桑联邦理工学院的丹尼尔·乌加特报道了另一个这样的变体：由碳组成的球壳嵌套构成的洋葱状结构。一些人认为它们像巨型富勒烯，尽管人们知道其外壳中含有许多晶体缺陷和断裂。具有空心中心的"洋葱"碳已被用于封装材料的研究，在其中心的巨大压强可以把石墨状碳变成金刚石。

巴克敏斯特富勒烯（C_{60}）的发现 [1] 和它的批量制备 [2] 已经激发了大量研究。最近，人们已将注意力转向其他弯曲的石墨网络，例如巨型富勒烯（$C_n, n > 100$）[3,4] 和碳纳米管 [5-8]。通常理论认为 [9]，石墨层之所以发生弯曲，其目的在于消除出现于生长中的结构边缘的高能悬挂键。这里我要报道在高分辨率电子显微镜中的炭黑粒子和微管形石墨结构对于强电子束照射的反应；这样的条件类似于高温环境，能使结构获得一定程度的流动性。随着照射增强，存在着从初始物质向由同心石墨层组成的准球形颗粒的渐变式重组织化。这为提出 [9] 的富勒烯成核理论增加了支持，而且进一步指出，平面型石墨可能不是碳在有限尺寸体系中最稳定的同素异形体。

一直以来人们都将 C_{60} 分子的显著稳定性归因于其高度对称性结构，其中碳原子位于截顶二十面体的顶点处 [1]。C_{60} 分子可以被看作是一个六角石墨层通过引入正五边形以消除所有悬挂键而卷曲成的一个空心球（直径为 7.1 Å）。对于所有的富勒烯，由 sp^2 轨道弯曲而产生的应力倾向于集中在五边形的顶点处。C_{60} 分子出色的稳定性归因于以下两个事实：它是不包含相邻五边形的最小碳笼，并且它的球状形态使应力得以对称地分布在所有原子上 [10]。

In addition to C_{60}, cylindrical carbon structures have been observed[5] in which the graphitic sheet has a helical arrangement. The natural question arises: how is it possible to generate such symmetrical, low-entropy forms from the random condensation of carbon vapour? Perhaps it is worthwhile to contemplate the ease with which these carbon hexagonal networks grow as curved or closed sheets rather than the traditionally planar ones. Chemists are conditioned to think of graphitic sheet structures as flat, where carbon atoms are bound in infinite hexagonal sheets, like chicken wire. In carbon vapour, pieces of graphite sheet would have many dangling bonds; they would have little reason to remain flat, and the physical tendency to reach the lowest energy level available would induce the sheets to eliminate their dangling bonds by curling up[12]. By heating and properly annealing pure carbon in the absence of other chemically active elements, and under conditions that favour sp^2 carbon network formation, it should be possible to synthesize curled nets and closed cages. In fact, this is the situation in arc discharges, which is the technique used at present to produce macroscopic quantities of fullerenes[2], metallofullerenes[13] and graphitic tubules[14].

Under the conditions of observation in an electron microscope, strong irradiation in some respects resembles a high-temperature regime, allowing structural fluidity; for example, amorphous carbon films usually develop slight graphitization under the electron beam. In particular, irradiation usually heats the sample by energy absorption and ruptures bonds through electron excitations. Furthermore, high-energy particles can transfer momentum to the nuclei, displacing atoms to interstitial lattice sites ("knock on"). Such conditions may be realized by electron bombardment in a high-resolution electron microscope (HREM), and consequently the evolution of a sample may be observed, even up to atomic details under favourable conditions. We must note, however, that electron-beam heating may not lead to the same result as thermal heating, because of the contribution of the excitation processes.

We have irradiated carbon soot in a 300-kV HREM microscope (Philips EM430 ST), using an electron dose up to 10–20 times higher than under normal operating conditions (the usual dose is 10–20 A cm^{-2}). Figure 1 shows a sequence of images of a group of irradiated graphitic particles, taken at 10-minute intervals. The original soot, collected in an arc-discharge apparatus, contains mostly nanometric needles formed by coaxial graphitic tubes, with some polyhedral graphitic particles formed by the junction of small flakes of planar graphite (Fig. 1a). All the particles are covered with a thin amorphous carbon layer. In the intermediate image of the sequence (Fig. 1b), particles now show more marked curvature and, in particular, the tubular structures are collapsing. At this stage, the amorphous carbon layer has graphitized epitaxially onto the particles. Finally (Fig. 1c), the electron annealing leads to a sample composed almost entirely of spherical particles. Detailed examination of the particles shows that they consist of an assembly of concentric spherical graphitic cages (see Fig. 2), the distance between layers agreeing with that for bulk graphite ($d_{002} = 3.34$ Å). The apparent disorder in the spherical shells arises as a consequence of the low electron dose necessary for taking the micrographs; under such conditions, the heating effect of the electron beam is insufficient to permit structural

918

除 C$_{60}$ 之外，还观测到了圆柱形碳结构 [5]，其中石墨层具有螺旋形排布方式。由此自然产生一个问题：碳蒸气的随机凝聚是以何种方式产生出这种对称的低熵形态的呢？也许以下问题是值得思考的，即碳的六边形网络作为弯曲或闭合层的生长比起传统的平面层生长更具有便易性。化学家习惯于认为石墨层结构是平面的，碳原子被限定于无限的六边形层中，就像铁丝网一样。在碳蒸气中，石墨层碎片可以含有很多悬挂键；它们很难保持平面形，而趋向于达到可能的最低能量的物理性质将会促使层通过卷曲消除其悬挂键 [12]。在没有其他化学活性元素存在，以及有利于 sp^2 碳网络形成的条件下，通过加热纯碳并适当地退火，应该有可能合成卷曲网状和闭合笼状的物质。实际上，这就是电弧放电的情况，这是一种目前用来大量制备富勒烯 [2]、金属富勒烯 [13] 和石墨微管 [14] 的技术。

在电子显微镜观测条件下，强烈的照射在某些方面类似于高温环境，使结构具有了流动性；例如，无定形碳薄膜在电子束照射下通常会产生轻微的石墨化。特别是，照射通常以能量吸收的方式加热样品并以电子激发的方式打断样品化学键。此外，高能粒子能将动量传递给核，使原子移动到晶格间隙位点（"撞出"）。利用高分辨率电子显微镜（HREM）中的电子轰击可以实现上述条件，同时可以观测到样品的变化过程，在有利条件下甚至可以观测到原子水平的细节。但是我们必须注意，由于激发过程的贡献，电子束加热可能不会导致与传统加热方式同样的结果。

我们在一台 300 kV HREM 显微镜（飞利浦 EM430 ST）中照射炭黑，使用的电子束剂量超过正常操作条件下的 10~20 倍（通常剂量为 10~20 A·cm^{-2}）。图 1 显示了一组经照射的石墨颗粒的图像序列，拍摄间隔为 10 分钟。初始炭黑是从电弧放电装置中收集到的，其中主要包含由共轴石墨管形成的纳米尺寸针状物，以及由小的平面型石墨薄片接合而形成的一些多面体石墨颗粒（图 1a）。所有颗粒上都覆盖着一层薄的无定形碳。在图像序列的中间部分（图 1b）里，颗粒呈现出更为明显的曲率，特别是，微管型结构正在瓦解。在这个阶段中，无定形碳层石墨化并外延到颗粒上。最后（图 1c），电子退火产生出一种几乎完全由球状颗粒组成的样品。对颗粒的详细检测表明，它们是由同心球形石墨笼的聚集体构成的（参见图 2），层与层之间的距离和块状石墨中的相吻合（d$_{002}$ = 3.34 Å）。球层中明显的无序性是由拍摄显微图像所必需的低电子剂量产生的；在这样的条件下，电子束的加热效应不足以使结构

reorganization back to the closed-shell form. Imaging on a much shorter timescale, however, permits the observation of more complete structures. The existence of these structures has already been proposed[15-17].

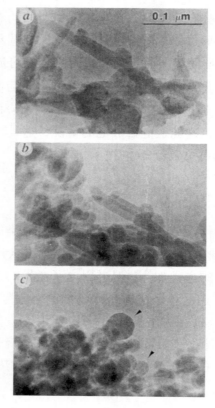

Fig. 1. Sequence of transmission electron micrographs of carbon soot subjected to strong electron beam irradiation. *a*, Original soot containing tubular or polyhedral graphitic particles; *b*, after 10 minutes of strong irradiation, there is a noticeable tendency for the particles forming the soot to become more spherical, especially the graphitic needles; *c*, after 20 minutes, the soot is nearly exclusively composed of quasi-spherical graphitic particles. Further irradiation does not produce significant observable changes in structure.

The final spherical structures do not correspond to the deformation of a tube into a sphere with the same number of atoms (see scheme for single-shell particles in Fig. 3*a*, *b*), but rather to the formation of a multiple-shell sphere with a very small central cage (Fig. 3*c*). The reduced dimension of the final inner shell (0.6–1 nm) allows an increase in the number of shells. Following Euler's theorem, any closed hexagonal network contains exactly 12 pentagonal rings; this is the case in the tube (Fig. 3*a*, the pentagons being situated at the hemispherical domes at the extremities of the cylinder) or in the spherical cage (Fig. 3*b*). The onion-like particle of Fig. 3*c* is formed by four closed shells; in consequence, it contains four times as many pentagons. Our results present clear experimental evidence of the spontaneous tendency of graphite to include pentagons in its hexagonal network and form curved structures. Hence, they support the dangling bond minimization scheme, proposed to explain the growth of fullerenes from carbon vapour[9].

重组回闭合壳层结构。不过，在短得多的时间尺度上的成像使我们得以观测更完整的结构。已有人提出这些结构是存在的 [15-17]。

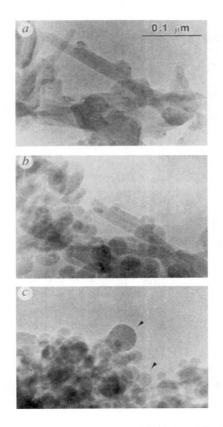

图 1. 炭黑遭到强电子束照射的透射电子显微图序列。a，含微管或多面体石墨颗粒的初始炭黑；b，强照射 10 分钟后，炭黑中的颗粒，尤其是石墨针状物中，出现了明显向球形转变的趋势；c，20 分钟后，炭黑基本上毫无例外地由准球形石墨颗粒组成。继续照射不再产生结构上可观测的显著变化。

最终的球形结构并不对应于具有相同原子数目的管到球的变形（参见图 3a、b 中单壳层颗粒的图解），而是形成包含一个很小的中心笼的多层球体（图 3c）。最内一层尺寸的减少（0.6~1 nm）使得壳层数目增加。根据欧拉定理，任一闭合六方网络恰好包含 12 个五边形环；这就是管（图 3a，五边形位于圆柱体末端的半球拱处）或者球形笼（图 3b）的情况。图 3c 中的洋葱状颗粒是由四个闭合壳层形成的。因此，它包含四倍的五边形数。我们的结果为石墨在其六边形网络中包含五边形并且形成弯曲结构的自发倾向提供了清晰的实验证据。因此，它们支持了为解释富勒烯能从碳蒸气中生长出来而提出的悬挂键数目最小化的理论 [9]。

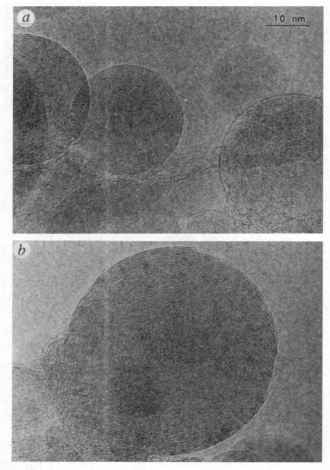

Fig. 2. Detailed structure of the graphitic particles marked with an arrow in Fig. 1c. Dark contrast rings correspond roughly to atomic positions, and the distance between rings corresponds to the (002) lattice parameter of bulk graphite. Note the remarkable sphericity of the particles.

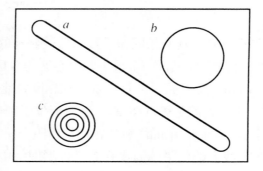

Fig. 3. Schematic representation of three-dimensional particles formed by an equal graphitic surface: a, cylindrical structure closed by hemispherical domes (diameter $\varnothing \approx 1$ nm and 13.7 nm long); b, spherical cage ($\varnothing \approx 3.74$ nm); c, onion-like structure formed by 4 shells ($\varnothing \approx 2.72$ nm), the central one being a C_{60} molecule.

922

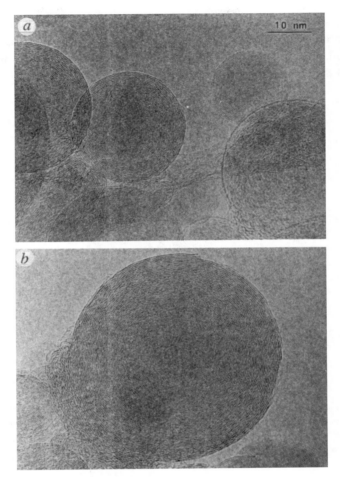

图 2. 图 1c 中箭头所指示的石墨颗粒的详细结构。暗衬度环大致上对应于原子的位置，而环之间的距离则对应于块状石墨的 (002) 晶格参数。注意颗粒明显为球形。

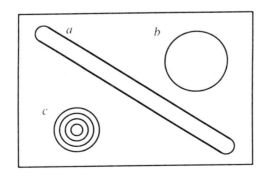

图 3. 由相等的石墨表面形成的三维结构示意图：a，用半球圆拱封口的圆柱形结构（直径 Ø ≈ 1 nm，长 13.7 nm）；b，球形笼（Ø ≈ 3.74 nm）；c，由四个壳层形成的洋葱状结构（Ø ≈ 2.72 nm），中心的那个是 C_{60} 分子。

Curved graphitic sheets can also be formed by irradiation of amorphous carbon particles (Fig. 4). The graphitic structures generated are naturally curled, and two nucleation centres are easily recognizable (marked with arrows in Fig. 4*b*), from which spherical particles will be formed. Further irradiation annealing leads to the separation of the two graphitic spheres.

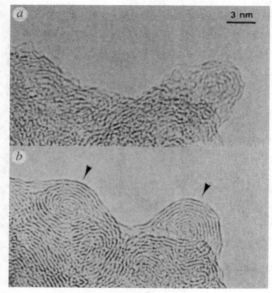

Fig. 4. Transmission electron micrographs of amorphous carbon subjected to electron irradiation. *a*, Original particle; *b*, after 10 minutes of strong irradiation, graphitization (marked with arrows) is present, and the sheets show a clear tendency to form closed cages. Further irradiation would lead to the separation of two graphitic spheres.

The formation mechanism for these multiple-shell spheres is based on irradiation-stimulated graphitization, and is rather different from the accretion mechanism originally considered in laser vaporization and arc-discharge experiments, which would produce spiral multiple-shell particles[9].

The sequence shown in Fig. 1 clearly reveals that if enough energy is provided, spherical structures are favoured over tubular ones. This observation agrees with the predictions made for giant fullerenes[18,19] (monolayers), but van der Waals interaction between the concentric layers should be included in order to compare calculations with the present experiments.

The "spherical graphite" that we have observed may attain a considerable size (47 nm in diameter and ~70 shells for the particle shown in Fig. 2*b*). In a few cases, we have even observed spheres several micrometres in diameter, although in this range of sizes a prolonged irradiation period is required before the particles become spherical. We should not rule out the possibility that even larger (possibly macroscopic) graphitic spheres could be generated by adequate annealing of carbon; the maximum size attainable will give

924

弯曲石墨层还能通过对无定形碳颗粒的照射而形成（图4）。所生成的石墨结构是天然弯曲的，并且很容易识别出两个成核中心（图4b 中以箭头标出），球形颗粒就从这里开始形成。继续照射退火导致两个石墨球形颗粒的分离。

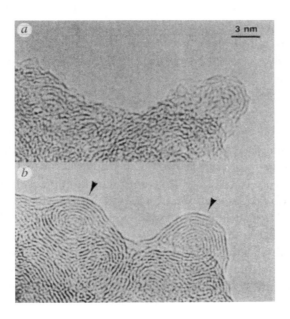

图 4. 接受电子束照射的无定形碳的透射电子显微图像。a，初始颗粒；b，经过 10 分钟强照射后，出现石墨化（用箭头标出），层呈现出清晰的形成闭合笼的倾向。继续照射会导致两个石墨球体的分离。

这些多壳层球体的形成机制是基于照射激发石墨化的原理，并且与最初在激光气化和电弧放电实验中所考虑的堆积机制有很大不同，后者会产生出螺旋形多壳层颗粒 [9]。

图 1 中显示的图像序列清楚地表明，如果提供足够的能量，球形结构比微管结构更容易形成。这一观测结果与对巨型富勒烯（单层）的预测 [18,19] 是一致的，但是要将计算结果与当前实验进行比较，则同心层之间的范德华相互作用也应包含在内。

我们所观测到的"球形石墨"可能具有相当大的尺寸（图 2b 中显示的颗粒，直径达到 47 nm，约 70 个壳层）。在少数情况下，我们甚至曾观测到直径达几个微米的球体，不过要达到这个范围的尺寸需要在颗粒变成球形之前延长照射时间。我们不应该排除下列可能性：更大的（可能是宏观水平的）石墨球体可以利用碳的充分退火而生产出来；所得到的最大尺寸将为我们提供关于闭合石墨层中存在的变形的

us information about the distortion present in the closed graphite sheets. The traditional idea that planar graphite is the most stable form of pure carbon would then have to be seriously reviewed: a flat graphite flake cannot be perfect, and includes many dangling bonds which are usually eliminated by attaching impurities (for example, hydrogen). The "spherical graphite" presented here is a pure carbon material, which has no dangling bonds, and moreover, having a spherical shape, allows a uniform distribution of the strain because of the out-of-plane geometry. Those of us accustomed to traditional planar graphite, initially surprised by the fascinating fullerenes, are now confronted with supplementary evidence that spherical carbon networks can be favoured under high temperature or strong irradiation regimes.

This notion also raises a point concerning the solid allotropes of carbon. When Krätschmer et al.[2] synthesized large amounts of the C_{60} molecule for the first time, they prepared a new, third form, of solid carbon (called fullerite), which is a three-dimensional packing of C_{60} spheres and is distinct from the two traditional crystalline carbon forms, graphite and diamond. Considering the observed tendency of graphite to form multiple-shell spheres ("onions"), of which single-shell fullerenes are only the first member, we speculate that fullerite is the first member of a family of new solid forms of carbon that could be formed by the packing of these onion-like graphitic spheres, interacting through van der Waals forces. Further experimental work will be needed to produce and isolate multishelled graphitic spheres, but a huge family of carbon materials awaits the skill of experimentalists.

(**359**, 707-709; 1992)

Daniel Ugarte
Institut de Physique Expérimentale, Ecole Polytechnique Fédérale de Lausanne, 1015 Lausanne, Switzerland

Received 7 September; accepted 2 October 1992.

References:

1. Kroto, H. W., Heath, J. R., O'Brien, S. C., Curl, R. F. & Smalley, R. E. *Nature* **318**, 162-163 (1985).
2. Krätschmer, W., Lamb, L. D., Fostiropoulos, K. & Huffman, D. *Nature* **347**, 354-358 (1990).
3. Kroto, H. W. & McKay, K. *Nature* **331**, 328-331 (1988).
4. Lamb, L. D. *et al. Science* **255**, 1413-1416 (1992).
5. Iijima, S. *Nature* **354**, 56-58 (1991).
6. Mintimire, J. W., Dunlap, B. I. & White, C. T. *Phys. Rev. Lett.* **68**, 631-634 (1992).
7. Hamada, N., Sawada, S. & Oshiyama, A. *Phys. Rev. Lett.* **68**, 1579-1581 (1992).
8. Tanaka, K., Okahara, K., Okada, M. & Yamade, T. *Chem. Phys. Lett.* **191**, 469-472 (1992).
9. Zhang, Q. L. *et al. J. Phys. Chem.* **90**, 525-528 (1986).
10. Kroto, H. W. *Nature* **329**, 529-531 (1987).
11. Bundy, F. P. *Physica* A**156**, 169-178 (1989).
12. Robertson, D. H., Brenner, D. W. & White, C. T. *J. Phys. Chem.* **96**, 6133-6135 (1992).
13. Chai, Y. *et al. J. Phys. Chem.* **95**, 7564-7568 (1991).
14. Ebbesen, T. W. & Ajayan, P. M. *Nature* **358**, 220-222 (1992).
15. Curl, R. F. & Smalley, R. E. *Scient. Am.* **265**, 32-41 (October, 1991).

信息。平面型石墨是纯碳的最稳定形态这一传统观念就不得不重新接受严肃的审视：平坦的石墨薄片不可能是完美的，其中包含很多悬挂键，它们通常是通过吸附杂质（例如氢）而得以消除的。这里所展示的"球形石墨"是一种纯净的碳物质，其中不含悬挂键，而且凭借其球形形状的非平面几何性质而使应力得到均匀分布。那些习惯于传统平面型石墨且最初为神奇的富勒烯而惊奇的研究者，现在必须面对足以证明在高温或强照射环境中更有利于球型碳网络形成的证据。

这一观念还引出了一个关于碳的固态同素异形体的问题。当克雷奇默等人[2]第一次合成大量 C_{60} 分子时，他们制备出了一种新型——第三种形式——的固态碳（称为富勒烯），它是 C_{60} 球体的三维堆积，有别于两种传统晶体形式的碳：石墨和金刚石。考虑到我们观测到的石墨形成多壳层球体（"洋葱"）的趋势——单壳层富勒烯只是第一位成员而已，我们猜测富勒烯固体是一族新的固态碳物质的第一位成员，这族固态碳物质可以通过范德华相互作用由这些洋葱状石墨球体堆积形成。要制备和分离多壳层石墨球体还需要进一步的实验研究，但是一大族碳材料正等待着实验科学家技能的发掘。

（王耀杨 翻译；顾镇南 审稿）

16. Iijima, S. *J. Cryst. Growth* **50**, 657-683 (1980).

17. Iijima, S. *J. Phys. Chem.* **91**, 3466-3467 (1987).

18. Adams, G. B., Sankey, O. F., Page, J. B., O'Keeffe, M. & Drabold, D. A. *Science* **256**, 1792-1795 (1992).

19. Scuseria, G. E. in *Buckminsterfullerene* (eds Billups, W. E. & Ciufolini, M. A.) (VCH, New York, in the press).

Acknowledgements. We thank H. W. Kroto and W. de Heer for discussions and comments, and D. Reinhard and B. D. Hall for critical reading of the manuscript.

Ordered Mesoporous Molecular Sieves Synthesized by a Liquid-Crystal Template Mechanism

C. T. Kresge *et al.*

Editor's Note

Zeolites, minerals threaded with pores narrow enough to "sieve" molecules by size, have been used for half a century to catalyse transformations of petroleum hydrocarbons. In the 1960s, synthetic versions of molecular sieves were made using organic molecules called surfactants as templates for pores of particular sizes. Here researchers at Mobil in Princeton report a major innovation in the templating of porous solids using organic scaffolds. They find that using a different class of surfactants produces orderly arrays of pores an order of magnitude wider than those of previous artificial zeolites. These so-called mesopores (middle-sized pores) seem to be imprinted by stacks of cylindrical aggregates of surfactants. This provided a general route to materials with regular and adjustable nanoscale structure.

Microporous and mesoporous inorganic solids (with pore diameters of $\leqslant 20$ Å and ~ 20–500 Å respectively)[1] have found great utility as catalysts and sorption media because of their large internal surface area. Typical microporous materials are the crystalline framework solids, such as zeolites[2], but the largest pore dimensions found so far are ~ 10–12 Å for some metallophosphates[3-5] and ~ 14 Å for the mineral cacoxenite[6]. Examples of mesoporous solids include silicas[7] and modified layered materials[8-11], but these are invariably amorphous or paracrystalline, with pores that are irregularly spaced and broadly distributed in size[8,12]. Pore size can be controlled by intercalation of layered silicates with a surfactant species[9,13], but the final product retains, in part, the layered nature of the precursor material. Here we report the synthesis of mesoporous solids from the calcination of aluminosilicate gels in the presence of surfactants. The material[14,15] possesses regular arrays of uniform channels, the dimensions of which can be tailored (in the range 16 Å to 100 Å or more) through the choice of surfactant, auxiliary chemicals and reaction conditions. We propose that the formation of these materials takes place by means of a liquid-crystal "templating" mechanism, in which the silicate material forms inorganic walls between ordered surfactant micelles.

MEMBERS of this family of materials, designated MCM-41, were first observed in electron micrographs of products from hydrothermal reactions of aluminosilicate gels in the presence of quaternary ammonium surfactants. We prepared the MCM-41

利用液晶模板机制合成的有序介孔分子筛

克雷斯吉等

编者按

沸石，一类含有孔道的矿物，其孔径小到足以按大小来"筛选"分子，将其用于石油碳氢化合物的催化转化已有半个世纪。早在20世纪60年代，人们就使用一种被称作表面活性剂的有机分子作为特定大小的孔的模板，实现了多种分子筛的合成。本文中，普林斯顿的美孚公司研究人员报道了以有机支架为模板制备多孔固体的重大创新。他们发现用不同的表面活性剂制备出的有序排列的孔比以前人造沸石的孔径大一个数量级。这些所谓的介孔（中等大小的孔）似乎是表面活性剂圆柱状聚集体堆积结构的印记。这为合成规则的纳米结构可调的材料提供了一种通用途径。

由于具有极大的内表面积，微孔和介孔无机固体（孔径分别为 ≤2 Å 和大约 20~500 Å）[1] 在作为催化剂和吸附介质方面具有重要用途。典型的微孔材料是诸如沸石 [2] 的具有晶体骨架的固体，迄今已观察到某些金属磷酸盐的孔径约为 10~12 Å[3-5]，黄磷铁矿的孔径约为 14 Å[6]，这些是目前在微孔材料中发现的最大孔径。介孔固体包括氧化硅基材料 [7] 和改性层状材料 [8-11] 等，但它们都是无定形或者次晶态的，孔的排列不规则且尺寸分布较宽 [8,12]。虽然孔的尺寸可以通过将表面活性物质插入层状硅酸盐来加以调控 [9,13]，但是最终产物仍然部分保留了原材料的层状性质。本文我们要报道的是，在有表面活性剂的条件下通过煅烧铝硅酸盐凝胶来合成介孔固体材料。所得材料 [14,15] 具有均匀孔道的规则排列结构，该孔道尺寸可以通过选取表面活性剂、辅助化学试剂和反应条件来进行调节（范围从 16 Å 到 100 Å 甚至更大）。我们认为，这些材料的制备是通过一种液晶"模板"机制来进行的，在有序排列的表面活性剂的胶束之间硅酸盐物质形成了无机墙体。

我们所合成的 MCM–41 属于这类介孔材料，它们最先是在含季铵类表面活性剂的铝硅酸盐凝胶完成水热反应后所得产物的电子显微照片中观察到的。我们用如下方法制备这里所表征的 MCM–41 分子筛：200 g 含 26%（重量比）十六烷基三甲基铵离子

molecular sieve characterized here as follows: 200 g of a solution containing 26 wt% hexadecyltrimethylammonium ion, as $C_{16}H_{33}(CH_3)_3N^+OH/Cl$ (~30% hydroxide), was combined with 2 g of Catapal alumina, 100 g of tetramethylammonium silicate solution (10% SiO_2, ratio of tetramethylammonium to $SiO_2 = 1$) and 25 g of a precipitated silica (HiSil), with stirring (molar ratio of $C_{16}H_{33}(CH_3)_3N^+$ to Si $\leqslant$ 1). This mixture was placed in a static autoclave at 150 °C for 48 hours. After cooling it to room temperature, we recovered the solid product by filtration on a Buchner funnel, washed it with water and dried it in air at ambient temperature. The as-synthesized product was then calcined at 540 °C for one hour in flowing nitrogen, followed by six hours in flowing air. The as-synthesized product contains over 40 wt% of the original surfactant as reflected by its composition (molar): 1 N, 19.6 C, 4.7 Si, 0.27 Al. In general, no special precautions (heating rate, atmosphere) are needed during the temperature ramping (from ambient temperature) and calcination processes.

Transmission electron microscopy (Fig. 1a) shows the regular hexagonal array of uniform channels characteristic of MCM-41. A representative electron diffraction pattern (Fig. 1b), with the MCM-41 in the same orientation, confirms the periodicity of the structure. For the sample described above, an interplanar spacing $d_{100} \approx 40$ Å was observed. In the corresponding powder X-ray diffraction pattern of the bulk sample (Fig. 2), the four peaks observed in the low-angle 2θ region can be indexed on a hexagonal unit cell with $a \approx 45$ Å ($2d_{100}/\sqrt{3}$). Generally, both electron and X-ray diffraction patterns show only a few low-order members of the $hk0$ subset of hexagonal reflections. The BET surface area of the preparation is $\geqslant 1,000$ m^2 g^{-1} with exceptionally high sorption capacities of >50 wt% cyclohexane at 40 torr, 49 wt% n-hexane at 40 torr, and 67 wt% benzene at 50 torr. The pore volume of this sample is 0.79 cm^3 g^{-1}. The range of pore volumes for MCM-41 samples is 0.7–1.2 cm^3 g^{-1}. Figure 3 shows N_2 adsorption isotherms for this material and for an amorphous mesoporous silica. The morphology of MCM-41 depends on synthesis conditions, but it is possible to obtain relatively large (~2 μm) hexagonal prisms of MCM-41, as seen in the scanning electron micrograph in Fig. 4.

（即 $C_{16}H_{33}(CH_3)_3N^+OH/Cl$）的溶液（约 30% 的氢氧化物），加上 2 g 氧化铝（商品名为 Catapal）、100 g 四甲基铵的硅酸盐溶液（10% SiO_2，四甲基铵离子与 SiO_2 的比例等于 1）和 25 g 沉淀的二氧化硅（HiSil），进行搅拌（$C_{16}H_{33}(CH_3)_3N^+$ 与 Si 的摩尔比 ≤1）。然后将该混合物转移至高压反应釜中，150 ℃ 陈化 48 小时。将其冷却到室温后，用布氏漏斗过滤回收得到固体产物，用去离子水洗涤后室温条件下干燥。接着，将原位合成产物于 540℃ 下先在氮气流中煅烧 1 小时，再在空气流中煅烧 6 小时。原位合成产物中包含重量比超过 40% 的初始表面活性剂，其（摩尔）组成含：1 N、19.6 C、4.7 Si、0.27 Al。一般来说，在（从室温）升温和煅烧过程中没有需要特别注意之处（加热速率，环境等）。

透射电子显微镜可观察到 MCM-41 特有的均匀孔道的规则六方排列（图 1a）。图 1b 为从具有同一取向的 MCM-41 样品中得到的一张有代表性的电子衍射图，可以证实结构的周期性。对于上述样品，可观测到晶面间距 $d_{100} \approx 40$ Å。在相应本体样品的 X 射线粉末衍射图（图 2）中，低角度 2θ 区域所出现的四个衍射峰可按 $a \approx 45$ Å（$2d_{100}/\sqrt{3}$）的六方晶胞结构进行指标化。通常，电子衍射和 X 射线衍射图案都只显示出几个低指数的 $hk0$ 六方衍射。按上述条件制得的产物的 BET 比表面积 ≥1,000 $m^2 \cdot g^{-1}$，具有极高的吸附能力，可在 40 torr 时吸附超过 50%（重量比）的环己烷，40 torr 时吸附 49%（重量比）的正己烷以及 50 torr 时吸附 67%（重量比）的苯。该样品的孔体积为 0.79 $cm^3 \cdot g^{-1}$。MCM-41 样品的孔体积范围是 0.7~1.2 $cm^3 \cdot g^{-1}$。图 3 给出了这种材料和无定形介孔二氧化硅的 N_2 吸附等温线。MCM-41 的形貌取决于合成的条件，但如图 4 中的扫描电子显微照片所示，我们也有可能得到较大孔径（约 2 μm）的 MCM-41 六方棱柱结构。

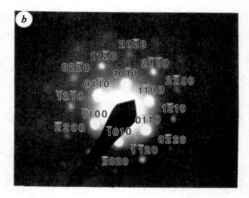

Fig. 1. *a*, Representative transmission electron micrograph of MCM-41. This image was obtained with a JEOL 200CX transmission electron microscope operated at 200 kV from a thin section prepared by ultramicrotomy. The instrument has an interpretable resolution of 4.5 Å and an effective 2-Å objective aperture was used to enhance image contrast. *b*, Representative electron micrograph of MCM-41. Selected area electron diffraction pattern indexed as the *hk*0 projection of a hexagonal unit cell with *a* = 45 Å.

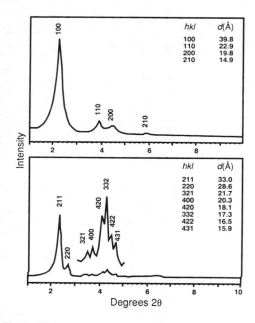

Fig. 2. *a*, Representative X-ray diffraction pattern of MCM-41. The pattern was obtained from a Scintag PAD automated diffraction system using Θ–Θ geometry, Cu Kα radiation (λ = 1.5418 Å) and an energy-dispersive detector. *b*, Representative X-ray diffraction pattern of cubic (*Ia3d*) phase. Inset is expansion of region 2Θ = 3–5°.

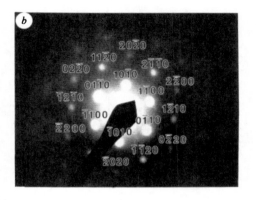

图 1. *a*，MCM–41 的典型透射电子显微照片。此图是从用超薄切片法制得的薄片样品上得到的，所用透射电子显微镜为 JEOL 200CX，加速电压为 200 kV。该仪器可靠的分辨率为 4.5 Å，并且使用了 2 Å 的有效物镜光阑以增强图像对比度。*b*，MCM–41 的典型电子衍射照片。选区电子衍射谱图按 *a* = 45 Å 的六方晶胞的 *hk*0 衍射进行了指标化。

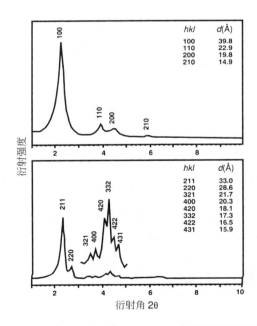

图 2. *a*，MCM–41 的典型 X 射线衍射图。本图由 Scintag PAD 自动衍射系统测得，仪器采用 Θ–Θ 扫描模式、Cu Kα 射线（λ = 1.5418 Å）及能量色散检测仪。*b*，立方（*Ia*3*d*）相结构的典型 X 射线衍射图。插图是 2Θ = 3°～5° 区域的放大。

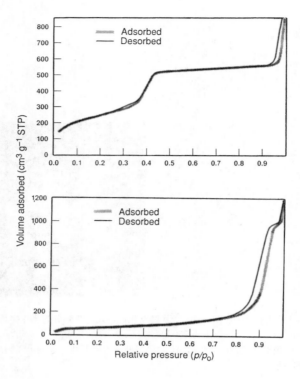

Fig. 3. a, N_2 adsorption isotherm for MCM-41. b, N_2 adsorption isotherm for amorphous silica (BET surface area 306 m² g⁻¹). These isotherms were obtained on a Micromeritics Digisorb 2600 adsorption instrument using standard procedures. The isotherm for this MCM-41 shows the inflection characteristic of capillary condensation within the pores, where the p/p_0 (relative N_2 pressure) position of the inflection point is related to the diameter of the pore being filled[26,27] ~40 Å. The significant adsorption at lower p/p_0 (~200 cm³ g⁻¹) is most probably due to monolayer coverage of the walls and not to the presence of microporous phases.

Fig. 4. Scanning electron micrograph of a MCM-41 sample. This micrograph was obtained on a JEOL JXA-840 scanning electron microscope using conventional sample preparation and imaging techniques.

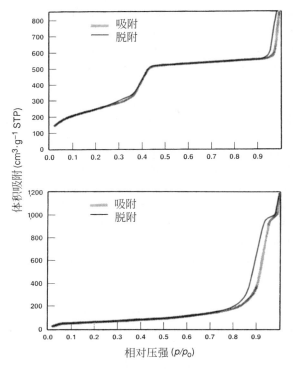

图 3. *a*，MCM–41 的 N$_2$ 吸附等温线。*b*，无定形二氧化硅（BET 比表面积为 306 m^2 · g^{-1}）的 N$_2$ 吸附等温线。这些等温线是在 Micromeritics Digisorb 2600 吸收装置上用标准程序测得的。MCM–41 的等温线上的拐点显示出孔内毛细凝聚的特征，拐点位置所对应的 p/p_0（相对 N$_2$ 压强）与被填充孔的直径（约 40 Å）有关 [26,27]。在较低 p/p_0 处（约 200 cm^3 · g^{-1}）的显著吸附极有可能是源于墙体上的单层覆盖而不是源于微孔相的存在。

图 4. MCM–41 样品的扫描电子显微照片。本显微照片是在 JEOL JXA–840 扫描电子显微镜下得到的。实验中采用了传统的样品制备方法和成像技术。

The nature of the ordering in the walls of MCM-41—that is, the degree to which the atoms are precisely ordered—is not fully understood. We have not detected any X-ray diffraction peaks with a non-zero l component. The large, regular pore channels of these materials would, however, make the $hk0$ reflections dominate, resulting in little scattering intensity along the c-axis.

The pore diameter of MCM-41 can be varied by changing the alkyl chain length of the cationic surfactants used in the synthesis procedure. For example, by substituting the dodecyltrimethylammonium ion ($C_{12}H_{25}(CH_3)_3N^+$) for hexadecyltrimethylammonium ion, we produced a sample of MCM-41 with 30-Å pore diameter. The C/N molar ratio for as-synthesized C_{12}-based MCM-41 is 15, which is consistent with the surfactant remaining intact. Another way of altering the pore diameter of MCM-41 is to add auxiliary hydrocarbons, such as alkylated benzene (for example 1,3,5-trimethylbenzene), to the synthesis mixture[16]. The incremental addition of 1,3,5-trimethylbenzene results in the concomitant increase of d_{100} and the pore diameter. Hexagonal phases with pore diameters up to ~100 Å have been characterized.

The microscopy and diffraction results presented above are strikingly similar (R. M. Dessau and C. D. Chang, personal communication) to those obtained[17-19] from lyotropic liquid-crystal phases which are produced in surfactant-water mixtures. These phases are ordered arrays of surfactant aggregates which occur at specific amphiphile concentrations[20,21]. One such phase, the "middle" or "H_1" phase, produces transmission electron microscope images[22] analogous to those of MCM-41. The H_1 phase is a hexagonal array of cylindrical micelles in which the hydrophobic hydrocarbon chains are gathered in the centre and the polar groups are arrayed on the surface, in contact with a continuous region of water surrounding the micelles[20]. The repeat dimensions of the MCM-41 prepared as described above are consistent with those determined for hexadecyltrimethylammonium-based liquid crystals, where cylinder-to-cylinder repeat distances of ~40 Å have been observed[20].

The observed dependence on alkyl chain length and the influence of auxiliary organic molecules on the resultant inorganic product are also consistent with two phenomena observed for liquid crystals. The diameter of hexagonal liquid-crystal phases prepared with anionic surfactants depends on the alkyl chain length of the surfactant[20,21]. Organic species may be solubilized inside the hydrophobic regions of micelles, causing an increase in micelle diameter[21,23]. Chemicals added to surfactant solutions can increase the porosity of amorphous adsorbants[24].

These similarities suggest that these mesoporous molecular sieves are formed by a "liquid-crystal templating" mechanism. In this mechanism (Fig. 5), inorganic material occupies the continuous solvent (water) region to create inorganic walls between the surfactant cylinders. It may be that encapsulation occurs because anionic aluminosilicate species enter the solvent region to balance the cationic hydrophilic surfaces of the micelles. Alternatively, it may be the introduction of the aluminosilicate species themselves that mediates the hexagonal ordering. Once an ordered array is established, subsequent thermal processing

938

MCM–41 墙体中的有序属性，即原子精确排列的有序程度，目前尚不完全清楚。我们没有检测到任何 $l \neq 0$ 的 X 射线衍射峰。这可能是由于材料中大的规则孔道使得 $hk0$ 衍射占主要地位，从而导致沿 c 轴的散射强度显得非常弱。

改变合成过程中所用阳离子表面活性剂的烷基链长度可以改变 MCM–41 的孔径大小。例如，用十二烷基三甲基铵离子（$C_{12}H_{25}(CH_3)_3N^+$）来代替十六烷基三甲基铵离子，我们制备出一种孔径为 30 Å 的 MCM–41 样品。所合成的基于 C_{12} 的 MCM–41 中，C/N 摩尔比为 15，这与未反应时的表面活性剂是一致的。另一种改变 MCM–41 孔径的方法是向合成混合物中添加辅助性的碳氢化合物，比如烷基苯（例如 1,3,5–三甲基苯）[16]。1,3,5–三甲基苯添加量的增多使得 d_{100} 和孔径随之相应增大。孔径高达约 100 Å 的六方相已经得到表征。

上文给出的显微和衍射结果与从表面活性剂 / 水混合体系所形成的溶致液晶相中得到的[17-19] 极为相似（德绍和张，个人交流）。那些溶致液晶相是在特定的双亲分子浓度下出现的表面活性剂聚集体的有序排列[20,21]。其中的一个相，即所谓"中间"或"H_1"相，能给出与 MCM–41 类似的透射电子显微图像[22]。H_1 相是一种圆柱形胶束的六方排列，表面活性剂的疏水性烃基链聚集在胶束中心；而极性基团则排列在胶束表面上，与胶束周围水的连续区域保持接触[20]。依上述方法制备的 MCM–41 的重复尺寸与基于十六烷基三甲基铵的液晶所决定的尺寸相吻合，在后者中观测到圆柱到圆柱的重复距离约为 40 Å[20]。

我们在对所得无机产物的研究中已观察到其对烷基链长的依赖性及辅助性有机分子对其的影响，这也与在液晶中观察到的两种现象相一致。用阴离子表面活性剂制备的六方液晶相的直径取决于表面活性剂的烷基链长度[20,21]。有机物可能溶入胶束的疏水区域，从而导致胶束直径增大[21,23]。向表面活性剂溶液中添加化学物质能够增加无定形吸附剂的多孔性[24]。

上述这些相似性意味着我们合成的介孔分子筛是通过一种"液晶模板"机制形成的。在这种机制（图 5）中，无机物质占据着连续溶剂（水）区域，从而在表面活性剂柱体之间形成无机墙体。产生这种包封的原因可能是由于铝硅酸盐的阴离子进入了溶剂区域以平衡胶束的阳离子亲水表面。而另一种可能性是，引入的铝硅酸盐类物质本身也许就可以介导六方有序排列。一旦建立了有序排列，随后的热处理

is used to remove the organic material and produce a stable mesoporous molecular sieve.

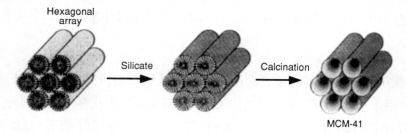

Fig. 5. Schematic drawing of the liquid-crystal templating mechanism. Hexagonal arrays of cylindrical micelles form (possibly mediated by the presence of silicate ions), with the polar groups of the surfactants (light grey) to the outside. Silicate species (dark grey) then occupy the spaces between the cylinders. The final calcination step burns off the original organic material, leaving hollow cylinders of inorganic material.

Although other workers[13] have produced mesoporous silicates with high surface areas, the mechanism used has been the intercalation of a guest (such as hexadecyltrimethylammonium chloride) into a layered host (such as kanemite). The mesopores of these materials are not an ordered regular array (as observed in MCM-41). The final product retains, in part, the layered nature of the kanemite precursor. Furthermore, the concentrations, reagents, pH and reaction conditions are not conducive for liquid-crystal formation and templating.

Additional strong evidence for the proposed liquid-crystal templating mechanism is the discovery of another member of this family[14,15] that mimics a liquid-crystal structure[25]. A representative powder X-ray diffraction pattern of a silicate molecular sieve with cubic symmetry ($Ia3d$) is given in Fig. 2. The cubic phase is prepared by increasing the molar ratio of $C_{16}H_{33}(CH_3)_3N^+$ to Si to values greater than one.

(**359**, 710-712; 1992)

C. T. Kresge[*], M. E. Leonowicz[*], W. J. Roth[*], J. C. Vartuli[*] & J. S. Beck[†]
Mobil Research and Development Corporation,
[*] Paulsboro Research Laboratory, Paulsboro, New Jersey 08066, USA
[†] Central Research Laboratory, Princeton, New Jersey 08543, USA

Received 1 May; accepted 1 September 1992.

References:
1. IUPAC Manual of Symbols and Terminology *Pure appl. Chem.* **31**, 578 (1972).
2. Meier, W. M. & Olson, D. H. *Atlas of Zeolite Structure Types*, 2nd Edn (Butterworths, London, 1988).
3. Davis, M. E., Saldarriaga, C., Montes, C., Garces, J. & Crowder, C. *Nature* **331**, 698-699 (1988).
4. Dessau, R. M., Schlenker, J. L. & Higgins, J. B. *Zeolites* **10**, 522-524 (1990).
5. Estermann, M., McCusker, L. B., Baerlocher, C., Merrouche, A. & Kessler, H. *Nature* **352**, 320-323 (1991).
6. Moore, P. B. & Shen, J. *Nature* **306**, 356-358 (1983).
7. Iler, R. K. *The Chemistry of Silica* (Wiley, New York, 1979).
8. Pinnavaia, T. J. *Science* **220**, 365-371 (1983).

可除去有机物并且产生稳定的介孔分子筛。

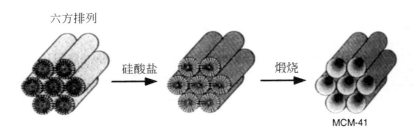

图 5. 液晶模板机制的示意图。表面活性剂的极性基团（浅灰色）指向外侧的圆柱形胶束形成六方排列
  （可能经由硅酸盐离子的介导）。然后，硅酸盐组分（深灰色）占据圆柱之间的空间。最后的煅烧步骤
  除去了初始有机物，而留下无机材料的空心圆柱体。

虽然其他研究者也已制备出了具有高比表面积的介孔硅酸盐，但他们所用的方法都是在层状主体中（例如水硅钠石）插入客体分子（例如十六烷基三甲基氯化铵）[13]。那些材料中的介孔并不具有有序的规则排列（即与在 MCM–41 中所观察到的不同）。并且，其最终产物仍然部分保留着水硅钠石前驱体的层状性质。此外，其所用的浓度、反应试剂、pH 和反应条件也不利于液晶的形成和模板作用。

进一步支持我们所提出的液晶模板机制的有力证据是对另一种这类材料的发现[14,15]，其结构也是模拟了一种液晶结构[25]。图 2 中给出了具有立方对称性（$Ia3d$）的硅酸盐分子筛的典型 X 射线粉末衍射图。该立方相是通过将 $C_{16}H_{33}(CH_3)_3N^+$ 与 Si 的摩尔比增加到超过 1 而制备得到的。

（王耀杨 翻译；陈尔强 审稿）

9. Landis, M. E. *et al. J. Am. Chem. Soc.* **113**, 3189-3190 (1991).

10. Vaughan, D. E. W. & Lussier, R. J. *Proc. 5th int. Conf. Zeolites* (ed. Rees, L. V. C.) 94-100 (Heyden, London, 1980).

11. Vaughan, D. E. W. *Am. Chem. Soc. Symp. Series* **368**, 308-325 (1988).

12. Tindwa, R. M., Ellis, D. K., Peng, G. Z. & Clearfield, A. *J. Chem. Soc. Faraday Trans. 1*, **81**, 545-548 (1985).

13. Yanagisawa, T., Shimizu, T., Kazuyuki, K. & Kato, C. *Bull. Chem. Soc. Jpn* **63**, 988-992 (1990).

14. Kresge, C. T., Leonowicz, M. E., Roth, W. J. & Vartuli, J. C. *U.S. Patent No. 5,098,684* (1992); *U.S. Patent No. 5,102,643* (1992).

15. Beck, J. S. *et al. U.S. Patent No. 5,108,725* (1992).

16. Beck, J. S. *U.S. Patent No. 5,057,296* (1991).

17. Ekwall, P. *Advances in Liquid Crystals*, Vol. 1 (ed. Brown, G. H.) (Academic, New York, 1971).

18. Ekwall, P., Mandell, L. & Fontell, K. *Liquid Crystals* (ed. Brown, G. H.) 325-334 (Gordon and Breach, London, 1969).

19. Luzzati, V. *Biological Membranes* (ed. Chapman, D.) 71-123 (Academic, New York, 1968).

20. Tiddy, G. J. T. *Phys. Rep.* **57**, No. 1, 1-46 (1980).

21. Winsor, P. A. *Chem. Rev.* **68**, No. 1, 1-40 (1968).

22. Goodman, J. F. & Clunie, J. S. *Electron Microscopy of Liquid Crystals. Liquid Crystals and Plastic Crystals*, Vol. 2 (eds. Gray, G. W. & Winsor, P. A.) 1-23 (Wiley, New York, 1974).

23. Speght, P. P. A., Skoulios, A. E. & Luzzati, V. *Acta cryst.* **14**, 866-872 (1961).

24. Komarov, V. S. & Kuznetsova, T. F. *Vesti Akad. Navuk BSSR* No. 2, 22-27 (1978).

25. Luzzati, V. & Speght, P. P. A. *Nature* **215**, 701-704, (1967).

26. Gregg, S. J. & Sing, K. S. W. *Adsorption, Surface Area, and Porosity*, 2nd Edn (Academic, New York, 1982).

27. Barrett, E. P., Joyner, L. G. & Halenda, P. P. *J. Am. Chem. Soc.* **73**, 373-380 (1951).

Acknowledgements. We thank the technical staff of the Paulsboro and Central Research Laboratories, Mobil Research and Development Corporation, for discussions. In particular, we thank C. D. Chang, R. M. Dessau and H. M. Princen for alerting us to references and for discussions, D. T. Geston and K. G. Simmons for assistance, J. B. Higgins and N. H. Goeke for the scanning electron micrograph, J. L. Schlenker for assistance in X-ray diffraction pattern indexing and Mobil Research and Development Corporation for its support.

Evidence for Massive Discharges of Icebergs into the North Atlantic Ocean during the Last Glacial Period

G. Bond *et al.*

Editor's Note

Studies of sediments in the North Atlantic Ocean had revealed layers of minerals thought to have been carried by icebergs and deposited when the ice melted. These "Heinrich layers", formed during the last ice age, were a mystery. Here oceanographer Gerard Bond and colleagues show that the deposits can be used to track the paths of icebergs from the coast of Canada, where they broke away from the Laurentide ice sheet. At this point the cause was puzzling, since no significant warming was known at those times. It is now thought that such Heinrich events, probably due to surges in the ice sheets, could have altered ocean circulation patterns, and North Atlantic climate, through freshening of sea water by melted ice.

Sediments in the North Atlantic ocean contain a series of layers that are rich in ice-rafted debris and unusually poor in foraminifera[1]. Here we present evidence that the most recent six of these "Heinrich layers", deposited between 14,000 and 70,000 years ago, record marked decreases in sea surface temperature and salinity, decreases in the flux of planktonic foraminifera to the sediments, and short-lived, massive discharges of icebergs originating in eastern Canada. The path of the icebergs, clearly marked by the presence of ice-rafted detrital carbonate, can be traced for more than 3,000 km—a remarkable distance, attesting to extreme cooling of surface waters and enormous amounts of drifting ice. The cause of these extreme events is puzzling. They may reflect repeated rapid advances of the Laurentide ice sheet, perhaps associated with reductions in air temperatures, yet temperature records from Greenland ice cores appear to exhibit only a weak corresponding signal. Moreover, the 5–10,000-yr intervals between the events are inconsistent with Milankovitch orbital periodicities, raising the question of what the ultimate cause of the postulated cooling may have been.

THE most detailed study of the sediment composing the Heinrich deposits has been made on cores from DSDP site 609[2] (Fig. 1). High percentages of ice-rafted detritus (IRD) and low concentrations of foraminifera clearly define the six deposits that formed during the last glacial period (Fig. 2). Foraminiferal stratigraphy indicates that these deposits correlate directly with the six deposits originally identified by Heinrich in the Dreizack seamount area[2] (Fig. 1). We have now traced Heinrich deposits in other cores from the North Atlantic and Labrador Sea (Fig. 1), demonstrating that they are widespread

末次冰期大量冰山流入北大西洋的证据

邦德等

编者按

对北大西洋海洋沉积物的研究显示，其矿物层是由冰山携带且当它们融化时沉积的，这些形成于末次冰期的"海因里希层"迄今仍是谜团。海洋学家杰勒德·邦德及其同事发现，这些沉积物可被用来追踪冰山从劳伦泰德冰盖断裂后沿加拿大海岸的运移路径。众所周知，由于末次冰期没有显著变暖，因此造成该现象的原因令人困惑。杰勒德·邦德及其同事认为这些"海因里希事件"（很可能由冰盖激增引起）有可能通过融化的冰淡化海水，从而改变海洋环流模式以及北大西洋的气候。

北大西洋海洋沉积物中含有一系列富含冰筏碎屑、贫有孔虫的沉积层，这些沉积层被称为"海因里希层"[1]。本文我们将证明，距今最近的沉积于 14,000~70,000 年前的六个"海因里希层"记录了海表温度和盐度显著下降、沉积物中浮游有孔虫通量减少以及发源于加拿大东部大量冰山的短暂排入。由冰筏碎屑碳酸盐所清楚标志的冰山运移路径可追踪到 3,000 km 以上——这是一段相当远的距离，证明了表层水体的急剧变冷和大量浮冰的存在。上述极端事件的成因令人迷惑不解，它们可能反映了劳伦泰德冰盖由于气温降低造成的多次快速前进过程，不过来自格陵兰岛冰芯的温度记录却仅显示出微弱的对应信号。而且，这些事件的间隔为 5,000~10,000 年，与米兰科维奇轨道周期不相符，由此引出一个问题：导致变冷事件的最终起因是什么？

关于海因里希沉积物组成的最详细研究是基于深海钻探计划（DSDP）609 站的岩芯[2]（图 1），极高的冰筏碎屑（IRD）百分比和较低的有孔虫含量清楚地界定了形成于末次冰期的六个沉积层序列（图 2）。有孔虫层显示，这些沉积序列与海因里希在德雷扎克海底山脉最初识别的六个沉积层有直接的联系[2]（图 1）。如今我们利用取自北大西洋和拉布拉多海的其他岩芯（图 1）来追踪海因里希沉积层，结果证明，这种沉积广泛分布于北大西洋。我们利用加速器质谱仪（AMS）对 DSDP 609 features of the North Atlantic ocean. Radiocarbon measurements by accelerator mass spectrometry (AMS) at DSDP site 609 date the first three deposits at ~14,300, ~21,000 and ~28,000 years (Table 1), and extrapolation of ^{14}C-based sedimentation rates dates the last three at ~41,000, ~52,000 and ~69,000 years (Fig. 1). Comparable AMS ages for the first three layers have been obtained from three other cores (Table 1).

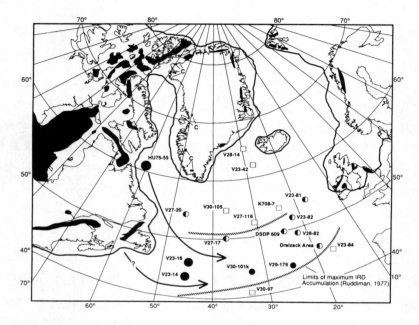

Fig. 1. Location of cores containing Heinrich deposits (deposits with unusually large concentrations of IRD and low amounts of foraminifera) and IRD unusually rich in limestone and dolomite grains. Filled circles indicate that carbonate-rich IRD is present in all Heinrich deposits identified; half-filled circles indicate that carbonate-rich IRD is absent in some of the Heinrich deposits identified; open squares indicate that carbonate-rich IRD is absent in all of the Heinrich layers identified (see Table 3). The solid black pattern is the distribution of limestone and dolomite bedrock (including submerged rocks in Hudson Bay and Hudson Strait) and the thick solid line is the approximate maximum limit of ice sheets during the last glaciation. Cs are small exposures of carbonate rocks. The westward increase in thicknesses of layers rich in carbonate IRD, indicated by increase in the size of the circles, and the widespread occurrence of limestone and dolomite in eastern Canada and northwestern Greenland are evidence that the carbonate-bearing icebergs originated in the Labrador Sea and Scotian Shelf regions. Their transit completely across the Atlantic was made possible by extreme cooling of surface waters, as indicated by the high percentages of the polar planktonic foraminifera *N. pachyderma* in the Heinrich layers (Fig. 2). The arrows show possible paths of iceberg transport.

946

站岩芯进行了放射性碳（¹⁴C）测年，定出最上面三个沉积层的年龄分别约为 14,300 年、21,000 年和 28,000 年（表 1），并根据 ¹⁴C 沉积速率推断，最下面三个沉积层的年龄分别约为 41,000 年、52,000 年和 69,000 年（图 1）。另外还测定了其他三根岩芯最顶部三个层的 AMS 年龄，以供比较（表 1）。

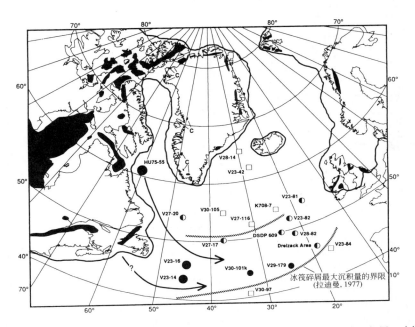

图 1. 含有海因里希沉积（具有异常高的冰筏碎屑密集度和较低的有孔虫含量）的岩芯位置，冰筏碎屑中石灰岩和白云岩颗粒异常丰富。黑色圆圈表示所有已识别出的海因里希沉积层中都存在富碳酸盐的冰筏碎屑；半填充圆圈表示部分海因里希沉积层中缺失富碳酸盐冰筏碎屑；白色方框表示所有海因里希层中均无富碳酸盐冰筏碎屑（见表 3）。黑色填充区表示石灰岩与白云岩基岩（包括哈得孙湾和哈得孙海峡中被淹没的部分）的分布，而粗实线则为末次冰期时冰盖大致的最大界限。C 表示较小的碳酸盐岩露头。富碳酸盐冰筏碎屑层向西逐渐变厚，厚度以圆圈大小的增加表示。加拿大东部和格陵兰岛西北部石灰岩与白云岩的广泛出现是携带碳酸盐岩的冰山发源于拉布拉多海和斯科舍陆架区的证据。表层水体极端冷却使得冰山穿越整个大西洋成为可能，其中表层水体极端冷却是从海因里希层中极地浮游有孔虫厚壁新方球虫（*N. pachyderma*）的高百分比看出的（图 2）。箭头表示冰山搬运的可能路径。

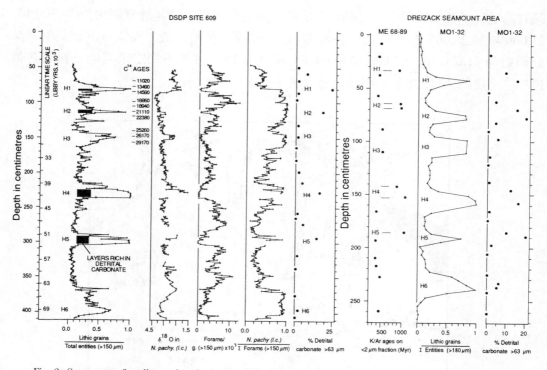

Fig. 2. Summary of radiometric, planktonic $\delta^{18}O$, foraminiferal and lithic measurements in cores from DSDP site 609 and from the Dreizack seamount area. The number of foraminifera size >150 μm per gram and the ratio of lithic grains to total entities >150 μm in cores from both localities defines the six deposits originally identified by Heinrich[1]. Microscopic examination indicates that low foraminiferal concentrations also occur in material <150 μm in the Heinrich layers. AMS C^{14} ages are from Table 1. The linear timescale begins at 175 cm (30,720 C^{14} years, Table 1), and is based on a mean sedimentation rate of 6 cm per 1,000 years given by C^{14} dating and by orbital tuning[27]. K/Ar ages from core Me 68–89 are from refs 6 and 7. The $\delta^{18}O$ measurements were made at Gif-sur-Yvette. ($\delta^{18}O = (^{18}O/^{16}O)_{sample}/(^{18}O/^{16}O)_{standard} - 1$, where standard is PDB.) The gaps in the ratio of *N. pachyderma* to total of foraminifera and in the $\delta^{18}O$ record in DSDP site 609 are intervals where the number of foraminifera is nearly zero. In these cores, four of the Heinrich deposits (H1, 2, 4 and 5) contain layers with unusually high percentages of carbonate IRD that was derived from sources in eastern Canada (Fig. 1). The black bars in DSDP 609 are the positions of these layers in the core as defined by their distinctive appearance in X-radiographs. The detrital carbonate constitutes 20% to 25% of the IRD in both the Dreizack area and at DSDP site 609, determined by line counting the > 63 μm fraction with a petrographic microscope. Based on visual estimates of DSDP site 609 material, detrital carbonate constitutes 40% to 60% of the <63 μm fraction. The detrital carbonate grains are rounded to subrounded and have fine-grained recrystallized textures. At one locality in the Dreizack area, core 244, oolites and fragments of echinoderms have been identified in the carbonate IRD. In addition, the layers rich in detrital carbonate have small amounts of fine-grained authigenic dolomite and unusually low porosities that average about one half that of typical deep sea muds (refs 8, 9). The clay mineralogy of layers H1, 2, 4 and 5 in the Mount Dreizack cores also is unusual, consisting of abundant material from freshly derived acidic and metamorphic rocks and lacking the smectitic products of weathered basalts found in the ambient sediment (refs 6, 28).

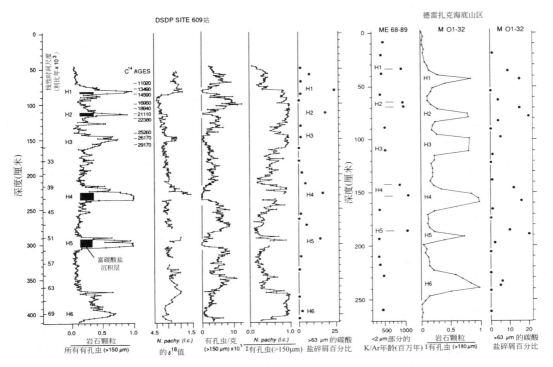

图 2. 来自 DSDP 609 站和德雷扎克海底山区岩芯的放射性测年、浮游有孔虫的 $\delta^{18}O$ 值、有孔虫和岩屑的测量结果。根据两地岩芯中每克沉积物所含直径大于 150 μm 的浮游有孔虫数量以及岩屑颗粒对于所有大于 150 μm 浮游有孔虫总量的比值确定出最早由海因里希识别出的六个沉积层 [1]。显微镜观察显示，海因里希层中在岩屑 < 150 μm 处也会出现较低密集度的有孔虫。AMS C^{14} 测年结果见表 1。线性时间尺度从 175 cm（C^{14} 测年结果为 30,720 年，表 1）处开始，是根据 C^{14} 定年和轨道调谐 [27] 得出的每 1,000 年 6 cm 的平均沉积速率确定的。Me 68-89 岩芯的 K/Ar 测年结果来自参考文献 6 和 7。$\delta^{18}O$ 测定是在吉夫－苏尔－伊薇特进行的。（$\delta^{18}O = (^{18}O/^{16}O)_{样品}/(^{18}O/^{16}O)_{标准}-1$，其中标准为 PDB。）DSDP 609 站中厚壁新方球虫相对于浮游有孔虫总量比值以及 $\delta^{18}O$ 记录的空缺为有孔虫数近乎为零处。在上述岩芯中，其中四个海因里希沉积层（H1、H2、H4 和 H5）含有异常高的碳酸盐冰筏碎屑（来自加拿大东部）百分比（图 1）。这些层在 DSDP 609 站岩芯中的位置根据 X 射线图的独特外观界定，并以黑色条带表示。在德雷扎克地区和 DSDP 609 站上碎屑碳酸盐组分均占到了冰筏碎屑的 20%~25%，该结果是在岩相显微镜下对大于 63 μm 部分进行行计数得到的。根据对 DSDP 609 站岩芯冰筏碎屑的目测估计，小于 63 μm 部分中碎屑碳酸盐占 40%~60%。碎屑碳酸盐颗粒均呈圆状到次圆状，具有细粒重结晶结构。在德雷扎克地区一个地点取得的 244 岩芯，其碳酸盐冰筏碎屑中发现了鲕粒岩和棘皮动物碎片。此外，富含碎屑碳酸盐的沉积层中还存在少量的细粒自生白云岩，且其孔隙度异常低，平均约为典型深海底泥的一半（见参考文献 8、9）。德雷扎克海山岩芯中 H1、H2、H4 和 H5 层的黏土矿物也有异常，由大量新形成的酸性变质岩物质组成，而缺少在周围沉积物中发现的玄武岩风化形成的蒙脱石产物（见参考文献 6、28）。

Table 1. AMS radiocarbon dates for DSDP 609, HU75-55, V23-81 and V23-16

Core	Depth (cm)			Corrected age* (years)	Error (years)
DSDP 609 (*G.b.*)		63–65		11,980†	120
DSDP 609		64–66		11,180‡	190
DSDP 609		69–70		11,020‡	190
DSDP 609		73–75		12,350‡	220
DSDP 609		**75–77**		**13,490‡**	**220**
DSDP 609 (*G.b.*)	**H1** {	**79–81**	←*Hc*	**13,250‡**	**090**
DSDP 609		**84–85**		**14,590‡**	**230**
DSDP 609		87–88		15,960‡	240
DSDP 609		90–91		16,360‡	150
DSDP 609		98–99		16,960‡	120
DSDP 609		105–107		18,940‡	220
DSDP 609		**110–111**		**19,970‡**	**330**
DSDP 609	**H2** {	**111–112**		**20,550§**	**260**
DSDP 609		**112–113**		**21,110‡**	**220**
DSDP 609		**115–116**	*Hc*	**21,370‡**	**220**
DSDP 609		118–120		22,380‡	340
DSDP 609 (*G.i.*)		139–141		25,260‡	440
DSDP 609		**143–144**		**26,570‡**	**490**
DSDP 609	**H3** {	**147–149**		**26,170‡**	**310**
DSDP 609		**153–155**		**29,170†**	**660**
DSDP 609		166–167		30,080‡	680
DSDP 609 (*G.i.*)		174–176		30,720†	730
HU75-55	H1→	81		13,235	190
HU75-55		116		14,610	105
HU75-55	H2→	181		19,455	210
HU75-55		250		21,105	240
V23-81		198–199		12,320§	220
V23-81	H1→	215–216		13,260§	210
V23-81		249–250		16,550‡	190
V23-81	H2→	264–265		18,530‡	240
V23-81		335–336		21,950‡	310
V23-81	H3→	340–341		23,090‡	370
V23-81		400–401		31,250‡	690
V23-81		418–419		30,150‡	770
V23-16	H1→	29–30		10,050‡	150
V23-16		54–55		15,370‡	220

表 1. DSDP 609、HU75-55、V23-81 和 V23-16 站的 AMS 放射性碳定年结果

岩芯	深度（cm）			校正年龄*（年）	误差(年)
DSDP 609 (*G.b.*)		63~65		11,980†	120
DSDP 609		64~66		11,180‡	190
DSDP 609		69~70		11,020‡	190
DSDP 609		73~75		12,350‡	220
DSDP 609	H1 {	**75~77**	←*Hc*	**13,490‡**	**220**
DSDP 609 (*G.b.*)		**79~81**		**13,250‡**	**090**
DSDP 609		**84~85**		**14,590‡**	**230**
DSDP 609		87~88		15,960‡	240
DSDP 609		90~91		16,360‡	150
DSDP 609		98~99		16,960‡	120
DSDP 609		105~107		18,940‡	220
DSDP 609	H2 {	**110~111**		**19,970‡**	**330**
DSDP 609		**111~112**		**20,550 §**	**260**
DSDP 609		**112~113**	*Hc*	**21,110‡**	**220**
DSDP 609		**115~116**		**21,370‡**	**220**
DSDP 609		118~120		22,380‡	340
DSDP 609 (*G.i.*)		139~141		25,260‡	440
DSDP 609	H3 {	**143~144**		**26,570‡**	**490**
DSDP 609		**147~149**		**26,170‡**	**310**
DSDP 609		**153~155**		**29,170†**	**660**
DSDP 609		166~167		30,080‡	680
DSDP 609 (*G.i.*)		174~176		30,720†	730
HU75-55	H1 →	81		13,235	190
HU75-55		116		14,610	105
HU75-55	H2 →	181		19,455	210
HU75-55		250		21,105	240
V23-81		198~199		12,320 §	220
V23-81	H1 →	215~216		13,260 §	210
V23-81		249~250		16,550‡	190
V23-81	H2 →	264~265		18,530‡	240
V23-81		335~336		21,950‡	310
V23-81	H3 →	340~341		23,090‡	370
V23-81		400~401		31,250‡	690
V23-81		418~419		30,150‡	770
V23-16	H1 →	29~30		10,050‡	150
V23-16		54~55		15,370‡	220

Continued

Core		Depth (cm)		Corrected age* (years)	Error (years)
V23-16	H2→	62–63		16,670‡	280
V23-16		144–145		23,400‡	390
V23-16	H3→	184–185		28,240‡	600
V23-16		207–208		31,230‡	880

* Corrected for assumed 400-yr difference between surface water carbon and atmospheric carbon. *G.b.* indicates analyses done on *G. bulloides*, *G.i.* indicates analyses done on *G. inflata*. All other measurements are on *N. pachyderma* (l.c.) H1 and so on are Heinrich deposits as defined by low foram concentrations (see for example Fig. 2). *Hc* refers to layers within Heinrich deposits that are rich in detrital carbonate IRD.

† Ref. 29.

‡ From analyses done in Zurich for this paper.

§ Ref. 19.

Table 2. Foraminifera and IRD sand flux estimates for DSDP 609

Depth interval (cm)		Radiocarbon time interval	Flux of foraminifera >150 µm (number cm⁻² yr⁻¹)	Flux of IRD >150 µm (number cm⁻² yr⁻¹)	
	64–74	1,270	29.31		3.78
H1 {	74–76	1,140	5.39		2.58
	76–84	1,100	7.40	Hc →	10.50
	84–87	1,370	6.34		3.14
	87–90	400	27.57		11.49
	90–105	2,580	26.87		6.07
H2 {	105–110	1,030	9.89		4.78
	110–112	1,140	4.45		2.85
	112–115	260	8.53	Hc →	20.15
	115–118	1,010	9.78		5.25
	118–139	2,880	17.24		4.17
H3 {	139–143	1,310	5.58		1.05
	143–153	2,600	1.97		2.13
	153–166	910	17.79		9.10
	166–174	540	22.76		7.02

Flux estimates were calculated using measured dry sample weights, grain and foram counts, radiocarbon age intervals and dry bulk density. Dry bulk density was calculated using wet bulk density and sediment porosity in ref. 20. Two equations were solved: flux = SI [Σ (pc) × ρ_{dd}]/Δt, and $\rho_{dd} = \rho_{wd} - (\Phi_s \times \rho_w)$, where SI is sampling interval, pc is particle count per gram. ρ_{dd} = dry bulk density, ρ_{wd} = wet bulk density, Φ_s is sediment porosity, ρ_w is density of sea water, and Δt is time interval based on radiocarbon dates. Because layers with carbonate IRD have higher densities than ambient sediment and they lack foraminifera, the IRD flux values for those layers are a minimum. The decrease in foraminifera flux in the H layers is too large to be an artefact of variations in density and porosity of typical glacial sediment[17].

岩芯	深度（cm）			校正年龄*（年）	误差(年)
V23-16	H2 →	62~63		16,670‡	280
V23-16		144~145		23,400‡	390
V23-16	H3 →	184~185		28,240‡	600
V23-16		207~208		31,230‡	880

* 对假定的表层水体中的碳与大气中的碳相差 400 年进行校正。*G.b.* 表示分析对象为泡抱球虫，*G.i.* 表示分析对象为 *G. inflata*（有孔虫的一种）。其他测定结果均根据厚壁新方球虫得到 (I.c.)，H1 等层是根据低有孔虫密集度确定出的海因里希沉积层（示例见图 2）。*Hc* 指的是海因里希沉积物中富含碎屑碳酸盐的冰筏碎屑层。

† 据参考文献 29；

‡ 在苏黎世为本文所做的分析结果；

§ 据参考文献 19。

表 2.　DSDP 609 站深海岩芯的有孔虫和冰筏碎屑通量估计

深度间隔 (cm)		放射性碳时间间隔	大于 150 μm 的有孔虫通量（个 cm^{-2} · yr^{-1}）	大于 150 μm 的冰筏碎屑通量（个 cm^{-2} · yr^{-1}）	
	64~74	1,270	29.31		3.78
H1	**74~76**	**1,140**	**5.39**		**2.58**
	76~84	**1,100**	**7.40**	*Hc* →	**10.50**
	84~87	**1,370**	**6.34**		**3.14**
	87~90	400	27.57		11.49
	90~105	2,580	26.87		6.07
H2	**105~110**	**1,030**	**9.89**		**4.78**
	110~112	**1,140**	**4.45**		**2.85**
	112~115	**260**	**8.53**	*Hc* →	**20.15**
	115~118	**1,010**	**9.78**		**5.25**
	118~139	2,880	17.24		4.17
H3	**139~143**	**1,310**	**5.58**		**1.05**
	143~153	**2,600**	**1.97**		**2.13**
	153~166	910	17.79		9.10
	166~174	540	22.76		7.02

通量估计是通过对已测定的样品干重、颗粒和有孔虫计数、放射性碳年龄间隔和干容重进行计算而得到的。干容重依据湿容重和参考文献 20 中的沉积物孔隙度计算得到。所解两个方程为：通量 = SI [∑ (pc)×ρ_{dd}]/ Δt，以及 ρ_{dd} = ρ_{wd} − (Φ_s×ρ_w)，其中 SI 为取样间隔，pc 为每克中的颗粒数，ρ_{dd} 为干容重，ρ_{wd} 为湿容重，Φ_s 为沉积物孔隙度，ρ_w 为海水密度，Δt 表示根据放射性碳定年得出的时间间隔。由于含碳酸盐冰筏碎屑层的密度高于周围沉积物，且其中缺少有孔虫，因此这些层的冰筏碎屑通量值最低。由于各 H 层中有孔虫通量大大降低，因而不是典型冰川沉积物的密度和孔隙度变化的产物[17]。

Table 3. Thicknesses of detrital carbonate-rich layers within Heinrich deposits (H)

Core	Latitude(N)	Longitude(W)	Water depth (m)	H1		H2		H3		H4		H5		H6	
				d	t	d	t	d	t	d	t	d	t	d	t
HU75-55	61° 30′	58° 39′	2,500	90	40	210	69	*	*	*	*	*	*	*	*
V23-16	46° 00′	45° 03′	2,813	45	25	120	35	205	20	270	50	375	8	550	12
V23-14	43° 24′	45° 15′	3,177	*	*	55	10	120	20	150	15	265	25	380	15
V28-82	49° 27′	22° 16′	3,935	60	5	98	15		*	192	23	*	*	*	*
V30-101k	44° 06′	32° 30′	3,504	37	3	52	8	80	5	98	4	*	*	*	*
DSDP 609	49° 53′	24° 14′	3,884	82	1	113	5	150	0	229	10	296	10	400	0
V29-179	44° 01′	24° 32′	3,331	60	2	83	3	120	1	200	4	*	*	*	*
MO1-32	47° 35′	28° 56′	4,070	42	3	78	7	105	0	157	12	192	5	236	0
V23-82	52° 35′	21° 56′	3,974	90	1	152	5	190	0	270	4	340	2	440	0
V23-81	54° 15′	16° 50′	2,393	220	1	329	3	383	0	495	3	584	2	760	0
V30-105	54° 31′	36° 30′	2,758	110	0	*	*	*	*	*	*	*	*	*	*
V27-17	50° 05′	37° 18′	4,054	33	0	49	5	70	2	95	3	*	*	147	2
V27-20	54° 00′	46° 12′	3,510	56	0	96	2	125	0	210	8	*	*	*	*
V27-116	52° 50′	30° 20′	3,202	43	0	65	0	*	*	*	*	*	*	*	*
V28-14	64° 47′	29° 34′	1,855	150	0	*	*	*	*	*	*	*	*	*	*
V23-42	62° 11′	27° 56′	1,514		NH	*	*	*	*	*	*	*	*	*	*
K708-7	53° 56′	24° 05′	3,502	40	0	100	0		NH		NH		NH	200	0
V30-97	41° 00′	32° 56′	3,371	70	0	*	*	*		*	*	*	*	*	
V23-82	46° 00′	16° 55′	4,513	50	0	*	*	100	*	*	*	*	*		

Core locations are given in Fig. 1. Thicknesses (t) and depths (d) are in centimetres; where layer rich in detrital carbonate is present, depths are at the approximate middle of that layer; otherwise depths are at the middle of the low foraminiferal zone. NH-No Heinrich deposit (that is, no deposit with low abundance of foraminifera) at expected depth. Data for identification and correlation of Heinrich deposits as follows: HU75-55, DSDP 609 (Table 1, refs 2, 4, 5); MO1-32 (ref. 1); V23-81 (refs 19, 21 and W. F. Ruddiman, unpublished data from the National Geophysical Data Center (NOAA); K708-7 (refs 21–23, and W. F. Ruddiman, NOAA unpublished data); V28-82 (% *N. pachyderma* from G.B. *et al.*, manuscript in preparation); V28-14 (refs 21, 23, 24); V23-16, V23-82, V23-83, V30-101k, V29-179, V30-105, V27-17, V27-20, V27-116, V23-42, V30-97 (refs 21, 23, 25, 26 and W. F. Ruddiman, NOAA unpublished data; and % *N. pachyderma* from G.B. *et al.*, manuscript in preparation). In V23-84 foraminiferal abundances have not been measured, but low coccolith zones occur at probable depths of H1 and H3 (ref. 26) and are taken as evidence of Heinrich deposits.
* No data available.

One of the most unusual properties of the Heinrich deposits is the presence of prominent layers with 20% to 25% detrital limestone and dolomite, a composition markedly different from that in the ambient glacial sediment which consists mostly of quartz and feldspar, variable amounts of black volcanic glass and only a few percent detrital carbonate (see for example Fig. 2). These distinctive layers have a well defined distribution in the northern Atlantic (Fig. 1; Table 3). In the southwest, all six Heinrich deposits contain a layer with abundant detrital carbonate. To the north and east, however, H3 and H6 lack these layers, and their IRD resembles that of the ambient sediment. Still farther to the north and in

表 3. 海因里希沉积层（H）中富碎屑碳酸盐层的厚度

岩芯	纬度(N)	经度（W）	水深(m)	H1		H2		H3		H4		H5		H6	
				d	t	d	t	d	t	d	t	d	t	d	t
HU75-55	61°30′	58°39′	2,500	90	40	210	69	*	*	*	*	*	*	*	*
V23-16	46°00′	45°03′	2,813	45	25	120	35	205	20	270	50	375	8	550	12
V23-14	43°24′	45°15′	3,177	*	*	55	10	120	20	150	15	265	25	380	15
V28-82	49°27′	22°16′	3,935	60	5	98	15	*	*	192	23	*	*	*	*
V30-101k	44°06′	32°30′	3,504	37	3	52	8	80	5	98	4	*	*	*	*
DSDP 609	49°53′	24°14′	3,884	82	1	113	5	150	0	229	10	296	10	400	0
V29-179	44°01′	24°32′	3,331	60	2	83	3	120	1	200	4	*	*	*	*
MO1-32	47°35′	28°56′	4,070	42	3	78	7	105	9	157	12	192	5	236	0
V23-82	52°35′	21°56′	3,974	90	1	152	5	190	0	270	4	340	2	440	0
V23-81	54°15′	16°50′	2,393	220	1	329	5	383	0	495	3	584	2	760	0
V30-105	54°31′	36°30′	2,758	110	0	*	*	*	*	*	*	*	*	*	*
V27-17	50°05′	37°18′	4,054	33	0	49	5	70	2	95	3	*	*	147	2
V27-20	54°00′	46°12′	3,510	56	0	96	5	125	0	210	8	*	*	*	*
V27-116	52°50′	30°20′	3,202	43	0	65	0	*	*	*	*	*	*	*	*
V28-14	64°47′	29°34′	1,855	150	0	*	*	*	*	*	*	*	*	*	*
V23-42	62°11′	27°56′	1,514		NH	*	*	*	*	*	*	*	*	*	*
K708-7	53°56′	24°05′	3,502	40	0	100	0	NH		NH		NH		200	0
V30-97	41°00′	32°56′	3,371	70	0	*	*	*	*	*	*	*	*	*	*
V23-82	46°00′	16°55′	4,513	50	0	*	*	100	0	*	*	*	*	*	*

岩芯位置见图 1。厚度 (t) 和深度 (d) 的单位均为厘米。在富碎屑碳酸盐层存在之处，其深度值为该层近似中间的深度；其他深度均为低密集度有孔虫带的中间深度。NH–No 表示海因里希沉积层（即不含低有孔虫丰度的沉积层）的预期深度。用于海因里希沉积的识别和相关性分析的数据如下：HU75-55；DSDP 609（表 1，见参考文献 2、4、5）；MO1-32（据文献 1）；V23-81（据文献 19、21 以及拉迪曼，来自美国国家地球物理数据中心（National Geophysical Data Center (NOAA)) 的未发表数据）；K708-7（据参考文献 21~23 以及拉迪曼，NOAA 未发表数据）；V28-82（厚壁新方球虫百分比含量，据杰勒德·邦德等，手稿准备中）；V28-14（据文献 21、23、24）；V23-16、V23-82、V23-83、V30-101k、V29-179、V30-105、V27-17、V27-20、V27-116、V23-42、V30-97（据文献 21、23、25、26 和拉迪曼，NOAA 未发表数据；以及杰勒德·邦德等的厚壁新方球虫百分含量，手稿准备中）。V23-84 站的有孔虫丰度未测量，但在 H1 和 H3 的可能深度上出现的低密集度颗石藻带（参见文献 26）可视为海因里希沉积层的证据。
* 无可用数据。

　　海因里希沉积层中最不寻常的特征之一是高含量的碎屑石灰岩与白云岩，含量为 20% 至 25%，该组成与周围冰川沉积物的组成有显著区别，后者主要由石英、长石和不定量的黑色火山玻璃构成，而碎屑碳酸盐则仅占几个百分点（示例见图 2）。这些特殊的沉积层在北大西洋中的分布非常明确（图 1，表 3）。在西南部，六个海因里希沉积层中均包含一个富含碎屑碳酸盐的层位。但向北和向东，H3 和 H6 中则缺少这样的层位，其中的冰筏碎屑反而与周围沉积物相似。而再往北以及最南端地

the southernmost samples, none of the Heinrich deposits identified so far contain detrital carbonate. Hence, layers rich in detrital carbonate are confined to the belt of high IRD accumulation that formed during the last glaciation[3] (Fig. 1).

Evidence of at least one source of the carbonate IRD has been found in the Labrador Sea (Fig. 1). Here, H1 and H2 contain thick layers rich in detrital carbonate (Tables 1–3) that was derived from nearby limestone and dolomite bedrock in Hudson Strait[4,5] (Fig. 1). A source in eastern Canada is further supported by the marked westward increase in thicknesses of the carbonate-rich layers (Fig. 1). In addition, in the Dreizack cores the <2-µm carbonate-free fraction in H1, 2, 4 and 5 has an average K/Ar age of 897 Myr, contrasting with average ages of 442 Myr for the >2-µm ambient glacial sediment[6,7] (Fig. 2). The older ages are evidence of detrital clay with large amounts of Precambrian material[6,7], ample sources of which occur in eastern Canada.

Two other features of the Heinrich deposits are worthy of mention. First, each layer rich in detrital carbonate accumulated rapidly. This is indicated by their sharp bases as revealed in X-radiographs of Dreizack[8,9] and DSDP site 609 cores, and by increased fluxes of lithic grains comprising the carbonate IRD in H1 and H2 (Table 2). Foraminifera are well preserved in these layers and our flux estimates are not affected by dissolution. Second, all six Heinrich deposits contain evidence of surface water with extremely low temperature, low flux of planktonic foraminifera and low salinity. In each deposit, the planktonic species *Neogloboquadrina pachyderma* (left-coiled) dominates the foraminifera population (Fig. 2), indicating deep southward penetration of polar water. In DSDP site 609, the flux of planktonic foraminifera of size >150 µm dropped markedly during formation of at least the first three deposits (Table 2). This implies a reduction in the number of foraminifera living in the surface water, although we note that dissolution of foraminifera has occurred in H3. A reduction in the number of foraminifera in surface water could be associated with changes in primary productivity, but it could also reflect other changes in surface water, associated directly with temperature or salinity. Conspicuous decreases in planktonic $\delta^{18}O$ also occur in all six of the Heinrich deposits (Fig. 2). As the foraminiferal assemblages dictate cold conditions, sea surface salinities must have dropped markedly during deposition of each layer.

The evidence we have so far allows us to propose a tentative explanation for Heinrich layers and their unusual mineralogy. First, we note that the layers with abundant detrital carbonate lie within but do not extend through the Heinrich deposits (Fig. 2). This leads us to view Heinrich deposits as a composite of two processes. One was a drop in sea surface temperatures accompanied by reduction of the flux of planktonic foraminifera, accounting in part for the high lithic to foraminifera ratios originally noted by Heinrich[1]. The other, indicated by rapid deposition of the carbonate-rich IRD, was a brief but massive discharge of icebergs, occurring within but not spanning the interval of low surface temperatures. The rapid deposition of this IRD overwhelmed the already reduced flux of foraminifera, producing layers within the Heinrich deposits nearly devoid of foraminifera (Fig. 2). We suggest that shortly after surface temperatures and foraminifera flux began to drop, ice

区的样品中，目前它识别出的海因里希沉积层中都不含碎屑碳酸盐。因此，富含碎屑碳酸盐的沉积层仅限于末次冰期期间形成的冰筏碎屑高度积累带上 [3]（图 1）。

在拉布拉多海我们发现了碳酸盐冰筏碎屑至少一个来源的证据（图 1）。此处，H1 和 H2 含有富碎屑碳酸盐的厚层（表 1~3），它们均来自邻近的哈得孙海峡的石灰岩和白云岩基岩 [4,5]（图 1）。富碳酸盐层向西明显变厚（图 1），进一步证明加拿大东部地区是一个来源地。此外，在德雷扎克地区的岩芯中，H1、H2、H4 和 H5 中小于 2 μm、不含碳酸盐的部分的平均 K/Ar 年龄为 8.97 亿年，而周围大于 2 μm 的冰川沉积物平均年龄为 4.42 亿年 [6,7]，两者形成鲜明对比（图 2）。较老的年龄说明碎屑黏土中存在大量前寒武纪的物质 [6,7]，而加拿大东部有许多这种较老的岩石。

海因里希沉积层的另外两个特征也值得一提。首先，每个富碎屑碳酸盐层都是快速沉积的。这既可以从德雷扎克 [8,9] 和 DSDP 609 站岩芯的 X 射线图中清晰的底部界限看出，也可以从 H1 和 H2 中组成碳酸盐冰筏碎屑的岩屑颗粒通量增加看出（表 2）。这些沉积层中的有孔虫保存完好，而且我们的通量估计并未受到分解作用的影响。其次，从六个海因里希沉积层中均能找到极低的表层水温度、低浮游有孔虫通量以及低盐度的证据。每个沉积层中，浮游种厚壁新方球虫（左旋）在有孔虫种群中占据绝对优势（图 2），说明极地水体向南方深部渗透。在 DSDP 609 站中，直径大于 150 μm 的浮游有孔虫通量在至少最上部三个沉积层形成时期明显减少（表 2）。这表明生活在表层水体中的有孔虫数量已经减少，尽管我们注意到在 H3 中有孔虫已经开始发生分解。表层水体中有孔虫数量的减少可能与初级生产力的变化有关，但也可能反映了表层水体的其他变化，即与温度或盐度有直接关系。六个海因里希沉积层中浮游有孔虫的 $\delta^{18}O$ 值均显著降低（图 2）。由于浮游有孔虫组合指示寒冷环境，因此，当每一个"海因里希层"沉积时海表盐度必定显著降低。

根据目前已有的证据，我们可以对海因里希层及其异常矿物学特征做出一个尝试性的解释。首先，我们注意到，海因里希沉积中出现富含碎屑碳酸盐的层位，但并未扩展到整个沉积层（图 2），这使我们将海因里希沉积层看作两个作用的复合产物。一个作用是海表温度的降低伴随着浮游有孔虫通量的减少，部分地导致了岩屑相对于有孔虫比率的升高，海因里希最早发现了这一点 [1]；另一个作用是短暂但大量的冰山流入，可以从富碳酸盐冰筏碎屑的快速沉积看出，这个过程发生在低表层水温时期内但并没有跨越整个低表层水温时段。冰筏碎屑的快速沉积量大大超出了本已减少的有孔虫通量，形成了海因里希沉积中几近缺失有孔虫的层位（图 2）。我们

streams in eastern Canada (and possibly in northwestern Greenland) began to advance rapidly, leading to massive calving as ice fronts reached maximum seaward positions. This led to the release of large amounts of glacier ice, much of it carbonate-bearing, into the Labrador Sea and perhaps into the Scotian shelf as well. Cold sea surface temperatures slowed melting and the icebergs drifted into the North Atlantic. Rapid transit of huge amounts of this ice eastward along the southern edge of the polar gyre led to rapid deposition of carbonate-rich IRD in a wide belt, reaching completely across the ocean during four of the events.

The absence of the carbonate-rich layers south of the IRD belt (Fig. 1) probably reflects complete melting of ice upon reaching warm water south of the glacial polar front[3]. Similarly, the absence of carbonate-rich IRD in H3 and H6 in cores within the belt is probably a consequence of warmer sea surface temperature causing melting of the ice before it could traverse the width of the Atlantic. The absence of the carbonate-rich IRD in virtually all of the Heinrich deposits identified farther north is consistent with the glacial circulation pattern in which discharge of ice from the Labrador Sea was carried southwards and then in a broad arc northeastwards along the southern boundary of the polar gyre[10].

Melting of the huge quantities of ice drifting across the North Atlantic must have been an important factor in the sudden lowering of surface salinities implied by the $\delta^{18}O$ measurements[1]. Assuming a $\delta^{18}O$ of $-35‰$ for glacial ice[11] and ignoring the decrease in temperature implied by the foraminiferal speciation, the $\sim 1‰$ $\delta^{18}O$ changes require mixing only about 1 part iceberg meltwater with about 30 parts sea water. We note that the accompanying salinity drop is probably enough to shut down the North Atlantic's thermohaline circulation.

Perhaps the most important result of our study is its evidence of repeated, rapid advances of ice sheets in eastern North America and the questions it raises about the cause of those events. One explanation is stochastic surging[2], but that does not account for evidence of extreme cooling of surface water and reduced flux of planktonic foraminifera before and after the discharge of ice into the ocean. The same evidence makes it unlikely that the discharges of ice and melt products were the sole cause of the lowered sea surface temperatures. If atmospheric cooling accompanied the shift of polar water southward, the ice advances may have been forced by falling temperatures. The time intervals between the successive Heinrich layers, however, are shorter than orbital precession cycles (19 and 23 kyr), raising the question of what would have caused the atmospheric cooling. So far, only H1 and H2 have been linked directly to advances of ice streams, and only in the limited area of Hudson Strait[4,5]. Our study raises questions of whether other parts of the Laurentide ice sheet discharged carbonate-bearing icebergs at the same times, whether there are glacial records of the older Heinrich events in eastern North America, and whether there were correlative advances of the Greenland, Fennoscandian and Barents Sea ice sheets[12-18]. If so, those will be the first indications that large portions of Northern Hemisphere ice sheets advanced synchronously on timescales less than those of

认为，表层温度和有孔虫通量开始下降后不久，加拿大东部（也有可能在格陵兰岛西北部）的冰流就开始快速向前推进，随着冰崖到达最大向海位置，大量的冰崩解，由此释放大量冰川冰（大部分含碳酸盐）进入拉布拉多海，或许也进入了斯科舍陆架。海表温度变冷减缓了冰山的融化，使它们能够漂至北大西洋。巨量冰体沿极地环流南缘向东运移，使得富含碳酸盐的冰筏碎屑在很宽的带上快速沉积下来，其中有四次事件中完全穿越了大西洋。

冰筏碎屑带（图 1）南部未出现富碳酸盐层，很可能反映了浮冰在到达冰川极锋以南的温暖水体后即完全融化 [3]。同样地，该带内岩芯中 H3 和 H6 层富碳酸盐冰筏碎屑的缺失则很可能是海表温度变暖引起浮冰在穿过大西洋之前即融化掉的结果。再往北，所有海因里希沉积中几乎未发现富碳酸盐冰筏碎屑，这与该处的冰川环流模式一致，在该模式中由拉布拉多海流出的浮冰向南搬运，然后又沿极地环流南边界呈宽弧形向东北流动 [10]。

巨量浮冰经过北大西洋时的融化肯定是 $\delta^{18}O$ 所反映的海表盐度骤降的一个重要因素 [1]。假设冰川冰的 $\delta^{18}O$ 为 –35‰ [11]，并忽略有孔虫物种形成所反映的温度降低，那么大约只需 1 份冰山融水与大约 30 份海水混合就可使 $\delta^{18}O$ 值改变 1‰。我们注意到随之发生的盐度降低很可能足以使北大西洋的温盐环流关闭。

本研究最重要的结论大概就是得到了关于北美洲东部冰盖多次快速前进的证据以及由此引出的上述事件的成因问题。对上述现象的一种解释是随机性的冰山的大量快速排入 [2]，但这无法解释表层水体极端冷却及浮冰流入海洋前后浮游有孔虫通量减少的证据。同样的证据亦表明，冰的排入及其融化不大可能是海表温度降低的唯一原因。倘若大气降温伴随着极地水的南流，那么冰进应该是受温度降低驱动的。然而，两个连续的海因里希层之间的时间间隔要短于轨道岁差周期（19,000 年和 23,000 年），由此引出大气降温的成因问题。到目前为止，仅 H1 和 H2 与冰流的前进的直接联系被证明，而且仅限于哈得孙海峡地区 [4,5]。从我们的研究中可引出许多问题：劳伦泰德冰盖其他部分排出富含碳酸盐的冰山是否在同一时期？北美洲东部是否存在更老海因里希事件的冰川记录？格陵兰岛、芬诺斯坎迪亚和巴伦支海冰盖是否也发生过同时代的推进 [12-18]？如果推进时代相同，那将首次表明北半球大部分冰盖均同步前进，其时间尺度小于米兰科维奇旋回，上述事件并没有被纳入当前

the Milankovitch cycles, events that are not incorporated in current models of ice-sheet dynamics.

(**360**, 245-249; 1992)

Gerard Bond[*], Hartmut Heinrich[†], Wallace Broecker[*], Laurent Labeyrie[‡], Jerry McManus[*], John Andrews[§], Sylvain Huon[||], Ruediger Jantschik[¶], Silke Clasen[#], Christine Simet[**], Kathy Tedesco[‡], Mieczyslawa Klas[*], Georges Bonani[††] & Susan Ivy

[*] Lamont-Doherty Geological Observatory, Palisades, New York 10964, USA

[†] Bundesamt für Seeschiffahrt und Hydrographie, Postfach 30 12 20, 2000 Hamburg 36, Germany

[‡] C.F.R. Laboratoire mixte CNRS-CEA, Domaine du CNRS, 91198, Gif-sur-Yvette Cedex, France

[§] Institute of Arctic and Alpine Research and Geological Sciences Box 450, University of Colorado, Boulder, Colorado 80309 USA

[||] Département de Minéralogie, 13 rue des Maraichers, CH-1211 Geneve 4, Switzerland

[¶] Institut de Géologie, 11, rue E. Argand, CH-2007 Neuchâtel, Switzerland

[#] Abteilung Sediment-Geologie, Institut für Geologie und Paläontologie, Goldschmidtstrasse 3, W-3400 Göttingen, Germany

[**] Institut für Geologie und Paläontologie, Sigwartstrasse10, 7400 Tübingen, Germany

[††] Institut für Mittelenergiephysik, ETH Honggerberg, CH-8093 Zurich, Switzerland

Received 8 May; accepted 8 October 1992.

References:

1. Heinrich, H. *Quat. Res.* **29**, 142-152 (1988).

2. Broecker, W. S., Bond, G., Klas, M., Clark, E. & McManus, J. *Clim. Dynam.* **6**, 265-273 (1992).

3. Ruddiman, W. *Geol. Soc. Am. Bull.* **88**, 1813-1827 (1977).

4. Andrews, J. T. & Tedesco, K. *Geology* (in the press).

5. Tedesco, K. & Andrews, J. T. *Eos* 72 (44), 271 (1992).

6. Jantschik, R. & Huon, S. *Ecol. Geol. Helv.* **85**, 195-212 (1992).

7. Huon, S., Jantschik, R., Kubler, B. & Fontignie, D. *Bull. Suisse Miner. Petrogr.* **21**, 275-280 (1991).

8. Jantschik, R. & Lohoff, R. thesis Univ. of Göttingen (1987).

9. Clausen, S., Jantschik, R. & Meischner, D. *Nachr. Dt. Geol. Ges.* **43**, 121 (1990).

10. Ruddiman, W. F. & McIntyre, A. *Science* **212**, 617-627 (1981).

11. Dansgaard, W. *et al. Science* **218**, 1273-1277 (1982).

12. Henrich, R., Kassens, H., Vogelsang, E. & Thiede, J. *Mar. Geol.* **86**, 283-319 (1989).

13. Wolf, T. C. W. *Geomar. Rep.* **5**, 92 (1991).

14. Henrich, R. in *Init. Rep. DSDP* 104 (eds Eldholm, O., Thiede, J. & Taylor, E.) 189-232 (U.S. Govt. Printing Office, Washington, DC, 1989).

15. Vogelsang, E. *Ber. Sonderforschungsber.* **313** (32), 136 (1990).

16. Bischof, J. *Ber. Sonderforschungsber.* **313** (30), 127 (1991).

17. Kassens, H. *Ber. Sonderforschungsber.* **313** (24), 115 (1990).

18. Birgisdóttir, L. *Ber. Sonderforschungsber.* **313** (34), 112 (1991).

19. Broecker, W. S. *et al. Paleoceanography* **3**, 1-19 (1988).

20. Ruddiman, W. F. *et al. Init. Rep. DSDP* **94**, 247-349 (U.S. Govt Printing Office, Washington, DC, 1987).

21. Ruddiman, W. F. & McIntyre, A. *Palaeogeogr. Palaeoclimatol. Palaeoecol.* **35**, 145-214 (1981).

22. Ruddiman, W. F., Sancetta, C. D. & McIntyre, A. *Phil. Trans. R. Soc. Lond.* B**280**, 119-142 (1977).

23. Ruddiman, W. F., McIntyre, A., Niebler-Hunt, V. & Durazzi, J. T. *Quat. Res.* **13**, 33-64 (1980).

24. Kellogg, T. B. in *Climate Changes on a Yearly to Millennial Basis* (eds Mörner, N. A. & Karlén) 123-133 (Reidel, Dordrecht, 1989).

25. Sancetta, C., Imbire, K. J., Kipp, N. G., McIntyre, A. & Ruddiman, W. F. *Quat. Res.* **2**, 363-367 (1972).

26. McIntyre, A., Ruddiman, W. F. & Jantzen, R. *Deep-Sea Res.* **19**, 61-77 (1972).

27. Ruddiman, W. F., Raymo, M. E., Martinson, D. G., Clement, B. M. & Backman, J. *Paleoceanography* **4**, 353-412 (1989).

28. Grousset, F. & Chesselet, R. *Earth Planet. Sci. Lett.* **78**, 271-287 (1986).

的冰盖动力模型中。

(齐红艳 翻译；聂军胜 审稿)

29. Broecher, W. S., Bond, G., Klas, M., Bonani, G. & Wolfli, W. *Paleoceanography* **5**, 469-477 (1990).

Acknowledgements. We thank D. MacAyeal and G. Denton for comments on the manuscript, and J. Thiede and T. Wolf for information on possible Heinrich events in the Norwegian Sea. This research was supported in part by the NSF and NOAA. Work on the Dreizack cores was supported by a DFG grant. The planktic $\delta^{18}O$ have been measured with the support of the French CNRS, CEA and CEE(EPOCH). We thank the Ocean Drilling Program for permission to sample cores from DSDP site 609. Support for the core collection of Lamont-Doherty Geological Observatory is provided by the NSF and the office of Naval Research.

Solar Cycle Length, Greenhouse Forcing and Global Climate

P. M. Kelly and T. M. L. Wigley

Editor's note

Although rising concentrations of greenhouse gases such as carbon dioxide are generally expected to increase global temperatures, climate models exploring this scenario did not seem to give temperatures trends that matched with observations. This led some to propose that the observed warming had other origins, perhaps decade-scale changes in the energy output of the Sun caused by the solar cycle. In this paper, Mick Kelly and Tom Wigley of the University of East Anglia, England, try to separate these influences. They find that when the solar-cycle influence is combined with greenhouse-gas effects, the agreement between modelling and observations is much better, although greenhouse gases still dominate the trend. Despite these and other similar results, some climate-change sceptics continue to insist that solar changes, not greenhouse gases, are to blame for global warming.

The recent rise in global-mean surface air temperature is widely thought to be the result of increasing atmospheric concentrations of greenhouse gases[1-3], but there are discrepancies between the predicted response of the atmosphere to this radiative forcing and the observed temperature changes[1-5]. Solar irradiance fluctuations have been proposed as a possible explanation for these discrepancies, and various solar properties (for example, radius[6], smoothed sunspot number[7] or cycle length[8]) have been suggested as proxies for solar irradiance variations in the absence of direct data. Here we model the effects of a combination of greenhouse and solar-cycle-length forcing and compare the results with observed temperatures. We find that this forcing combination can explain many features of the temperature record, although the results must be interpreted cautiously; even with optimized solar forcing, most of the recent warming trend is explained by greenhouse forcing.

W E use an upwelling-diffusion energy-balance climate model[4,5] to simulate the effects of greenhouse and solar forcing over the period 1765 to 1985. In a series of analyses, we vary the climate sensitivity and a scaling factor linking changes in solar cycle length to radiative forcing, and determine the best fit between annual modelled and observed global-mean (land-plus-marine) temperature[9,10] by maximizing the explained variance over the period 1861–1985 (following ref. 11).

太阳活动周期长度、温室强迫与全球气候

凯利，威格利

编者按

尽管全球气温的升高被认为是由于像二氧化碳之类的温室气体浓度的升高引起的，但气候模式在模拟这种特定辐射强迫情景时却没有得出与观测结果相吻合的温度趋势。在这种情况下，有人提出已观测到的全球变暖是由一些其他的原因引起的，例如，由太阳活动十一年周期所导致的太阳辐射输出能量的变化。本文中，来自英格兰东安格利亚大学的米克·凯利和汤姆·威格利试图区分开这些影响。凯利和威格利发现在温室气体和太阳周期的共同作用下，模拟结果和观测值之间吻合得比较好，虽然温室气体仍在变化趋势中占主导地位。尽管存在这一结果及其他类似的结论，一些对气候变化持怀疑态度的人仍坚持认为是太阳输出能量变化而非温室气体引起了全球变暖。

人们普遍认为近年来全球平均地表气温的上升是大气中温室气体浓度升高的结果 [1-3]，但据此计算出的大气对该辐射强迫下的响应与实际观测到的温度变化之间却存在差异 [1-5]。有学者提出，太阳辐照度波动可能是造成这种差异的一个原因，同时，由于缺乏直接数据，许多太阳属性（例如，半径 [6]、平滑太阳黑子数 [7]、太阳活动周期长度 [8]）已被视为衡量太阳辐照度变化的替代性指标。本文我们将利用模式来研究温室强迫因子与太阳活动周期长度强迫因子共同作用下的情况，并将所得结果与实测温度值进行对比。我们发现：两种强迫因子的组合可以更好地解释温度记录中的许多特征，尽管对于结果的解释需要谨慎；另外，即使充分考虑订正过的太阳辐射强迫，最近的气候变暖趋势仍主要是由温室强迫所导致的。

我们采用一个考虑了上涌－耗散过程的能量平衡气候模式 [4,5] 来模拟 1765~1985 年间温室强迫因子和太阳强迫因子的效应。通过改变气候敏感度、太阳活动周期长度和辐射强迫之间的比例因子，进行一系列分析，然后通过最大化 1861~1985 年间的解释方差来调整模式模拟的结果，使之与实测全球年平均（包括陆地和海洋）温度 [9,10] 拟合得最好（据参考文献 11）。

We use two records of greenhouse forcing and allied effects. The first, "history 1", is taken from ref. 12. The second, "history 2", has been derived by Wigley and Raper (their "middle" aerosol forcing case)[13] on the basis of a recent re-evaluation of the forcing associated with, *inter alia*, ozone depletion and sulphur dioxide emissions[14]. The climate sensitivity is specified by the equilibrium global-mean warming for a change in forcing (of any origin) equivalent to a doubling of the CO_2 concentration, $\Delta T_{2\times}$, and is allowed to vary between 0.5 and 5.5 °C. This exceeds the range of uncertainty associated with cloud feedback and other processes, 1.5 to 4.5 °C, based on general circulation model calculations[1]. We assume a simple linear relationship between irradiance and cycle length, consistent with ref. 8. The solar forcing term is defined by $\Delta Q_s = \beta \Delta L$, where ΔQ_s is the solar forcing change at the top of the troposphere, ΔL refers to the series of cycle-length departures from the 1765–1985 mean and β is a solar forcing scaling factor (W m^{-2} yr^{-1}). β is varied between -1.0 and $+0.5$ which implies a range of -3 to $+2$ W m^{-2} for ΔQ_s (-1.3 to $+0.8\%$ irradiance change). We make use of two cycle length records, that presented by Friis-Christensen and Lassen[8], FCL, and our own estimate, KW (Fig. 1).

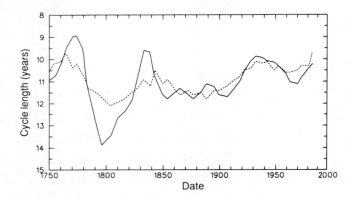

Fig. 1. The two solar cycle length records. Solid line: record derived in this paper (KW). Dashed line: record derived by Friis-Christensen and Lassen[8] (FCL). KW is derived from the same basic sunspot data set as FCL but the raw maximum-to-maximum and minimum-to-minimum length series were combined into a single series before applying a 7-term binomial filter. Differences between the records arise mainly because of the different bandwidths of the filters used. We have used the FCL record as published, although we found that they omitted two minor troughs around 1800 and that a different length for the final solar cycle is obtained when making use of the most recently available data.

Considerable margins of uncertainty are associated with the best-fit climate sensitivities identified in an analysis of this type[3]. First and foremost, we are intentionally considering a limited subset of the potential causes of recent longer-term climate change. Other mechanisms must have played a part[2-5] and their inclusion could alter the best-fit climate sensitivities significantly and lead to improved values for the explained variance. (Some mechanisms, such as internal climate variability[3-5], provide an alternative explanation for the discrepancies between the modelled response to greenhouse forcing and observed trends.) Second, uncertainties exist in the data records used in the analysis and aspects of model formulation, although these are well documented[1]. These problems are unlikely to affect the relative levels of the greenhouse and solar contributions, but they could well influence their absolute levels.

966

我们采用了两条温室强迫曲线，以及温室强迫和太阳辐射的联合效应纪录。其一，"历史记录 1"，从参考文献 12 中获得。其二，"历史记录 2"，是由威格利和雷珀[13] 新近对尤其与臭氧亏损和二氧化硫排放有关的强迫的重新评估得到[14]（这里只取他们文中的"中等"气溶胶强迫情景）。气候敏感度用由强迫因子的改变（任一起因）引起的全球平均变暖程度来表示，相当于 CO_2 浓度加倍所产生的升温即 $\Delta T_{2\times}$，其变化范围是 0.5~5.5 ℃。该范围超出了根据大气环流模式计算出的考虑了云层反馈及其他反馈作用导致的不确定性的范围 1.5~4.5 ℃ [1]。我们假定辐照度与太阳活动周期长度之间为简单的线性关系，与参考文献 8 一致。太阳辐射强迫可被定义为：$\Delta Q_s = \beta \Delta L$，其中 ΔQ_s 为对流层顶太阳辐射的变化，ΔL 代表太阳活动周期长度相对于 1765~1985 年平均值的偏差，β 为太阳辐射强迫的比例因子（$W \cdot m^{-2} \cdot yr^{-1}$）。$\beta$ 在 –1.0 至 + 0.5 之间变化，也就意味着 ΔQ_s 的变化范围为 –3 $W \cdot m^{-2}$ 到 +2 $W \cdot m^{-2}$（相当于太阳辐照度变化 –1.3% ~ +0.8%）。我们采用的两个太阳活动周期长度序列，分别为弗里斯－克里斯滕森和拉森[8] 提供的 FCL 数据和我们自己测量的 KW 数据（图 1）。

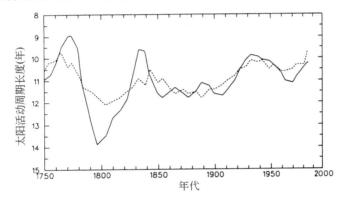

图 1. 本文采用的两条太阳活动周期长度记录。实线：本文得到的记录（KW）。虚线：弗里斯－克里斯滕森和拉森[8] 得到的记录（FCL）。KW 所用的太阳黑子数据和 FCL 是一样的，只是在应用二次多项式滤波器之前将最大值对最大值、最小值对最小值的原始数据合并为了一个序列。两个记录之间的差别主要是由于采用的滤波器带宽不同所致。我们利用了发表过的 FCL 记录，尽管我们发现他们漏掉了 1800 年前后的两个小波谷，由此导致在应用最新数据时得到不同的太阳周期长度。

在该类分析中，最佳拟合气候敏感度有很大的不确定性[3]。首先，我们有意只考虑引起近代长期气候变化众多潜在原因中的一小部分。其他机制也会起到一定作用[2-5]，它们的加入可显著改变对最佳拟合气候敏感度的估计，并会导致解释方差值的进一步增加（例如，气候的内变率[3-5] 就为单纯考虑温室强迫的模拟结果与实测变暖趋势间的差异提供了另一种解释）。其次，分析中使用的观测数据和气候模式中的一些参数存在不确定性，尽管这些数据记录得很完善[1]。这些问题不太可能会影响温室效应与太阳辐射贡献量的相对水平，但却会对其绝对水平有很大影响。

We consider first greenhouse forcing alone (Table 1). For history 1, the best fit occurs when $\Delta T_{2\times} = 1.5\ °C$, with 50.9% of the variance in the observed temperature record accounted for. For history 2, the best fit occurs at a higher climate sensitivity, $\Delta T_{2\times} = 3.7\ °C$, as the global forcing is not as great. This simulation explains 55.7% of the temperature variance. These simulations capture the magnitude of the observed long-term trend in a realistic fashion, but the observed and simulated series differ noticeably on the decade-to-decade timescale (Fig. 2a and b).

Table 1. Effect of different forcings

Forcing.		$\Delta T_{2\times}(°C)$	$\beta\ (W\ m^{-2}\ yr^{-1})$	Explained variance (%)		
Greenhouse	Solar			Greenhouse	Solar	Total
History 1	None	1.5		50.9		50.9
History 2	None	3.7		55.7		55.7
History 1	KW	0.9	−0.58	39.2	21.6	60.8
History 2	KW	2.0	−0.29	41.2	19.4	60.6
History 1	FCL	0.8	−0.59	34.5	21.1	55.6
History 2	FCL	2.2	−0.21	44.8	12.8	57.6
None	KW	25.4	−0.27		61.6	61.6
None	FCL	12.0	−0.31		59.5	59.5

The climate sensitivity, $\Delta T_{2\times}$, solar forcing scaling factor, β, and percentage of the observed temperature variance explained for the best-fit simulations associated with the greenhouse-forcing-alone, greenhouse-plus-solar and solar-forcing-alone analyses. History 1, greenhouse forcing[12]; History 2, greenhouse plus aerosol forcing[13]; KW, present cycle-length record; FCL, Friis-Christensen and Lassen cycle-length record[8].

We now combine greenhouse and solar forcing to determine whether a better fit between modelled and observed temperature can be obtained by including the solar component. For history 1 and the KW solar record, the best fit occurs at $\Delta T_{2\times} = 0.9\ °C$ and $\beta = -0.58$. With history 2 and the KW record, the best fit is for $\Delta T_{2\times} = 2.0\ °C$ and $\beta = -0.29$. The variance explained by these two simulations is 60.8% and 60.6%, respectively. The results based on the FCL record are similar, although the variance explained is slightly less (Table 1). The solar term clearly improves the agreement between the modelled and observed series (Fig. 2c–f); in particular, the marked warming around 1930 and the stable temperatures during the 1950s are better represented. If the explained variance is partitioned into greenhouse and solar components, greenhouse forcing has the strongest influence in all cases although the solar contribution is not negligible (Table 1).

首先，我们仅考虑温室强迫（表1）。对于历史记录1，当 $\Delta T_{2\times} = 1.5\,℃$ 时达到最佳拟合，此时温室强迫在实测温度记录中的解释方差为50.9%。在历史记录2中，最佳拟合出现在较高的气候敏感度上，$\Delta T_{2\times} = 3.7\,℃$，而全球强迫则并没有这么大。它对温度的解释方差为55.7%。上述模拟结果真实地反映了实测气候长期变化的趋势，但在年代际时间尺度上，实测值与模拟值之间差异明显（图2a和b）。

表1. 不同强迫因子的影响

强迫因子		$\Delta T_{2\times}$（℃）	β（W·m^{-2}·yr^{-1}）	解释方差（%）		
温室强迫	太阳辐射强迫			温室强迫	太阳辐射强迫	总和
历史记录1	无	1.5		50.9		50.9
历史记录2	无	3.7		55.7		55.7
历史记录1	KW	0.9	−0.58	39.2	21.6	60.8
历史记录2	KW	2.0	−0.29	41.2	19.4	60.6
历史记录1	FCL	0.8	−0.59	34.5	21.1	55.6
历史记录2	FCL	2.2	−0.21	44.8	12.8	57.6
无	KW	25.4	−0.27		61.6	61.6
无	FCL	12.0	−0.31		59.5	59.5

$\Delta T_{2\times}$ 为气候敏感度，β 表示太阳辐射强迫的比例因子，分别计算出了仅考虑温室强迫因子、温室强迫因子＋太阳辐射强迫因子和仅太阳辐射强迫因子时，最佳拟合模拟结果对实测温度的解释方差百分比。历史记录1为温室强迫因子[12]；历史记录2为温室强迫因子＋气溶胶强迫因子[13]；KW为目前的太阳活动周期长度记录；FCL为弗里斯－克里斯滕森和拉森的周期长度记录[8]。

现在我们结合温室强迫和太阳辐射强迫，以确定是否包含太阳辐射强迫后可得到模拟与实测温度之间更好的拟合结果。对于历史记录1和KW太阳辐射记录，最佳拟合结果出现在 $\Delta T_{2\times}=0.9\,℃$，$\beta=-0.58$ 时。对历史记录2和KW记录，最佳拟合结果出现在 $\Delta T_{2\times}=2.0\,℃$，$\beta=-0.29$ 时。两次模拟结果的解释方差分别为60.8%和60.6%。根据FCL记录得到的结果与此类似，只是其解释方差略低（表1）。太阳辐射强迫显著提高了模拟结果与实测值之间的一致性（图2c~f）；特别是对1930年前后出现的明显变暖和20世纪50年代温度较平稳的特征，都反映得更好。如果把解释方差分解为温室强迫和太阳辐射强迫两个分量，则无论何种情况下温室强迫的影响均最大，尽管太阳辐射强迫的贡献也不可忽略（表1）。

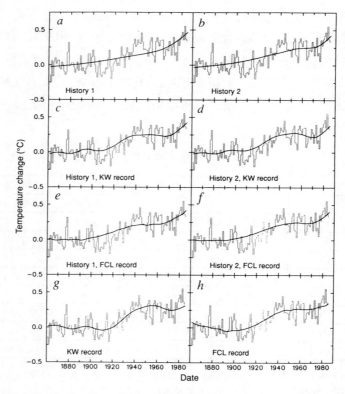

Fig. 2. Comparison of modelled (thick) and observed (thin) global-mean surface air temperature changes as departures from the 1861–1900 mean. (See Table 1 for associated CO_2-doubling temperatures and solar forcing scaling factors.) We use global-mean (land-plus-marine) temperature[10] as it is the best available indicator for the Earth as a whole[9,10,17]. Ref. 8 used the Northern Hemisphere, land-based temperature record as an indicator of global change, claiming these data to be superior to the full global data set, but this is incorrect[9,10]. Before calculation of the explained variance, both simulated and observed temperatures have been adjusted to have the same 1861–1900 mean. We have not filtered the annual data to avoid both a subjective decision on filter characteristics and the inflation of explained variance at the expense of loss of degrees of freedom. *a*, Greenhouse forcing alone, history 1. *b*, Greenhouse forcing alone, history 2. *c*, Greenhouse, history 1, and solar, KW record, forcing. *d*, Greenhouse, history 2, and solar, KW record, forcing. *e*, Greenhouse, history 1, and solar, FCL record, forcing. *f*, Greenhouse, history 2, and solar, FCL record, forcing. *g*, Solar forcing alone, KW record. *h*, Solar forcing alone, FCL record.

Finally, we consider solar forcing alone. No best fit occurs within the specified range of $\Delta T_{2\times}$ whichever cycle length record is used. The optimal pairing of β and $\Delta T_{2\times}$ is found at $\Delta T_{2\times} = 25\,°C$ for the KW record and at $\Delta T_{2\times} = 12\,°C$ for the FCL record. The variance explained by this pair of experiments is close to 60%, and the visual correspondence between the simulated and observed temperature series is good (Fig. 2*g* and *h*). Although these results might be considered implausible because of the extreme climate sensitivities implied, the explained variance at more reasonable climate sensitivities within the upper half of the accepted range of uncertainty, 1.5 to 4.5 °C, remains above 55%. Nevertheless, the overall credibility of the experiment with solar forcing alone must be considered low, as it is illogical to neglect greenhouse forcing given the well-established case for its existence[1,2].

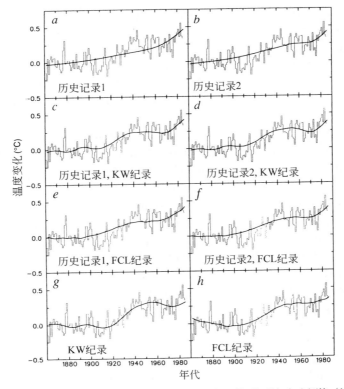

图 2. 全球地表平均气温相对于 1861~1900 年平均值的变化的模拟值（粗线）与实测值（细线）对比。（相应的 CO_2 浓度加倍的温度及太阳辐射强迫比例因子见表 1。）我们采用全球平均（陆地＋海洋）温度 [10]，是因为总体来看它是地球温度的最佳可用指标 [9,10,17]。参考文献 8 采用了北半球的陆地温度作为全球温度变化的指标，并称这些数据优于全球数据组合，但这是错误的 [9,10]。在计算解释方差之前，我们将观测和模拟的温度值调整为与 1861~1900 年的平均值相同。我们并未过滤年平均数据，以避免对滤波特征的主观影响，也避免降低样本的自由度以虚假地提高解释方差。a，仅温室强迫，历史记录 1。b，仅温室强迫，历史记录 2。c，温室强迫，历史记录 1 和 KW 太阳辐射强迫记录。d，温室强迫，历史记录 2 和 KW 太阳辐射强迫记录。e，温室强迫，历史记录 1 和 FCL 太阳辐射强迫记录。f，温室强迫，历史记录 2 和 FCL 太阳辐射强迫记录。g，仅太阳辐射强迫，KW 记录。h，仅太阳辐射强迫，FCL 记录。

　　最后，我们考虑仅有太阳辐射强迫的情况。不管采用哪条周期长度记录，在指定的 $\Delta T_{2\times}$ 范围内都未能找到最佳拟合点。对于 KW 记录，理想的 β 和 $\Delta T_{2\times}$ 组合出现在 $\Delta T_{2\times} = 25\,℃$ 时，而对于 FCL 记录，$\Delta T_{2\times} = 12\,℃$ 时最理想。这两组实验的解释方差接近 60%，并且模拟结果与实测温度序列之间看起来一致性也较好（图 2g 和 h）。虽然这些结果可能会因为其中暗含极高的气候敏感度而显得不可信，但当气候敏感度较合理，位于可接受的不确定范围 1.5~4.5 ℃ 内的高值区时，其解释方差也可保持在 55% 以上。但无论如何，可以认为仅考虑太阳辐射强迫的实验结果可信度很低，因为不管怎样，在很好地证明温室强迫存在 [1,2] 的情况下，再去忽略它是不合逻辑的。

We now assess the plausibility of the greenhouse-plus-solar simulations in terms of their implied climate sensitivities and solar forcing ranges. The best-fit results using history 1 imply climate sensitivities below the accepted range, but they are not beyond the bounds of possibility. For history 2, the implied climate sensitivities are within the accepted range. We next compare the range of past variations in solar irradiance implied by the best-fit values of β with what is known from other sources. The solar and greenhouse components of the radiative forcing for the four best-fit cases are shown in Fig. 3. For the twentieth century as a whole, the variations in solar irradiance implied by the analyses are within the bounds of possibility. For earlier times, though, there are reasons for doubting certain simulations. For history 1 and the KW solar record, the implied variation in solar irradiance before 1850 is much greater than current estimates of the potential range of variability of this quantity. For example, the solar forcing increases by about 2.5 W m^{-2} from 1795 to 1834, an increase of more than 1% in irradiance. Such a change is unlikely. It is well beyond both the departure necessary to account for the Little Ice Age[15] and, more important, beyond the range of potential departures estimated from astronomical data[16]. In two of the other cases (history 2, KW record; history 1, FCL record), the implied irradiance variations about the year 1800 border on inconsistency with the independent evidence cited above. Only in the case of history 2 and the FCL record are the implied irradiance changes compatible with that evidence. In this case, the maximum change over a 40-year period is −0.5 W m^{-2} (−0.21%) from 1765 to 1804. A nonlinear $\Delta Q_s - \Delta L$ relationship may reduce the range of implied solar changes before 1900, but there is no evidence available at present to support a more complex relationship than assumed here.

In summary, our results provide circumstantial support for the hypothesized link between solar cycle length and irradiance. Even in the optimal cases considered here, however, the solar contribution to recent global-mean temperature change is much less than that due to increasing greenhouse gas concentrations and other anthropogenic effects. The value of cycle length data is limited because our results show considerable sensitivity to the filtering method used to construct the record. This implies large uncertainties in the cycle-length-based record of solar irradiance changes over and above those associated with the optimization procedure used to deduce β. The physical mechanism underlying the proposed link between solar output and cycle length must be better understood before cycle length can be used with confidence as a proxy for irradiance changes.

下面我们从气候敏感度和太阳辐射强迫范围两方面评估一下"温室强迫 + 太阳辐射强迫"驱动模拟的合理性。利用历史记录 1 得到的最佳拟合结果中，气候敏感度低于可接受范围，但并未超出可能范围。对于历史记录 2，其气候敏感度处于可接受范围内。下一步我们将 β 处于最佳拟合值时对应的太阳辐照度变化范围与其他数据源所给出的范围相比较。四种最佳拟合情况下的太阳辐射强迫和温室强迫见图 3。对于二十世纪，总体上分析得出的太阳辐照度的变化处于可能的范围以内。对于更早时期，某些模拟结果却值得怀疑。根据历史记录 1 和 KW 太阳辐射记录，1850 年以前的太阳辐照度变化远远大于目前对其潜在变化范围所作的估计。例如，1795~1834 年间太阳辐射强迫升高了 2.5 W·m⁻²，意味着辐照度升高了超过 1%。这么大的变化量是不太可能的，它远远超出了形成小冰期 [15] 必要的偏差，更为重要的是，它甚至超出了根据天文数据估计出的可能偏差范围 [16]。在其他两种情况中（历史记录 2，KW 记录；历史记录 1，FCL 记录），1800 年前后的辐照度变化与上文提到的独立证据也不一致。只有在历史记录 2 和 FCL 记录的情况下，所得到的辐照度变化与上文证据一致。在此个例中，1765~1804 年的 40 年间太阳辐照度的最大变化量为 –0.5 W·m⁻²（–0.21%）。除此以外，ΔQ_s 和 ΔL 之间的非线性关系有可能缩小 1900 年之前太阳辐射强度的变化范围，但目前还没有能够支持两者之间存在更复杂关系的证据。

总之，本研究结果为太阳活动周期长度和太阳辐照度之间的假设关系提供了详尽的证据。但即使在本文所列的最理想的情况下，太阳辐射强迫对近期全球变暖的贡献仍远小于增加的温室气体浓度及其他人类活动所带来的影响。太阳活动周期长度的数据价值有限，因为本研究结果对构建记录所采用的滤波方法很敏感。这意味着，根据周期长度得出的太阳辐照度变化存在很大的不确定性，超过推导 β 时采用的优化处理过程产生的不确定性。要想有把握地将太阳活动周期长度作为辐照度变化的替代指标，还需要进一步认识太阳周期长度与太阳辐照度之间的关系及其背后的物理机制。

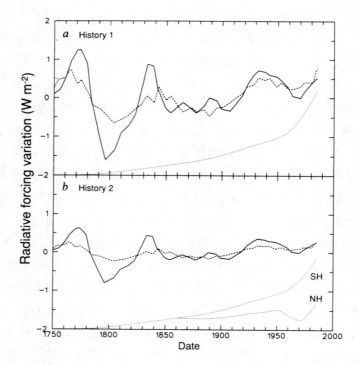

Fig. 3. solar forcing variations (W m⁻²) implied by the best-fit estimates of the solar forcing scaling factor. *a*, KW (solid line) and FCL (dashed line) cycle-length records, with global history 1 greenhouse forcing (dotted, offset by −2 W m⁻²). *b*, KW (solid line) and FCL (dashed line) cycle-length records, with history 2 greenhouse plus aerosol forcing for the Northern Hemisphere, NH, and Southern Hemisphere, SH (dotted, offset by −2 W m⁻²). The greenhouse plus aerosol forcing in this case is hemisphere-specific because of the differential effects of the sulphate aerosol contribution.

Note added in proof: The accompanying paper by Schlesinger and Ramankutty, which was shown to us after we had submitted this paper, also considers the relative importance of greenhouse, sulphate aerosol and solar forcing. There are minor differences in the results which arise mainly because we use the latest IPCC temperature data[10] and include stratospheric ozone depletion feedback in history 2 (ref. 13). In addition, the model formulation and parameter values used[13] differ slightly between the two analyses.

(**360**, 328-330; 1992)

P. M. Kelly and T. M. L. Wigley
Climatic Research Unit, University of East Anglia, Norwich NR4 7TJ, UK

Received 7 July; accepted 19 October 1992.

References:

1. Houghton, J. T., Jenkins, G. J. & Ephraums, J. J. (eds) *Climate Change: The IPCC Scientific Assessment* (Cambridge Univ. Press, 1990).

2. Hansen, J. E. & Lacis, A. A. *Nature* **346**, 713-719 (1990).

3. Wigley, T. M. L. & Raper, S. C. B. in *Climate Change: Science, Impacts and Policy* (eds Jäger, J. & Ferguson, H. L.) 231-242 (Cambridge Univ. Press, 1991).

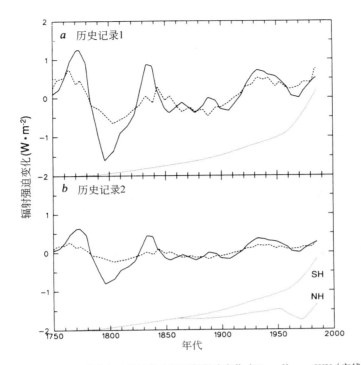

图 3. 由太阳辐射强迫比例因子最佳拟合估计的太阳辐射强迫变化（W·m⁻²）。a，KW（实线）和 FCL（虚线）的太阳周期长度记录，以及全球历史记录 1 下的温室强迫（点虚线，抵消了 −2 W·m⁻² 的太阳辐射强度）。b，KW（实线）和 FCL（虚线）周期长度记录，以及历史记录 2 下北半球（NH）和南半球（SH）的温室强迫加上气溶胶强迫记录（点虚线，抵消了 −2 W·m⁻² 的太阳辐射强度）。这里温室强迫加气溶胶强迫分为南北半球，是因为两个半球的硫酸盐气溶胶贡献不同。

附加说明：我们是在本文提交后才见到施莱辛格和拉曼库迪的文章的，他们的文章也讨论了温室强迫、硫酸盐气溶胶强迫和太阳辐射强迫的相对重要性。我们得到的结果和他们的有微小差异，主要是由于我们采用了政府间气候变化专门委员会（IPCC）最新的温度数据[10]，并且在历史记录 2 中包含了平流层臭氧损耗反馈（参考文献 13）。此外，两种分析方法所采用的模式构建和参数值[13]也略有不同。

（齐红艳 翻译；闻新宇 审稿）

4. Wigley, T. M. L. & Raper, S. C. B. *Nature* **330**, 127-131 (1987).

5. Wigley, T. M. L. & Raper, S. C. B. *Nature* **344**, 324-327 (1990).

6. Gilliland, R. L. *Clim. Change* **4**, 111-131 (1982).

7. Reid, G. C. *Nature* **329**, 142-143 (1987).

8. Friis-Christensen, E. & Lassen, K. *Science* **254**, 698-700 (1991).

9. Folland, C. K., Karl, T. R. & Vinnikov, K. Ya. in *Climate Change: The IPCC Scientific Assessment* (eds Houghton, J. T., Jenkins, G. J. & Ephraums, J. J.) 195-238 (Cambridge Univ. Press, 1990).

10. Folland, C. K. *et al.* in *Climate Change 1992: Supplementary Report to the IPCC Scientific Assessment* (eds Houghton, J. T., Callander, B. A. & Varney, S. K.) 135-170 (Cambridge Univ. Press, 1992).

11. Kelly, P. M. & Wigley, T. M. L. *Nature* **347**, 460-462 (1990).

12. Shine, K. P., Derwent, R. G., Wuebbles, D. J. & Morcrette, J.-J. in *Climate Change: The IPCC Scientific Assessment* (eds Houghton, J. T., Jenkins, G. J. & Ephraums, J. J.) 41-68 (Cambridge Univ. Press, 1990).

13. Wigley, T. M. L. & Raper, S. C. B. *Nature* **357**, 293-300 (1992).

14. Isaksen, I. S. A. *et al.* in *Climate Change 1992: Supplementary Report to the IPCC Scientific Assessment* (eds Houghton, J. T., Callander, B. A. & Varney, S. K.) 47-67 (Cambridge Univ. Press, 1992).

15. Wigley, T. M. L. & Kelly, P. M. *Phil. Trans. R. Soc.* A**330**, 547-560 (1990).

16. Baliunas, S. & Jastrow, R. *Nature* **348**, 520-523 (1990).

17. Jones, P. D., Wigley, T. M. L. & Farmer, G. in *Greenhouse-Gas-Induced Climatic Change: A Critical Appraisal of Simulations and Observations* (ed. Schlesinger, M. E.) 153-172 (Elsevier, 1991).

Acknowledgements. This analysis was supported by the US Department of Energy, Atmospheric and Climate Research Division.

Implications for Global Warming of Intercycle Solar Irradiance Variations

M. E. Schlesinger and N. Ramankutty

Editor's Note

In the early 1990s, some climate researchers argued that the observed warming of the earth was caused more by variations in heat output by the Sun than by greenhouse gases released through human activity. It was a minority view, but an influential one, argued forcefully for example by the US think tank the George Marshall Institute. This paper by climatologists Michael Schlesinger and Navin Ramankutty is one of several that debunk the notion that changes in solar output can be held accountable for twentieth-century climate change. The authors run computer models of climate for plausible solar variations, and find that these alone cannot account for the modern temperature trends—the dominant contribution to global warming, they say, comes from greenhouse gases.

Following earlier studies[1-6], attention has recently been directed again to the possibility that long-term solar irradiance variations, rather than increased greenhouse gas concentrations, have been the dominant cause of the observed rise in global-mean surface temperature from the mid-nineteenth century to the present. Friis-Christensen and Lassen[7] report a high correlation (0.95; ref. 8) between the variable period of the "11-year" sunspot cycle and the mean Northern Hemisphere land surface temperature from 1865 to 1985. The Marshall Institute report[9] concludes that "… the sun has been the controlling influence on climate in the last 100 years, with the greenhouse effect playing a smaller role." Here we explore the implication that such putative solar irradiance variations would have for global warming. Our results provide strong circumstantial evidence that there have been intercycle variations in solar irradiance which have contributed to the observed temperature changes since 1856. However, we find that since the nineteenth century, greenhouse gases, not solar irradiance variations, have been the dominant contributor to the observed temperature changes.

WE use a hemispherically resolving version[10] of our simple climate–ocean model which we used for IPCC/90 (ref. 11) and other studies[12-14]. The model calculates the change in hemispheric-mean surface air temperature (ΔT_a) and ocean temperatures as a function of depth resulting from a change in hemispheric-mean net radiation at the tropopause due to external cause(s). The temperature change ΔT_a generates an opposing change in tropopause radiative flux, $-\lambda \Delta T_a$, where λ is a prescribed sensitivity parameter which implicitly includes the effects of changes in feedback quantities—for example, water

太阳辐照度周期性变化对全球变暖的意义

施莱辛格，拉曼库迪

编者按：

20 世纪 90 年代早期，关于引起全球气候变暖的因子，一些气候学家认为太阳辐射的变化要比人类活动排放的温室气体重要很多。虽然持这种观点的人不多，但影响力很强，比如美国的智囊团乔治·马歇尔研究所就持有这种观点。在本文中，气候学家迈克尔·施莱辛格和纳温·拉曼库迪证明了 20 世纪气候变化是由太阳辐射变化所导致的这一观点是错误的。他们运用计算机气候模式模拟太阳辐射变化对气候变化的影响，发现只有太阳辐射变化并不能解释现代气温变化的趋势，他们认为引起全球变暖的主要因素是温室气体。

接着早期的研究 [1-6]，科学家的注意力近年来又转向了太阳辐照度长期变化而非升高的温室气体浓度，认为前者可能是 19 世纪中期到现在全球地表平均温度升高的主要原因。弗里斯－克里斯滕森和拉森 [7] 报告了太阳黑子 11 年周期的变化时间与北半球 1865 年到 1985 年间陆地表面平均温度之间存在着很高的相关性（0.95；参考文献 8）。马歇尔研究所的报告 [9] 断定："……过去一百年中，太阳对气候影响起主导作用，而温室气体的作用较小"。本文将要探讨这种推断的太阳辐照度变化对全球变暖的意义。我们的研究结果有力地旁证了太阳辐照度在周期之间存在着变化，这对 1856 年以来观测到的温度变化有一定的贡献。但是，我们发现自 19 世纪以来，对全球温度变化起主导作用的是温室气体而不是太阳辐照度变化。

本研究中，我们使用了一个简单的气候－海洋模式的半球尺度版本 [10]，该模式曾经用于 IPCC/90（编者注：政府间气候变化专门委员会第一次评估报告，于 1990 年发布）（参考文献 11）和其他的研究 [12-14] 中。模式计算了由于外部强迫导致对流层顶半球平均净辐射量变化而引起的半球地表平均气温的变化（ΔT_a）和海洋不同深度上的温度变化。由这个温度变化 ΔT_a 产生一个对流层顶辐射通量的相反变化 $-\lambda\Delta T_a$，这里 λ 是个给定的敏感性参数，该参数隐含了比如水汽、云量、雪冰等反馈量以及温度变

vapour, clouds, and snow and ice—as well as in temperature. We assume that the same λ is valid for each of the radiative forcings studied here. Earlier studies indicate that the error associated with this assumption is small, as simple climate models reproduce the response of more-complex climate models[15,16] and these show similar responses to CO_2 and solar-constant changes[17]. For convenience we write $\lambda = \Delta F_{2\times}/\Delta T_{2\times}$, where $\Delta T_{2\times}$ is a prescribed equilibrium value of ΔT_a resulting from a radiative forcing equivalent to that for doubling the CO_2 concentration, $\Delta F_{2\times} = 4.4 \text{ W m}^{-2}$ (ref. 18). The latter is based on radiative-transfer-model calculations for standard and doubled CO_2 (such as ICRCCM[19]) which do not include any solar-variability effects.

The model is forced by time-dependent tropopause radiative changes due to increasing greenhouse gases (GHGs), intercycle solar irradiance variations and increasing anthropogenic sulphate aerosols (ASAs). The forcing for GHGs is

$$\Delta F_{GHG}(t) = 4.4 \; \frac{\ln [C(t)/C(1765)]}{\ln 2}$$

where $C(t)$ is the historical annual-mean equivalent-carbon-dioxide concentration from 1765 to 1990 determined from IPCC/90 (ref. 18). The intercycle solar-irradiance forcing is taken as $\Delta F_{Sun}(t) = \beta[P_0 - P(t)]$, where $P(t)$ is the length of the "11-year" sunspot cycle given by Gleissberg[20] for June 1638 to December 1744 and Friis-Christensen and Lassen[7] for January 1745 to June 1985, $P_0 = 11.018$ yr is the average cycle period over June 1638 to June 1985, and β represents the putative variation of solar irradiance with respect to P. We ignore here intra-cycle solar-irradiance forcing[21] because studies have shown its temperature response to be negligibly small[22-25]. The forcing due to increasing ASAs is taken to be

$$\Delta F_{SO_4}(t) = \Delta F_{SO_4}(1978) \; \frac{Q_{SO_2-S}(t)}{Q_{SO_2-S}(1978)}$$

where $Q_{SO_2-S}(t)$ is an estimated emission rate of sulphur in the form of SO_2 from 1860 through 1985 and $\Delta F_{SO_4}(1978)$ is the radiative forcing of ASAs in 1978, this being the year for which Charlson et al.[26] made detailed radiative-transfer calculations for the part of ΔF_{SO_4} contributed by the clear atmosphere. But because both the clear and cloudy parts of ΔF_{SO_4} are uncertain[10,26], we prescribe ΔF_{SO_4} from zero to -1.7 W m^{-2} on the basis of an uncertainty analysis of ΔF_{SO_4} for the clear atmosphere combined with a rough estimate of ΔF_{SO_4} for the cloudy atmosphere[10].

We estimate $\Delta T_{2\times}$ for three cases: (1) GHG without and with ASA; (2) Sun without and with ASA; and (3) GHG + Sun without and with ASA. Case (2) cannot occur by itself, however, because, for any climate sensitivity λ, the radiative forcing due to the observed increase in GHGs will induce a warming which cannot be ignored. Consequently, case (2) is included here only as an informative comparison with case (1), a case which can exist alone if $\beta = 0$.

化的影响。我们假定相同的 λ 值对这里研究的每个辐射强迫因子都是有效的。早前的研究指出这样的假设引起的误差非常小，因为简单的气候模式能够再现较为复杂的气候模式[15,16]的响应，并且这些简单模式显示对 CO_2 和太阳常数变化[17]的响应类似。为了方便起见，让 $\lambda = \Delta F_{2\times}/\Delta T_{2\times}$，这里 $\Delta T_{2\times}$ 是 ΔT_a 的一个给定的平衡值，ΔT_a 的这一平衡值是由辐射强迫等效于 2 倍的 CO_2 浓度引起的地表平均气温变化，$\Delta F_{2\times} = 4.4$ W·m^{-2}（参考文献 18）。$\Delta F_{2\times}$ 是根据辐射传输模式对标准的及 2 倍的 CO_2 浓度计算得到的（比如 ICRCCM[19]），这种计算不包括任何太阳辐射变化的影响。

　　模式是由随时间变化的对流层顶辐射变化所驱动的，而辐射变化是由于温室气体（GHGs）增加、太阳辐照度周期间变化和不断增加的人类活动产生的硫酸盐气溶胶（ASAs）引起的。温室气体的强迫表示为：

$$\Delta F_{GHG}(t) = 4.4 \, \frac{\ln [C(t)/C(1765)]}{\ln 2}$$

其中，$C(t)$ 是由 IPCC/90 给出的从 1765 年到 1990 年这一时段年平均等效 CO_2 浓度（参考文献 18）。太阳辐照度周期间变化的强迫表示为：$\Delta F_{Sun}(t) = \beta[P_0-P(t)]$，这里，$P(t)$ 是"11 年"太阳黑子周期的长度，由格莱斯贝格[20]根据 1638 年 6 月到 1744 年 12 月的资料以及弗里斯－克里斯滕森和拉森[7] 1745 年 1 月到 1985 年 6 月的资料所确定；$P_0 = 11.018$ 年是 1638 年 6 月到 1985 年 6 月平均的周期长度；β 表示推断的关于 P 的太阳辐照度变化。这里，我们忽略了周期内的太阳辐照度变化的强迫[21]，因为有研究已经显示温度对其响应非常小，可以忽略不计[22-25]。由于人类排放的硫酸盐气溶胶增加而造成的辐射强迫表示为：

$$\Delta F_{SO_4}(t) = \Delta F_{SO_4}(1978) \, \frac{Q_{SO_2-S}(t)}{Q_{SO_2-S}(1978)}$$

其中，$Q_{SO_2-S}(t)$ 代表在 1860 年到 1985 年期间以 SO_2 形式排放的硫的估算排放率，$\Delta F_{SO_4}(1978)$ 是 1978 年硫酸盐气溶胶的辐射强迫，正是在 1978 年，查尔森等[26]在辐射传输模式下对晴空大气对于 ΔF_{SO_4} 的贡献部分进行了详尽计算。但是由于有云和晴空条件下大气的 ΔF_{SO_4} 都具有不确定性[10,26]，我们根据晴空条件下 ΔF_{SO_4} 的不确定性分析以及有云条件下对 ΔF_{SO_4} 的粗略估算，给定 ΔF_{SO_4} 的范围是 0 到 -1.7 W·m^{-2}[10]。

　　我们估算了三种情形下的 $\Delta T_{2\times}$ 值：（1）不考虑和考虑 ASA 条件下的 GHG 情况；（2）不考虑和考虑 ASA 条件下的太阳辐射情况；（3）不考虑和考虑 ASA 条件下的 GHG 加太阳辐射的情况。然而，第（2）种情况并不会单独发生，因为对于任何气候敏感因子 λ，温室气体增加导致的辐射强迫会引发不可忽略的升温。因此，在这里引入第（2）种情形的目的只是为了与第（1）种情形（这种情形在 $\beta = 0$ 时可单独存在）作一个有价值的对比。

For GHG alone and GHG with ASA, the model was run for many values of $\Delta T_{2\times}$, each beginning at $t_0 =$ June 1638 with $\Delta T_m(t_0) = 0$, where ΔT_m is the global average of the model's changes in mixed-layer temperature over ocean and air temperature over land, and extending through June 1985. The model results were then compared with observations of the departure of global-mean, annual-mean temperature from its 1951–80 average, $\delta T_0(t)$. This comparison was necessary because only these temperature departures have been compiled, not the actual temperatures themselves (ref. 27, updated and extended by C. Folland, D. Parker and R. Hacket, Hadley Centre, UK Meteorological Office). For each $\Delta T_{2\times}$, the root-mean-square error (RMSE) of model-simulated annual-mean temperature departure, $\delta T_m(t) = \Delta T_m(t) + \delta T_{PI}$, to $\delta T_0(t)$ was calculated from January 1856 through June 1985, with the pre-industrial average temperature anomaly, δT_{PI}, determined such that the RMSE was minimized[10]. The $\Delta T_{2\times}$ giving the smallest RMSE was then chosen. The same procedure was performed for Sun alone and Sun with ASA, and for GHG plus Sun, both without and with ASA, except that both $\Delta T_{2\times}$ and β were determined to minimize the RMSE. We have also run the model from 1745 to 1985 without the Gleissberg data[20] and obtained virtually identical results.

Figure 1 presents plots of $\Delta T_{2\times}$, β, the unexplained standard deviation (USD: standard deviation of $\delta T_0(t) - \delta T_m(t)$ as a percentage of the standard deviation of $\delta T_0(t)$), and the residual linear trend (RLT: trend of $\delta T_0(t) - \delta T_m(t)$) against $\Delta F_{SO_4}(1978)$. For $\Delta F_{SO_4}(1978) = 0$, Fig. 1 shows that adding solar forcing with $\beta = 0.867$ W m^{-2} yr^{-1} to GHG forcing (going from point a to e) reduces $\Delta T_{2\times}$ from 1.4 °C to 0.7 °C, USD from 72.5% to 67.7%, and RLT from 0.015 °C per century to -0.005 °C per century. Removing GHG forcing to leave Sun alone (e to c) reduces β to 0.300 W m^{-2} yr^{-1}, increases $\Delta T_{2\times}$ to 9.6 °C, and increases RLT to 0.029 °C per century. As negative ASA forcing is added for GHG alone and GHG plus Sun, $\Delta T_{2\times}$ increases nonlinearly[10], USD decreases to minima at $\Delta F_{SO_4}(1978)$ $= -1.2$ and -1.5 W m^{-2}, respectively, and the magnitude of RLT decreases to minima at $\Delta F_{SO_4}(1978) = -1.3$ and -1.4 W m^{-2}, respectively. In marked contrast, decreasing $\Delta F_{SO_4}(1978)$ for Sun alone causes $\Delta T_{2\times}$ to decrease toward zero and β to rapidly increase such that both USD and RLT increase to constant values for $\Delta F_{SO_4}(1978) \leqslant -0.4$ W m^{-2}. The ratio of $\Delta T_{2\times}$ for GHG plus Sun to $\Delta T_{2\times}$ for GHG alone decreases with decreasing $\Delta F_{SO_4}(1978)$ from 0.52 for $\Delta F_{SO_4}(1978) = 0$.

Figure 2 illustrates the simulated temperature anomalies, δT_m, in comparison with the observed temperature anomaly, δT_0, for points a to f in Fig. 1. Points a, c and e have zero sulphate forcing, points b and f have $\Delta F_{SO_4}(1978) = -1.1$ W m^{-2}, the central estimate of the previously mentioned uncertainty analysis[10], and point d is an example near $\Delta F_{SO_4}(1978) = -0.4$ W m^{-2} where $\Delta T_{2\times} \approx 0$ for Sun alone. For GHG alone and GHG with $\Delta F_{SO_4}(1978) = -1.1$ W m^{-2} (Fig. 2A), δT_m respectively equals $\delta T_{PI} = -0.34$ °C and -0.53 °C until 1765 when GHG forcing begins. Thereafter, δT_m monotonically increases to 1985 when the global warming, $\Delta T_m(t) = \delta T_m(t) - \delta T_{PI}$, is 0.52 °C and 0.75 °C, respectively. In contrast, the δT_m values for Sun alone and Sun with $\Delta F_{SO_4}(1978) = -0.3$ W m^{-2} (Fig.

对于只有 GHG 和 GHG 加 ASA 的情形，模式分别在多个 $\Delta T_{2\times}$ 值下运行，每次运行开始于 $t_0 = 1638$ 年 6 月，此时 $\Delta T_m(t_0) = 0$，这里 ΔT_m 是该模式的海洋混合层温度和陆地大气温度变化的全球平均值，模式一直运行到 1985 年 6 月。接下来，将模式结果与实测的全球和年平均温度相对于 1951~1980 年平均温度的偏差值 $\delta T_0(t)$ 进行比较。这样比较是必要的，因为目前只能获得这些温度的偏差值，而不是真实的温度值本身（参考文献 27，由英国气象局哈德莱中心的福兰德、帕克和哈克特更新和扩展）。对每一个 $\Delta T_{2\times}$，计算了模式模拟的从 1856 年 1 月到 1985 年 6 月年平均温度偏差 $\delta T_m(t)$（$\delta T_m(t) = \Delta T_m(t) + \delta T_{PI}$）相对于 $\delta T_0(t)$ 的均方根误差。其中 δT_{PI} 是工业化前平均温度异常，当均方根误差为最小值时就得到 δT_{PI} 的值[10]。然后选择产生最小均方根误差的 $\Delta T_{2\times}$ 值。针对其他强迫情形——仅有太阳辐射和太阳辐射加 ASA 的情况、考虑和不考虑 ASA 的 GHG 加太阳辐射的情况，也进行同样的计算，除了 $\Delta T_{2\times}$ 和 β 均已经确定下来，以使均方根误差最小化。我们还在不使用格莱斯贝格数据[20]的条件下运行了模式，计算 1745 年到 1985 年的情况，获得了几乎一样的结果。

图 1 展示了 $\Delta T_{2\times}$、β、未解释标准差（USD：$\delta T_0(t) - \delta T_m(t)$ 的标准偏差占 $\delta T_0(t)$ 标准偏差的百分比）和残差线性趋势（RLT：$\delta T_0(t) - \delta T_m(t)$ 的趋势）相对于 ΔF_{SO_4}（1978）的关系图。当 ΔF_{SO_4}（1978）= 0，图 1 显示把太阳辐射强迫 $\beta = 0.867$ W·m⁻²·yr⁻¹ 加到 GHG 强迫上（从 a 点到 e 点）可以使 $\Delta T_{2\times}$ 从 1.4 ℃ 减小到 0.7 ℃，USD 从 72.5% 减小到 67.7%，RLT 值从每世纪 0.015 ℃ 减小到每世纪 −0.005 ℃。除去 GHG 强迫只保留太阳辐射强迫（从 e 点到 c 点）使得 β 减小到 0.300 W·m⁻²·yr⁻¹，$\Delta T_{2\times}$ 增加到 9.6 ℃，RLT 增加到每世纪 0.029 ℃。当将负的 ASA 强迫加入只有 GHG 强迫和 GHG 强迫加太阳辐射强迫两种情况时，$\Delta T_{2\times}$ 呈现非线性增加趋势[10]，USD 分别在 ΔF_{SO_4}（1978）= −1.2 W·m⁻² 和 −1.5 W·m⁻² 时达到最低值，并且 RLT 的幅度分别在 ΔF_{SO_4}（1978）= −1.3 W·m⁻² 和 −1.4 W·m⁻² 时降到最低值。形成巨大反差的是在仅有太阳辐射强迫的情况下减小 ΔF_{SO_4}（1978），可以使 $\Delta T_{2\times}$ 向 0 逼近，而 β 迅速增加，以至于 USD 和 RLT 在 ΔF_{SO_4}（1978）≤ −0.4 W·m⁻² 时增加到定值。GHG 强迫加太阳辐射强迫情况下的 $\Delta T_{2\times}$ 与仅有 GHG 强迫情况下的 $\Delta T_{2\times}$ 的比值在 ΔF_{SO_4}（1978）= 0 时为 0.52，并随着 ΔF_{SO_4}（1978）的减小而降低。

图 2 展示了模拟的温度异常值 δT_m 与观测到的图 1 中 a 点到 f 点的温度异常值 δT_0 的比较。在 a、c 和 e 点人类排放的硫酸盐气溶胶强迫为 0，在 b 和 f 点，ΔF_{SO_4}（1978）= −1.1 W·m⁻²，是前面提及的不确定性分析[10]的中间估计值，而 d 点是只有太阳辐射强迫情况下当 ΔF_{SO_4} 接近 −0.4 W·m⁻² 时，$\Delta T_{2\times} \approx 0$ 的一个例子。对于只有 GHG 强迫和具有 ΔF_{SO_4}（1978）= −1.1 W·m⁻² 的 GHG 的情况（图 2A），直到 1765 年 GHG 强迫开始前，δT_m 分别等于 $\delta T_{PI} = -0.34$ ℃ 和 −0.53 ℃。从那以后 δT_m 就一直单调增

2B) oscillate about $\delta T_{PI} = -0.13$ °C, with maxima in the eighteenth, nineteenth and twentieth centuries. For Sun alone, the eighteenth- and twentieth-century maxima are comparable, whereas for Sun plus ASA the eighteenth-century maximum is larger. For GHG plus Sun (Fig. 2C), δT_m oscillates about $\delta T_{PI} = -0.26$ °C with no noticeable trend until about 1900. By 1922, δT_m exceeds its eighteenth-century maximum, continues to increase until 1944, remains nearly constant until 1966, and then increases to $\Delta T_m(1985)$ = 0.42 °C. For GHG plus Sun with $\Delta F_{SO_4}(1978) = -1.1$ W m^{-2}, δT_m oscillates about $\delta T_{PI} = -0.35$ °C until 1911 when δT_m exceeds its nineteenth-century maximum. Thereafter, δT_m increases to 1946, remains nearly constant until 1971, and then increases to $\Delta T_m(1985)$ = 0.55 °C.

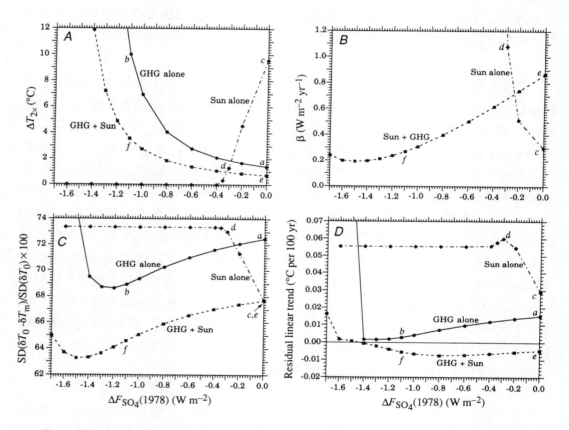

Fig. 1. Variation with ASA forcing, $\Delta F_{SO_4}(1978)$, of (A) climate sensitivity, $\Delta T_{2\times}$; (B) intercycle solar-irradiance parameter, β; (C) unexplained standard deviation, USD; and (D) residual linear trend, RLT.

加，直到 1985 年，全球增暖值 $\Delta T_{\mathrm{m}}(t) = \delta T_{\mathrm{m}}(t) - \delta T_{\mathrm{PI}}$ 分别为 0.52 ℃和 0.75 ℃。相对的，只有太阳辐射强迫和 $\Delta F_{\mathrm{SO_4}}(1978) = -0.3\,\mathrm{W \cdot m^{-2}}$ 的太阳辐射强迫情况下的 δT_{m} 值在 $\delta T_{\mathrm{PI}} = -0.13$ ℃左右振荡（图 2B），最大波动值出现在 18 世纪、19 世纪和 20 世纪。对于只有太阳辐射强迫的情况，18 世纪和 20 世纪的最大值相当，而对于太阳辐射强迫加 ASA 强迫的情况，18 世纪的最大值比较大。对于 GHG 加太阳辐射强迫，δT_{m} 值在 $\delta T_{\mathrm{PI}} = -0.26$ ℃左右振荡（图 2C），直到大约 1900 年才有明显的趋势。到 1922 年，δT_{m} 超过其 18 世纪的最大值，继续增加直到 1944 年，然后一直保持稳定到 1966 年，之后增加到 $\Delta T_{\mathrm{m}}(1985) = 0.42$ ℃。对于 GHG 加上太阳辐射强迫并且 $\Delta F_{\mathrm{SO_4}}(1978) = -1.1\,\mathrm{W \cdot m^{-2}}$ 的情况，δT_{m} 值在 $\delta T_{\mathrm{PI}} = -0.35$ ℃左右振荡，直到 1911 年 δT_{m} 超过其 19 世纪最大值。从 1911 年到 1946 年，δT_{m} 保持增长，然后基本保持稳定直到 1971 年，最后增加到 $\Delta T_{\mathrm{m}}(1985) = 0.55$ ℃。

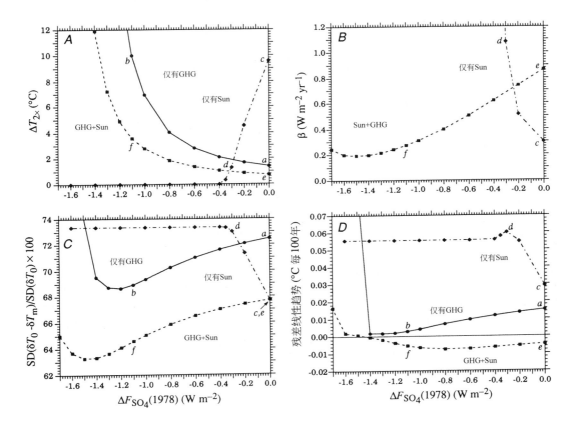

图 1. ASA 导致的辐射强迫 $\Delta F_{\mathrm{SO_4}}(1978)$ 而引起的参数变化：（A）气候敏感性，$\Delta T_{2\times}$；（B）周期间太阳辐照度参数，β；（C）未解释标准差，USD；（D）残差线性趋势，RLT。

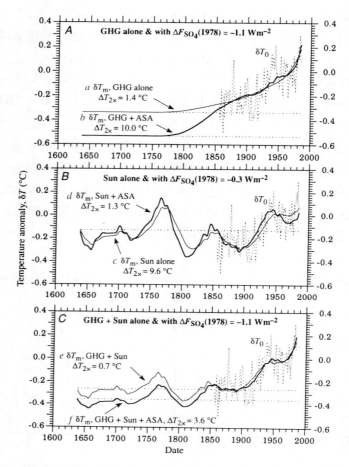

Fig. 2. Comparison of the simulated and observed temperature anomalies, δT_m and δT_0, for points a–f in Fig. 1. Dashed lines show the pre-industrial temperature anomaly, δT_{Pi}.

The contributions of the individual forcing components to $\Delta T_m(t)$ are presented in Fig. 3. For GHG plus Sun (Fig. 3a) the temperature change due to GHG permanently exceeds the magnitude of the temperature change due to the Sun after 1894, and their difference increases to a maximum of 0.19 °C in 1982. The same is true for GHG plus Sun with $\Delta F_{SO_4}(1978) = -1.1$ W m^{-2} (Fig. 3b), but beginning in 1827 and increasing to a maximum difference of 0.93 °C in 1985. These results do not support the conclusion of the Marshall Institute report[9], which we quoted in our opening paragraph.

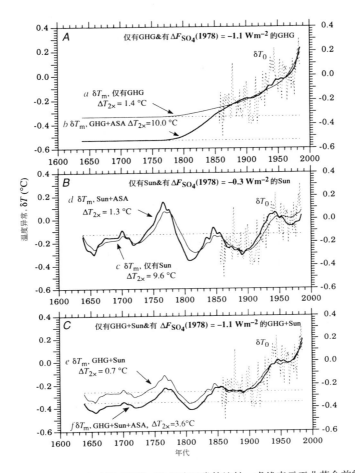

图 2. 图 1 中 $a \sim f$ 点模拟的 δT_m 和实际观测的 δT_0 温度异常值比较。虚线表示工业革命前的温度异常值，δT_{Pl}。

单个强迫因子对 $\Delta T_m(t)$ 的贡献如图 3 所示。对于 GHG 加太阳辐射强迫的情况（图 3a），1894 年之后由 GHG 导致的温度变化持续超过由于太阳辐射强迫导致的温度变化的幅度，并且他们的差值在 1982 年增加到最大值 0.19 ℃。对 GHG 加太阳辐射且 $\Delta F_{SO_4}(1978) = -1.1 \ W \cdot m^{-2}$ 的情况（图 3b）也是如此，但是开始时间在 1827 年，在 1985 年差值增加到最大值 0.93 ℃。这些结果并不支持本文开始引用的马歇尔研究所报告[9] 的结论。

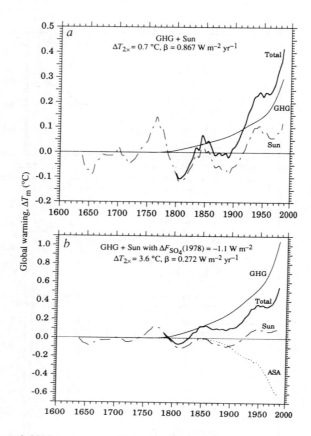

Fig. 3. Contributions of GHGs, intercycle solar variations and ASAs to global warming, ΔT_m. The heavy line for the total ΔT_m("Total") is not shown before 1801 in a and 1785 in b so that solar contribution (Sun) can be seen.

Figure 4 presents the intercycle solar-irradiance anomaly, $\Delta S = \Delta F_{Sun}[4/(1-\alpha_p)]$, with $\alpha_p = 0.3$ the planetary albedo, for the two cases of Fig. 3, both in W m^{-2} and as a percentage of the mean solar irradiance measured from 1980 to 1989 by the Solar Maximum Satellite (SMS), $S_0 = 1,367.5$ W m^{-2} (ref. 21, and R. C. Willson, personal communication). The intra-cycle solar-irradiance variation given by the standard deviation of the SMS observations, $\sigma(\text{intra}) = 0.6$ W m^{-2} (0.044% of S_0; R. C. Willson, personal communication), is also shown for comparison. For GHG plus Sun with $\Delta F_{SO_4}(1978) = -1.1$ W m^{-2}, ΔS ranges from -1.6 W m^{-2} to 2.1 W m^{-2} (-0.12% to 0.15%), with a standard deviation $\sigma(\text{inter}) = 0.85$ W m^{-2} (0.062%). This intercycle variation is within the "several tenths of a percent" estimated by Baliunas and Jastrow[28] from observations of the visual-brightness and magnetic-activity variations of 74 solar-type stars. For GHG plus Sun without ASA, ΔS ranges from -5.3 W m^{-2} to 6.5 W m^{-2} (-0.38% to 0.48%), with $\sigma(\text{inter}) = 2.71$ W m^{-2} (0.198%). This intercycle variation is within the 0.1–3% variation found by Lockwood et $al.$[29] for 25 solar-type stars. Consequently, our results constitute strong evidence, albeit circumstantial, that there have been variations in solar irradiance which have contributed to the observed temperature changes since 1856.

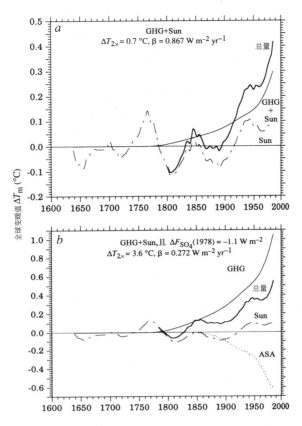

图 3. GHG、太阳辐射周期间变化和 ASA 对全球变暖值 ΔT_m 的贡献。粗实线表示的总的 ΔT_m 值在 1801 年（a）和 1785 年（b）以前的部分没有在图中显示，这样可以清楚看出太阳辐射强迫的贡献。

　　图 4 展示的是图 3 中两种情况的周期间太阳辐照度异常值，$\Delta S = \Delta F_{\text{Sun}}[4/(1-\alpha_p)]$，其中 $\alpha_p = 0.3$，为行星反照率，两者均以 $W \cdot m^{-2}$ 为单位，且以 1980 年到 1989 年间由太阳峰年卫星 (SMS) 测量的平均太阳辐照度 ($S_0 = 1,367.5\ W \cdot m^{-2}$) 的百分率表示（参考文献 21 以及威尔森，个人交流）。同时给出由太阳峰年卫星观测的标准偏差 $\sigma(\text{intra}) = 0.6\ W \cdot m^{-2}$，($S_0$ 的 0.044%；威尔森，个人交流）得到的太阳辐照度周期内变化以进行比较。对于 GHG 加太阳辐射强迫且 $\Delta F_{\text{SO}_4}(1978) = -1.1\ W \cdot m^{-2}$ 的情况，ΔS 值的范围从 $-1.6\ W \cdot m^{-2}$ 到 $2.1\ W \cdot m^{-2}$ 之间（-0.12% 到 0.15%），其中的标准偏差 $\sigma(\text{inter}) = 0.85\ W \cdot m^{-2}(0.062\%)$。这一周期间的变化在"百分之几十"的范围内，这个范围由巴柳纳斯和贾斯特罗 [28] 通过对 74 颗太阳型恒星视觉亮度与磁场活动变化的观测而估算得出。对于 GHG 加太阳辐射而没有 ASA 的情况，ΔS 值的范围从 $-5.3\ W \cdot m^{-2}$ 到 $6.5\ W \cdot m^{-2}$（-0.38% 到 0.48%），其中的标准偏差 $\sigma(\text{inter}) = 2.71\ W \cdot m^{-2}(0.198\%)$。这个周期间的变化在 0.1%~3% 之间，该范围由洛克伍德等 [29] 通过对 25 颗太阳型恒星的观测所发现。因此，我们的结果（尽管是间接的）提供了强有力的证据，证明太阳辐照度是变化的，这种变化对 1856 年以来观测到的温度变化是有贡献的。

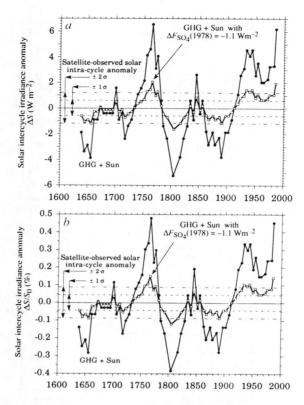

Fig. 4. Intercycle solar-irradiance variation for the two cases of Fig. 3, ΔS (*a*) and $\Delta S/S_0$ (*b*), where $S_0 =$ 1,367.5 W m^{-2} is the mean solar irradiance measured by the Solar Maximum Satellite (SMS) from 1980 to 1989. The values of $\pm\sigma$ and $\pm 2\sigma$ for the SMS observations, $\sigma(\text{intra}) = 0.6$ W m^{-2} (0.044% of S_0), are also shown.

It can be argued that past intercycle solar-irradiance variations may have been larger than those used herein based on estimating β to minimize the RMSE between δT_m and δT_0. Although it is likely that significantly larger irradiance variations would have been detected by past ground-based observations[30], conclusive evidence must await future satellite observations spanning several solar cycles. Regrettably, this evidence will be acquired too late to influence contemporary greenhouse policy. Nevertheless, our present evidence indicates that GHGs will continue to dominate global warming, but that inclusion of the Sun's past influence reduces the estimate of $\Delta T_{2\times}$ by at least 48%. This does not necessarily mean that $\Delta T_{2\times}$ is small because, as shown here, the uncertain negative radiative forcing by ASAs (and biomass burning[31]) can increase $\Delta T_{2\times}$ significantly. Clearly, it is imperative to reduce this uncertainty.

The accompanying paper[32] also considers the relationship between solar forcing, greenhouse forcing and climate change.

(**360**, 330-333; 1992)

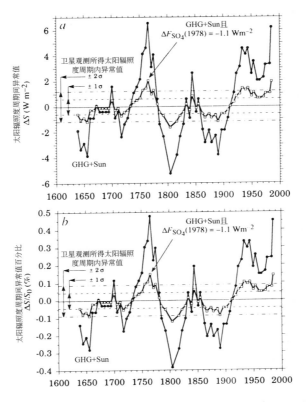

图 4. 图 3 中两种情况下太阳辐照度的周期间变化 ΔS (a) 和 $\Delta S/S$ (b)，这里 $S_0 = 1{,}367.5\,\mathrm{W \cdot m^{-2}}$，是 1980 年到 1989 年间太阳峰年卫星 (SMS) 所测量的太阳平均辐照度。图中也显示了太阳峰年卫星观测值的标准偏差 $\pm\sigma$、$\pm 2\sigma$ 以及 $\sigma(\mathrm{intra}) = 0.6\,\mathrm{W \cdot m^{-2}}$($S_0$ 的 0.044%)。

  可以认为过去的太阳辐照度周期间变化可能大于这里根据估算 β 来最小化 δT_{m} 和 δT_0 之间的均方根误差而得到的太阳辐照度变化值。尽管通过过去的地面仪器探测可能会得到明显较大的太阳辐照度变化[30]，但是结论性的证据还需要等待未来跨越数个太阳周期的卫星观测资料才能得出。遗憾的是，获得这样的证据需要的时间太长以至于无法对当今的温室气体相关政策施加影响。尽管如此，我们目前的证据表明，GHG 将继续主导全球变暖，不过加上太阳过去的影响可以把 $\Delta T_{2\times}$ 的估计值减小至少 48%。这并不意味着 $\Delta T_{2\times}$ 一定是很小的，因为，正如本文所示，由 ASA（和生物质燃烧[31]）导致不确定的负辐射强迫可以极大地增加 $\Delta T_{2\times}$ 值。显然，减少这种不确定性是势在必行的。

  类似的研究[32]也考虑到了太阳辐射强迫、温室气体强迫与气候变化之间的关系。

（许向科 翻译；陈文 审稿）

Michael E. Schlesinger and Navin Ramankutty

Department of Atmospheric Sciences, University of Illinois at Urbana-Champaign, 105 South Gregory Avenue, Urbana, Illinois 61801, USA

Received 27 July; accepted 19 October 1992.

References:

1. Hansen, J. *et al. Science* **213**, 957-966 (1981).

2. Gilliland, R. L. *Clim. Change* **4**, 111-131 (1982).

3. Gilliland, R. L. & Schneider, S. H. *Nature* **310**, 38-41 (1984).

4. Reid, G. C. *Nature* **329**, 142-143 (1987).

5. Seitz, F., Jastrow, R. & Nierenberg, W. A. *Scientific Perspectives on the Greenhouse Problem* (George C. Marshall Institute, Washington DC, 1989).

6. Reid, G. C. *J. Geophys. Res.* **96**, 2835-2844 (1991).

7. Friis-Christensen, E. & Lassen, K. *Science* **254**, 698-700 (1991).

8. Kerr, R. A. *Science* **254**, 652-653 (1991).

9. Jastrow, R., Nierenberg, W. & Seitz, F. *Global Warming Update: Recent Scientific Findings* (George C. Marshall Institute, Washington DC, 1992).

10. Schlesinger, M. E., Jiang, X. & Charlson, R. J. in *Climate Change and Energy Policy. Proc. int. Conf. Global Climate Change: Its Mitigation Through Improved Production and Use of Energy* (eds Rosen, L. & Glasser, R.) 75-108 (American Institute of Physics, New York, 1992).

11. Houghton, J. T., Jenkins, G. J. & Ephraums, J. J. (eds) *Climate Change: The IPCC Scientific Assessment* (Cambridge Univ. Press, 1990).

12. Schlesinger, M. E. & Jiang, X. *Nature* **350**, 219-221 (1991).

13. Hammitt, J. K., Lempert, R. J. & Schlesinger, M. E. *Nature* **357**, 315-318 (1992).

14. Schlesinger, M. E. *Eos* **73**, 325-327 (1992).

15. Schlesinger, M. E. in *Understanding Climate Change* (eds Berger, A., Dickinson, R. E. & Kidson, J. W.), Geophys. Monogr. 52, 177-187 (American Geophysical Union, Washington DC 1989).

16. Schlesinger, M. E. & Jiang, X. *J. Clim.* **3**, 1297-1315 (1990).

17. Manabe, S. & Wetherald, R. T. *J. atmos. Sci.* **37**, 99-118 (1980).

18. Shine, K. P., Derwent, R. G., Wuebbles, D. J. & Morcrette J.-J. in *Climate Change: The IPCC Scientific Assessment* (eds Houghton, J. T., Jenkins, G. J. & Ephraums, J. J.) 41-68 (Cambridge Univ. Press, 1990).

19. Luther, F. M. *et al. Bull. Am. Met. Soc.* **69**, 40-48 (1988).

20. Gleissberg, W. *Terrestr. Magnet. Atmos. Electr.* **49**, 243-244 (1944).

21. Willson, R. C. & Hudson, H. S. *Nature* **351**, 42-44 (1991).

22. Hoffert, M. I., Frei, A. & Narayanan, V. K. *Clim. Change* **13**, 267-285 (1988).

23. Hoffert, M. I. in *Greenhouse-Gas-Induced Climatic Change: A Critical Appraisal of Simulations and Observations* (ed. Schlesinger, M. E.) 413-428 (Elsevier, Amsterdam, 1991).

24. Wigley, T. M. L. & Raper, S. C. B. *Geophys. Res. Lett.* **17**, 2169-2172 (1990).

25. Kelly, P. M. & Wigley, T. M. L. *Nature* **347**, 460-462 (1990).

26. Charlson, R. J., Langner, J., Rodhe, H., Leovy, C. B. & Warren, S. G. *Tellus* **43**, 152-163 (1991).

27. Folland, C. K., Karl, T. R. & Vinnikov, K. Y. in *Climate Change: The IPCC Scientific Assessment* (eds Houghton, J. T., Jenkins, G. J. & Ephraums, J. J.) 195-238 (Cambridge Univ. Press, 1990).

28. Baliunas, S. & Jastrow, R. *Nature* **348**, 520-523 (1990).

29. Lockwood, G. W. *et al. Nature* (in the press).

30. Fröhlich, C. in *The Solar Output and its Variation* (ed. White, O. R.) 93-109 (Colorado Associated Univ. Press, Boulder, 1977).

31. Penner, J. E., Dickinson, R. E. & O'Neill, C. A. *Science* **256**, 1432-1433 (1992).

32. Kelly, P. M. & Wigley, T. M. L. *Nature* **360**, 328-330 (1992).

Acknowledgements. We thank C. Folland, D. Parker and R. Hackett for the IPCC monthly surface temperature anomaly data; J. McKinnon for the monthly sunspot record; R. Willson for the mean and standard deviation of the solar constant observed by the Solar Maximum Satellite; and A. Ghanem for assisting in the digitization of the solar-cycle length data. This research was supported by the US NSF and the US Department of Energy, Carbon Dioxide Research Program, Office of Health and Environmental Research.

Appendix: Index by Subject
附录：学科分类目录

Physics
物理

Chemistry
化学

Biology
生物

Astronomy
天文

Geoscience
地球科学